OPERATIONS MANAGEMENT

SUSTAINABILITY AND SUPPLY CHAIN MANAGEMENT

THIRD CANADIAN EDITION

JAY HEIZER
Texas Lutheran University

BARRY RENDER
Graduate School of Business, Rollins College

CHUCK MUNSON
Carson College of Business, Washington State University

PAUL GRIFFIN
Humber Institute of Technology and Advanced Learning

 Pearson

To Kathryn Ann Heizer

—JH

To Donna, Charlie, Jesse, and Reva
and to Howard G. Kornacki, the teacher who taught
me to love math

—BR

To Suzanne, Alexandra, Kenna, Ryan, and
Robert Kathleen

—PG

Pearson Canada Inc., 26 Prince Andrew Place, North York, Ontario M3C 2H4.

ISBN 978-0-13-483807-6

Library and Archives Canada Cataloguing in Publication

Heizer, Jay, author
    Operations management : sustainability and supply chain management/Jay Heizer, Barry Render, Chuck Munson, Paul Griffin. -- Third Canadian edition.

Includes bibliographical references and indexes.
ISBN 978-0-13-483807-6 (softcover)

    1. Production management--Textbooks. 2. Textbooks.
I. Render, Barry, author II. Munson, Chuck, author III. Griffin, Paul, 1961-, author IV. Title.

TS155.H3726 2018   658.5   C2018-904040-8

About the Authors

Jay Heizer Professor Emeritus, the Jesse H. Jones Chair of Business Administration, Texas Lutheran University, Seguin, Texas. He received his B.B.A. and M.B.A. from the University of North Texas and his Ph.D. in Management and Statistics from Arizona State University. He was previously a member of the faculty at the University of Memphis, the University of Oklahoma, Virginia Commonwealth University, and the University of Richmond. He has also held visiting positions at Boston University, George Mason University, the Czech Management Center, and the Otto-Von-Guericke University, Magdeburg.

Dr. Heizer's industrial experience is extensive. He learned the practical side of operations management as a machinist apprentice at Foringer and Company, as a production planner for Westinghouse Airbrake, and at General Dynamics, where he worked in engineering administration. In addition, he has been actively involved in consulting in the OM and MIS areas for a variety of organizations, including Philip Morris, Firestone, Dixie Container Corporation, Columbia Industries, and Tenneco. He holds the CPIM certification from APICS—the Association for Operations Management.

Professor Heizer has co-authored five books and has published more than 30 articles on a variety of management topics. His papers have appeared in the *Academy of Management Journal, Journal of Purchasing, Personnel Psychology, Production & Inventory Control Management, APICS—The Performance Advantage, Journal of Management History, IIE Solutions, and Engineering Management*, among others. He has taught operations management courses in undergraduate, graduate, and executive programs.

Barry Render Professor Emeritus, the Charles Harwood Professor of Operations Management, Crummer Graduate School of Business, Rollins College, Winter Park, Florida. He received his B.S. in Mathematics and Physics at Roosevelt University, and his M.S. in Operations Research and Ph.D. in Quantitative Analysis at the University of Cincinnati. He previously taught at George Washington University, University of New Orleans, Boston University, and George Mason University, where he held the Mason Foundation Professorship in Decision Sciences and was Chair of the Decision Sciences Department. Dr. Render has also worked in the aerospace industry for General Electric, McDonnell Douglas, and NASA.

Professor Render has co-authored 10 textbooks for Prentice Hall, including *Managerial Decision Modeling with Spreadsheets, Quantitative Analysis for Management, Service Management, Introduction to Management Science,* and *Cases and Readings in Management Science. Quantitative Analysis for Management*, now in its 11th edition, is a leading text in that discipline in the United States and globally. Dr. Render's more than 100 articles on a variety of management topics have appeared in *Decision Sciences, Production and Operations Management, Interfaces, Information and Management, Journal of Management Information Systems, Socio-Economic Planning Sciences, IIE Solutions,* and *Operations Management Review*, among others.

Dr. Render has been honoured as an AACSB Fellow and was twice named a Senior Fulbright Scholar. He was Vice President of the Decision Science Institute Southeast Region and served as Software Review Editor for *Decision Line* for six years and as Editor of the *New York Times* Operations Management special issues for five years. From 1984 to 1993, Dr. Render was President of Management Service Associates of Virginia, Inc., whose technology clients included the FBI, the U.S. Navy, Fairfax County, Virginia, and C&P Telephone. He is currently Consulting Editor to *Financial Times Press*.

Dr. Render has taught operations management courses in Rollins College's MBA and Executive MBA programs. He has received that school's Welsh Award as leading Professor and was selected by Roosevelt University as the 1996 recipient of the St. Claire Drake Award for Outstanding Scholarship. In 2005, Dr. Render received the Rollins College MBA Student Award for Best Overall Course, and in 2009 was named Professor of the Year by full-time MBA students.

Chuck Munson Professor of Operations Management, Carson College of Business, Washington State University, Pullman, Washington. He received his BSBA *summa cum laude* in finance, along with his MSBA and Ph.D. in operations management, from Washington University in St. Louis. For two years, he served as Associate Dean for Graduate Programs in Business at Washington State. He also worked for three years as a financial analyst for Contel Telephone Corporation.

Professor Munson serves as a senior editor for *Production and Operations Management*, and he serves on the editorial review board of four other journals. He has published more than 25 articles in such journals as *Production and Operations Management, IIE Transactions, Decision Sciences, Naval Research Logistics, European Journal of Operational Research, Journal of the Operational Research Society,* and *Annals of Operations Research.* He is editor of the book *The Supply Chain Management Casebook: Comprehensive Coverage and Best Practices in SCM,* and he has co-authored the research monograph *Quantity Discounts: An Overview and Practical Guide for Buyers and Sellers.* He is also coauthor of *Managerial Decision Modeling with Spreadsheets* (4th edition), published by Pearson.

Dr. Munson has taught operations management core and elective courses at the undergraduate, MBA, and Ph.D. levels at Washington State University. He has also conducted several teaching workshops at international conferences and for Ph.D. students at Washington State University. His major awards include being a Founding Board Member of the Washington State University President's Teaching Academy (2004); winning the WSU College of Business Outstanding Teaching Award (2001 and 2015), Research Award (2004), and Service Award (2009 and 2013); and being named the WSU MBA Professor of the Year (2000 and 2008).

Paul Griffin Associate Dean, Business Degrees, Humber Institute of Technology & Advanced Learning, Toronto, Ontario, Canada. He received his Ph.D. in Management from the University of Bradford in the United Kingdom and has also achieved 18 professional designations, including Chartered Professional Accountant (CPA), Certified Management Accountant (CMA), Certified General Accountant (CGA), Certified Financial Planner (CFP), Fellow of the Canadian Securities Institute (FCSI), and several others.

Before joining academia, Dr. Griffin was engaged in the financial services sector for over 20 years and was most recently the National Director of Operations and Compliance at ING Canada. He remains an active member of several boards and committees, most notably the Insurance Institute of Canada's Ethics Advisory Board and the Financial Services Commission of Ontario's Advisory Board, and he serves as Chair of the Education Committee and Board of Directors for the Canadian Institute of Financial Planning. Before becoming Associate Dean at Humber, Dr. Griffin was a Professor and taught operations management, accounting, finance, and marketing. During that time, he received the Award of Excellence for Outstanding Academic Contribution.

Dr. Griffin continues to write for practitioner-targeted publications and develops a continuous stream of technical manuals, materials, and courses for both the academic and industrial sectors. He remains an active member of the Editorial Advisory Board for the *Journal of Financial Planning.*

Brief Table of Contents

Table of Contents

Preface

Welcome to your operations management (OM) course and to the third Canadian edition of this textbook. This text presents a state-of-the-art view of the activities of the operations function from a Canadian perspective. Operations is an exciting and dynamic area of management that has a profound effect on the productivity of both services and manufacturing. Indeed, few other activities have so much impact on the quality of your life. The goal of this book is to present a broad introduction to the field of operations in a realistic, meaningful, and practical manner. OM includes a blend of subject areas, including accounting, industrial engineering, management, management science, and statistics. Whether you are pursuing a career in the operations field or not, you will likely be working with people in operations. Therefore, having a solid understanding of the role of operations in an organization is of substantial benefit to you. This text will also help you understand how OM affects society and your life. Certainly, you will better understand what goes on behind the scenes when you buy a coffee at Tim Hortons, take a flight from Edmonton to Vancouver, place an order with Amazon.ca, or enter a Canadian hospital for medical care.

Although many readers of this book are not OM majors, students studying marketing, finance, accounting, and MIS will hopefully find the material both interesting and useful as they develop a fundamental working knowledge of the operations side of the firm.

ABOUT THE THIRD CANADIAN EDITION

The goal of this third Canadian edition is to retain the features and strengths that have made this book so successful over the years while bringing a new Canadian perspective to the text. Readers will find examples of Canadian companies and success stories woven throughout the book with cases drawn from the manufacturing and service industry taken from both the private and public sectors. The text describes many Canadian locations and uses Canadian data when available. Readers can follow the story of the construction of a hockey arena as a recurring case study that touches upon many aspects of OM in a familiar setting. It is also important to acknowledge the global nature of today's business environment. Operations management is a discipline that encompasses both the local and the international, with global considerations affecting everything from location strategies to scheduling and transportation. This third Canadian edition therefore retains many of the best and most familiar U.S. and international examples.

NEW TO THIS EDITION

We've made significant revisions to this edition, and we want to share some of the changes with you.

Five New Video Case Studies Featuring Alaska Airlines In this edition we take you behind the scenes of Alaska Airlines, consistently rated as one of the top carriers in North America. This fascinating organization opened its doors—and planes—so we could examine leading-edge OM in the airline industry. We observe the quality program at Alaska Air (Chapter 6), the process analysis behind the airline's 20-minute baggage retrieval guarantee (Chapter 7), how Alaska empowers its employees (Chapter 10), the airline's use of Lean, 5s, kaizen, and Gemba walks (Chapter 16), and the complexities of scheduling (Module B). These videos, and other video case studies that feature real companies, can be found in MyLab Operations Management.

New Sustainability in the Supply Chain Supplement 5 We have enhanced the coverage of sustainability in this edition with the inclusion of a brand-new supplement that covers the topics of corporate social responsibility, design and production for sustainability, and regulations and industry standards.

Creating Your Own Excel Spreadsheets We continue to provide two free decision support software programs, Excel OM for Windows and Mac and POM for Windows, to help you and your students solve homework problems and case studies. These excellent packages are found in MyLab Operations Management's Download Center.

Many instructors also encourage students to develop their own Excel spreadsheet models to tackle OM issues. With this edition we provide numerous examples at chapter end on how to do so. "Creating Your Own Excel Spreadsheets" examples now appear in Chapters 2, 4, 8, 12, and Supplement 6, Supplement 7, and Modules A, and F. We hope these 8 samples will help expand students' spreadsheet capabilities.

Expanding and Reordering Our Set of Homework Problems We believe that a vast selection of quality homework problems, ranging from easy to challenging (denoted by one to four dots), is critical for both instructors and students. Instructors need a broad selection of problems to choose from for homework, quizzes, and exams—without reusing the same set from semester to semester. We take pride in having more problems than any other OM text. We added dozens of new problems this edition.

Further, with the majority of our adopters now using the MyLab Operations Management learning system in their classes, we have reorganized all the homework problems—both those appearing in the printed text and the additional homework problems that are available in MyLab Operations Management—by topic heading. We identify all problems by topic.

The list of all problems by topic also appears at the end of each boxed example as well as in the Rapid Review that closes each chapter. These handy references should make it easier to assign problems for homework, quizzes, and exams. A rich set of assignable problems and cases makes the learning experience more complete and pedagogically sound.

Lean Operations In previous editions we sought to explicitly differentiate the concepts of just-in-time, Lean, and the Toyota Production System in Chapter 16. However, there is significant overlap and interchangeability among those three concepts, so we have revised Chapter 16 to incorporate the three concepts into an overall concept of "Lean". The chapter suggests that students view Lean as a comprehensive integrated operations strategy that sustains competitive advantage and results in increased returns to all stakeholders.

In addition, the following changes have been made for the third Canadian edition:
- New section on strategic planning, core competencies, and outsourcing added to Chapter 2.
- Coverage of agile and waterfall approaches to project management have been revised in Chapter 3.
- New section on supply chain management in Chapter 4.
- Added coverage of sustainability and life cycle assessment (LCA) to Chapter 5.
- New section on ISO 9000 International Quality Standards in Chapter 6.
- Coverage of bottleneck analysis in Supplement 7 has been completely revised.
- Added coverage of supplier certification, contracting, and centralized purchasing to Chapter 11.
- Added section on warehouse storage to Supplement 11.
- Coverage of economic order quantity enhanced with new section on period order quantity in Chapter 14.
- Added coverage of finite and infinite loading to Chapter 15.
- Added coverage of Lean sustainability to Chapter 16.
- Added coverage of parallel redundancy to Chapter 17.
- New examples and case studies throughout the text.

MyLab Operations Management Resources In addition to our video case studies and our Excel OM and POM for Windows software, we provide the following resources in MyLab Operations Management:
- Excel OM data files: Prepared for specific examples, these files allow users to solve all the marked text examples without reentering data.
- Active Models: These are Excel-based OM simulations, designed to help students understand the quantitative methods shown in the textbook examples. Students may change the

data to see how the changes affect the answers. These files are available in the Download Center.

- Online Tutorial Chapters: "Statistical Tools for Managers," "Acceptance Sampling," "The Simplex Method of Linear Programming," "The MODI and VAM Methods of Solving Transportation Problems," and "Vehicle Routing and Scheduling" are provided as additional material.
- Additional case studies: These case studies supplement the ones in the text.
- Virtual office hours videos: Professors Heizer, Render, and Munson walk students through the Solved Problems in a series of 5- to 20-minute explanations.

ACKNOWLEDGMENTS

We wish to acknowledge the contributions of the following reviewers who provided feedback during the development of the manuscript.

Farid Albehadili,
University of Prince Edward Island

Elkafi Hassini,
McMaster University

Gary Llewellyn Evans,
University of Prince Edward Island

Sam Lampropoulos,
George Brown College

Scott Hadley,
Sheridan College

David Roberts,
Southern Alberta Institute of Technology

Publishing a textbook requires the work of many talented individuals to handle the specialized tasks of development, photography, graphic design, illustration, editing, and production, to name only a few. I would like to thank Scott Hardie, Portfolio Manager; and Jennifer Murray, Content Developer, for her editorial guidance throughout the writing stage. I also thank the rest of the talented team: John Polanszky, Content Manager; Pippa Kennard and Christine Selvan, Project Managers; Sally Glover, Copy Editor; the team at Pearson CSC, and, finally, Spencer Snell, Marketing Manager.

But most of all, I thank my wife, Suzanne, and my children, Alexandra and Kathleen; my granddaughter, Kenna; plus Ryan and Robert, family and extended family, friends, and colleagues. I couldn't have done it without all of their support.

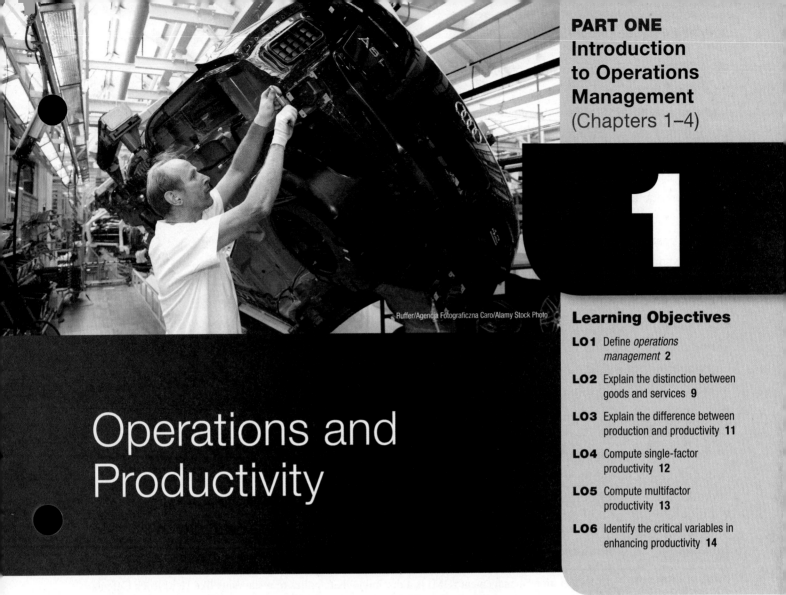

Ruffer/Agencja Fotograficzna Caro/Alamy Stock Photo

1

Operations and Productivity

Learning Objectives

LO1 Define *operations management* 2

LO2 Explain the distinction between goods and services 9

LO3 Explain the difference between production and productivity 11

LO4 Compute single-factor productivity 12

LO5 Compute multifactor productivity 13

LO6 Identify the critical variables in enhancing productivity 14

Operations Management at Hard Rock Cafe

Operations managers throughout the world are producing products daily to provide for the well-being of society. These products take on a multitude of forms, including auto parts at Magna International, motion pictures at DreamWorks Studios, rides at Disney World, and food at Hard Rock Cafe. These firms produce thousands of complex products every day—to be delivered as the customer ordered them, when the customer wants them, and where the customer wants them. Hard Rock does this for over 35 million guests worldwide every year. This is a challenging task, and the operations manager's job—whether at Magna International, DreamWorks, Disney, or Hard Rock—is demanding.

Orlando-based Hard Rock Cafe opened its first restaurant in London in 1971, making it over four decades old and the granddaddy of theme restaurants. Although other theme restaurants have come and gone, Hard Rock is still going strong, with 150 restaurants in 53 countries—and new restaurants opening each year. Hard Rock made its name with rock music memorabilia, having started when Eric Clapton, a regular customer, marked his favourite bar stool by hanging his guitar on the wall in the London cafe. Now Hard

< **Global Company Profile Hard Rock Cafe**

1

Rock has 70 000 items and millions of dollars invested in memorabilia. To keep customers coming back time and again, Hard Rock creates value in the form of good food and entertainment.

The operations managers at Hard Rock Cafe at Universal Studios in Orlando provide more than 3500 custom products—in this case, meals—every day. These products are designed, tested, and then analyzed for cost of ingredients, labour requirements, and customer satisfaction. On approval, menu items are put into production—and then only if the ingredients are available from qualified suppliers. The production process—from receiving, to cold storage, to grilling or baking or frying, and a dozen other steps—is designed and maintained to yield a quality meal. Operations managers, using the best people they can recruit and train, also prepare effective employee schedules and design efficient layouts.

Managers who successfully design and deliver goods and services throughout the world understand operations. In this textbook, we look not only at how

Hard Rock Cafe in Orlando, Florida, prepares over 3500 meals each day. Seating more than 1500 people, it is one of the largest restaurants in the world. But Hard Rock's operations managers serve the hot food hot and the cold food cold.

Andre Jenny/Alamy Stock Photo

Hard Rock's managers create value but also at how operations managers in other services, as well as in manufacturing, do so. Operations management is demanding, challenging, and exciting. It affects our lives every day. Ultimately, operations managers determine how well we live.

What Is Operations Management?

LO1 Define *operations management*

VIDEO 1.1
Operations Management at Hard Rock

VIDEO 1.2
Operations Management at Frito-Lay

Production
The creation of goods and services.

Operations management (OM)
Activities that relate to the creation of goods and services through the transformation of inputs to outputs.

Operations management (OM) is a discipline that applies to restaurants like Hard Rock Cafe as well as to factories like Ford and Whirlpool. The techniques of OM apply throughout the world to virtually all productive enterprises. It doesn't matter if the application is in an office, a hospital, a restaurant, a department store, or a factory—the production of goods and services requires operations management. And the *efficient* production of goods and services requires effective application of the concepts, tools, and techniques of OM that we introduce in this book.

As we progress through this text, we will discover how to manage operations in a changing global economy. An array of informative examples, charts, text discussions, and pictures illustrate concepts and provide information. We will see how operations managers create the goods and services that enrich our lives.

In this chapter, we first define *operations management*, explaining its heritage and exploring the exciting role operations managers play in a huge variety of organizations. Then we discuss production and productivity in both goods- and service-producing firms. This is followed by a discussion of operations in the service sector and the challenge of managing an effective and efficient production system.

Production is the creation of goods and services. **Operations management (OM)** is the set of activities that creates value in the form of goods and services by transforming inputs into outputs. Activities creating goods and services take place in all organizations. In manufacturing firms, the production activities that create goods are usually quite obvious. In them, we can see the creation of a tangible product such as a Sony TV or a Harley-Davidson motorcycle.

In an organization that does not create a tangible good or product, the production function may be less obvious. We often call these activities *services*. The services may be "hidden" from the public and even from the customer. The product may take such forms as the transfer of funds from a savings account to a chequing account, the transplant of a human organ, the filling of an empty seat on an airplane, or the education of a student. Regardless of whether the end product is a good or service, the production activities that go on in the organization are often referred to as operations, or *operations management*.

Organizing to Produce Goods and Services

To create goods and services, all organizations perform three functions (see Figure 1.1). These functions are the necessary ingredients not only for production but also for an organization's survival. They are:

1. *Marketing*, which generates the demand, or at least takes the order for a product or service (nothing happens until there is a sale).

Let's begin by defining what this course is about.

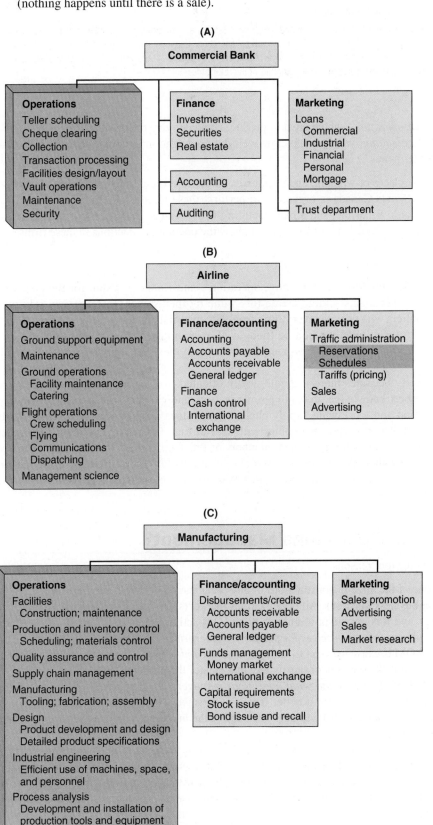

FIGURE 1.1

Organization Charts for Two Service Organizations and One Manufacturing Organization

(A) A bank, (B) an airline, and (C) a manufacturing organization. The blue areas are OM activities.

(A)

Commercial Bank

Operations
Teller scheduling
Cheque clearing
Collection
Transaction processing
Facilities design/layout
Vault operations
Maintenance
Security

Finance
Investments
Securities
Real estate

Accounting

Auditing

Marketing
Loans
  Commercial
  Industrial
  Financial
  Personal
  Mortgage

Trust department

(B)

Airline

Operations
Ground support equipment
Maintenance
Ground operations
  Facility maintenance
  Catering
Flight operations
  Crew scheduling
  Flying
  Communications
  Dispatching
Management science

Finance/accounting
Accounting
  Accounts payable
  Accounts receivable
  General ledger
Finance
  Cash control
  International
    exchange

Marketing
Traffic administration
  Reservations
  Schedules
  Tariffs (pricing)
Sales
Advertising

(C)

Manufacturing

Operations
Facilities
  Construction; maintenance
Production and inventory control
  Scheduling; materials control
Quality assurance and control
Supply chain management
Manufacturing
  Tooling; fabrication; assembly
Design
  Product development and design
  Detailed product specifications
Industrial engineering
  Efficient use of machines, space,
  and personnel
Process analysis
  Development and installation of
  production tools and equipment

Finance/accounting
Disbursements/credits
  Accounts receivable
  Accounts payable
  General ledger
Funds management
  Money market
  International exchange
Capital requirements
  Stock issue
  Bond issue and recall

Marketing
Sales promotion
Advertising
Sales
Market research

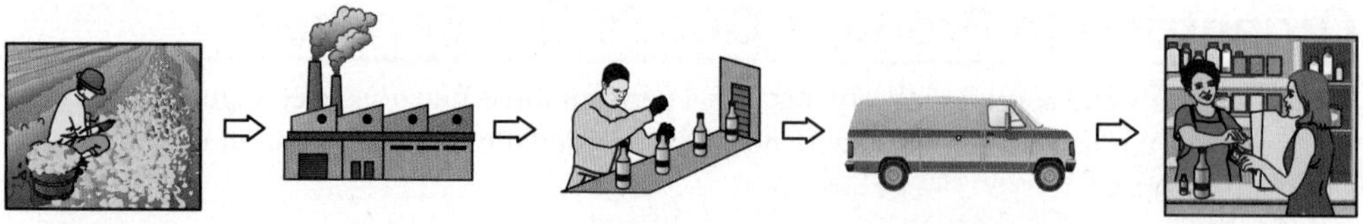

Farmer   Syrup   Bottler   Distributor   Retailer
              producer

FIGURE 1.2 Soft Drink Supply Chain

A supply chain for a bottle of Coke requires a beet or sugar cane farmer, a syrup producer, a bottler, a distributor, and a retailer, each adding value to satisfy a customer. Only with collaborations between all members of the supply chain can efficiency and customer satisfaction be maximized. The supply chain, in general, starts with the provider of basic raw materials and continues all the way to the final customer at the retail store.

2. *Production/operations*, which creates, produces, and delivers the product.
3. *Finance/accounting*, which tracks how well the organization is doing, pays the bills, and collects the money.

Universities, places of worship, and businesses all perform these functions. Even a volunteer group such as Scouts Canada is organized to perform these three basic functions. Figure 1.1 shows how a bank, an airline, and a manufacturing firm organize themselves to perform these functions. The blue-shaded areas of Figure 1.1 show the operations functions in these firms.

THE SUPPLY CHAIN

Supply chain

A global network of organizations and activities that supplies a firm with goods and services.

Through the three functions—marketing, operations, and finance—value for the customer is created. However, firms seldom create this value by themselves. Instead, they rely on a variety of suppliers who provide everything from raw materials to accounting services. These suppliers, when taken together, can be thought of as a supply chain. A **supply chain** (see Figure 1.2) is a global network of organizations and activities that supply a firm with goods and services.

As our society becomes more technologically oriented, we see increasing specialization. Specialized expert knowledge, instant communication, and cheaper transportation also foster specialization and worldwide supply chains. It just does not pay for a firm to try to do everything itself. The expertise that comes with specialization exists up and down the supply chain, adding value at each step. When members of the supply chain collaborate to achieve high levels of customer satisfaction, we have a tremendous force for efficiency and competitive advantage. Competition in the 21st century is no longer between companies; it is between supply chains.

Why Study Operations Management?

We study OM for four reasons:

1. OM is one of the three major functions of any organization, and it is integrally related to all the other business functions. All organizations market (sell), finance (account), and produce (operate), and it is important to know how the OM activity functions. Therefore, we study *how people organize themselves for productive enterprise.*
2. We study OM because we want to know *how goods and services are produced.* The production function is the segment of our society that creates the products and services we use.
3. We study OM to *understand what operations managers do.* Regardless of your job in an organization, you can perform better if you understand what operations managers do. In addition, understanding OM will help you explore the numerous and lucrative career opportunities in the field.
4. We study OM *because it is such a costly part of an organization.* A large percentage of the revenue of most firms is spent in the OM function. Indeed, OM provides a major opportunity for an organization to improve its profitability and enhance its service to society. Example 1 considers how a firm might increase its profitability via the production function.

Fisher Technologies is a small firm that must double its dollar contribution to fixed cost and profit in order to be profitable enough to purchase the next generation of production equipment. Management has determined that if the firm fails to increase its contribution, its bank will not make the loan and the equipment cannot be purchased. If the firm cannot purchase the equipment, the limitations of the old equipment will force Fisher to go out of business and, in doing so, put its employees out of work and discontinue producing goods and services for its customers.

APPROACH ▶ Table 1.1 shows a simple profit-and-loss statement and three strategic options (marketing, finance/accounting, and operations) for the firm. The first option is a *marketing option*, where good marketing management may increase sales by 50%. By increasing sales by 50%, contribution will in turn increase 71%. But increasing sales 50% may be difficult; it may even be impossible.

EXAMPLE 1

Examining the Options for Increasing Contribution

Table 1.1

Options for Increasing Contribution

	Current	Marketing Option[a] Increase Sales Revenue 50%	Finance/ Accounting Option[b] Reduce Finance Costs 50%	OM Option[c] Reduce Production Costs 20%
Sales	$100 000	$ 150 000	$100 000	$100 000
Costs of goods	−80 000	−120 000	−80 000	−64 000
Gross margin	20 000	30 000	20 000	36 000
Finance costs	−6 000	−6 000	−3 000	−6 000
Subtotal	14 000	24 000	17 000	30 000
Taxes at 25%	−3 500	−6 000	−4 250	−7 500
Contribution[d]	$ 10 500	$ 18 000	$ 12 750	$ 22 500

[a] Increasing sales 50% increases contribution by $7500, or 71% (= 7500/10 500).
[b] Reducing finance costs 50% increases contribution by $2250, or 21% (= 2250/10 500).
[c] Reducing production costs 20% increases contribution by $12 000, or 114% (= 12 000/10 500).
[d] Contribution to fixed costs (excluding finance costs) and profit.

The second option is a *finance/accounting option*, where finance costs are cut in half through good financial management. But even a reduction of 50% is still inadequate for generating the necessary increase in contribution. Contribution is increased by only 21%.

The third option is an *OM option*, where management reduces production costs by 20% and increases contribution by 114%.

SOLUTION ▶ Given the conditions of our brief example, Fisher Technologies has increased contribution from $10 500 to $22 500. It may now have a bank willing to lend it additional funds.

INSIGHT ▶ The OM option not only yields the greatest improvement in contribution but also may be the only feasible option. Increasing sales by 50% and decreasing finance costs by 50% may both be virtually impossible. Reducing operations costs by 20% may be difficult but feasible.

LEARNING EXERCISE ▶ What is the impact of only a 15% decrease in costs in the OM option? [Answer: A $19 500 contribution; approximately an 86% increase.]

Example 1 underscores the importance of an effective operations activity of a firm. Development of increasingly effective operations is the approach taken by many companies as they face growing global competition.

What Operations Managers Do

All good managers perform the basic functions of the management process. The **management process** consists of *planning*, *organizing*, *staffing*, *leading*, and *controlling*. Operations managers apply this management process to the decisions they make in the OM function. The 10 major decisions of OM are shown in Table 1.2. Successfully addressing each of these decisions requires planning, organizing, staffing, leading, and controlling. Typical issues relevant to these decisions and the chapter in which each is discussed are also shown.

An operations manager must successfully address the 10 decisions around which this text is organized.

Management process
The application of planning, organizing, staffing, leading, and controlling to the achievement of objectives.

Table 1.2
**10 Critical Decisions
of Operations Management**

10 Decision Areas	Issues	Chapter(s)
1. Design of goods and services	What good or service should we offer? How should we design these products?	5
2. Managing quality	How do we define the quality? Who is responsible for quality?	6, Supplement 6
3. Process and capacity design	What process and what capacity will these products require? What equipment and technology are necessary for these processes?	7, Supplement 7
4. Location strategy	Where should we put the facility? On what criteria should we base the location decision?	8
5. Layout strategy	How should we arrange the facility? How large must the facility be to meet our plan?	9
6. Human resources and job design	How do we provide a reasonable work environment? How much can we expect our employees to produce?	10
7. Supply chain management	Should we make or buy this component? Who should be our suppliers, and how can we integrate them into our strategy?	11, Supplement 11
8. Inventory, material requirements planning, and JIT (just-in-time)	How much inventory of each item should we have? When do we reorder?	12, 14, 16
9. Intermediate and short-term scheduling	Are we better off keeping people on the payroll during slowdowns? Which job do we perform next?	13, 15
10. Maintenance	Who is responsible for maintenance?	17

STUDENT | TIP

Current OM emphasis on quality and supply chain has increased job opportunities in these 10 areas.

WHERE ARE THE OM JOBS?

How does one get started on a career in operations? The 10 OM decisions identified in Table 1.2 are made by individuals who work in the disciplines shown in the blue areas of Figure 1.1. Competent business students who know their accounting, statistics, finance, and OM have an opportunity to assume entry-level positions in all of these areas. As you read this text, identify disciplines that can assist you in making these decisions, then take courses in those areas. The more background an OM student has in accounting, statistics, information systems, and mathematics, the more job opportunities will be available. About 40% of all jobs are in OM.

The following professional organizations provide various certifications that may enhance your education and be of help in your career:

- APICS, the Association for Operations Management (**www.apics.org**)
- Standards Council of Canada (**www.scc.ca**)
- Institute for Supply Management (ISM) (**www.instituteforsupplymanagement.org**)
- Project Management Institute (PMI) (**www.pmi.org**)
- Council of Supply Chain Management Professionals (**www.cscmp.org**)

Figure 1.3 shows some possible job opportunities.

The Heritage of Operations Management

The field of OM is relatively young, but its history is rich and interesting. Our lives and the OM discipline have been enhanced by the innovations and contributions of numerous individuals. We now introduce a few of these people, and we provide a summary of significant events in operations management in Figure 1.4.

Eli Whitney (1800) is credited for the early popularization of interchangeable parts, which was achieved through standardization and quality control. Through a contract he signed with the

| Operations Management Positions |
| SEARCH JOBS |

| Date | Job Title |

1/15 **Plant Manager**

Division of Fortune 1000 company seeks plant manager for plant located in the Vancouver area. This plant manufactures loading dock equipment for commercial markets. The candidate must be experienced in plant management including expertise in production planning, purchasing, and inventory management. Good written and oral communication skills are a must, along with excellent application of skills in managing people.

2/23 **Operations Analyst**

Expanding national coffee shop: top 10 "Best Places to Work" wants junior-level systems analyst to join our excellent store improvement team. Business or I.E. degree, work methods, labour standards, ergonomics, cost accounting knowledge a plus. This is a hands-on job and excellent opportunity for a team player with good people skills. West coast location. Some travel required.

3/18 **Quality Manager**

Several openings exist in our small package processing facilities in Montreal and Winnipeg for quality managers. These highly visible positions require extensive use of statistical tools to monitor all aspects of service, timeliness, and workload measurement. The work involves (1) a combination of hands-on applications and detailed analysis using databases and spreadsheets, (2) process audits to identify areas for improvement, and (3) management of implementation of changes. Positions involve night hours and weekends. Send résumé.

4/6 **Supply Chain Manager and Planner**

Responsibilities entail negotiating contracts and establishing long-term relationships with suppliers. We will rely on the selected candidate to maintain accuracy in the purchasing system, invoices, and product returns. A bachelor's degree and up to two years' related experience are required. Working knowledge of MRP, ability to use feedback to master scheduling and suppliers and consolidate orders for best price and delivery are necessary. Proficiency in all PC Windows applications, particularly Excel and Word, is essential. Knowledge of Oracle business systems is a plus. Effective verbal and written communication skills are essential.

5/14 **Process Improvement Consultants**

An expanding consulting firm is seeking consultants to design and implement lean production and cycle time reduction plans in both service and manufacturing processes. Our firm is currently working with an international bank to improve its back office operations, as well as with several manufacturing firms. A business degree required; APICS certification a plus.

FIGURE 1.3 **Many Opportunities Exist for Operations Managers**

Cost Focus		Quality Focus	Customization Focus
Early Concepts **1776–1880**	**Mass Production Era** **1910–1980**	**Lean Production Era** **1980–1995**	**Mass Customization Era** **1995–2015**
Labour Specialization (Smith, Babbage)	Moving Assembly Line (Ford/Sorensen)	Just-in-Time (JIT)	Globalization
Standardized Parts (Whitney)	Statistical Sampling (Shewhart)	Computer-Aided Design (CAD)	Internet/Ecommerce
	Economic Order Quantity (Harris)	Electronic Data Interchange (EDI)	Enterprise Resource Planning
Scientific Management Era **1880–1910**		Total Quality Management (TQM)	International Quality Standards (ISO)
Gantt Charts (Gantt)	Linear Programming	Baldrige Award	Finite Scheduling
Motion & Time Studies (Gilbreth)	PERT/CPM (DuPont)	Empowerment	Supply Chain Management
Process Analysis (Taylor)	Material Requirements Planning (MRP)	Kanbans	Mass Customization
Queuing Theory (Erlang)			Build-to-Order
			Sustainability

FIGURE 1.4 **Significant Events in Operations Management**

U.S. government for 10 000 muskets, he was able to command a premium price because of their interchangeable parts.

Frederick W. Taylor (1881), known as the father of scientific management, contributed to personnel selection, planning and scheduling, motion study, and the now popular field of ergonomics. One of his major contributions was his belief that management should be much more resourceful and aggressive in the improvement of work methods. Taylor and his colleagues, Henry L. Gantt and Frank and Lillian Gilbreth, were among the first to systematically seek the best way to produce.

Another of Taylor's contributions was the belief that management should assume more responsibility for:

1. Matching employees to the right job.
2. Providing the proper training.
3. Providing proper work methods and tools.
4. Establishing legitimate incentives for work to be accomplished.

By 1913, Henry Ford and Charles Sorensen combined what they knew about standardized parts with the quasi-assembly lines of the meatpacking and mail-order industries and added the revolutionary concept of the assembly line, where men stood still and material moved.

Quality control is another historically significant contribution to the field of OM. Walter Shewhart (1924) combined his knowledge of statistics with the need for quality control and provided the foundations for statistical sampling in quality control. W. Edwards Deming (1950) believed, as did Frederick Taylor, that management must do more to improve the work environment and processes so that quality can be improved.

Operations management will continue to progress with contributions from other disciplines, including *industrial engineering* and *management science*. These disciplines, along with statistics, management, and economics, contribute to improved models and decision making.

Innovations from the *physical sciences* (biology, anatomy, chemistry, and physics) have also contributed to advances in OM. These innovations include new adhesives, faster integrated circuits, gamma rays to sanitize food products, and higher-quality glass for LCD and plasma TVs. Innovation in products and processes often depends on advances in the physical sciences.

Especially important contributions to OM have come from *information technology*, which we define as the systematic processing of data to yield information. Information technology—with wireless links, internet, and ecommerce—is reducing costs and accelerating communication.

Decisions in operations management require individuals who are well versed in management science, in information technology, and often in one of the biological or physical sciences. In this textbook, we look at the diverse ways a student can prepare for a career in operations management.

Operations in the Service Sector

Manufacturers produce a tangible product, while service products are often intangible. But many products are a combination of a good and a service, which complicates the definition of a service. Even the Canadian government has trouble generating a consistent definition. Because definitions vary, much of the data and statistics generated about the service sector are inconsistent. However, we define **services** as including repair and maintenance, government, food and lodging, transportation, insurance, trade, financial, real estate, education, law, medicine, entertainment, and other professional occupations.

Services
Economic activities that typically produce an intangible product (such as education, entertainment, lodging, government, financial, and health services).

DIFFERENCES BETWEEN GOODS AND SERVICES

LO2 Explain the distinction between goods and services

Let's examine some of the differences between goods and services:

- Services are usually *intangible* (for example, your purchase of a ride in an empty airline seat between two cities) as opposed to a tangible good.
- Services are often *produced and consumed simultaneously*; there is no stored inventory. For instance, the beauty salon produces a haircut that is "consumed" simultaneously, or the doctor produces an operation that is "consumed" as it is produced. We have not yet figured out how to inventory haircuts or appendectomies.
- Services are often *unique*. Your mix of financial coverage, such as investments and insurance policies, may not be the same as anyone else's, just as the medical procedure or a haircut produced for you is not exactly like anyone else's.
- Services have *high customer interaction*. Services are often difficult to standardize, automate, and make as efficient as we would like because customer interaction demands uniqueness. In fact, in many cases this uniqueness is what the customer is paying for; therefore, the operations manager must ensure that the product is designed (i.e., customized) so that it can be delivered in the required unique manner.
- Services have *inconsistent product definition*. Product definition may be rigorous, as in the case of an auto insurance policy, but inconsistent because policyholders change cars and policies mature.
- Services are often *knowledge based*, as in the case of educational, medical, and legal services, and therefore hard to automate.
- Services are frequently *dispersed*. Dispersion occurs because services are frequently brought to the client/customer via a local office, a retail outlet, or even a house call.

The activities of the operations function are often very similar for both goods and services. For instance, both goods and services must have quality standards established, and both must be designed and processed on a schedule in a facility where human resources are employed.

Having made the distinction between goods and services, we should point out that, in many cases, the distinction is not clear-cut. In reality, almost all services and almost all goods are a mixture of a service and a tangible product. Even services such as consulting may require a tangible report. Similarly, the sale of most goods includes a service. For instance, many products have the service components of financing and delivery (e.g., automobile sales). Many also require after-sale training and maintenance (e.g., office copiers and machinery). "Service" activities may also be an integral part of production. Human resource activities, logistics, accounting, training, field service, and repair are all service activities, but they take place within a manufacturing organization. Very few services are "pure," meaning they have no tangible component. Counselling may be one of the exceptions.

GROWTH OF SERVICES

Services constitute the largest economic sector in postindustrial societies. Until about 1900, many Canadians were employed in agriculture. Increased agricultural productivity allowed people to leave the farm and seek employment in the city. Similarly, manufacturing employment has decreased in North America in the past 30 years. The Canadian market tends to follow U.S. trends, as can be seen in the following comparison. The changes in U.S. agriculture, manufacturing, and service employment are shown in Figure 1.5. Although the number of people employed in manufacturing has decreased since 1950, each person is now producing almost 20 times more than in 1950. Services became the dominant employer in the early 1920s, with manufacturing employment peaking at about 32% in 1950. The huge productivity increases in

FIGURE 1.5
U.S. Agriculture, Manufacturing, and Service Employment
Source: U.S. Bureau of Labor Statistics.

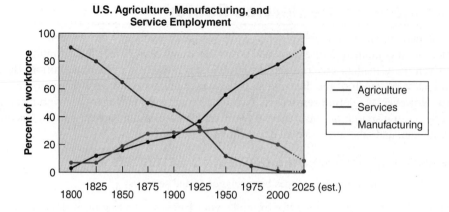

U.S. Agriculture, Manufacturing, and Service Employment

Service sector

The segment of the economy that includes trade, financial, lodging, education, legal, medical, and other professional occupations.

STUDENT | TIP

Service jobs with their operations component are growing as a percentage of all jobs.

agriculture and manufacturing have allowed more of our economic resources to be devoted to services. Consequently, much of the world can now enjoy the pleasures of education, health services, entertainment, and myriad other things that we call services. Examples of firms and percentage of employment in the Canadian **service sector** are shown in Table 1.3. The table also provides employment percentages for the nonservice sectors of manufacturing, construction, utilities, agriculture, and mining on the bottom five lines.

SERVICE PAY

Although there is a common perception that service industries are low paying, in fact, many service jobs pay very well. Operations managers in the maintenance facility of an airline are very

Table 1.3

Examples of Organizations in Each Sector

Sector	Example	Percent of All Jobs
Service-Producing Sector		
Trade	Hudson Bay Company; Real Canadian Superstore	15%
Transportation and warehousing	WestJet; Maritime–Ontario Freight Lines Limited	5%
Finance, insurance, real estate, and leasing	Royal Bank; Manulife	6%
Professional, scientific, and technical services	Borden Ladner Gervais Law Firm	8%
Business, building, and other support services[1]	Edmonton Waste Management Centre; Carlson Wagonlit Travel	4%
Educational services	McGill University	7%
Health care and social assistance	SickKids Hospital	12%
Information, culture, and recreation	Calgary Flames; Princess of Wales Theatre	5%
Accommodation and food services	Tim Hortons; Royal York Hotel	6%
Other Services	Joe's Barber Shop; ABC Landscaping	4%
Public administration	Province of Manitoba; City of Hamilton	6%
Goods-Producing Sector		22%
Agriculture	Farming Operations	2%
Forestry, fishing, mining, quarrying, oil, and gas[2]	Canadian Mining Company Inc.; Dome Pacific Logging Ltd.	2%
Utilities	Ontario Power Generation	1%
Construction	PCL Construction Management Inc.	7%
Manufacturing	Magna International Inc.	10%

[1] Formerly "Management of companies, administrative, and other support services."
[2] Also referred to as "Natural resources."

Source: Statistics Canada, CANSIM, table 282-0008 and Catalogue no. 71F0004XCB.

well paid, as are the operations managers who supervise computer services to the financial community. However, the accommodation and food services sectors followed by the arts, recreation, and entertainment sectors offer the lowest average weekly pay levels in Canada.

New Challenges in Operations Management

Operations managers work in an exciting and dynamic environment that is the result of a variety of challenging forces, from globalization of world trade to the transfer of ideas, products, and money at electronic speeds. Let's look at some of these challenges:

- *Global focus:* The rapid decline in communication and transportation costs has made markets global. Similarly, resources in the form of capital, materials, talent, and labour are also now global. As a result, countries throughout the world are contributing to globalization as they vie for economic growth. Operations managers are rapidly seeking creative designs, efficient production, and high-quality goods via international collaboration.
- *Supply chain partnering:* Shorter product life cycles, demanding customers, and fast changes in technology, materials, and processes require supply chain partners to be in tune with the needs of end users. And because suppliers may be able to contribute unique expertise, operations managers are outsourcing and building long-term partnerships with critical players in the supply chain.
- *Sustainability:* Operations managers' continuing battle to improve productivity is concerned with designing products and processes that are ecologically sustainable. This means designing green products and packaging that minimize resource use, can be recycled or reused, and are generally environmentally friendly.
- *Rapid product development:* Technology combined with rapid international communication of news, entertainment, and lifestyles is dramatically chopping away at the lifespan of products. OM is answering with new management structures, enhanced collaboration, digital technology, and creative alliances that are more responsive and effective.
- *Mass customization:* Once managers recognize the world as the marketplace, the cultural and individual differences become quite obvious. In a world where consumers are increasingly aware of innovation and options, substantial pressure is placed on firms to respond in a creative way. And OM must rapidly respond with product designs and flexible production processes that cater to the individual whims of consumers. The goal is to produce customized products, whenever and wherever needed.
- *Lean operations:* Lean is the management model sweeping the world and providing the standard against which operations managers must compete. Lean can be thought of as the driving force in a well-run operation, where the customer is satisfied, employees are respected, and waste does not exist. The theme of this text is to build organizations that are more efficient, where management creates enriched jobs that help employees engage in continuous improvement and where goods and services are produced and delivered when and where the customer desires them. These ideas are captured in the phrase *Lean*.

These trends are part of the exciting OM challenges currently facing operations managers.

The Productivity Challenge

The creation of goods and services requires changing resources into goods and services. The more efficiently we make this change, the more productive we are and the more value is added to the good or service provided. **Productivity** is the ratio of outputs (goods and services) divided by the inputs (resources, such as labour and capital) (see Figure 1.6). The operations manager's job is to enhance (improve) this ratio of outputs to inputs. Improving productivity means improving efficiency. *Efficiency* means doing the job well—with a minimum of resources and waste. Note the distinction between being *efficient*, which implies doing the job well, and being *effective*, which means doing the right thing. A job well done—say, by applying the 10 decisions of operations management—helps us be *efficient*; developing and using the correct strategy helps us be *effective*.

FIGURE 1.6

The Economic System Adds Value by Transforming Inputs to Outputs

An effective feedback loop evaluates performance against a strategy or standard. It also evaluates customer satisfaction and sends signals to managers controlling the inputs and transformation process.

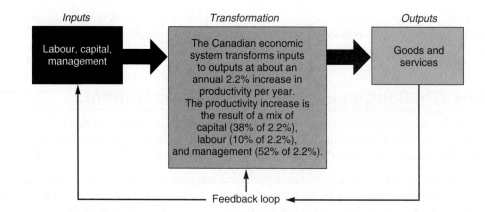

This improvement can be achieved in two ways: reducing inputs while keeping output constant, or increasing output while keeping inputs constant. Both represent an improvement in productivity. In an economic sense, inputs are labour, capital, and management, which are integrated into a production system. Management creates this production system, which provides the conversion of inputs to outputs. Outputs are goods and services, including such diverse items as guns, butter, education, improved judicial systems, and ski resorts. *Production* is the making of goods and services. High production may imply only that more people are working and that employment levels are high (low unemployment), but it does not imply high *productivity*.

Measurement of productivity is an excellent way to evaluate a country's ability to provide an improving standard of living for its people. *Only through increases in productivity can the standard of living improve.* Moreover, only through increases in productivity can labour, capital, and management receive additional payments. If returns to labour, capital, or management are increased without increased productivity, prices rise. On the other hand, downward pressure is placed on prices when productivity increases, because more is being produced with the same resources.

The benefits of increased productivity are illustrated in the *OM in Action* box "Improving Productivity at Starbucks". Since 1973, labour productivity in Canada has experienced an annual rate of growth averaging approximately 1.25%, down considerably from the previous level of 3.00% during the period between 1961 and 1973. An increase of one percentage point in this performance would almost double the annual growth rate to 2.25%. Such a growth rate in labour productivity would mean that the average level of labour productivity in Canada would double every 32 years, not every 58 years as it will with a 1.25% growth rate. Moreover, if our labour productivity level were to double every 32 years, then (in the absence of major demographic effects) so would Canada's standard of living.

PRODUCTIVITY MEASUREMENT

LO4 Compute single-factor productivity

In this text, we examine how to improve productivity through operations management. Productivity is a significant issue for the world and one that the operations manager is uniquely qualified to address.

The measurement of productivity can be quite direct. Such is the case when productivity is measured by labour-hours per tonne of a specific type of steel. Although labour-hours are a common measure of input, other measures such as capital (dollars invested), materials (tonnes of ore), or energy (kilowatts of electricity) can be used.[1] An example of this can be summarized in the following equation:

$$\text{Productivity} = \frac{\text{Units produced}}{\text{Input used}} \quad \text{(1-1)}$$

---

[1] The quality and time period are assumed to remain constant.

OM in Action   Improving Productivity at Starbucks

"This is a game of seconds . . ." says Silva Peterson, whom Starbucks has put in charge of saving seconds. Her team of 10 analysts is constantly asking themselves: "How can we shave time off this?"

Peterson's analysis suggested that there were some obvious opportunities. First, stop requiring signatures on credit card purchases under $25. This sliced 8 seconds off the transaction time at the cash register.

Then analysts noticed that Starbucks's largest cold beverage, the Venti size, required two bending and digging motions to scoop up enough ice. The scoop was too small. Redesign of the scoop provided the proper amount in one motion and cut 14 seconds off the average time of one minute.

Third were new espresso machines; with the push of a button, the machines grind coffee beans and brew. This allowed the server, called a "barista" in Starbucks's vocabulary, to do other things. The savings: about 12 seconds per espresso shot.

As a result, operations improvements at Starbucks outlets have increased the average yearly volume by nearly $200 000, to about $940 000 in the past six years. This is a 27% improvement in productivity—about 4.5% per year. In the service industry, a 4.5% per year increase is very tasty.

Sources: Based on *The Wall Street Journal* (August 4, 2009): A1, A10 and (April 12, 2005): B2:B7; *Industrial Engineer* (January 2006): 66; and www.finfacts.com, October 6, 2005.

For example, if units produced = 1000 and labour-hours used is 250, then:

$$\text{Single-factor productivity} = \frac{\text{Units produced}}{\text{Labour-hours used}} = \frac{1000}{250} = 4 \text{ units per labour-hour}$$

The use of just one resource input to measure productivity, as shown in Equation (1-1), is known as **single-factor productivity**. However, a broader view of productivity is **multifactor productivity**, which includes all inputs (e.g., capital, labour, material, energy). Multifactor productivity is also known as *total factor productivity*. Multifactor productivity is calculated by combining the input units as shown here:

$$\text{Multifactor productivity} = \frac{\text{Output}}{\text{Labour} + \text{Material} + \text{Energy} + \text{Capital} + \text{Miscellaneous}} \quad \text{(1-2)}$$

To aid in the computation of multifactor productivity, the individual inputs (the denominator) can be expressed in dollars and summed as shown in Example 2.

LO5 Compute multifactor productivity

Single-factor productivity
Indicates the ratio of the goods and services produced (outputs) to one resource (input).

Multifactor productivity
Indicates the ratio of the goods and services produced (outputs) to many or all resources (inputs).

Collins Title wants to evaluate its labour and multifactor productivity with a new computerized title-search system. The company has a staff of four, each working eight hours per day (for a payroll cost of $640/day) and overhead expenses of $400 per day. Collins processes and closes on eight titles each day. The new computerized title-search system will allow the processing of 14 titles per day. Although the staff, their work hours, and pay are the same, the overhead expenses are now $800 per day.

APPROACH ▶ Collins uses Equation (1-1) to compute labour productivity and Equation (1-2) to compute multifactor productivity.

SOLUTION ▶

$$\text{Labour productivity with the old system:} \frac{8 \text{ titles per day}}{32 \text{ labour-hours}} = 0.25 \text{ titles per labour-hour}$$

$$\text{Labour productivity with the new system:} \frac{14 \text{ titles per day}}{32 \text{ labour-hours}} = 0.4375 \text{ titles per labour-hour}$$

$$\text{Multifactor productivity with the old system:} \frac{8 \text{ titles per day}}{\$640 + 400} = 0.0077 \text{ titles per dollar}$$

$$\text{Multifactor productivity with the new system:} \frac{14 \text{ titles per day}}{\$640 + 800} = 0.0097 \text{ titles per dollar}$$

EXAMPLE 2

Computing Single-Factor and Multifactor Gains in Productivity

Labour productivity has increased from 0.25 to 0.4375. The change is $(0.4375 - 0.25)/0.25 = 0.75$, or a 75% increase in labour productivity. Multifactor productivity has increased from 0.0077 to 0.0097. This change is $(0.0097 - 0.0077)/0.0077 = 0.26$, or a 26% increase in multifactor productivity.

INSIGHT ▶ Both the labour (single-factor) and multifactor productivity measures show an increase in productivity. However, the multifactor measure provides a better picture of the increase because it includes all the costs connected with the increase in output.

LEARNING EXERCISE ▶ If the overhead goes to \$960 (rather than \$800), what is the multifactor productivity? [Answer: 0.00875.]

RELATED PROBLEMS ▶ 1.1, 1.2, 1.5, 1.6, 1.7, 1.8, 1.9, 1.11, 1.12, 1.14, 1.15

Use of productivity measures aids managers in determining how well they are doing. But results from the two measures can be expected to vary. If labour productivity growth is entirely the result of capital spending, measuring just labour distorts the results. Multifactor productivity is usually better but more complicated. Labour productivity is the more popular measure. The multifactor-productivity measures provide better information about the trade-offs among factors, but substantial measurement problems remain. Some of these measurement problems are:

1. *Quality* may change while the quantity of inputs and outputs remains constant. Compare an HDTV of this decade with a black-and-white TV of the 1950s. Both are TVs, but few people would deny that the quality has improved. The unit of measure—a TV—is the same, but the quality has changed.
2. *External elements* may cause an increase or a decrease in productivity for which the system under study may not be directly responsible. A more reliable electric power service may greatly improve production, thereby improving the firm's productivity because of this support system rather than because of managerial decisions made within the firm.
3. *Precise units of measure* may be lacking. Not all automobiles require the same inputs: Some cars are subcompacts; others are 911 Turbo Porsches.

Productivity measurement is particularly difficult in the service sector, where the end product can be hard to define. For example, economic statistics ignore the quality of your haircut, the outcome of a court case, or service at a retail store. In some cases, adjustments are made for the quality of the product sold but *not* for the quality of the sales presentation or the advantage of a broader product selection. Productivity measurements require specific inputs and outputs, but a free economy is producing worth—what people want—which includes convenience, speed, and safety. Traditional measures of outputs may be a very poor measure of these other measures of worth. Note the quality-measurement problems in a law office, where each case is different, altering the accuracy of the measure "cases per labour-hour" or "cases per employee".

PRODUCTIVITY VARIABLES

Productivity variables

The three factors critical to productivity improvement—labour, capital and management.

As we saw in Figure 1.6, productivity increases are dependent on three **productivity variables**:

1. *Labour*, which contributes about 10% of the annual increase.
2. *Capital*, which contributes about 38% of the annual increase.
3. *Management*, which contributes about 52% of the annual increase.

These three factors are critical to improved productivity. They represent the broad areas in which managers can take action to improve productivity.

LO6 Identify the critical variables in enhancing productivity

LABOUR Improvement in the contribution of labour to productivity is the result of a healthier, better-educated, and better-nourished labour force. Some increase may also be attributed to a shorter work week. Historically, about 10% of the annual improvement in productivity is attributed to improvement in the quality of labour. Three key variables for improved labour productivity are:

1. Basic education appropriate for an effective labour force.
2. Diet of the labour force.
3. Social overhead that makes labour available, such as transportation and sanitation.

6 yds	If $9y + 3 = 6y + 15$ then $y =$
4 yds	_____ 1 _____ 4
What is the area of this rectangle?	_____ 2 _____ 6

_____ 4 square yds
_____ 6 square yds
_____ 10 square yds
_____ 20 square yds
_____ 24 square yds

Which of the following is true about 84% of 100?

_____ It is greater than 100

_____ It is less than 100

_____ It is equal to 100

FIGURE 1.7

About Half of the 17-Year-Olds in the United States Cannot Correctly Answer Questions of This Type

STUDENT TIP

Perhaps as many as 25% of North American workers lack the basic skills needed for their current job.

Illiteracy and poor diets are major impediments to productivity, costing countries up to 20% of their productivity. Infrastructure that yields clean drinking water and sanitation is also an opportunity for improved productivity, as well as an opportunity for better health, in much of the world.

In developed nations, the challenge becomes *maintaining and enhancing the skills of labour* in the midst of rapidly expanding technology and knowledge. Recent data suggest that the average American 17-year-old knows significantly less mathematics than the average Japanese person of the same age, and about half cannot answer the questions in Figure 1.7. Moreover, more than 38% of U.S. job applicants tested for basic skills were deficient in reading, writing, or math.[2]

Overcoming shortcomings in the quality of labour while other countries have a better labour force is a major challenge. Perhaps improvements can be found not only through increasing competence of labour but also via *better utilized labour with a stronger commitment*. Training, motivation, team building, and the human resource strategies discussed in Chapter 10, as well as improved education, may be among the many techniques that will contribute to increased labour productivity. Improvements in labour productivity are possible; however, they can be expected to be increasingly difficult and expensive.

CAPITAL Human beings are tool-using animals. Capital investment provides those tools. Capital investment has increased in Canada most years except during a few very severe recession periods. Accumulated capital investment has increased in Canada at a compound annual growth rate of 4.5%.

Inflation and taxes increase the cost of capital, making capital investment increasingly expensive. When the capital invested per employee drops, we can expect a drop in productivity. Using labour rather than capital may reduce unemployment in the short run, but it also makes economies less productive and therefore lowers wages in the long run. Capital investment is often necessary but seldom sufficient in the battle for increased productivity.

The trade-off between capital and labour is continually in flux. The higher the cost of capital, the more projects requiring capital are "squeezed out": they are not pursued because the potential return on investment for a given risk has been reduced. Managers adjust their investment plans to changes in capital cost.

MANAGEMENT Management is a factor of production and an economic resource. Management is responsible for ensuring that labour and capital are effectively used to increase productivity. Management accounts for over half of the annual increase in productivity. This increase includes improvements made through the use of knowledge and the application of technology.

Using knowledge and technology is critical in postindustrial societies. Consequently, postindustrial societies are also known as knowledge societies. A **knowledge society** is one in which much of the labour force has migrated from manual work to technical and information-processing tasks requiring ongoing education. The required education and training are important high-cost items that are the responsibility of operations managers as they build organizations and workforces. The expanding knowledge base of contemporary society requires that managers use *technology and knowledge effectively*.

Knowledge society

A society in which much of the labour force has migrated from manual work to work based on knowledge.

---

[2] "Can't Read, Can't Count," *Scientific American* (October 2001): 24; and "Economic Time Bomb: U.S. Teens Are among Worst at Math," *The Wall Street Journal* (December 7, 2004): B1.

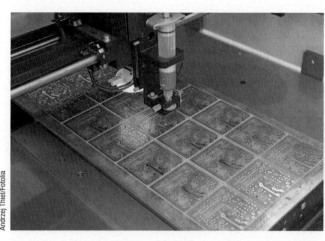

The effective use of capital often means finding the proper trade-off between investment in capital assets (automation, left) and human assets (a manual process, right). While there are risks connected with any investment, the cost of capital and physical investments is fairly clear-cut, but the cost of employees has many hidden costs, including fringe benefits, social insurance, and legal constraints on hiring, employment, and termination.

Siemens, the multibillion-dollar German conglomerate, has long been known for its apprentice programs in its home country. Because education is often the key to efficient operations in a technological society, Siemens has spread its apprentice-training programs to its international plants. These programs are laying the foundation for the highly skilled workforce that is essential for global competitiveness.

More effective use of capital also contributes to productivity. It falls to the operations manager, as a productivity catalyst, to select the best new capital investments as well as to improve the productivity of existing investments.

The productivity challenge is difficult. A country cannot be a world-class competitor with second-class inputs. Poorly educated labour, inadequate capital, and dated technology are second-class inputs. High productivity and high-quality outputs require high-quality inputs, including good operations managers.

PRODUCTIVITY AND THE SERVICE SECTOR

The service sector provides a special challenge to the accurate measurement of productivity and productivity improvement. The traditional analytical framework of economic theory is based primarily on goods-producing activities. Consequently, most published economic data relate to goods production. But the data do indicate that, as our contemporary service economy has increased in size, we have had slower growth in productivity.

Productivity of the service sector has proven difficult to improve because service sector work is:

1. Typically labour intensive (e.g., counselling, teaching).
2. Frequently focused on unique individual attributes or desires (e.g., investment advice).
3. Often an intellectual task performed by professionals (e.g., medical diagnosis).
4. Often difficult to mechanize and automate (e.g., a haircut).
5. Often difficult to evaluate for quality (e.g., performance of a law firm).

OM in Action — Taco Bell Improves Productivity and Goes Green to Lower Costs

Founded in 1962 by Glenn Bell, Taco Bell seeks competitive advantage via low cost. Like many other services, Taco Bell relies on its operations management to improve productivity and reduce cost.

Its menu and meals are designed to be easy to prepare. Taco Bell has shifted a substantial portion of food preparation to suppliers who can perform food processing more efficiently than a stand-alone restaurant. Ground beef is precooked prior to arrival and then reheated, as are many dishes that arrive in plastic boil bags for easy sanitary reheating. Similarly, tortillas arrive already fried and onions arrive prediced. Efficient layout and automation has cut to eight seconds the time needed to prepare tacos and burritos and has cut time in the drive-through lines by one minute. These advances have been combined with training and empowerment to increase the span of management from one supervisor for five restaurants to one supervisor for 30 or more.

Operations managers at Taco Bell believe they have cut in-store labour by 15 hours per day and reduced floor space by more than 50%. The result is a store that can handle twice the volume with half the labour.

In 2010, Taco Bell completed the rollout of its new Grill-to-Order kitchens by installing water- and energy-saving grills that conserve over a billion litres of water and 200 million kWh of electricity each year. This "green"-inspired cooking method also saves the company's 5600 restaurants $17 million per year.

Effective operations management has resulted in productivity increases that support Taco Bell's low-cost strategy. Taco Bell is now the fast-food low-cost leader with a 73% share of the Mexican fast-food market.

Sources: Based on *Energy Business Journal* (May 12, 2008): 111; *Harvard Business Review* (July/August 2008): 118; and J. Hueter and W. Swart, *Interfaces* (January–February 1998): 75–91.

The more intellectual and personal the task, the more difficult it is to achieve increases in productivity. Low-productivity improvement in the service sector is also attributable to the growth of low-productivity activities in the service sector. These include activities not previously a part of the measured economy, such as child care, food preparation, house cleaning, and laundry service. These activities have moved out of the home and into the measured economy as more and more women have joined the workforce. Inclusion of these activities has probably resulted in lower measured productivity for the service sector, although, in fact, actual productivity has probably increased because these activities are now more efficiently produced than previously.

However, in spite of the difficulty of improving productivity in the service sector, improvements are being made, and there are a multitude of ways to make these improvements. Indeed, what can be done when management pays attention to how work actually gets done is astonishing!

Although the evidence indicates that all industrialized countries have the same problem with service productivity, the United States remains the world leader in overall productivity *and* service productivity. Retailing is twice as productive in the United States as in Japan, where laws protect shopkeepers from discount chains. The U.S. telephone industry is at least twice as productive as Germany's. However, because productivity is central to the operations manager's job and because the service sector is so large, we take special note in this text of how to improve productivity in the service sector. (See, for instance, the *OM in Action* box "Taco Bell Improves Productivity and Goes Green to Lower Costs.")

Ethics, Social Responsibility, and Sustainability

STUDENT TIP

Ethics must drive all of a manager's decisions.

Operations managers are subjected to constant changes and challenges. The systems they build to convert resources into goods and services are complex. The physical and social environments change, as do laws and values. These changes present a variety of challenges that come from the conflicting perspectives of stakeholders such as customers, distributors, suppliers, owners, lenders, and employees. These stakeholders, as well as government agencies at various levels, require constant monitoring and thoughtful responses.

Identifying ethical and socially responsible responses while building productive systems is not always clear-cut. Among the many ethical challenges facing operations managers are:

- Efficiently developing and producing safe, quality products.
- Maintaining a sustainable environment.
- Providing a safe workplace.
- Honouring stakeholder commitments.

OM in Action   Magna International

In operations management, balancing the interests of the various stakeholders associated with a company can be challenging at the best of times. To add to the challenge, progressive organizations are now placing the needs of society high on the priority list and have declared their corporate social responsibility. Automotive parts manufacturer Magna International is an example of one of these companies.

Magna has publicly stated that it is committed to supporting the basic fabric of society through a number of programs, volunteer work, and charitable activities. Magna's "Corporate Constitution" allocates a maximum of 2% of its pretax profits to support charitable and nonprofit organizations, and it has pledged support to many programs dealing with health, culture, education, sports, and politics. Magna's executive officers have expressed their desire to continuously improve the quality of life in each of the communities in which their employees work and live.

Magna International's "Corporate Constitution" publicly declares and defines the rights of its employees and investors to participate in its profits and growth, while also imposing specified disciplines on management. This constitution strikes a balance between employees, investors,

society, and management. This business philosophy was introduced by the company's founder, Frank Stronach, in 1971—it is known as "Fair Enterprise" and is at the heart of Magna's operating structure.

Magna International actively supports the concept of corporate social responsibility.

Source: Based on www.magna.com/about-magna/our-culture /corporate-constitution.

Managers must do all of this in an ethical and socially responsible way while meeting the demands of the marketplace. If operations managers have a *moral awareness and focus on increasing productivity* in a system where all stakeholders have a voice, then many of the ethical challenges will be successfully addressed (for example, see the *OM in Action* box "Magna International"). The organization will use fewer resources, the employees will be committed, the market will be satisfied, and the ethical climate will be enhanced. Throughout this text, we note ways in which operations managers can take ethical and socially responsible actions while successfully addressing these challenges of the market. We also conclude each chapter with an Ethical Dilemma exercise.

CHAPTER SUMMARY

Operations, marketing, and finance/accounting are the three functions basic to all organizations. The operations function creates goods and services. Much of the progress of operations management has been made in the 20th century, but since the beginning of time, humankind has been attempting to improve its material well-being. Operations managers are key players in the battle to improve productivity.

As societies become increasingly affluent, more of their resources are devoted to services. In Canada, more than three-quarters of the workforce is employed in the service sector. Productivity improvements are difficult to achieve, but operations managers are the primary vehicle for making improvements.

ETHICAL DILEMMA

Major corporations with overseas subcontractors (such as IKEA in Bangladesh, Unilever in India, and Nike in China) have been criticized, often with substantial negative publicity, when children as young as 10 have been found working in the subcontractor's facilities. The standard response is to perform an audit and then enhance controls so it does not happen again. In one such case, a 10-year-old

was terminated. Shortly thereafter, the family, without the 10-year-old's contribution to the family income, lost its modest home, and the 10-year-old was left to scrounge in the local dump for scraps of metal. Was the decision to hire the 10-year-old ethical? Was the decision to terminate the 10-year-old ethical?

Discussion Questions

1. Why should one study operations management?
2. Identify four people who have contributed to the theory and techniques of operations management.
3. Briefly describe the contributions of the four individuals identified in the preceding question.
4. Figure 1.1 outlines the operations, finance/accounting, and marketing functions of three organizations. Prepare a chart similar to Figure 1.1 outlining the same functions for one of the following:
   a. newspaper
   b. drugstore
   c. college library
   d. summer camp
   e. small costume-jewellery factory
5. Answer Question 4 for some other organization, perhaps an organization where you have worked.
6. What are the three basic functions of a firm?
7. Name the 10 decision areas of operations management.
8. Name four areas that are significant to improving labour productivity.
9. Canada, and indeed much of the world, has been described as a *knowledge society*. How does this affect productivity measurement and the comparison of productivity between Canada and other countries?
10. What are the measurement problems that occur when one attempts to measure productivity?
11. Mass customization and rapid product development were identified as current trends in modern manufacturing operations. What is the relationship, if any, between these trends? Can you cite any examples?
12. What are the five reasons productivity is difficult to improve in the service sector?
13. Describe some of the actions taken by Taco Bell to increase productivity that have resulted in Taco Bell's ability to serve "twice the volume with half the labour".

Solved Problems Virtual Office Hours help is available at MyLab Operations Management.

▼ SOLVED PROBLEM 1.1

Productivity can be measured in a variety of ways, such as by labour, capital, energy, material usage, and so on. At Modern Lumber, Inc., Art Binley, president and producer of apple crates sold to growers, has been able, with his current equipment, to produce 240 crates per 100 logs. He currently purchases 100 logs per day, and each log requires three labour-hours to process. He believes that he can hire a professional buyer who can buy a better-quality log at the same cost. If this is the case, he can increase his production to 260 crates per 100 logs. His labour-hours will increase by eight hours per day.

What will be the impact on productivity (measured in crates per labour-hour) if the buyer is hired?

▼ SOLUTION

(a) Current labour productivity $= \dfrac{240 \text{ crates}}{100 \text{ logs} \times 3 \text{ hours/log}}$

$= \dfrac{240}{300}$

$= 0.8$ crate per labour-hour

(b) Labour productivity with buyer

$= \dfrac{260 \text{ crates}}{100 \text{ logs} \times 3 \text{ hours/log} + 8 \text{ hours}}$

$= \dfrac{260}{308}$

$= 0.844$ crates per labour-hour

Using current productivity (0.80 from part [a]) as a base, the increase will be 5.5% (= 0.844/0.8 = 1.055, or a 5.5% increase).

▼ SOLVED PROBLEM 1.2

Art Binley has decided to look at his productivity from a multifactor (total factor productivity) perspective (refer to Solved Problem 1.1). To do so, he has determined his labour, capital, energy, and material usage and decided to use dollars as the common denominator. His total labour-hours are now 300 per day and will increase to 308 per day. His capital and energy costs will remain constant at $350 and $150 per day, respectively. Material costs for the 100 logs per day are $1000 and will remain the same. Because he pays an average of $10 per hour (with fringes), Binley determines his productivity increase as follows:

▼ SOLUTION

	Current System		**System with Professional Buyer**	
Labour:	300 h @ $10/h = $3000		308 h @ $10/h =	$3080
Material:	100 logs/day 1000			1000
Capital:	350			350
Energy:	150			150
Total Cost:	$4500			$4580
Multifactor productivity of current system:			Multifactor productivity of proposed system:	
= 240 crates/$4500 = 0.0533 crates/dollar			= 260 crates/$4580 = 0.0568 crates/dollar	

Using current productivity (0.0533) as a base, the increase will be 0.066. That is, 0.0568/0.0533 = 1.066, or a 6.6% increase.

Problems*

•• **1.1** John Lucy makes wooden boxes in which to ship motorcycles. John and his three employees invest a total of 40 hours per day making 120 boxes.
a) What is their productivity?
b) John and his employees have discussed redesigning the process to improve efficiency. If they can increase the rate to 125 boxes per day, what will be their new productivity?
c) What will be their unit *increase* in productivity per hour?
d) What will be their percentage change in productivity? **Px**

•• **1.2** Riverside Metal Works produces cast bronze valves on a 10-person assembly line. On a recent day, 160 valves were produced during an eight-hour shift.
a) Calculate the labour productivity of the line.
b) The manager at Riverside changed the layout and was able to increase production to 180 units per eight-hour shift. What is the new labour productivity per labour-hour?
c) What is the percentage of productivity increase? **Px**

•• **1.3** This year, Benson, Inc., will produce 57 600 hot water heaters at its plant in Saskatoon, Saskatchewan, in order to meet expected global demand. To accomplish this, each labourer at the Saskatoon plant will work 160 hours per month. If the labour productivity at the plant is 0.15 hot water heaters per labour-hour, how many labourers are employed at the plant?

•• **1.4** As a library or internet assignment, find the U.S. productivity rate (increase) last year for the (a) national economy, (b) manufacturing sector, and (c) service sector.

•• **1.5** Aditi produces "Final Exam Care Packages" for resale. She is currently working a total of five hours per day to produce 100 care packages.
a) What is Aditi's productivity?
b) Aditi thinks that by redesigning the package, she can increase her total productivity to 133 care packages per day. What will be her new productivity?
c) What will be the percentage increase in productivity if Aditi makes the change? **Px**

•• **1.6** Eric Lafleur makes billiard balls in his New Brunswick plant. With recent increases in his costs, he has a newfound interest in efficiency. Eric is interested in determining the productivity of his organization. He would like to know if his organization is maintaining the manufacturing average of 3% increase in productivity. He has the following data representing a month from last year and an equivalent month this year:

	Last Year	**Now**
Units produced	1 000	1 000
Labour (hours)	300	275
Resin (kilograms)	50	45
Capital invested ($)	10 000	11 000
Energy (BTU)	3 000	2 850

Show the productivity percentage change for each category, and then determine the improvement for labour-hours, the typical standard for comparison. **Px**

•• **1.7** Eric Lafleur (using data from Problem 1.6) determines his costs to be as follows:
• *Labour:* $10 per hour
• *Resin:* $5 per kilogram
• *Capital expense:* 1% per month of investment
• *Energy:* $0.50 per BTU
Show the percentage change in productivity for one month last year versus one month this year, on a multifactor basis with dollars as the common denominator. **Px**

•• **1.8** Kleen Karpet cleaned 65 rugs in October, consuming the following resources:

Labour:	520 hours at $13 per hour
Solvent:	100 gallons at $5 per gallon
Machine rental:	20 days at $50 per day

a) What is the labour productivity per dollar?
b) What is the multifactor productivity? **Px**

•• **1.9** David Upton is president of Upton Manufacturing, a producer of Go-Kart tires. Upton makes 1000 tires per day with the following resources:

Labour:	400 hours per day @ $12.50 per hour
Raw material:	20 000 pounds per day @ $1 per pound
Energy:	$5000 per day
Capital costs:	$10 000 per day

a) What is the labour productivity per labour-hour for these tires at Upton Manufacturing?
b) What is the multifactor productivity for these tires at Upton Manufacturing?
c) What is the percent change in multifactor productivity if Upton can reduce the energy bill by $1000 per day without cutting production or changing any other inputs? **Px**

•• **1.10** Sawyer's, a local bakery, is worried about increased costs—particularly energy. Last year's records provide a fairly good estimate of the parameters for this year. Judy Sawyer, the owner, does not believe things have changed much, but she did invest an additional $3000 for modifications to the bakery's ovens to make them more energy efficient. The modifications were supposed to make the ovens at least 15% more efficient. Sawyer has asked you to check the energy savings of the new ovens and also to look over other measures of the bakery's productivity to see if the modifications were beneficial. You have the following data to work with:

	Last Year	**Now**
Production (dozen)	1 500	1 500
Labour (hours)	350	325
Capital investment ($)	15 000	18 000
Energy (BTU)	3 000	2 750

Px

•• **1.11** Cunningham Performance Auto, Inc., modifies 375 autos per year. The manager, Peter Cunningham, is interested in obtaining a measure of overall performance. He has asked you to provide him with a multifactor measure of last year's performance as a benchmark for future comparison. You have assembled the following data. Resource inputs were: labour, 10 000 hours; 500 suspension and engine modification kits; and energy, 100 000 kilowatt-hours.

---

* Note: **Px** means the problem may be solved with POM for Windows and/or Excel OM.

Average labour cost last year was $20 per hour, kits cost $1000 each, and energy costs were $3 per kilowatt-hour. What do you tell Cunningham? **Px**

•• **1.12** Halifax Seafood makes 500 wooden packing boxes for fresh seafood per day, working in two 10-hour shifts. Due to increased demand, plant managers have decided to operate three eight-hour shifts instead. The plant is now able to produce 650 boxes per day.
a) Calculate the company's productivity before the change in work rules and after the change.
b) What is the percentage increase in productivity?
c) If production is increased to 700 boxes per day, what is the new productivity? **Px**

•• **1.13** Marjatta Viitasalo operates a bakery in Thunder Bay, Ontario. Because of its excellent product and excellent location, demand has increased by 25% in the last year. On far too many occasions, customers have not been able to purchase the bread of their choice. Because of the size of the store, no new ovens can be added. At a staff meeting, one employee suggested ways to load the ovens differently so that more loaves of bread can be baked at one time. This new process will require that the ovens be loaded by hand, requiring additional manpower. This is the only thing to be changed. If the bakery makes 1500 loaves per month with a labour productivity of 2.344 loaves per labour-hour, how many workers will Viitasalo need to add? (*Hint:* Each employee works 160 hours per month.)

•• **1.14** Refer to Problem 1.13. The pay will be $8 per hour for employees. Marjatta Viitasalo can also improve the yield by purchasing a new blender. The new blender will mean an increase in her investment. This added investment has a cost of $100 per month, but she will achieve the same output (an increase to 1875) as the change in labour-hours. Which is the better decision?

a) Show the productivity change, in loaves per dollar, with an increase in labour cost (from 640 to 800 hours).
b) Show the new productivity, in loaves per dollar, with only an increase in investment ($100 per month more).
c) Show the percent productivity change for labour and investment.

•• **1.15** Refer to Problems 1.13 and 1.14. If Marjatta Viitasalo's utility costs remain constant at $500 per month, labour at $8 per hour, and cost of ingredients at $0.35 per loaf, but Viitasalo does not purchase the blender suggested in Problem 1.14, what will the productivity of the bakery be? What will be the percent increase or decrease?

•• **1.16** In December, General Motors produced 6600 customized vans at its plant in Windsor. The labour productivity at this plant is known to have been 0.10 vans per labour-hour during that month; 300 labourers were employed at the plant that month.
a) How many hours did the average labourer work that month?
b) If productivity can be increased to 0.11 vans per hour, how many hours would the average labourer work that month?

•• **1.17** Natalie Attired runs a small job shop where garments are made. The job shop employs eight workers. Each worker is paid $10 per hour. During the first week of March, each worker worked 45 hours. Together, they produced a batch of 132 garments. Of these garments, 52 were "seconds" (meaning that they were flawed). The seconds were sold for $90 each at a factory outlet store. The remaining 80 garments were sold to retail outlets at a price of $198 per garment. What was the labour productivity, in dollars per labour-hour, at this job shop during the first week of March?

CASE STUDIES

National Air Express

National Air Express is a competitive air-express firm with offices around the country. Mohammed Chaudry, the Ottawa station manager, is preparing his quarterly budget report, which will be presented at the Eastern regional meeting next week. He is very concerned about adding capital expense to the operation when business has not increased appreciably. This has been the worst first quarter he can remember, with snowstorms, freezing rain, and bitter cold. He has asked Martha Lewis, field services supervisor, to help him review the available data and offer possible solutions.

Service Methods

National Air offers door-to-door overnight air-express delivery within Canada. Chaudry and Lewis manage a fleet of 24 trucks to handle freight in the Ottawa area. Routes are assigned by area, usually delineated by postal codes, major streets, or key geographical features, such as the Ottawa River. Pickups are generally handled between 3:00 p.m. and 6:00 p.m., Monday through Friday. Driver routes are a combination of regularly scheduled daily stops and pickups that the customer calls in as needed. These call-in pickups are dispatched by radio to the driver. Most call-in customers want as late a pickup as possible, just before closing (usually at 5:00 p.m.).

When the driver arrives at each pickup location, he or she provides supplies as necessary (an envelope or box if requested) and must receive a completed air waybill for each package. Because the industry is extremely competitive, a professional, courteous driver is essential to retaining customers. Therefore, Chaudry has always been concerned that drivers not rush a customer to complete his or her package and paperwork.

Budget Considerations

Chaudry and Lewis have found that they have been unable to meet their customers' requests for a scheduled pickup on many occasions in the past quarter. Although, on average, drivers are not handling any more business, they are unable on some days to arrive at each location on time. Chaudry does not think he can justify increasing costs by $1200 per week for additional trucks and drivers while productivity (measured in shipments per truck/day) has remained flat. The company has established itself as the low-cost operator in the industry but has at the same time committed itself to offering quality service and value for its customers.

Discussion Questions

1. Is the productivity measure of shipments per day per truck still useful? Are there alternatives that might be more effective?
2. What, if anything, can be done to reduce the daily variability in pickup call-ins? Can the driver be expected to be at several locations at once at 5:00 p.m.?
3. How should package pickup performance be measured? Are standards useful in an environment that is affected by the weather, traffic, and other random variables? Are other companies having similar problems?

Source: Adapted from a case by Phil Pugliese under the supervision of Professor Marilyn M. Helms, University of Tennessee at Chattanooga. Reprinted by permission.

Frito-Lay: Operations Management in Manufacturing

Frito-Lay, the massive Dallas, Texas-based subsidiary of PepsiCo, has 38 plants and 48 000 employees in North America. Seven of Frito-Lay's 41 brands exceed $1 billion in sales: Fritos, Lay's, Cheetos, Ruffles, Tostitos, Doritos, and Walker's Potato Chips. Operations are the focus of the firm—from designing products for new markets, to meeting changing consumer preferences, to adjusting to rising commodity costs, to subtle issues involving flavours and preservatives—OM is under constant cost, time, quality, and market pressure. Here is a look at how the 10 decisions of OM are applied at this food processor.

In the food industry, product development kitchens experiment with new products, submit them to focus groups, and perform test marketing. Once the product specifications have been set, processes capable of meeting those specifications and the necessary quality standards are created. At Frito-Lay, quality begins at the farm, with onsite inspection of the potatoes used in Ruffles and the corn used in Fritos. Quality continues throughout the manufacturing process, with visual inspections and with statistical process control of product variables such as oil, moisture, seasoning, salt, thickness, and weight. Additional quality evaluations are conducted throughout shipment, receipt, production, packaging, and delivery.

The production process at Frito-Lay is designed for large volumes and small variety, using expensive special-purpose equipment, and with swift movement of material through the facility. Product-focused facilities, such as Frito-Lay's, typically have high capital costs, tight schedules, and rapid processing. Frito-Lay's facilities are located regionally to aid in the rapid delivery of products because freshness is a critical issue. Sanitary issues and necessarily fast processing of products put a premium on an efficient layout. Production lines are designed for balanced throughput and high utilization. Cross-trained workers, who handle a variety of production lines, have promotion paths identified for their particular skill set. The company rewards employees with medical, retirement, and education plans. Its turnover is very low.

The supply chain is integral to success in the food industry; vendors must be chosen with great care. Moreover, the finished food product is highly dependent on perishable raw materials. Consequently, the supply chain brings raw material (potatoes, corn, etc.) to the plant securely and rapidly to meet tight production schedules. For instance, potatoes are picked in St. Augustine, Florida, unloaded at the Orlando plant, processed, packaged, and shipped from the plant, all in under 12 hours. The requirement for fresh product requires on-time, just-in-time deliveries combined with both low raw material and finished goods inventories. The continuous-flow nature of the specialized equipment in the production process permits little work-in-process inventory. The plants usually run 24/7. This means that there are four shifts of employees each week.

Tight scheduling to ensure the proper mix of fresh finished goods on automated equipment requires reliable systems and effective maintenance. Frito-Lay's workforce is trained to recognize problems early, and professional maintenance personnel are available on every shift. Downtime is very costly and can lead to late deliveries, making maintenance a high priority.

Discussion Questions*

1. From your knowledge of production processes and from the case and the video, identify how each of the 10 decisions of OM is applied at Frito-Lay.
2. How would you determine the productivity of the production process at Frito-Lay?
3. How are the 10 decisions of OM different when applied by the operations manager of a production process such as Frito-Lay versus a service organization such as Hard Rock Cafe? (See the Hard Rock Cafe video case below.)

_____

* You may wish to view the video that accompanies this case before addressing these questions.

Sources: Professors Beverly Amer (Northern Arizona University), Barry Render (Rollins College), and Jay Heizer (Texas Lutheran University).

Hard Rock Cafe: Operations Management in Services

Since its inception in 1971, Hard Rock has grown from a modest London pub to a global power managing 150 cafes, 13 hotels/casinos, live music venues, and a huge annual Rockfest concert. This puts Hard Rock firmly in the service industry—a sector that employs over 75% of the people in the United States. Hard Rock moved its world headquarters to Orlando, Florida, in 1988 and has expanded to more than 40 locations throughout the United States, serving over 100 000 meals each day. Hard Rock chefs are modifying the menu from classic American—burgers and chicken wings—to include

higher-end items such as stuffed veal chops and lobster tails. Just as taste in music changes over time, so does Hard Rock Cafe, with new menus, layouts, memorabilia, services, and strategies.

At Orlando's Universal Studios, a traditional tourist destination, Hard Rock Cafe serves over 3500 meals each day. The cafe employs about 400 people. Most are employed in the restaurant, but some work in the retail shop. Retail is now a standard and increasingly prominent feature in Hard Rock Cafes (since close to 48% of revenue comes from this source). Cafe employees include kitchen and wait staff, hostesses, and bartenders. Hard Rock employees are not only competent in their job skills but are also passionate about music and have engaging personalities. Cafe staff is scheduled down to 15-minute intervals to meet seasonal and daily demand changes in the tourist environment of Orlando. Surveys are done on a regular basis to evaluate quality of food and service at the cafe. Scores are rated on a 1 to 7 scale, and if the score is not a 7, the food or service is considered a failure.

Hard Rock is adding a new emphasis on live music and is redesigning its restaurants to accommodate the changing tastes. Since Eric Clapton hung his guitar on the wall to mark his favourite bar stool, Hard Rock has become the world's leading collector and exhibitor of rock 'n' roll memorabilia, with changing exhibits at its cafes throughout the world. The collection includes thousands of pieces, valued at $40 million. In keeping with the times, Hard Rock also maintains a website, **www.hardrock.com**, which receives over 100 000 hits per week, and a weekly cable television program on VH-1. Hard Rock's brand recognition, at 92%, is one of the highest in the world.

Discussion Questions*

1. From your knowledge of restaurants, the video, the *Global Company Profile* that opens this chapter, and the case itself, identify how each of the 10 decisions of operations management is applied at Hard Rock Cafe.
2. How would you determine the productivity of the kitchen staff and wait staff at Hard Rock?
3. How are the 10 decisions of OM different when applied to the operations manager of a service operation such as Hard Rock versus an automobile company such as Ford Motor Company?

* You may wish to view the video that accompanies this case before addressing these questions.

CHAPTER 1 | RAPID REVIEW

MyLab Operations Management

Main Heading	Review Material	
WHAT IS OPERATIONS MANAGEMENT? (p. 2)	• **Production**—The creation of goods and services. • **Operations management (OM)**—Activities that relate to the creation of goods and services through the transformation of inputs to outputs.	**VIDEO 1.1** Operations Management at Hard Rock **VIDEO 1.2** Operations Management at Frito-Lay
ORGANIZING TO PRODUCE GOODS AND SERVICES (pp. 3–4)	All organizations perform three functions to create goods and services: 1. *Marketing*, which generates demand 2. *Production/operations*, which creates the product 3. *Finance/accounting*, which tracks how well the organization is doing, pays the bills, and collects the money	
THE SUPPLY CHAIN (p. 4)	• **Supply chain**—A global network of organizations and activities that supplies a firm with goods and services.	
WHY STUDY OPERATIONS MANAGEMENT? (pp. 4–5)	We study OM for four reasons: 1. To learn how people organize themselves for productive enterprise 2. To learn how goods and services are produced 3. To understand what operations managers do 4. Because OM is a costly part of an organization	
WHAT OPERATIONS MANAGERS DO (pp.5–6)	• **Management process**—The application of planning, organizing, staffing, leading, and controlling to achieve objectives.Ten major decisions are required of operations managers: 1. Design of goods and services 2. Managing quality 3. Process strategy 4. Location strategy 5. Layout strategy 6. Human resources 7. Supply chain management 8. Inventory management 9. Scheduling 10. Maintenance About 40% of all jobs are in OM. Operations managers possess job titles such as plant manager, quality manager, process-improvement consultant, and operations analyst.	

Main Heading	Review Material	
THE HERITAGE OF OPERATIONS MANAGEMENT (pp. 6–8)	Significant events in modern OM can be classified into five eras: 1. Early concepts (1776–1880)—Labour specialization (Smith, Babbage), standardized parts (Whitney) 2. Scientific management (1880–1910)—Gantt charts (Gantt), motion and time studies (Gilbreth), process analysis (Taylor), queuing theory (Erlang) 3. Mass production (1910–1980)—Assembly line (Ford/Sorensen), statistical sampling (Shewhart), economic order quantity (Harris), linear programming (Dantzig), PERT/CPM (DuPont), material requirements planning 4. Lean production (1980–1995)—Just-in-time, computer-aided design, electronic data interchange, total quality management, Baldrige Award, empowerment, kanbans 5. Mass customization (1995–2005)—Globalization, internet/ecommerce, enterprise resource planning, international quality standards, finite scheduling, supply chain management, mass customization, build-to-order, sustainability 6. Globalization era (2005–2020)—Global supply chains, growth of transnational organizations, instant communications, sustainability, ethics in a global work force, logistics and shipping	
OPERATIONS IN THE SERVICE SECTOR (pp. 9–11)	• **Services**—Economic activities that typically produce an intangible product (such as education, entertainment, lodging, government, financial, and health services). Almost all services and almost all goods are a mixture of a service and a tangible product. • **Service sector**—The segment of the economy that includes trade, finance, lodging, education, law, medicine, and other professional occupations. Services now constitute the largest economic sector in postindustrial societies. The huge productivity increases in agriculture and manufacturing have allowed more of our economic resources to be devoted to services. Many service jobs pay very well.	
NEW CHALLENGES IN OPERATIONS MANAGEMENT (p. 11)	Some of the current challenges for operations managers include: • Global focus; international collaboration • Rapid product development; design collaboration • Environmentally sensitive production; green manufacturing; sustainability • Mass customization • Supply chain partnering; joint ventures; alliances • Lean operations; continuous improvement and elimination of waste	
THE PRODUCTIVITY CHALLENGE (pp. 11–17)	• **Productivity**—The ratio of outputs (goods and services) divided by one or more inputs (such as labour, capital, or management). High production means producing many units, while high productivity means producing units efficiently. Only through increases in productivity can the standard of living of a country improve. Canadian productivity has averaged over 3% for the past half century. $$\text{Productivity} = \frac{\text{Units produced}}{\text{Input used}} \qquad \textbf{(1-1)}$$ • **Single-factor productivity**—Indicates the ratio of one resource (input) to the goods and services produced (outputs). • **Multifactor productivity**—Indicates the ratio of many or all resources (inputs) to the goods and services produced (outputs). Also called *total factor productivity*. Multifactor Productivity $$= \frac{\text{Output}}{\text{Labour + Material + Energy + Capital + Miscellaneous}} \qquad \textbf{(1-2)}$$	Problems: 1.1–1.17 Virtual Office Hours for Solved Problems: 1.1, 1.2

MyLab Operations Management

Main Heading	Review Material
	Measurement problems with productivity include: (1) the quality may change, (2) external elements may interfere, and (3) precise units of measure may be lacking.
	• **Productivity variables**—The three factors critical to productivity improvement are labour (10%), capital (38%), and management (52%).
	• **Knowledge society**—A society in which much of the labour force has migrated from manual work to work based on knowledge.
ETHICS, SOCIAL RESPONSIBILITY, AND SUSTAINABILITY (pp. 17–18)	Among the many ethical challenges facing operations managers are (1) efficiently developing and producing safe, quality products; (2) maintaining a clean environment; (3) providing a safe workplace; and (4) honouring stakeholder commitments.

Self-Test

■ **Before taking the self-test,** refer to the learning objectives listed at the beginning of the chapter and the key terms listed at the end of the chapter.

LO1 Productivity increases when:
a) inputs increase while outputs remain the same.
b) inputs decrease while outputs remain the same.
c) outputs decrease while inputs remain the same.
d) inputs and outputs increase proportionately.
e) inputs increase at the same rate as outputs.

LO2 Services often:
a) are tangible.
b) are standardized.
c) are knowledge based.
d) are low in customer interaction.
e) have consistent product definition.

LO3 Productivity:
a) can use many factors as the numerator.
b) is the same thing as production.
c) increases at about 0.5% per year.
d) is dependent upon labour, management, and capital.
e) is the same thing as effectiveness.

LO4 Single-factor productivity:
a) remains constant.
b) is never constant.

c) usually uses labour as a factor.
d) seldom uses labour as a factor.
e) uses management as a factor.

LO5 Multifactor productivity:
a) remains constant.
b) is never constant.
c) usually uses substitutes as common variables for the factors of production.
d) seldom uses labour as a factor.
e) always uses management as a factor.

LO6 Productivity increases each year in Canada are a result of three factors:
a) labour, capital, management
b) engineering, labour, capital
c) engineering, capital, quality control
d) engineering, labour, data processing
e) engineering, capital, data processing

Answers: LO1. b; LO2. c; LO3. d; LO4. c; LO5. c; LO6. a

MyLab Operations Management

Most of these questions can be found in MyLab Operations Management. Visit MyLab Operations Management to access cases, videos, downloadable software, and much more. MyLab Operations Management Management also features a personalized Study Plan that helps you identify which chapter concepts you've mastered and guides you towards study tools for additional practice.

2

Learning Objectives

LO1 Define *mission* and *strategy* 32

LO2 Identify and explain three strategic approaches to competitive advantage 32

LO3 Identify and define the 10 decisions of operations management 36

LO4 Understand the significance of key success factors and core competencies 41

LO5 Identify and explain four global operations strategy options 47

Operations Strategy in a Global Environment

Global > Company Profile Boeing

Boeing's Global Strategy Yields Competitive Advantage

Boeing's strategy for its 787 Dreamliner is unique from both an engineering and a global perspective.

The Dreamliner incorporates the latest in a wide range of aerospace technologies, from airframe and engine design to super-lightweight titanium-graphite laminate, carbon-fibre and epoxy, and composites. Another innovation is the electronic monitoring system that allows the airplane to report maintenance requirements to ground-based computer systems. Boeing has also worked with General Electric and Rolls-Royce to develop more efficient engines. The advances in engine technology contribute as much as 8% of the increased fuel/payload efficiency of the new airplane, representing a nearly two-generation jump in technology.

This state-of-the-art Boeing 787 is also *global*. Led by Boeing at its Everett, Washington, facility, an international team of aerospace companies developed the airplane. New technologies, new design, new manufacturing processes, and committed international suppliers are helping Boeing and its partners achieve unprecedented levels of performance in design, manufacture, and operation.

The 787 is global not only because it has a range of 13 800 km but also because it is built all over the world—with a huge financial risk of over US $5 billion, Boeing needed partners. The global nature of both technology and the aircraft market meant finding exceptional developers and suppliers, wherever they might be. It also meant finding firms willing to step up to the risk associated with a very expensive new product. These partners not only spread the risk but also bring commitment to the table. Countries that have a stake in the 787 are more likely to buy from Boeing than from the European competitor Airbus Industrie.

Boeing teamed with more than 20 international systems suppliers to develop technologies and design concepts for the 787. Boeing found its 787 partners in over a dozen countries; a few of them are shown in the table.

State-of-the-art composite sections of the 787 are built around the world and shipped to Boeing for final assembly.

Some of the International Suppliers of Boeing 787 Components

Latecoere	France	Passenger doors
Labinal	France	Wiring
Dassault	France	Design and PLM software
Messier-Bugatti	France	Electric brakes
Thales	France	Electrical power conversion system and integrated standby flight display
Messier-Dowty	France	Landing gear structure
Diehl	Germany	Interior lighting
Cobham	United Kingdom	Fuel pumps and valves
Rolls-Royce	United Kingdom	Engines
Smiths Aerospace	United Kingdom	Central computer system
BAE Systems	United Kingdom	Electronics
Alenia Aeronautica	Italy	Upper centre fuselage and horizontal stabilizer
Toray Industries	Japan	Carbon fibre for wing and tail units
Fuji Heavy Industries	Japan	Centre wing box
Kawasaki Heavy Industries	Japan	Forward fuselage, fixed sections of wing, landing gear wheel well
Teijin Seiki	Japan	Hydraulic actuators
Mitsubishi Heavy Industries	Japan	Wing box
Chengdu Aircraft Group	China	Rudder
Hafei Aviation	China	Parts
Korean Airlines	South Korea	Wingtips
Saab	Sweden	Cargo and access doors

The Japanese companies Toray, Teijin Seiki, Fuji, Kawasaki, and Mitsubishi are producing over 35% of the project, providing whole composite fuselage sections. Italy's Alenia Aeronautica is building an additional 10% of the plane.

Many North American companies—including Crane Aerospace, Fairchild Controls, Goodrich, General Dynamics, Hamilton Sundstrand, Honeywell, Moog, Parker Hannifin, Rockwell Collins, and Triumph Group—are also suppliers. Boeing has 70% to 80% of the Dreamliner built by other companies. And even some of the portion built by Boeing is produced at Boeing facilities outside the United States, in Australia and Canada.

The Dreamliner is efficient, has a global range, and is made from components produced around the world. The result: a state-of-the-art airplane reflecting the global nature of business in the 21st century and one of the fastest-selling commercial jets in history.

A Global View of Operations and Supply Chains

Today's operations manager must have a global view of operations strategy. Since the early 1990s, nearly 3 billion people in developing countries have overcome the cultural, religious, ethnic, and political barriers that constrain productivity and are now players on the global economic stage. As these barriers disappear, simultaneous advances are being made in technology, reliable shipping, and cheap communication. The unsurprising result is the growth of world trade (see Figure 2.1), global capital markets, and the international movement of people. This means increasing economic integration and interdependence of countries—in a word, globalization. In response, organizations are hastily extending their operations globally with innovative strategies. For instance:

- Boeing is competitive because both its sales and production are worldwide.
- Italy's Benetton moves inventory to stores around the world faster than its competition by building flexibility into design, production, and distribution.
- Sony purchases components from suppliers in Thailand, Malaysia, and elsewhere around the world for assembly in its electronic products.
- Volvo, considered a Swedish company, was recently controlled by a U.S. company (Ford) and has been subsequently acquired by Geely of China. But the current Volvo S40 is built in Belgium on a platform shared with the Mazda 3 (built in Japan) and the Ford Focus (built in Europe.)

Globalization means that domestic production and exporting may no longer be a viable business model; local production and exporting no longer guarantee success or even survival. There are new standards of global competitiveness that impact quality, variety, customization, convenience, timeliness, and cost. The globalization of strategy contributes efficiency and adds value to products and services, but it also complicates the operations manager's job. Complexity, risk, and competition are intensified; companies must carefully account for them.

FIGURE 2.1

Growth of World Trade as a Percent of World GDP

Source: World Bank; World Trade Organization; and IMF.

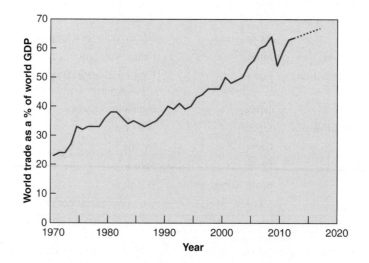

OM in Action   Cartoon Production at Home in Manila

Fred Flintstone is not from Bedrock. He is actually from Manila, capital of the Philippines. So are Tom and Jerry, Aladdin, and Donald Duck. More than 90% of North American television cartoons are produced in Asia and India, with the Philippines leading the way. With their competitive advantage of English as an official language and a strong familiarity with North American culture, animation companies in Manila now employ more than 1700 people. Filipinos understand Western culture, and "You need to have a group of artists that can understand the humour that goes with it," says Bill Dennis, a Hanna-Barbera executive.

Major studios like Disney, Marvel, Warner Brothers, and Hanna-Barbera send *storyboards*—cartoon action outlines—and voice tracks to the Philippines. Artists there draw, paint, and film about 20 000 sketches for a 30-minute episode. The cost of $130 000 to produce an episode in the Philippines compares with $160 000 in Korea and $500 000 in the United States.

Sources: Journal of Global Information Technology Management (2007): 1–6; *The New York Times* (February 26, 2004): A29; and *The Wall Street Journal* (August 9, 2005): D8.

We have identified six reasons why domestic business operations decide to change to some form of international operation. They are:

1. Reduce costs (labour, taxes, tariffs, etc.).
2. Improve the supply chain.
3. Provide better goods and services.
4. Understand markets.
5. Learn to improve operations.
6. Attract and retain global talent.

Let us examine, in turn, each of the six reasons.

REDUCE COSTS

Many international operations seek to take advantage of the tangible opportunities to reduce their costs. Foreign locations with lower wages can help lower both direct and indirect costs. (See the *OM in Action* box "Cartoon Production at Home in Manila.") Less stringent government regulations on a wide variety of operations practices (e.g., environmental control, health and safety, etc.) reduce costs. Opportunities to cut the cost of taxes and tariffs also encourage foreign operations. In Mexico, the creation of **maquiladoras** (free-trade zones) allows manufacturers to cut their costs of taxation by paying only on the value added by Mexican workers. If a Canadian manufacturer brings a $500 machine to a maquiladora operation for assembly work costing $25, tariff duties will be charged only on the $25 of work performed in Mexico.

Shifting low-skilled jobs to another country has several potential advantages. First, and most obviously, the firm may reduce costs. Second, moving the lower-skilled jobs to a lower-cost location frees higher-cost workers for more valuable tasks. Third, reducing wage costs allows the savings to be invested in improved products and facilities (and the retraining of existing workers, if necessary) at the home location. The impact of this approach is shown in the *OM in Action* box, "Going Global to Compete".

Trade agreements have also helped reduce tariffs and thereby reduce the cost of operating facilities in foreign countries. The **World Trade Organization (WTO)** has helped reduce tariffs from 40% in 1940 to less than 3% today. Another important trade agreement is the **United States, Mexico, Canada Agreement (USMCA)**. USMCA seeks to phase out all trade and tariff barriers among Canada, Mexico, and the United States. Other trade agreements that are accelerating global trade include APEC (the Pacific Rim countries), SEATO (Australia, New Zealand, Japan, Hong Kong, South Korea, New Guinea, and Chile), MERCOSUR (Argentina, Brazil, Paraguay, and Uruguay), and CAFTA (Central America, Dominican Republic, and the United States).

Another trading group is the **European Union (EU)**.[1] The European Union has reduced trade barriers among the participating European nations through standardization and a common

Maquiladoras
Mexican factories located along the U.S.–Mexico border that receive preferential tariff treatment.

World Trade Organization (WTO)
An international organization that promotes world trade by lowering barriers to the free flow of goods across borders.

United States, Mexico, Canada Agreement (USMCA)
A free trade agreement between Canada, Mexico, and the United States.

European Union (EU)
A European trade group that has 28 member states as of 2015.

---

[1] The 28 members of the European Union (EU) as of 2015 were Austria, Belgium, Bulgaria, Croatia, Cyprus, Czech Republic, Denmark, Estonia, Finland, France, Germany, Greece, Hungary, Ireland, Italy, Latvia, Lithuania, Luxembourg, Malta, Netherlands, Poland, Portugal, Romania, Slovakia, Slovenia, Spain, Sweden, and the United Kingdom. Not all have adopted the euro. In addition, Albania, Montenegro, Serbia, Macedonia, and Turkey are candidates for entry into the EU.

OM in Action   Going Global to Compete

Headquartered in Montreal and founded in 1880, Bell Canada is one of Canada's prominent players in wireless telecommunications, controlling about 30% of the domestic market. Approximately 50% of Bell Canada's revenue stems from its wireless initiatives. It is active in contracting suitable vendors as part of outsourcing key voice-based projects for its satellite TV, Bell Mobility, Solo Mobility, and internet divisions. Bell Canada intends to outsource these particular projects via fixed payouts as part of a deal worth roughly between $25 million and $30 million per year. India is the beneficiary of these outsourced contracts, and the projects include inbound customer contact. Bell remains watchful for outsourcing partners with strong competencies in managing this type of front-end work.

In a similar fashion, the Canadian Bar Association reported through its in-house magazine about the "commoditization" of legal services, and noted a trend toward outsourcing certain aspects of legal work. Although the concept is fairly new to Canadian lawyers, firms that do engage in it suggest they provide hourly savings of up to 75%.

Resourceful organizations, such as Bell Canada and these law firms, use a global perspective to become more efficient, which allows them to develop new products, retrain employees, and invest in new plant and equipment.

Sources: Ottawa Citizen (2006); and www.bell.ca.

currency, the euro. However, this major Canadian trading partner, with 503 million people, is also placing some of the world's most restrictive conditions on products sold in the EU. Everything from recycling standards to automobile bumpers to hormone-free farm products must meet EU standards, complicating international trade.

IMPROVE THE SUPPLY CHAIN

The supply chain can often be improved by locating facilities in countries where unique resources are available. These resources may be expertise, labour, or raw material. For example, a trend is evident in which precious metals companies are relocating to the mining regions of northern Ontario. Auto-styling studios from throughout the world are migrating to the auto Mecca of southern California to ensure the necessary expertise in contemporary auto design. Similarly, world athletic shoe production has migrated from South Korea to Guangzhou, China: this location takes advantage of the low-cost labour and production competence in a city where 40 000 people work making athletic shoes for the world. And a perfume essence manufacturer wants a presence in Grasse, France, where much of the world's perfume essences are prepared from the flowers of the Mediterranean.

PROVIDE BETTER GOODS AND SERVICES

Although the characteristics of goods and services can be objective and measurable (e.g., number of on-time deliveries), they can also be subjective and less measurable (e.g., sensitivity to culture). We need an ever better understanding of differences in culture and of the way business is handled in different countries. Improved understanding as the result of a local presence permits firms to customize products and services to meet unique cultural needs in foreign markets.

Another reason to have international operations is to reduce response time to meet customers' changing product and service requirements. Customers who purchase goods and services from Canadian firms are increasingly located in foreign countries. Providing them with quick and adequate service is often improved by locating facilities in their home countries.

UNDERSTAND MARKETS

Because international operations require interaction with foreign customers, suppliers, and other competitive businesses, international firms inevitably learn about opportunities for new products and services. Europe led the way with cell phone innovations, and now the Japanese lead with the latest cell phone fads. Knowledge of these markets helps firms not only understand where the market is going but also diversify their customer base, add production flexibility, and smooth the business cycle.

Another reason to go into foreign markets is the opportunity to expand the *life cycle* (i.e., stages a product goes through; see Chapter 5) of an existing product. While some products in

A worldwide strategy places added burdens on operations management. Because of regional differences, designers and manufacturers must adapt their products to suit their various markets. A common example of the market differences involves automobiles and the need to place the driver on either the right or the left due to the local roadways and infrastructure.

Canada are in a "mature" stage of their product life cycle, they may represent state-of-the-art products in less-developed countries. For example, the market for personal computers could be characterized as "mature" in Canada but as in the "introductory" stage in many developing countries, such as Vietnam and Myanmar (Burma).

LEARN TO IMPROVE OPERATIONS

Learning does not take place in isolation. Firms serve themselves and their customers well when they remain open to the free flow of ideas. For example, General Motors found that it could improve operations by jointly building and running, with the Japanese, an auto assembly plant in San Jose, California. This strategy allowed GM to contribute its capital and knowledge of North American labour and environmental laws while the Japanese contributed production and inventory ideas. Similarly, operations managers have improved equipment and layout by learning from the ergonomic competence of the Scandinavians.

ATTRACT AND RETAIN GLOBAL TALENT

Global organizations can attract and retain better employees by offering more employment opportunities. They need people in all functional areas and areas of expertise worldwide. Global firms can recruit and retain good employees because they provide both greater growth opportunities and insulation against unemployment during times of economic downturn. During economic downturns in one country or continent, a global firm has the means to relocate unneeded personnel to more prosperous locations.

So, to recap, successfully achieving a competitive advantage in our shrinking world means maximizing all of the possible opportunities, from tangible to intangible, that international operations can offer.

Cultural and Ethical Issues

While there are great forces driving firms towards globalization, many challenges remain. One of these challenges is reconciling differences in social and cultural behaviour. With issues ranging from bribery, to child labour, to the environment, managers sometimes do not know how to respond when operating in a different culture. What one country's culture deems acceptable may be considered unacceptable or illegal in another. It is not by chance that there are fewer female managers in the Middle East than in India.

As the owner of a Guatemala plant said, "The ethics of the world markets is very clear: Manufacturers will move wherever it is cheapest or most convenient to their interests."

In the last decade, changes in international laws, agreements, and codes of conduct have been applied to define ethical behaviour among managers around the world. The WTO, for example, helps to make uniform the protection of both governments and industries from foreign firms that engage in unethical conduct. Even on issues where significant differences between cultures exist, as in the area of bribery or the protection of intellectual property, global uniformity is slowly being accepted by most nations.

In spite of cultural and ethical differences, we live in a period of extraordinary mobility of capital, information, goods, and even people. We can expect this to continue. The financial sector, the telecommunications sector, and the logistics infrastructure of the world are healthy institutions that foster efficient and effective use of capital, information, and goods. Globalization, with all its opportunities and risks, is here and will continue. It must be embraced as managers develop their missions and strategies.

Developing Missions and Strategies

STUDENT TIP

Getting an education and managing an organization both require a mission and a strategy.

LO1 Define *mission* and *strategy*

Mission
The purpose or rationale for an organization's existence.

An effective operations management effort must have a *mission* so it knows where it is going and a *strategy* so it knows how to get there. This is the case for a small domestic organization as well as a large international organization.

MISSION

Economic success, indeed survival, is the result of identifying missions to satisfy a customer's needs and wants. We define the organization's **mission** as its purpose—what it will contribute to society. Mission statements provide boundaries and focus for organizations and the concept around which the firm can rally. The mission states the rationale for the organization's existence. Developing a good strategy is difficult, but it is much easier if the mission has been well defined. Figure 2.2 provides examples of mission statements.

Once an organization's mission has been decided, each functional area within the firm determines its supporting mission. By *functional area,* we mean the major disciplines required by the firm, such as marketing, finance/accounting, and production/operations. Missions for each function are developed to support the firm's overall mission. Then within that function, lower-level supporting missions are established for the OM functions. Figure 2.3 provides such a hierarchy of sample missions.

STRATEGY

Strategy
How an organization expects to achieve its missions and goals.

VIDEO 2.1
Operations Strategy at Regal Marine

With the mission established, strategy and its implementation can begin. **Strategy** is an organization's action plan to achieve the mission. Each functional area has a strategy for achieving its mission and for helping the organization reach the overall mission. These strategies exploit opportunities and strengths, neutralize threats, and avoid weaknesses. In the following sections, we will describe how strategies are developed and implemented.

Firms achieve missions in three conceptual ways: (1) differentiation, (2) cost leadership, and (3) response. This means operations managers are called on to deliver goods and services that are (1) *better*, or at least different, (2) *cheaper*, and (3) more *responsive*. Operations managers translate these *strategic concepts* into tangible tasks to be accomplished. Any one or combination of

LO2 Identify and explain three strategic approaches to competitive advantage

FIGURE 2.2

Mission Statements for Three Organizations

Royal Canadian Mounted Police
The RCMP is Canada's national police service. Proud of our traditions and confident in meeting future challenges, we commit to preserve the peace, uphold the law and provide quality service in partnership with our communities.
Source: Mission Statement for Royal Canadian Mounted Police. Reprinted with permission.
Hard Rock Cafe
Our Mission: To spread the spirit of rock 'n roll by creating authentic experiences that rock.
Source: Mission Statement for Hard Rock Café, Hard Rock Café International (USA), Inc. Reprinted with permission.
Arnold Palmer Hospital
Arnold Palmer Hospital for Children provides state of the art, family-centered healthcare focused on restoring the joy of childhood in an environment of compassion, healing and hope.
Source: Mission Statement from Arnold Palmer Hospital for Children. Copyright © by Orlando Health. Reprinted with permission.

Sample Company Mission
To manufacture and service an innovative, growing, and profitable worldwide microwave communications business that exceeds our customers' expectations.

Sample Operations Management Mission
To produce products consistent with the company's mission as the worldwide low-cost manufacturer.

Sample OM Department Missions	
Product design	To design and produce products and services with outstanding quality and inherent customer value.
Quality management	To attain the exceptional value that is consistent with our company mission and marketing objectives by close attention to design, procurement, production, and field service opportunities.
Process design	To determine, design, and produce the production process and equipment that will be compatible with low-cost product, high quality, and a good quality of work life at economical cost.
Location	To locate, design, and build efficient and economical facilities that will yield high value to the company, its employees, and the community.
Layout design	To achieve, through skill, imagination, and resourcefulness in layout and work methods, production effectiveness and efficiency while supporting a high quality of work life.
Human resources	To provide a good quality of work life, with well-designed, safe, rewarding jobs, stable employment, and equitable pay, in exchange for outstanding individual contribution from employees at all levels.
Supply chain management	To collaborate with suppliers to develop innovative products from stable, effective, and efficient sources of supply.
Inventory	To achieve low investment in inventory consistent with high customer service levels and high facility utilization.
Scheduling	To achieve high levels of throughput and timely customer delivery through effective scheduling.
Maintenance	To achieve high utilization of facilities and equipment by effective preventive maintenance and prompt repair of facilities and equipment.

these three strategic concepts can generate a system that has a unique advantage over competitors. For example, Hunter Fan has differentiated itself as a premier maker of quality ceiling fans that lower heating and cooling costs for its customers. Nucor Steel, on the other hand, satisfies customers by being the lowest-cost steel producer in the world. And Dell achieves rapid response by building personal computers with each customer's requested software in a matter of hours.

Clearly, strategies differ. And each strategy puts different demands on operations management. Hunter Fan's strategy is one of *differentiating* itself via quality from others in the industry. Nucor focuses on value at *low cost*, and Dell's dominant strategy is quick, reliable *response*.

Achieving Competitive Advantage Through Operations

Each of the three strategies provides an opportunity for operations managers to achieve competitive advantage. **Competitive advantage** implies the creation of a system that has a unique advantage over competitors. The idea is to create customer value in an efficient and sustainable

Competitive advantage
The creation of a unique advantage over competitors.

STUDENT TIP

For many organizations, the operations function provides *the* competitive advantage.

way. Pure forms of these strategies may exist, but operations managers will more likely be called on to implement some combination of them. Let us briefly look at how managers achieve competitive advantage via *differentiation*, *low cost*, and *response*.

COMPETING ON DIFFERENTIATION

Safeskin Corporation is number one in latex exam gloves because it has differentiated itself and its products. It did so by producing gloves that were designed to prevent allergic reactions about which doctors were complaining. When other glove makers caught up, Safeskin developed hypoallergenic gloves. Then it added texture to its gloves. Then it developed a synthetic disposable glove for those allergic to latex—always staying ahead of the competition. Safeskin's strategy is to develop a reputation for designing and producing reliable state-of-the-art gloves, thereby differentiating itself.

Differentiation is concerned with providing *uniqueness*. A firm's opportunities for creating uniqueness are not located within a particular function or activity but can arise in virtually everything the firm does. Moreover, because most products include some service, and most services include some product, the opportunities for creating this uniqueness are limited only by imagination. Indeed, **differentiation** should be thought of as going beyond both physical characteristics and service attributes to encompass everything about the product or service that influences the value that the customers derive from it. Therefore, effective operations managers assist in defining everything about a product or service that will influence the potential value to the customer. This may be the convenience of a broad product line, product features, or a service related to the product. Such services can manifest themselves through convenience (location of distribution centres, stores, or branches), training, product delivery and installation, or repair and maintenance services.

In the service sector, one option for extending product differentiation is through an *experience*. Differentiation by experience in services is a manifestation of the growing "experience economy". The idea of **experience differentiation** is to engage the customer—to use people's five senses so they become immersed, or even an active participant, in the product. Disney does this with the Magic Kingdom. People no longer just go on a ride; they are immersed in the Magic Kingdom—surrounded by a dynamic visual and sound experience that complements the physical ride. Some rides further engage the customer by having them steer the ride or shoot targets or villains.

Theme restaurants, such as Hard Rock Cafe, likewise differentiate themselves by providing an "experience". Hard Rock engages the customer with classic rock music, big-screen rock videos, memorabilia, and staff who can tell stories. In many instances, a full-time guide is available to explain the displays, and there is always a convenient retail store so the guest can take home a tangible part of the experience. The result is a "dining experience" rather than just a meal. In a less dramatic way, both Tim Hortons and your local supermarket deliver an experience when they provide music and the aroma of brewing coffee or freshly baked bread.

COMPETING ON COST

Porter Airlines has been a consistent success while other North American airlines have lost billions of dollars. Porter has done this by fulfilling a need for low-cost and short-hop flights. Its operations strategy has included use of secondary airports and terminals, few fare options, smaller crews, and no expensive ticket offices.

Additionally, and less obviously, Porter has very effectively matched capacity to demand and effectively utilized this capacity. It has done this by designing a route structure that matches the capacity of its Bombardier Q400, the only plane in its fleet. Second, it achieves more air miles than other airlines through faster turnarounds—its planes are on the ground less.

One driver of a low-cost strategy is a facility that is effectively utilized. Porter and others with low-cost strategies understand this and utilize resources effectively. Identifying the optimum size (and investment) allows firms to spread overhead costs, providing a cost advantage. For instance, Walmart continues to pursue its low-cost strategy with superstores that are open 24 hours a day. For more than 50 years, it has successfully grabbed market share. Walmart has driven down store overhead costs, shrinkage, and distribution costs. Its rapid transportation of goods, reduced warehousing costs, and direct shipment from manufacturers have resulted in high inventory turnover and made it a low-cost leader.

Differentiation

Distinguishing the offerings of an organization in a way that the customer perceives as adding value.

Experience differentiation

Engaging a customer with a product through imaginative use of the five senses, so the customer "experiences" the product.

VIDEO 2.2
Hard Rock's Global Strategy

Low-cost leadership entails achieving maximum *value*, as defined by your customer. It requires examining each of the 10 OM decisions in a relentless effort to drive down costs while meeting customer expectations of value. A low-cost strategy does *not* imply low value or low quality.

Low-cost leadership
Achieving maximum value, as perceived by the customer.

COMPETING ON RESPONSE

The third strategy option is response. Response is often thought of as *flexible* response, but it also refers to *reliable* and *quick* response. Indeed, we define **response** as including the entire range of values related to timely product development and delivery, as well as reliable scheduling and flexible performance.

Response
A set of values related to rapid, flexible, and reliable performance.

Flexible response may be thought of as the ability to match changes in a marketplace where design innovations and volumes fluctuate substantially.

Hewlett-Packard is an exceptional example of a firm that has demonstrated flexibility in both design and volume changes in the volatile world of personal computers. HP's products often have a life cycle of months, and volume and cost changes during that brief life cycle are dramatic. However, HP has been successful at institutionalizing the ability to change products and volume to respond to dramatic changes in product design and costs—thus building a *sustainable competitive advantage*.

The second aspect of response is the *reliability* of scheduling. One way the German machine industry has maintained its competitiveness despite having the world's highest labour costs is through reliable response. This response manifests itself in reliable scheduling. German machine firms have meaningful schedules—and they perform to these schedules. Moreover, the results of these schedules are communicated to the customer, and the customer can, in turn, rely on them. Consequently, the competitive advantage generated through reliable response has value to the end customer. This is also true for organizations such as grocerygateway.com, where reliability in scheduling and adhering to these schedules is an expectation of customers.

The third aspect of response is *quickness*. Whether it is a production system at a Toyota plant, a pizza delivered in five minutes by Pizza Hut, or customized phone products delivered in three days from Motorola, the operations manager who develops systems that respond quickly can have a competitive advantage.

In practice, differentiation, low cost, and response can increase productivity and generate a sustainable competitive advantage (see Figure 2.4). Proper implementation of the following decisions by operations managers will allow these advantages to be achieved.

Whether it is because of a busy lifestyle or other reasons, customers can shop at home for groceries by placing an order with *grocerygateway.com* and arranging for a delivery time within a 90-minute window. Reliability is vital for this type of service.

Ken Faught/Toronto Star/Getty Images

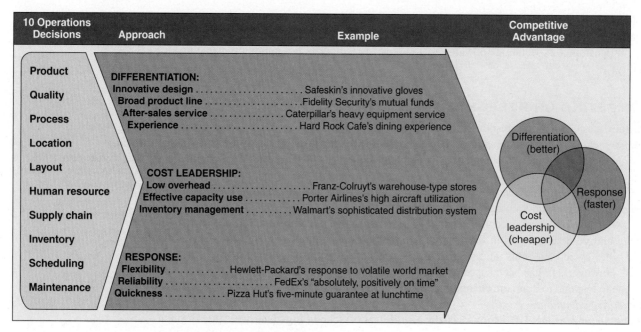

10 Operations Decisions	Approach	Example	Competitive Advantage

Product
Quality
Process
Location
Layout
Human resource
Supply chain
Inventory
Scheduling
Maintenance

DIFFERENTIATION:
Innovative design . . . . Safeskin's innovative gloves
Broad product line .Fidelity Security's mutual funds
After-sales service . . . . Caterpillar's heavy equipment service
Experience . . . . Hard Rock Cafe's dining experience

COST LEADERSHIP:
Low overhead . . . . Franz-Colruyt's warehouse-type stores
Effective capacity use . . . . Porter Airlines's high aircraft utilization
Inventory management . . . . Walmart's sophisticated distribution system

RESPONSE:
Flexibility . . . . Hewlett-Packard's response to volatile world market
Reliability . . . . FedEx's "absolutely, positively on time"
Quickness . . . . Pizza Hut's five-minute guarantee at lunchtime

Differentiation (better)
Response (faster)
Cost leadership (cheaper)

FIGURE 2.4 Achieving Competitive Advantage Through Operations

Operations decisions

The strategic decisions of OM are goods and service design, quality, process and capacity design, location selection, layout design, human resources and job design, supply chain management, inventory, scheduling, and maintenance.

LO3 Identify and define the 10 decisions of operations management

10 Strategic OM Decisions

Differentiation, low cost, and response can be achieved when managers make effective decisions in 10 areas of OM. These are collectively known as **operations decisions**. The 10 decisions of OM that support missions and implement strategies are:

1. *Goods and service design:* Designing goods and services defines much of the transformation process. Costs, quality, and human resource decisions are often determined by design decisions. Designs usually determine the lower limits of cost and the upper limits of quality.
2. *Quality:* The customer's quality expectations must be determined and policies and procedures established to identify and achieve that quality.
3. *Process and capacity design:* Process options are available for products and services. Process decisions commit management to specific technology, quality, human resource use, and maintenance. These expenses and capital commitments determine much of the firm's basic cost structure.
4. *Location selection:* Facility location decisions for both manufacturing and service organizations may determine the firm's ultimate success. Errors made at this juncture may overwhelm other efficiencies.
5. *Layout design:* Material flows, capacity needs, personnel levels, technology decisions, and inventory requirements influence layout.
6. *Human resources and job design:* People are an integral and expensive part of the total system design. Therefore, the quality of work life provided, the talent and skills required, and their costs must be determined.
7. *Supply chain management:* These decisions determine what is to be made and what is to be purchased. Consideration is also given to quality, delivery, and innovation, all at a satisfactory price. Mutual trust between buyer and supplier is necessary for effective purchasing.
8. *Inventory:* Inventory decisions can be optimized only when customer satisfaction, suppliers, production schedules, and human resource planning are considered.
9. *Scheduling:* Feasible and efficient schedules of production must be developed; the demands on human resources and facilities must be determined and controlled.
10. *Maintenance:* Decisions must be made regarding desired levels of reliability and stability, and systems must be established to maintain that reliability and stability.

Table 2.1

The Differences Between Goods and Services Influence How the 10 Operations Management Decisions Are Applied

Operations Decisions	Goods	Services
Goods and services design	Product is usually tangible (a computer).	Product is not tangible. A new range of product attributes (a smile).
Quality	Many objective quality standards (battery life).	Many subjective quality standards (nice colour).
Process and capacity design	Customer is not involved in most of the process (auto assembly).	Customer may be directly involved in the process (a haircut). Capacity must match demand to avoid lost sales (customers often avoid waiting).
Location selection	May need to be near raw materials or labour force (steel plant near ore).	May need to be near customer (car rental).
Layout design	Layout can enhance production efficiency (assembly line).	Can enhance product as well as production (layout of a classroom or a fine-dining restaurant).
Human resources and job design	Workforce focused on technical skills (stonemason). Labour standards can be consistent (assembly line employee). Output-based wage system possible (garment sewing).	Direct workforce usually needs to be able to interact well with customer (bank teller); labour standards vary depending on customer requirements (legal cases).
Supply chain management	Supply chain relationships critical to final product.	Supply chain relationships important but may not be critical.
Inventory	Raw materials, work-in-process, and finished goods may be inventoried (beer).	Most services cannot be stored; so other ways must be found to accommodate fluctuations in demand (can't store haircuts, but even the hair salon has an inventory of supplies).
Scheduling	Ability to inventory may allow levelling of production rates (lawn mowers).	Often concerned with meeting the customer's immediate schedule with human resources.
Maintenance	Maintenance is often preventive and takes place at the production site.	Maintenance is often "repair" and takes place at the customer's site.

STUDENT TIP

The production of both goods and services requires execution of the 10 OM decisions.

Operations managers implement these 10 decisions by identifying key tasks and the staffing needed to achieve them. However, the implementation of decisions is influenced by a variety of issues, including a product's proportion of goods and services (see Table 2.1). Few products are either all goods or all services. Although the 10 decisions remain the same for both goods and services, their relative importance and method of implementation depend on this ratio of goods and services. Throughout this text, we discuss how strategy is selected and implemented for both goods and services through these 10 operations management decisions.

Let's look at an example of strategy development through one of the 10 decisions.

Pierre Alexander has just completed culinary school and is ready to open his own restaurant. After examining both the external environment and his prospective strengths and weaknesses, he makes a decision on the mission for his restaurant, which he defines as, "To provide outstanding French fine dining for the people of Calgary."

APPROACH ▶ Alexander's supporting operations strategy is to ignore the options of *cost leadership* and *quick response* and focus on *differentiation*. Consequently, his operations strategy requires him to evaluate product designs (menus and meals) and selection of process, layout, and location. He must also evaluate the human resources, suppliers, inventory, scheduling, and maintenance that will support his mission as well as a differentiation strategy.

EXAMPLE 1

Strategy Development

SOLUTION ▶ Examining just one of these 10 decisions, *process design*, requires that Alexander consider the issues presented in the following figure.

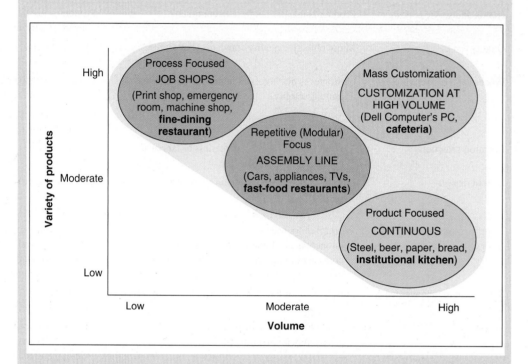

The first option is to operate in the lower right corner of the figure above, where he could produce high volumes of food with a limited variety, much as in an institutional kitchen. Such a process could produce large volumes of standard items such as baked goods and mashed potatoes prepared with state-of-the-art automated equipment. Alexander concludes that this is not an acceptable process option.

Alternatively, he can move to the middle of the figure, where he could produce more variety and lower volumes. Here, he would have less automation and use prepared modular components for meals, much as a fast-food restaurant does. Again, he deems such process designs inappropriate for his mission.

Another option is to move to the upper right corner and produce a high volume of customized meals, but neither Alexander nor anyone else knows how to do this with gourmet meals.

Finally, Alexander can design a process that operates in the upper left corner of the figure, which requires little automation but lends itself to high variety. This process option suggests that he build an extremely flexible kitchen suitable for a wide variety of custom meals catering to the whims of each customer. With little automation, such a process would be suitable for a huge variety. This process strategy will support his mission and desired product differentiation. Only with a process such as this can he provide the fine French-style gourmet dining that he has in mind.

INSIGHT ▶ By considering the options inherent in each of the 10 OM decisions, managers—Alexander, in this case—can make decisions that support the mission.

LEARNING EXERCISE ▶ If Alexander's mission were to offer less expensive meals and reduce the variety offered but still do so with a French flair, what might his process strategy be? [Answer: Alexander might try a repetitive (modular) strategy and mimic the La Madeleine cafeteria-style restaurants. The La Madeleine chain has more than 60 locations and would be a good model for Alexander to mirror. It has the approach, atmosphere, style, and menu he is seeking.]

The 10 decisions of operations management are implemented in ways that provide competitive advantage, not just for fine-dining restaurants, but for all the goods and services that enrich our lives. How this might be done for two drug companies—one seeking a competitive advantage via differentiation, and the other via low cost—is shown in Table 2.2.

Table 2.2

Operations Strategies of Two Drug Companies

	Brand Name Drugs, Inc.	Generic Drug Corp.
Competitive Advantage	**Product Differentiation**	**Low Cost**
Product Selection and Design	Heavy R&D investment; extensive labs; focus on development in a broad range of drug categories	Low R&D investment; focus on development of generic drugs
Quality	Quality is major priority; standards exceed regulatory requirements	Meets regulatory requirements on a country-by-country basis, as necessary
Process	Product and modular production process; tries to have long product runs in specialized facilities; builds capacity ahead of demand	Process focused; general production processes; "job shop" approach, short-run production; focus on high utilization
Location	Still located in city where it was founded	Recently moved to low-tax, low-labour-cost environment
Layout	Layout supports automated product-focused production	Layout supports process-focused "job shop" practices
Human Resources	Hire the best; nationwide searches	Very experienced top executives provide direction; other personnel paid below industry average
Supply Chain	Long-term supplier relationships	Tends to purchase competitively to find bargains
Inventory	Maintains high finished goods inventory primarily to ensure all demands are met	Process focus drives up work-in-process inventory; finished goods inventory tends to be low
Scheduling	Centralized production planning	Many short-run products complicate scheduling
Maintenance	Highly trained staff; extensive parts inventory	Highly trained staff to meet changing demands

Issues in Operations Strategy

Whether the OM strategy is differentiation, cost, or response (as shown earlier in Figure 2.4), OM is a critical player. Therefore, prior to establishing and attempting to implement a strategy, some alternative perspectives may be helpful. One perspective is to take a **resources view**. This means thinking in terms of the financial, physical, human, and technological resources available and ensuring that the potential strategy is compatible with those resources. Another perspective is Porter's value chain analysis.[2] **Value chain analysis** is used to identify activities that represent strengths, or potential strengths, and may be opportunities for developing competitive advantage. These are areas where the firm adds its unique *value* through product research, design, human resources, supply chain management, process innovation, or quality management. Porter also suggests analysis of competitors via what he calls his **five forces model**.[3] These potential competing forces are immediate rivals, potential entrants, customers, suppliers, and substitute products.

In addition to the competitive environment, the operations manager needs to understand that the firm is operating in a system with many other external factors. These factors range from political, to legal, to cultural. They influence strategy development and execution and require constant scanning of the environment.

The firm itself is also undergoing constant change. Everything from resources, to technology, to product life cycles is in flux. Consider the significant changes required within the firm as its products move from introduction, to growth, to maturity, and to decline (see Figure 2.5). These internal changes, combined with external changes, require strategies that are dynamic.

In this chapter's *Global Company Profile*, Boeing provides an example of how strategy must change as technology and the environment change. Boeing can now build planes from carbon fibre, using a global supply chain. Like many other OM strategies, Boeing's strategy has changed with technology and globalization. Microsoft has also had to adapt quickly to a changing

An effective strategy finds the optimum fit for the firm's resources in the dynamic environment.

Resources view

A method managers use to evaluate the resources at their disposal and manage or alter them to achieve competitive advantage.

Value chain analysis

A way to identify those elements in the product/service chain that uniquely add value.

Five forces model

A method of analyzing the five forces in the competitive environment.

---

[2] M. E. Porter, *Competitive Advantage: Creating and Sustaining Superior Performance*. New York, NY: The Free Press, 1985.

[3] Michael E. Porter, *Competitive Strategy: Techniques for Analyzing Industries and Competitors*. New York, NY: The Free Press, 1980, 1998.

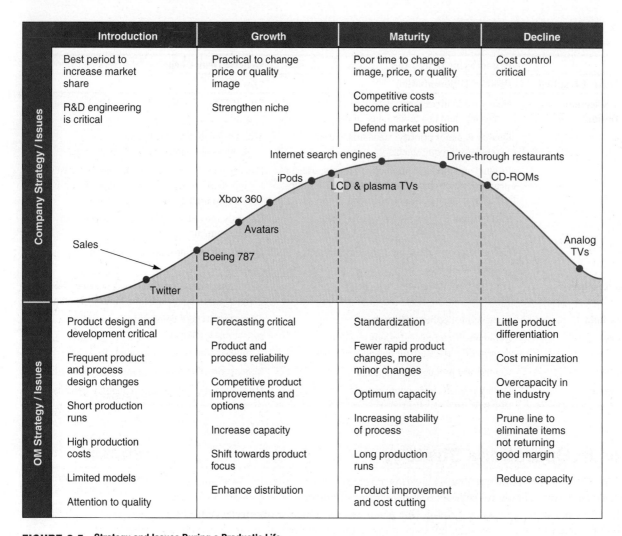

	Introduction	Growth	Maturity	Decline
Company Strategy / Issues	Best period to increase market share R&D engineering is critical	Practical to change price or quality image Strengthen niche	Poor time to change image, price, or quality Competitive costs become critical Defend market position	Cost control critical
OM Strategy / Issues	Product design and development critical Frequent product and process design changes Short production runs High production costs Limited models Attention to quality	Forecasting critical Product and process reliability Competitive product improvements and options Increase capacity Shift towards product focus Enhance distribution	Standardization Fewer rapid product changes, more minor changes Optimum capacity Increasing stability of process Long production runs Product improvement and cost cutting	Little product differentiation Cost minimization Overcapacity in the industry Prune line to eliminate items not returning good margin Reduce capacity

On the sales curve (left to right): Twitter, Sales, Boeing 787, Avatars, Xbox 360, iPods, Internet search engines, LCD & plasma TVs, Drive-through restaurants, CD-ROMs, Analog TVs

FIGURE 2.5 **Strategy and Issues During a Product's Life**

environment. Faster processors, new computer languages, changing customer preferences, increased security issues, the internet, the cloud, and Google have all driven changes at Microsoft. These forces have moved Microsoft's product strategy from operating systems to office products, to internet service provider, and now to integrator of computers, cell phones, games, and television via the cloud.

The more thorough the analysis and understanding of both the external and internal factors, the more likely that a firm can find the optimum use of its resources. Once a firm understands itself and the environment, a SWOT analysis, which we discuss next, is in order.

Strategy Development and Implementation

A **SWOT analysis** is a formal review of the internal *strengths* and *weaknesses* and the external *opportunities* and *threats*. Beginning with SWOT analyses, organizations position themselves, through their strategy, to have a competitive advantage. A firm may have excellent design skills or great talent at identifying outstanding locations. However, it may recognize limitations of its manufacturing process or in finding good suppliers. The idea is to maximize opportunities and minimize threats in the environment while maximizing the advantages of the organization's strengths and minimizing the weaknesses. Any preconceived ideas about mission are then re-evaluated to ensure they are consistent with the SWOT analysis. Subsequently, a strategy for achieving the mission is developed. This strategy is continually evaluated against the value provided to customers and competitive realities. The process is shown in Figure 2.6. From this process, key success factors are identified.

Analyze the Environment
Identify the strengths, weaknesses, opportunities, and threats.
Understand the environment, customers, industry, and competitors.

Determine the Corporate Mission
State the reason for the firm's existence, and identify the value it wishes to create.

Form a Strategy
Build a competitive advantage, such as low price, design or volume flexibility, quality, quick delivery, dependability, after-sale services, or broad product lines.

FIGURE 2.6
Strategy Development Process

KEY SUCCESS FACTORS AND CORE COMPETENCIES

Because no firm does everything exceptionally well, a successful strategy requires determining the firm's critical success factors and core competencies. **Key success factors (KSFs)** are those activities that are necessary for a firm to achieve its goals. Key success factors can be so significant that a firm must get them right to survive in the industry. A KSF for McDonald's, for example, is layout. Without a play area, an effective drive-through, and an efficient kitchen, McDonald's cannot be successful. KSFs are often necessary, but not sufficient for competitive advantage. On the other hand, **core competencies** are the set of unique skills, talents, and capabilities that a firm does at a world-class standard. They allow a firm to set itself apart and develop a competitive advantage. Organizations that prosper identify their core competencies and nurture them. While McDonald's KSFs may include layout, its core competency may be consistency and quality. Honda Motors's core competency is gas-powered engines—engines for automobiles, motorcycles, lawn mowers, generators, snow blowers, and more. The idea is to build KSFs and core competencies that provide a competitive advantage and support a successful strategy and mission. A core competency may be a subset of KSFs or a combination of KSFs. The operations manager begins this inquiry by asking:

- "What tasks must be done particularly well for a given strategy to succeed?"
- "Which activities will help the OM function provide a competitive advantage?"
- "Which elements contain the highest likelihood of failure, and which require additional commitment of managerial, monetary, technological, and human resources?"

Only by identifying and strengthening key success factors and core competencies can an organization achieve sustainable competitive advantage.

In this text-book, we focus on the 10 OM decisions that typically include the KSFs. Potential KSFs for marketing, finance, and operations are shown in Figure 2.7. The 10 OM decisions we develop in this text provide an excellent initial checklist for determining KSFs and identifying core competencies within the operations function. For instance, the 10 decisions, related KSFs, and core

LO4 Understand the significance of key success factors and core competencies

Key success factors (KSFs)
Activities or factors that are *key* to achieving competitive advantage.

Core competencies
A set of skills, talents, and activities in which a firm is particularly strong.

All images: American Honda Motor Co., Inc.

Julie Lucht/Shutterstock

Honda's core competency is the design and manufacture of gas-powered engines. This competency has allowed Honda to become a leader in the design and manufacture of a wide range of gas-powered products. Tens of millions of these products are shipped around the world.

FIGURE 2.7

Implement Strategy by Identifying and Executing Key Success Factors That Support Core Competencies

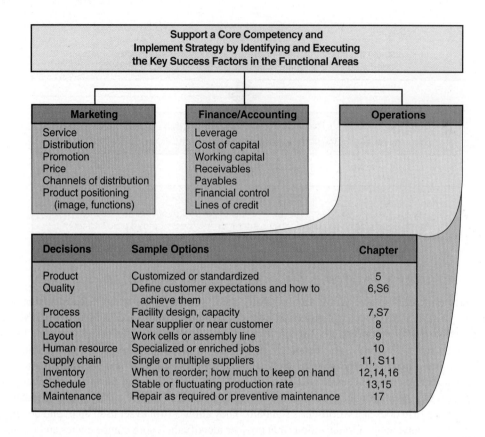

Support a Core Competency and Implement Strategy by Identifying and Executing the Key Success Factors in the Functional Areas

Marketing
Service
Distribution
Promotion
Price
Channels of distribution
Product positioning
   (image, functions)

Finance/Accounting
Leverage
Cost of capital
Working capital
Receivables
Payables
Financial control
Lines of credit

Operations

Decisions	Sample Options	Chapter
Product	Customized or standardized	5
Quality	Define customer expectations and how to achieve them	6,S6
Process	Facility design, capacity	7,S7
Location	Near supplier or near customer	8
Layout	Work cells or assembly line	9
Human resource	Specialized or enriched jobs	10
Supply chain	Single or multiple suppliers	11, S11
Inventory	When to reorder; how much to keep on hand	12,14,16
Schedule	Stable or fluctuating production rate	13,15
Maintenance	Repair as required or preventive maintenance	17

competencies can allow a firm to differentiate its product or service. That differentiation may be via a core competency of innovation and new products, where the KSFs are product design and speed to market, as is the case for 3M and Rubbermaid. Similarly, differentiation may be via quality, where the core competency is institutionalizing quality, as at Toyota. Differentiation may also be via maintenance, where the KSFs are product reliability and after-sale service, as is the case at IBM and Canon.

Whatever the KSFs and core competencies, they must be supported by the related activities. One approach to identifying the activities is an **activity map**, which links competitive advantage, KSFs, and supporting activities. For example, Figure 2.8 shows how Porter Airlines, whose core competency is operations, built a set of integrated activities to support its low-cost competitive advantage. Notice how the KSFs support operations and in turn are supported by other activities. The activities fit together and reinforce each other. And the better they fit and reinforce each other, the more sustainable the competitive advantage. By focusing on enhancing its core competency and KSFs with a supporting set of activities, Porter Airlines has become one of the great airline success stories.

Activity map

A graphical link of competitive advantage, KSFs, and supporting activities.

BUILD AND STAFF THE ORGANIZATION

The operations manager's job is a three-step process. Once a strategy and key success factors have been identified, the second step is to group the necessary activities into an organizational structure. The third step is to staff it with personnel who will get the job done. The manager works with subordinate managers to build plans, budgets, and programs that will successfully implement strategies that achieve missions. Firms tackle this organization of the operations function in a variety of ways. The organization charts shown in Chapter 1 (Figure 1.1) indicate the way some firms have organized to perform the required activities.

INTEGRATE OM WITH OTHER ACTIVITIES

The organization of the operations function and its relationship to other parts of the organization vary with the OM mission. Moreover, the operations function is most likely to be successful when the operations strategy is integrated with other functional areas of the firm, such as marketing, finance, information technology, and human resources. In this way, all of the areas support the company's objectives. For example, short-term scheduling in the airline industry is dominated by volatile customer travel patterns. Day-of-week preference, holidays, seasonality, school schedules, and so on all play a role in changing flight schedules. Consequently, airline

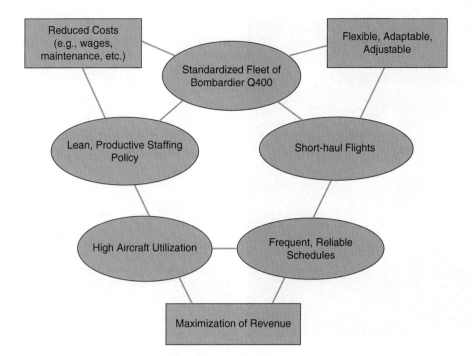

FIGURE 2.8
Activity Mapping of Porter Airlines's Low-Cost Competitive Advantage
To achieve a low-cost competitive advantage, Porter Airlines addresses a number of key success factors. As the figure illustrates, a low-cost advantage is highly dependent on a very well-run operations function.

scheduling, although an OM activity, can be a part of marketing. Effective scheduling in the trucking industry is reflected in the amount of time trucks travel loaded. However, scheduling of trucks requires information from delivery and pickup points, drivers, and other parts of the organization. When the OM function results in effective scheduling in the air passenger and commercial trucking industries, a competitive advantage can exist.

The operations manager transforms inputs into outputs. The transformations may be in terms of storage, transportation, manufacturing, dissemination of information, and utility of the product or service. *The operations manager's job is to implement an OM strategy, provide competitive advantage, and increase productivity.*

Strategic Planning, Core Competencies, and Outsourcing

As organizations develop missions, goals, and strategies, they identify their strengths—what they do as well as or better than their competitors—as their *core competencies*. By contrast, *noncore activities*, which can be a sizable portion of an organization's total business, are good candidates for outsourcing. **Outsourcing** is transferring activities that have traditionally been internal to external suppliers.

Outsourcing
Transferring a firm's activities that have traditionally been internal to external suppliers.

Outsourcing is not a new concept, but it does add complexity and risk to the supply chain. Because of its potential, outsourcing continues to expand. The expansion is accelerating due to three global trends: (1) increased technological expertise, (2) more reliable and cheaper transportation, and (3) the rapid development and deployment of advancements in telecommunications and computers. This rich combination of economic advances is contributing to both lower cost and more specialization. As a result more firms are candidates for outsourcing of noncore activities.

Outsourcing implies an agreement (typically a legally binding contract) with an external organization. The classic make-or-buy decision, concerning which products to make and which to buy, is the basis of outsourcing. When firms such as Apple find that their core competency is in creativity, innovation, and product design, they may want to outsource manufacturing.

Outsourcing manufacturing is an extension of the long-standing practice of *subcontracting* production activities, which when done on a continuing basis is known as *contract manufacturing*. Contract manufacturing is becoming standard practice in many industries, from computers to automobiles. For instance, Johnson & Johnson, like many other big drug companies whose core competency is research and development, often farms out manufacturing to contractors. On the other hand, Sony's core competency is electromechanical design of chips. This is its core competency, but Sony is also one of the best in the world when it comes to rapid response and specialized production of these

Keith Dannemiller/Alamy Stock Photo

Contract manufacturers such as Flextronics provide outsourcing service to IBM, Cisco Systems, HP, Microsoft, Sony, Nortel, Ericsson, and Sun, among many others. Flextronics is a high-quality producer that has won over 450 awards, including the Malcolm Baldrige Award. One of the side benefits of outsourcing is that client firms such as IBM can actually improve their performance by using the competencies of an outstanding firm like Flextronics. But there are risks involved in outsourcing.

chips. Therefore, Sony finds that it wants to be its own *manufacturer*, while specialized providers come up with major innovations in such areas as software, human resources, and distribution. These areas are the providers' business, not Sony's, and the provider may very well be better at it than Sony.

Other examples of outsourcing noncore activities include:

- DuPont's legal services routed to the Philippines
- IBM's handing of travel services and payroll and Hewlett-Packard's provision of IT services to P&G
- Production of the Audi A4 convertible and Mercedes CLK convertible by Wilhelm Karmann in Osnabruck, Germany
- Blue Cross sending hip resurfacing surgery patients to India

Managers evaluate their strategies and core competencies and ask themselves how to use the assets entrusted to them. Do they want to be the company that does low-margin work at 3%–4% or the innovative firm that makes a 30%–40% margin? PC and iPad contract manufacturers in China and Taiwan earn 3%–4%, but Apple, which innovates, designs, and sells, has a margin 10 times as large.

THE THEORY OF COMPARATIVE ADVANTAGE

Theory of comparative advantage

A theory which states that countries benefit from specializing in (and exporting) goods and services in which they have relative advantage, and they benefit from importing goods and services in which they have a relative disadvantage.

The motivation for international outsourcing comes from the **theory of comparative advantage**. This theory focuses on the economic concept of relative advantage. According to the theory, if an external provider, regardless of its geographic location, can perform activities more productively than the purchasing firm, then the external provider should do the work. This allows the purchasing firm to focus on what it does best—its core competencies. Consistent with the theory of comparative advantage, outsourcing continues to grow. But outsourcing the wrong activities can be a disaster. And even outsourcing noncore activities has risks.

RISKS OF OUTSOURCING

STUDENT TIP

The substantial risk of outsourcing requires managers to invest in the effort to make sure they do it right.

Risk management starts with a realistic analysis of uncertainty and results in a strategy that minimizes the impact of these uncertainties. Indeed, outsourcing *is* risky, with roughly half of all outsourcing agreements failing because of inadequate planning and analysis. Timely delivery and quality standards can be major problems, as can underestimating increases in inventory and logistics costs. Some potential advantages and disadvantages of outsourcing are shown in Table 2.3. A survey of North American companies found that, as a group, those that outsourced customer service saw a drop in their score on the American Consumer Satisfaction Index. The declines were roughly the same whether companies outsourced domestically or overseas.[4]

---

[4] J. Whitaker, M. S. Krishnan, and C. Fornell. "How Offshore Outsourcing Affects Customer Satisfaction." The Wall Street Journal (July 7, 2008): R4.

Table 2.3

Potential Advantages and Disadvantages of Outsourcing

Advantages	Disadvantages
Cost savings	Increased logistics and inventory costs
Gaining outside expertise that comes with specialization	Loss of control (quality, delivery, etc.)
Improving operations and service	Potential creation of future competition
Maintaining a focus on core competencies	Negative impact on employees
Accessing outside technology	Risks may not manifest themselves for years

However, when outsourcing is overseas, additional issues must be considered. These issues include financial attractiveness, people skills and availability, and the general business environment. Another risk of outsourcing overseas is the political backlash that results from moving jobs to foreign countries. The perceived loss of jobs has fuelled anti-outsourcing rhetoric. This rhetoric is contributing to a process known as *reshoring*, the return of business activity to the originating country. (See the *OM in Action* box "Reshoring to Smaller Towns in North America".)

In addition to the external risks, operations managers must deal with other issues that outsourcing brings. These include: (1) reduced employment levels, (2) changes in facility requirements, (3) potential adjustments to quality control systems and manufacturing processes, and (4) expanded logistics issues, including insurance, tariffs, customs, and timing.

To summarize, managers can find substantial efficiencies in outsourcing noncore activities, but they must be cautious in outsourcing those elements of the product or service that provide a competitive advantage. The next section provides a methodology that helps analyze the outsourcing decision process.

RATING OUTSOURCE PROVIDERS

Research indicates that the most common reason for the failure of outsourcing agreements is that the decisions are made without sufficient analysis. The *factor rating method* provides an objective way to evaluate outsource providers. We assign points for each factor to each provider and then importance weights to each of the factors. We now apply the technique in Example 2 to compare outsourcing providers being considered by a firm.

OM in Action   Reshoring to Smaller Towns in North America

North American companies continue their global search for efficiency by outsourcing call centres and back-office operations, but many find they need to look no farther than a place like Dubuque, Iowa.

To North American firms facing quality problems with their outsourcing operations overseas and bad publicity at home, small-town America is emerging as a pleasant alternative. Dubuque (population 57,313), Nacogdoches, Texas (population 29,914), or Twin Falls, Idaho (population 34,469), may be the perfect call centre location. Even though the pay is low, the jobs are some of the best available to small-town residents.

By moving out of big cities to the cheaper labour and real estate of small towns, companies can save millions and still increase productivity. A call centre in a town that just lost its major manufacturing plant finds the jobs easy to fill.

IBM, which has been criticized in the past for moving jobs to India and other offshore locations, picked Dubuque for its new remote computer-services centre with 1300 jobs.

Taking advantage of even cheaper wages in other countries will not stop soon, though. Is India the unstoppable overseas call centre capital that people think it is? Not at all. Despite its population of 1.3 billion, only a small percentage of its workers have the language skills and technical education to work in Western-style industries. Already, India has been warned that if call centres can't recruit at reasonable wages, its jobs will move to the Philippines, South Africa, and Ghana. And indeed, Dell, Apple, and Britain's Powergen are reshoring from Indian call centres, claiming their costs had become too high.

Fredrik Renander/Alamy Stock Photo

Sources: Industry Week (August 5, 2014) and The Wall Street Journal, (November 27, 2013).

EXAMPLE **2**

**Rating Provider
Selection Criteria**

National Architects, Inc., a Vancouver-based designer of high-rise office buildings, has decided to outsource its information technology (IT) function. Three outsourcing providers are being actively considered: one in Canada, one in India, and one in Israel.

APPROACH ▶ National's VP–Operations, Susan Cholette, has made a list of seven criteria she considers critical. After putting together a committee of four other VPs, she has rated each firm (boldface type, on a 1–5 scale, with 5 being highest) and has also placed an importance weight on each of the factors, as shown in Table 2.4.

Table 2.4

Factor Ratings Applied to National Architects's Potential IT Outsourcing Providers

FACTOR (CRITERION)*	IMPORTANCE WEIGHT	OUTSOURCE PROVIDERS		
		BIM (CANADA)	S.P.C. (INDIA)	TELCO (ISRAEL)
1. Can reduce operating costs	.2	.2 × 3 = .6	.2 × 3 = .6	.2 × 5 = 1.0
2. Can reduce capital investment	.2	.2 × 4 = .8	.2 × 3 = .6	.2 × 3 = .6
3. Skilled personnel	.2	.2 × 5 = 1.0	.2 × 4 = 8	.2 × 3 = .6
4. Can improve quality	.1	.1 × 4 = .4	.1 × 5 = .5	.1 × 2 = .2
5. Can gain access to technology not in company	.1	.1 × 5 = .5	.1 × 3 = .3	.1 × 5 = .5
6. Can create additional capacity	.1	.1 × 4 = .4	.1 × 2 = .2	.1 × 4 = .4
7. Aligns with policy/philosophy/culture	.1	.1 × 2 = .2	.1 × 3 = .3	.1 × 5 = .5
Total Weighted Score		3.9	3.3	3.8

*These seven major criteria are based on a survey of 165 procurement executives, as reported in J. Schildhouse, *Inside Supply Management* (December 2005): 22–29.

SOLUTION ▶ Susan multiplies each rating by the weight and sums the products in each column to generate a total score for each outsourcing provider. She selects BIM, which has the highest overall rating.

INSIGHT ▶ When the total scores are as close (3.9 vs. 3.8) as they are in this case, it is important to examine the sensitivity of the results to inputs. For example, if one of the importance weights or factor scores changes even marginally, the final selection may change. Management preference may also play a role here.

LEARNING EXERCISE ▶ Susan decides that "Skilled personnel" should instead get a weight of 0.1 and "Aligns with policy/philosophy/culture" should increase to 0.2. How do the total scores change? [Answer: BIM = 3.6, S.P.C. = 3.2, and Telco = 4.0, so Telco would be selected.]

RELATED PROBLEMS ▶ 2.8–2.12

EXCEL OM Data File **Ch02Ex2.xlsx** can be found in **MyLab Operations Management.**

Most North American toy companies now outsource their production to Chinese manufacturers. Cost savings are significant, but there are several downsides, including loss of control over such issues as quality. A few years ago, Mattel had to recall 10.5 million Elmos, Big Birds, and SpongeBobs. These made-in-China toys contained excessive levels of lead in their paint. More recently, quality issues have dealt with poisonous pet food, tainted milk products, and contaminated sheetrock.

Global Operations Strategy Options

As we suggested earlier in this chapter, many operations strategies now require an international dimension. We tend to call a firm with an international dimension an international business or a multinational corporation. An **international business** is any firm that engages in international trade or investment. This is a broad category and is the opposite of a domestic, or local, firm.

A **multinational corporation (MNC)** is a firm with *extensive* international business involvement. MNCs buy resources, create goods or services, and sell goods or services in a variety of countries. The term *multinational corporation* applies to most of the world's large, well-known businesses. Bombardier is a good example of an MNC. It has a presence in 60 countries worldwide, including 76 production and engineering sites. Bombardier acquires parts and raw materials from around the world, and ships its finished products (including planes, trains, and buses) to its customers wherever they may be.

Operations managers of international and multinational firms approach global opportunities with one of four operations strategies: *international*, *multidomestic*, *global*, or *transnational* (see Figure 2.9). The matrix of Figure 2.9 has a vertical axis of cost reduction and a horizontal axis of local responsiveness. Local responsiveness implies quick response and/or the differentiation necessary for the local market. The operations manager must know how to position the firm in this matrix. Let us briefly examine each of the four strategies.

INTERNATIONAL STRATEGY

An **international strategy** uses exports and licences to penetrate the global arena. As Figure 2.9 suggests, the international strategy is the least advantageous, with little local responsiveness and little cost advantage. There is little responsiveness because we are exporting or licensing goods from the home country. And the cost advantages may be few because we are using the existing production process at some distance from the new market. However, an international strategy is

STUDENT TIP

Firms that ignore the global economy will not survive.

International business
A firm that engages in cross-border transactions.

Multinational corporation (MNC)
A firm that has extensive involvement in international business, owning or controlling facilities in more than one country.

LO5 Identify and explain four global operations strategy options

International strategy
A strategy in which global markets are penetrated using exports and licences.

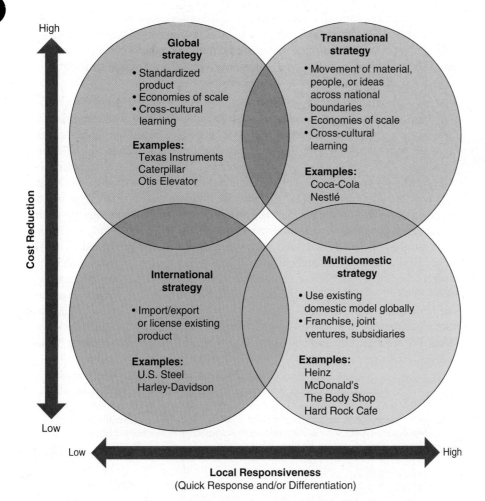

FIGURE 2.9

Four International Operations Strategies

Source: Based on M. Hitt, R. D. Ireland, and R. E. Hoskisson, *Strategic Management, Competitiveness and Globalization*, 7th ed. (Cincinnati: Southwestern College Publishing, 2009).

often the easiest, as exports can require little change in existing operations, and licensing agreements often leave much of the risk to the licensee.

MULTIDOMESTIC STRATEGY

Multidomestic strategy

A strategy in which operating decisions are decentralized to each country to enhance local responsiveness.

The **multidomestic strategy** has decentralized authority with substantial autonomy at each business. Organizationally, these are typically subsidiaries, franchises, or joint ventures with substantial independence. The advantage of this strategy is maximizing a competitive response for the local market; however, the strategy has little or no cost advantage. Many food producers, such as Heinz, use a multidomestic strategy to accommodate local tastes because global integration of the production process is not critical. The concept is one of "We were successful in the home market; let's export the management talent and processes, not necessarily the product, to accommodate another market." McDonald's is operating primarily as a multidomestic, which gives it the local responsiveness needed to modify its menu country by country. McDonald's can then serve beer in Germany, wine in France, McHuevo (poached egg hamburger) in Uruguay, and hamburgers without beef in India. With over 2000 restaurants in Japan and a presence for more than a generation, McDonald's is thought to have been invented in Japan, according to the average Japanese family. Interestingly, McDonald's prefers to call itself *multilocal*.[5]

GLOBAL STRATEGY

Global strategy

A strategy in which operating decisions are centralized and headquarters coordinates the standardization and learning between facilities.

A **global strategy** has a high degree of centralization, with headquarters coordinating the organization to seek out standardization and learning between plants, thus generating economies of scale. This strategy is appropriate when the strategic focus is cost reduction but has little to recommend it when the demand for local responsiveness is high. Caterpillar, the world leader in earth moving equipment, and Texas Instruments, a world leader in semiconductors, pursue global strategies. Caterpillar and Texas Instruments find this strategy advantageous because the end products are similar throughout the world. Earth moving equipment is the same in Nigeria as in Prince Edward Island, which allows Caterpillar to have individual factories focus on a limited line of products to be shipped worldwide. This results in economies of scale and learning within each facility. A global strategy also allows Texas Instruments to build optimum-size plants with similar processes and to then maximize learning by aggressive communication between plants. The result is an effective cost reduction advantage for Texas Instruments.

TRANSNATIONAL STRATEGY

Transnational strategy

A strategy that combines the benefits of global-scale efficiencies with the benefits of local responsiveness.

A **transnational strategy** exploits the economies of scale and learning, as well as pressure for responsiveness, by recognizing that core competence does not reside in just the "home" country but can exist anywhere in the organization. *Transnational* describes a condition in which material, people, and ideas cross—or *transgress*—national boundaries. These firms have the potential to pursue all three operations strategies (i.e., differentiation, low cost, and response). Such firms can be thought of as "world companies" whose country identity is not as important as its interdependent network of worldwide operations. Key activities in a transnational company are neither centralized in the parent company nor decentralized so that each subsidiary can carry out its own tasks on a local basis. Instead, the resources and activities are dispersed, but specialized, so as to be both efficient and flexible in an interdependent network. Nestlé is a good example of such a company. Although it is legally Swiss, 95% of its assets are held and 98% of its sales are made outside Switzerland. Fewer than 10% of its workers are Swiss. Similarly, service firms such as Asea Brown Boveri (an engineering firm that is Swedish but headquartered in Switzerland), Reuters (a news agency), Bertelsmann (a publisher), and Citicorp (a banking corporation) can be viewed as transnationals. We can expect the national identities of these transnationals to continue to fade.

---

[5] James L. Watson, ed., *Golden Arches East: McDonald's in East Asia* (Stanford University Press, 1997): 12. *Note:* McDonald's also operates with some of the advantages of a global organization. By using very similar product lines throughout the world, McDonald's obtains some of the standardization advantages of a global strategy. However, it manages to retain the advantages of a multidomestic strategy.

In a continuing fierce worldwide battle, both Komatsu and Caterpillar seek global advantage in the heavy equipment market. As Komatsu (left) moved west to the United Kingdom, Caterpillar (right) moved east, with 13 facilities and joint ventures in China. Both firms are building equipment throughout the world as cost and logistics dictate. Their global strategies allow production to move as markets, risk, and exchange rates dictate.

CHAPTER | SUMMARY

Global operations provide an increase in both the challenges and opportunities for operations managers. Although the task is challenging, operations managers can and do improve productivity. They can build and manage OM functions that contribute in a significant way to competitiveness. Organizations identify their strengths and weaknesses. They then develop effective missions and strategies that account for these strengths and weaknesses and complement the opportunities and threats in the environment. If this procedure is performed well, the organization can have competitive advantage through some combination of product differentiation, low cost, and response. This competitive advantage is often achieved via a move to international, multidomestic, global, or transnational strategies.

Effective use of resources, whether domestic or international, is the responsibility of the professional manager, and professional managers are among the few in our society who *can* achieve this performance. The challenge is great, and the rewards to the manager and to society substantial.

ETHICAL | DILEMMA

As a manufacturer of athletic shoes whose image, indeed performance, is widely regarded as socially responsible, you find your costs increasing. Traditionally, your athletic shoes have been made in Indonesia and South Korea. Although the ease of doing business in those countries has been improving, wage rates have also been increasing. The labour-cost differential between your present suppliers and a contractor who will get the shoes made in China now exceeds $1 per pair. Your sales next year are projected to be 10 million pairs, and your analysis suggests that this cost differential is not offset by any other tangible costs; you face only the political risk and potential damage to your commitment to social responsibility. Thus, this $1 per pair savings should flow directly to your bottom line. There is no doubt that the Chinese government engages in censorship, remains repressive, and is a long way from a democracy. Moreover, you will have little or no control over working conditions, sexual harassment, and pollution. What do you do, and on what basis do you make your decision?

Discussion Questions

1. Based on the descriptions and analyses in this chapter, would Boeing be better described as a global firm or a transnational firm? Discuss.
2. List six reasons to internationalize operations.
3. Coca-Cola is called a global product. Does this mean that it is formulated in the same way throughout the world? Discuss.
4. Define *mission*.
5. Define *strategy*.
6. Describe how an organization's *mission* and *strategy* have different purposes.
7. Identify the mission and strategy of your automobile repair garage. What are the manifestations of the 10 OM decisions at the garage? That is, how is each of the 10 decisions accomplished?
8. As a library or internet assignment, identify the mission of a firm and the strategy that supports that mission.
9. How does an OM strategy change during a product's life cycle?
10. There are three primary ways to achieve competitive advantage. Provide an example, not included in the text, of each. Support your choices.
11. Given the discussion of Porter Airlines in the text, define an *operations* strategy for that firm.
12. How must an operations strategy integrate with marketing and accounting?
13. How would you summarize outsourcing trends?
14. What potential cost-saving advantages might firms experience by using outsourcing?
15. What internal issues must managers address when outsourcing?
16. How should a company select an outsourcing provider?
17. What are some of the possible consequences of poor outsourcing?
18. What global operations strategy is most descriptive of McDonald's?

Solved Problems Virtual Office Hours help is available at MyLab Operations Management.

▼ SOLVED PROBLEM 2.1

The global tire industry continues to consolidate. Michelin buys Goodrich and Uniroyal and builds plants throughout the world. Bridgestone buys Firestone, expands its research budget, and focuses on world markets. Goodyear spends almost 4% of its sales revenue on research. These three aggressive firms have come to dominate the world tire market, with total market share approaching 60%. And the German tire maker Continental AG has strengthened its position as fourth in the world, with a dominant presence in Germany. Against this formidable array, the old-line Italian tire company Pirelli SpA found it difficult to respond effectively. Although Pirelli still had 5% of the market, it was losing millions of dollars per year while the competition was getting stronger. Tires are a tough, competitive business that rewards companies having strong market shares and long production runs. Pirelli has some strengths: an outstanding reputation for excellent high-performance tires and an innovative manufacturing function.

Use a SWOT analysis to establish a feasible strategy for Pirelli.

▼ SOLUTION

First, find an opportunity in the world tire market that avoids the threat of the mass-market onslaught by the big three tire makers. Second, utilize the internal marketing strength represented by Pirelli's strong brand name and history of winning World Rally Championships. Third, maximize the internal innovative capabilities of the operations function.

To achieve these goals, Pirelli made a strategic shift out of low-margin standard tires and into higher-margin performance tires. Pirelli established deals with luxury brands Jaguar, BMW, Maserati, Ferrari, Bentley, and Lotus Elise and established itself as a provider of a large share of tires on new Porsches, S-class Mercedes, and Saabs. As a result, more than 70% of the company's tire production is now high-performance tires. People are willing to pay a premium for Pirellis.

The operations function continued to focus its design efforts on performance tires and developing a system of modular tire manufacture that allows much faster switching between models. This modular system, combined with investments in new manufacturing flexibility, has driven batch sizes down to as small as 150 to 200, making small-lot performance tires economically feasible. Manufacturing innovations at Pirelli have streamlined the production process, moving it from a 14-step process to a three-step process. A threat from the Big Three going after the performance market remains, but Pirelli has bypassed its weakness of having a small market share. The firm now has 24 plants in 12 countries and a presence in more than 160 countries, with sales exceeding $4.5 billion.

Sources: Just Auto (February 2009): 14–15 and (December 2008): 14–15; *Hoover's Company Records* (October 15, 2005): 41369; and www.pirelli.com/corporate/en/investors/pirelli_at_glance/default.html.

Using Software to Solve Outsourcing Problems

Excel, Excel OM, and POM for Windows may be used to solve many of the problems in this chapter.

CREATING YOUR OWN EXCEL SPREADSHEETS

Program 2.1 illustrates how to build an Excel spreadsheet for the data in Example 2. In this example the factor rating method is used to compare National Architects's three potential outsourcing providers.

This program provides the data inputs for seven important factors, including their weights (0.0–1.0) and ratings (1–5 scale where 5 is the highest rating) for each country. As we

see, BIM is most highly rated, with a 3.9 score, versus 3.3 for S.P.C. and 3.8 for Telco.

✗ USING EXCEL OM

Excel OM (free with your text and also found in MyLab Operations Management) may be used to solve Example 2 (with the Factor Rating module).

P USING POM FOR WINDOWS

POM for Windows also includes a factor rating module. For details, refer to Appendix IV. POM for Windows is also found in MyLab Operations Management and can solve all problems labeled with a **P**.

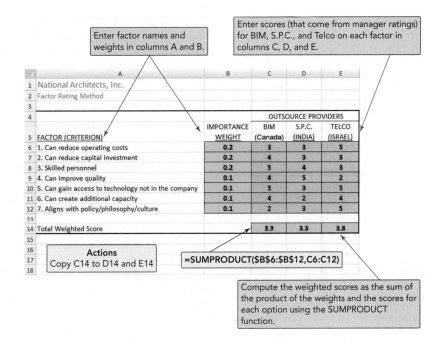

Enter factor names and weights in columns A and B.

Enter scores (that come from manager ratings) for BIM, S.P.C., and Telco on each factor in columns C, D, and E.

	A	B	C	D	E
1	National Architects, Inc.				
2	Factor Rating Method				
3					
4			OUTSOURCE PROVIDERS		
5	FACTOR (CRITERION)	IMPORTANCE WEIGHT	BIM (Canada)	S.P.C. (INDIA)	TELCO (ISRAEL)
6	1. Can reduce operating costs	0.2	3	3	5
7	2. Can reduce capital investment	0.2	4	3	3
8	3. Skilled personnel	0.2	5	4	3
9	4. Can improve quality	0.1	4	5	2
10	5. Can gain access to technology not in the company	0.1	5	3	5
11	6. Can create additional capacity	0.1	4	2	4
12	7. Aligns with policy/philosophy/culture	0.1	2	3	5
13					
14	Total Weighted Score		3.9	3.3	3.8
15					
16	**Actions**				
17	Copy C14 to D14 and E14				
18					

=SUMPRODUCT($B$6:$B$12,C6:C12)

Compute the weighted scores as the sum of the product of the weights and the scores for each option using the SUMPRODUCT function.

PROGRAM 2.1

Using Excel to Develop a Factor Rating Analysis, With Data from Example 2.

Problems
Note: **Px** means the problem may be solved with POM for Windows and/or Excel OM.

Problems 2.1–2.3 relate to *A Global View of Operations and Supply Chains*

•• **2.1** Match the product with the proper parent company and country in the table below:

Product	Parent Company	Country
Arrow Shirts	Volkswagen	1. France
Braun Household Appliances	Bidermann International	2. Great Britain
Volvo Autos	Bridgestone	3. Germany
Firestone Tires	Campbell Soup	4. Japan
Godiva Chocolate	Credit Lyonnais	5. United States
Häagen-Dazs Ice Cream (USA)	Tata	6. Switzerland
Jaguar Autos	Procter & Gamble	7. China
MGM Movies	Michelin	8. India
Lamborghini Autos	Nestlé	
Goodrich Tires	Geely	
Alpo Pet Foods		

•• **2.2** Based on the corruption perception index developed by Transparency International (www.transparency.org), rank the following countries from most corrupt to least: Venezuela, Denmark, the United States, Switzerland, and China.

•• **2.3** Based on the competitiveness ranking developed by the Global Competitiveness Index (www.weforum.org), rank the following countries from most competitive to least: Mexico, Switzerland, the United States, and China.

Problems 2.4 and 2.5 relate to *Achieving Competitive Advantage Through Operations*

• **2.4** The text provides three primary strategic approaches (differentiation, cost, and response) for achieving competitive advantage. Provide an example of each not given in the text. Support your choices. (*Hint:* Note the examples provided in the text.)

•• **2.5** Within the food service industry (restaurants that serve meals to customers, but not just fast food), find examples of firms that have sustained competitive advantage by competing on the basis of (1) cost leadership, (2) response, and (3) differentiation. Cite one example in each category; provide a sentence or two in support of each choice. Do not use fast-food chains for all categories. (*Hint:* A "99¢ menu" is very easily copied and is not a good source of sustained advantage.)

Problem 2.6 relates to *Issues in Operations Strategy*

••• **2.6** Identify how changes within an organization affect the OM strategy for a company. For instance, discuss what impact the following internal factors might have on OM strategy:
a) Maturing of a product.
b) Technology innovation in the manufacturing process.
c) Changes in laptop computer design that builds in wireless technology.

Problem 2.7 relates to *Strategy Development and Implementation*

••• **2.7** Identify how changes in the external environment affect the OM strategy for a company. For instance, discuss what impact the following external factors might have on OM strategy:
a) Major increases in oil prices.
b) Water- and air-quality legislation.
c) Fewer young prospective employees entering the labour market.
d) Inflation versus stable prices.
e) Legislation moving health insurance from a pretax benefit to taxable income.

Problems 2.8–2.12 relate to *Strategic Planning, Core Competencies, and Outsourcing*

•• **2.8** Claudia Pragram Technologies, Inc., has narrowed its choice of outsourcing provider to two firms located in different countries. Pragram wants to decide which one of the two countries is the better choice, based on risk-avoidance criteria. She has polled her executives and established four criteria. The resulting ratings for the two countries are presented in the table below, where 1 is a lower risk and 3 is a higher risk.

Selection Criterion	England	Mexico
Price of service from outsourcer	2	3
Nearness of facilities to client	3	1
Level of technology	1	3
History of successful outsourcing	1	2

The executives have determined four criteria weightings: Price, with a weight of 0.1; Nearness, with 0.6; Technology, with 0.2; and History, with 0.1.

a) Using the factor rating method, which country would you select?
b) Double each of the weights used in part (a) (to 0.2, 1.2, 0.4, and 0.2, respectively). What effect does this have on your answer? Why? **Px**

•• **2.9** Ranga Ramasesh is the operations manager for a firm that is trying to decide which one of four countries it should research for possible outsourcing providers. The first step is to select a country based on cultural risk factors, which are critical to eventual business success with the provider. Ranga has reviewed outsourcing provider directories and found that the four countries in the table that follows have an ample number of providers from which they can choose. To aid in the country selection step, he has enlisted the aid of a cultural expert, John Wang, who has provided ratings of the various criteria in the table. The resulting ratings are on a 1 to 10 scale, where 1 is a low risk and 10 is a high risk.

John has also determined six criteria weightings: Trust, with a weight of 0.4; Quality, with 0.2; Religious, with 0.1; Individualism, with 0.1; Time, with 0.1; and Uncertainty, with 0.1. Using the factor rating method, which country should Ranga select? **Px**

Culture Selection Criterion	Mexico	Panama	Costa Rica	Peru
Trust	1	2	2	1
Society value of quality work	7	10	9	10
Religious attitudes	3	3	3	5
Individualism attitudes	5	2	4	8
Time orientation attitudes	4	6	7	3
Uncertainty avoidance attitudes	3	2	4	2

•• **2.10** Fernando Garza's firm wishes to use factor rating to help select an outsourcing provider of logistics services.

a) With weights from 1–5 (5 highest) and ratings 1–100 (100 highest), use the following table to help Garza make his decision:

		Rating of Logistics Providers		
Criterion	Weight	Overnight Shipping	Worldwide Delivery	United Freight
Quality	5	90	80	75
Delivery	3	70	85	70
Cost	2	70	80	95

b) Garza decides to increase the weights for quality, delivery, and cost to 10, 6, and 4, respectively. How does this change your conclusions? Why?
c) If Overnight Shipping's ratings for each of the factors increase by 10%, what are the new results? **Px**

••• **2.11** Walker Accounting Software is marketed to small accounting firms throughout the United States and Canada. Owner George Walker has decided to outsource the company's help desk and is considering three providers: Manila Call Center (Philippines), Delhi Services (India), and Moscow Bell (Russia). The following table summarizes the data Walker has assembled. Which outsourcing firm has the best rating? (Higher weights imply higher importance and higher ratings imply more desirable providers.) **Px**

		Provider Ratings		
Criterion	Importance Weight	Manila	Delhi	Moscow
Flexibility	0.5	5	1	9
Trustworthiness	0.1	5	5	2
Price	0.2	4	3	6
Delivery	0.2	5	6	6

•••• **2.12** Rao Technologies, a Quebec-based high-tech manufacturer, is considering outsourcing some of its electronics production. Four firms have responded to its request for bids, and CEO Mohan Rao has started to perform an analysis on the scores his OM team has entered in the table below.

		Ratings of Outsource Providers			
Factor	Weight	A	B	C	D
Labour	*w*	5	4	3	5
Quality procedures	30	2	3	5	1
Logistics system	5	3	4	3	5
Price	25	5	3	4	4
Trustworthiness	5	3	2	3	5
Technology in place	15	2	5	4	4
Management team	15	5	4	2	1

Weights are on a scale from 1 through 30, and the outsourcing provider scores are on a scale of 1 through 5. The weight for the labour factor is shown as a *w* because Rao's OM team cannot agree on a value for this weight. For what range of values of *w*, if any, is company C a recommended outsourcing provider, according to the factor rating method?

Problem 2.13 relates to *Global Operations Strategy Options*

•• **2.13** Does Boeing practice a multinational operations strategy, a global operations strategy, or a transnational operations strategy? Support your choice with specific references to Boeing's operations and the characteristics of each type of organization.

CASE STUDIES

Mr. Lube

A substantial market exists for automobile tune-ups, oil changes, and lubrication service for the more than 12 million cars on Canadian roads. Some of this demand is filled by full-service auto dealerships, some by Canadian Tire, and some by other tire/service dealers. However, Mr. Lube, Great Canadian Oil Change, Jiffy Lube, and others have also developed strategies to accommodate this opportunity.

Mr. Lube stations perform oil changes, lubrication, and interior cleaning in a spotless environment. The buildings are clean, freshly painted, and often surrounded by neatly trimmed landscaping and clean parking areas. To facilitate fast service, cars can be driven though the facility. At Mr. Lube, the customer is greeted by service representatives who take their order, which typically includes fluid checks (oil, water, brake fluid, transmission fluid, and differential grease) and the necessary lubrication, as well as filter changes for air and oil. Service personnel in neat uniforms then move into action. The standard team has one person checking fluid levels under the hood, another in the garage pit removing the oil filter, draining the oil, checking the differential and transmission, and lubricating as necessary. Precise task assignments and good training are designed to move the car into and out of the bay in minutes. The idea is to charge no more, and hopefully less, than gas stations, automotive repair chains, and auto dealers. While doing so, Mr. Lube strives to provide better service than its competitors.

Discussion Questions

1. What constitutes the mission of Mr. Lube?
2. How does the Mr. Lube operations strategy provide competitive advantage? (*Hint:* Evaluate how Mr. Lube's traditional competitors perform the 10 decisions of operations management compared to how Mr. Lube performs them.)
3. Is it likely that Mr. Lube has increased productivity over its more traditional competitors? Why? How would we measure productivity in this industry?

Video Case | Operations Strategy at Regal Marine

Regal Marine, one of the United States's 10 largest power-boat manufacturers, achieves its mission—providing luxury performance boats to customers worldwide—using the strategy of differentiation. It differentiates its products through constant innovation, unique features, and high quality. Increasing sales at the Orlando, Florida, family-owned firm suggest that the strategy is working.

As a quality boat manufacturer, Regal Marine starts with continuous innovation, as reflected in computer-aided design (CAD), high-quality moulds, and close tolerances that are controlled through both defect charts and rigorous visual inspection. In-house quality is not enough, however. Because a product is only as good as the parts put into it, Regal has established close ties with a large number of its suppliers to ensure both flexibility and perfect parts. With the help of these suppliers, Regal can profitably produce a product line of 22 boats, ranging from the $14 000 19-foot boat to the $500 000 44-foot Commodore yacht.

"We build boats," says VP Tim Kuck, "but we're really in the 'fun' business. Our competition includes not only 300 other boat, canoe, and yacht manufacturers in our $17 billion industry, but home theatres, the internet, and all kinds of alternative family entertainment." Fortunately, Regal has been paying down debt and increasing market share.

Regal has also joined with scores of other independent boat makers in the American Boatbuilders Association. Through economies of scale in procurement, Regal is able to navigate against billion-dollar competitor Brunswick (maker of the Sea Ray and Bayliner brands). The *Global Company Profile* featuring Regal Marine (which opens Chapter 5) provides further background on Regal and its strategy.

Discussion Questions*

1. State Regal Marine's mission in your own words.
2. Identify the strengths, weaknesses, opportunities, and threats that are relevant to the strategy of Regal Marine.
3. How would you define Regal's strategy?
4. How would each of the 10 operations management decisions apply to operations decision making at Regal Marine?

* You may wish to view the video that accompanies this case before addressing these questions.

Video Case | Hard Rock Cafe's Global Strategy

Hard Rock brings the concept of the "experience economy" to its cafe operation. The strategy incorporates a unique "experience" into its operations. This innovation is somewhat akin to mass customization in manufacturing. At Hard Rock, the experience concept is to provide not only a custom meal from the menu but also a dining event that includes a unique visual and sound experience not duplicated anywhere else in the world. This strategy is succeeding. Other theme restaurants have come and gone while Hard Rock continues to grow. As Professor Constantinos Markides of the London Business School says, "The trick is not to play the game better than the competition, but to develop and play an altogether different game."* At Hard Rock, the different game is the experience game.

From the opening of its first cafe in London in 1971, during the British rock music explosion, Hard Rock has been serving food and rock music with equal enthusiasm. Hard Rock Cafe has two Canadian outlets, more than 40 U.S. locations, about a dozen in Europe, and the remainder scattered throughout the world, from Bangkok and Beijing to Beirut. New construction, leases, and investment in remodelling are long term; a global strategy means special consideration of political risk, currency risk, and social norms in a context of a brand fit. Although Hard Rock is one of the most recognized brands in the world, this does not mean its cafe is a natural everywhere. Special consideration must be given to the supply chain for the restaurant and its accompanying retail store. About 48% of a typical cafe's sales are from merchandise.

The Hard Rock Cafe business model is well defined, but because of various risk factors and differences in business practices and employment law, Hard Rock elects to franchise about half of its cafes. Social norms and preferences often suggest some tweaking of menus for local taste. For instance, Hard Rock focuses less on hamburgers and beef and more on fish and lobster in its British cafes.

Because 70% of Hard Rock's guests are tourists, recent years have found it expanding to "destination" cities. While this has been a winning strategy for decades, allowing the firm to grow from one London cafe to 145 facilities in 60 countries, it has made Hard Rock susceptible to economic fluctuations that hit the tourist business hardest. So Hard Rock is signing a long-term lease for a new location in Nottingham, England, to join recently opened

cafes in Manchester and Birmingham—cities that are not standard tourist destinations. At the same time, menus are being upgraded. Hopefully, repeat business from locals in these cities will smooth demand and make Hard Rock less dependent on tourists.

Discussion Questions†

1. Identify the strategy changes that have taken place at Hard Rock Cafe since its founding in 1971.
2. As Hard Rock Cafe has changed its strategy, how have its responses to some of the 10 decisions of OM changed?
3. Where does Hard Rock fit within the four international operations strategies outlined in Figure 2.9? Explain your answer.

---

* Constantinos Markides, "Strategic Innovation," *MIT Sloan Management Review* 38, no. 3 (spring 1997): 9.
† You may wish to view the video that accompanies the case before addressing these questions.

▶**Additional Case Study:** Visit **MyLab Operations Management** for this free case study: **Motorola's Global Strategy:** Focuses on Motorola's international strategy.

CHAPTER 2 │ RAPID REVIEW

MyLab Operations
Management

Main Heading	Review Material
A GLOBAL VIEW OF OPERATIONS AND SUPPLY CHAINS (pp. 28–31)	Domestic business operations decide to change to some form of international operations for six main reasons: 1. Reduce costs (labour, taxes, tariffs, etc.) 2. Improve supply chain 3. Provide better goods and services 4. Understand markets 5. Learn to improve operations 6. Attract and retain global talent • **Maquiladoras**—Mexican factories located along the U.S.–Mexico border that receive preferential tariff treatment. • **World Trade Organization (WTO)**—An international organization that promotes world trade by lowering barriers to the free flow of goods across borders. • **United States, Mexico, Canada Agreement (USMCA)**—A free trade agreement between Canada, Mexico, and the United States. • **European Union (EU)**—A European trade group that has 28 member states as of 2015. Other trade agreements include APEC (the Pacific Rim countries), SEATO (Australia, New Zealand, Japan, Hong Kong, South Korea, New Guinea, and Chile), MERCOSUR (Argentina, Brazil, Paraguay, and Uruguay), and CAFTA (Central America, the Dominican Republic, and the United States). The World Trade Organization helps to make uniform the protection of both governments and industries from foreign firms that engage in unethical conduct.
CULTURAL AND ETHICAL ISSUES (pp. 31–32)	Globalization involves many challenges, including reconciling differences in social and cultural behaviour.

MyLab Operations Management

Main Heading	Review Material	
DEVELOPING MISSIONS AND STRATEGIES (pp. 32–33)	An effective operations management effort must have a *mission* so it knows where it is going and a *strategy* so it knows how to get there. • **Mission**—The purpose or rationale for an organization's existence. • **Strategy**—How an organization expects to achieve its missions and goals. The three strategic approaches to competitive advantage are: 1. Differentiation 2. Cost leadership 3. Response	**VIDEO 2.1** Operations Strategy at Regal Marine
ACHIEVING COMPETITIVE ADVANTAGE THROUGH OPERATIONS (pp. 33–36)	• **Competitive advantage**—The creation of a unique advantage over competitors. • **Differentiation**—Distinguishing the offerings of an organization in a way that the customer perceives as adding value. • **Experience differentiation**—Engaging a customer with a product through imaginative use of the five senses, so the customer "experiences" the product. • **Low-cost leadership**—Achieving maximum value, as perceived by the customer. • **Response**—A set of values related to rapid, flexible, and reliable performance. Differentiation can be attained, for example, through innovative design, by providing a broad product line, by offering excellent after-sale service, or through adding a sensory experience to the product or service offering. Cost leadership can be attained, for example, via low overhead, effective capacity use, or efficient inventory management. Response can be attained, for example, by offering a flexible product line, reliable scheduling, or speedy delivery.	**VIDEO 2.2** Hard Rock's Global Strategy
10 STRATEGIC OM DECISIONS (pp. 36–39)	• **Operations decisions**—The strategic decisions of OM are goods and service design, quality, process and capacity design, location selection, layout design, human resources and job design, supply chain management, inventory, scheduling, and maintenance.	
ISSUES IN OPERATIONS STRATEGY (pp. 39–40)	• **Resources view**—A method managers use to evaluate the resources at their disposal and manage or alter them to achieve competitive advantage. • **Value chain analysis**—A way to identify the elements in the product/service chain that uniquely add value. • **Five forces model**—A method of analyzing the five forces in the competitive environment. The potential competing forces in Porter's five forces model are (1) immediate rivals, (2) potential entrants, (3) customers, (4) suppliers, and (5) substitute products. Different issues are emphasized during different stages of the product life cycle: • **Introduction**—Company strategy: Best period to increase market share, R&D engineering is critical. OM strategy: Product design and development critical, frequent product and process design changes, short production runs, high production costs, limited models, attention to quality. • **Growth**—Company strategy: Practical to change price or quality image, strengthen niche. OM strategy: Forecasting critical, product and process reliability, competitive product improvements and options, increase capacity, shift towards product focus, enhance distribution. • **Maturity**—Company strategy: Poor time to change image or price or quality, competitive costs become critical, defend market position. OM strategy: Standardization, less rapid product changes (more minor changes), optimum capacity, increasing stability of process, long production runs, product improvement, and cost cutting. • **Decline**—Company strategy: Cost control critical. OM strategy: Little product differentiation, cost minimization, overcapacity in the industry, prune line to eliminate items not returning good margin, reduce capacity.	

Main Heading	Review Material	
STRATEGY DEVELOPMENT AND IMPLEMENTATION (pp. 40–43)	• **SWOT analysis**—A method of determining internal strengths and weaknesses and external opportunities and threats. The strategy development process first involves performing environmental analysis, followed by determining the corporate mission, and finally forming a strategy. • **Key success factors (KSFs)**—Activities or factors that are key to achieving competitive advantage. • **Core competencies**—A set of skills, talents, and activities in which a firm is particularly strong. A core competency may be a subset of, or a combination of, KSFs. • **Activity map**—A graphical link of competitive advantage, KSFs, and supporting activities. An operations manager's job is to implement an OM strategy, provide competitive advantage, and increase productivity.	Virtual Office Hours for Solved Problem: 2.1
STRATEGIC PLANNING, CORE COMPETENCIES, AND OUTSOURCING (pp. 43–46)	• **Outsourcing**—Transferring a firm's activities that have traditionally been internal to external suppliers • **Theory of comparative advantage**—A theory which states that countries benefit from specializing in (and exporting) goods and services in which they have relative advantage, and they benefit from importing goods and services in which they have a relative disadvantage.	
GLOBAL OPERATIONS STRATEGY OPTIONS (pp. 47–49)	• **International business**—A firm that engages in cross-border transactions. • **Multinational corporation (MNC)**—A firm that has extensive involvement in international business, owning or controlling facilities in more than one country. • **International strategy**—A strategy in which global markets are penetrated using exports and licences. • **Multidomestic strategy**—A strategy in which operating decisions are decentralized to each country to enhance local responsiveness. • **Global strategy**—A strategy in which operating decisions are centralized and headquarters coordinates the standardization and learning between facilities. • **Transnational strategy**—A strategy that combines the benefits of global-scale efficiencies with the benefits of local responsiveness. These firms transgress national boundaries. The four operations strategies for approaching global opportunities can be classified according to local responsiveness and cost reduction: 1. **International**—Little local responsiveness and little cost advantage 2. **Multidomestic**—Significant local responsiveness but little cost advantage 3. **Global**—Little local responsiveness but significant cost advantage 4. **Transnational**—Significant local responsiveness and significant cost advantage	

Self-Test

■ **Before taking the self-test,** refer to the learning objectives listed at the beginning of the chapter.

LO1 A mission statement is beneficial to an organization because it:
   a) is a statement of the organization's purpose.
   b) provides a basis for the organization's culture.
   c) identifies important constituencies.
   d) details specific income goals.
   e) ensures profitability.

LO2 The three strategic approaches to competitive advantage are
   _____, _____, and _____.

LO3 Core competencies are those strengths in a firm that include:
   a) specialized skills.
   b) unique production methods.
   c) proprietary information/knowledge.
   d) things a company does better than others.
   e) all of the above.

LO4 Evaluating outsourcing providers by comparing their weighted average scores involves:
   a) factor rating analysis.
   b) cost-volume analysis.
   c) transportation model analysis.
   d) linear regression analysis.
   e) crossover analysis.

LO5 A company that is organized across international boundaries, with decentralized authority and substantial autonomy at each business via subsidiaries, franchises, or joint ventures, has:
   a) a global strategy.
   b) a transnational strategy.
   c) an international strategy.
   d) a multidomestic strategy.

Answers: LO1. a; LO2. differentiation, cost leadership, response; LO3. e; LO4. a; LO5. c.

MyLab Operations Management

Most of these questions can be found in MyLab Operations Management. Visit MyLab Operations Management to access cases, videos, downloadable software, and much more. MyLab Operations Management Management also features a personalized Study Plan that helps you identify which chapter concepts you've mastered and guides you towards study tools for additional practice.

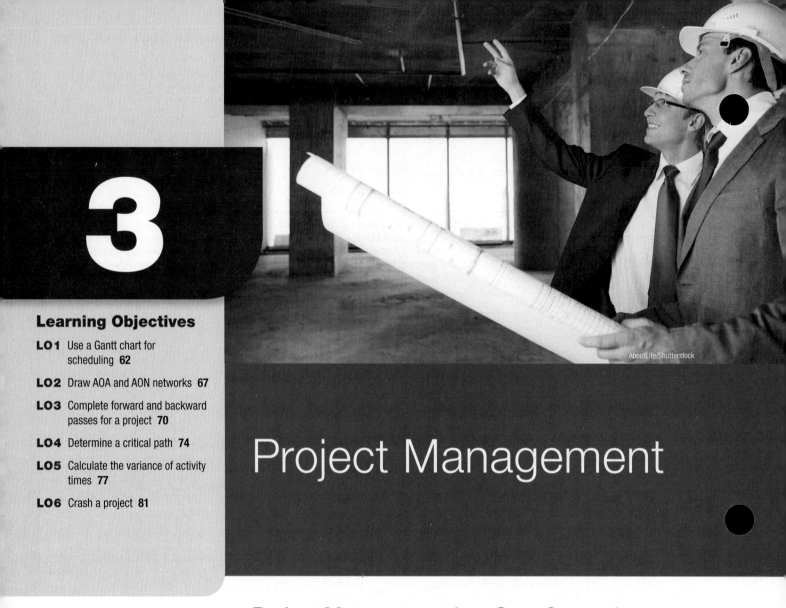

AboutLife/Shutterstock

3

Project Management

Global > Company Profile EllisDon

Project Management Is a Core Strength for EllisDon

Doing a good job is commendable, but in the construction industry it is imperative that it is also done on time, every time, and at each step during the process. Excellence in project management is a defining factor in successful companies.

EllisDon is a Canadian leader in engineering and construction project management. It is self-described as a project management service that takes a "hands-on" approach. The company's belief is that by becoming deeply involved in a project, it can ensure that the job is completed as the owner intended. This level of commitment and involvement aids in foreseeing issues, thus allowing challenges to be faced head-on and resolved faster.

EllisDon works with clients to keep its projects on track from project conception through to the selection of consultants, planning, tendering, and finally completion, closeout, and commissioning. In instances where EllisDon is not the builder of the project, it oversees all the work, manages the consultants, and reports the progress to the owner.

The company has a wealth of experience and knowledge, having worked on projects of all sizes and complexities in a wide variety of locations around the world. It has also built solid relationships with architects, engineers, and subcontractors. This network of expertise is a valuable resource for project management in this industry.

On the global scene, EllisDon is the project manager for the Palm Jumeirah in Dubai, United Arab Emirates. This is a property development project using land reclamation to create an artificial archipelago so large that it can be seen from space; upon completion, it is anticipated it will be visible from the moon. It contains apartment buildings, town houses, plus food and retail outlets.

The following is a list of some of the company's other more notable current projects, both those that are completed and ongoing:

- Increased expansion at the Calgary Airport.
- Union Station (Toronto) renovation and expansion.
- Design-builder for the Halifax 4-Pad Arena.
- General contractor for additions to the Hamilton Community Centre for the City of Richmond, British Columbia.
- Construction manager for George Brown College's Waterfront Campus.
- Construction of the SickKids (Hospital) Research Tower.

Construction of the SickKids (Hospital) Research Tower.

- Construction management contract for the Ritz-Carlton, Toronto, and the Residences at the Ritz-Carlton.
- Construction work on the Saskatoon Police Headquarters.
- Engineer-procure-construct contract for an ethanol plant for Terra Grain Fuels, Inc., of Regina, Saskatchewan.

EllisDon's excellence in project management continues to provide a competitive advantage. Due to the company's reputation and experience in project management, it is not difficult to understand why EllisDon is a Canadian success story.

Source: www.ellisdon.com.

The Importance of Project Management

When EllisDon, the subject of the opening *Global Company Profile*, received confirmation that it was awarded the contract to be the project manager for the Palm Jumeirah in Dubai, United Arab Emirates, it had to mobilize a large force of subcontractors, workers, construction professionals, and engineers. The project management team was also required to ensure ongoing access to physical resources and an uninterrupted flow of supplies. Similarly, when Hard Rock Cafe sponsors Rockfest, hosting more than 100 000 fans at its annual concert, the project manager begins planning some nine months earlier. Using the software package Microsoft Project, described in this chapter, each of the hundreds of details can be monitored and controlled. When a band can't reach the Rockfest site by bus because of massive traffic jams, Hard Rock's project manager is ready with a helicopter backup.

EllisDon and Hard Rock Cafe are just two examples of firms that face modern phenomena: growing project complexity and collapsing product/service life cycles. This change stems from awareness of the strategic value of time-based competition and a quality mandate for continuous improvement. Each new product/service introduction is a unique event—a project. In addition, projects are a common part of our everyday life, whether we are planning a wedding or a surprise birthday party, remodelling a house, or preparing a semester-long class project.

VIDEO 3.1
Project Management at Hard Rock's Rockfest

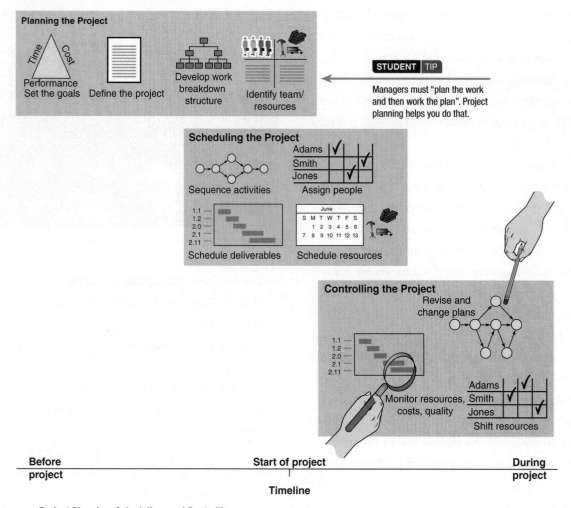

FIGURE 3.1 Project Planning, Scheduling, and Controlling

Scheduling projects is a difficult challenge for operations managers. The stakes in project management are high, and cost overruns and unnecessary delays occur due to poor scheduling and poor controls.

Projects that take months or years to complete are usually developed outside the normal production system. Project organizations within the firm may be set up to handle such jobs and are often disbanded when the project is complete. On other occasions, managers find projects just a part of their job. The management of projects involves three phases (see Figure 3.1):

1. *Planning:* This phase includes goal setting, defining the project, and team organization.
2. *Scheduling:* This phase relates people, money, and supplies to specific activities and relates activities to each other.
3. *Controlling:* Here, the firm monitors resources, costs, quality, and budgets. It also revises or changes plans and shifts resources to meet time and cost demands.

We begin this chapter with a brief overview of these functions. We also describe three popular techniques to allow managers to plan, schedule, and control—Gantt charts, the program evaluation and review technique (PERT), and the critical path method (CPM).

Project Planning

Project organization

An organization formed to ensure that programs (projects) receive the proper management and attention.

Projects can be defined as a series of related tasks directed towards a major output. In some firms, a **project organization** is developed to make sure existing programs continue to run smoothly on a day-to-day basis while new projects are successfully completed.

For companies with multiple large projects, such as a construction firm, a project organization is an effective way of assigning the people and physical resources needed. It is a temporary

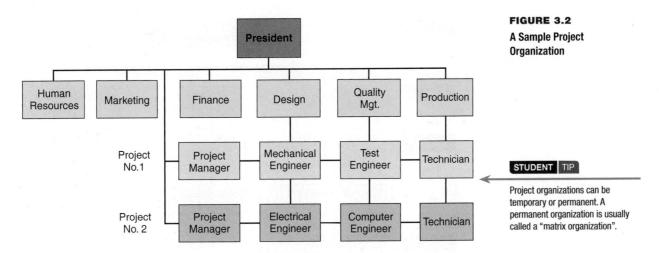

FIGURE 3.2

A Sample Project Organization

organization structure designed to achieve results by using specialists from throughout the firm. NASA and many other organizations use the project approach. You may recall Project Gemini and Project Apollo, terms used to describe teams that NASA organized to reach space exploration objectives.

The project organization works best when:

1. Work can be defined with a specific goal and deadline.
2. The job is unique or somewhat unfamiliar to the existing organization.
3. The work contains complex interrelated tasks requiring specialized skills.
4. The project is temporary but critical to the organization.
5. The project cuts across organizational lines.

THE PROJECT MANAGER

An example of a project organization is shown in Figure 3.2. Project team members are temporarily assigned to a project and report to the project manager. The manager heading the project coordinates activities with other departments and reports directly to top management. Project managers receive high visibility in a firm and are responsible for making sure that (1) all necessary activities are finished in proper sequence and on time; (2) the project comes in within budget; (3) the project meets its quality goals; and (4) the people assigned to the project receive the motivation, direction, and information needed to do their jobs. This means that project managers should be good coaches and communicators, and be able to organize activities from a variety of disciplines.

ETHICAL ISSUES FACED IN PROJECT MANAGEMENT Project managers not only have high visibility but also face ethical decisions on a daily basis. How they act establishes the code of conduct for the project. Project managers often deal with (1) offers of gifts from contractors, (2) pressure to alter status reports to mask the reality of delays, (3) false reports for charges of time and expenses, and (4) pressures to compromise quality to meet bonus or penalty schedules.

Using the Project Management Institute's (**www.pmi.org**) ethical codes is one means of trying to establish standards. Research has shown that without good leadership and a strong organizational culture, most people follow their own sets of ethical standards and values.[1]

WORK BREAKDOWN STRUCTURE

The project management team begins its task well in advance of project execution so that a plan can be developed. One of its first steps is to carefully establish the project's objectives, then break the project down into manageable parts. This **work breakdown structure (WBS)** defines the project by dividing it into its major subcomponents (or tasks), which are then subdivided into

Work breakdown structure (WBS)

A hierarchical description of a project into more and more detailed components.

---

[1] See Hilder Helgadottir, "The Ethical Dimension of Project Management," *International Journal of Project Management* 26, no. 7 (October 2008): 743–748.

FIGURE 3.3
Work Breakdown Structure

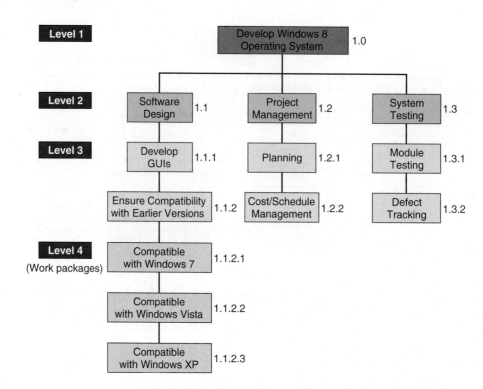

more detailed components, and finally into a set of activities and their related costs. The division of the project into smaller and smaller tasks can be difficult but is critical to managing the project and to scheduling success. Gross requirements for people, supplies, and equipment are also estimated in this planning phase.

The work breakdown structure typically decreases in size from top to bottom and is indented like this:

Level

1   Project

2   Major tasks in the project

3   Subtasks in major tasks

4   Activities (or "work packages") to be completed

This hierarchical framework can be illustrated with the development of Microsoft's operating system Windows 8. As we see in Figure 3.3, the project, creating a new operating system, is labelled 1.0. The first step is to identify the major tasks in the project (level 2). Three examples would be software design (1.1), project management (1.2), and system testing (1.3). Two major subtasks for 1.1 are development of graphical user interfaces (GUIs) (1.1.1) and creating compatibility with previous versions of Windows (1.1.2). The major subtasks for 1.1.2 are level 4 activities, such as creating a team to handle compatibility with Windows 7 (1.1.2.1), creating a team for Windows Vista (1.1.2.2), and creating a team for Windows XP (1.1.2.3). There are usually many level 4 activities.

Project Scheduling

Project scheduling involves sequencing and allotting time to all project activities. At this stage, managers decide how long each activity will take and compute how many people and what materials will be needed at each stage of production. Managers also chart separate schedules for personnel needs by type of skill (management, engineering, or pouring concrete, for example). Charts also can be developed for scheduling materials.

One popular project scheduling approach is the Gantt chart. **Gantt charts** are low-cost means of helping managers make sure that (1) activities are planned, (2) order of performance is documented, (3) activity time estimates are recorded, and (4) overall project time is developed. As Figure 3.4 shows, Gantt charts are easy to understand. Horizontal bars are drawn for each project activity along a timeline. This illustration of a routine servicing of a Delta jetliner during a 40-minute lay-

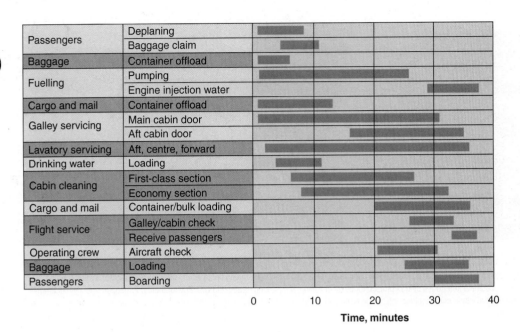

FIGURE 3.4

Gantt Chart of Service Activities for a Delta Jet during a 40-Minute Layover

Delta hopes to save U.S. $50 million a year with this turnaround time, which is a reduction from its traditional 60-minute routine.

over shows that Gantt charts also can be used for scheduling repetitive operations. In this case, the chart helps point out potential delays. The *OM in Action* box on Delta provides additional insights.

On simple projects, scheduling charts such as these permit managers to observe the progress of each activity and to spot and tackle problem areas. Gantt charts do not adequately illustrate the interrelationships between the activities and the resources, however.

PERT and CPM, the two widely used network techniques that we shall discuss shortly, *do* have the ability to consider precedence relationships and interdependency of activities. On complex projects, the scheduling of which is almost always computerized, PERT and CPM thus have an edge over the simpler Gantt charts. Even on huge projects, though, Gantt charts can be used as summaries of project status and may complement the other network approaches.

To summarize, whatever the approach taken by a project manager, project scheduling serves several purposes:

1. It shows the relationship of each activity to others and to the whole project.
2. It identifies the precedence relationships among activities.
3. It encourages the setting of realistic time and cost estimates for each activity.
4. It helps make better use of people, money, and material resources by identifying critical bottlenecks in the project.

OM in Action   Delta's Ground Crew Orchestrates a Smooth Takeoff

Flight 574's engines screech its arrival as the jet lumbers down Richmond's taxiway with 140 passengers arriving from Atlanta. In 40 minutes, the plane is to be airborne again.

However, before this jet can depart, there is business to attend to: passengers, luggage, and cargo to unload and load; thousands of gallons of jet fuel and countless drinks to restock; cabin and restrooms to clean; toilet holding tanks to drain; and engines, wings, and landing gear to inspect.

The 10-person ground crew knows that a miscue anywhere—a broken cargo loader, lost baggage, misdirected passengers—can mean a late departure and trigger a chain reaction of headaches from Richmond to Atlanta to every destination of a connecting flight.

Carla Sutera, the operations manager for Delta's Richmond International Airport, views the turnaround operation like a pit boss awaiting a race car. Trained crews are in place for Flight 574, with baggage carts and tractors, hydraulic cargo loaders, a truck to load food and drinks, another to lift the cleanup crew, another to put fuel on, and a fourth to take water off. The "pit crew" usually performs so smoothly that most passengers never suspect the proportions of the effort. Gantt charts, such as the one in Figure 3.4, aid Delta and other airlines with the staffing and scheduling that are needed for this task.

Sources: Knight Ridder Tribune Business News (July 16, 2005): 1 and (November 21, 2002): 1.

Construction of the new 11-storey building at Arnold Palmer Hospital in Orlando, Florida, was an enormous project for the hospital administration. The photo on the left shows the first six floors under construction. The photo on the right shows the building as completed two years later. Prior to beginning actual construction, regulatory and funding issues added, as they do with most projects, substantial time to the overall project. Cities have zoning and parking issues; the U.S. Environmental Protection Agency has drainage and waste issues; and regulatory authorities have their own requirements, as do issuers of bonds. The $100 million, four-year project at Arnold Palmer Hospital is discussed in the Video Case Study at the end of this chapter.

Project Controlling

STUDENT TIP

Software has revolutionized project control.

VIDEO 3.2
Project Management at Arnold Palmer Hospital

The control of projects, like the control of any management system, involves close monitoring of resources, costs, quality, and budgets. Control also means using a feedback loop to revise the project plan and having the ability to shift resources to where they are needed most. Computerized PERT/CPM reports and charts are widely available today on personal computers. Some of the more popular of these programs are Oracle Primavera (by Oracle), MindView (by Match Ware), HP Project (by Hewlett-Packard), Fast Track (by AEC Software), and Microsoft Project (by Microsoft Corp.), which we illustrate in this chapter.

These programs produce a broad variety of reports, including (1) detailed cost breakdowns for each task, (2) total program labour curves, (3) cost distribution tables, (4) functional cost and hour summaries, (5) raw material and expenditure forecasts, (6) variance reports, (7) time analysis reports, and (8) work status reports.

Controlling projects can be difficult. The stakes are high; cost overruns and unnecessary delays can occur due to poor planning, scheduling, and controls. Some projects are "well-defined," whereas others may be "ill-defined". Projects typically only become well-defined after detailed extensive initial planning and careful definition of required inputs, resources, processes, and outputs. Well-established projects where constraints are known (e.g., buildings and roads) and engineered products (e.g., airplanes and cars) with well-defined specifications and drawings may

---

OM in Action   Agile Project Management at Mastek

Agile project management has changed the way that Mastek Corp., in Mumbai, India, develops its educational software products. On a traditional well-defined project, managers are actively involved in directing work and telling their team what needs to be done—a style often referred to as a step-by-step waterfall style of project management.

Agile project management is different. In the early stages, the project manager creates a high-level plan, based on outline requirements and a high-level view of the solution. From that point, the end project is created iteratively and incrementally, with each increment building on the output of steps preceding it.

The principles of agile are essentially communication and transparency. Instead of waiting for something to be

delivered, with limited understanding of the desired end result, there are numerous checkpoints and feedback loops to track progress.

Agile provides Mastek the ability to keep costs under control. Without agile, the cost of quality increases. "It's much harder to correct mistakes when a software product is nearing its final phase of development," says a company executive. "It's much better to develop it as you go along. I think agile project management would help any software developer."

Sources: AMPG International (2015) and www.cprime.com (2012).

fall into this category. Well-defined projects are assumed to have changes small enough to be managed without substantially revising plans. They use what is called a *waterfall* approach, where the project progresses smoothly, in a step-by-step manner, through each phase to completion.

But many projects, such as software development (e.g., 3-D games) and new technology (e.g., landing the Mars land rover) are ill-defined. These projects require what is known as an *agile* style of management with collaboration and constant feedback to adjust to the many unknowns of the evolving technology and project specifications. The *OM in Action* box "Agile Project Management at Mastek" provides such an example. Most projects fall somewhere between waterfall and agile.

Project Management Techniques: PERT and CPM

Program evaluation and review technique (PERT) and the **critical path method (CPM)** were both developed in the 1950s to help managers schedule, monitor, and control large and complex projects. CPM arrived first, in 1957, as a tool developed by J. E. Kelly of Remington Rand and M. R. Walker of DuPont to assist in the building and maintenance of chemical plants at DuPont. Independently, PERT was developed in 1958 for the U.S. Navy.

THE FRAMEWORK OF PERT AND CPM

PERT and CPM both follow six basic steps:

1. Define the project and prepare the work breakdown structure.
2. Develop the relationships among the activities. Decide which activities must precede and which must follow others.
3. Draw the network connecting all the activities.
4. Assign time and/or cost estimates to each activity.
5. Compute the *longest* time path through the network. This is called the **critical path**.
6. Use the network to help plan, schedule, monitor, and control the project.

Step 5, finding the critical path, is a major part of controlling a project. The activities on the critical path represent tasks that will delay the entire project if they are not completed on time. Managers can gain the flexibility needed to complete critical tasks by identifying noncritical activities and replanning, rescheduling, and reallocating labour and financial resources.

Although PERT and CPM differ to some extent in terminology and in the construction of the network, their objectives are the same. Furthermore, the analysis used in both techniques is very similar. The major difference is that PERT employs three time estimates for each activity. These time estimates are used to compute expected values and standard deviations for the activity. CPM makes the assumption that activity times are known with certainty and hence requires only one time factor for each activity. For an example of large project that put these principles into action see the *OM in Action* box "Rebuilding the Electricity Grid in China".

For purposes of illustration, the rest of this section concentrates on a discussion of PERT. Most of the comments and procedures described, however, apply just as well to CPM.

PERT and CPM are important because they can help answer questions such as the following about projects with thousands of activities:

1. When will the entire project be completed?
2. What are the critical activities or tasks in the project—that is, which activities will delay the entire project if they are late?
3. Which are the noncritical activities—the ones that can run late without delaying the whole project's completion?
4. What is the probability that the project will be completed by a specific date?
5. At any particular date, is the project on schedule, behind schedule, or ahead of schedule?
6. On any given date, is the money spent equal to, less than, or greater than the budgeted amount?
7. Are there enough resources available to finish the project on time?
8. If the project is to be finished in a shorter amount of time, what is the best way to accomplish this goal at the least cost?

STUDENT TIP

To use project management software, you first need to understand the next two sections in this chapter.

Program evaluation and review technique (PERT)
A project management technique that employs three time estimates for each activity.

Critical path method (CPM)
A project management technique that uses only one time factor per activity.

Critical path
The computed *longest* time path(s) through a network.

NETWORK DIAGRAMS AND APPROACHES

Activity-on-node (AON)
A network diagram in which nodes designate activities.

Activity-on-arrow (AOA)
A network diagram in which arrows designate activities.

The first step in a PERT or CPM network is to divide the entire project into significant activities in accordance with the work breakdown structure. There are two approaches for drawing a project network: **activity on node (AON)** and **activity on arrow (AOA)**. Under the AON convention, *nodes* designate activities. Under AOA, *arrows* represent activities. Activities consume time and resources. The basic difference between AON and AOA is that the nodes in an AON diagram represent activities. In an AOA network, the nodes represent the starting and finishing times of an activity and are also called *events*. So nodes in AOA consume neither time nor resources.

Figure 3.5 illustrates both conventions for a small portion of the airline turnaround Gantt chart (in Figure 3.4). The examples provide some background for understanding six common activity relationships in networks. In Figure 3.5(a), activity A must be finished before activity B is started, and B must, in turn, be completed before C begins. Activity A might represent "deplaning passengers," while B is "cabin cleaning," and C is "boarding new passengers".

Dummy activity
An activity having no time that is inserted into a network to maintain the logic of the network.

Figures 3.5(e) and 3.5(f) illustrate that the AOA approach sometimes needs the addition of a **dummy activity** to clarify relationships. A dummy activity consumes no time or resources but is required when a network has two activities with identical starting and ending events, or when two or more follow some, but not all, "preceding" activities. The use of dummy activities is also

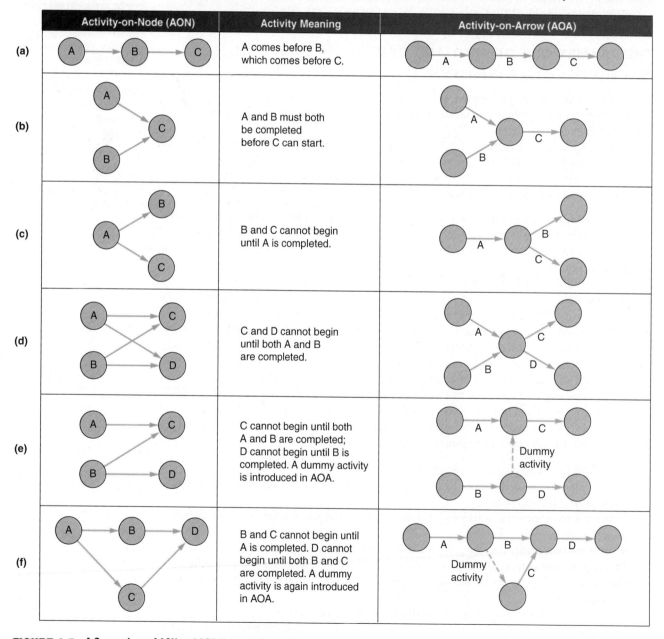

FIGURE 3.5 A Comparison of AON and AOA Network Conventions

important when computer software is employed to determine project completion time. A dummy activity has a completion time of zero and is shown graphically with a dashed line.

Although both AON and AOA are popular in practice, many of the project management software packages, including Microsoft Project, use AON networks. For this reason, although we illustrate both types of networks in the next examples, we focus on AON networks in subsequent discussions in this chapter.

ACTIVITY-ON-NODE EXAMPLE

EXAMPLE 1

Activity-on-Node for Environmental Problem at Hamilton Paper

Hamilton Paper Manufacturing, Inc., located near downtown Hamilton, has long been delaying the expense of installing air pollution control equipment in its facility. The province has recently given the manufacturer 16 weeks to install a complex air filter system. Hamilton Paper has been warned that it may be forced to close the facility unless the device is installed in the allotted time. Joni Steinberg, the plant manager, wants to make sure that installation of the filtering system progresses smoothly and on time.

Given the following information, develop a table showing activity precedence relationships.

APPROACH ▶ Hamilton Paper has identified the eight activities that need to be performed in order for the project to be completed. When the project begins, two activities can be simultaneously started: building the internal components for the device (activity A) and making the modifications necessary for the floor and roof (activity B). The construction of the collection stack (activity C) can begin when the internal components are completed. Pouring the concrete floor and installation of the frame (activity D) can be started as soon as the internal components are completed and the roof and floor have been modified.

After the collection stack has been constructed, two activities can begin: building the high-temperature burner (activity E) and installing the pollution control system (activity F). The air pollution device can be installed (activity G) after the concrete floor has been poured, the frame has been installed, and the high-temperature burner has been built. Finally, after the control system and pollution device have been installed, the system can be inspected and tested (activity H).

SOLUTION ▶ Activities and precedence relationships may seem rather confusing when they are presented in this descriptive form. It is therefore convenient to list all the activity information in a table, as shown in Table 3.1. We see in the table that activity A is listed as an *immediate predecessor* of activity C. Likewise, both activities D and E must be performed prior to starting activity G.

LO2 Draw AOA and AON networks

Table 3.1
Hamilton Paper Manufacturing's Activities and Predecessors

Activity	Description	Immediate Predecessors
A	Build internal components	—
B	Modify roof and floor	—
C	Construct collection stack	A
D	Pour concrete and install frame	A, B
E	Build high-temperature burner	C
F	Install pollution control system	C
G	Install air pollution device	D, E
H	Inspect and test	F, G

INSIGHT ▶ To complete a network, all predecessors must be clearly defined.

LEARNING EXERCISE ▶ What is the impact on the sequence of activities if provincial approval is required after *Inspect and test?* [Answer: The immediate predecessor for the new activity would be H, *Inspect and test*, with *Provincial approval* as the last activity, I.]

Note that in Example 1, it is enough to list just the *immediate predecessors* for each activity. For instance, in Table 3.1, since activity A precedes activity C, and activity C precedes activity E, the fact that activity A precedes activity E is *implicit*. This relationship need not be explicitly shown in the activity precedence relationships.

When there are many activities in a project with fairly complicated precedence relationships, it is difficult for an individual to comprehend the complexity of the project from just the tabular information. In such cases, a visual representation of the project, using a *project network*, is convenient and useful. A project network is a diagram of all the activities and the precedence relationships that exist between these activities in a project. Example 2 illustrates how to construct a project network for Hamilton Paper Manufacturing.

EXAMPLE 2

AON Graph for Hamilton Paper

Draw the AON network for Hamilton Paper, using the data in Example 1.

APPROACH ▶ In the AON approach, we denote each activity by a node. The lines, or arrows, represent the precedence relationships between the activities.

SOLUTION ▶ In this example, there are two activities (A and B) that do not have any predecessors. We draw separate nodes for each of these activities, as shown in Figure 3.6. Although not required, it is usually convenient to have a unique starting activity for a project. We have therefore included a dummy activity called Start in Figure 3.6. This dummy activity does not really exist and takes up zero time and resources. Activity Start is an immediate predecessor for both activities A and B, and serves as the unique starting activity for the entire project.

FIGURE 3.6

Beginning AON Network for Hamilton Paper

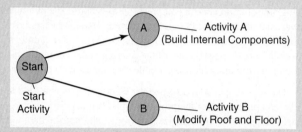

We now show the precedence relationships using lines with arrow symbols. For example, an arrow from activity Start to activity A indicates that Start is a predecessor for activity A. In a similar fashion, we draw an arrow from Start to B.

Next, we add a new node for activity C. Since activity A precedes activity C, we draw an arrow from node A to node C. Likewise, we first draw a node to represent activity D. Then, since activities A and B both precede activity D, we draw arrows from A to D and from B to D (see Figure 3.7).

FIGURE 3.7

Intermediate AON Network for Hamilton Paper

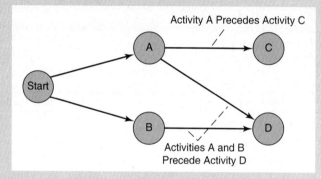

We proceed in this fashion, adding a separate node for each activity and a separate line for each precedence relationship that exists. The complete AON project network for the Hamilton Paper Manufacturing project is shown in Figure 3.8.

FIGURE 3.8

Complete AON Network for Hamilton Paper

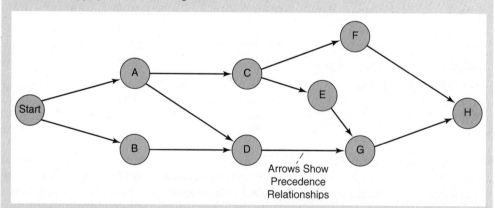

INSIGHT ▶ Drawing a project network properly takes some time and experience. We would like the lines to be straight and arrows to move to the right when possible.

LEARNING EXERCISE ▶ If *Provincial approval* occurs after *Inspect and test*, what is the impact on the graph? [Answer: A straight line is extended to the right beyond H to reflect the additional activity.]

RELATED PROBLEMS ▶ 3.3, 3.6, 3.7, 3.9a, 3.10, 3.12, 3.15a

When we first draw a project network, it is not unusual that we place our nodes (activities) in the network in such a fashion that the arrows (precedence relationships) are not straight lines. That is, the lines could be intersecting each other, and even facing in opposite directions. For example, if we had switched the location of the nodes for activities E and F in Figure 3.8, the lines from F to H and E to G would have intersected. Although such a project network is perfectly valid, it is good practice to have a well-drawn network. One rule that we especially recommend is to place the nodes in such a fashion that all arrows point in the same direction. To achieve this, we suggest that you first draw a rough draft of the network, making sure all the relationships are shown. Then you can redraw the network to make appropriate changes in the location of the nodes.

As with the unique starting node, it is convenient to have the project network finish with a unique ending node. In the Hamilton Paper example, it turns out that a unique activity, H, is the last activity in the project. We therefore automatically have a unique ending node.

In situations in which a project has multiple ending activities, we include a "dummy" ending activity. This dummy activity has all the multiple ending activities in the project as immediate predecessors. We illustrate this type of situation in Solved Problem 3.2 at the end of this chapter.

ACTIVITY-ON-ARROW EXAMPLE

We saw earlier that in an AOA project network we can represent activities by arrows. A node represents an *event*, which marks the start or completion time of an activity. We usually identify an event (node) by a number.

Draw the complete AOA project network for Hamilton Paper's problem.

APPROACH ▶ Using the data from Table 3.1 in Example 1, draw one activity at a time, starting with A.

SOLUTION ▶ We see that activity A starts at event 1 and ends at event 2. Likewise, activity B starts at event 1 and ends at event 3. Activity C, whose only immediate predecessor is activity A, starts at node 2 and ends at node 4. Activity D, however, has two predecessors (i.e., A and B). Hence, we need both activities A and B to end at event 3, so that activity D can start at that event. However, we cannot have multiple activities with common starting and ending nodes in an AOA network. To overcome this difficulty, in such cases, we may need to add a dummy line (activity) to enforce the precedence relationship. The dummy activity, shown in Figure 3.9 as a dashed line, is inserted between events 2 and 3 to make the diagram reflect the precedence between A and D. The remainder of the AOA project network for Hamilton Paper's example is also shown.

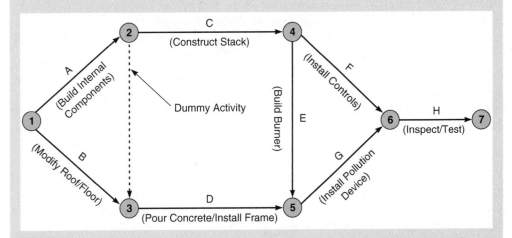

INSIGHT ▶ Dummy activities are common in AOA networks. They do not really exist in the project and take zero time.

LEARNING EXERCISE ▶ A new activity, *Provincial approval*, follows activity H. Add it to Figure 3.9. [Answer: Insert an arrowed line from node 7, which ends at a new node 8, and is labelled I (Provincial Approval).]

RELATED PROBLEMS ▶ 3.4, 3.5, 3.9b

EXAMPLE 3

Activity-on-Arrow for Hamilton Paper

FIGURE 3.9

Complete AOA Network (With Dummy Activity) for Hamilton Paper

STUDENT TIP

The dummy activity consumes no time, but note how it changes precedence. Now activity D cannot begin until *both* B and the dummy are complete.

Determining the Project Schedule

Critical path analysis

A process to find the most effective sequence of activities that helps determine a project schedule.

Look back at Figure 3.8 (in Example 2) for a moment to see Hamilton Paper's completed AON project network. Once this project network has been drawn to show all the activities and their precedence relationships, the next step is to determine the project schedule. That is, we need to identify the planned starting and ending time for each activity.

Let us assume Hamilton Paper estimates the time required for each activity, in weeks, as shown in Table 3.2. The table indicates that the total time for all eight of the company's activities is 25 weeks. However, since several activities can take place simultaneously, it is clear that the total project completion time may be less than 25 weeks. To find out just how long the project will take, we perform the **critical path analysis** for the network.

Table 3.2

Time Estimates for Hamilton Paper Manufacturing

Activity	Description	Time (weeks)
A	Build internal components	2
B	Modify roof and floor	3
C	Construct collection stack	2
D	Pour concrete and install frame	4
E	Build high-temperature burner	4
F	Install pollution control system	3
G	Install air pollution device	5
H	Inspect and test	2
	Total time (weeks)	25

As mentioned earlier, the critical path is the *longest* time path through the network. To find the critical path, we calculate two distinct starting and ending times for each activity. These are defined as follows:

Earliest start (ES) = earliest time at which an activity can start, assuming all predecessors have been completed
Earliest finish (EF) = earliest time at which an activity can be finished
Latest start (LS) = latest time at which an activity can start so as not to delay the completion time of the entire project
Latest finish (LF) = latest time by which an activity has to finish so as not to delay the completion time of the entire project

We use a two-pass process, consisting of a forward pass and a backward pass, to determine these time schedules for each activity. The early start and finish times (ES and EF) are determined during the **forward pass**. The late start and finish times (LS and LF) are determined during the backward pass.

Forward pass

A process that identifies all the early start and early finish times.

FORWARD PASS

To clearly show the activity schedules on the project network, we use the notation shown in Figure 3.10. The ES of an activity is shown in the top left corner of the node denoting that activity. The EF is shown in the top right corner. The latest times, LS and LF, are shown in the bottom left and bottom right corners, respectively.

EARLIEST START TIME RULE Before an activity can start, all of its immediate predecessors must be finished:

- If an activity has only a single immediate predecessor, its ES equals the EF of the predecessor.
- If an activity has multiple immediate predecessors, its ES is the maximum of all EF values of its predecessors. That is,

$$ES = Max \{EF \text{ of all immediate predecessors}\} \qquad \text{(3-1)}$$

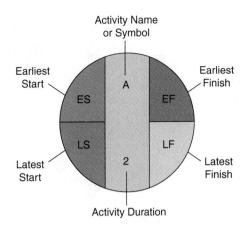

Activity Name or Symbol
Earliest Start
Earliest Finish
Latest Start
Latest Finish
Activity Duration

FIGURE 3.10
Notation Used in Nodes for Forward and Backward Passes

EARLIEST FINISH RULE The earliest finish time (EF) of an activity is the sum of its earliest start time (ES) and its activity time. That is,

$$EF = ES + \text{Activity time} \qquad (3\text{-}2)$$

Calculate the earliest start and finish times for the activities in the Hamilton Paper Manufacturing project.

APPROACH ▶ Use Table 3.2, which contains the activity times. Complete the project network for the company's project, along with the ES and EF values for all activities.

SOLUTION ▶ With the help of Figure 3.11, we describe how these values are calculated.

Since activity Start has no predecessors, we begin by setting its ES to 0. That is, activity Start can begin at time 0, which is the same as the beginning of week 1. If activity Start has an ES of 0, its EF is also 0, since its activity time is 0.

Next, we consider activities A and B, both of which have only Start as an immediate predecessor. Using the earliest start time rule, the ES for both activities A and B equals 0, which is the EF of activity Start. Now, using the earliest finish time rule, the EF for A is 2 (= 0 + 2), and the EF for B is 3 (= 0 + 3).

Since activity A precedes activity C, the ES of C equals the EF of A (= 2). The EF of C is therefore 4 (= 2 + 2).

We now come to activity D. Both activities A and B are immediate predecessors for B. Whereas A has an EF of 2, activity B has an EF of 3. Using the earliest start time rule, we compute the ES of activity D as follows:

$$\text{ES of D} = \text{Max(EF of A, EF of B)} = \text{Max}(2, 3) = 3$$

The EF of D equals 7 (= 3 + 4). Next, both activities E and F have activity C as their only immediate predecessor. Therefore, the ES for both E and F equals 4 (= EF of C). The EF of E is 8 (= 4 + 4), and the EF of F is 7 (= 4 + 3).

Activity G has both activities D and E as predecessors. Using the earliest start time rule, its ES is therefore the maximum of the EF of D and the EF of E. Hence, the ES of activity G equals 8 (= maximum of 7 and 8), and its EF equals 13 (= 8 + 5).

Finally, we come to activity H. Since it also has two predecessors, F and G, the ES of H is the maximum EF of these two activities. That is, the ES of H equals 13 (= maximum of 13 and 7). This implies that the EF of H is 15 (= 13 + 2). Since H is the last activity in the project, this also implies that the earliest time in which the entire project can be completed is 15 weeks.

INSIGHT ▶ The ES of an activity that has only one predecessor is simply the EF of that predecessor. For an activity with more than one predecessor, we must carefully examine the EFs of all immediate predecessors and choose the largest one.

LEARNING EXERCISE ▶ A new activity I, *Provincial Approval*, takes one week. Its predecessor is activity H. What are I's ES and EF? [Answer: 15, 16.]

RELATED PROBLEMS ▶ 3.11, 3.14c

EXCEL OM Data File **Ch03Ex4.xlsx** can be found at **MyLab Operations Management**.

EXAMPLE **4**
Computing Earliest Start and Finish Times for Hamilton Paper

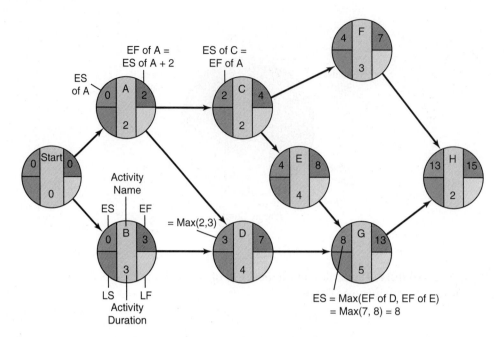

FIGURE 3.11 Earliest Start and Earliest Finish Times for Hamilton Paper

Although the forward pass allows us to determine the earliest project completion time, it does not identify the critical path. To identify this path, we need to now conduct the backward pass to determine the LS and LF values for all activities.

BACKWARD PASS

Backward pass

A process that identifies all the late start and late finish times.

Just as the forward pass began with the first activity in the project, the **backward pass** begins with the last activity in the project. For each activity, we first determine its LF value, followed by its LS value. The following two rules are used in this process.

LATEST FINISH TIME RULE This rule is again based on the fact that before an activity can start, all of its immediate predecessors must be finished:

- If an activity is an immediate predecessor for just a single activity, its LF equals the LS of the activity that immediately follows it.
- If an activity is an immediate predecessor to more than one activity, its LF is the minimum of all LS values of all activities that immediately follow it. That is:

$$LF = Min\{LS \text{ of all immediate following activities}\} \tag{3-3}$$

LATEST START TIME RULE The latest start time (LS) of an activity is the difference of its latest finish time (LF) and its activity time. That is:

$$LS = LF - Activity \text{ time} \tag{3-4}$$

EXAMPLE 5

Computing Latest Start and Finish Times for Hamilton Paper

Calculate the latest start and finish times for each activity in Hamilton Paper's pollution project.

APPROACH ▶ Figure 3.12 shows the complete project network for Hamilton Paper, along with LS and LF values for all activities. In what follows, we see how these values were calculated.

SOLUTION ▶ We begin by assigning an LF value of 15 weeks for activity H. That is, we specify that the latest finish time for the entire project is the same as its earliest finish time. Using the latest start time rule, the LS of activity H is equal to 13 (= 15 − 2).

Since activity H is the lone succeeding activity for both activities F and G, the LF for both F and G equals 13. This implies that the LS of G is 8 (= 13 − 5), and the LS of F is 10 (= 13 − 3).

Proceeding in this fashion, we see that the LF of E is 8 (= LS of G) and its LS is 4 (= 8 − 4). Likewise, the LF of D is 8 (= LS of G) and its LS is 4 (= 8 − 4).

We now consider activity C, which is an immediate predecessor to two activities: E and F. Using the latest finish time rule, we compute the LF of activity C as follows:

$$\text{LF of C} = \text{Min(LS of E, LS of F)} = \text{Min}(4, 10) = 4$$

The LS of C is computed as 2 (= 4 − 2). Next, we compute the LF of B as 4 (= LS of D), and its LS as 1 (= 4 − 3).

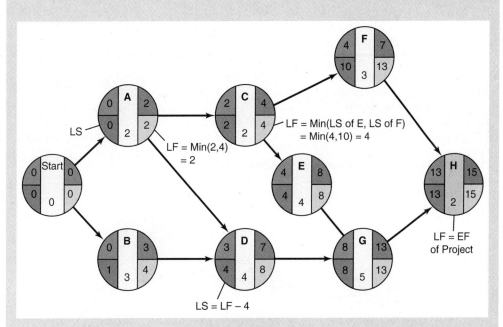

FIGURE 3.12
Latest Start and Finish Times Are Now Added

We now consider activity A. We compute its LF as 2 (= minimum of LS of C and LS of D). Hence, the LS of activity A is 0 (= 2 − 2). Finally, both the LF and LS of activity Start are equal to 0.

INSIGHT ▶ The LF of an activity that is the predecessor of only one activity is just the LS of that following activity. If the activity is the predecessor to more than one activity, its LF is the smallest LS value of all activities that follow immediately.

LEARNING EXERCISE ▶ A new activity I, *Provincial approval*, takes one week. Its predecessor is activity H. What are I's LS and LF? [Answer: 15, 16.]

RELATED PROBLEMS ▶ 3.11, 3.14c.

CALCULATING SLACK TIME AND IDENTIFYING THE CRITICAL PATH(S)

After we have computed the earliest and latest times for all activities, it is a simple matter to find the amount of **slack time**[2] that each activity has. Slack is the length of time an activity can be delayed without delaying the entire project. Mathematically:

Slack time
Free time for an activity.

$$\text{Slack} = \text{LS} - \text{ES} \quad \text{or} \quad \text{Slack} = \text{LF} - \text{EF} \qquad \text{(3-5)}$$

Calculate the slack for the activities in the Hamilton Paper project.

APPROACH ▶ Start with the data in Figure 3.12 in Example 5 and develop Table 3.3 one line at a time.

SOLUTION ▶ Table 3.3 summarizes the ES, EF, LS, LF, and slack time for all of the firm's activities. Activity B, for example, has one week of slack time since its LS is 1 and its ES is 0 (alternatively, its

EXAMPLE 6

Calculating Slack Times for Hamilton Paper

---

[2] Slack time may also be referred to as *free time, free float,* or *free slack.*

Table 3.3

Hamilton Paper's Schedule and Slack Times

Activity	Earliest Start ES	Earliest Finish EF	Latest Start LS	Latest Finish	Slack LS – ES	On Critical Path
A	0	2	0	2	0	Yes
B	0	3	1	4	1	No
C	2	4	2	4	0	Yes
D	3	7	4	8	1	No
E	4	8	4	8	0	Yes
F	4	7	10	13	6	No
G	8	13	8	13	0	Yes
H	13	15	13	15	0	Yes

LF is 4 and its EF is 3). This means that activity B can be delayed by up to one week, and the whole project can still be finished in 15 weeks.

On the other hand, activities A, C, E, G, and H have *no* slack time. This means that none of them can be delayed without delaying the entire project. Conversely, if plant manager Joni Steinberg wants to reduce the total project times, she will have to reduce the length of one of these activities.

Figure 3.13 shows the slack computed for each activity.

FIGURE 3.13

Slack Times Are Now Computed and Added

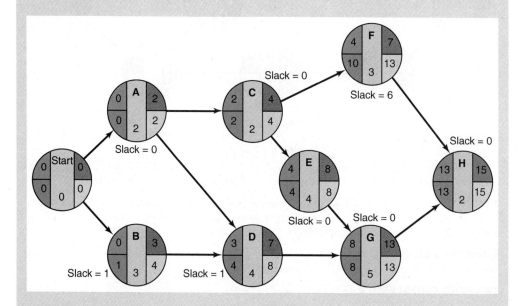

INSIGHT ▶ Slack may be computed from either early/late starts or early/late finishes. The key is to find which activities have zero slack.

LEARNING EXERCISE ▶ A new activity I, *Provincial approval*, follows activity H and takes one week. Is it on the critical path? [Answer: Yes, its LS − ES = 0.]

RELATED PROBLEMS ▶ 3.6, 3.11, 3.27

ACTIVE MODEL 3.1 This example is further illustrated in Active Model 3.1 at **MyLab Operations Management**.

LO4 Determine a critical path

The activities with zero slack are called *critical activities* and are said to be on the critical path. The critical path is a continuous path through the project network that:

- Starts at the first activity in the project (Start in our example).
- Terminates at the last activity in the project (H in our example).
- Includes only critical activities (i.e., activities with no slack time).

Show Hamilton Paper's critical path and find the project completion time.

EXAMPLE 7

Showing Critical Path With Blue Arrows

APPROACH ► We use Table 3.3 and Figure 3.14. Figure 3.14 indicates that the total project completion time of 15 weeks corresponds to the longest path in the network. That path is Start-A-C-E-G-H in network form. It is shown with thick blue arrows.

INSIGHT ► The critical path follows the activities with slack = 0. This is considered the longest path through the network.

LEARNING EXERCISE ► Why are activities B, D, and F not on the path with the thick blue line? [Answer: They are not critical and have slack values of 1, 1, and 6 weeks, respectively.]

FIGURE 3.14
The Critical Path Is Now Shown in Five Thick Blue Lines

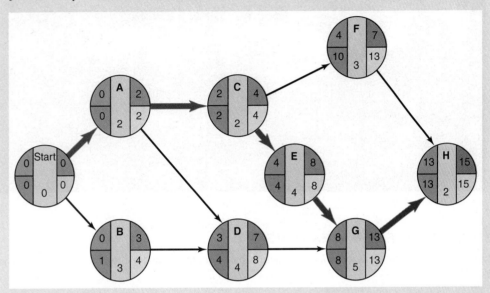

RELATED PROBLEMS ► 3.3, 3.4, 3.5, 3.6, 3.7, 3.12, 3.14b, 3.15, 3.17, 3.20a, 3.22a, 3.23, 3.26

TOTAL SLACK TIME Look again at the project network in Figure 3.14. Consider activities B and D, which have slack of one week each. Does it mean that we can delay *each* activity by one week, and still complete the project in 15 weeks? The answer is no.

Let's assume that activity B is delayed by one week. It has used up its slack of one week and now has an EF of 4. This implies that activity D now has an ES of 4 and an EF of 8. Note that these are also its LS and LF values, respectively. That is, activity D also has no slack time now. Essentially, the slack of one week that activities B and D had is, for that path, *shared* between them. Delaying either activity by one week causes not only that activity, but also the other activity, to lose its slack. This type of a slack time is referred to as **total slack**. Typically, when two or more noncritical activities appear successively in a path, they share total slack.

Total slack
Time shared among more than one activity.

Variability in Activity Times

STUDENT TIP

PERT's ability to handle three time estimates for each activity enables us to compute the probability that we can complete the project by a target date.

In identifying all earliest and latest times so far, and the associated critical path(s), we have adopted the CPM approach of assuming that all activity times are known and fixed constants. That is, there is no variability in activity times. However, in practice, it is likely that activity completion times vary depending on various factors.

For example, building internal components (activity A) for Hamilton Paper Manufacturing is estimated to finish in two weeks. Clearly, factors such as late arrival of raw materials, absence of key personnel, and so on, could delay this activity. Suppose activity A actually ends up taking three weeks. Since A is on the critical path, the entire project will now be delayed by one week to 16 weeks. If we had anticipated completion of this project in 15 weeks, we would obviously miss our deadline.

Although some activities may be relatively less prone to delays, others could be extremely susceptible to delays. For example, activity B (modify roof and floor) could be heavily dependent on weather conditions. A spell of bad weather could significantly affect its completion time.

This means that we cannot ignore the impact of variability in activity times when deciding the schedule for a project. PERT addresses this issue.

To plan, monitor, and control the huge number of details involved in sponsoring a rock festival attended by more than 100 000 fans, managers use Microsoft Project and the tools discussed in this chapter. The Video Case Study "Managing Hard Rock's Rockfest," at the end of the chapter, provides more details of the management task.

Tim Coggin/Alamy Stock Photo

THREE TIME ESTIMATES IN PERT

In PERT, we employ a probability distribution based on three time estimates for each activity, as follows:

Optimistic time

The "best" activity completion time that could be obtained in a PERT network.

Pessimistic time

The "worst" activity time that could be expected in a PERT network.

Most likely time

The most probable time to complete an activity in a PERT network.

Optimistic time (a) = time an activity will take if everything goes as planned. In estimating this value, there should be only a small probability (say, 1/100) that the activity time will be less than a.

Pessimistic time (b) = time an activity will take assuming very unfavourable conditions. In estimating this value, there should also be only a small probability (also, 1/100) that the activity time will be greater than b.

Most likely time (m) = most realistic estimate of the time required to complete an activity.

When using PERT, we often assume that activity time estimates follow the beta probability distribution (see Figure 3.15). This continuous distribution is often appropriate for determining the expected value and variance for activity completion times.

To find the *expected activity time*, t, the beta distribution weights the three time estimates as follows:

$$t = (a + 4m + b)/6 \qquad \text{(3-6)}$$

That is, the most likely time (m) is given four times the weight as the optimistic time (a) and pessimistic time (b). The time estimate t computed using Equation 3-6 for each activity is used in the project network to compute all earliest and latest times.

FIGURE 3.15

Beta Probability Distribution With Three Time Estimates

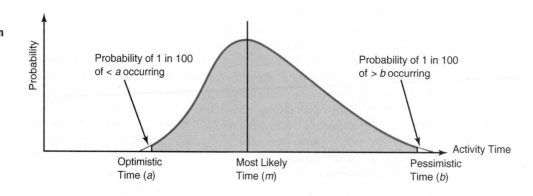

To compute the *dispersion* or *variance of activity completion time*, we use the formula:[3]

$$\text{Variance } [(b - a)/6]2 \tag{3-7}$$

Joni Steinberg and the project management team at Hamilton Paper want an expected time and variance for activity F (*Installing the pollution control system*) where: $$a = 1 \text{ week}, m = 2 \text{ weeks}, b = 9 \text{ weeks}$$ **APPROACH** ▶ Use Equations 3-6 and 3-7 to compute the expected time and variance for F. **SOLUTION** ▶ The expected time for activity F is: $$t = \frac{a + 4m + b}{6} = \frac{1 + 4(2) + 9}{6} = \frac{18}{6} = 3 \text{ weeks}$$ The variance for activity F is: $$\text{Variance} = \left[\frac{(b - a)}{6}\right]^2 = \left[\frac{(9 - 1)}{6}\right]^2 = \left(\frac{8}{6}\right)^2 = \frac{64}{36} = 1.78$$	**EXAMPLE** **8** **Expected Times and Variances for Hamilton Paper** **LO5** Calculate the variance of activity times

INSIGHT ▶ Steinberg now has information that allows her to understand and manage activity F. The expected time is, in fact, the activity time used in our earlier computation and identification of the critical path.

LEARNING EXERCISE ▶ Review the expected times and variances for all of the other activities in the project. These are shown in Table 3.4.

Table 3.4

Time Estimates (in Weeks) for Hamilton Paper's Project

Activity	Optimistic a	Most Likely m	Pessimistic b	Expected Time $t = (a + 4m + b)/6$	Variance $[(b - a)/6]^2$
A	1	2	3	2	$[(3 - 1)/6]^2 = 4/36 = 0.11$
B	2	3	4	3	$[(4 - 2)/6]^2 = 4/36 = 0.11$
C	1	2	3	2	$[(3 - 1)/6]^2 = 4/36 = 0.11$
D	2	4	6	4	$[(6 - 2)/6]^2 = 16/36 = 0.44$
E	1	4	7	4	$[(7 - 1)/6]^2 = 36/36 = 1.00$
F	1	2	9	3	$[(9 - 1)/6]^2 = 64/36 = 1.78$
G	3	4	11	5	$[(11 - 3)/6]^2 = 64/36 = 1.78$
H	1	2	3	2	$[(3 - 1)/6]^2 = 4/36 = 0.11$

STUDENT TIP

Can you see why the variance is higher in some activities than in others? Note the spread between the optimistic and pessimistic times.

RELATED PROBLEMS ▶ 3.13, 3.14a, 3.17ab, 3.21a

EXCEL OM Data File **Ch03Ex8.xlsx** can be found at **MyLab Operations Management.**

PROBABILITY OF PROJECT COMPLETION

The critical path analysis helped us determine that Hamilton Paper's expected project completion time is 15 weeks. Joni Steinberg knows, however, that there is significant variation in the time estimates for several activities. Variation in activities that are on the critical path can affect the overall project completion time—possibly delaying it. This is one occurrence that worries the plant manager considerably.

PERT uses the variance of critical path activities to help determine the variance of the overall project. Project variance is computed by summing variances of *critical* activities:

$$\sigma_p^2 = \text{Project variance} = \sum(\text{variances of activities on critical path}) \tag{3-8}$$

---

[3] This formula is based on the statistical concept that from one end of the beta distribution to the other is 6 standard deviations (± 3 standard deviations from the mean). Since $(b - a)$ is 6 standard deviations, the variance is $[(b - a)/6]^2$.

This ship is being built at the Hyundai shipyard, Asia's largest shipbuilder, in Korea. Managing this project uses the same techniques as managing the remodelling of a store or installing a new production line.

Kim Hong-Ji/Reuters

EXAMPLE 9

Computing Project Variance and Standard Deviation for Hamilton Paper

Hamilton Paper's managers now wish to know the project's variance and standard deviation.

APPROACH ▶ Because the activities are independent, we can add the variances of the activities on the critical path and then take the square root to determine the project's standard deviation.

SOLUTION ▶ From Example 8 (Table 3.4), we have the variances of all of the activities on the critical path. Specifically, we know that the variance of activity A is 0.11, variance of activity C is 0.11, variance of activity E is 1.00, variance of activity G is 1.78, and variance of activity H is 0.11.

Compute the total project variance and project standard deviation:

$$\text{Project variance } \sigma_p^2 = 0.11 + 0.11 + 1.00 + 1.78 + 0.11 = 3.11$$

which implies:

$$\text{Project standard deviation } (\sigma_P) = \sqrt{\text{Project variance}} = \sqrt{3.11} = 1.76 \text{ weeks}$$

INSIGHT ▶ Management now has an estimate not only of expected completion time for the project but also of the standard deviation of that estimate.

LEARNING EXERCISE ▶ If the variance for activity A is actually 0.30 (instead of 0.11), what is the new project standard deviation? [Answer: 1.817.]

RELATED PROBLEM ▶ 3.17e

How can this information be used to help answer questions regarding the probability of finishing the project on time? PERT makes two more assumptions: (1) total project completion times follow a normal probability distribution, and (2) activity times are statistically independent. With these assumptions, the bell-shaped normal curve shown in Figure 3.16 can be used to

FIGURE 3.16

Probability Distribution for Project Completion Times at Hamilton Paper

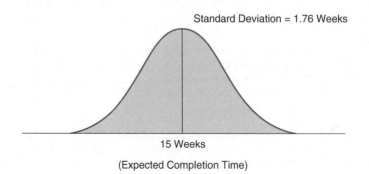

Standard Deviation = 1.76 Weeks

15 Weeks

(Expected Completion Time)

represent project completion dates. This normal curve implies that there is a 50% chance that the manufacturer's project completion time will be less than 15 weeks and a 50% chance that it will exceed 15 weeks.

EXAMPLE 10

Probability of Completing a Project on Time

Joni Steinberg would like to find the probability that her project will be finished on or before the 16-week provincial deadline.

APPROACH ▶ To do so, she needs to determine the appropriate area under the normal curve. This is the area to the left of the 16th week.

SOLUTION ▶ The standard normal equation can be applied as follows:

$$Z = (\text{Due date} - \text{Expected date of completion})/\sigma_p \qquad \text{(3-9)}$$
$$= (16 \text{ weeks} - 15 \text{ weeks})/1.76 \text{ weeks} = 0.57$$

where Z is the number of standard deviations the due date or target date lies from the mean or expected date.

Referring to the Normal Table in Appendix I, we find a Z-value of 0.57 to the right of the mean indicates a probability of 0.7157. Thus, there is a 71.57% chance that the pollution control equipment can be put in place in 16 weeks or less. This is shown in Figure 3.17.

STUDENT TIP

Here is a chance to review your statistical skills and use of a normal distribution table (Appendix I).

FIGURE 3.17
Probability That Hamilton Paper Will Meet the 16-Week Deadline

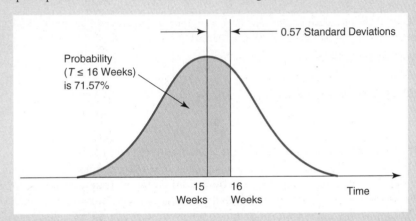

INSIGHT ▶ The shaded area to the left of the 16th week (71.57%) represents the probability that the project will be completed in less than 16 weeks.

LEARNING EXERCISE ▶ What is the probability that the project will be completed on or before the 17th week? [Answer: About 87.2%.]

RELATED PROBLEMS ▶ 3.14d, 3.17f, 3.21de, 3.22b, 3.24

DETERMINING PROJECT COMPLETION TIME FOR A GIVEN CONFIDENCE LEVEL Let's say Joni Steinberg is worried that there is only a 71.57% chance that the pollution control equipment can be put in place in 16 weeks or less. She thinks that it may be possible to plead with the environmental group for more time. However, before she approaches the group, she wants to arm herself with sufficient information about the project. Specifically, she wants to find the deadline by which she has a 99% chance of completing the project. She hopes to use her analysis to convince the group to agree to this extended deadline.

Clearly, this due date would be greater than 16 weeks. However, what is the exact value of this new due date? To answer this question, we again use the assumption that Hamilton Paper's project completion time follows a normal probability distribution with a mean of 15 weeks and a standard deviation of 1.76 weeks.

Joni Steinberg wants to find the due date that gives her company's project a 99% chance of *on-time* completion.

APPROACH ▶ She first needs to compute the Z-value corresponding to 99%, as shown in Figure 3.18. Mathematically, this is similar to Example 10, except the unknown is now Z rather than the due date.

EXAMPLE 11

Computing Probability for Any Completion Date

FIGURE 3.18

Z-Value for 99% Probability of Project Completion at Hamilton Paper

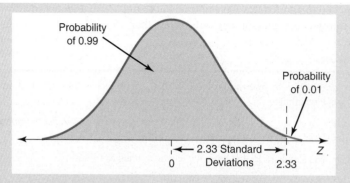

Probability of 0.99

Probability of 0.01

2.33 Standard Deviations

0   2.33   *Z*

SOLUTION ▶ Referring again to the Normal Table in Appendix I, we identify a Z-value of 2.33 as being closest to the probability of 0.99. That is, Steinberg's due date should be 2.33 standard deviations above the mean project completion time. Starting with the standard normal equation (see Equation 3-9), we can solve for the due date and rewrite the equation as:

$$\text{Due date} = \text{Expected completion time} + (Z \times \sigma_p) \qquad \textbf{(3-10)}$$
$$= 15 + (2.33 \times 1.76) = 19.1 \text{ weeks}$$

INSIGHT ▶ If Steinberg can get the environmental group to agree to give her a new deadline of 19.1 weeks (or more), she can be 99% sure of finishing the project on time.

LEARNING EXERCISE ▶ What due date gives the project a 95% chance of on-time completion? [Answer: About 17.9 weeks.]

RELATED PROBLEMS ▶ 3.22c, 3.24e

VARIABILITY IN COMPLETION TIME OF NONCRITICAL PATHS In our discussion so far, we have focused exclusively on the variability in the completion times of activities on the critical path. This seems logical since these activities are, by definition, the more important activities in a project network. However, when there is variability in activity times, it is important that we also investigate the variability in the completion times of activities on *noncritical* paths.

Consider, for example, activity D in Hamilton Paper's project. Recall from Figure 3.14 in Example 7 that this is a noncritical activity, with a slack time of one week. We have therefore not considered the variability in D's time in computing the probabilities of project completion times. We observe, however, that D has a variance of 0.44 (see Table 3.4 in Example 8). In fact, the pessimistic completion time for D is six weeks. This means that if D ends up taking its pessimistic time to finish, the project will not finish in 15 weeks, even though D is not a critical activity.

For this reason, when we find probabilities of project completion times, it may be necessary for us not to focus only on the critical path(s). Indeed, some research has suggested that expending project resources to reduce the variability of activities not on the critical path can be an effective element in project management.[4] We may need also to compute these probabilities for noncritical paths, especially those that have relatively large variances. It is possible for a noncritical path to have a smaller probability of completion within a due date, when compared with the critical path. Determining the variance and probability of completion for a noncritical path is done in the same manner as Examples 9 and 10.

WHAT PROJECT MANAGEMENT HAS PROVIDED SO FAR Project management techniques have thus far been able to provide Joni Steinberg with several valuable pieces of management information:

1. The project's expected completion date is 15 weeks.
2. There is a 71.57% chance that the equipment will be in place within the 16-week deadline. PERT analysis can easily find the probability of finishing by any date Steinberg is interested in.

---

[4] F. M. Pokladnik, T. F. Anthony, R. R. Hill, and G. Ulrich, "A Fresh Look at Estimated Project Duration: Noncritical Path Activity Contribution to Project Variance in PERT/CPM," *Proceedings of the 2003 Southwest Decision Science Conference*, Houston.

3. Five activities (A, C, E, G, and H) are on the critical path. If any one of these is delayed for any reason, the entire project will be delayed.
4. Three activities (B, D, and F) are not critical and have some slack time built in. This means that Steinberg can borrow from their resources, and, if necessary, she may be able to speed up the whole project.
5. A detailed schedule of activity starting and ending dates, slack, and critical path activities has been made available (see Table 3.3 in Example 6).

Cost–Time Trade-Offs and Project Crashing

While managing a project, it is not uncommon for a project manager to be faced with either (or both) of the following situations: (1) the project is behind schedule, and (2) the scheduled project completion time has been moved forward. In either situation, some or all of the remaining activities need to be speeded up (usually by adding resources) to finish the project by the desired due date. The process by which we shorten the duration of a project in the cheapest manner possible is called project **crashing**.

The critical path method (CPM) is a technique in which each activity has a *normal* or *standard* time that we use in our computations. Associated with this normal time is the *normal cost* of the activity. However, another time in project management is the *crash time*, which is defined as the shortest duration required to complete an activity. Associated with this crash time is the *crash cost* of the activity. Usually, we can shorten an activity by adding extra resources (e.g., equipment, people) to it. Hence, it is logical for the crash cost of an activity to be higher than its normal cost.

Crashing
Shortening activity time in a network to reduce time on the critical path so total completion time is reduced.

The amount by which an activity can be shortened (i.e., the difference between its normal time and crash time) depends on the activity in question. We may not be able to shorten some activities at all. For example, if a casting needs to be heat-treated in the furnace for 48 hours, adding more resources does not help shorten the time. In contrast, we may be able to shorten some activities significantly (e.g., frame a house in three days instead of 10 days by using three times as many workers).

Likewise, the cost of crashing (or shortening) an activity depends on the nature of the activity. Managers are usually interested in speeding up a project at the least additional cost. Hence, when choosing which activities to crash, and by how much, we need to ensure the following:

- The amount by which an activity is crashed is, in fact, permissible.
- Taken together, the shortened activity durations will enable us to finish the project by the due date.
- The total cost of crashing is as small as possible.

LO6 Crash a project

Crashing a project involves four steps:

STEP 1: Compute the crash cost per week (or other time period) for each activity in the network. If crash costs are linear over time, the following formula can be used:

$$\text{Crash cost per period} = \frac{(\text{Crash cost} - \text{Normal cost})}{(\text{Normal time} - \text{Crash time})} \qquad \text{(3-11)}$$

STEP 2: Using the current activity times, find the critical path(s) in the project network. Identify the critical activities.

STEP 3: If there is only one critical path, then select the activity on this critical path that (a) can still be crashed and (b) has the smallest crash cost per period. Crash this activity by one period.

If there is more than one critical path, then select one activity from each critical path such that (a) each selected activity can still be crashed and (b) the total crash cost per period of *all* selected activities is the smallest. Crash each activity by one period. Note that the same activity may be common to more than one critical path.

STEP 4: Update all activity times. If the desired due date has been reached, stop. If not, return to Step 2.

We illustrate project crashing in Example 12.

EXAMPLE **12**

Project Crashing to Meet a Deadline at Hamilton Paper

Suppose that Hamilton Paper Manufacturing has been given only 13 weeks (instead of 16 weeks) to install the new pollution control equipment or face a court-ordered shutdown. As you recall, the length of Joni Steinberg's critical path was 15 weeks, but she must now complete the project in 13 weeks.

APPROACH ▶ Steinberg needs to determine which activities to crash, and by how much, to meet this 13-week due date. Naturally, Steinberg is interested in speeding up the project by two weeks, at the least additional cost.

SOLUTION ▶ The company's normal and crash times, and normal and crash costs, are shown in Table 3.5. Note, for example, that activity B's normal time is three weeks (the estimate used in computing the critical path), and its crash time is one week. This means that activity B can be shortened by up to two weeks if extra resources are provided. The cost of these additional resources is $4000 (= difference between the crash cost of $34 000 and the normal cost of $30 000). If we assume that the crashing cost is linear over time (i.e., the cost is the same each week), activity B's crash cost per week is $2000 (= $4000/2).

Table 3.5

Normal and Crash Data for Hamilton Paper Manufacturing

Activity	Time (Weeks) Normal	Time (Weeks) Crash	Cost ($) Normal	Cost ($) Crash	Crash Cost per Week ($)	Critical Path?
A	2	1	22 000	22 750	750	Yes
B	3	1	30 000	34 000	2 000	No
C	2	1	26 000	27 000	1 000	Yes
D	4	3	48 000	49 000	1 000	No
E	4	2	56 000	58 000	1 000	Yes
F	3	2	30 000	30 500	500	No
G	5	2	80 000	84 500	1 500	Yes
H	2	1	16 000	19 000	3 000	Yes

This calculation for activity B is shown in Figure 3.19. Crash costs for all other activities can be computed in a similar fashion.

FIGURE 3.19

Crash and Normal Times and Costs for Activity B

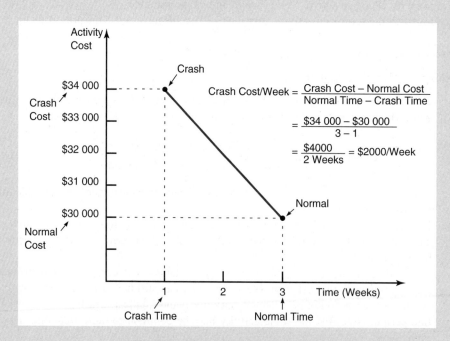

Steps 2, 3, and 4 can now be applied to reduce Hamilton Paper's project completion time at a minimum cost. We show the project network for Hamilton Paper again in Figure 3.20.

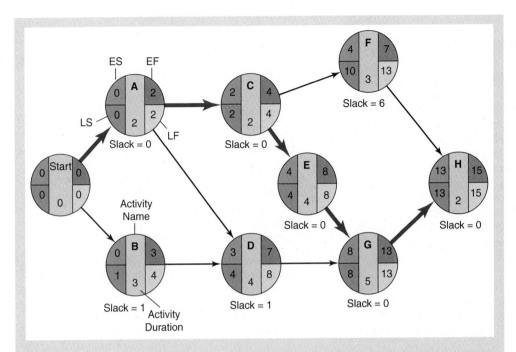

FIGURE 3.20
Critical Path and Slack Times for Hamilton Paper

The current critical path (using normal times) is Start-A-C-E-G-H, in which Start is just a dummy starting activity. Of these critical activities, activity A has the lowest crash cost per week of $750. Joni Steinberg should therefore crash activity A by one week to reduce the project completion time to 14 weeks. The cost is an additional $750. Note that activity A cannot be crashed any further, since it has reached its crash limit of one week.

At this stage, the original path Start-A-C-E-G-H remains critical with a completion time of 14 weeks. However, a new path Start-B-D-G-H is also critical now, with a completion time of 14 weeks. Hence, any further crashing must be done to both critical paths.

On each of these critical paths, we need to identify one activity that can still be crashed. We also want the total cost of crashing an activity on each path to be the smallest. We might be tempted to simply pick the activities with the smallest crash cost per period in each path. If we did this, we would select activity C from the first path and activity D from the second path. The total crash cost would then be $2000 (= $1000 + $1000).

But we spot that activity G is common to both paths. That is, by crashing activity G, we will simultaneously reduce the completion time of both paths. Even though the $1500 crash cost for activity G is higher than that for activities C and D, we would still prefer crashing G, since the total crashing cost will now be only $1500 (compared with the $2000 if we crash C and D).

INSIGHT ▶ To crash the project down to 13 weeks, Steinberg should crash activity A by one week, and activity G by one week. The total additional cost will be $2250 (= $750 + $1500). This is important because many contracts for projects include bonuses or penalties for early or late finishes.

LEARNING EXERCISE ▶ Say the crash cost for activity B is $31 000 instead of $34 000. How does this change the answer? [Answer: No change.]

RELATED PROBLEMS ▶ 3.16, 3.18, 3.19, 3.20, 3.25

EXCEL OM Data File **Ch03Ex12.xlsx** can be found at **MyLab Operations Management.**

A Critique of PERT and CPM

STUDENT TIP

As a critique of our discussions of PERT, here are some of its features about which operations managers need to be aware:

Every technique has shortfalls as well as strengths. It is important to know both.

ADVANTAGES

1. Especially useful when scheduling and controlling large projects.
2. Straightforward concept and not mathematically complex.
3. Graphical networks help highlight relationships among project activities.

OM in Action   Rebuilding the Electricity Grid in China

Due to its rapidly expanding economy and steady growth, China has been striving to rebuild its infrastructure and utilities. Among these many needs is a requirement for a robust and stable electricity grid. To meet the demand for electricity, China contracted Atomic Energy of Canada Limited (AECL) in order to construct two 728 megawatt CANDU reactors at Qinshan in the eastern part of the country (roughly 125 km south of Shanghai). The project was mutually beneficial to both countries. In particular, China was able to secure a contract with an organization with a proven track record, while Canada was fortunate to export human and physical resources for a high-profile project and derive significant revenue and goodwill.

Largely thanks to excellent project management, the project was completed four months ahead of schedule and under budget. Currently, the project has the record for the shortest construction schedule ever completed

for a nuclear power plant in that country. In fact, several significant milestones were achieved and records were set. These include:

- The first CANDU unit (Unit 1) was operating commercially 43 days ahead of schedule and was the first of its kind ever built in China.
- Unit 1 also boasted the shortest construction period for a nuclear plant in the country (54 months).
- Unit 2 was launched into commercial operation 112 days ahead of plan.
- The entire project was completed 10% below budget.

The foregoing demonstrates the value of good planning and solid project management. The benefits are tangible to all stakeholders.

Source: www.cna.ca.

---

4.   Critical path and slack time analyses help pinpoint activities that need to be closely watched.
5.   Project documentation and graphs point out who is responsible for various activities.
6.   Applicable to a wide variety of projects.
7.   Useful in monitoring not only schedules but costs as well.

LIMITATIONS

1.   Project activities have to be clearly defined, independent, and stable in their relationships.
2.   Precedence relationships must be specified and networked together.
3.   Time estimates tend to be subjective and are subject to fudging by managers who fear the dangers of being overly optimistic or not pessimistic enough.
4.   There is the inherent danger of placing too much emphasis on the longest, or critical, path. Near-critical paths need to be monitored closely as well.

STUDENT TIP

Now that you understand the workings of PERT and CPM, you are ready to master this useful program. Knowing such software gives you an edge over others in the job market.

Hamilton Paper Co. Activities		
Activity	Time (weeks)	Prede-cessors
A	2	—
B	3	—
C	2	A
D	4	A, B
E	4	C
F	3	C
G	5	D, E
H	2	F, G

Using Microsoft Project to Manage Projects

The approaches discussed so far are effective for managing small projects. However, for large or complex projects, specialized project management software is much preferred. In this section, we provide a brief introduction to the most popular example of such specialized software, Microsoft Project. A time-limited version of Microsoft Project may be requested directly from Microsoft.

Microsoft Project is extremely useful in drawing project networks, identifying the project schedule, and managing project costs and other resources.

ENTERING DATA

Let us again consider the Hamilton Paper Manufacturing project. Recall that this project has eight activities (repeated in the margin). The first step is to define the activities and their precedence relationships. To do so, we select File|New to open a blank project. We type the project start date (as July 1), then enter all activity information (see Program 3.1). For each activity (or task, as Microsoft Project calls it), we fill in the name and duration. The description of the activity is also placed in the *Task Name* column in Program 3.1. As we enter activities and durations, the software automatically inserts start and finish dates.

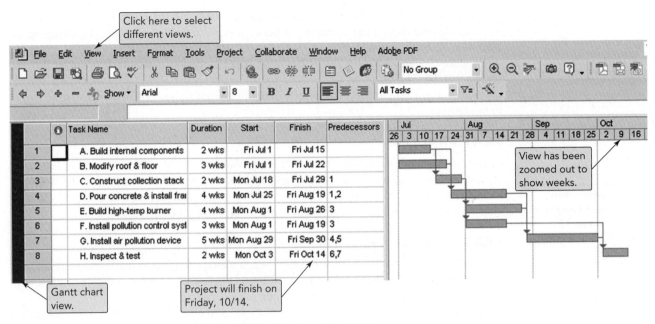

PROGRAM 3.1 Gantt Chart in Microsoft Project for Hamilton Paper Manufacturing

Source: Courtesy of Microsoft Corporation.

The next step is to define precedence relationships between these activities. To do so, we enter the relevant activity numbers (e.g., 1, 2) in the *Predecessors* column.

VIEWING THE PROJECT SCHEDULE

When all links have been defined, the complete project schedule can be viewed as a Gantt chart. We can also select View|Network Diagram to view the schedule as a project network (shown in Program 3.2). The critical path is shown in red on the screen in the network diagram. We can click on any of the activities in the project network to view details of the activities. Likewise, we can easily add or remove activities from the project network. Each time we do so, Microsoft

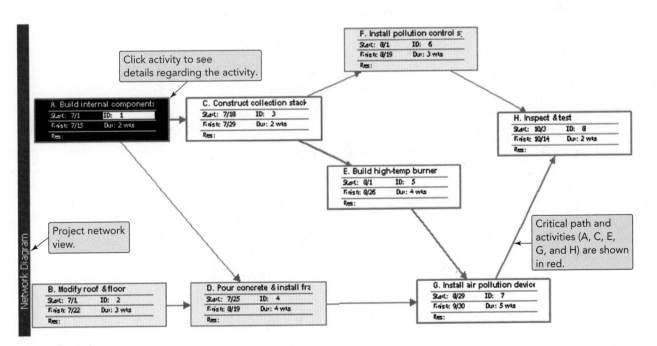

PROGRAM 3.2 Project Network in Microsoft Project for Hamilton Paper Manufacturing

Source: Courtesy of Microsoft Corporation.

Project automatically updates all start dates, finish dates, and the critical path(s). If desired, we can manually change the layout of the network (e.g., reposition activities) by changing the options in Format|Layout.

Programs 3.1 and 3.2 show that if Hamilton Paper's project starts July 1, it can be finished on October 14. The start and finish dates for all activities are also clearly identified. Project management software, we see, can greatly simplify the scheduling procedures discussed earlier in this chapter.

PERT ANALYSIS

Microsoft Project does not perform the PERT probability calculations discussed in Examples 10 and 11. However, by clicking View|Toolbars|PERT Analysis, we can get Microsoft Project to allow us to enter optimistic, most likely, and pessimistic times for each activity. We can then choose to view Gantt charts based on any of these three times for each activity.

TRACKING THE TIME STATUS OF A PROJECT

Perhaps the biggest advantage of using software to manage projects is that it can track the progress of the project. In this regard, Microsoft Project has many features available to track individual activities in terms of time, cost, resource usage, and so on.

An easy way to track the time progress of tasks is to enter the percent of work completed for each task. One way to do so is to double-click on any activity in the *Task Name* column in Program 3.1. A window is displayed that allows us to enter the percent of work completed for each task.

The table in the margin provides data regarding the percent of each of Hamilton Paper's activities as of today. (Assume that today is Friday, August 12, that is, the end of the sixth week of the project schedule.)

As shown in Program 3.3, the Gantt chart immediately reflects this updated information by drawing a thick line within each activity's bar. The length of this line is proportional to the percent of that activity's work that has been completed.

How do we know if we are on schedule? Notice that there is a vertical line shown on the Gantt chart corresponding to today's date. Microsoft Project will automatically move this line to correspond with the current date. If the project is on schedule, we should see all bars to the *left* of today's line indicate that they have been completed. For example, Program 3.3 shows that activities A, B, and C are on schedule. In contrast, activities D, E, and F appear to be behind schedule. These activities need to be investigated further to determine the reason for the delay. This type of easy *visual* information is what makes such software so useful in practice for project management.

Activity	Completed
A	100
B	100
C	100
D	10
E	20
F	20
G	0
H	0

Pollution Project Percentage Completed on Aug. 12

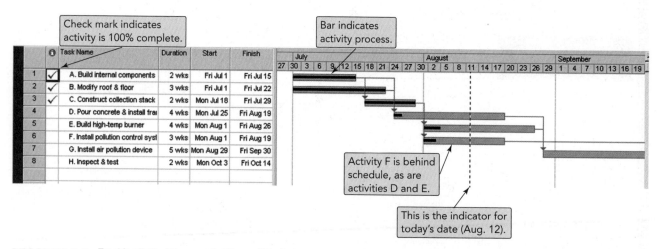

PROGRAM 3.3 Tracking Project Progress in Microsoft Project

Source: Courtesy of Microsoft Corporation.

We encourage you to download a time-limited version of Microsoft Project directly from Microsoft and to create a project network for work you are currently doing.

CHAPTER SUMMARY

PERT, CPM, and other scheduling techniques have proven to be valuable tools in controlling large and complex projects. Managers use such techniques to segment projects into discrete activities (work breakdown structures), identifying specific resources and time requirements for each. With PERT and CPM, managers can understand the status of each activity, including its earliest start, latest start, earliest finish, and latest finish (ES, LS, EF, and LF) times. By controlling the trade-off between ES and LS, managers can identify the activities that have slack and can address resource allocation, perhaps by smoothing resources. Effective project management also allows managers to focus on the activities that are critical to timely project completion. By understanding the project's critical path, they know where crashing makes the most economic sense.

Good project management also allows firms to efficiently create products and services for global markets and to respond effectively to global competition. Microsoft Project, illustrated in this chapter, is one of a wide variety of software packages available to help managers handle network modelling problems.

The models described in this chapter require good management practices, detailed work breakdown structures, clear responsibilities assigned to activities, and straightforward and timely reporting systems. All are critical parts of project management.

ETHICAL DILEMMA

Two examples of massively mismanaged projects are TAURUS and the Canadian federal government long-gun registry. The first, formally called the London Stock Exchange Automation Project, cost U.S. $575 million before it was finally abandoned. Although most IT projects have a reputation for cost overruns, delays, and underperformance, TAURUS set a new standard.

As unfortunate as the TAURUS case may be, the Canadian federal government's long-gun registry was worse. In addition to the registry being a divisive issue and its value being questioned, the costs of implementing and maintaining the system mushroomed out of control. Taxpayers were initially expected to contribute $2 million of the budget while registration fees were expected to cover the remaining costs. By the time the registry was scrapped in 2012, estimates of the cost of the program exceeded $1 billion.

Read about one of these two projects (or another of your choice) and explain why it faced such problems. How and why do project managers allow such massive endeavours to fall into such a state? What do you think are the causes?

Discussion Questions

1. Give an example of a situation in which project management is needed.
2. Explain the purpose of project organization.
3. What are the three phases involved in the management of a large project?
4. What are some of the questions that can be answered with PERT and CPM?
5. Define *work breakdown structure*. How is it used?
6. What is the use of Gantt charts in project management?
7. What is the difference between an activity-on-arrow (AOA) network and an activity-on-node (AON) network? Which is primarily used in this chapter?
8. What is the significance of the critical path?
9. What would a project manager have to do to crash an activity?
10. Describe how expected activity times and variances can be computed in a PERT network.
11. Define *early start*, *early finish*, *late finish*, and *late start* times.
12. Students are sometimes confused by the concept of critical path and want to believe that it is the *shortest* path through a network. Convincingly explain why this is not so.
13. What are dummy activities? Why are they used in activity-on-arrow (AOA) project networks?
14. What are the three time estimates used with PERT?
15. Would a project manager ever consider crashing a noncritical activity in a project network? Explain convincingly.
16. How is the variance of the total project computed in PERT?
17. Describe the meaning of slack, and discuss how it can be determined.
18. How can we determine the probability that a project will be completed by a certain date? What assumptions are made in this computation?
19. Name some of the widely used project management software programs.
20. What is the difference between the waterfall approach and agile project management?

Using Software to Solve Project Management Problems

In addition to the Microsoft Project software just illustrated, both Excel OM and POM for Windows are available to readers of this text as project management tools.

✗ USING EXCEL OM

Excel OM has a Project Scheduling module. Program 3.4 uses the data from the Hamilton Paper Manufacturing example in this chapter (see Examples 4 and 5). The PERT/CPM analysis also handles activities with three time estimates.

PROGRAM 3.4
Excel OM's Use of Hamilton Paper Manufacturing's Data from Examples 4 and 5

Source: Courtesy of Microsoft Corporation.

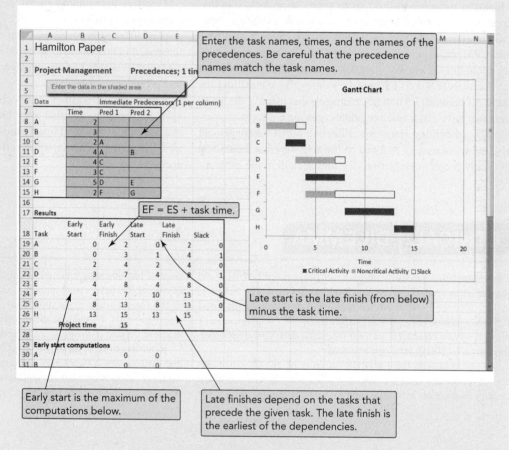

Enter the task names, times, and the names of the precedences. Be careful that the precedence names match the task names.

EF = ES + task time.

Late start is the late finish (from below) minus the task time.

Early start is the maximum of the computations below.

Late finishes depend on the tasks that precede the given task. The late finish is the earliest of the dependencies.

𝑷 USING POM FOR WINDOWS

The POM for Windows Project Scheduling module can also find the expected project completion time for a CPM and PERT network with either one or three time estimates. POM for Windows also performs project crashing. For further details, refer to Appendix IV.

Solved Problems Virtual Office Hours help is available at MyLab Operations Management.

▼ SOLVED PROBLEM 3.1

Construct an AON network based on the following:

Activity	Immediate Predecessor(s)
A	—
B	—
C	—
D	A, B
E	C

▼ SOLUTION

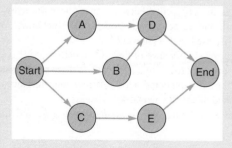

▼ **SOLVED PROBLEM 3.2**

Insert a dummy activity and event to correct the following AOA network:

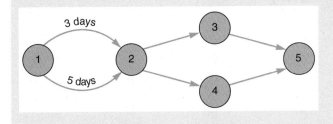

▼ **SOLUTION**

Since we cannot have two activities starting and ending at the same node, we add the following dummy activity and dummy event to obtain the correct AOA network:

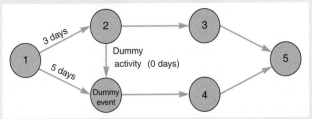

▼ **SOLVED PROBLEM 3.3**

Calculate the critical path, project completion time T, and project variance σ_p^2 based on the following AON network information:

Activity	Time	Variance	ES	EF	LS	LF	Slack
A	2	$\frac{2}{6}$	0	2	0	2	0
B	3	$\frac{2}{6}$	0	3	1	4	1
C	2	$\frac{4}{6}$	2	4	2	4	0
D	4	$\frac{4}{6}$	3	7	4	8	1
E	4	$\frac{2}{6}$	4	8	4	8	0
F	3	$\frac{1}{6}$	4	7	10	13	6
G	5	$\frac{1}{6}$	8	13	8	13	0

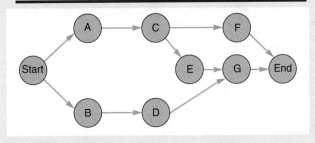

▼ **SOLUTION**

We conclude that the critical path is Start–A–C–E–G–End:

$$\text{Total project time} = T = 2 + 2 + 4 + 5 = 13$$

and

$$\sigma_p^2 = \sum \text{Variances on the critical path} = \frac{2}{6} + \frac{4}{6} + \frac{2}{6} + \frac{1}{6} = \frac{9}{6} = 1.5$$

▼ **SOLVED PROBLEM 3.4**

To complete the wing assembly for an experimental aircraft, Jim Gilbert has laid out the seven major activities involved. These activities have been labelled A through G in the following table, which also shows their estimated completion times (in weeks) and immediate predecessors. Determine the expected time and variance for each activity:

Activity	a	m	b	Immediate Predecessors
A	1	2	3	—
B	2	3	4	—
C	4	5	6	A
D	8	9	10	B
E	2	5	8	C, D
F	4	5	6	D
G	1	2	3	E

▼ **SOLUTION**

Expected times and variances can be computed using Equations (3-6) and (3-7). The results are summarized in the following table:

Activity	Expected Time (in weeks)	Variance
A	2	$\frac{1}{9}$
B	3	$\frac{1}{9}$
C	5	$\frac{1}{9}$
D	9	$\frac{1}{9}$
E	5	1
F	5	$\frac{1}{9}$
G	2	$\frac{1}{9}$

▼ SOLVED PROBLEM 3.5

Referring to Solved Problem 3.4, now Jim Gilbert would like to determine the critical path for the entire wing assembly project as well as the expected completion time for the total project. In addition, he would like to determine the earliest and latest start and finish times for all activities.

▼ SOLUTION

The AON network for Gilbert's project is shown in Figure 3.21. Note that this project has multiple activities (A and B) with no immediate predecessors, and multiple activities (F and G) with no successors. Hence, in addition to a unique starting activity (Start), we have included a unique finishing activity (End) for the project.

Figure 3.21 shows the earliest and latest times for all activities. The results are also summarized in the following table:

Activity	Activity Time				
	ES	EF	LS	LF	Slack
A	0	2	5	7	5
B	0	3	0	3	0
C	2	7	7	12	5
D	3	12	3	12	0
E	12	17	12	17	0
F	12	17	14	19	2
G	17	19	17	19	0

Expected project length = 19 weeks
Variance of the critical path = 1.333
Standard deviation of the critical path = 1.155 weeks

The activities along the critical path are B, D, E, and G. These activities have zero slack as shown in the table.

FIGURE 3.21

Critical Path for Solved Problem 3.5

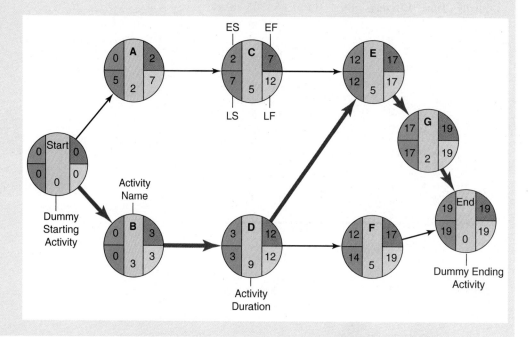

▼ SOLVED PROBLEM 3.6

The following information has been computed from a project:

Expected total project time $= T = 62$ weeks
Project variance $(\sigma_p^2) = 81$

What is the probability that the project will be completed 18 weeks *before* its expected completion date?

▼ SOLUTION

The desired completion date is 18 weeks before the expected completion date, 62 weeks. The desired completion date is 44 (or 62 − 18) weeks:

$$\sigma_p = \sqrt{\text{Project variance}}$$

$$Z = \frac{\text{Due date} - \text{Expected completion date}}{\sigma_p}$$

$$= \frac{44 - 62}{9} = \frac{-18}{9} = -2.0$$

The normal curve appears as follows:

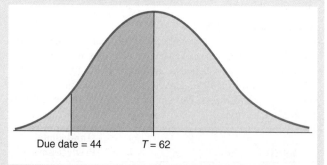

Due date = 44   T = 62

Because the normal curve is symmetrical and table values are calculated for positive values of Z, the area desired is equal to 1 − (table value). For $Z = +2.0$, the area from the table is 0.97725. Thus, the area corresponding to a Z-value of −2.0 is 0.02275 (or 1 − 0.97725). Hence, the probability of completing the project 18 weeks before the expected completion date is approximately 0.023, or 2.3%.

▼ SOLVED PROBLEM 3.7

Determine the least cost of reducing the project completion date by three months based on the following information:

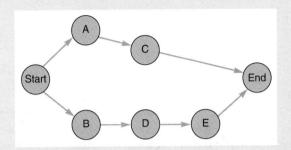

Activity	Normal Time (months)	Crash Time (months)	Normal Cost	Crash Cost
A	6	4	$2000	$2400
B	7	5	3000	3500
C	7	6	1000	1300
D	6	4	2000	2600
E	9	8	8800	9000

▼ SOLUTION

The first step in this problem is to compute ES, EF, LS, LF, and slack for each activity:

Activity	ES	EF	LS	LF	Slack
A	0	6	9	15	9
B	0	7	0	7	0
C	6	13	15	22	9
D	7	13	7	13	0
E	13	22	13	22	0

The critical path consists of activities B, D, and E.

Next, crash cost/month must be computed for each activity:

Activity	Normal Time – Crash Time	Crash Cost – Normal Cost	Crash Cost/ Month	Critical Path?
A	2	$400	$200/month	No
B	2	500	250/month	Yes
C	1	300	300/month	No
D	2	600	300/month	Yes
E	1	200	200/month	Yes

Finally, we will select that activity on the critical path with the smallest crash cost/month. This is activity E. Thus, we can reduce the total project completion date by one month for an additional cost of $200. We still need to reduce the project completion date by two more months. This reduction can be achieved at least cost along the critical path by reducing activity B by two months for an additional cost of $500. Neither reduction has an effect on noncritical activities. This solution is summarized in the following table:

Activity	Months Reduced	Cost
E	1	$200
B	2	500
		Total: $700

Problems*

• **3.1** The work breakdown structure for building a house (levels 1 and 2) is shown below:

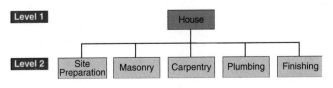

a) Add two level 3 activities to each of the level 2 activities to provide more detail to the WBS.
b) Select one of your level 3 activities and add two level 4 activities below it.

•• **3.2** Robert Mefford has been nominated as a candidate to run for a seat as a member of Parliament representing Bonavista South. He views his eight-month campaign for office as a major project and wishes to create a work breakdown structure (WBS) to

---

* *Note:* **℞X** means the problem may be solved with POM for Windows and/or Excel OM.

help control the detailed scheduling. So far, he has developed the following pieces of the WBS:

Level	Level ID No.	Activity
1	1.0	Develop political campaign
2	1.1	Fund-raising plan
3	1.11	_____
3	1.12	_____
3	1.13	_____
2	1.2	Develop a position on major issues
3	1.21	_____
3	1.22	_____
3	1.23	_____
2	1.3	Staffing for campaign
3	1.31	_____
3	1.32	_____
3	1.33	_____
3	1.34	_____
2	1.4	Paperwork compliance for candidacy
3	1.41	_____
3	1.42	_____
2	1.5	Ethical plan/issues
3	1.51	_____

Help Mr. Mefford by providing details where the blank lines appear. Are there any other major (level 2) activities to create? If so, add an ID number 1.6 and insert them.

•   **3.3** Draw the activity-on-node (AON) project network associated with the following activities for Dave Carhart's consulting company project. How long should it take Dave and his team to complete this project? What are the critical path activities?

Activity	Immediate Predecessor(s)	Time (days)
A	—	3
B	A	4
C	A	6
D	B	6
E	B	4
F	C	4
G	D	6
H	E, F	8

•   **3.4** Given the activities whose sequence is described by the following table, draw the appropriate activity-on-arrow (AOA) network diagram.
a) Which activities are on the critical path?
b) What is the length of the critical path?

Activity	Immediate Predecessor(s)	Time (days)
A	—	5
B	A	2
C	A	4
D	B	5
E	B	5
F	C	5
G	E, F	2
H	D	3
I	G, H	5

•   **3.5** Using AOA, diagram the network described below for Roni Zuckerman's construction project. Calculate its critical path. How long is the minimum duration of this network?

Activity	Nodes	Time (weeks)	Activity	Nodes	Time (weeks)
J	1–2	10	N	3–4	2
K	1–3	8	O	4–5	7
L	2–4	6	P	3–5	5
M	2–3	3			

•   **3.6** Anju Chaudhary is developing a program in leadership training for middle-level managers. She has listed a number of activities that must be completed before a training program of this nature could be conducted. The activities, immediate predecessors, and times appear in the accompanying table:

Activity	Immediate Predecessor(s)	Time (days)
A	—	2
B	—	5
C	—	1
D	B	10
E	A, D	3
F	C	6
G	E, F	8

a) Develop an AON network for this problem.
b) What is the critical path?
c) What is the total project completion time?
d) What is the slack time for each individual activity?

••   **3.7** Task time estimates for a production line setup project at Robert Klassen's Ontario factory are as follows:

Activity	Time (in hours)	Immediate Predecessors
A	6.0	—
B	7.2	—
C	5.0	A
D	6.0	B, C
E	4.5	B, C
F	7.7	D
G	4.0	E, F

a) Draw the project network using AON.
b) Identify the critical path.
c) What is the expected project length?
d) Draw a Gantt chart for the project.

•• **3.8** The City of Lethbridge has decided to build a botanical garden and picnic area in the heart of the city for the recreation of its citizens. The precedence table for all the activities required to construct this area successfully is given below. Draw the Gantt chart for the whole construction activity.

Code	Activity	Description	Time (in hours)	Immediate Predecessor(s)
A	Planning	Find location; determine resource requirements	20	None
B	Purchasing	Requisition of lumber and sand	60	Planning
C	Excavation	Dig and grade	100	Planning
D	Sawing	Saw lumber into appropriate sizes	30	Purchasing
E	Placement	Position lumber in correct locations	20	Sawing, excavation
F	Assembly	Nail lumber together	10	Placement
G	Infill	Put sand in and under the equipment	20	Assembly
H	Outfill	Put dirt around the equipment	10	Assembly
I	Decoration	Put grass all over the garden, landscape, paint	30	Infill, outfill

•• **3.9** Refer to the table in Problem 3.8.
a) Draw the AON network for the construction activity.
b) Draw the AOA network for the construction activity.

• **3.10** The activities needed to build an experimental chemical contaminant tracking machine at Charlie Cook Corp. are listed in the following table. Construct an AON network for these activities.

Activity	Immediate Predecessor(s)	Activity	Immediate Predecessor(s)
A	—	E	B
B	—	F	B
C	A	G	C, E
D	A	H	D, F

• **3.11** Charlie Cook (see Problem 3.10) was able to determine the activity times for constructing his chemical contaminant tracking machine. Cook would like to determine ES, EF, LS, LF, and slack for each activity. The total project completion time and the critical path should also be determined. Here are the activity times:

Activity	Time (weeks)	Activity	Time (weeks)
A	6	E	4
B	7	F	6
C	3	G	10
D	2	H	7

• **3.12** The activities described by the following table are given for the Duplaga Corporation:

Activity	Immediate Predecessor(s)	Time
A	—	9
B	A	7
C	A	3
D	B	6
E	B	9
F	C	4
G	E, F	6
H	D	5
I	G, H	3

a) Draw the appropriate AON PERT diagram for Annelise Duplaga's management team.
b) Find the critical path.
c) What is the project completion time?

• **3.13** A small renovation of a Hard Rock Cafe gift shop has six activities (in hours). For the following estimates of a, m, and b, calculate the expected time and the standard deviation for each activity:

Activity	a	m	b
A	11	15	19
B	27	31	41
C	18	18	18
D	8	13	19
E	17	18	20
F	16	19	22

•• **3.14** McGee Carpet and Trim installs carpet in commercial offices. Andrea McGee has been very concerned with the amount of time it took to complete several recent jobs. Some of her workers are very unreliable. A list of activities and their optimistic completion time, the most likely completion time, and the pessimistic completion time (all in days) for a new contract are given in the following table:

Activity	Time (days) a	m	b	Immediate Predecessor(s)
A	3	6	8	—
B	2	4	4	—
C	1	2	3	—
D	6	7	8	C
E	2	4	6	B, D
F	6	10	14	A, E
G	1	2	4	A, E
H	3	6	9	F
I	10	11	12	G
J	14	16	20	C
K	2	8	10	H, I

a) Determine the expected completion time and variance for each activity.
b) Determine the total project completion time and the critical path for the project.

c) Determine ES, EF, LS, LF, and slack for each activity.
d) What is the probability that McGee Carpet and Trim will finish the project in 40 days or less?

•• 3.15 The following is a table of activities associated with a project at Bill Figg Enterprises, their durations, and what activities each must precede:

Activity	Duration (weeks)	Precedes
A (start)	1	B, C
B	1	E
C	4	F
E	2	F
F (end)	2	—

a) Draw an AON diagram of the project, including activity durations.
b) Define the critical path, listing all critical activities in chronological order.
c) What is the project duration (in weeks)?
d) What is the slack (in weeks) associated with any and all noncritical paths through the project?

•• 3.16 Assume that the activities in Problem 3.15 have the following costs to shorten: A, $300/week; B, $100/week; C, $200/week; E, $100/week; and F, $400/week. Assume also that you can crash an activity down to zero weeks in duration and that every week you can shorten the project is worth $250 to you. What activities would you crash? What is the total crashing cost?

••• 3.17 Thabo Mbeki, president of Mbeki Construction, has developed the tasks, durations, and predecessor relationships in the following table for building new motels. Draw the AON network and answer the questions that follow.

Activity	Immediate Predecessor(s)	*Time Estimates (in weeks)* Optimistic	Most Likely	Pessimistic
A	—	4	8	10
B	A	2	8	24
C	A	8	12	16
D	A	4	6	10
E	B	1	2	3
F	E, C	6	8	20
G	E, C	2	3	4
H	F	2	2	2
I	F	6	6	6
J	D, G, H	4	6	12
K	I, J	2	2	3

a) What is the expected (estimated) time for activity C?
b) What is the variance for activity C?
c) Based on the calculation of estimated times, what is the critical path?
d) What is the estimated time of the critical path?
e) What is the activity variance along the critical path?
f) What is the probability of completion of the project before week 36?

••• 3.18 What is the minimum cost of crashing by four days the following project that James Walters manages at Athabasca University?

Activity	Normal Time (days)	Crash Time (days)	Normal Cost	Crash Cost	Immediate Predecessor(s)
A	6	5	$ 900	$1000	—
B	8	6	300	400	—
C	4	3	500	600	—
D	5	3	900	1200	A
E	8	5	1000	1600	C

•• 3.19 Three activities are candidates for crashing on a project network for a large computer installation (all are, of course, critical). Activity details are in the following table:

Activity	Predecessor	Normal Time	Normal Cost	Crash Time	Crash Cost
A	—	7 days	$6000	6 days	$6600
B	A	4 days	1200	2 days	3000
C	B	11 days	4000	9 days	6000

a) What action would you take to reduce the critical path by one day?
b) Assuming no other paths become critical, what action would you take to reduce the critical path one additional day?
c) What is the total cost of the two-day reduction?

••• 3.20 Development of a new deluxe version of a particular software product is being considered by Ravi Behara's software house. The activities necessary for the completion of this project are listed in the following table:

Activity	Normal Time (weeks)	Crash Time (weeks)	Normal Cost	Crash Cost	Immediate Predecessor(s)
A	4	3	$2000	$2600	—
B	2	1	2200	2800	—
C	3	3	500	500	—
D	8	4	2300	2600	A
E	6	3	900	1200	B
F	3	2	3000	4200	C
G	4	2	1400	2000	D, E

a) What is the project completion date?
b) What is the total cost required for completing this project on normal time?
c) If you wish to reduce the time required to complete this project by one week, which activity should be crashed, and how much will this increase the total cost?
d) What is the maximum time that can be crashed? How much would costs increase?

••• 3.21 The estimated times and immediate predecessors for the activities in a project at Caesar Douglas's retinal scanning company are given in the following table. Assume that the activity times are independent.

	Immediate	Time (weeks)		
Activity	Predecessor	a	m	b
A	—	9	10	11
B	—	4	10	16
C	A	9	10	11
D	B	5	8	11

a) Calculate the expected time and variance for each activity.

b) What is the expected completion time of the critical path? What is the expected completion time of the other path in the network?

c) What is the variance of the critical path? What is the variance of the other path in the network?

d) If the time to complete path A–C is normally distributed, what is the probability that this path will be finished in 22 weeks or less?

e) If the time to complete path B–D is normally distributed, what is the probability that this path will be finished in 22 weeks or less?

f) Explain why the probability that the *critical path* will be finished in 22 weeks or less is not necessarily the probability that the *project* will be finished in 22 weeks or less.

••• **3.22** Jack Kanet Manufacturing produces custom-built pollution control devices for medium-size steel mills. The most recent project undertaken by Jack requires 14 different activities.

a) Jack's managers would like to determine the total project completion time (in days) and those activities that lie along the critical path. The appropriate data are shown in the following table.

b) What is the probability of being done in 53 days?

c) What date results in a 99% probability of completion?

Activity	Immediate Predecessor(s)	Optimistic Time	Most Likely Time	Pessimistic Time
A	—	4	6	7
B	—	1	2	3
C	A	6	6	6
D	A	5	8	11
E	B, C	1	9	18
F	D	2	3	6
G	D	1	7	8
H	E, F	4	4	6
I	G, H	1	6	8
J	I	2	5	7
K	I	8	9	11
L	J	2	4	6
M	K	1	2	3
N	L, M	6	8	10

••• **3.23** A firm hired to coordinate the release of the movie *Goon* (starring Jay Baruchel) identified 16 activities to be completed before the release of the film.

a) How many weeks in advance of the film release should the promoter have started its marketing campaign? What is the critical path? The tasks (in time units of weeks) are as follows:

Activity	Immediate Predecessors	Optimist Time	Most Likely Time	Pessimistic Time
A	—	1	2	4
B	—	3	3.5	4
C	—	10	12	13
D	—	4	5	7
E	—	2	4	5
F	A	6	7	8
G	B	2	4	5.5
H	C	5	7.7	9
I	C	9.9	10	12
J	C	2	4	5
K	D	2	4	6
L	E	2	4	6
M	F, G, H	5	6	6.5
N	J, K, L	1	1.1	2
O	I, M	5	7	8
P	N	5	7	9

b) If activities I and J were not necessary, what impact would this have on the critical path and the number of weeks needed to complete the marketing campaign?

•• **3.24** Using PERT, Jennifer Benson was able to determine that the expected project completion time for the construction of a pleasure yacht is 21 months, and the project variance is 4.

a) What is the probability that the project will be completed in 17 months?

b) What is the probability that the project will be completed in 20 months?

c) What is the probability that the project will be completed in 23 months?

d) What is the probability that the project will be completed in 25 months?

e) What is the due date that yields a 95% chance of completion?

••• **3.25** Bolling Electronics manufactures DVD players for commercial use. W. Blaker Bolling, president of Bolling Electronics, is contemplating producing DVD players for home use. The activities necessary to build an experimental model and related data are given in the following table:

Activity	Normal Time (weeks)	Crash Time (weeks)	Normal Cost ($)	Crash Cost ($)	Immediate Predecessor(s)
A	3	2	1000	1600	—
B	2	1	2000	2700	—
C	1	1	300	300	—
D	7	3	1300	1600	A
E	6	3	850	1000	B
F	2	1	4000	5000	C
G	4	2	1500	2000	D, E

a) What is the project completion date?

b) Crash this project to 10 weeks at the least cost.

c) Crash this project to seven weeks (which is the maximum it can be crashed) at the least cost.

• • •   3.26 The Maser is a new custom-designed sports car. An analysis of the task of building the Maser reveals the following list of relevant activities, their immediate predecessors, and their duration:[5]

a) Draw a network diagram for the project.

b) Mark the critical path and state its length.

c) If the Maser had to be completed two days earlier, would it help to:
  i) Buy preassembled transmissions and drivetrains?
  ii) Install robots to halve engine-building time?
  iii) Speed delivery of special accessories by three days?

d) How might resources be borrowed from activities on the noncritical path to speed activities on the critical path?

Job Letter	Description	Immediate Predecessor(s)	Normal Time (days)
A	Start	—	0
B	Design	A	8
C	Order special accessories	B	0.1
D	Build frame	B	1
E	Build doors	B	1
F	Attach axles, wheels, gas tank	D	1
G	Build body shell	B	2
H	Build transmission and drivetrain	B	3
I	Fit doors to body shell	G, E	1
J	Build engine	B	4
K	Bench-test engine	J	2
L	Assemble chassis	F, H, K	1
M	Road test chassis	L	0.5
N	Paint body	I	2
O	Install wiring	N	1
P	Install interior	N	1.5
Q	Accept delivery of special accessories	C	5
R	Mount body and accessories on chassis	M, O, P, Q	1
S	Road test car	R	0.5
T	Attach exterior trim	S	1
U	Finish	T	0

[5] *Source:* STONER, MANAGEMENT 3RD EDTN., 3rd Ed., ©1986. Reprinted and Electronically reproduced by permission of Pearson Education, Inc., New York, NY..

CASE STUDIES

Fast Creek Lightning: (A)*

Fast Creek is a city in south central Saskatchewan located along the Trans-Canada Highway. Fast Creek has a population of just over 27 000 residents and is a regional hub for the many smaller towns and hundreds of farms in the surrounding area. Fast Creek is a transportation and industrial centre, and has several federal and provincial government offices.

Fast Creek is also a sports centre, and its junior hockey team, the Fast Creek Lightning, have a long history of success in the Central Hockey League but have not won a major trophy in close to 10 years. To reach their long-desired goal of winning the league championship and reaching the Memorial Cup final, the Lightning have hired the legendary Scotty Beauchamp as head coach.

One of Beauchamp's demands on joining the Lightning had been a new arena. With attendance increasing, Lightning executives and city officials began to face the issue head-on. After six months of study, much political arm wrestling, and some serious financial analysis, Keith MacLennan, owner of the Lightning, had reached a decision to expand the capacity at the current arena.

---

* This integrated study runs throughout the text. Other issues facing Fast Creek's hockey expansion include (B) forecasting game attendance (Chapter 4); (C) quality of facilities (Chapter 6); (D) break-even analysis for food services (Supplement 7 MyLab Operations Management); (E) location of the new arena (Chapter 8 MyLab Operations Management); (F) inventory planning of hockey programs (Chapter 12 MyLab Operations Management); and (G) scheduling of site security officers/staff for game days (Chapter 13). Recurring cases are also available in a separate file for instructors using the PCL.

Adding over a thousand seats, including many luxury boxes, would not please everyone. The influential Beauchamp had argued the need for a first-class arena, with state-of-the-art training facilities and a palatial office appropriate for a future hall of fame coach. But the decision was made, and everyone, including the coach, would learn to live with it.

The job now was to get construction going immediately after the 2016 season ended. This would allow exactly 270 days until the 2017 season opening game. The contractor, Hill Construction, signed his contract. Bob Hill looked at the tasks his engineers had outlined and looked MacLennan in the eye. "I guarantee the team will be able to take to the ice on schedule next season," he said with a sense of confidence. "I sure hope so," replied MacLennan. "The contract penalty of $10 000 per day for running late is nothing compared to what Coach Beauchamp will do to you if our opening game with Saskatoon is delayed or cancelled." Hill, sweating slightly, did not need to respond. In hockey-crazy Saskatchewan, Hill Construction would be in trouble if the 270-day target was missed.

Back in his office, Hill again reviewed the data (see Table 3.6) and noted that optimistic time estimates could be used as crash times. He then gathered his foremen. "Folks, if we're not 75% sure we'll finish this stadium in less than 270 days, I want this project crashed! Give me the cost figures for a target date of 250 days—also for 240 days. I want to be early, not just on time!"

Discussion Questions

1. Develop a network drawing for Hill Construction, and determine the critical path. How long is the project expected to take?
2. What is the probability of finishing in 270 days?
3. If it is necessary to crash to 250 or 240 days, how would Hill do so, and at what costs? As noted in the case, assume that optimistic time estimates can be used as crash times.

Table 3.6 Fast Creek Lightning Project

Activity	Description	Predecessor(s)	Optimistic	Most Likely	Pessimistic	Crash Cost/Day
			Time Estimates (days)			
A	Bonding, insurance, tax structuring	—	20	30	40	$1500
B	Foundation, concrete footings for boxes	A	20	65	80	3500
C	Upgrading box seating	A	50	60	100	4000
D	Upgrading walkways, stairwells, elevators	C	30	50	100	1900
E	Interior wiring, lathes	B	25	30	35	9500
F	Inspection approvals	E	0.1	0.1	0.1	0
G	Plumbing	D, F	25	30	35	2500
H	Painting	G	10	20	30	2000
I	Hardware/AC/metal workings	H	20	25	60	2000
J	Tile/carpet/windows	H	8	10	12	6000
K	Inspection	J	0.1	0.1	0.1	0
L	Final detail work/cleanup	I, K	20	25	60	4500

Video Case — Project Management at Arnold Palmer Hospital

The equivalent of a new kindergarten class is born every day at Orlando's Arnold Palmer Hospital. With more than 12 300 births in 2005 in a hospital that was designed in 1989 for a capacity of 6500 births a year, the newborn intensive care unit was stretched to the limit. Moreover, with continuing strong population growth in central Florida, the hospital was often full. It was clear that new facilities were needed. After much analysis, forecasting, and discussion, the management team decided to build a new 273-bed building across the street from the existing hospital. But the facility had to be built in accordance with the hospital's "Guiding Principles" and its uniqueness as a health centre dedicated to the specialized needs of women and infants. Those Guiding Principles are: *Family-centred focus, a healing environment where privacy and dignity are respected, sanctuary of caring that includes warm, serene surroundings with natural lighting, sincere and dedicated staff providing the highest quality care, and patient-centred flow and function.*

The vice-president of business development, Karl Hodges, wanted a hospital that was designed from the inside out by the people who understood the Guiding Principles, who knew most about the current system, and who were going to use the new system, namely, the doctors and nurses. Hodges and his staff spent 13 months discussing expansion needs with this group, as well as with patients and the community, before developing a proposal for the new facility on December 17, 2001. An administrative team created 35 user groups, which held over 1000 planning meetings (lasting from 45 minutes to a whole day). They even created a "Supreme Court" to deal with conflicting views on the multifaceted issues facing the new hospital.

Funding and regulatory issues added substantial complexity to this major expansion, and Hodges was very concerned that the project stays on time and within budget. Tom Hyatt, director of facility development, was given the task of onsite manager of the U.S. $100 million project, in addition to overseeing ongoing renovations, expansions, and other projects. The activities in the multiyear project for the new building at Arnold Palmer are shown in Table 3.7.

Table 3.7 Expansion Planning and Arnold Palmer Hospital Construction Activities and Times[a]

Activity	Scheduled Time	Precedence Activity(ies)
1. Proposal and review	1 month	—
2. Establish master schedule	2 weeks	1
3. Architect selection process	5 weeks	1
4. Survey whole campus and its needs	1 month	1
5. Conceptual architect's plans	6 weeks	3
6. Cost estimating	2 months	2, 4, 5
7. Deliver plans to board for consideration/decision	1 month	6
8. Surveys/regulatory review	6 weeks	6
9. Construction manager selection	9 weeks	6
10. State review of need for more hospital beds ("Certificate of Need")	3.5 months	7, 8
11. Design drawings	4 months	10
12. Construction documents	5 months	9, 11
13. Site preparation/demolish existing building	9 weeks	11
14. Construction start/building pad	2 months	12, 13
15. Relocate utilities	6 weeks	12
16. Deep foundations	2 months	14
17. Building structure in place	9 months	16
18. Exterior skin/roofing	4 months	17
19. Interior buildout	12 months	17
20. Building inspections	5 weeks	15, 19
21. Occupancy	1 month	20

[a] This list of activities is abbreviated for the purposes of this case study. For simplification, assume each week = 0.25 months (i.e., 2 weeks = 0.5 month, 6 weeks = 1.5 months, etc.).

Discussion Questions*

1. Develop the network for planning and construction of the new hospital at Arnold Palmer.
2. What is the critical path, and how long is the project expected to take?
3. Why is the construction of this 11-storey building any more complex than construction of an equivalent office building?
4. What percent of the whole project duration was spent in planning that occurred prior to the proposal and reviews? Prior to the actual building construction? Why?

* You may wish to view the video accompanying this case before addressing these questions.

Video Case — Managing Hard Rock's Rockfest

At the Hard Rock Cafe, like many organizations, project management is a key planning tool. With Hard Rock's constant growth in hotels and cafes, remodelling of existing cafes, scheduling for Hard Rock Live concert and event venues, and planning the annual Rockfest, managers rely on project management techniques and software to maintain schedule and budget performance.

"Without Microsoft Project," says Hard Rock vice-president Chris Tomasso, "there is no way to keep so many people on the same page." Tomasso is in charge of the Rockfest event, which is attended by well over 100 000 enthusiastic fans. The challenge is pulling it off within a tight nine-month planning horizon. As the event approaches, Tomasso devotes greater energy to its activities. For the first three months, Tomasso updates his Microsoft Project charts monthly. Then at the six-month mark, he updates his progress weekly. At the nine-month mark, he checks and corrects his schedule twice a week.

Early in the project management process, Tomasso identifies 10 major tasks (called level 2 activities in a work breakdown structure, or WBS)[†]: talent booking, ticketing, marketing/PR, online promotion, television, show production, travel, sponsorships, operations, and merchandising. Using a WBS, each of these is further divided into a series of subtasks. Table 3.8 identifies 26 of the major activities and subactivities, their immediate predecessors, and time estimates. Tomasso enters all these into the Microsoft Project software.[‡] Tomasso alters the Microsoft Project document and the timeline as the project progresses. "It's okay to change it as long as you keep on track," he states.

[†] The level 1 activity is the Rockfest concert itself.
[‡] There are actually 127 activities used by Tomasso; the list is abbreviated for this case study.

The day of the rock concert itself is not the end of the project planning. "It's nothing but surprises. A band not being able to get to the venue because of traffic jams is a surprise, but an 'anticipated' surprise. We had a helicopter on stand-by ready to fly the band in," says Tomasso.

On completion of Rockfest in July, Tomasso and his team have a three-month reprieve before starting the project planning process again.

Discussion Questions*

1. Identify the critical path and its activities for Rockfest. How long does the project take?

2. Which activities have a slack time of eight weeks or more?
3. Identify five major challenges a project manager faces in events such as this one.
4. Why is a work breakdown structure useful in a project such as this? Take the 26 activities and break them into what you think should be level 2, level 3, and level 4 tasks.

* You may wish to view the video accompanying this case before addressing these questions.

Table 3.8 Some of the Major Activities and Subactivities in the Rockfest Plan

Activity	Description	Predecessor(s)	Time (weeks)
A	Finalize site and building contracts	—	7
B	Select local promoter	A	3
C	Hire production manager	A	3
D	Design promotional website	B	5
E	Set TV deal	D	6
F	Hire director	E	4
G	Plan for TV camera placement	F	2
H	Target headline entertainers	B	4
I	Target support entertainers	H	4
J	Travel accommodations for talent	I	10
K	Set venue capacity	C	2
L	Ticketmaster contract	D, K	3
M	Onsite ticketing	L	8
N	Sound and staging	C	6
O	Passes and stage credentials	G, R	7
P	Travel accommodations for staff	B	20
Q	Hire sponsor coordinator	B	4
R	Finalize sponsors	Q	4
S	Define/place signage for sponsors	R, X	3
T	Hire operations manager	A	4
U	Develop site plan	T	6
V	Hire security director	T	7
W	Set police/fire security plan	V	4
X	Power, plumbing, AC, toilet services	U	8
Y	Secure merchandise deals	B	6
Z	Online merchandise sales	Y	6

▶**Additional Case Study:** Visit **MyLab Operations Management** for this case study:
Shale Oil Company: This oil refinery must shutdown for maintenance of a major piece of equipment.

CHAPTER 3 | RAPID REVIEW

MyLab Operations Management

Main Heading	Review Material	
THE IMPORTANCE OF PROJECT MANAGEMENT (pp. 59–60)	The management of projects involves three phases: 1. **Planning**—This phase includes goal setting, defining the project, and team organization. 2. **Scheduling**—This phase relates people, money, and supplies to specific activities and relates activities to each other. 3. **Controlling**—Here, the firm monitors resources, costs, quality, and budgets. It also revises or changes plans and shifts resources to meet time and cost demands.	**VIDEO 3.1** Project Management at Hard Rock's Rockfest
PROJECT PLANNING (pp. 60–62)	Projects can be defined as a series of related tasks directed towards a major output. • **Project organization**—An organization formed to ensure that programs (projects) receive the proper management and attention. • **Work breakdown structure (WBS)**—A hierarchical description of a project into more and more detailed components.	Problem 3.1
PROJECT SCHEDULING (pp. 62–63)	• **Gantt charts**—Planning charts used to schedule resources and allocate time. Project scheduling serves several purposes: 1. It shows the relationship of each activity to others and to the whole project. 2. It identifies the precedence relationships among activities. 3. It encourages the setting of realistic time and cost estimates for each activity. 4. It helps make better use of people, money, and material resources by identifying critical bottlenecks in the project.	Problem 3.8
PROJECT CONTROLLING (pp. 64–65)	Computerized programs produce a broad variety of PERT/CPM reports, including (1) detailed cost breakdowns for each task, (2) total program labour curves, (3) cost distribution tables, (4) functional cost and hour summaries, (5) raw material and expenditure forecasts, (6) variance reports, (7) time analysis reports, and (8) work status reports.	**VIDEO 3.2** Project Management at Arnold Palmer Hospital
PROJECT MANAGEMENT TECHNIQUES: PERT AND CPM (pp. 65–69)	• **Program evaluation and review technique (PERT)**—A project management technique that employs three time estimates for each activity. • **Critical path method (CPM)**—A project management technique that uses only one time factor per activity. • **Critical path**—The computed *longest* time path(s) through a network. PERT and CPM both follow six basic steps. The activities on the critical path will delay the entire project if they are not completed on time. • **Activity-on-node (AON)**—A network diagram in which nodes designate activities. • **Activity-on-arrow (AOA)**—A network diagram in which arrows designate activities. In an AOA network, the nodes represent the starting and finishing times of an activity and are also called *events*. • **Dummy activity**—An activity having no time that is inserted into a network to maintain the logic of the network. A dummy ending activity can be added to the end of an AON diagram for a project that has multiple ending activities.	Problems: 3.3–3.7, 3.9, 3.10, 3.12, 3.15 Virtual Office Hours for Solved Problems: 3.1, 3.2

MyLab Operations Management

Main Heading	Review Material	
DETERMINING THE PROJECT SCHEDULE (pp. 70–75)	• **Critical path analysis**— A process to find the most effective sequence of activities that helps determine a project schedule. To find the critical path, we calculate two distinct starting and ending times for each activity: • *Earliest start (ES)* = Earliest time at which an activity can start, assuming that all predecessors have been completed. • *Earliest finish (EF)* = Earliest time at which an activity can be finished. • *Latest start (LS)* = Latest time at which an activity can start, without delaying the completion time of the entire project. • *Latest finish (LF)* = Latest time by which an activity has to finish so as not to delay the completion time of the entire project.	Problems: 3.11, 3.14, 3.15, 3.17, 3.20, 3.22, 3.23, 3.26
	• **Forward pass**—A process that identifies all the early start and early finish times. $\quad ES$ = Maximum EF of all immediate predecessor **(3-1)** $\quad EF = ES$ + Activity time **(3-2)** • **Backward pass**—A process that identifies all the late start and late finish times. $\quad LF$ = Minimum LS of all immediate following activities **(3-3)** $\quad LS = LF$ − Activity time **(3-4)** • **Slack time**—Free time for an activity. $\quad$ Slack = $LS - ES$ or Slack = $LF - EF$ **(3-5)** The activities with zero slack are called *critical activities* and are said to be on the critical path. The critical path is a continuous path through the project network that starts at the first activity in the project, terminates at the last activity in the project, and includes only critical activities.	Virtual Office Hours for Solved Problem: 3.3 **ACTIVE MODEL 3.1**
VARIABILITY IN ACTIVITY TIMES (pp. 75–81)	• **Total slack**—Time shared among more than one activity. • **Optimistic time** (*a*)—The "best" activity completion time that could be obtained in a PERT network. • **Pessimistic time** (*b*)—The "worst" activity time that could be expected in a PERT network. • **Most likely time** (*m*)—The most probable time to complete an activity in a PERT network. When using PERT, we often assume that activity time estimates follow the beta distribution. $\quad$ Expected activity time $t = (a + 4m + b)/6$ **(3-6)** $\quad$ Variance of Activity Completion Time $= (b - a)/6^2$ **(3-7)** $\quad \sigma_p^2$ = project variance $= \sum$ (variances of activities on critical path) **(3-8)** $\quad Z$ = (Due date − expected data of completion)$/\sigma_p$ **(3-9)** $\quad$ Due date = Expected completion time + $(Z \times \sigma_p)$ **(3-10)**	Problems: 3.13, 3.14. 3.21, 3.24 Virtual Office Hours for Solved Problems: 3.4, 3.5, 3.6
COST–TIME TRADE-OFFS AND PROJECT CRASHING (pp. 81–83)	• **Crashing**—Shortening activity time in a network to reduce time on the critical path so total completion time is reduced. $\quad$ Crash cost per period $= \dfrac{(\text{Crash cost} - \text{Normal cost})}{(\text{Normal time} - \text{Crash time})}$ **(3-11)**	Problems: 3.16, 3.18, 3.19, 3.25 Virtual Office Hours for Solved Problem: 3.7
A CRITIQUE OF PERT AND CPM (pp. 83–84)	As with every technique for problem solving, PERT and CPM have a number of advantages as well as several limitations.	
USING MICROSOFT PROJECT TO MANAGE PROJECTS (pp. 84–87)	Microsoft Project, the most popular example of specialized project management software, is extremely useful in drawing project networks, identifying the project schedule, and managing project costs and other resources.	

Self-Test

■ **Before taking the self-test,** refer to the learning objectives listed at the beginning of the chapter and the key terms listed at the end of the chapter.

LO1 Which of the following statements regarding Gantt charts is true?
   a) Gantt charts give a timeline and precedence relationships for each activity of a project.
   b) Gantt charts use the four standard spines: Methods, Materials, Manpower, and Machinery.
   c) Gantt charts are visual devices that show the duration of activities in a project.
   d) Gantt charts are expensive.
   e) All of the above are true.

LO2 Which of the following is true about AOA and AON networks?
   a) In AOA, arrows represent activities.
   b) In AON, nodes represent activities.
   c) Activities consume time and resources.
   d) Nodes are also called *events* in AOA.
   e) All of the above.

LO3 Slack time equals:
   a) $ES + t$.
   b) $LS - ES$.
   c) zero.
   d) $EF - ES$.

LO4 The critical path of a network is the:
   a) shortest time path through the network.
   b) path with the fewest activities.
   c) path with the most activities.
   d) longest time path through the network.

LO5 PERT analysis computes the variance of the total project completion time as:
   a) the sum of the variances of all activities in the project.
   b) the sum of the variances of all activities on the critical path.
   c) the sum of the variances of all activities not on the critical path.
   d) the variance of the final activity of the project.

LO6 The crash cost per period:
   a) is the difference in costs divided by the difference in times (crash and normal).
   b) is considered to be linear in the range between normal and crash.
   c) needs to be determined so that the smallest cost values on the critical path can be considered for time reduction first.
   d) all of the above.

Answers: LO1. c; LO2. e; LO3. b; LO4. d; LO5. b; LO6. d.

MyLab Operations Management

Most of these questions can be found in MyLab Operations Management. Visit MyLab Operations Management to access cases, videos, downloadable software, and much more. MyLab Operations Management Management also features a personalized Study Plan that helps you identify which chapter concepts you've mastered and guides you towards study tools for additional practice.

pedrosek/Shutterstock

4

Forecasting

Forecasting Provides a Competitive Advantage for Disney

When it comes to the world's most respected brands, Walt Disney Parks & Resorts is a visible leader. Although the monarch of this magic kingdom is no man but a mouse—Mickey Mouse—it is CEO, Robert Iger, who daily manages the entertainment giant.

Disney's global portfolio includes Shanghai Disney (2016), Hong Kong Disneyland (2005), Disneyland Paris (1992), and Tokyo Disneyland (1983). But it is the Walt Disney World Resort (in Florida) and Disneyland Resort (in California) that drive profits in this U.S. $50 billion corporation, which is ranked in the top 100 in both the *Fortune* 500 and the *Financial Times* Global 500.

Revenues at Disney are all about people—how many visit the parks and how they spend money while there. When Iger receives a daily report from his six theme parks near Orlando, the report contains only two numbers: the *forecast* of yesterday's attendance at the parks (Magic Kingdom, Epcot, Disney's Animal Kingdom, Disney's Hollywood Studios, Typhoon Lagoon, and Blizzard Beach) and the *actual* attendance. An error close to zero is expected. Iger takes his forecasts very seriously.

< Global Company Profile Walt Disney Parks & Resorts

103

The forecasting team at Walt Disney World Resort doesn't just do a daily prediction, however, and Iger is not its only customer. The team also provides daily, weekly, monthly, annual, and five-year forecasts to the labour management, maintenance, operations, finance, and park scheduling departments. Forecasters use judgmental models, econometric models, moving-average models, and regression analysis.

With 20% of Walt Disney World Resort's customers coming from outside the United States, its economic model includes variables such as gross domestic product (GDP), cross-exchange rates, and arrivals into the United States. Disney also uses 35 analysts and 70 field people to survey 1 million people each year. The surveys—administered to guests at the parks and its 20 hotels, to employees, and to travel industry professionals—examine future travel plans and experiences at the parks. This helps forecast not only the attendance but behaviour at each ride (e.g., how long people will wait, how many times they will ride). Inputs to the monthly forecasting model include airline specials, speeches by the chair of the Federal Reserve, and Wall Street trends. Disney even monitors 3000 school districts inside and outside the United States for holiday/vacation schedules. With this approach, Disney's five-year attendance forecast yields just a 5% error on average. Its annual forecasts have a 0% to 3% error.

Attendance forecasts for the parks drive a whole slew of management decisions. For example, capacity on any day can be increased by opening at 8:00 a.m. instead of the usual 9:00 a.m., by opening more shows or rides, by adding more food/beverage carts (9 million hamburgers and 50 million Cokes are sold per year!), and by bringing in more employees (called

Mickey and Minnie Mouse, and other Disney characters, with Cinderella's Castle in the background, provide the public image of Disney to the world. Forecasts drive the work schedules of 58 000 cast members working at Walt Disney World Resort near Orlando.

Kelly/Mooney Photography/Corbis Documentary/Getty Images

"cast members"). Cast members are scheduled in 15-minute intervals throughout the parks for flexibility. Demand can be managed by limiting the number of guests admitted to the parks, with the "FAST PASS" reservation system, and by shifting crowds from rides to more street parades.

At Disney, forecasting is a key driver in the company's success and competitive advantage.

STUDENT TIP

An increasingly complex world economy makes forecasting challenging.

What Is Forecasting?

Every day, managers like those at Disney make decisions without knowing what will happen in the future. They order inventory without knowing what sales will be, purchase new equipment despite uncertainty about demand for products, and make investments without knowing what profits will be. Managers are always trying to make better estimates of what will happen in the future in the face of uncertainty. Making good estimates is the main purpose of forecasting.

In this chapter, we examine different types of forecasts and present a variety of forecasting models. Our purpose is to show that there are many ways for managers to forecast. We also provide an overview of business sales forecasting and describe how to prepare, monitor, and judge the accuracy of a forecast. Good forecasts are an *essential* part of efficient service and manufacturing operations.

Forecasting is the art and science of predicting future events. Forecasting may involve taking historical data and projecting them into the future with some sort of mathematical model. It may be a subjective or intuitive prediction. Or it may involve a combination of these—that is, a mathematical model adjusted by a manager's good judgment.

Forecasting
The art and science of predicting future events.

As we introduce different forecasting techniques in this chapter, you will see that there is seldom one superior method. What works best in one firm under one set of conditions may be a complete disaster in another organization, or even in a different department of the same firm. In addition, you will see that there are limits as to what can be expected from forecasts. They are seldom, if ever, perfect. They are also costly and time-consuming to prepare and monitor.

Few businesses, however, can afford to avoid the process of forecasting by just waiting to see what happens and then taking their chances. Effective planning in both the short run and long run depends on a forecast of demand for the company's products.

FORECASTING TIME HORIZONS

A forecast is usually classified by the *future time horizon* that it covers. Time horizons fall into three categories:

LO1 Understand the three time horizons and which models apply for each

1. *Short-range forecast:* This forecast has a time span of up to one year but is generally less than three months. It is used for planning purchasing, job scheduling, workforce levels, job assignments, and production levels.
2. *Medium-range forecast:* A medium-range, or intermediate, forecast generally spans from three months to three years. It is useful in sales planning, production planning and budgeting, cash budgeting, and analysis of various operating plans.
3. *Long-range forecast:* Generally three years or more in time span, long-range forecasts are used in planning for new products, capital expenditures, facility location or expansion, and research and development.

Medium- and long-range forecasts are distinguished from short-range forecasts by three features:

1. First, intermediate and long-run forecasts *deal with more comprehensive issues* and support management decisions regarding planning and products, plants, and processes. Implementing some facility decisions, such as GM's decision to open a new Brazilian manufacturing plant, can take five to eight years from inception to completion.
2. Second, short-term forecasting usually *employs different methodologies* than longer-term forecasting. Mathematical techniques, such as moving averages, exponential smoothing, and trend extrapolation (all of which we shall examine shortly), are common to short-run projections. Broader, *less* quantitative methods are useful in predicting such issues as whether a new product, like the optical disk recorder, should be introduced into a company's product line.
3. Finally, as you would expect, short-range forecasts *tend to be more accurate* than longer-range forecasts. Factors that influence demand change every day. Thus, as the time horizon lengthens, it is likely that forecast accuracy will diminish. It almost goes without saying, then, that sales forecasts must be updated regularly to maintain their value and integrity. After each sales period, forecasts should be reviewed and revised.

THE INFLUENCE OF PRODUCT LIFE CYCLE

Another factor to consider when developing sales forecasts, especially longer ones, is product life cycle. Products, and even services, do not sell at a constant level throughout their lives. Most successful products pass through four stages: (1) introduction, (2) growth, (3) maturity, and (4) decline.

Products in the first two stages of the life cycle (such as virtual reality and the Boeing 787 Dreamliner) need longer forecasts than those in the maturity and decline stages (such as large SUVs and skateboards). Forecasts that reflect life cycle are useful in projecting different staffing levels, inventory levels, and factory capacity as the product passes from the first to the last stage. The challenge of introducing new products is treated in more detail in Chapter 5.

TYPES OF FORECASTS

Organizations use three major types of forecasts in planning future operations:

1. **Economic forecasts** address the business cycle by predicting inflation rates, money supplies, housing starts, and other planning indicators.
2. **Technological forecasts** are concerned with rates of technological progress, which can result in the birth of exciting new products, requiring new plants and equipment.
3. **Demand forecasts** are projections of demand for a company's products or services. These forecasts, also called *sales forecasts*, drive a company's production, capacity, and scheduling systems and serve as inputs to financial, marketing, and personnel planning.

Economic and technological forecasting are specialized techniques that may fall outside the role of the operations manager. The emphasis in this book will therefore be on demand forecasting.

The Strategic Importance of Forecasting

Good forecasts are of critical importance in all aspects of a business: *The forecast is the only estimate of demand until actual demand becomes known.* Forecasts of demand therefore drive decisions in many areas. Let's look at the impact of product demand forecast on three activities:

1. Supply chain management.
2. Human resources.
3. Capacity.

SUPPLY CHAIN MANAGEMENT

Good supplier relations and the ensuing advantages in product innovation, cost, and speed to market depend on accurate forecasts. Here are just three examples:

- Apple has built an effective global system where it controls nearly every piece of the supply chain, from product design to retail store. With rapid communication and accurate data shared up and down the supply chain, innovation is enhanced, inventory costs are reduced, and speed to market is improved. Once a product goes on sale, Apple tracks demand by the hour for each store and adjusts production forecasts daily. At Apple, forecasts for its supply chain are a strategic weapon.
- Toyota develops sophisticated car forecasts with input from a variety of sources, including dealers. But forecasting the demand for accessories such as navigation systems, custom wheels, spoilers, and so on is particularly difficult. And there are over 1000 items that vary by model and colour. As a result, Toyota not only reviews reams of data with regard to vehicles that have been built and wholesaled but also looks in detail at vehicle forecasts before it makes judgments about the future accessory demand. When this is done correctly, the result is an efficient supply chain and satisfied customers.
- Walmart collaborates with suppliers such as Sara Lee and Procter & Gamble to make sure the right item is available at the right time in the right place and at the right price. For instance, in hurricane season, Walmart's ability to analyze 700 million store–item combinations means it can forecast that not only flashlights but also Pop-Tarts and beer sell at seven times the normal demand rate. These forecasting systems are known as *collaborative planning, forecasting, and replenishment* (CPFR). They combine the intelligence of multiple supply chain partners. The goal of CPFR is to create significantly more accurate information that can power the supply chain to greater sales and profits.

HUMAN RESOURCES

Hiring, training, and laying off workers all depend on anticipated demand. If the human resources department must hire additional workers without warning, the amount of training declines and the quality of the workforce suffers. A large chemical firm almost lost its biggest customer when a quick expansion to around-the-clock shifts led to a total breakdown in quality control on the second and third shifts.

CAPACITY

When capacity is inadequate, the resulting shortages can lead to loss of customers and market share. This is exactly what happened to Nabisco when it underestimated the huge demand for its new low-fat Snackwell's Devil's Food Cookies. Even with production lines working overtime, Nabisco could not keep up with demand, and it lost customers. Amazon made the same error with its Kindle. On the other hand, when excess capacity exists, costs can skyrocket.

Seven Steps in the Forecasting System

Forecasting follows seven basic steps. We use Disney World, the focus of this chapter's *Global Company Profile*, as an example of each step:

1. *Determine the use of the forecast*: Disney uses park attendance forecasts to drive decisions about staffing, opening times, ride availability, and food supplies.
2. *Select the items to be forecasted:* For Disney World, there are six main parks. A forecast of daily attendance at each is the main number that determines labour, maintenance, and scheduling.
3. *Determine the time horizon of the forecast:* Is it for the short, medium, or long term? Disney develops daily, weekly, monthly, annual, and five-year forecasts.
4. *Select the forecasting model(s):* Disney uses a variety of statistical models that we shall discuss, including moving averages, econometrics, and regression analysis. It also employs judgmental, or nonquantitative, models.
5. *Gather the data needed to make the forecast:* Disney's forecasting team employs 35 analysts and 70 field personnel to survey 1 million people/businesses every year. Disney also uses a firm called Global Insights for travel industry forecasts and gathers data on exchange rates, arrivals into the United States, airline specials, Wall Street trends, and school vacation schedules.
6. *Make the forecast.*
7. *Validate and implement the results:* At Disney, forecasts are reviewed daily at the highest levels to make sure that the model, assumptions, and data are valid. Error measures are applied; then the forecasts are used to schedule personnel down to 15-minute intervals.

These seven steps present a systematic way of initiating, designing, and implementing a forecasting system. When the system is to be used to generate forecasts regularly over time, data must be routinely collected. Then actual computations are usually made by computer.

Regardless of the system that firms like Disney use, each company faces several realities:

- Forecasts are seldom perfect. This means that outside factors that we cannot predict or control often impact the forecast. Companies need to allow for this reality.
- Most forecasting techniques assume that there is some underlying stability in the system. Consequently, some firms automate their predictions using computerized forecasting software, and then closely monitor only the product items whose demand is erratic.
- Both product family and aggregated forecasts are more accurate than individual product forecasts. Disney, for example, aggregates daily attendance forecasts by park. This approach helps balance the over- and underpredictions of each of the six attractions.

Forecasting Approaches

STUDENT TIP

Forecasting is part science and part art.

There are two general approaches to forecasting, just as there are two ways to tackle all decision modelling. One is a quantitative analysis; the other is a qualitative approach. **Quantitative forecasts** use a variety of mathematical models that rely on historical data and/or associative variables to forecast demand. Subjective or **qualitative forecasts** incorporate such factors as the decision maker's intuition, emotions, personal experiences, and value system in reaching a forecast. Some firms use one approach and some use the other. In practice, a combination of the two is usually most effective.

Quantitative forecasts
Forecasts that employ mathematical modelling to forecast demand.

Qualitative forecasts
Forecasts that incorporate such factors as the decision maker's intuition, emotions, personal experiences, and value system.

OVERVIEW OF QUALITATIVE METHODS

In this section, we consider four different *qualitative* forecasting techniques:

1. **Jury of executive opinion**: Under this method, the opinions of a group of high-level experts or managers, often in combination with statistical models, are pooled to arrive at a group estimate of demand. Bristol-Myers Squibb Company, for example, uses 220 well-known research scientists as its jury of executive opinion to get a grasp on future trends in the world of medical research.
2. **Delphi method**: There are three different types of participants in the Delphi method: decision makers, staff personnel, and respondents. Decision makers usually consist of a group

LO2 Explain when to use each of the four qualitative models

Jury of executive opinion
A forecasting technique that uses the opinion of a small group of high-level managers to form a group estimate of demand.

Delphi method

A forecasting technique using a group process that allows experts to make forecasts.

Sales force composite

A forecasting technique based on salespersons' estimates of expected sales.

Consumer market survey

A forecasting method that solicits input from customers or potential customers regarding future purchasing plans.

of five to 10 experts who will be making the actual forecast. Staff personnel assist decision makers by preparing, distributing, collecting, and summarizing a series of questionnaires and survey results. The respondents are a group of people, often located in different places, whose judgments are valued. This group provides inputs to the decision makers before the forecast is made.

3. **Sales force composite**: In this approach, each salesperson estimates what sales will be in his or her region. These forecasts are then reviewed to ensure that they are realistic. Then they are combined at the district and national levels to reach an overall forecast. A variation of this approach occurs at Lexus, where every quarter Lexus dealers have a "make meeting". At this meeting, they talk about what is selling, in what colours, and with what options, so the factory knows what to build.

4. **Consumer market survey**: This method solicits input from customers or potential customers regarding future purchasing plans. It can help not only in preparing a forecast but also in improving product design and planning for new products. The consumer market survey and sales force composite methods can, however, suffer from overly optimistic forecasts that arise from customer input. The 2001 crash of the telecommunication industry was the result of overexpansion to meet "explosive customer demand". Where did these data come from? Oplink Communications, a Nortel Networks supplier, says its "company forecasts over the last few years were based mainly on informal conversations with customers."[1]

OVERVIEW OF QUANTITATIVE METHODS

Five quantitative forecasting methods, all of which use historical data, are described in this chapter. They fall into two categories:

1. Naive approach
2. Moving averages
3. Exponential smoothing   **Time-series models**
4. Trend projection
5. Linear regression   **Associative model**

Time series

A forecasting technique that uses a series of past data points to make a forecast.

TIME-SERIES MODELS Time-series models predict on the assumption that the future is a function of the past. In other words, they look at what has happened over a period of time and use a series of past data to make a forecast. If we are predicting sales of lawn mowers, we use the past sales for lawn mowers to make the forecasts.

ASSOCIATIVE MODELS Associative models, such as linear regression, incorporate the variables or factors that might influence the quantity being forecast. For example, an associative model for lawn mower sales might use factors such as new housing starts, advertising budget, and competitors' prices.

Time-Series Forecasting

A time series is based on a sequence of evenly spaced (weekly, monthly, quarterly, and so on) data points. Examples include weekly sales of Sher-Wood hockey sticks, quarterly earnings reports of Bell Canada stock, daily shipments of Labatt's beer, and annual consumer price indices. Forecasting time-series data implies that future values are predicted *only* from past values and that other variables, no matter how potentially valuable, may be ignored.

DECOMPOSITION OF A TIME SERIES

Analyzing time series means breaking down past data into components and then projecting them forward. A time series has four components:

1. *Trend* is the gradual upward or downward movement of the data over time. Changes in income, population, age distribution, or cultural views may account for movement in trend.

---

[1] "Lousy Sales Forecasts Helped Fuel the Telecom Mess," *The Wall Street Journal* (July 9, 2001): B1–B4.

2. *Seasonality* is a data pattern that repeats itself after a period of days, weeks, months, or quarters. There are six common seasonality patterns:

Period of Pattern	"Season" Length	Number of "Seasons" in Pattern
Week	Day	7
Month	Week	$4-4\frac{1}{2}$
Month	Day	28–31
Year	Quarter	4
Year	Month	12
Year	Week	52

Restaurants and barber shops, for example, experience weekly seasons, with Saturday being the peak of business. Beer distributors forecast yearly patterns, with monthly seasons. Three "seasons"—May, July, and September—each contain a big beer-drinking holiday.

3. *Cycles* are patterns in the data that occur every several years. They are usually tied into the business cycle and are of major importance in short-term business analysis and planning. Predicting business cycles is difficult because they may be affected by political events or by international turmoil.

4. *Random variations* are "blips" in the data caused by chance and unusual situations. They follow no discernible pattern, so they cannot be predicted.

Figure 4.1 illustrates a demand over a four-year period. It shows the average, trend, seasonal components, and random variations around the demand curve. The average demand is the sum of the demand for each period divided by the number of data periods.

NAIVE APPROACH

The simplest way to forecast is to assume that demand in the next period will be equal to demand in the most recent period. In other words, if sales of a product—say, Nokia cell phones—were 68 units in January, we can forecast that February's sales will also be 68 phones. Does this make any sense? It turns out that for some product lines, this **naive approach** is the most cost-effective and efficient objective forecasting model. At least it provides a starting point against which more sophisticated models that follow can be compared.

Naive approach

A forecasting technique that assumes that demand in the next period is equal to demand in the most recent period.

MOVING AVERAGES

Moving-averages forecasts use a number of historical actual data values to generate a forecast. Moving averages are useful *if we can assume that market demands will stay fairly steady over time*. A four-month moving average is found by simply summing the demand during the past four months and dividing by four. With each passing month, the most recent month's data are added to the sum of the previous three months' data, and the earliest month is dropped. This practice tends to smooth out short-term irregularities in the data series.

Moving averages

A forecasting method that uses an average of the *n* most recent periods of data to forecast the next period.

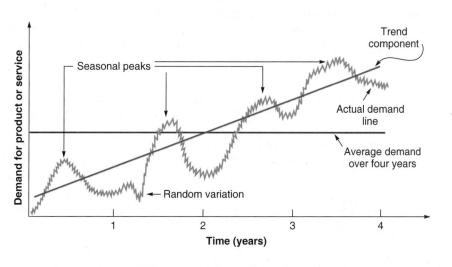

FIGURE 4.1

Demand Charted Over Four Years with the Growth Trend and Seasonality Indicated

Mathematically, the simple moving average (which serves as an estimate of the next period's demand) is expressed as

$$\text{Moving average} = \frac{\Sigma \text{ demand in previous } n \text{ periods}}{n} \qquad (4\text{-}1)$$

where n is the number of periods in the moving average—for example, four, five, or six months, respectively, for a four-, five-, or six-period moving average.

Example 1 shows how moving averages are calculated.

EXAMPLE 1

Determining the Moving Average

Donna's Garden Supply wants a three-month moving-average forecast, including a forecast for next January, for shed sales.

APPROACH ▶ Storage shed sales are shown in the middle column of the table. A three-month moving average appears on the right.

Month	Actual Shed Sales	Three-Month Moving Average
January	10	
February	12	
March	13	
April	16	$(10 + 12 + 13)/3 = 11\frac{2}{3}$
May	19	$(12 + 13 + 16)/3 = 13\frac{2}{3}$
June	23	$(13 + 16 + 19)/3 = 16$
July	26	$(16 + 19 + 23)/3 = 19\frac{1}{3}$
August	30	$(19 + 23 + 26)/3 = 22\frac{2}{3}$
September	28	$(23 + 26 + 30)/3 = 26\frac{1}{3}$
October	18	$(26 + 30 + 28)/3 = 28$
November	16	$(30 + 28 + 18)/3 = 25\frac{1}{3}$
December	14	$(28 + 18 + 16)/3 = 20\frac{2}{3}$

SOLUTION ▶ The forecast for December is $20\frac{2}{3}$. To project the demand for sheds in the coming January, we sum the October, November, and December sales and divide by three: January forecast $=$ $(18 + 16 + 14)/3 = 16$.

INSIGHT ▶ Management now has a forecast that averages sales for the last three months. It is easy to use and understand.

LEARNING EXERCISE ▶ If actual sales in December were 18 (rather than 14), what is the new January forecast? [Answer: $17\frac{1}{3}$]

RELATED PROBLEMS ▶ 4.1a, 4.2b, 4.5a, 4.6, 4.8ab, 4.10a, 4.13b, 4.15, 4.47

EXCEL OM Data File **Ch04Ex1.xlsx** can be found at **MyLab Operations Management.**

ACTIVE MODEL 4.1 This example is further illustrated in Active Model 4.1 at **MyLab Operations Management.**

LO3 Apply the naive, moving-average, exponential smoothing, and trend methods

When a detectable trend or pattern is present, *weights* can be used to place more emphasis on recent values. This practice makes forecasting techniques more responsive to changes because more recent periods may be more heavily weighted. Choice of weights is somewhat arbitrary because there is no set formula to determine them. Therefore, deciding which weights to use requires some experience. For example, if the latest month or period is weighted too heavily, the forecast may reflect a large unusual change in the demand or sales pattern too quickly.

A weighted moving average may be expressed mathematically as:

$$\text{Weighted moving average} = \frac{\Sigma \text{ (Weight for period } n)(\text{Demand in period } n)}{\Sigma \text{Weights}} \qquad (4\text{-}2)$$

Example 2 shows how to calculate a weighted moving average.

EXAMPLE 2

Determining the
Weighted Moving
Average

Donna's Garden Supply (see Example 1) wants to forecast storage shed sales by weighting the past three months, with more weight given to recent data to make them more significant.

APPROACH ▶ Assign more weight to recent data, as follows:

Weights Applied	Period
3	Last month
2	2 months ago
1	3 months ago
$\overline{6}$	Sum of weights

Forecast for this month =

$$\frac{3 \times \text{Sales last mo.} + 2 \times \text{Sales 2 mos. ago} + 1 \times \text{Sales 3 mos. ago}}{\text{Sum of the weights}}$$

SOLUTION ▶ The results of this weighted average forecast are as follows:

Month	Actual Shed Sales	Three-Month Weighted Moving Average
January	10	
February	12	
March	13	
April	16	$[(3 \times 13) + (2 \times 12) + (10)]/6 = 12\frac{1}{6}$
May	19	$[(3 \times 16) + (2 \times 13) + (12)]/6 = 14\frac{1}{3}$
June	23	$[(3 \times 19) + (2 \times 16) + (13)]/6 = 17$
July	26	$[(3 \times 23) + (2 \times 19) + (16)]/6 = 20\frac{1}{2}$
August	30	$[(3 \times 26) + (2 \times 23) + (19)]/6 = 23\frac{5}{6}$
September	28	$[(3 \times 30) + (2 \times 26) + (23)]/6 = 27\frac{1}{2}$
October	18	$[(3 \times 28) + (2 \times 30) + (26)]/6 = 28\frac{1}{3}$
November	16	$[(3 \times 18) + (2 \times 28) + (30)]/6 = 23\frac{1}{3}$
December	14	$[(3 \times 16) + (2 \times 18) + (28)]/6 = 18\frac{2}{3}$

INSIGHT ▶ In this particular forecasting situation, you can see that more heavily weighting the latest month provides a much more accurate projection.

LEARNING EXERCISE ▶ If the assigned weights were 0.50, 0.33, and 0.17 (instead of 3, 2, and 1), what is the forecast for January's weighted moving average? Why? [Answer: There is no change.] These are the same *relative* weights. Note that the sum of the weights is 1 now, so there is no need for a denominator. When the weights sum to 1, calculations tend to be simpler.

RELATED PROBLEMS ▶ 4.1b, 4.2c, 4.5c, 4.6, 4.7, 4.10b

EXCEL OM Data file **Ch04Ex2.xlsx** can be found at **MyLab Operations Management.**

Both simple and weighted moving averages are effective in smoothing out sudden fluctuations in the demand pattern to provide stable estimates. Moving averages do, however, present three problems:

1. Increasing the size of *n* (the number of periods averaged) does smooth out fluctuations better, but it makes the method less sensitive to *real* changes in the data.
2. Moving averages cannot pick up trends very well. Because they are averages, they will always stay within past levels and will not predict changes to either higher or lower levels. That is, they *lag* the actual values.
3. Moving averages require extensive records of past data.

FIGURE 4.2

Actual Demand vs. Moving-Average and Weighted–Moving-Average Methods for Donna's Garden Supply

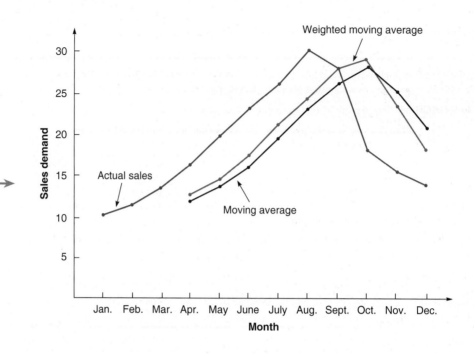

Figure 4.2, a plot of the data in Examples 1 and 2, illustrates the lag effect of the moving-average models. Note that both the moving-average and weighted moving average lines lag the actual demand. The weighted moving average, however, usually reacts more quickly to demand changes. Even in periods of downturn (see November and December), it more closely tracks the demand.

EXPONENTIAL SMOOTHING

Exponential smoothing

A weighted moving average forecasting technique in which data points are weighted by an exponential function.

Exponential smoothing is a sophisticated weighted moving average forecasting method that is still fairly easy to use. It involves very *little* recordkeeping of past data. The basic exponential smoothing formula can be shown as follows:

$$\text{New forecast} = \text{Last period's forecast}$$
$$+ \alpha (\text{Last period's actual demand} - \text{Last period's forecast}) \qquad \textbf{(4-3)}$$

Smoothing constant

The weighting factor, α, used in an exponential smoothing forecast, a number between 0 and 1.

where α is a weight, or **smoothing constant**, chosen by the forecaster, that has a value between 0 and 1. Equation (4-3) can also be written mathematically as:

$$F_t = F_{t-1} + \alpha(A_{t-1} - F_{t-1}) \qquad \textbf{(4-4)}$$

where
F_t = new forecast
F_{t-1} = previous period's forecast
α = smoothing (or weighting) constant ($0 \le \alpha \le 1$)
A_{t-1} = previous period's actual demand

The concept is not complex. The latest estimate of demand is equal to the old estimate adjusted by a fraction of the difference between the last period's actual demand and the old estimate. Example 3 shows how to use exponential smoothing to derive a forecast.

EXAMPLE 3

Determining a Forecast Via Exponential Smoothing

In January, a car dealer predicted February demand for 142 Ford Mustangs. Actual February demand was 153 autos. Using a smoothing constant chosen by management of $\alpha = 0.20$, the dealer wants to forecast March demand using the exponential smoothing model.

APPROACH ▶ The exponential smoothing model in Equations (4-3) and (4-4) can be applied.

SOLUTION ▶ Substituting the sample data into the formula, we obtain:

New forecast (for March demand) = 142 + 0.2(153 − 142) = 142 + 2.2

= 144.2

Thus, the March demand forecast for Ford Mustangs is rounded to 144.

INSIGHT ▶ Using just two pieces of data, the forecast and the actual demand, plus a smoothing constant, we developed a forecast of 144 Ford Mustangs for March.

LEARNING EXERCISE ▶ If the smoothing constant is changed to 0.30, what is the new forecast? [Answer: 145.3]

RELATED PROBLEMS ▶ 4.1c, 4.3, 4.4, 4.5d, 4.6, 4.9d 4.11, 4.12, 4.13a, 4.17, 4.18, 4.37, 4.43, 4.47, 4.49

The *smoothing constant*, α, is generally in the range from 0.05 to 0.50 for business applications. It can be changed to give more weight to recent data (when α is high) or more weight to past data (when α is low). When α reaches the extreme of 1.0, then in Equation (4-4), $F_t = 1.0A_{t-1}$. All the older values drop out, and the forecast becomes identical to the naive model mentioned earlier in this chapter. That is, the forecast for the next period is just the same as this period's demand.

The following table helps illustrate this concept. For example, when $\alpha = 0.5$, we can see that the new forecast is based almost entirely on demand in the last three or four periods. When $\alpha = 0.1$, the forecast places little weight on recent demand and takes many periods (about 19) of historical values into account.

		Weight Assigned to			
Smoothing Constant	Most Recent Period (α)	2nd Most Recent Period $\alpha(1-\alpha)$	3rd Most Recent Period $\alpha(1-\alpha)^2$	4th Most Recent Period $\alpha(1-\alpha)^3$	5th Most Recent Period $\alpha(1-\alpha)^4$
$\alpha = 0.1$	0.1	0.09	0.081	0.073	0.066
$\alpha = 0.5$	0.5	0.25	0.125	0.063	0.031

SELECTING THE SMOOTHING CONSTANT The exponential smoothing approach is easy to use, and it has been successfully applied in virtually every type of business. However, the appropriate value of the smoothing constant, α, can make the difference between an accurate forecast and an inaccurate forecast. High values of α are chosen when the underlying average is likely to change. Low values of α are used when the underlying average is fairly stable. In picking a value for the smoothing constant, the objective is to obtain the most accurate forecast.

STUDENT TIP
The forecast error tells us how well the model performed against itself using past data.

MEASURING FORECAST ERROR

The overall accuracy of any forecasting model—moving average, exponential smoothing, or other—can be determined by comparing the forecasted values with the actual or observed values. If F_t denotes the forecast in period t, and A_t denotes the actual demand in period t, the *forecast error* (or deviation) is defined as:

$$\text{Forecast error} = \text{Actual demand} - \text{Forecast value} = A_t - F_t$$

LO4 Compute three measures of forecast accuracy

Several measures are used in practice to calculate the overall forecast error. These measures can be used to compare different forecasting models, as well as to monitor forecasts to ensure they are performing well. Three of the most popular measures are mean absolute deviation (MAD), mean squared error (MSE), and mean absolute percent error (MAPE). We now describe and give an example of each.

MEAN ABSOLUTE DEVIATION The first measure of the overall forecast error for a model is the **mean absolute deviation (MAD)**. This value is computed by taking the sum of the absolute values of the individual forecast errors (deviations) and dividing by the number of periods of data (n):

Mean absolute deviation (MAD)
A measure of the overall forecast error for a model.

$$\text{MAD} = \frac{\Sigma |\text{Actual} - \text{Forecast}|}{n} \qquad \text{(4-5)}$$

Example 4 applies MAD, as a measure of overall forecast error, by testing two values of α.

EXAMPLE 4
Determining the Mean Absolute Deviation (MAD)

During the past eight quarters, the Port of Halifax has unloaded large quantities of grain from ships. The port's operations manager wants to test the use of exponential smoothing to see how well the technique works in predicting tonnage unloaded. He guesses that the forecast of grain unloaded in the first quarter was 175 tonnes. Two values of α are to be examined: $\alpha = 0.10$ and $\alpha = 0.50$.

APPROACH ▶ Compare the actual data with the data we forecast (using each of the two α-values) and then find the absolute deviation and MADs.

SOLUTION ▶ The following table shows the *detailed* calculations for $\alpha = 0.10$ only:

Quarter	Actual Tonnage Unloaded	Forecast with $\alpha = 0.10$	Forecast with $\alpha = 0.50$
1	180	175	175
2	168	175.50 = 175.00 + 0.10(180 − 175)	177.50
3	159	174.75 = 175.50 + 0.10(168 − 175.50)	172.75
4	175	173.18 = 174.75 + 0.10(159 − 174.75)	165.88
5	190	173.36 = 173.18 + 0.10(175 − 173.18)	170.44
6	205	175.02 = 173.36 + 0.10(190 − 173.36)	180.22
7	180	178.02 = 175.02 + 0.10(205 − 175.02)	192.61
8	182	178.22 = 178.02 + 0.10(180 − 178.02)	186.30
9	?	178.59 = 178.22 + 0.10(182 − 178.22)	184.15

To evaluate the accuracy of each smoothing constant, we can compute forecast errors in terms of absolute deviations and MADs:

Quarter	Actual Tonnage Unloaded	Forecast with $\alpha = 0.10$	Absolute Deviation for $\alpha = 0.10$	Forecast with $\alpha = 0.50$	Absolute Deviation for $\alpha = 0.50$
1	180	175	5.00	175	5.00
2	168	175.50	7.50	177.50	9.50
3	159	174.75	15.75	172.75	13.75
4	175	173.18	1.82	165.88	9.12
5	190	173.36	16.64	170.44	19.56
6	205	175.02	29.98	180.22	24.78
7	180	178.02	1.98	192.61	12.61
8	182	178.22	3.78	186.30	4.30
		Sum of absolute deviations:	82.45		98.62
	$\text{MAD} = \dfrac{\Sigma \lvert \text{Deviations} \rvert}{n}$		10.31		12.33

INSIGHT ▶ On the basis of this comparison of the two MADs, a smoothing constant of $\alpha = 0.10$ is preferred to $\alpha = 0.50$ because its MAD is smaller.

LEARNING EXERCISE ▶ If the smoothing constant is changed from $\alpha = 0.10$ to $\alpha = 0.20$, what is the new MAD? [Answer: 10.21.]

RELATED PROBLEMS ▶ 4.5b, 4.8c, 4.9c, 4.14, 4.23, 4.37a

EXCEL OM Data File **Ch04Ex4a.xlsx** and **Ch04Ex4b.xlsx** can be found at **MyLab Operations Management**.

ACTIVE MODEL 4.2 This example is further illustrated in Active Model 4.2 at **MyLab Operations Management**.

Most computerized forecasting software includes a feature that automatically finds the smoothing constant with the lowest forecast error. Some software modifies the α-value if errors become larger than acceptable.

MEAN SQUARED ERROR The **mean squared error (MSE)** is a second way of measuring overall forecast error. MSE is the average of the squared differences between the forecasted and observed values. Its formula is:

Mean squared error (MSE)
The average of the squared differences between the forecasted and observed values.

$$\text{MSE} = \frac{\Sigma(\text{Forecast errors})^2}{n} \qquad \textbf{(4-6)}$$

Example 5 finds the MSE for the Port of Halifax introduced in Example 4.

The operations manager for the Port of Halifax now wants to compute MSE for $\alpha = 0.10$.

APPROACH ▶ Use the same forecast data for $\alpha = 0.10$ from Example 4, then compute the MSE using Equation (4-6).

SOLUTION ▶

Quarter	Actual Tonnage Unloaded	Forecast for $\alpha = 0.10$	(Error)^2
1	180	175	$5^2 = 25$
2	168	175.50	$(-7.5)^2 = 56.25$
3	159	174.75	$(-15.75)^2 = 248.06$
4	175	173.18	$(1.82)^2 = 3.33$
5	190	173.36	$(16.64)^2 = 276.89$
6	205	175.02	$(29.98)^2 = 898.70$
7	180	178.02	$(1.98)^2 = 3.92$
8	182	178.22	$(3.78)^2 = 14.31$
			Sum of errors squared $= 1526.46$

$$\text{MSE} = \frac{\Sigma(\text{Forecast errors})^2}{n} = 1526.46/8 = 190.8$$

INSIGHT ▶ Is this MSE $= 190.8$ good or bad? It all depends on the MSEs for other forecasting approaches. A low MSE is better because we want to minimize MSE. MSE exaggerates errors because it squares them.

LEARNING EXERCISE ▶ Find the MSE for $\alpha = 0.50$. [Answer: MSE $= 195.24$. The result indicates that $\alpha = 0.10$ is a better choice because we seek a lower MSE. Coincidentally, this is the same conclusion we reached using MAD in Example 4.]

RELATED PROBLEMS ▶ 4.8d, 4.14, 4.20

EXAMPLE 5

Determining the Mean Squared Error (MSE)

A drawback of using the MSE is that it tends to accentuate large deviations due to the squared term. For example, if the forecast error for period 1 is twice as large as the error for period 2, the squared error in period 1 is four times as large as that for period 2. Hence, using MSE as the measure of forecast error typically indicates that we prefer to have several smaller deviations rather than even one large deviation.

MEAN ABSOLUTE PERCENT ERROR A problem with both the MAD and MSE is that their values depend on the magnitude of the item being forecast. If the forecast item is measured in thousands, the MAD and MSE values can be very large. To avoid this problem, we can use the **mean absolute percent error (MAPE)**. This is computed as the average of the absolute difference between the forecasted and actual values, expressed as a percentage of the actual values. That is, if we have forecasted and actual values for n periods, the MAPE is calculated as:

Mean absolute percent error (MAPE)
The average of the absolute differences between the forecast and actual values, expressed as a percentage of actual values.

$$\text{MAPE} = \frac{\sum_{i=1}^{n} 100|\text{Actual}_i - \text{Forecast}_i|/\text{Actual}_i}{n} \qquad \textbf{(4-7)}$$

Example 6 illustrates the calculations using the data from Examples 4 and 5.

Determining the Mean Absolute Percent Error (MAPE)

The Port of Halifax wants to now calculate the MAPE when $\alpha = 0.10$.

APPROACH ▶ Equation (4-7) is applied to the forecast data computed in Example 4.

SOLUTION ▶

Quarter	Actual Tonnage Unloaded	Forecast for $\alpha = 0.10$	Absolute Percent Error 100(|error|/actual)
1	180	175.00	100(5/180) = 2.78%
2	168	175.50	100(7.5/168) = 4.46%
3	159	174.75	100(15.75/159) = 9.90%
4	175	173.18	100(1.82/175) = 1.05%
5	190	173.36	100(16.64/190) = 8.76%
6	205	175.02	100(29.98/205) = 14.62%
7	180	178.02	100(1.98/180) = 1.10%
8	182	178.22	100(3.78/182) = 2.08%
			Sum of % errors = 44.75%

$$\text{MAPE} = \frac{\Sigma \text{ absolute percent errors}}{n} = \frac{44.75\%}{8} = 5.59\%$$

INSIGHT ▶ MAPE expresses the error as a percentage of the actual values, undistorted by a single large value.

LEARNING EXERCISE ▶ What is MAPE when α is 0.50? [Answer: MAPE = 6.75%. As was the case with MAD and MSE, the $\alpha = 0.1$ was preferable for this series of data.]

RELATED PROBLEMS ▶ 4.8e, 4.33c

The MAPE is perhaps the easiest measure to interpret. For example, a result that the MAPE is 6% is a clear statement that is not dependent on issues such as the magnitude of the input data. Table 4.1 summarizes how MAD, MSE, and MAPE differ.

EXPONENTIAL SMOOTHING WITH TREND ADJUSTMENT

Simple exponential smoothing, the technique we just illustrated in Examples 3 to 6, is like any other moving-average technique: It fails to respond to trends. Other forecasting techniques that can deal with trends are certainly available. However, because exponential smoothing is such a popular modelling approach in business, let us look at it in more detail.

Here is why exponential smoothing must be modified when a trend is present. Assume that demand for our product or service has been increasing by 100 units per month and that we have

Table 4.1 **Comparison of Measures of Forecast Error**

Measure	Meaning	Equation		Application to chapter example
Mean absolute deviation (MAD)	How much the forecast missed the target	$$\text{MAD} = \frac{\Sigma\|\text{Actual} - \text{Forecast}\|}{n}$$	(4-5)	For $\alpha = 0.10$ in Example 4, the forecast for grain unloaded was off by an average of 10.31 tonnes.
Mean squared error (MSE)	The square of how much the forecast missed the target	$$\text{MSE} = \frac{\Sigma(\text{Forecast errors})^2}{n}$$	(4-6)	For $\alpha = .10$ in Example 5, the square of the forecast error was 190.8. This number does not have a physical meaning but is useful when compared to the MSE of another forecast.
Mean absolute percent error (MAPE)	The average percent error	$$\text{MAPE} = \frac{\sum_{i=1}^{n} 100\|\text{Actual}_i - \text{Forecast}_i\|/\text{Actual}_i}{n}$$	(4-7)	For $\alpha = .10$ in Example 6, the forecast is off by 5.59% on average. As in Examples 4 and 5, some forecasts were too high, and some were low.

4. Estimate next year's total annual demand.
5. Divide this estimate of total annual demand by the number of seasons, and then multiply it by the seasonal index for that month. This provides the *seasonal forecast*.

Example 9 illustrates this procedure as it computes seasonal indices from historical data.

EXAMPLE 9

Determining Seasonal Indices

A Winnipeg distributor of Sony laptop computers wants to develop monthly indices for sales. Data from 2016–2018, by month, are available.

APPROACH ▶ Follow the five steps listed above.

SOLUTION ▶

Month	2016	2017	2018	Average 2016–2018 Demand	Average Monthly Demand[a]	Seasonal Index[b]
		Demand				
Jan.	80	85	105	90	94	0.957 (= 90/94)
Feb.	70	85	85	80	94	0.851 (= 80/94)
Mar.	80	93	82	85	94	0.904 (= 85/94)
Apr.	90	95	115	100	94	1.064 (= 100/94)
May	113	125	131	123	94	1.309 (= 123/4)
June	110	115	120	115	94	1.223 (= 115/94)
July	100	102	113	105	94	1.117 (= 105/94)
Aug.	88	102	110	100	94	1.064 (= 100/94)
Sept.	85	90	95	90	94	0.957 (= 90/94)
Oct.	77	78	85	80	94	0.851 (= 80/94)
Nov.	75	82	83	80	94	0.851 (= 80/94)
Dec.	82	78	80	80	94	0.851 (= 80/94)

Total average annual demand = 1128

[a]Average monthly demand $= \dfrac{1128}{12 \text{ months}} = 94$ [b]Seasonal index $= \dfrac{\text{Average 2016–2018 monthly demand}}{\text{Average monthly demand}}$

If we expected the 2019 annual demand for computers to be 1200 units, we would use these seasonal indices to forecast the monthly demand as follows:

Month	Demand	Month	Demand
Jan.	$\frac{1200}{12} \times 0.957 = 96$	July	$\frac{1200}{12} \times 1.117 = 112$
Feb.	$\frac{1200}{12} \times 0.851 = 85$	Aug.	$\frac{1200}{12} \times 1.064 = 106$
Mar	$\frac{1200}{12} \times 0.904 = 90$	Sept.	$\frac{1200}{12} \times 0.957 = 96$
Apr.	$\frac{1200}{12} \times 1.064 = 106$	Oct.	$\frac{1200}{12} \times 0.851 = 85$
May	$\frac{1200}{12} \times 1.309 = 131$	Nov.	$\frac{1200}{12} \times 0.851 = 85$
June	$\frac{1200}{12} \times 1.223 = 122$	Dec.	$\frac{1200}{12} \times 0.851 = 85$

INSIGHT ▶ Think of these indices as percentages of average sales. The average sales (without seasonality) would be 94, but with seasonality, sales fluctuate from 85% to 131% of average.

LEARNING EXERCISE ▶ If 2019 annual demand is 1150 laptops (instead of 1200), what will the January, February, and March forecasts be? [Answer: 91.7, 81.5, and 86.6, which can be rounded to 92, 82, and 87.]

RELATED PROBLEMS ▶ 4.27, 4.28

EXCEL OM Data File **Ch04Ex9.xlsx** can be found at **MyLab Operations Management.**

For simplicity, only three periods are used for each monthly index in the preceding example. Example 10 illustrates how indices that have already been prepared can be applied to adjust trend-line forecasts for seasonality.

Applying Both Trend and Seasonal Indices

San Diego Hospital wants to improve its forecasting by applying both trend and seasonal indices to 66 months of data it has collected. It will then forecast "patient-days" over the coming year.

APPROACH ▶ A trend line is created; then monthly seasonal indices are computed. Finally, a multiplicative seasonal model is used to forecast months 67 to 78.

SOLUTION ▶ Using 66 months of adult inpatient hospital days, the following equation was computed:

$$\hat{y} = 8090 + 21.5x$$

where
$$\hat{y} = \text{patient-days}$$
$$x = \text{time, in months}$$

Based on this model, which reflects only trend data, the hospital forecasts patient-days for the next month (period 67) to be:

$$\text{Patient-days} = 8090 + (21.5)(67) = 9530 (\text{trend only})$$

While this model, as plotted in Figure 4.6, recognized the upward trend line in the demand for inpatient services, it ignored the seasonality that the administration knew to be present.

FIGURE 4.6

Trend Data for San Diego Hospital

Source: From "Modern Methods Improve Hospital Forecasting" by W. E. Sterk and E. G. Shryock from *Healthcare Financial Management*, Vol. 41, no. 3, p. 97. Reprinted by permission of Healthcare Financial Management Association.

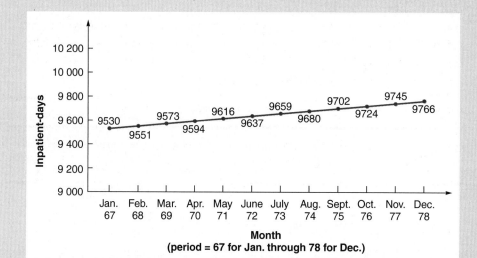

The following table provides seasonal indices based on the same 66 months. Such seasonal data, by the way, were found to be typical of hospitals nationwide.

Seasonality Indices for Adult Inpatient-Days at San Diego Hospital

Month	Seasonality Index	Month	Seasonality Index
January	1.04	July	1.03
February	0.97	August	1.04
March	1.02	September	0.97
April	1.01	October	1.00
May	0.99	November	0.96
June	0.99	December	0.98

These seasonal indices are graphed in Figure 4.7. Note that January, March, July, and August seem to exhibit significantly higher patient-days on average, while February, September, November, and December experience lower patient-days.

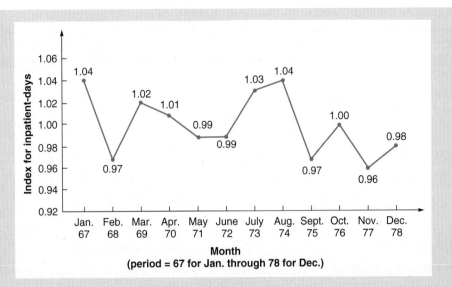

FIGURE 4.7

Seasonal Index for San Diego Hospital

However, neither the trend data nor the seasonal data alone provide a reasonable forecast for the hospital. Only when the hospital multiplied the trend-adjusted data times the appropriate seasonal index did it obtain good forecasts. Thus, for period 67 (January):

Patient-days = (Trend-adjusted forecast) (Monthly seasonal index) = (9530)(1.04) = 9911

The patient-days for each month are:

Period	67	68	69	70	71	72	73	74	75	76	77	78
Month	Jan.	Feb.	March	April	May	June	July	Aug.	Sept.	Oct.	Nov.	Dec.
Forecast with Trend and Seasonality	9911	9265	9764	9691	9520	9542	9949	10 068	9411	9724	9355	9572

A graph showing the forecast that combines both trend and seasonality appears in Figure 4.8.

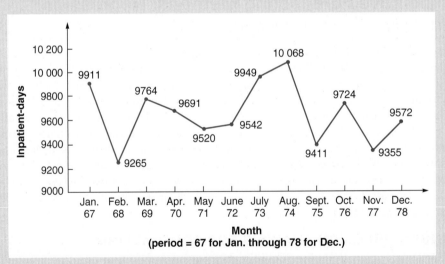

FIGURE 4.8

Combined Trend and Seasonal Forecast

INSIGHT ▶ Notice that with trend only, the September forecast is 9702, but with both trend and seasonal adjustments, the forecast is 9411. By combining trend and seasonal data, the hospital was better able to forecast patient-days and the related staffing and budgeting vital to effective operations.

LEARNING EXERCISE ▶ If the slope of the trend line for patient-days is 22.0 (rather than 21.5) and the index for December is 0.99 (instead of 0.98), what is the new forecast for December patient-days? [Answer: 9708.]

RELATED PROBLEMS ▶ 4.26, 4.29

Example 11 further illustrates seasonality for quarterly data at a department store.

RELATED PROBLEMS ▶ 4.26, 4.29

EXAMPLE 11

Adjusting Trend Data With Seasonal Indices

Management at Davis's Department Store has used time-series regression to forecast retail sales for the next four quarters. Sales estimates are $100 000, $120 000, $140 000, and $160 000 for the respective quarters. Seasonal indices for the four quarters have been found to be 1.30, 0.90, 0.70, and 1.10, respectively.

APPROACH ▶ To compute a seasonalized or adjusted sales forecast, we just multiply each seasonal index by the appropriate trend forecast:

$$\hat{y}_{seasonal} = Index \times \hat{y}_{trend\ forecast}$$

SOLUTION ▶   Quarter I: $\hat{y}_I = (1.30)(\$100\ 000) = \$130\ 000$

Quarter II: $\hat{y}_{II} = (0.90)(\$120\ 000) = \$108\ 000$

Quarter III: $\hat{y}_{III} = (0.70)(\$140\ 000) = \$98\ 000$

Quarter IV: $\hat{y}_{IV} = (1.10)(\$160\ 000) = \$176\ 000$

INSIGHT ▶ The straight-line trend forecast is now adjusted to reflect the seasonal changes.

LEARNING EXERCISE ▶ If the sales forecast for Quarter IV was 180 000 (rather than 160 000), what would be the seasonally adjusted forecast? [Answer: $198 000.]

RELATED PROBLEMS ▶ 4.26, 4.29

CYCLICAL VARIATIONS IN DATA

Cycles

Patterns in the data that occur every several years.

Cycles are like seasonal variations in data but occur every several *years*, not weeks, months, or quarters. Forecasting cyclical variations in a time series is difficult. This is because cycles include a wide variety of factors that cause the economy to go from recession to expansion to recession over a period of years. These factors include national or industry-wide overexpansion in times of euphoria and contraction in times of concern. Forecasting demand for individual products can also be driven by product life cycles—the stages products go through from introduction through decline. Life cycles exist for virtually all products; striking examples include floppy disks, video recorders, and the original Game Boy. We leave cyclical analysis to forecasting texts.

Developing associative techniques of variables that affect one another is our next topic.

Associative Forecasting Methods: Regression and Correlation Analysis

STUDENT TIP

We now deal with the same mathematical model that we saw earlier, the least squares method. But we use any potential "cause-and-effect" variable as *x*.

Unlike time-series forecasting, *associative forecasting* models usually consider *several* variables that are related to the quantity being predicted. Once these related variables have been found, a statistical model is built and used to forecast the item of interest. This approach is more powerful than the time-series methods that use only the historical values for the forecasted variable.

Many factors can be considered in an associative analysis. For example, the sales of Dell PCs may be related to Dell's advertising budget, the company's prices, competitors' prices and promotional strategies, and even the nation's economy and unemployment rates. In this case, PC sales would be called the *dependent variable*, and the other variables would be called *independent variables*. The manager's job is to develop *the best statistical relationship between PC sales and the independent variables*. The most common quantitative associative forecasting model is **linear-regression analysis**.

Linear-regression analysis

A straight-line mathematical model to describe the functional relationships between independent and dependent variables.

USING REGRESSION ANALYSIS FOR FORECASTING

We can use the same mathematical model that we employed in the least squares method of trend projection to perform a linear-regression analysis. The dependent variables that we want to forecast will still be $\hat{y}$. But now the independent variable, x, need no longer be time. We use the equation:

$$\hat{y} = a + bx$$

LO6 Conduct a regression and correlation analysis

where $\hat{y}$ = value of the dependent variable (in our example, sales)
              a = y-axis intercept
              b = slope of the regression line
              x = independent variable

Example 12 shows how to use linear regression.

EXAMPLE 12

Computing a Linear Regression Equation

Nodel Construction Company renovates old homes in North Bay, Ontario. Over time, the company has found that its dollar volume of renovation work is dependent on the North Bay area payroll. Management wants to establish a mathematical relationship to help predict sales.

APPROACH ▶ Nodel's VP of operations has prepared the following table, which lists company revenues and the amount of money earned by wage earners in North Bay during the past six years:

Nodel's Sales (in $ millions), y	Area Payroll (in $ billions), x	Nodel's Sales (in $ millions), y	Area Payroll (in $ billions), x
2.0	1	2.0	2
3.0	3	2.0	1
2.5	4	3.5	7

The VP needs to determine whether there is a straight-line (linear) relationship between area payroll and sales. He plots the known data on a scatter diagram:

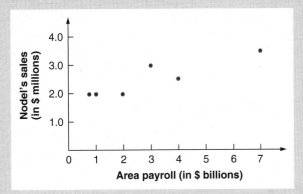

STUDENT TIP

A scatter diagram is a powerful data analysis tool. It helps quickly size up the relationship between two variables.

From the six data points, there appears to be a slight positive relationship between the independent variable (payroll) and the dependent variable (sales): As payroll increases, Nodel's sales tend to be higher.

SOLUTION ▶ We can find a mathematical equation by using the least squares regression approach:

Sales, y	Payroll, x	x^2	xy
2.0	1	1	2.0
3.0	3	9	9.0
2.5	4	16	10.0
2.0	2	4	4.0
2.0	1	1	2.0
3.5	7	49	24.5
$\Sigma y = 15.0$	$\Sigma x = 18$	$\Sigma x^2 = 80$	$\Sigma xy = 51.5$

$$\bar{x} = \frac{\Sigma x}{6} = \frac{18}{6} = 3$$

$$\bar{y} = \frac{\Sigma y}{6} = \frac{15}{6} = 2.5$$

$$b = \frac{\Sigma xy - n\bar{x}\bar{y}}{\Sigma x^2 n\bar{x}^2} = \frac{51.5 - (6)(3)(2.5)}{80 - (6)(3)^2} = 0.25$$

$$a = \bar{y} - b\bar{x} = 2.5 - (2.5)(3) = 1.75$$

The estimated regression equation, therefore, is:

$$\hat{y} = 1.75 + 0.25x$$

or:

$$\text{Sales} = 1.75 + 0.25(\text{payroll})$$

> If the local chamber of commerce predicts that the North Bay area payroll will be $6 billion next year, we can estimate sales for Nodel with the regression equation:
>
> $$\text{Sales(in \$ millions)} = 1.75 + 0.25(6)$$
> $$= 1.75 + 1.50 = 3.25$$
>
> or:
>
> $$\text{Sales} = \$3\,250\,000$$
>
> **INSIGHT ▶** Given our assumptions of a straight-line relationship between payroll and sales, we now have an indication of the slope of that relationship: on average, sales increase at the rate of a million dollars for every quarter billion dollars in the local area payroll. This is because $b = 0.25$.
>
> **LEARNING EXERCISE ▶** What are Nodel's sales when the local payroll is $8 billion? [Answer: $3.75 million.]
>
> **RELATED PROBLEMS ▶** 4.24, 4.30, 4.31, 4.32, 4.33, 4.35, 4.38, 4.40, 4.41, 4.46, 4.48, 4.49
>
> **EXCEL OM** Data file Ch4Ex12.xlsx can be found at **MyLab Operations Management.**

The final part of Example 12 shows a central weakness of associative forecasting methods like regression. Even when we have computed a regression equation, we must provide a forecast of the independent variable x—in this case, payroll—before estimating the dependent variable y for the next time period. Although this is not a problem for all forecasts, you can imagine the difficulty of determining future values of *some* common independent variables (such as unemployment rates, gross national product, price indices, and so on).

STANDARD ERROR OF THE ESTIMATE

The forecast of $3 250 000 for Nodel's sales in Example 12 is called a *point estimate* of y. The point estimate is really the *mean*, or *expected value*, of a distribution of possible values of sales. Figure 4.9 illustrates this concept.

FIGURE 4.9

Distribution About the Point Estimate of $3.25 Million Sales

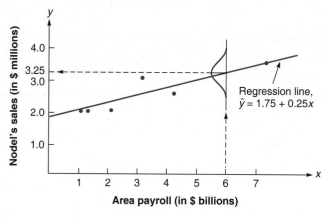

Standard error of the estimate

A measure of variability around the regression line—its standard deviation.

To measure the accuracy of the regression estimates, we must compute the **standard error of the estimate**, $S_{y,x}$. This computation is called the *standard deviation of the regression*. It measures the error from the dependent variable, y, to the regression line, rather than to the mean. Equation (4-14) is a similar expression to that found in most statistics books for computing the standard deviation of an arithmetic mean:

$$S_{y,x} = \sqrt{\frac{\Sigma(y - y_c)^2}{n - 2}} \tag{4-14}$$

where y = y-value of each data point

             y_c = computed value of the dependent variable, from the regression equation

             n = number of data points

Equation (4-15) below may look more complex, but it is actually an easier-to-use version of Equation (4-14). Both formulas provide the same answer and can be used in setting up prediction intervals around the point estimate:[3]

---

[3] When the sample size is large ($n > 30$), the prediction interval value of y can be computed using normal tables. When the number of observations is small, the t-distribution is appropriate. See D. Groebner et al., *Business Statistics*, 8th ed. (Upper Saddle River, NJ: Prentice Hall, 2011).

Glidden Paints' assembly lines fill thousands of cans per hour. To predict demand, the firm uses associative forecasting methods such as linear regression, with independent variables such as disposable personal income and GNP. Although housing starts would be a natural variable, Glidden found that it correlated poorly with past sales. It turns out that most Glidden paint is sold through retailers to customers who already own homes or businesses.

$$S_{y,x} = \sqrt{\frac{\Sigma y^2 - a\Sigma y - b\Sigma xy}{n - 2}} \qquad \text{(4-15)}$$

Example 13 shows how we would calculate the standard error of the estimate in Example 12.

Nodel's VP of operations now wants to know the error associated with the regression line computed in Example 12.

APPROACH ▶ Compute the standard error of the estimate, $S_{y,x}$, using Equation (4-15).

SOLUTION ▶ The only number we need that is not available to solve for $S_{y,x}$ is Σy^2. Some quick addition reveals $\Sigma y^2 = 39.5$. Therefore:

$$S_{y,x} = \sqrt{\frac{\Sigma y^2 - a\Sigma y - b\Sigma xy}{n - 2}}$$

$$= \sqrt{\frac{39.5 - 1.75(15) - 0.25(51.5)}{6 - 2}}$$

$$= \sqrt{0.09375} = 0.306 \text{ (in \$ millions)}$$

The standard error of the estimate is then $306 000 in sales.

INSIGHT ▶ The interpretation of the standard error of the estimate is similar to the standard deviation; namely, ±1 standard deviation = 0.6827. So there is a 68.27% chance of sales being ±$306 000 from the point estimate of $3 250 000.

LEARNING EXERCISE ▶ What is the probability sales will exceed $3 556 000? [Answer: About 16%.]

RELATED PROBLEMS ▶ 4.41e, 4.48b

EXAMPLE 13

Computing the Standard Error of the Estimate

CORRELATION COEFFICIENTS FOR REGRESSION LINES

The regression equation is one way of expressing the nature of the relationship between two variables. Regression lines are not cause-and-effect relationships. They merely describe the relationships among variables. The regression equation shows how one variable relates to the value and changes in another variable.

Another way to evaluate the relationship between two variables is to compute the **coefficient of correlation**. This measure expresses the degree or strength of the linear relationship. Usually identified as r, the coefficient of correlation can be any number between +1 and −1. Figure 4.10 illustrates what different values of r might look like.

Coefficient of correlation
A measure of the strength of the relationship between two variables.

FIGURE 4.10

Four Values of the Correlation Coefficient

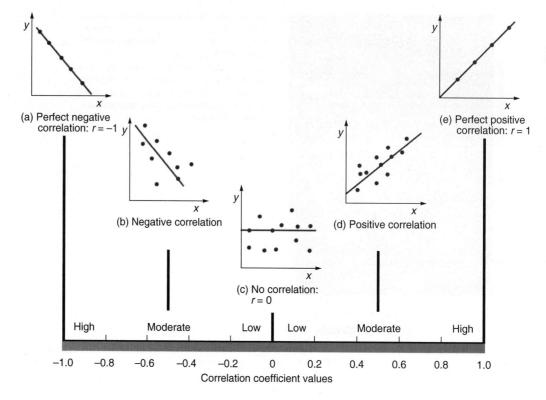

(a) Perfect negative correlation: $r = -1$

(b) Negative correlation

(c) No correlation: $r = 0$

(d) Positive correlation

(e) Perfect positive correlation: $r = 1$

High	Moderate	Low		Low	Moderate	High

| −1.0 | −0.8 | −0.6 | −0.4 | −0.2 | 0 | 0.2 | 0.4 | 0.6 | 0.8 | 1.0 |

Correlation coefficient values

To compute r, we use much of the same data needed earlier to calculate a and b for the regression line. The rather lengthy equation for r is:

$$r = \frac{n\Sigma xy - \Sigma x \Sigma y}{\sqrt{[n\Sigma x^2 - (\Sigma x)^2][n\Sigma y^2 - (\Sigma y)^2]}} \qquad \text{(4-16)}$$

Example 14 shows how to calculate the coefficient of correlation for the data given in Examples 12 and 13.

EXAMPLE 14

Determining the Coefficient of Correlation

In Example 12, we looked at the relationship between Nodel Construction Company's renovation sales and payroll in its hometown of North Bay. The VP now wants to know the strength of the association between area payroll and sales.

APPROACH ▶ We compute the r value using Equation (4-16). We need first to add one more column of calculations—for y^2.

SOLUTION ▶ The data, including the column for y^2 and the calculations, are shown here:

y	x	x^2	xy	y^2
2.0	1	1	2.0	4.0
3.0	3	9	9.0	9.0
2.5	4	16	10.0	6.25
2.0	2	4	4.0	4.0
2.0	1	1	2.0	4.0
3.5	7	49	24.5	12.25
$\Sigma y = 15.0$	$\Sigma x = 18$	$\Sigma x^2 = 80$	$\Sigma xy = 51.5$	$\Sigma y^2 = 39.5$

$$r = \frac{(6)(51.5) - (18)(15.0)}{\sqrt{[(6)(80) - (18)^2][(6)(39.5) - (15.0)^2]}}$$

$$= \frac{309 - 270}{\sqrt{(156)(12)}} = \frac{39}{\sqrt{1872}}$$

$$= \frac{39}{43.3} = 0.901$$

INSIGHT ▶ This *r* of 0.901 appears to be a significant correlation and helps confirm the closeness of the relationship between the two variables.

LEARNING EXERCISE ▶ If the coefficient of correlation was −0.901 rather than +0.901, what would this tell you? [Answer: The negative correlation would tell you that as payroll went up, Nodel's sales went down—a rather unlikely occurrence that would suggest you recheck your math.]

RELATED PROBLEMS ▶ 4.24d, 4.35d, 4.38c, 4.41f, 4.48b

Although the coefficient of correlation is the measure most commonly used to describe the relationship between two variables, another measure does exist. It is called the **coefficient of determination** and is simply the square of the coefficient of correlation—namely, r^2. The value of r^2 will always be a positive number in the range $0 \le r^2 \le 1$. The coefficient of determination is the percentage of variation in the dependent variable (*y*) that is explained by the regression equation. In Nodel's case, the value of r^2 is 0.81, indicating that 81% of the total variation is explained by the regression equation.

Coefficient of determination
A measure of the amount of variation in the dependent variable about its mean that is explained by the regression equation.

MULTIPLE-REGRESSION ANALYSIS

Multiple regression is a practical extension of the simple regression model we just explored. It allows us to build a model with several independent variables instead of just one variable. For example, if Nodel Construction wanted to include average annual interest rates in its model for forecasting renovation sales, the proper equation would be:

Multiple regression
An associative forecasting method with more than one independent variable.

$$\hat{y} = a + b_1x_1 + b_2x_2 \tag{4-17}$$

where $\quad \hat{y}$ = dependent variable, sales
$\quad a$ = a constant, the *y* intercept
$\quad x_1$ and x_2 = values of the two independent variables, area payroll and interest rates, respectively
$\quad b_1$ and b_2 = coefficients for the two independent variables

The mathematics of multiple regression becomes quite complex (and is usually tackled by computer), so we leave the formulas for a, b_1, and b_2 to statistics textbooks. However, Example 15 shows how to interpret Equation (4-17) in forecasting Nodel's sales.

Nodel Construction wants to see the impact of a second independent variable, interest rates, on its sales.

APPROACH ▶ The new multiple-regression line for Nodel Construction, calculated by computer software, is:

$$\hat{y} = 1.80 + 0.30x_1 - 5.0x_2$$

We also find that the new coefficient of correlation is 0.96, implying that the inclusion of the variable x_2, interest rates, adds even more strength to the linear relationship.

SOLUTION ▶ We can now estimate Nodel's sales if we substitute values for next year's payroll and interest rate. If North Bay's payroll will be $6 billion and the interest rate will be 0.12 (= 12%), sales will be forecast as:

$$\text{Sales(\$ millions)} = 1.80 + 0.30(6) - 5.0(0.12)$$
$$= 1.8 + 1.8 - 0.6$$
$$= 3.0$$

or:

$$\text{Sales} = \$3\,000\,000$$

INSIGHT ▶ By using both variables—payroll and interest rates—Nodel now has a sales forecast of $3 million and a higher coefficient of correlation. This suggests a stronger relationship between the two variables and a more accurate estimate of sales.

LEARNING EXERCISE ▶ If interest rates were only 6%, what would be the sales forecast? [Answer: 1.8 + 1.8 − 5.0(0.06) = 3.3, or $3 300 000.]

RELATED PROBLEMS ▶ 4.34, 4.36

EXAMPLE 15

Using a Multiple-Regression Equation

STUDENT TIP

Using a tracking signal is a good
way to make sure the forecasting
system is continuing to do a good
job.

Monitoring and Controlling Forecasts

Once a forecast has been completed, it should not be forgotten. No manager wants to be reminded that his or her forecast is horribly inaccurate, but a firm needs to determine why actual demand (or whatever variable is being examined) differed significantly from that projected. If the forecaster is accurate, that individual usually makes sure that everyone is aware of his or her talents. Very seldom does one read articles in *Report on Business, Financial Times*, or *The Wall Street Journal*, however, about money managers who are consistently off by 25% in their stock market forecasts.

One way to monitor forecasts to ensure that they are performing well is to use a tracking signal. A **tracking signal** is a measurement of how well a forecast is predicting actual values. As forecasts are updated every week, month, or quarter, the newly available demand data are compared to the forecast values.

The tracking signal is computed as the cumulative error divided by the *mean absolute deviation (MAD)*:

Tracking signal

A measurement of how well
a forecast is predicting actual
values.

$$\text{(Tracking signal)} = \frac{\text{Cumulative error}}{\text{MAD}}$$

$$= \frac{\Sigma(\text{Actual demand in period } i - \text{Forecast demand in period } i)}{\text{MAD}} \quad \textbf{(4-18)}$$

Where

$$\text{(MAD)} = \frac{\Sigma |\text{Actual} - \text{Forecast}|}{n}$$

LO7 Use a tracking signal

as seen earlier, in Equation (4-5).

Positive tracking signals indicate that demand is *greater* than forecast. *Negative* signals mean that demand is *less* than forecast. A good tracking signal—that is, one with a low cumulative error—has about as much positive error as it has negative error. In other words, small deviations are okay, but positive and negative errors should balance one another so that the tracking signal centres closely around zero. A consistent tendency for forecasts to be greater or less than the actual values (i.e., for a high absolute cumulative error) is called a **bias** error. Bias can occur if, for example, the wrong variables or trend line are used or if a seasonal index is misapplied.

Bias

A forecast that is consistently
higher or consistently lower than
actual values of a time series.

Once tracking signals are calculated, they are compared with predetermined control limits. When a tracking signal exceeds an upper or lower limit, there is a problem with the forecasting method, and management may want to re-evaluate the way it forecasts demand. Figure 4.11 shows the graph of a tracking signal that is exceeding the range of acceptable variation. If the model being used is exponential smoothing, perhaps the smoothing constant needs to be readjusted.

How do firms decide what the upper and lower tracking limits should be? There is no single answer, but they try to find reasonable values—in other words, limits not so low as to be triggered with every small forecast error and not so high as to allow bad forecasts to be regularly overlooked. One MAD is equivalent to approximately 0.8 standard deviation, ±2 MADs = ±1.6 standard deviations, ±3 MADs = ±2.4 standard deviations, and ±4 MADs = ±3.2 standard deviations. This fact suggests that for a forecast to be "in control," 89% of the errors are expected to fall within ±2 MADs, 98% within ±3 MADs, or 99.9% within ±4 MADs.[4]

FIGURE 4.11

A Plot of Tracking Signals

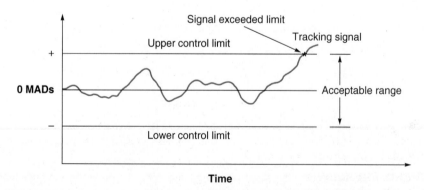

<hr>

[4] To prove these three percentages to yourself, just set up a normal curve for ±1.6 standard deviations (*z*-values). Using the normal table in Appendix I, you find that the area under the curve is 0.89. This represents ±2 MADs. Likewise, ±3 MADs = ±2.4 standard deviations encompass 98% of the area, and so on for ±4 MADs.

Example 16 shows how the tracking signal and cumulative error can be computed.

EXAMPLE **16**

Computing the Tracking Signal at Carlson's Bakery

Carlson's Bakery wants to evaluate performance of its croissant forecast.

APPROACH ▶ Develop a tracking signal for the forecast and see if it stays within acceptable limits, which we define as ±4 MADs.

SOLUTION ▶ Using the forecast and demand data for the past six quarters for croissant sales, we develop a tracking signal in the table below:

Quarter	Actual Demand	Forecast Demand	Error	Cumulative Error	Absolute Forecast Error	Cumulative Absolute Forecast Error	MAD	Tracking Signal (Cumulative Error/MAD)
1	90	100	−10	−10	10	10	10.0	−10/10 = −1
2	95	100	−5	−15	5	15	7.5	−15/7.5 = −2
3	115	100	+15	0	15	30	10.0	0/10 = 0
4	100	110	−10	−10	10	40	10.0	−10/10 = −1
5	125	110	+15	+5	15	55	11.0	+5/11 = +0.5
6	140	110	+30	+35	30	85	14.2	+35/14.2 = +2.5

$$\text{At the end of quarter 6, MAD} = \frac{\Sigma\,|\text{Forecast errors}|}{n} = \frac{85}{6} = 14.2$$

$$\text{and Tracking signal} = \frac{\text{Cumulative error}}{\text{MAD}} = \frac{35}{14.2} = 2.5\ \text{MADs}$$

INSIGHT ▶ Because the tracking signal drifted from −2 MAD to +2.5 MAD (between 1.6 and 2.0 standard deviations), we can conclude that it is within acceptable limits.

LEARNING EXERCISE ▶ If actual demand in quarter 6 was 130 (rather than 140), what would be the MAD and resulting tracking signal? [Answer: MAD for quarter 6 would be 12.5, and the tracking signal for period 6 would be 2 MADs.]

RELATED PROBLEMS ▶ 4.37, 4.45

ADAPTIVE SMOOTHING

Adaptive forecasting refers to computer monitoring of tracking signals and self-adjustment if a signal passes a preset limit. For example, when applied to exponential smoothing, the α and β coefficients are first selected on the basis of values that minimize error forecasts and then adjusted accordingly whenever the computer notes an errant tracking signal. This process is called **adaptive smoothing**.

FOCUS FORECASTING

Rather than adapt by choosing a smoothing constant, computers allow us to try a variety of forecasting models. Such an approach is called focus forecasting. **Focus forecasting** is based on two principles:

1. Sophisticated forecasting models are not always better than simple ones.
2. There is no single technique that should be used for all products or services.

Bernard Smith, inventory manager for American Hardware Supply, coined the term *focus forecasting*. Smith's job was to forecast quantities for 100 000 hardware products purchased by American's 21 buyers.[5] He found that buyers neither trusted nor understood the exponential smoothing model then in use. Instead, they used very simple approaches of their own. So Smith developed his new computerized system for selecting forecasting methods.

Smith chose to test seven forecasting methods. They ranged from the simple ones that buyers used (such as the naive approach) to statistical models. Every month, Smith applied the forecasts of all seven models to each item in stock. In these simulated trials, the forecast values were subtracted from the most recent actual demands, giving a simulated forecast error. The forecast

Adaptive smoothing

An approach to exponential smoothing forecasting in which the smoothing constant is automatically changed to keep errors to a minimum.

Focus forecasting

Forecasting that tries a variety of computer models and selects the best one for a particular application.

---

[5] Bernard T. Smith, *Focus Forecasting: Computer Techniques for Inventory Control* (Boston, MA: CBI Publishing, 1978).

method yielding the least error is selected by the computer, which then uses it to make next month's forecast. Although buyers still have an override capability, American Hardware finds that focus forecasting provides excellent results.

Forecasting in the Service Sector

Forecasting in the service sector presents some unusual challenges. A major technique in the retail sector is tracking demand by maintaining good short-term records. For instance, a barbershop catering to men expects peak flows on Fridays and Saturdays. Indeed, most barbershops are closed on Sunday and Monday, and many call in extra help on Friday and Saturday. A downtown restaurant, on the other hand, may need to track conventions and holidays for effective short-term forecasting. The *OM in Action* box "Forecasting at FedEx's Customer Service Centres" provides an example of a major service sector industry, the call centre.

SPECIALTY RETAIL SHOPS

Specialty retail facilities, such as flower shops, may have other unusual demand patterns, and those patterns will differ depending on the holiday. When Valentine's Day falls on a weekend, for example, flowers can't be delivered to offices, and those romantically inclined are likely to celebrate with outings rather than flowers. If a holiday falls on a Monday, some of the celebration may also take place on the weekend, reducing flower sales. However, when Valentine's Day falls midweek, busy midweek schedules often make flowers the optimal way to celebrate. Because flowers for Mother's Day are to be delivered on Saturday or Sunday, this holiday forecast varies less. Due to special demand patterns, many service firms maintain records of sales, noting not only the day of the week but also unusual events, including the weather, so that patterns and correlations that influence demand can be developed.

FAST-FOOD RESTAURANTS

Fast-food restaurants are well aware not only of weekly, daily, and hourly but even quarter-hourly (15-minute) variations in demands that influence sales. Therefore, detailed forecasts of demand are needed. Figure 4.12(a) shows the hourly forecast for a typical fast-food restaurant. Note the lunchtime and dinnertime peaks. This contrasts to the mid-morning and mid-afternoon peaks at FedEx's call centre in Figure 4.12(b).

Firms such as Taco Bell now use point-of-sale computers that track sales every quarter-hour. Taco Bell found that a six-week moving average was the forecasting technique that minimized its mean squared error (MSE) of these quarter-hour forecasts. Building this forecasting

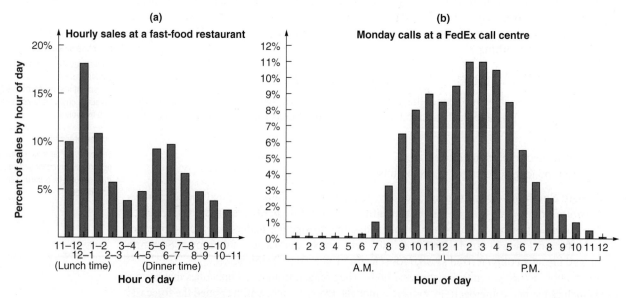

FIGURE 4.12   Forecasts Are Unique: Note the Variations between (a) Hourly Sales at a Fast-Food Restaurant and (b) Hourly Call Volume at FedEx

Source: Based on historical data: see Journal of Business Forecasting (Winter 1999–2000): 6–11.

OM in Action — Forecasting at FedEx's Customer Service Centres

The world's largest express shipping company, FedEx, generates US $38 billion in revenues, using 675 planes, 44 000 trucks, and a workforce of 145 000 in 220 countries. To support this global network, the company has 51 customer service call centres, whose service goal is to answer 90% of all calls within 20 seconds. With a half-million daily calls just in the United States, FedEx makes extensive use of forecasting models for staffing decisions and to ensure that customer satisfaction levels stay the highest in the industry.

FedEx's forecasting and modelling department makes several different forecasts. *One-year* and *five-year* models predict number of calls, average handle time, and staffing needs. They break forecasts into weekday, Saturday, and Sunday and then use the Delphi method and time-series analysis.

FedEx's *tactical forecasts* are monthly and use eight years of historical daily data. This time-series model

addresses month, day of week, and day of month to predict caller volume. Finally, the *operational forecast* uses a weighted moving average and six weeks of data to project the number of calls on a half-hourly basis.

FedEx's forecasts are consistently accurate to within 1% to 2% of actual call volumes. This means coverage needs are met, service levels are maintained, and costs are controlled.

Sources: Hoover's Company Records (July 1, 2009): 10552; *Baseline* (January 2005): 54; and *Journal of Business Forecasting* (Winter 1999–2000): 7–11.

methodology into each of Taco Bell's 6500 stores' computers, the model makes weekly projections of customer transactions. These in turn are used by store managers to schedule staff, who begin in 15-minute increments, not one-hour blocks as in other industries. The forecasting model has been so successful that Taco Bell has increased customer service while documenting more than U.S. $50 million in labour cost savings in four years of use.[6]

CHAPTER SUMMARY

Forecasts are a critical part of the operations manager's function. Demand forecasts drive a firm's production, capacity, and scheduling systems and affect the financial, marketing, and personnel planning functions.

There are a variety of qualitative and quantitative forecasting techniques. Qualitative approaches employ judgment, experience, intuition, and a host of other factors that are difficult to quantify. Quantitative forecasting uses historical data and causal, or associative, relations to project future demands. The Rapid Review for this chapter summarizes the formulas we introduced in quantitative forecasting. Forecast calculations are seldom performed by hand. Most operations managers turn to software packages such as Forecast PRO, NCSS, Minitab, Systat, Statgraphics, SAS, SPSS, or Excel.

No forecasting method is perfect under all conditions. And even once management has found a satisfactory approach, it must still monitor and control forecasts to make sure errors do not get out of hand. Forecasting can often be a very challenging, but rewarding, part of managing.

ETHICAL DILEMMA

In 2017, the board of regents responsible for all public higher-education funding in a major Canadian city hired a consultant to develop a series of enrolment forecasting models, one for each college. These models used historical data and exponential smoothing to forecast the following year's enrolments. Based on the model, which included a smoothing constant (α) for each school, each institution's budget was set by the board. The head of the board personally selected each smoothing constant based on what she called her "gut reactions and political acumen".

What do you think the advantages and disadvantages of this system are? Answer from the perspective of (a) the board of regents and (b) the president of each school. How can this model be abused, and what can be done to remove any biases? How can a *regression model* be used to produce results that favour one forecast over another?

---

[6] J. Hueter and W. Swart, "An Integrated Labor Management System for Taco Bell," *Interfaces* 28, no. 1 (January–February 1998): 75–91.

Discussion Questions

1. What is a qualitative forecasting model, and when is its use appropriate?
2. Identify and briefly describe the two general forecasting approaches.
3. Identify the three forecasting time horizons. State an approximate duration for each.
4. Briefly describe the steps that are used to develop a forecasting system.
5. A sceptical manager asks what medium-range forecasts can be used for. Give the manager three possible uses/purposes.
6. Explain why such forecasting devices as moving averages, weighted moving averages, and exponential smoothing are not well suited for data series that have trends.
7. What is the basic difference between a weighted moving average and exponential smoothing?
8. What three methods are used to determine the accuracy of any given forecasting method? How would you determine whether time-series regression or exponential smoothing is better in a specific application?
9. Research and briefly describe the Delphi technique. How would it be used by an employer you have worked for?
10. What is the primary difference between a time-series model and an associative model?

11. Define *time series*.
12. What effect does the value of the smoothing constant have on the weight given to the recent values?
13. Explain the value of seasonal indices in forecasting. How are seasonal patterns different from cyclical patterns?
14. Which forecasting technique can place the most emphasis on recent values? How does it do this?
15. In your own words, explain adaptive forecasting.
16. What is the purpose of a tracking signal?
17. Explain, in your own words, the meaning of the correlation coefficient. Discuss the meaning of a negative value of the correlation coefficient.
18. What is the difference between a dependent and an independent variable?
19. Give examples of industries that are affected by seasonality. Why would these businesses want to filter out seasonality?
20. Give examples of industries in which demand forecasting is dependent on the demand for other products.
21. What happens to the ability to forecast for periods further into the future?

Using Software in Forecasting

This section presents three ways to solve forecasting problems with computer software. First, you can create your own Excel spreadsheets to develop forecasts. Second, you can use the Excel OM software that comes with the text and is found on our text website. Third, POM for Windows is another program that is located on our website at **MyLab Operations Management.**

CREATING YOUR OWN EXCEL SPREADSHEETS

Excel spreadsheets (and spreadsheets in general) are frequently used in forecasting. Exponential smoothing, trend analysis, and regression analysis (simple and multiple) are supported by built-in Excel functions.

Program 4.1 illustrates how to build an Excel forecast for the data in Example 8. The goal for N.Y. Edison is to create a trend analysis of the year 1 to year 7 data. As an alternative, you may want to experiment with Excel's built-in regression analysis. To do so, under the **Data** menu bar selection choose

PROGRAM 4.1

Using Excel to Develop Your Own Forecast, With Data From Example 8

Source: Courtesy of Microsoft Corporation.

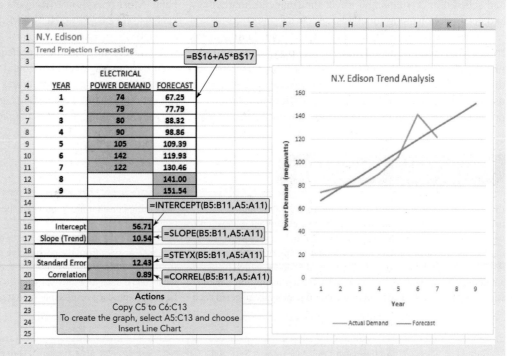

Data Analysis, then **Regression**. Enter your Y and X data into two columns (say A and B). When the regression window appears, enter the Y and X ranges, then select **OK**. Excel offers several plots and tables to those interested in more rigorous analysis of regression problems.

Computations			
Value	**Cell**	**Excel Formula**	**Action**
Trend line column	D4	=$B$16+$B$17*C4	Copy to D5:D14
		(or =TREND($B$4:$B$10,$C$4:$C$10,C4))	
Intercept	B16	=INTERCEPT(B4:B10, C4:C10)	
Slope (trend)	B17	=SLOPE(B4:B10, C4:C10)	
Standard error	B19	=STEYX(B4:B10, C4:C10)	
Correlation	B20	=CORREL(B4:B10, C4:C10)	

As an alternative, you may want to experiment with Excel's built-in regression analysis. To do so, under the *Data* menu bar selection choose *Data Analysis*, then *Regression*. Enter your Y and X data into two columns (say, B and C). When the regression window appears, enter the Y and X ranges, then select *OK*. Excel offers several plots and tables to those interested in more rigorous analysis of regression problems.

X USING EXCEL OM

Excel OM's forecasting module has five components: (1) moving averages, (2) weighted moving averages, (3) exponential smoothing, (4) regression (with one variable only), and (5) decomposition. Excel OM's error analysis is much more complete than that available with the Excel add-in.

Program 4.2 illustrates Excel OM's input and output, using Example 2's weighted moving average data.

P USING POM FOR WINDOWS

POM for Windows can project moving averages (both simple and weighted), handle exponential smoothing (both simple and trend adjusted), forecast with least squares trend projection, and solve linear-regression (associative) models. A summary screen of error analysis and a graph of the data can also be generated. As a special example of exponential smoothing adaptive forecasting, when using an α of 0, POM for Windows will find the α value that yields the minimum MAD.

Appendix IV provides further details.

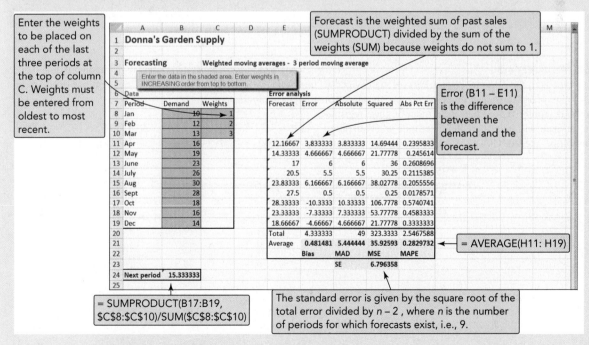

PROGRAM 4.2 **Analysis of Excel OM's Weighted Moving Average Program, Using Data From Example 2 as Input**

Source: Courtesy of Microsoft Corporation.

Solved Problems Virtual Office Hours help is available at MyLab Operations Management.

▼ SOLVED PROBLEM 4.1

Sales of Chevrolet's popular Camaro grew steadily at auto dealerships in Alberta during five years (see table below). The sales manager had predicted in 2013 that 2014 sales would be 410 Camaros. Using exponential smoothing with a weight of $\alpha = 0.30$, develop forecasts for 2015 through 2019.

Year	Sales	Forecast
2014	450	410
2015	495	
2016	518	
2017	563	
2018	584	
2019	?	

▼ SOLUTION

Year	Forecast
2014	410.0
2015	$422.0 = 410 + 0.3(450 - 410)$
2016	$443.9 = 422 + 0.3(495 - 422)$
2017	$466.1 = 443.9 + 0.3(518 - 443.9)$
2018	$495.2 = 466.1 + 0.3(563 - 466.1)$
2019	$521.8 = 495.2 + 0.3(584 - 495.2)$

▼ SOLVED PROBLEM 4.2

In Example 7, we applied trend-adjusted exponential smoothing to forecast demand for a piece of pollution control equipment for months 2 and 3 (out of nine months of data provided). Let us now continue this process for month 4. We want to confirm the forecast for month 4 shown in Table 4.2 and Figure 4.3.

For month 4, $A_4 = 19$, with $\alpha = 0.2$, and $\beta = 0.4$.

▼ SOLUTION

$$F_4 = \alpha A_3 + (1 - \alpha)(F_3 + T_3)$$
$$= (0.2)(20) + (1 - 0.2)(15.18 + 2.10)$$
$$= 4.0 + (0.8)(17.28)$$
$$= 4.0 + 13.82$$
$$= 17.82$$
$$T_4 = \beta(F_4 - F_3) + (1 - \beta)T_3$$
$$= (0.4)(17.82 - 15.18) + (1 - 0.4)(2.10)$$
$$= (0.4)(2.64) + (0.6)(2.10)$$
$$= 1.056 + 1.26$$
$$= 2.32$$
$$FIT_4 = 17.82 + 2.32$$
$$= 20.14$$

▼ SOLVED PROBLEM 4.3

Room registrations in the Toronto Towers Plaza Hotel have been recorded for nine years. To project future occupancy, management would like to determine the mathematical trend of guest registration. This estimate will help the hotel determine whether future expansion will be needed. Given the following time-series data, develop a regression equation relating registrations to time (e.g., a trend equation). Then forecast year 11 registrations. Room registrations are in the thousands:

Year 1: 17   Year 2: 16   Year 3: 16   Year 4: 21   Year 5: 20
Year 6: 20   Year 7: 23   Year 8: 25   Year 9: 24

▼ SOLUTION

Year, x	Registrants, y (in thousands)	x^2	xy
1	17	1	17
2	16	4	32
3	16	9	48
4	21	16	84
5	20	25	100
6	20	36	120
7	23	49	161
8	25	64	200
9	24	81	216
$\Sigma x = 45$	$\Sigma y = 182$	$\Sigma x^2 = 285$	$\Sigma xy = 978$

$$b = \frac{\Sigma xy - n\bar{x}\bar{y}}{\Sigma x^2 - n\bar{x}^2} = \frac{978 - (9)(5)(20.22)}{285 - (9)(25)} = \frac{978 - 909.9}{285 - 225} = \frac{68.1}{60} = 1.135$$

$$a = \bar{y} - b\bar{x} = 20.22 - (1.135)(5) = 20.22 - 5.675 = 14.545$$

$$\hat{y}(\text{registrations}) = 14.545 + 1.135x$$

The projection of registrations in the year 11 is:

$$\hat{y} = 14.545 + (1.135)(11) = 27.03$$
or 27 030 guests in year 11

▼ SOLVED PROBLEM 4.4

Quarterly demand for Ford F150 pickups at a St. John's auto dealer is forecast with the equation:

$$\hat{y} = 10 + 3x$$

where x = quarters, and:

Quarter I of 2014 = 0
Quarter II of 2014 = 1
Quarter III of 2014 = 2
Quarter IV of 2014 = 3
Quarter I of 2015 = 4
and so on

and:

$$\hat{y} = \text{quarterly demand}$$

The demand for trucks is seasonal, and the indices for Quarters I, II, III, and IV are 0.80, 1.00, 1.30, and 0.90, respectively. Forecast demand for each quarter of 2016. Then, seasonalize each forecast to adjust for quarterly variations.

▼ SOLUTION

Quarter II of 2015 is coded $x = 5$; Quarter III of 2015, $x = 6$; and Quarter IV of 2015, $x = 7$. Hence, Quarter I of 2016 is coded $x = 8$; Quarter II, $x = 9$; and so on.

$$\hat{y}(2016 \text{ Quarter I}) = 10 + 3(8) = 34$$
$$\hat{y}(2016 \text{ Quarter II}) = 10 + 3(9) = 37$$
$$\hat{y}(2016 \text{ Quarter III}) = 10 + 3(10) = 40$$
$$\hat{y}(2016 \text{ Quarter IV}) = 10 + 3(11) = 43$$

Adjusted forecast = (0.80)(34) = 27.2
Adjusted forecast = (1.00)(37) = 37
Adjusted forecast = (1.30)(40) = 52
Adjusted forecast = (0.90)(43) = 38.7

Problems*

• 4.1 The following gives the number of units of type A blood used at Woodlawn Hospital in the past six weeks:

Week Of	Pints Used
August 31	360
September 7	389
September 14	410
September 21	381
September 28	368
October 5	374

a) Forecast the demand for the week of October 12 using a three-week moving average.
b) Use a three-week weighted moving average, with weights of 0.1, 0.3, and 0.6, using 0.6 for the most recent week. Forecast demand for the week of October 12.
c) Compute the forecast for the week of October 12 using exponential smoothing with a forecast for August 31 of 360 and $\alpha = 0.2$. **PX**

•• 4.2

Year	1	2	3	4	5	6	7	8	9	10	11
Demand	7	9	5	9	13	8	12	13	9	11	7

a) Plot the above data on a graph. Do you observe any trend, cycles, or random variations?
b) Starting in year 4 and going to year 12, forecast demand using a three-year moving average. Plot your forecast on the same graph as the original data.
c) Starting in year 4 and going to year 12, forecast demand using a three-year moving average with weights of 0.1, 0.3, and 0.6, using 0.6 for the most recent year. Plot this forecast on the same graph.
d) As you compare forecasts with the original data, which seems to give the better results? **PX**

• 4.3 Refer to Problem 4.2. Develop a forecast for years 2 through 12 using exponential smoothing with $\alpha = 0.4$ and a forecast for year 1 of 6. Plot your new forecast on a graph with the actual data and the naive forecast. Based on a visual inspection, which forecast is better? **PX**

• 4.4 A cheque-processing centre uses exponential smoothing to forecast the number of incoming cheques each month. The number of cheques received in June was 40 million, while the forecast was 42 million. A smoothing constant of 0.2 is used.
a) What is the forecast for July?
b) If the centre received 45 million cheques in July, what would be the forecast for August?
c) Why might this be an inappropriate forecasting method for this situation? **PX**

* *Note:* **PX** means the problem may be solved with POM for windows and/or Excel OM.

•• **4.5** The Bonavista Patient Transfer Company is considering the purchase of a new ambulance. The decision will rest partly on the anticipated distance to be driven next year. The kilometres driven during the past five years are as follows:

Year	Distance (km)
1	3000
2	4000
3	3400
4	3800
5	3700

a) Forecast the number of kilometres for next year using a two-year moving average.
b) Find the MAD based on the two-year moving-average forecast in part (a). (*Hint:* You will have only three years of matched data.)
c) Use a weighted two-year moving average with weights of 0.4 and 0.6 to forecast next year's mileage. (The weight of 0.6 is for the most recent year.) What MAD results from using this approach to forecasting? (*Hint:* You will have only three years of matched data.)
d) Compute the forecast for year 6 using exponential smoothing, an initial forecast for year 1 of 3000 kilometres and $\alpha = 0.5$. **Px**

•• **4.6** The monthly sales for Telco Batteries, Inc., were as follows:

Month	Sales
January	20
February	21
March	15
April	14
May	13
June	16
July	17
August	18
September	20
October	20
November	21
December	23

a) Plot the monthly sales data.
b) Forecast January sales using each of the following:
   i) Naive method.
   ii) A three-month moving average.
   iii) A six-month weighted average using 0.1, 0.1, 0.1, 0.2, 0.2, and 0.3, with the heaviest weights applied to the most recent months.
   iv) Exponential smoothing using an $\alpha = 0.3$ and a September forecast of 18.
   v) A trend projection.
c) With the data given, which method would allow you to forecast next March's sales? **Px**

•• **4.7** The actual demand for the patients at Moncton Medical Clinic for the first six weeks of this year follows:

Week	Actual No. of Patients
1	65
2	62
3	70
4	48
5	63
6	52

Clinic administrator Marc Schniederjans wants you to forecast patient demand at the clinic for week 7 by using this data. You decide to use a weighted moving average method to find this forecast. Your method uses four actual demand levels, with weights of 0.333 on the present period, 0.25 one period ago, 0.25 two periods ago, and 0.167 three periods ago.
a) What is the value of your forecast? **Px**
b) If instead the weights were 20, 15, 15, and 10, respectively, how would the forecast change? Explain why.
c) What if the weights were 0.40, 0.30, 0.20, and 0.10, respectively? Now what is the forecast for week 7?

• **4.8** A Canadian tourist travelling to Miami learned that the local temperatures in Fahrenheit for the last week were as follows: 93, 94, 93, 95, 96, 88, 90 (yesterday).
a) Forecast the high temperature today, using a three-day moving average.
b) Forecast the high temperature today, using a two-day moving average.
c) Calculate the mean absolute deviation based on a two-day moving average.
d) Compute the mean squared error for the two-day moving average.
e) Calculate the mean absolute percent error for the two-day moving average. **Px**

••• **4.9** Dell uses the CR5 chip in some of its laptop computers. The prices for the chip during the past 12 months were as follows:

Month	Price per Chip	Month	Price per Chip
January	$1.80	July	$1.80
February	1.67	August	1.83
March	1.70	September	1.70
April	1.85	October	1.65
May	1.90	November	1.70
June	1.87	December	1.75

a) Use a two-month moving average on all the data and plot the averages and the prices.
b) Use a three-month moving average and add the three-month plot to the graph created in part (a).
c) Which is better (using the mean absolute deviation): the two-month average or the three-month average?
d) Compute the forecasts for each month using exponential smoothing, with an initial forecast for January of $1.80. Use $\alpha = 0.1$, then $\alpha = 0.3$, and finally $\alpha = 0.5$. Using MAD, which α is the best? **Px**

•• **4.10** Data collected on the yearly registrations for a Six Sigma seminar at the Quality College are shown in the following table:

Year	1	2	3	4	5	6	7	8	9	10	11
Registrations (000)	4	6	4	5	10	8	7	9	12	14	15

a) Develop a three-year moving average to forecast registrations from year 4 to year 12.
b) Estimate demand again for years 4 to 12 with a three-year weighted moving average in which registrations in the most recent year are given a weight of 2, and registrations in the other two years are each given a weight of 1.
c) Graph the original data and the two forecasts. Which of the two forecasting methods seems better? **Px**

· 4.11 Use exponential smoothing with a smoothing constant of 0.3 to forecast the registrations at the seminar given in Problem 4.10. To begin the procedure, assume that the forecast for year 1 was 5000 people signing up.
a) What is the MAD? **Px**
b) What is the MSE?

·· 4.12 Consider the following actual and forecast demand levels for Big Mac hamburgers at a local McDonald's restaurant:

Day	Actual Demand	Forecast Demand
Monday	88	88
Tuesday	72	88
Wednesday	68	84
Thursday	48	80
Friday		

The forecast for Monday was derived by observing Monday's demand level and setting Monday's forecast level equal to this demand level. Subsequent forecasts were derived by using exponential smoothing with a smoothing constant of 0.25. Using this exponential smoothing method, what is the forecast for Big Mac demand for Friday? **Px**

··· 4.13 As you can see in the following table, demand for heart transplant surgery at Vancouver General Hospital has increased steadily in the past few years:

Year	1	2	3	4	5	6
Heart Transplants	45	50	52	56	58	?

The director of medical services predicted six years ago that demand in year 1 would be 41 surgeries.
a) Use exponential smoothing, first with a smoothing constant of 0.6 and then with one of 0.9, to develop forecasts for years 2 through 6.
b) Use a three-year moving average to forecast demand in years 4, 5, and 6.
c) Use the trend projection method to forecast demand in years 1 through 6.
d) With MAD as the criterion, which of the four forecasting methods is best? **Px**

·· 4.14 Following are two weekly forecasts made by two different methods for the number of litres of gasoline, in thousands, demanded at a local gasoline station. Also shown are actual demand levels, in thousands of litres:

	Forecasts		
Week	Method 1	Method 2	Actual Demand
1	0.90	0.80	0.70
2	1.05	1.20	1.00
3	0.95	0.90	1.00
4	1.20	1.11	1.00

What are the MAD and MSE for each method?

· 4.15 Refer to Solved Problem 4.1. Use a three-year moving average to forecast the sales of Chevrolet Camaros in Alberta through 2016. What is the MAD? **Px**

· 4.16 Refer to Solved Problem 4.1. Using the trend projection method, develop a forecast for the sales of Chevrolet Camaros in Alberta through 2016. What is the MAD? **Px**

· 4.17 Refer to Solved Problem 4.1. Using smoothing constants of 0.6 and 0.9, develop forecasts for the sales of Chevrolet Camaros. What effect did the smoothing constant have on the forecast? Use MAD to determine which of the three smoothing constants (0.3, 0.6, or 0.9) gives the most accurate forecast. **Px**

···· 4.18 Consider the following actual (A_t) and forecast (F_t) demand levels for a product:

Time Period, T	Actual Demand, A_t	Forecast Demand, F_t
1	50	50
2	42	50
3	56	48
4	46	50
5		

The first forecast, F_1, was derived by observing A_1 and setting F_1 equal to A_1. Subsequent forecasts were derived by exponential smoothing. Using the exponential smoothing method, find the forecast for time period 5. (*Hint:* You need first to find the smoothing constant, α.)

··· 4.19 Income at the law firm Smith and Jones for the period February to July was as follows:

Month	February	March	April	May	June	July
Income (in $000s)	70.0	68.5	64.8	71.7	71.3	72.8

Use trend-adjusted exponential smoothing to forecast the law firm's August income. Assume that the initial forecast for February is $65 000 and the initial trend adjustment is 0. The smoothing constants selected are $\alpha = 0.1$ and $\beta = 0.2$. **Px**

··· 4.20 Resolve Problem 4.19 with $\alpha = 0.1$ and $\beta = 0.8$. Using MSE, determine which smoothing constants provide a better forecast. **Px**

· 4.21 Refer to the trend-adjusted exponential smoothing illustration in Example 7. Using $\alpha = 0.2$ and $\beta = 0.4$, we forecast sales for nine months, showing the detailed calculations for months 2 and 3. In Solved Problem 4.2, we continued the process for month 4. In this problem, show your calculations for months 5 and 6 for F_t, T_t, and FIT_t. **Px**

· 4.22 Refer to Problem 4.21. Complete the trend-adjusted exponential smoothing forecast computations for periods 7, 8, and 9. Confirm that your numbers for F_t, T_t, and FIT_t match those in Table 4.2. **Px**

·· 4.23 Sales of vegetable dehydrators at Bud Banis's discount department store in Gander over the past year are shown below. Management prepared a forecast using a combination of exponential smoothing and its collective judgment for the four months March, April, May, and June:

Month	Unit Sales	Management's Forecast
July	100	
August	93	
September	96	
October	110	
November	124	
December	119	
January	92	
February	83	
March	101	120
April	96	114
May	89	110
June	108	108

a) Compute MAD and MAPE for management's technique.
b) Do management's results outperform (i.e., have smaller MAD and MAPE than) a naive forecast?
c) Which forecast do you recommend, based on lower forecast error?

•• **4.24** Howard Weiss, owner of a musical instrument distributorship, thinks that demand for bass drums may be related to the number of television appearances by the popular group Stone Temple Pilots during the previous month. Weiss has collected the data shown in the following table:

Demand for Bass Drums	3	6	7	5	10	7
Stone Temple Pilots' TV Appearances	3	4	7	6	8	5

a) Graph these data to see whether a linear equation might describe the relationship between the group's television shows and bass drum sales.
b) Use the least squares regression method to derive a forecasting equation.
c) What is your estimate for bass drum sales if the Stone Temple Pilots performed on TV nine times last month?
d) What are the correlation coefficient (r) and the coefficient of determination (r^2) for this model, and what do they mean? **Px**

• **4.25** The following gives the number of accidents that occurred on a section of the Trans-Canada Highway during the past four months:

Month	Number of Accidents
January	30
February	40
March	60
April	90

Forecast the number of accidents that will occur in May, using least squares regression to derive a trend equation. **Px**

• **4.26** In the past, Arup Mukherjee's tire dealership in Sudbury sold an average of 1000 radials each year. In the past two years, 200 and 250, respectively, were sold in fall, 350 and 300 in winter, 150 and 165 in spring, and 300 and 285 in summer. With a major expansion planned, Mukherjee projects sales next year to increase to 1200 radials. What will be the demand during each season?

•• **4.27** Mark Cotteleer owns a company that manufactures canoes. Actual demand for Mark's canoes during each season in 2015 through 2018 was as follows:

Season	Year 2015	2016	2017	2018
Winter	1400	1200	1000	900
Spring	1500	1400	1600	1500
Summer	1000	2100	2000	1900
Fall	600	750	650	500

Mark has forecasted that annual demand for his canoes in 2019 will equal 5600 canoes. Based on this data and the multiplicative seasonal model, what will the demand level be for Mark's canoes in the spring of 2019?

•• **4.28** Attendance at Victoria's newest theme park has been as follows:

Quarter	Guests (in thousands)	Quarter	Guests (in thousands)
Winter 2015	73	Summer 2016	124
Spring 2015	104	Fall 2016	52
Summer 2015	168	Winter 2017	89
Fall 2015	74	Spring 2017	146
Winter 2016	65	Summer 2017	205
Spring 2016	82	Fall 2017	98

Compute seasonal indices using all of the data. **Px**

• **4.29** Central Electric Company estimates its demand trend line (in millions of kilowatt hours) to be:

$$D = 77 + 0.43Q$$

where Q refers to the sequential quarter number and $Q = 1$ for winter of year 1. In addition, the multiplicative seasonal factors are as follows:

Quarter	Factor (Index)
Winter	0.8
Spring	1.1
Summer	1.4
Fall	0.7

Forecast energy use for the four quarters of year 26, beginning with winter.

• **4.30** Brian Buckley has developed the following forecasting model:

$$\hat{y} = 36 + 4.3x$$

where $\hat{y}$ = demand for Aztec air conditioners and
x = the outside temperature (°F)

a) Forecast demand for the Aztec when the temperature is 70°F.
b) What is demand when the temperature is 80°F?
c) What is demand when the temperature is 90°F? **Px**

•• **4.31** Coffee Palace's manager, Joe Felan, suspects that demand for mocha latte coffees depends on the price being charged. Based on historical observations, Joe has gathered the following data, which show the numbers of these coffees sold over six different price values:

Price	Number Sold
$2.70	760
$3.50	510
$2.00	980
$4.20	250
$3.10	320
$4.05	480

Using these data, how many mocha latte coffees would be forecast to be sold according to simple linear regression if the price per cup were $2.80? **Px**

• **4.32** The following data relate the sales figures of the bar in Marty and Polly Starr's small bed-and-breakfast inn in Summerside, Prince Edward Island, to the number of guests registered that week:

Week	Guests	Bar Sales
1	16	$330
2	12	270
3	18	380
4	14	300

a) Perform a linear regression that relates bar sales to guests (not to time).
b) If the forecast is for 20 guests next week, what are the sales expected to be? **Px**

• **4.33** The number of transistors (in millions) made at a plant in Japan during the past five years follows:

Year	Transistors
1	140
2	160
3	190
4	200
5	210

a) Forecast the number of transistors to be made next year, using linear regression.
b) Compute the mean squared error (MSE) when using linear regression.
c) Compute the mean absolute percent error (MAPE). **Px**

• **4.34** The number of auto accidents in a certain region is related to the regional number of registered automobiles in thousands (X_1), alcoholic beverage sales in $10 000s (X_2), and rainfall in inches (X_3). Furthermore, the regression formula has been calculated as:

$$Y = a + b_1X_1 + b_2X_2 + b_3X_3$$

where Y = number of automobile accidents
$a = 7.5$
$b_1 = 3.5$
$b_2 = 4.5$
$b_3 = 2.5$

Calculate the expected number of automobile accidents under conditions (a), (b), and (c):

	X_1	X_2	X_3
(a)	2	3	0
(b)	3	5	1
(c)	4	7	2

•• **4.35** John Howard, a Toronto real estate developer, has devised a regression model to help determine residential housing prices in southern Ontario. The model was developed using recent sales in a particular neighbourhood. The price (Y) of the house is based on the size (square footage = X) of the house. The model is:

$$Y = 13\ 473 + 37.65X$$

The coefficient of correlation for the model is 0.63.
a) Use the model to predict the selling price of a house that is 1860 square feet.
b) An 1860-square-feet house recently sold for $95 000. Explain why this is not what the model predicted.

c) If you were going to use multiple regression to develop such a model, what other quantitative variables might you include?
d) What is the value of the coefficient of determination in this problem? **Px**

• **4.36** Accountants at the firm Michael Vest, Chartered Accountants, believed that several travelling executives were submitting unusually high travel vouchers when they returned from business trips. First, they took a sample of 200 vouchers submitted from the past year. Then they developed the following multiple-regression equation relating expected travel cost to number of days on the road (x_1) and distance travelled (x_2) in kilometres:

$$\hat{y} = \$90.00 + \$48.50x_1 + \$0.40x_2$$

The coefficient of correlation computed was 0.68.
a) If Wanda Fennell returns from a 300-kilometre trip that took her out of town for five days, what is the expected amount she should claim as expenses?
b) Fennell submitted a reimbursement request for $685. What should the accountant do?
c) Should any other variables be included? Which ones? Why? **Px**

•• **4.37** Sales of music stands at Johnny Ho's music store in Burnaby over the past 10 weeks are shown in the table.

Week	Demand	Week	Demand
1	20	6	29
2	21	7	36
3	28	8	22
4	37	9	25
5	25	10	28

a) Forecast demand for each week, including week 10, using exponential smoothing with $\alpha = 0.5$ (initial forecast = 20).
b) Compute the MAD.
c) Compute the tracking signal. **Px**

•• **4.38** City government has collected the following data on annual sales tax collections and new car registrations:

Annual Sales Tax Collections (in millions)	1.0	1.4	1.9	2.0	1.8	2.1	2.3
New Car Registrations (in thousands)	10	12	15	16	14	17	20

Determine the following:
a) The least squares regression equation.
b) Using the results of part (a), find the estimated sales tax collections if new car registrations total 22 000.
c) The coefficients of correlation and determination. **Px**

•• **4.39** Dr. Susan Sweeney, an Edmonton psychologist, specializes in treating patients who are agoraphobic (i.e., afraid to leave their homes). The following table indicates how many patients Dr. Sweeney has seen each year for the past 10 years. It also indicates what the robbery rate was in Edmonton during the same year:

Year	1	2	3	4	5	6	7	8	9	10
Number of Patients	36	33	40	41	40	55	60	54	58	61
Robbery Rate per 1000 Population	58.3	61.1	73.4	75.7	81.1	89.0	101.1	94.8	103.3	116.2

Using trend analysis, predict the number of patients Dr. Sweeney will see in years 11 and 12 as a function of time. How well does the model fit the data? **Px**

•• **4.40** Using the data in Problem 4.39, apply linear regression to study the relationship between the robbery rate and Dr. Sweeney's patient load. If the robbery rate increases to 131.2 in year 11, how many phobic patients will Dr. Sweeney treat? If the robbery rate drops to 90.6, what is the patient projection? **Px**

••• **4.41** Bus and subway ridership for the summer months in London, England, is believed to be tied heavily to the number of tourists visiting the city. During the past 12 years, the following data have been obtained:

Year (summer months)	Number of Tourists (in millions)	Ridership (in millions)
1	7	1.5
2	2	1.0
3	6	1.3
4	4	1.5
5	14	2.5
6	15	2.7
7	16	2.4
8	12	2.0
9	14	2.7
10	20	4.4
11	15	3.4
12	7	1.7

a) Plot these data and decide if a linear model is reasonable.
b) Develop a regression relationship.
c) What is expected ridership if 10 million tourists visit London in a year?
d) Explain the predicted ridership if there are no tourists at all.
e) What is the standard error of the estimate?
f) What is the model's correlation coefficient and coefficient of determination? **Px**

••• **4.42** Ontario Power Generation has been collecting data on demand for electric power in its western subregion for only the past two years. Those data are shown in the table below.

Month	Demand in Megawatts Last Year	This Year
January	5	17
February	6	14
March	10	20
April	13	23
May	18	30
June	15	38
July	23	44
August	26	41
September	21	33
October	15	23
November	12	26
December	14	17

To plan for expansion and to arrange to borrow power from neighbouring utilities during peak periods, the utility needs to be able to forecast demand for each month next year. However, the standard forecasting models discussed in this chapter will not fit the data observed for the two years.
a) What are the weaknesses of standard forecasting techniques as applied to this set of data?
b) Because known models are not appropriate here, propose your own approach to forecasting. Although there is no perfect solution to tackling data such as these (in other words, there are no 100% right or wrong answers), justify your model.
c) Forecast demand for each month next year using the model you propose.

••• **4.43** Emergency calls to the 911 system of Winnipeg for the past 24 weeks are shown in the following table:

Week	1	2	3	4	5	6	7	8	9	10	11	12
Calls	50	35	25	40	45	35	20	30	35	20	15	40
Week	13	14	15	16	17	18	19	20	21	22	23	24
Calls	55	35	25	55	55	40	35	60	75	50	40	65

a) Compute the exponentially smoothed forecast of calls for each week. Assume an initial forecast of 50 calls in the first week, and use $\alpha = 0.2$. What is the forecast for week 25?
b) Reforecast each period using $\alpha = 0.6$.
c) Actual calls during week 25 were 85. Which smoothing constant provides a superior forecast? Explain and justify the measure of error you used. **Px**

••• **4.44** Using the 911 call data in Problem 4.43, forecast calls for weeks 2 through 25 with a trend-adjusted exponential smoothing model. Assume an initial forecast for 50 calls for week 1 and an initial trend of zero. Use smoothing constants of $\alpha = 0.3$ and $\beta = 0.2$. Is this model better than that of Problem 4.43? What adjustment might be useful for further improvement? (Again, assume that actual calls in week 25 were 85.) **Px**

••• **4.45** The following are monthly actual and forecast demand levels for May through December for units of a product manufactured by the N. Tamimi Pharmaceutical Company:

Month	Actual Demand	Forecast Demand
May	100	100
June	80	104
July	110	99
August	115	101
September	105	104
October	110	104
November	125	105
December	120	109

What is the value of the tracking signal as of the end of December?

•• **4.46** Thirteen students entered the business program at Hillcrest College two years ago. The following table indicates what students scored on their initial placement math exams and their grade point averages (GPAs) after students were in the Hillcrest program for two years.

Student	A	B	C	D	E	F	G
Exam Score	421	377	585	690	608	390	415
GPA	2.90	2.93	3.00	3.45	3.66	2.88	2.15

Student	H	I	J	K	L	M
Exam Score	481	729	501	613	709	366
GPA	2.53	3.22	1.99	2.75	3.90	1.60

a) Is there a meaningful relationship between their initial placement math scores and grades?

b) If a student scores a 350, what do you think his or her GPA will be?

c) What about a student who scores 800?

••• **4.47** City Cycles has just started selling the new Z-10 mountain bike, with monthly sales as shown in the table. First, co-owner Amit wants to forecast by exponential smoothing by initially setting February's forecast equal to January's sales with $\alpha = 0.1$. Co-owner Barbara wants to use a three-period moving average.

	Sales	Amit	Barbara	Amit's Error	Barbara's Error
January	400	—			
February	380	400			
March	410				
April	375				
May					

a) Is there a strong linear trend in sales over time?

b) Fill in the table with what Amit and Barbara each forecast for May and the earlier months, as relevant.

c) Assume that May's actual sales figure turns out to be 405. Complete the table's columns and then calculate the mean absolute deviation for both Amit's and Barbara's methods.

d) Based on these calculations, which method seems more accurate? **Px**

•• **4.48** Sundar Balakrishnan, the general manager of Precision Engineering Corporation (PEC), thinks that his firm's engineering services contracted to highway construction firms are directly related to the volume of highway construction business contracted with companies in his geographic area. He wonders if this is really so and, if it is, can this information help him plan his operations better by forecasting the quantity of his engineering services required by construction firms in each quarter of the year? The following table presents the sales of his services and total amounts of contracts for highway construction over the past eight quarters:

Quarter	1	2	3	4	5	6	7	8
Sales of PEC Services (in $ thousands)	8	10	15	9	12	13	12	16
Contracts Released (in $ thousands)	153	172	197	178	185	199	205	226

a) Using this data, develop a regression equation for predicting the level of demand of Precision's services.

b) Determine the coefficient of correlation and the standard error of the estimate. **Px**

•••• **4.49** Western Provincial Trust Company is proud of its long tradition in Canada. It has bucked the trend of financial and liquidity problems that has repeatedly plagued the industry. Deposits have increased slowly but surely over the years, despite recessions in 1983, 1988, 1991, 2001, and 2008. Management believes it is necessary to have a long-range strategic plan including a one-year forecast and preferably even a give-year forecast of deposits. They examine the past deposit data and also contrast it against the provincial gross domestic product (GDP) over the same 44 years. The resulting data are in the following table:

Year	Deposits[a]	GDP[b]	Year	Deposits[a]	GDP[b]
1966	0.25	0.4	1988	6.2	2.5
1967	0.24	0.4	1989	4.1	2.8
1968	0.24	0.5	1990	4.5	2.9
1969	0.26	0.7	1991	6.1	3.4
1970	0.25	0.9	1992	7.7	3.8
1971	0.30	1.0	1993	10.1	4.1
1972	0.31	1.4	1994	15.2	4.0
1973	0.32	1.7	1995	18.1	4.0
1974	0.24	1.3	1996	24.1	3.9
1975	0.26	1.2	1997	25.6	3.8
1976	0.25	1.1	1998	30.3	3.8
1977	0.33	0.9	1999	36.0	3.7
1978	0.50	1.2	2000	31.1	4.1
1979	0.95	1.2	2001	31.7	4.1
1980	1.70	1.2	2002	38.5	4.0
1981	2.3	1.6	2003	47.9	4.5
1982	2.8	1.5	2004	49.1	4.6
1983	2.8	1.6	2005	55.8	4.5
1984	2.7	1.7	2006	70.1	4.6
1985	3.9	1.9	2007	70.9	4.6
1986	4.9	1.9	2008	79.1	4.7
1987	5.3	2.3	2009	94.0	5.0

[a]In $ millions.

[b]In $ billions.

a) Using exponential smoothing, with $\alpha = 0.6$, then trend analysis, and finally linear regression, discuss which forecasting model fits best for Western Provincial's strategic plan. Justify the selection of one model over another.

b) Carefully examine the data. Can you make a case for excluding a portion of the information? Why? Would that change your choice of model? **Px**

CASE STUDIES

Fast Creek Lightning: (B)*

Fast Creek is a city in south central Saskatchewan located along the Trans-Canada Highway. Fast Creek has a population of just over 27 000 residents and is a regional hub for the many smaller towns and hundreds of farms in the surrounding area. Fast Creek is a transportation and industrial centre, and has several federal and provincial government offices.

Fast Creek is also a sports centre, and its junior hockey team, the Fast Creek Lightning, has a long history of success in the Central Hockey League but has not won a major trophy in close to 10 years. Since the legendary Scotty Beauchamp was hired as head coach in 2011 (in the hopes of winning the elusive league and national championship), total attendance at home games for each month has increased. Prior to Beauchamp's arrival, attendance averaged 25 000 to 29 000 per month (or between 5000 and 5800 tickets for each of the five home games per month). Season ticket sales bumped up by almost 2000 just with the announcement of the new coach's arrival. The Fast Creek Lightning are ready to move to the big time!

The immediate issue facing the Lightning, however, is not the championship. It is capacity. The existing Fast Creek arena, built in 1953, has seating for 10 800 fans. The following table indicates total home game attendance each month of the season for the past six years.

One of Beauchamp's demands on joining the Lightning had been a new arena. With attendance increasing, Lightning executives and city officials have begun to face the issue head-on. Beauchamp would like a state-of-the-art training facility solely for his players as an additional feature of any expansion.

The Lightning's owner, Keith MacLennan, has decided it is time for his vice-president of development to forecast when the existing arena will "max out". The expansion is, in his mind, a given. But MacLennan needs to know how long he could wait. He also seeks a revenue projection, assuming an average ticket price of $50 in 2017–2018 and a 5% increase each season in future prices.

Discussion Questions

1. Develop a forecasting model, justifying its selection over other forecasting techniques, and project attendance through the 2018–2019 season.

2. What revenues are to be expected in the 2017–2018 and 2018–2019 seasons?
3. Discuss the team's options.

Month	2011–2012	2012–2013	2013–2014
November	34 200	36 100	35 900
December[a]	39 800	40 200	46 500
January	38 200	39 100	43 100
February[b]	26 900	25 300	27 900
March	35 100	36 200	39 200

Month	2014–2015	2015–2016	2016–2017
November	41 900	42 500	46 900
December[a]	46 100	48 200	50 100
January	43 900	44 200	45 900
February[b]	30 100	33 900	36 300
March	40 500	47 800	49 900

[a]Every December, Fast Creek hosts a Holiday Classic weekend with special promotions and an old-timers' game that draws large crowds

[b]A popular week-long winter carnival in nearby Helmsville every February has a negative impact on attendance.

*This integrated study runs throughout the text. Issues facing Fast Creek's hockey expansion include (A) managing the arena project (Chapter 3); (C) quality of facilities (Chapter 6); (D) break-even analysis for food services (Supplement 7 MyLab Operations Management); (E) location of the new arena (Chapter 8 MyLab Operations Management); (F) inventory planning of hockey programs (Chapter 12 MyLab Operations Management); and (G) scheduling of campus security officers/staff for game days (Chapter 13). Recurring cases are also available in a separate file for instructors using the PCL.

Video Case | Forecasting at Hard Rock Cafe

With the growth of Hard Rock Cafe—from one pub in London in 1971 to more than 145 restaurants in 60 countries today—came a corporate-wide demand for better forecasting. Hard Rock uses long-range forecasting in setting a capacity plan and intermediate-term forecasting for locking in contracts for leather goods (used in jackets) and for such food items as beef, chicken, and pork. Its short-term sales forecasts are conducted each month, by cafe, and then aggregated for a headquarters view.

The heart of the sales forecasting system is the point-of-sale system (POS), which, in effect, captures transaction data on nearly every person who walks through a cafe's door. The sale of each entrée represents one customer; the entrée sales data are transmitted daily to the Orlando corporate headquarters' database. There, the financial team, headed by Todd Lindsey, begins the forecast

process. Lindsey forecasts monthly guest counts, retail sales, banquet sales, and concert sales (if applicable) at each cafe. The general managers of individual cafes tap into the same database to prepare a daily forecast for their sites. A cafe manager pulls up prior years' sales for that day, adding information from the local chamber of commerce or tourist board on upcoming events such as a major convention, sporting event, or concert in the city where the cafe is located. The daily forecast is further broken into hourly sales, which drives employee scheduling. An hourly forecast of $5500 in sales translates into 19 workstations, which are further broken down into a specific number of wait staff, hosts, bartenders, and kitchen staff. Computerized scheduling software plugs people in based on their availability. Variances between forecast and actual sales are then examined to see why errors occurred.

Hard Rock doesn't limit its use of forecasting tools to sales. To evaluate managers and set bonuses, a three-year weighted moving average is applied to cafe sales. If cafe general managers exceed their targets, a bonus is computed. Todd Lindsey, at corporate headquarters, applies weights of 40% to the most recent year's sales, 40% to the year before, and 20% to sales two years ago in reaching his moving average.

An even more sophisticated application of statistics is found in Hard Rock's menu planning. Using multiple regression, managers can compute the impact on demand of other menu items if the price of one item is changed. For example, if the price of a cheeseburger increases from $7.99 to $8.99, Hard Rock can predict the effect this will have on sales of chicken sandwiches, pork sandwiches, and salads. Managers do the same analysis on menu placement, with the centre section driving higher sales volumes. When an item such as a hamburger is moved off the centre to one of the side flaps, the corresponding effect on related items, say French fries, is determined.

Discussion Questions*

1. Describe three different forecasting applications at Hard Rock. Name three other areas in which you think Hard Rock could use forecasting models.

2. What is the role of the POS system in forecasting at Hard Rock?
3. Justify the use of the weighting system used for evaluating managers for annual bonuses.
4. Name several variables besides those mentioned in the case that could be used as good predictors of daily sales in each cafe.
5. At Hard Rock's Moscow restaurant, the manager is trying to evaluate how a new advertising campaign affects guest counts. Using data for the past 10 months (see the table), develop a least-squares regression relationship and then forecast the expected guest count when advertising is $65 000.

Hard Rock's Moscow Cafe[a]

Month	1	2	3	4	5	6	7	8	9	10
Guest count (in thousands)	21	24	27	32	29	37	43	43	54	66
Advertising (in $ thousands)	14	17	25	25	35	35	45	50	60	60

[a]These figures are used for purposes of this case study.

*You may wish to view the video that accompanies this case before addressing these questions.

▶Additional Case Study: Visit **MyLab Operations Management** for this case study:
North-South Airlines: Reflects the merger of two airlines and addresses their maintenance costs.

CHAPTER 4 | RAPID REVIEW

MyLab
Operations
Management

Main Heading	Review Material	
WHAT IS FORECASTING? (pp. 104–106)	• **Forecasting**—The art and science of predicting future events. • **Economic forecasts**—Planning indicators that are valuable in helping organizations prepare medium- to long-range forecasts. • **Technological forecasts**—Long-term forecasts concerned with the rates of technological progress. • **Demand forecasts**—Projections of a company's sales for each time period in the planning horizon.	
THE STRATEGIC IMPORTANCE OF FORECASTING (pp. 106–107)	*The forecast is the only estimate of demand until actual demand becomes known.* Forecasts of demand drive decisions in many areas, including *Human resources, Capacity, Supply chain management.*	**VIDEO 4.1** Forecasting at Hard Rock Cafe
SEVEN STEPS IN THE FORECASTING SYSTEM (p. 107)	Forecasting follows seven basic steps: (1) Determine the use of the forecast; (2) Select the items to be forecasted; (3) Determine the time horizon of the forecast; (4) Select the forecasting model(s); (5) Gather the data needed to make the forecast; (6) Make the forecast; (7) Validate and implement the results.	
FORECASTING APPROACHES (pp. 107–108)	• **Quantitative forecasts**—Forecasts that employ mathematical modelling to forecast demand. • **Qualitative forecasts**—Forecasts that incorporate factors such as the decision maker's intuition, emotions, personal experiences, and value system. • **Jury of executive opinion**—A forecasting technique that uses the opinion of a small group of high-level managers to form a group estimate of demand.	

Main Heading	Review Material	

- **Delphi method**—A forecasting technique using a group process that allows experts to make forecasts.
- **Sales force composite**—A forecasting technique based on salespersons' estimates of expected sales.
- **Consumer market survey**—A forecasting method that solicits input from customers or potential customers regarding future purchasing plans.
- **Time series**—A forecasting technique that uses a series of past data points to make a forecast.

TIME-SERIES FORECASTING
(pp. 108–126)

- **Naive approach**—A forecasting technique that assumes that demand in the next period is equal to demand in the most recent period.
- **Moving averages**—A forecasting method that uses an average of the n most recent periods of data to forecast the next period.

$$\text{Moving average} = \frac{\Sigma \text{Demand in previous } n \text{ periods}}{n} \quad \textbf{(4-1)}$$

$$\text{Weighted moving average} = \frac{\Sigma(\text{Weight for period } n)\,(\text{Demand in period } n)}{\Sigma \text{Weights}} \quad \textbf{(4-2)}$$

- **Exponential smoothing**—A weighted moving average forecasting technique in which data points are weighted by an exponential function.
- **Smoothing constant**—The weighting factor, α, used in an exponential smoothing forecast, a number between 0 and 1.

$$\text{New forecast} = \text{Last period's forecast} + \alpha$$
$$(\text{Last period's actual demand} - \text{Last period's forecast}) \quad \textbf{(4-3)}$$

$$\text{Exponential smoothing formula: } F_t = F_{t-1} + \alpha(A_{t-1} - F_{t-1}) \quad \textbf{(4-4)}$$

where F_t = new forecast

F_{t-1} = previous period's forecast

α = smoothing (or weighting) constant $(0 \le \alpha \le 1)$

A_{t-1} = previous period's actual demand

- **Mean absolute deviation (MAD)**—A measure of the overall forecast error for a model.

$$\text{MAD} = \frac{\Sigma |\text{Actual} - \text{Forecast}|}{n} \quad \textbf{(4-5)}$$

- **Mean squared error (MSE)**—The average of the squared differences between the forecasted and observed values.

$$\text{MSE} = \frac{\Sigma(\text{Forecast errors})^2}{n} \quad \textbf{(4-6)}$$

- **Mean absolute percent error (MAPE)**—The average of the absolute differences between the forecast and actual values, expressed as a percentage of actual values.

$$\text{MAPE} = \frac{\sum_{i=1}^{n} 100 |\text{Actual}_t - \text{Forecast}_t| / \text{Actual}_t}{n} \quad \textbf{(4-7)}$$

Exponential Smoothing With Trend Adjustment

Forecast including trend (FIT_t) = Exponentially smoothed forecast (F_t)
+ Exponentially smoothed trend (T_t) $\quad \textbf{(4-8)}$

- **Trend projection**—A time-series forecasting method that fits a trend line to a series of historical data points and then projects the line into the future for forecasts.

Forecast including trend (FIT_t) = Exponentially smoothed forecast (F_t)
+ Exponentially smoothed trend (T_t) $\quad \textbf{(4-8)}$

$$F_t = \alpha(A_{t-1}) + (1 - \alpha)(F_{t-1} + T_{t-1}) \quad \textbf{(4-9)}$$

Problems: 4.1–4.23, 4.25–4.29, 4.33, 4.37, 4.39, 4.43, 4.44, 4.47, 4.49

Virtual Office Hours for Solved Problems: 4.2–4.4

ACTIVE MODELS 4.1–4.4

Main Heading	Review Material	

$$T_t = \beta(F_t - F_{t-1}) + (1 - \beta)T_{t-1} \qquad \textbf{(4-10)}$$

where F_t = exponentially smoothed forecast of the data series in period t

T_t = exponentially smoothed trend in period t

A_t = actual demand in period t

α = smoothing constant for the average $(0 \leq \alpha \leq 1)$

β = smoothing constant for the trend $(0 \leq \beta \leq 1)$

Trend Projection and Regression Analysis

$$\hat{y} = a + bx, \text{ where } b = \frac{\Sigma xy - n\bar{x}\bar{y}}{\Sigma x^2 - n\bar{x}^2}, \text{ and } a = \bar{y} - b\bar{x} \quad \textbf{(4-11),(4-12),(4-13)}$$

- **Seasonal variations**—Regular upward or downward movements in a time series that tie to recurring events.
- **Cycles**—Patterns in the data that occur every several years.

ASSOCIATIVE FORECASTING METHODS: REGRESSION AND CORRELATION ANALYSIS (pp. 126–131)

- **Linear-regression analysis**—A straight-line mathematical model to describe the functional relationships between independent and dependent variables.
- **Standard error of the estimate**—A measure of variability around the regression line—its standard deviation.

$$S_{y,x} = \sqrt{\frac{\Sigma(y - y_c)^2}{n - 2}} \qquad \textbf{(4-14)}$$

$$S_{y,x} = \sqrt{\frac{\Sigma y^2 - a\Sigma y - b\Sigma xy}{n - 2}} \qquad \textbf{(4-15)}$$

- **Coefficient of correlation**—A measure of the strength of the relationship between two variables.

$$r = \frac{n\Sigma xy - \Sigma x\Sigma y}{\sqrt{[n\Sigma x^2 - (\Sigma x)^2][n\Sigma y^2 - (\Sigma y)^2]}} \qquad \textbf{(4-16)}$$

- **Coefficient of determination**—A measure of the amount of variation in the dependent variable about its mean that is explained by the regression equation.
- **Multiple regression**—An associative forecasting method with more than one independent variable.

$$\text{Multiple-regression forecast:} \quad \hat{y} = a + b_1 x_1 + b_2 x_2 \quad \textbf{(4-17)}$$

Problems: 4.24, 4.30–4.32, 4.34–4.36, 4.38, 4.40, 4.41, 4.46, 4.48

MONITORING AND CONTROLLING FORECASTS (pp. 132–134)

- **Tracking signal**—A measurement of how well the forecast is predicting actual values.

$$(\text{Tracking signal}) = \frac{\text{Cumulative error}}{\text{MAD}}$$

$$= \frac{\Sigma(\text{Actual demand in period } i - \text{Forecast demand in period } i)}{\text{MAD}}$$

$$\text{Where} \quad (\text{MAD}) = \frac{\Sigma|\text{Actual} - \text{Forecast}|}{n} \qquad \textbf{(4-18)}$$

- **Bias**—A forecast that is consistently higher or consistently lower than actual values of a time series.
- **Adaptive smoothing**—An approach to exponential smoothing forecasting in which the smoothing constant is automatically changed to keep errors to a minimum.
- **Focus forecasting**—Forecasting that tries a variety of computer models and selects the best one for a particular application.

Problems: 4.37, 4.45

Main Heading	Review Material
FORECASTING IN THE SERVICE SECTOR (pp. 134–135)	Service sector forecasting may require good short-term demand records, even per 15-minute intervals. Demand during holidays or specific weather events may also need to be tracked.

Self-Test

- **Before taking the self-test,** refer to the learning objectives listed at the beginning of the chapter and the key terms listed at the end of the chapter.

LO1 Forecasting time horizons include:
a) long range.
b) medium range.
c) short range.
d) all of the above.

LO2 Qualitative methods of forecasting include:
a) sales force composite.
b) jury of executive opinion.
c) consumer market survey.
d) exponential smoothing.
e) all except (d).

LO3 The difference between a *moving-average* model and an *exponential smoothing* model is that _____.

LO4 Three popular measures of forecast accuracy are:
a) total error, average error, and mean error.
b) average error, median error, and maximum error.
c) median error, minimum error, and maximum absolute error.
d) mean absolute deviation, mean squared error, and mean absolute percent error.

LO5 Average demand for iPods in Apple store in Rome, Italy, is 800 units per month. The May monthly index is 1.25. What is the seasonally adjusted sales forecast for May?
a) 640 units
b) 798.75 units
c) 800 units
d) 1000 units
e) cannot be calculated with the information given

LO6 The main difference between simple and multiple regression is _____.

LO7 The tracking signal is the:
a) standard error of the estimate.
b) cumulative error.
c) mean absolute deviation (MAD).
d) ratio of the cumulative error to MAD.
e) mean absolute percent error (MAPE).

Answers: LO1. d; LO2. e; LO3. exponential smoothing is a weighted moving average model in which all prior values are weighted with a set of exponentially declining weights; LO4. d; LO5. d; LO6. simple regression has only one independent variable; LO7. d.

MyLab Operations Management

Most of these questions can be found in MyLab Operations Management. Visit MyLab Operations Management to access cases, videos, downloadable software, and much more. MyLab Operations Management Management also features a personalized Study Plan that helps you identify which chapter concepts you've mastered and guides you towards study tools for additional practice.

Jochen Tack/Alamy Stock Photo

5

Design of Goods and Services

Product Strategy Provides Competitive Advantage at Regal Marine

Thirty years after its founding by potato farmer Paul Kuck, Regal Marine has become a powerful force on the waters of the world. The world's third-largest boat manufacturer (by global sales), Regal exports to 30 countries, including Russia and China. Almost one-third of its sales are overseas.

Product design is critical in the highly competitive pleasure boat business: "We keep in touch with our customers and we respond to the marketplace," says Kuck. "We're introducing six new models this year alone. I'd say we're definitely on the aggressive end of the spectrum."

With changing consumer tastes, compounded by material changes and ever-improving marine engineering, the design function is under constant pressure. Added to these pressures is the constant issue of cost competitiveness combined with the need to provide good value for customers.

Consequently, Regal Marine is a frequent user of computer-aided design (CAD). New designs come to life via Regal's three-dimensional CAD system borrowed from automotive technology. Regal's naval architects' goal is to

< Global
Company
Profile
Regal
Marine

151

continue to reduce the time from concept to proto-type to production. The sophisticated CAD system not only has reduced product development time but also has reduced problems with tooling and production, resulting in a superior product.

All of Regal's products, from its $14 000 5.7-metre boat to the $500 000 13-metre Commodore yacht, follow a similar production process. Hulls and decks are separately hand-produced by spraying pre-formed moulds with three to five layers of a fibreglass lami-nate. The hulls and decks harden and are removed to become the lower and upper structure of the boat. As they move to the assembly line, they are joined and components are added at each workstation.

Wooden components, precut in-house by computer-driven routers, are delivered on a just-in-time basis for installation at one station. Engines—one of the few purchased components—are installed at another station. Racks of electrical wiring harnesses, engi-neered and rigged in-house, are then installed. An

Once a hull has been pulled from the mould, it travels down a monorail assembly path. JIT inventory delivers engines, wiring, seats, flooring, and interiors when needed.

in-house upholstery department delivers customized seats, beds, dashboards, or other cushioned compo-nents. Finally, chrome fixtures are put in place, and the boat is sent to Regal's test tank for watertight, gauge, and system inspection.

Goods and Services Selection

Global firms like Regal Marine know that the basis for an organization's existence is the good or service it provides society. Great products are the keys to success. Anything less than an excellent product strategy can be devastating to a firm. To maximize the potential for success, top companies focus on only a few products and then concentrate on those products. For instance, Honda's focus is engines. Virtually all of Honda's sales (autos, motorcycles, generators, lawn mowers) are based on its outstanding engine technology. Likewise, Intel's focus is on microprocessors, and Michelin's is on tires. However, because most products have a limited and even predictable life cycle, companies must constantly be looking for new products to design, develop, and take to market. Good opera-tions managers insist on strong communication among customer, product, processes, and suppliers, which results in a high success rate for their new products. 3M's goal is to produce 30% of its profit from products introduced in the last four years. Benchmarks vary by industry, of course; Regal introduces six new boats a year, and Rubbermaid introduces a new product each day!

One product strategy is to build particular competence in customizing an established family of goods or services. This approach allows the customer to choose product variations while reinforcing the organization's strength. Dell Computer, for example, has built a huge market by delivering computers with the exact hardware and software desired by end users. And Dell does it fast—it understands that speed to market is imperative to gain a competitive edge.

Note that many service firms also refer to their offerings as products. For instance, when Allstate Insurance offers a new homeowner's policy, it is referred to as a new "product". Similarly, when CIBC opens a mortgage department, it offers a number of new mortgage "products". Although the term *product* may often refer to tangible goods, it also refers to offer-ings by service organizations.

Product decision

The selection, definition, and design of products.

An effective product strategy links product decisions with investment, market share, and prod-uct life cycle, and defines the breadth of the product line. The *objective of the **product decision** is to develop and implement a product strategy that meets the demands of the marketplace with a competitive advantage*. As one of the 10 decisions of OM, product strategy may focus on develop-ing a competitive advantage via differentiation, low cost, rapid response, or a combination of these.

Product Design Can Manifest Itself in Concepts, Technology, and Packaging. Whether it is a design focused on style at Nike (a), the application of technology at Samsung (b), or a new container at Sherwin Williams (c), operations managers need to remind themselves that the creative process is ongoing with major implications for production.

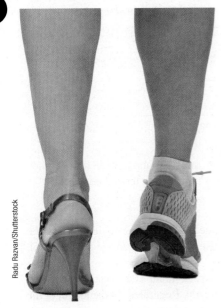

(a) Concepts: Nike, in its creative way, has moved athletic shoes from utilitarian necessities into glamorous accessories and in the process is constantly reinventing all parts of the shoe, including the heel.

(b) Technology: Samsung's latest technology: radical new smartphones that are bendable.

(c) Packaging: Dutch Boy's Ready to Roll contains 2.5 gallons of paint and has a built-in roller tray.

PRODUCT STRATEGY OPTIONS SUPPORT COMPETITIVE ADVANTAGE

A world of options exists in the selection, definition, and design of products. Product selection is choosing the good or service to provide to customers or clients. For instance, hospitals specialize in various types of patients and medical procedures. In consultation with a province's Ministry of Health, it could be determined that the public is best served if a particular hospital will operate as a general-purpose hospital, a maternity hospital, or, as in the case of the Canadian hospital Shouldice, will specialize in hernias. Hospitals select their products when they decide what kind of hospital to be. Numerous other options exist for hospitals, just as they exist for Taco Bell and Toyota.

Service organizations like Shouldice Hospital *differentiate* themselves through their product. Shouldice differentiates itself by offering a distinctly unique and high-quality product. Its world-renowned specialization in hernia repair service is so effective it allows patients to return to normal living in eight days as opposed to the average two weeks—and with very few complications. The entire production system is designed for this one product. Local anaesthetics are used, patients enter and leave the operating room on their own, rooms are spartan, and meals are served in a common dining room, encouraging patients to get out of bed for meals and join their fellows in the lounge. As Shouldice has demonstrated, product selection affects the entire production system.

Taco Bell has developed and executed a *low-cost* strategy through product design. By designing a product (its menu) that can be produced with a minimum of labour in small kitchens, Taco Bell has developed a product line that is both low cost and high value. Successful product design has allowed Taco Bell to increase the food content of its products from 27¢ to 45¢ of each sales dollar.

Toyota's strategy is *rapid response* to changing consumer demand. By executing the fastest automobile design in the industry, Toyota has driven the speed of product development down to well under two years in an industry whose standard is still over two years. The shorter design time allows Toyota to get a car to market before consumer tastes change and to do so with the latest technology and innovations.

Product decisions are fundamental to an organization's strategy and have major implications throughout the operations function. For instance, GM's steering columns are a good example of the strong role product design plays in both quality and efficiency. The redesigned steering column has a simpler design, with about 30% fewer parts than its predecessor. The result: Assembly

FIGURE 5.1
Product Life Cycle, Sales, Cost, and Profit

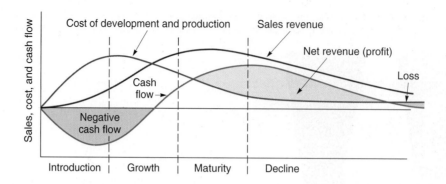

time is one-third that of the older column, and the new column's quality is about seven times higher. As an added bonus, machinery on the new line costs a third less than that on the old line.

PRODUCT LIFE CYCLES

LO1 Define *product life cycle*

Products are born. They live and they die. They are cast aside by a changing society. It may be helpful to think of a product's life as divided into four phases. Those phases are *introduction*, *growth*, *maturity*, and *decline*.

Product life cycles may be a matter of a few hours (a newspaper), months (seasonal fashions and personal computers), years (video cassette tapes), or decades (cars). Regardless of the length of the cycle, the task for the operations manager is the same: to design a system that helps introduce new products successfully. If the operations function cannot perform effectively at this stage, the firm may be saddled with losers—products that cannot be produced efficiently or perhaps at all.

Figure 5.1 shows the four life cycle stages and the relationship of product sales, cash flow, and profit over the life cycle of a product. Note that typically a firm has a negative cash flow while it develops a product. When the product is successful, those losses may be recovered. Eventually, the successful product may yield a profit prior to its decline. However, the profit is fleeting—hence, the constant demand for new products.

LIFE CYCLE AND STRATEGY

Just as operations managers must be prepared to develop new products, they must also be prepared to develop *strategies* for new and *existing* products. Periodic examination of products is appropriate because *strategies change as products move through their life cycle*. Successful product strategies require determining the best strategy for each product based on its position in its life cycle. A firm, therefore, identifies products or families of products and their position in the life cycle. Let us review some strategy options as products move through their life cycles.

INTRODUCTORY PHASE Because products in the introductory phase are still being "fine-tuned" for the market, as are their production techniques, they may warrant unusual expenditures for (1) research, (2) product development, (3) process modification and enhancement, and (4) supplier development. For example, when cellular phones were first introduced, the features desired by the public were still being determined. At the same time, operations managers were still groping for the best manufacturing techniques.

GROWTH PHASE In the growth phase, product design has begun to stabilize, and effective forecasting of capacity requirements is necessary. Adding capacity or enhancing existing capacity to accommodate the increase in product demand may be necessary.

MATURITY PHASE By the time a product is mature, competitors are established. So high-volume, innovative production may be appropriate. Improved cost control, reduction in options, and a paring down of the product line may be effective or necessary for profitability and market share.

DECLINE PHASE Management may need to be ruthless with those products whose life cycle is at an end. Dying products are typically poor products in which to invest resources and managerial talent. Unless dying products make some unique contribution to the firm's reputation or its product line or can be sold with an unusually high contribution, their production should be terminated.[1]

---

[1] *Contribution* is defined as the difference between direct cost and selling price. Direct costs are labour and material that go into the product.

PRODUCT-BY-VALUE ANALYSIS

The effective operations manager selects items that show the greatest promise. This is the Pareto principle (i.e., focus on the critical few, not the trivial many) applied to product mix: Resources are to be invested in the critical few and not the trivial many. **Product-by-value analysis** lists products in descending order of their *individual dollar contribution* to the firm. It also lists the *total annual dollar contribution* of the product. Low contribution on a per-unit basis by a particular product may look substantially different if it represents a large portion of the company's sales.

A product-by-value report allows management to evaluate possible strategies for each product. These may include increasing cash flow (e.g., increasing contribution by raising selling price or lowering cost), increasing market penetration (improving quality and/or reducing cost or price), or reducing costs (improving the production process). The report may also tell management which product offerings should be eliminated and which fail to justify further investment in research and development or capital equipment. Product-by-value analysis focuses management's attention on the strategic direction for each product.

Product-by-value analysis
A list of products, in descending order of their individual dollar contribution to the firm, as well as the *total annual dollar contribution* of the product.

Generating New Products

STUDENT TIP
Societies reward those who supply new products that reflect their needs.

Because products die; because products must be weeded out and replaced; because firms generate most of their revenue and profit from new products—product selection, definition, and design take place on a continuing basis. Consider recent product changes: TV to HDTV, radio to satellite radio, coffee shop to Starbucks lifestyle coffee, travelling circus to Cirque du Soleil, land line to cell phone, cell phone to smartphone, Walkman to iPod, an Internet of digital information to an Internet of "things"—and the list goes on. Knowing how to find and develop new products successfully is a requirement.

NEW PRODUCT OPPORTUNITIES

Aggressive new product development requires that organizations build structures internally that have open communication with customers, innovative organizational cultures, aggressive R&D, strong leadership, formal incentives, and training. Only then can a firm profitably and energetically focus on specific opportunities such as the following:

1. *Understanding the customer* is the premier issue in new product development. Many commercially important products are initially thought of and even prototyped by users rather than producers. Such products tend to be developed by "lead users"—companies, organizations, or individuals that are well ahead of market trends and have needs that go far beyond those of average users. The operations manager must be "tuned in" to the market and particularly to these innovative lead users.
2. *Economic change* brings increasing levels of affluence in the long run but economic cycles and price changes in the short run. In the long run, for instance, more and more people can afford automobiles, but in the short run, a recession may weaken the demand for automobiles.
3. *Sociological and demographic change* may appear in such factors as decreasing family size. This trend alters the size preference for homes, apartments, and automobiles.
4. *Technological change* makes possible everything from cell phones to iPads to artificial hearts.
5. *Political/legal change* brings about new trade agreements, tariffs, and government requirements.
6. Other changes may be brought about through *market practice*, *professional standards*, *suppliers*, and *distributors*.

Operations managers must be aware of these dynamics and be able to anticipate changes in product opportunities, the products themselves, product volume, and product mix.

IMPORTANCE OF NEW PRODUCTS

The importance of new products cannot be overestimated. As Figure 5.2(a) shows, leading companies generate a substantial portion of their sales from products less than five years old. Even Disney (Figure 5.2(b)) needs new theme parks to boost attendance. And giant Cisco Systems is expanding from its core business of making routers and switches into building its own computer servers (Figure 5.2(c)). The need for new products is why Gillette developed its multi blade

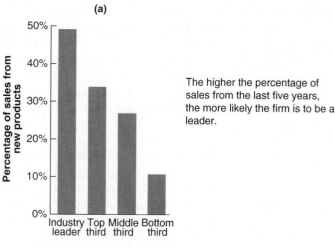

(a)

The higher the percentage of sales from the last five years, the more likely the firm is to be a leader.

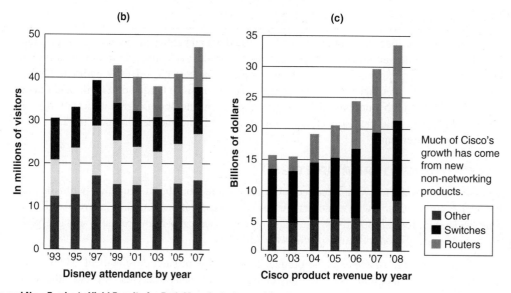

Disney World innovates with new parks, rides, and attractions to boost attendance.

■ Magic Kingdom
▫ Epcot
■ Disney's Hollywood Studios
■ Animal Kingdom

Much of Cisco's growth has come from new non-networking products.

■ Other
■ Switches
▪ Routers

FIGURE 5.2 Innovation and New Products Yield Results for Both Manufacturing and Services

razors, in spite of continuing high sales of its phenomenally successful Sensor razor, and why Disney innovates in spite of being the leading family entertainment company in the world.

Despite constant efforts to introduce viable new products, many new products do not succeed. Indeed, for General Mills to come up with a winner in the breakfast cereal market—defined as a cereal that gets a scant half of 1% of the market—isn't easy. Among the top 10 brands of cereal, the youngest, Honey Nut Cheerios, was created in 1979. DuPont estimates that it takes 250 ideas to yield one *marketable* product.[2]

As one can see, product selection, definition, and design occur frequently—perhaps hundreds of times for each financially successful product. Operations managers and their organizations must be able to accept risk and tolerate failure. They must accommodate a high volume of new product ideas while maintaining the activities to which they are already committed.

STUDENT TIP

Motorola went through 3000 working models before it developed its first pocket cell phone.

Product Development

PRODUCT DEVELOPMENT SYSTEM

An effective product strategy links product decisions with cash flow, market dynamics, product life cycle, and the organization's capabilities. A firm must have the cash for product development, understand the changes constantly taking place in the marketplace, and have the necessary

[2] Rosabeth Kanter, John Kao, and Fred Wiersema, *Innovation Breakthrough Thinking at 3M, DuPont, GE, Pfizer, and Rubbermaid* (New York, NY: HarperBusiness, 1997).

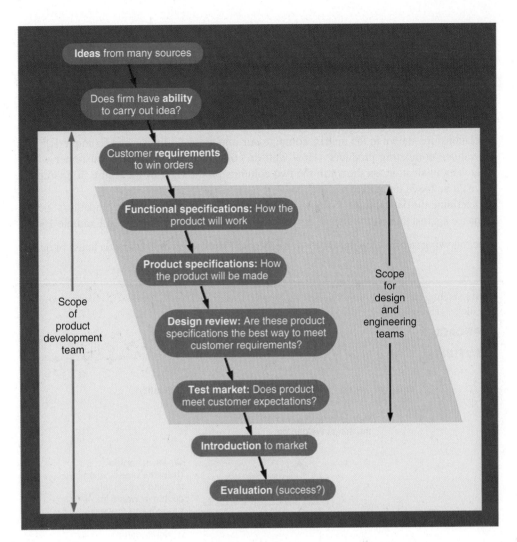

FIGURE 5.3
Product Development Stages
Product concepts are developed from a variety of sources, both external and internal to the firm. Concepts that survive the product idea stage progress through various stages, with nearly constant review, feedback, and evaluation in a highly participative environment to minimize failure.

talents and resources available. The product development system may well determine not only product success but also the firm's future. Figure 5.3 shows the stages of product development. In this system, product options go through a series of steps, each having its own screening and evaluation criteria but providing a continuing flow of information to prior steps.

The screening process extends to the operations function. Optimum product development depends not only on support from other parts of the firm but also on the successful integration of all 10 of the OM decisions, from product design to maintenance. Identifying products that appear likely to capture market share, be cost effective, and be profitable, but are in fact very difficult to produce, may lead to failure rather than success.

QUALITY FUNCTION DEPLOYMENT (QFD)

Quality function deployment (QFD) refers to both (1) determining what will satisfy the customer and (2) translating those customer desires into the target design. The idea is to capture a rich understanding of customer wants and to identify alternative process solutions. This information is then integrated into the evolving product design. QFD is used early in the design process to help determine *what will satisfy the customer* and *where to deploy quality efforts.*

One of the tools of QFD is the house of quality. The **house of quality** is a graphic technique for defining the relationship between customer desires and product (or service). Only by defining this relationship in a rigorous way can operations managers design products and processes with features desired by customers. Defining this relationship is the first step in building a world-class production system. To build the house of quality, we perform seven basic steps:

1. Identify customer *wants*. (What do prospective customers want in this product?)
2. Identify *how* the good/service will satisfy customer wants. (Identify specific product characteristics, features, or attributes and show how they will satisfy customer *wants*.)

LO2 Describe a product development system

Quality function deployment (QFD)
A process for determining customer requirements (customer "wants") and translating them into the attributes (the "hows") that each functional area can understand and act on.

LO3 Build a house of quality

House of quality
A part of the QFD process that utilizes a planning matrix to relate customer "wants" to "how" the firm is going to meet those "wants".

3. Relate customer *wants* to product *hows*. (Build a matrix, as in Example 1, that shows this relationship.)
4. Identify relationships between the firm's *hows*. (How do our *hows* tie together? For instance, in the following example, there is a high relationship between low electricity requirements and auto focus, auto exposure, and a paint pallet because they all require electricity. This relationship is shown in the "roof" of the house in Example 1.)
5. Develop importance ratings. (Using the *customer's* importance ratings and weights for the relationships shown in the matrix, compute *our* importance ratings, as in Example 1.)
6. Evaluate competing products. (How well do competing products meet customer wants? Such an evaluation, as shown in the two columns on the right of the figure in Example 1, would be based on market research.)
7. Determine the desirable technical attributes, your performance, and the competitors' performance against these attributes. (This is done at the bottom of the figure in Example 1.)

The following step-by-step illustration for Example 1 shows how to construct a house of quality.

EXAMPLE 1

Constructing a House of Quality

Great Cameras, Inc., wants a methodology that strengthens its ability to meet customer desires with its new digital camera.

APPROACH ▶ Use QFD's house of quality.

SOLUTION ▶ Build the house of quality for Great Cameras, Inc. We do so here going step by step.

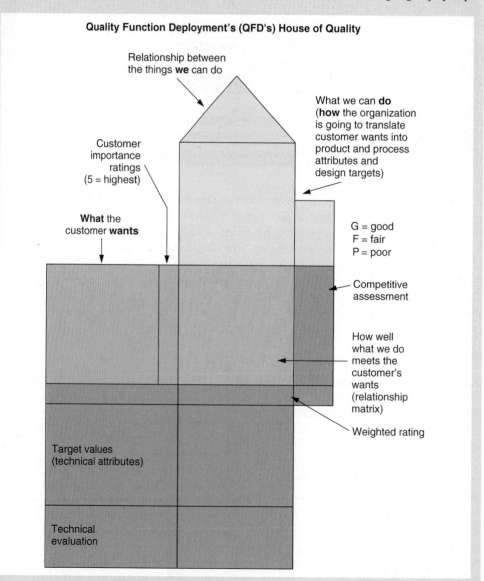

Quality Function Deployment's (QFD's) House of Quality

First, through market research, Great Cameras, Inc., determined what the customer *wants*. Those *wants* are shown on the left of the house of quality. Second, the product development team determined *how* the organization is going to translate those customer *wants* into product design and process attribute targets. These *hows* are entered across the top portion of the house of quality.

	Low electricity requirements	Aluminum components	Auto focus	Auto exposure	Paint pallet	Ergonomic design
Lightweight						
Easy to use						
Reliable						
Easy to hold steady						
Colour correction						

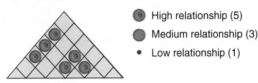

- ◉ High relationship (5)
- ⬤ Medium relationship (3)
- • Low relationship (1)

Third, the team evaluated each of the customer *wants* against the *hows*. In the relationship matrix of the house, the team evaluated how well its design meets customer needs. Fourth, the "roof" of the house indicates the relationship between the attributes. Fifth, the team developed importance ratings for its design attributes on the bottom row of the table. This was done by assigning values (5 for high, 3 for medium, and 1 for low) to each entry in the relationship matrix, and then multiplying each of these values by the customer's importance rating. The values in the "Our importance ratings" row provide a ranking of how to proceed with product and process design, with the highest values being the most critical to a successful product.

	Low electricity requirements	Aluminum components	Auto focus	Auto exposure	Paint pallet	Ergonomic design
3	•	⬤				•
4	•		⬤	⬤	⬤	⬤
5	⬤		⬤	⬤	⬤	
2						◉
1					◉	
Our importance ratings	22	9	27	27	32	25

of $25 = (1 \times 3) + (3 \times 4) + (2 \times 5)$

Sixth, the house of quality is also used for the evaluation of *competitors*. The two columns on the right indicate how market research thinks competitors A and B satisfy customer wants (Good, Fair, or Poor). Products from other firms and even the proposed product can be added next to company B.

Seventh, the team identifies the technical attributes and evaluates how well Great Cameras, Inc., and its competitors address these attributes. Here, the team decided on the noted technical attributes.

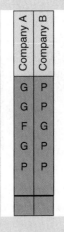

Company A	Company B
G	P
G	P
F	G
G	P
P	P

0.5 A	75%	2' to ∞	2 circuits	Failure 1 per 10,000	Panel ranking
0.7	60%	yes	1	ok	G
0.6	50%	yes	2	ok	F
0.5	75%	yes	2	ok	G

INSIGHT ▶ QFD provides an analytical tool that structures design features and technical issues, as well as providing importance rankings and competitor comparison.

LEARNING EXERCISE ▶ If the market research for another country indicates that "lightweight" has the most important customer ranking (5), and reliability is 3, what is the new total importance ranking for low electricity requirements, aluminum components, and ergonomic design? [Answer: 18, 15, 27, respectively.]

RELATED PROBLEMS ▶ 5.1, 5.2, 5.3, 5.4

Another use of QFD is to show how the quality effort will be *deployed*. As Figure 5.4 shows, *design characteristics* of House 1 become the inputs to House 2, which are satisfied by *specific components* of the product. Similarly, the concept is carried to House 3, where the specific components are to be satisfied through particular *production processes*. Once those production processes are defined, they become requirements of House 4 to be satisfied by a *quality plan* that will ensure conformance of those processes. The quality plan is a set of specific tolerances, procedures, methods, and sampling techniques that will ensure that the production process meets the customer requirements.

Much of the QFD effort is devoted to meeting customer requirements with design characteristics (House 1 in Figure 5.4), and its importance is not to be underestimated. However, the *sequence* of houses is a very effective way of identifying, communicating, and allocating resources throughout the system. The series of houses helps operations managers determine where to *deploy* quality resources. In this way we meet customer requirements, produce quality products, and win orders.

ORGANIZING FOR PRODUCT DEVELOPMENT

Let's look at four approaches to organizing for product development. *First*, the traditional North American approach to product development is an organization with distinct departments: a research and development department to do the necessary research; an engineering department to design the product; a manufacturing engineering department to design a product that can be produced; and a production department that produces the product. The distinct advantage of this approach is that fixed duties and responsibilities exist. The distinct disadvantage is lack of forward thinking: How will downstream departments in the process deal with the concepts, ideas, and designs presented to them, and ultimately what will the customer think of the product?

A *second* and popular approach is to assign a product manager to "champion" the product through the product development system and related organizations.

However, a *third*, and perhaps the best, product development approach used in North America seems to be the use of teams. Such teams are known variously as *product development teams, design for manufacturability teams*, and *value engineering teams*.

The Japanese use a *fourth* approach. They bypass the team issue by not subdividing organizations into research and development, engineering, production, and so forth. Consistent with

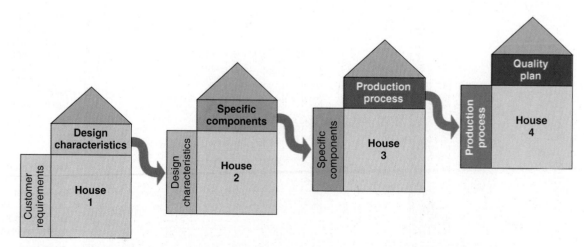

FIGURE 5.4 House of Quality Sequence Indicates How to Deploy Resources to Achieve Customer Requirements

the Japanese style of group effort and teamwork, these activities are all in one organization. Japanese culture and management style are more collegial and the organization less structured than in most Western countries. Therefore, the Japanese find it unnecessary to have "teams" provide the necessary communication and coordination. However, the typical Western style, and the conventional wisdom, is to use teams.

Product development teams are charged with the responsibility of moving from market requirements for a product to achieving a product success (refer to Figure 5.3). Such teams often include representatives from marketing, manufacturing, purchasing, quality assurance, and field service personnel. Many teams also include representatives from vendors. Regardless of the formal nature of the product development effort, research suggests that success is more likely in an open, highly participative environment where those with potential contributions are allowed to make them. The objective of a product development team is to make the good or service a success. This includes marketability, manufacturability, and serviceability.

Use of such teams is also called **concurrent engineering** and implies a team representing all affected areas (known as a *cross-functional* team). Concurrent engineering also implies speedier product development through simultaneous performance of various aspects of product development.[3] The team approach is the dominant structure for product development by leading organizations in North America.

Product development teams
Teams charged with moving from market requirements for a product to achieving product success.

Concurrent engineering
Use of participating teams in design and engineering activities.

MANUFACTURABILITY AND VALUE ENGINEERING

Manufacturability and value engineering activities are concerned with improvement of design and specifications at the research, development, design, and production stages of product development. In addition to immediate, obvious cost reduction, design for manufacturability and value engineering may produce other benefits. These include:

Manufacturability and value engineering
Activities that help improve a product's design, production, maintainability, and use.

1. Reduced complexity of the product.
2. Reduction of environmental impact.
3. Additional standardization of components.
4. Improvement of functional aspects of the product.
5. Improved job design and job safety.
6. Improved maintainability (serviceability) of the product.
7. Robust design.

Manufacturability and value engineering activities may be the best cost-avoidance technique available to operations management. They yield value improvement by focusing on achieving the functional specifications necessary to meet customer requirements in an optimal way. Value engineering programs, when effectively managed, typically reduce costs between 15% and 70% without reducing quality. Some studies have indicated that for every dollar spent on value engineering, $10 to $25 in savings can be realized.

Product design affects virtually all aspects of operating expense and sustainability. Consequently, the development process needs to ensure a thorough evaluation of design prior to a commitment to produce. The cost reduction achieved for a specific bracket via value engineering is shown in Figure 5.5.

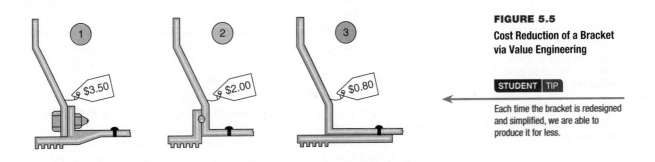

FIGURE 5.5

Cost Reduction of a Bracket via Value Engineering

STUDENT TIP

Each time the bracket is redesigned and simplified, we are able to produce it for less.

---

[3] Firms that have high technological or product change in their competitive environment tend to use more concurrent engineering practices. See X. Koufteros, M. Vonderembse, and W. Doll, "Concurrent Engineering and Its Consequences," *Journal of Operations Management* 19, no. 1 (January 2001): 97–115.

Issues for Product Design

In addition to developing an effective system and organization structure for product development, several *techniques* are important to the design of a product. We will now review six of these: (1) robust design, (2) modular design, (3) computer-aided design (CAD) and computer-aided manufacturing (CAM), (4) virtual reality technology, (5) value analysis, and (6) sustainability/life cycle assessment (LCA).

ROBUST DESIGN

Robust design
A design that can be produced to requirements even with unfavourable conditions in the production process.

Robust design means that the product is designed so that small variations in production or assembly do not adversely affect the product. For instance, Lucent developed an integrated circuit that could be used in many products to amplify voice signals. As originally designed, the circuit had to be manufactured very expensively to avoid variations in the strength of the signal. But after testing and analyzing the design, Lucent engineers realized that if the resistance of the circuit was reduced—a minor change with no associated costs—the circuit would be far less sensitive to manufacturing variations. The result was a 40% improvement in quality.

MODULAR DESIGN

Modular designs
Designs in which parts or components of a product are subdivided into modules that are easily interchanged or replaced.

Products designed in easily segmented components are known as **modular designs**. Modular designs offer flexibility to both production and marketing. Operations managers find modularity helpful because it makes product development, production, and subsequent changes easier. Moreover, marketing may like modularity because it adds flexibility to the ways customers can be satisfied. For instance, virtually all premium high-fidelity sound systems are produced and sold this way. The customization provided by modularity allows customers to mix and match to their own taste. This is also the approach taken by Harley-Davidson, where relatively few different engines, chassis, gas tanks, and suspension systems are mixed to produce a huge variety of motorcycles. It has been estimated that many automobile manufacturers can, by mixing the available modules, never make two cars alike. This same concept of modularity is carried over to many industries, from airframe manufacturers to fast-food restaurants. Airbus uses the same wing modules on several planes, just as McDonald's and Harvey's use relatively few modules (cheese, lettuce, buns, sauces, pickles, meat patties, French fries, etc.) to make a variety of meals.

COMPUTER-AIDED DESIGN (CAD)

Computer-aided design (CAD)
Interactive use of a computer to develop and document a product.

Computer-aided design (CAD) is the use of computers to interactively design products and prepare engineering documentation. The use and variety of CAD software is extensive and is rapidly expanding. CAD software allows designers to use three-dimensional drawings to save time and money by shortening development cycles for virtually all products. The speed and ease with which sophisticated designs can be manipulated, analyzed, and modified with CAD makes the review of numerous options possible before final commitments are made. Faster development, better products, accurate flow of information to other departments—all contribute to a tremendous payoff for CAD. The payoff is particularly significant because most product costs are determined at the design stage.

Design for manufacture and assembly (DFMA)
Software that allows designers to look at the effect of design on manufacturing of the product.

One extension of CAD is **design for manufacture and assembly (DFMA)** software, which focuses on the effect of design on assembly. It allows designers to examine the integration of product designs before the product is manufactured. For instance, DFMA allows automobile designers to examine how a transmission will be placed in a car on the production line, even while both the transmission and the car are still in the design stage.

3-D object modelling
An extension of CAD that builds small prototypes.

A second CAD extension is **3-D object modelling**. The technology is particularly useful for small prototype development. 3-D object modelling rapidly builds up a model in very thin layers of synthetic materials for evaluation. This technology speeds development by avoiding a more lengthy and formal manufacturing process. 3-D printers, costing as little as $5000, are also now available. Shoemaker Timberland, Inc., uses this technology to allow footwear designers to see their constructions overnight rather than waiting a week for model-makers to carve them.

At the Next GEN Science Fair in 2011, visitors are intrigued by advances in 3-D printers and the ability to capture intricate details of objects onto paper.

Liu Yilin Xinhua News Agency/Newscom

Some CAD systems have moved to the internet through ecommerce, where they link computerized design with purchasing, outsourcing, manufacturing, and long-term maintenance. This move supports rapid product change and the growing trend towards "mass customization". With CAD on the internet, customers can enter a supplier's design libraries and make design changes. The supplier's software can then automatically generate the drawings, update the bill of material, and prepare instructions for the supplier's production process. The result is customized products produced faster and at less expense.

As product life cycles shorten and design becomes more complex, collaboration among departments, facilities, and suppliers throughout the world becomes critical. The potential of such collaboration has proven so important that a standard for its exchange has been developed, known as the **standard for the exchange of product data (STEP)**. STEP permits manufacturers to express 3-D product information in a standard format so it can be exchanged internationally, allowing geographically dispersed manufacturers to integrate design, manufacture, and support processes.[4]

Standard for the exchange of product data (STEP)

A standard that provides a format allowing the electronic transmittal of three-dimensional data.

COMPUTER-AIDED MANUFACTURING (CAM)

Computer-aided manufacturing (CAM) refers to the use of specialized computer programs to direct and control manufacturing equipment. When computer-aided design (CAD) information is translated into instructions for computer-aided manufacturing (CAM), the result of these two technologies is CAD/CAM.

Computer-aided manufacturing (CAM)

The use of information technology to control machinery.

The benefits of CAD and CAM include:

1. *Product quality:* CAD permits the designer to investigate more alternatives, potential problems, and dangers.
2. *Shorter design time:* A shorter design phase lowers cost and allows a more rapid response to the market.
3. *Production cost reductions:* Reduced inventory, more efficient use of personnel through improved scheduling, and faster implementation of design changes lower costs.
4. *Database availability:* Provides information for other manufacturing software and accurate product data so everyone is operating from the same information, resulting in dramatic cost reductions.

---

[4] The STEP format is documented in the European Community's standard ISO 10303.

5. *New range of capabilities:* For instance, the abilities to rotate and depict objects in three-dimensional form, to check clearances, to relate parts and attachments, and to improve the use of numerically controlled machine tools all provide new capability for manufacturing. CAD/CAM removes substantial detail work, allowing designers to concentrate on the conceptual and imaginative aspects of their task.

VIRTUAL REALITY TECHNOLOGY

Virtual reality
A visual form of communication in which images substitute for reality and typically allow the user to respond interactively.

Virtual reality is a visual form of communication in which images substitute for the real thing but still allow the user to respond interactively. The roots of virtual reality technology in operations are in computer-aided design. Once design information is in a CAD system, it is also in electronic digital form for other uses, such as developing 3-D layouts of everything from restaurants to amusement parks. Changes to mechanical design, restaurant layouts, or amusement park rides are much less expensive at the design stage than later.

VALUE ANALYSIS

Value analysis
A review of successful products that takes place during the production process.

Although value engineering focuses on *preproduction* design improvement, value analysis, a related technique, takes place *during* the production process, when it is clear that a new product is a success. **Value analysis** seeks improvements that lead to either a better product, or a product made more economically, or a product with less environmental impact. The techniques and advantages for value analysis are the same as for value engineering, although minor changes in implementation may be necessary because value analysis is taking place while the product is being produced.

SUSTAINABILITY AND LIFE CYCLE ASSESSMENT (LCA)

Product design requires that managers evaluate product options. Addressing sustainability and life cycle assessment (LCA) are two ways of doing this. *Sustainability* means meeting the needs of the present without compromising the ability of future generations to meet their needs. An LCA is a formal evaluation of the environmental impact of a product. Both sustainability and LCA are discussed in depth in the supplement to this chapter.

Fast communication, rapid technological change, and short product life cycles push product development.

Time-Based Competition

As product life cycles shorten, the need for faster product development increases. Additionally, as technological sophistication of new products increases, so do the expense and risk. For instance, drug firms invest an average of 12 to 15 years and $1 billion before receiving regulatory approval of each new drug. And even then, only one of five will actually be a success. Those operations managers who master this art of product development continually gain on slower product developers. To the swift goes the competitive advantage. This concept is called **time-based competition**.

Time-based competition
Competition based on time, rapidly developing products and moving them to market.

Often, the first company into production may have its product adopted for use in a variety of applications that will generate sales for years. It may become the "standard". Consequently, there is often more concern with getting the product to market than with optimum product design or process efficiency. Even so, rapid introduction to the market may be good management because, until competition begins to introduce copies or improved versions, the product can sometimes be priced high enough to justify somewhat inefficient production design and methods.

LO4 Describe how time-based competition is implemented by OM

Because time-based competition is so important, instead of developing new products from scratch (which has been the focus thus far in this chapter) a number of other strategies can be used. Figure 5.6 shows a continuum that goes from new, internally developed products (on the lower left) to "alliances". *Enhancements* and *migrations* use the organization's existing product strengths for innovation and therefore are typically faster while at the same time being less risky than developing entirely new products. Enhancements may be changes in colour, size, weight, or features, such as are taking place with cell phones (see *OM in Action* box "Chasing Fads in the Cell Phone Industry"), or even changes in commercial aircraft. Boeing's enhancements of the 737 since its introduction in 1967 have made the 737 the largest-selling commercial aircraft in history. Boeing also uses its engineering prowess in air frames

Product Development Continuum

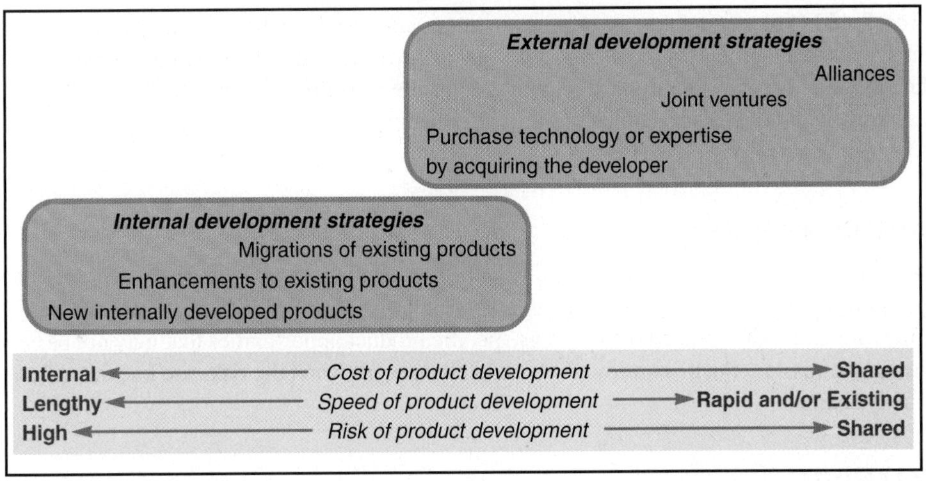

FIGURE 5.6

Product Development Continuum

External development strategies

Alliances

Joint ventures

Purchase technology or expertise by acquiring the developer

Internal development strategies

Migrations of existing products

Enhancements to existing products

New internally developed products

Internal ←	Cost of product development	→ Shared
Lengthy ←	Speed of product development	→ Rapid and/or Existing
High ←	Risk of product development	→ Shared

STUDENT TIP

Managers seek a variety of approaches to obtain speed to market. The president of one U.S. firm says: "If I miss one product cycle, I'm dead."

to *migrate* from one model to the next. This allows Boeing to speed development while reducing both cost and risk for new designs. This approach is also referred to as building on *product platforms*. Black & Decker has used its "platform" expertise in hand-powered tools to build a leading position in that market. Similarly, Hewlett-Packard has done the same in the printer business. Enhancements and migrations are a way of building on existing expertise and extending a product's life cycle.

The product development strategies on the lower left of Figure 5.6 are *internal* development strategies, while the three approaches we now introduce can be thought of as *external* development strategies. Firms use both. The external strategies are (1) purchase the technology, (2) establish joint ventures, and (3) develop alliances.

OM in Action   Chasing Fads in the Cell Phone Industry

In the shrinking world marketplace, innovations that appeal to customers in one region rapidly become global trends. The process shakes up the structure of one industry after another, from computers to automobiles to consumer electronics.

Nowhere has this impact been greater in recent years than in the cell phone industry. The industry sells about 1.3 billion phones each year, but product life cycle is short. Competition is intense. Higher margins go to the innovator—and manufacturers that jump on an emerging trend early can reap substantial rewards. The swiftest Chinese manufacturers, such as Ningbo Bird and TCL, now replace some phone models after just six months. In the past, Motorola, Nokia, and other industry veterans enjoyed what are now considered long life cycles—two years. New styles and technological advances in cell phones constantly appear somewhere in the world. Wired, well-travelled consumers seek the latest innovation; local retailers rush to offer it; and telecommunication providers order it.

Contemporary cell phones may be a curvy, boxy, or clamshell fashion item; have a tiny keyboard for quick and easy typing or a more limited number pad for a phone; have a built-in radio or a digital music player; have a camera, internet access, or TV clips; function on cellular or wireless (Wi-Fi) networks; or have games or personal organizers. Mattel and Nokia even have Barbie phones for preteen girls, complete with prepaid minutes, customized ringtones, and faceplates. The rapid changes in features and demand are forcing manufacturers into a frenzied race to keep up or simply to pull out.

"We got out of the handset business because we couldn't keep up with the cycle times," says Jeffrey Belk, Marketing VP for Qualcomm Inc., the San Diego company that now focuses on making handset chips.

Developing new products is always a challenge, but in the dynamic global marketplace of cell phones, product development takes on new technology and new markets at breakneck speed.

Sources: Supply Chain Management Review (October 2007): 28; *The Wall Street Journal* (October 30, 2003): A1 and (September 8, 2004): D5; and *International Business Times* (March 3, 2009).

PURCHASING TECHNOLOGY BY ACQUIRING A FIRM

Microsoft and Cisco Systems are examples of companies on the cutting edge of technology that often speed development by *acquiring entrepreneurial firms* that have already developed the technology that fits their mission. The issue then becomes fitting the purchased organization, its technology, its product lines, and its culture into the buying firm, rather than an issue of product development.

JOINT VENTURES

Joint ventures
Firms establishing joint ownership to pursue new products or markets.

Joint ventures are combined ownership, usually between just two firms, to form a new entity. Ownership can be 50–50, or one owner can assume a larger portion to ensure tighter control. Joint ventures are often appropriate for exploiting specific product opportunities that may not be central to the firm's mission. Such ventures are more likely to work when the risks are known and can be equitably shared.

ALLIANCES

Alliances
Cooperative agreements that allow firms to remain independent, but cooperatively pursue strategies consistent with their individual missions.

Alliances are cooperative agreements that allow firms to remain independent but use complementing strengths to pursue strategies consistent with their individual missions. When new products are central to the mission, but substantial resources are required and sizable risk is present, then alliances may be a good strategy for product development. Alliances are particularly beneficial when the products to be developed also have technologies that are in ferment. For example, Microsoft is pursuing a number of alliances with a variety of companies to deal with the convergence of computing, the internet, and television broadcasting. Alliances in this case are appropriate because the technological unknowns, capital demands, and risks are significant. Similarly, three firms—Mercedes Benz, Ford Motor, and Ballard Power Systems—have formed an alliance to develop "green" cars powered by fuel cells. However, alliances are much more difficult to achieve and maintain than are joint ventures because of the ambiguities associated with them. It may be helpful to think of an alliance as an incomplete contract between the firms. The firms remain separate.

Enhancements, migration, acquisitions, joint ventures, and alliances are all strategies for speeding product development. Moreover, they typically reduce the risk associated with product development while enhancing the human and capital resources available.

STUDENT TIP

Before anything can be produced, a product's functions and attributes must be defined.

LO5 Describe how products and services are defined by OM

Defining a Product

Once new goods or services are selected for introduction, they must be defined. First, a good or service is defined in terms of its *functions*—that is, what the product is to *do*. The product is then designed, and the firm determines how the functions are to be achieved. Management typically has a variety of options as to how a product should achieve its functional purpose. For instance, when an alarm clock is produced, aspects of design such as the colour, size, or location of buttons may make substantial differences in ease of manufacture, quality, and market acceptance.

Rigorous specifications of a product are necessary to assure efficient production. Equipment, layout, and human resources cannot be determined until the product is defined, designed, and documented. Therefore, every organization needs documents to define its products. This is true of everything from meat patties, to cheese, to computers, to medical procedures. In the case of cheese, a written specification is typical. Indeed, written specifications or standard grades exist and provide the definition for many products. For instance, Cheddar cheese has a written description that specifies the characteristics necessary for each Department of Justice grade. A portion of the Department of Justice grade requirements for Cheddar cheese is shown in Figure 5.7. Similarly, McDonald's has 60 specifications for potatoes that are to be made into French fries.

Engineering drawing
A drawing that shows the dimensions, tolerances, materials, and finishes of a component.

Most manufactured items as well as their components are defined by a drawing, usually referred to as an engineering drawing. An **engineering drawing** shows the dimensions, tolerances, materials, and finishes of a component. The engineering drawing will be an item on a

FIGURE 5.7

Grade Requirements for Cheddar Cheese

Source: www.justice.gc.ca (2) and (3) [Repealed, SOR/98-216, s. 7] SOR/88-195, s. 1; SOR/98-216, s. 7.

Grade Requirements for Cheddar Cheese

13. (1) Cheddar cheese may be graded Canada 1 if the cheese meets the requirements of section 4 and subsection 6(3), and

(a) its flavour and aroma are typical and desirable;

(b) its body is reasonably compact and firm;

(c) its texture is smooth;

(d) its surface is clean, smooth and unbroken;

(e) except in the case of marbled cheddar cheese, its colour is uniform and characteristic of cheddar cheese; and

(f) the cheese is uniform in size and regular in shape.

bill of material. An engineering drawing is shown in Figure 5.8. The **bill of material (BOM)** lists the components, their description, and the quantity of each required to make one unit of a product. A bill of material for a manufactured item is shown in Figure 5.9(a). Note that subassemblies and components (lower-level items) are indented at each level to indicate their subordinate position. An engineering drawing shows how to make one item on the bill of material.

In the food-service industry, bills of material manifest themselves in *portion-control standards*. The portion-control standard for Hard Rock Cafe's hickory BBQ bacon cheeseburger is shown in Figure 5.9(b). In a more complex product, a bill of material is referenced on other bills of material of which they are a part. In this manner, subunits (subassemblies) are part of the next higher unit (their parent bill of material) that ultimately makes a final product. In addition to being defined by written specifications, portion-control documents, or bills of material, products can be defined in other ways. For example, products such as chemicals, paints, and petroleum may be defined by formulas or proportions that describe how they are to be made. Movies are defined by scripts, and insurance coverage by legal documents known as policies.

Bill of material (BOM)

A list of the components, their description, and the quantity of each required to make one unit of a product.

MAKE-OR-BUY DECISIONS

For many components of products, firms have the option of producing the components themselves or purchasing them from outside sources. Choosing between these options is known as the make-or-buy decision. The **make-or-buy decision** distinguishes between what the firm wants to *produce* and what it wants to *purchase*. Because of variations in quality, cost, and delivery schedules, the make-or-buy decision is critical to product definition. Many items can be purchased as a "standard item" produced by someone else. Examples are the standard bolts listed on the bill of material shown in Figure 5.9(a), for which there will be SAE (Society of Automotive Engineers) specifications. Therefore, there typically is no need for the firm to duplicate this specification in another document.

Make-or-buy decision

The choice between producing a component or a service and purchasing it from an outside source.

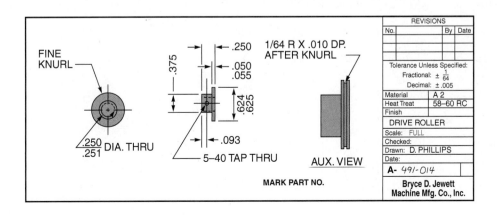

FIGURE 5.8

Engineering Drawings Such as This One Show Dimensions, Tolerances, Materials, and Finishes

FIGURE 5.9

Bills of Material Take Different Forms in (a) Manufacturing Plant and (b) Restaurant, but in Both Cases, the Product Must Be Defined

(a) **Bill of Material for a Panel Weldment**

NUMBER	DESCRIPTION	QTY
A 60–71	PANEL WELDM'T	1
A 60–7	LOWER ROLLER ASSM.	1
R 60–17	ROLLER	1
R 60–428	PIN	1
P 60–2	LOCKNUT	1
A 60–72	GUIDE ASSM. REAR	1
R 60–57–1	SUPPORT ANGLE	1
A 60–4	ROLLER ASSEM.	1
02–50–1150	BOLT	1
A 60–73	GUIDE ASSM. FRONT	1
A 60–74	SUPPORT WELDM'T	1
R 60–99	WEAR PLATE	1
02–50–1150	BOLT	1

(b) **Hard Rock Cafe's Hickory BBQ Bacon Cheeseburger**

DESCRIPTION	QTY
Bun	1
Hamburger patty	8 oz.
Cheddar cheese	2 slices
Bacon	2 strips
BBQ onions	1/2 cup
Hickory BBQ sauce	1 oz.
Burger set	
Lettuce	1 leaf
Tomato	1 slice
Red onion	4 rings
Pickle	1 slice
French fries	5 oz.
Seasoned salt	1 tsp.
11-inch plate	1
HRC flag	1

STUDENT TIP

Hard Rock's recipe here serves the same purpose as a bill of material in a factory: It defines the product for production.

GROUP TECHNOLOGY

Group technology

A product and component coding system that specifies the type of processing and the parameters of the processing; it allows similar products to be grouped.

Engineering drawings may also include codes to facilitate group technology. **Group technology** requires that components be identified by a coding scheme that specifies the type of processing (such as drilling) and the parameters of the processing (such as size). This facilitates standardization of materials, components, and processes as well as the identification of families of parts. As families of parts are identified, activities and machines can be grouped to minimize setups, routings, and material handling. An example of how families of parts may be grouped is shown in Figure 5.10. Group technology provides a systematic way to review a family of components to see if an existing component might suffice on a new project. Using existing or standard components eliminates all the costs connected with the design and development of the new part, which is a major cost reduction. For these reasons, successful implementation of group technology leads to the following advantages:

1. Improved design (because more design time can be devoted to fewer components).
2. Reduced raw material and purchases.
3. Simplified production planning and control.
4. Improved layout, routing, and machine loading.
5. Reduced tooling setup time, and work-in-process and production time.

The application of group technology helps the entire organization, as many costs are reduced.

FIGURE 5.10

A Variety of Group Technology Coding Schemes Move Manufactured Components from (a) Ungrouped to (b) Grouped (families of parts)

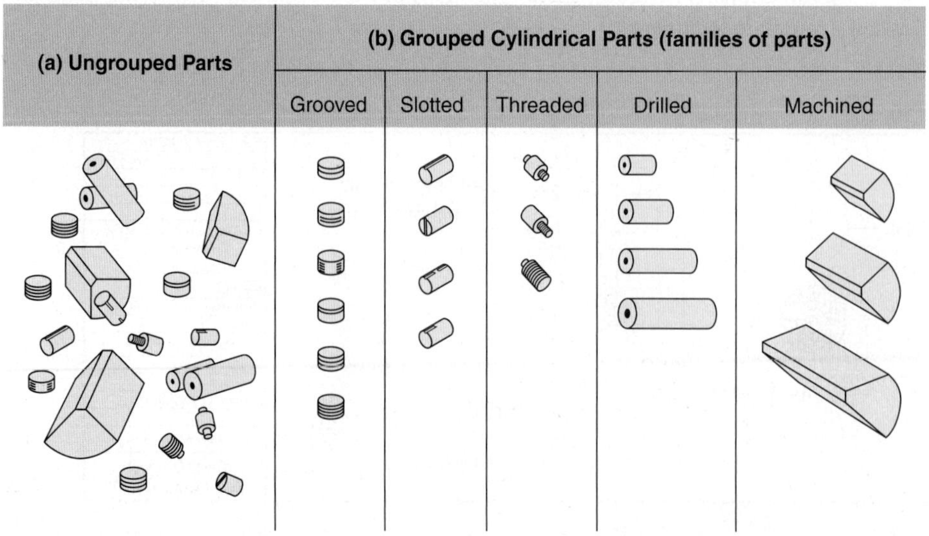

(a) Ungrouped Parts	(b) Grouped Cylindrical Parts (families of parts)				
	Grooved	Slotted	Threaded	Drilled	Machined

Documents for Production

Once a product is selected, designed, and ready for production, production is assisted by a variety of documents. We will briefly review some of these.

An **assembly drawing** simply shows an exploded view of the product. An assembly drawing is usually a three-dimensional drawing, known as an *isometric drawing*; the relative locations of components are drawn in relation to each other to show how to assemble the unit (see Figure 5.11(a)).

The **assembly chart** shows in schematic form how a product is assembled. Manufactured components, purchased components, or a combination of both may be shown on an assembly chart. The assembly chart identifies the point of production at which components flow into subassemblies and ultimately into a final product. An example of an assembly chart is shown in Figure 5.11(b).

The **route sheet** lists the operations necessary to produce the component with the material specified in the bill of material. The route sheet for an item will have one entry for each operation to be performed on the item. When route sheets include specific methods of operation and labour standards, they are often known as *process sheets*.

The **work order** is an instruction to make a given quantity of a particular item, usually to a given schedule. The order ticket that a waiter in your favourite restaurant writes down is a work order. In a hospital or factory, the work order is a more formal document that provides authorization to draw various pharmaceuticals or items from inventory, to perform various functions, and to assign personnel to perform those functions.

An **engineering change notice (ECN)** changes some aspect of the product's definition or documentation, such as an engineering drawing or a bill of material. For a complex product that has a long manufacturing cycle, such as a Boeing 777, the changes may be so numerous that no two 777s are built exactly alike—which is indeed the case. Such dynamic design change has fostered the development of a discipline known as configuration management, which is concerned with product identification, control, and documentation. **Configuration management** is the system by which a product's planned and changing configurations are accurately identified and for which control and accountability of change are maintained.

PRODUCT LIFE CYCLE MANAGEMENT (PLM)

Product life cycle management (PLM) is an umbrella of software programs that attempts to bring together phases of product design and manufacture—including tying together many of the techniques discussed in the prior two sections, *Defining a Product* and *Documents for Production*. The idea behind PLM software is that product design and manufacture decisions can be performed more creatively, faster, and more economically when the data are integrated and consistent.

Production personnel need clear, specific documents to help them make the product.

LO6 Describe the documents needed for production

Assembly drawing
An exploded view of the product.

Assembly chart
A graphic means of identifying how components flow into subassemblies and final products.

Route sheet
A listing of the operations necessary to produce a component with the material specified in the bill of material.

Work order
An instruction to make a given quantity of a particular item.

Engineering change notice (ECN)
A correction or modification of an engineering drawing or bill of material.

Configuration management
A system by which a product's planned and changing components are accurately identified.

Product life cycle management (PLM)
Software programs that tie together many phases of product design and manufacture.

(a) Assembly Drawing

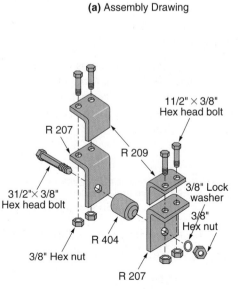

(b) Assembly Chart

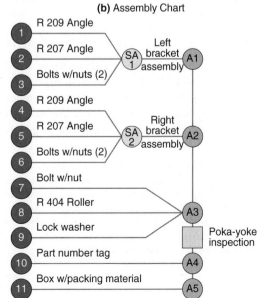

FIGURE 5.11

Assembly Drawing and Assembly Chart

Each year, the J.R. Simplot Company potato processing facilities in North America, Australia, China, and New Zealand produce billions of pounds of French fries and formed potato products for quick-service restaurants and other foodservice customers around the world (left photo). Sixty specifications (including a special blend of frying oil, a unique steaming process, and exact time and temperature for prefrying and drying) define how these potatoes become French fries. Further, 40% of all French fries must be 2 to 3 inches long, 40% must be over 3 inches long, and a few shorter ones constitute the final 20%. Quality control personnel use a micrometer to measure the fries (right photo).

Although there is not one standard, PLM products often start with product design (CAD/CAM); move on to design for manufacture and assembly (DFMA); and then into product routing, materials, layout, assembly, maintenance, and even environmental issues.[5] Integration of these tasks makes sense because many of these decisions areas require overlapping pieces of data. PLM software is now a tool of many large organizations, including Bombardier, Lockheed Martin, GE, Procter & Gamble, Toyota, and Boeing. Boeing estimates that PLM will cut final assembly of its 787 jet from two weeks to three days. PLM is now finding its way into medium and small manufacture as well.

Shorter life cycles, more technologically challenging products, more regulations about materials and manufacturing processes, and more environmental issues all make PLM an appealing tool for operations managers.

Service Design

STUDENT TIP

Services also need to be defined and documented.

LO7 Explain how the customer participates in the design and delivery of services

Process–chain–network (PCN) analysis

Analysis that focuses on the ways in which processes can be designed to optimize interaction between firms and their customers.

Process chain

A sequence of steps that accomplishes an identifiable purpose (of providing value to process participants).

Much of our discussion so far has focused on what we can call tangible products—that is, goods. On the other side of the product coin are, of course, services. Service industries include banking, finance, insurance, transportation, and communications. The products offered by service firms range from a medical procedure that leaves only the tiniest scar after an appendectomy, to a shampoo and cut at a hair salon, to a great sandwich. Designing services is challenging because they have a unique characteristic—customer interaction.

PROCESS–CHAIN–NETWORK (PCN) ANALYSIS

Process–chain–network (PCN) analysis, developed by Professor Scott Sampson, focuses on the ways in which processes can be designed to optimize interaction between firms and their customers.[6] A **process chain** is a sequence of steps that accomplishes an activity, such as building a home, completing a tax return, or preparing a sandwich. A process participant can be a manufacturer, a service provider, or a customer. A network is a set of participants.

---

[5] Some PLM vendors include supply chain elements such as sourcing, material management, and vendor evaluation in their packages, but in most instances, these are considered part of the ERP systems discussed along with MRP in Chapter 14. See, for instance, SAP PLM (**www.mySAP.com**), Parametric Technology Corp. (**www.ptc.com**), UGS Corp. (**www.ugs.com**), and Proplanner (**www.proplanner.com**).

[6] See Scott Sampson, "Visualizing Service Operations," *Journal of Service Research* (May 2012). More details about PCN analysis are available at **services.byu.edu**.

Each participant has a process domain that includes the set of activities over which it has control. The domain and interactions between two participants for sandwich preparation are shown in the PCN diagram (Figure 5.12). The activities are organized into three process regions for each participant:

1. The direct interaction region includes process steps that involve interaction between participants. For example, a sandwich buyer directly interacts with employees of a sandwich store (e.g., Subway, in the middle of Figure 5.12).
2. The surrogate (substitute) interaction region includes process steps in which one participant is acting on another participant's resources, such as their information, materials, or technologies. This occurs when the sandwich supplier is making sandwiches in the restaurant kitchen (left side of Figure 5.12) or, alternatively, when the customer has access to buffet ingredients and assembles the sandwich himself (right side of the figure). Under surrogate interaction, direct interaction is limited.
3. The independent processing region includes steps in which the sandwich supplier and/or the sandwich customer is acting on resources where each has maximum control. Most make-to-stock production fits in this region (left side of Figure 5.12; think of the firm that assembles all those prepackaged sandwiches available in vending machines and convenience stores). Similarly, those sandwiches built at home occur to the right, in the customer's independent processing domain.

All three process regions have similar operating issues—quality control, facility location and layout, job design, inventory, and so on—but the appropriate way of handling the issues differs across regions. Service operations exist only within the area of direct and surrogate interaction.

From the operations manager's perspective, the valuable aspect of PCN analysis is insight to aid in positioning and designing processes that can achieve strategic objectives. A firm's operations are strategic in that they can define what type of business the firm is in and what value proposition it desires to provide to customers. For example, a firm may assume a low-cost strategy, operating on the left of Figure 5.12 as a manufacturer of premade sandwiches. Other firms (e.g., Subway) adopt a differentiation strategy with high customer interaction. Each of the process regions depicts a unique operational strategy.

Firms wanting to achieve high economies of scale or more control in their operations should probably position towards the independent processing region of their process domain. Firms intending to provide a value offering that focuses on customization should be positioned more

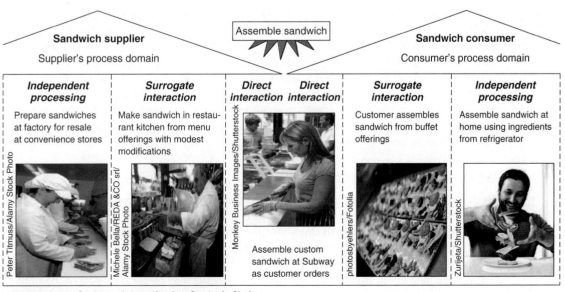

FIGURE 5.12 Customer Interaction Is a Strategic Choice

towards the consumer's process domain. PCN analysis can be applied in a wide variety of business settings.

ADDING SERVICE EFFICIENCY

Service productivity is notoriously low, in part because of customer involvement in the design or delivery of the service, or both. This complicates the product design challenge. We will now discuss a number of ways to increase service efficiency and, among these, several ways to limit this interaction.

LIMIT THE OPTIONS Because customers may participate in the design of the service (e.g., for a funeral or a hairstyle), design specifications may take the form of everything from a menu (in a restaurant), to a list of options (for a funeral), to a verbal description (a hairstyle). However, by providing a list of options (in the case of the funeral) or a series of photographs (in the case of the hairstyle), ambiguity may be reduced. An early resolution of the product's definition can aid efficiency as well as aid in meeting customer expectations.

DELAY CUSTOMIZATION Design the product so that customization is delayed as late in the process as possible. This is the way a hair salon operates. Although shampoo and condition are done in a standard way with lower-cost labour, the colour and styling (customizing) are done last. It is also the way most restaurants operate: How would you like your meal cooked? Which dressing would you prefer with your salad?

MODULARIZATION Modularize the service so that customization takes the form of changing modules. This strategy allows for "custom" services to be designed as standard modular entities. Just as modular design allows you to buy a high-fidelity sound system with just the features you want, modular flexibility also lets you buy meals, clothes, and insurance on a mix-and-match (modular) basis. Investments (portfolios of stocks and bonds) and education (university and college curricula) are examples of how the modular approach can be used to customize a service.

AUTOMATION Divide the service into small parts and identify those parts that lend themselves to automation. For instance, by isolating cheque-cashing activity via ATM, banks have been very effective at designing a product that both increases customer service and reduces costs. Similarly, airlines have moved to ticketless service via kiosks. A technique such as kiosks reduces both costs and lines at airports—thereby increasing customer satisfaction—and providing a win–win "product" design.

MOMENT OF TRUTH High customer interaction means that in the service industry there is a moment of truth when the relationship between the provider and the customer is crucial. At that moment, the customer's satisfaction with the service is defined. The moment of truth is the moment that exemplifies, enhances, or detracts from the customer's expectations. That moment may be as simple as a smile from a Starbucks barista or having the checkout clerk focus on you rather than talking over his shoulder to the clerk at the next counter. Moments of truth can occur when you order at McDonald's, get a haircut, or register for college courses. The operations manager's task is to identify moments of truth and design operations that meet or exceed the customer's expectations.

DOCUMENTS FOR SERVICES

Because of the high customer interaction of most services, the documents for moving the product to production are different from those used in goods-producing operations. The documentation for a service will often take the form of explicit *job instructions* that specify what is to happen at the moment of truth. For instance, regardless of how good a pharmacy's products may be in terms of variety, access to brand names and generic equivalents, and so forth, if the moment of truth is not done well, the product may be poorly received. Example 2 shows the kind of documentation a pharmacy may use to move a product (drive-up pharmacy) to "production". In a telemarketing service, the product design is communicated to production personnel in the form of a *telephone script*, while a *storyboard* is used for movie and TV production.

EXAMPLE 2

Service Documentation for Production

Nova Scotia Pharmaceuticals wants to ensure effective delivery of service to its drive-up customers.

APPROACH ▶ Develop a "production" document for the pharmacists at the drive-up window that provides the information necessary to do an effective job.

SOLUTION ▶

Documentation for Pharmacists at Drive-Up Windows

Customers who use the drive-up windows rather than walk up to the counter require a different customer relations technique. The distance and machinery between the pharmacist and the customer raises communication barriers. Guidelines to ensure good customer relations at the drive-up window are:

- Be especially discreet when talking to the customer through the microphone.
- Provide written instructions for customers who must fill out forms you provide.
- Mark lines to be completed or attach a note with instructions.
- Always say "please" and "thank you" when speaking through the microphone.
- Establish eye contact with the customer if the distance allows it.
- If a transaction requires that the customer park the car and walk up to the counter, apologize for the inconvenience.

INSIGHT ▶ By providing documentation in the form of a script/guideline for pharmacists, the likelihood of effective communication and a good product/service is improved.

LEARNING EXERCISE: ▶ Modify the guidelines above to show how they would be different for a drive-through restaurant. [Answer: Written instructions, marking lines to be completed, or coming into the store are seldom necessary, but techniques for making change and proper transfer of the order should be included.]

RELATED PROBLEM: ▶ 5.7

Application of Decision Trees to Product Design

STUDENT TIP

A decision tree is a great tool for thinking through a problem.

Decision trees can be used for new product decisions as well as for a wide variety of other management problems. They are particularly helpful when there are a series of decisions and various outcomes that lead to *subsequent* decisions followed by other outcomes. To form a decision tree, we use the following procedure:

1. Be sure that all possible alternatives and states of nature are included in the tree. This includes an alternative of "doing nothing".
2. Payoffs are entered at the end of the appropriate branch. This is the place to develop the payoff of achieving this branch.
3. The objective is to determine the expected value of each course of action. We accomplish this by starting at the end of the tree (the right-hand side) and working towards the beginning of the tree (the left), calculating values at each step and "pruning" alternatives that are not as good as others from the same node.

Example 3 shows the use of a decision tree applied to product design.

Decision Tree Applied to Product Design

Silicon, Inc., a semiconductor manufacturer, is investigating the possibility of producing and marketing a microprocessor. Undertaking this project will require either purchasing a sophisticated CAD system or hiring and training several additional engineers. The market for the product could be either favourable or unfavourable. Silicon, Inc., of course, has the option of not developing the new product at all.

With favourable acceptance by the market, sales would be 25 000 processors selling for $100 each. With unfavourable acceptance, sales would be only 8000 processors selling for $100 each. The cost of CAD equipment is $500 000, but that of hiring and training three new engineers is only $375 000. However, manufacturing costs should drop from $50 each when manufacturing without CAD, to $40 each when manufacturing with CAD.

The probability of favourable acceptance of the new microprocessor is 0.40; the probability of unfavourable acceptance is 0.60.

APPROACH ▶ Use of a decision tree seems appropriate as Silicon, Inc., has the basic ingredients: a choice of decisions, probabilities, and payoffs.

SOLUTION ▶ In Figure 5.13, we draw a decision tree with a branch for each of the three decisions, assign the respective probabilities payoff for each branch, and then compute the respective expected monetary values (EMVs). The EMVs have been circled at each step of the decision tree. For the top branch:

$$\text{EMV (purchase CAD system)} = (0.4)(\$1\ 000\ 000) + (0.6)(-\$20\ 000)$$

$$= \$388\ 000$$

This figure represents the results that will occur if Silicon, Inc., purchases CAD.

The expected value of hiring and training engineers is the second series of branches:

FIGURE 5.13

Decision Tree for Development of a New Product

The manager's options are to purchase CAD, hire/train engineers, or do nothing. Purchasing CAD has the highest expected monetary value (EMV).

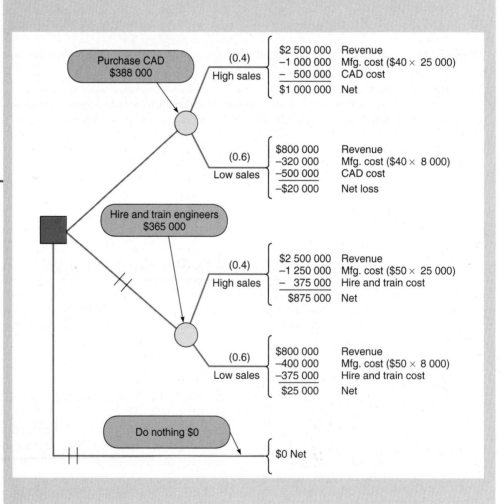

$$\text{EMV(Hire/train engineers)} = (0.4)(\$875\ 000) + (0.6)(\$25\ 000)$$

$$= \$365\ 000$$

The EMV of doing nothing is $0.

Because the top branch has the highest expected monetary value (an EMV of $388 000 versus $365 000 versus $0), it represents the best decision. Management should purchase the CAD system.

INSIGHT ▶ Use of the decision tree provides both objectivity and structure to our analysis of the Silicon, Inc., decision.

LEARNING EXERCISE ▶ If Silicon, Inc., thinks the probabilities of high sales and low sales may be equal, at 0.5 each, what is the best decision? [Answer: Purchase CAD remains the best decision, but with an EMV of $490 000.]

RELATED PROBLEMS ▶ 5.10, 5.11, 5.12, 5.13, 5.14, 5.15, 5.16, 5.18

ACTIVE MODEL 5.1 This example is further illustrated in Active Model 5.1 at **MyLab Operations Management**.

Transition to Production

STUDENT TIP

One of the arts of management is knowing when a product should move from development to production.

Eventually, a product, whether a good or service, has been selected, designed, and defined. It has progressed from an idea to a functional definition, and then perhaps to a design. Now, management must make a decision as to further development and production or termination of the product idea. One of the arts of modern management is knowing when to move a product from development to production; this move is known as *transition to production*. The product development staff is always interested in making improvements in a product. Because this staff tends to see product development as evolutionary, they may never have a completed product, but as we noted earlier, the cost of late product introduction is high. Although these conflicting pressures exist, management must make a decision—more development or production.

Once this decision is made, there is usually a period of trial production to ensure that the design is indeed producible. This is the manufacturability test. This trial also gives the operations staff the opportunity to develop proper tooling, quality control procedures, and training of personnel to ensure that production can be initiated successfully. Finally, when the product is deemed both marketable and producible, line management will assume responsibility.

Some companies appoint a *project manager*; others use *product development teams* to ensure that the transition from development to production is successful. Both approaches allow a wide range of resources and talents to be brought to bear to ensure satisfactory production of a product that is still in flux. A third approach is *integration of the product development and manufacturing organizations*. This approach allows for easy shifting of resources between the two organizations as needs change. The operations manager's job is to make the transition from R&D to production seamless.

CHAPTER SUMMARY

Effective product strategy requires selecting, designing, and defining a product and then transitioning that product to production. Only when this strategy is carried out effectively can the production function contribute its maximum to the organization. The operations manager must build a product development system that has the ability to conceive, design, and produce products that will yield a competitive advantage for the firm. As products move through their life cycle (introduction, growth, maturity, and decline), the options that the operations manager should pursue change. Both manufactured and service products have a variety of techniques available to aid in performing this activity efficiently.

Written specifications, bills of material, and engineering drawings aid in defining products. Similarly, assembly drawings, assembly charts, route sheets, and work orders are often used to assist in the actual production of the product. Once a product is in production, value analysis is appropriate to ensure maximum product value. Engineering change notices and configuration management provide product documentation.

ETHICAL | DILEMMA

Madhu Ranadive, president of Davisville Toy Company, Inc., in Stratford, Ontario, has just reviewed the design of a new pull-toy locomotive for one- to three-year-olds. Madhu's design and marketing staff are very enthusiastic about the market for the product and the potential of follow-on circus train cars. The sales manager is looking forward to a very good reception at the annual toy show in Toronto next month. Madhu is delighted as well, since she is faced with a layoff if orders do not improve.

Madhu's production people have worked out the manufacturing issues and produced a successful pilot run. However, the quality testing staff suggests that under certain conditions, a hook to attach cars to the locomotive and the crank for the bell can be broken off. This is an issue because children can choke on small parts such as these. In the quality test, one- to three-year-olds were unable to break off these parts; there were *no* failures. But when the test simulated the force of an adult tossing the locomotive into a toy box or a five-year-old throwing it on the floor, there were failures. The estimate is that one of the two parts can be broken off four times out of 100 000 throws. Neither the design nor the material people

knows how to make the toy safer and still perform as designed. The failure rate is low and certainly normal for this type of toy, but not at the Six Sigma level that Madhu's firm strives for. And, of course, someone, someday may sue. A child choking on the broken part is a serious matter.

The design of successful, ethically produced, new products, as suggested in this chapter, is a complex task. What should Madhu do?

Nikolay Dimitrow - ecobo/Shutterstock

Discussion Questions

1. Why is it necessary to document a product explicitly?
2. What techniques do we use to define a product?
3. In what ways are product strategies linked to product decisions?
4. Once a product is defined, what documents are used to assist production personnel in its manufacture?
5. What is time-based competition?
6. Describe the differences between joint ventures and alliances.
7. Describe four organizational approaches to product development. Which of these is generally thought to be best?
8. Explain what is meant by robust design.
9. What are three specific ways in which computer-aided design (CAD) benefits the design engineer?
10. What information is contained in a bill of material?
11. What information is contained in an engineering drawing?
12. What information is contained in an assembly chart? In a process sheet?
13. Explain what is meant in service design by the "moment of truth".
14. Explain how the house of quality translates customer desires into product/service attributes.
15. What is meant by *sustainability* in the context of operations management?
16. What strategic advantages does computer-aided design provide?
17. What is a process chain?
18. Why are the direct interaction and surrogate interaction regions in a PCN diagram important in service design?
19. Why are documents for service useful? Provide examples of four types.

Solved Problem Virtual Office Hours help is available at MyLab Operations Management.

▼ SOLVED PROBLEM 5.1

Sarah King, president of King Electronics, Inc., has two design options for her new line of high-resolution cathode-ray tubes (CRTs) for CAD workstations. The life cycle sales forecast for the CRT is 100 000 units.

Design option A has a 0.90 probability of yielding 59 good CRTs per 100 and a 0.10 probability of yielding 64 good CRTs per 100. This design will cost $1 000 000.

Design option B has a 0.80 probability of yielding 64 good units per 100 and a 0.20 probability of yielding 59 good units per 100. This design will cost $1 350 000.

Good or bad, each CRT will cost $75. Each good CRT will sell for $150. Bad CRTs are destroyed and have no salvage value. We ignore any disposal costs in this problem.

▼ SOLUTION

We draw the decision tree to reflect the two decisions and the probabilities associated with each decision. We then determine the payoff associated with each branch. The resulting tree is shown in Figure 5.14.

For design A:

$$EMV(\text{design A}) = (0.9)(\$350\ 000) + (0.1)(\$1\ 100\ 000)$$
$$= \$425\ 000$$

For design B:

$$EMV(\text{design B}) = (0.8)(\$750\ 000) + (0.2)(\$0)$$
$$= \$600\ 000$$

The highest payoff is design option B, at $600 000.

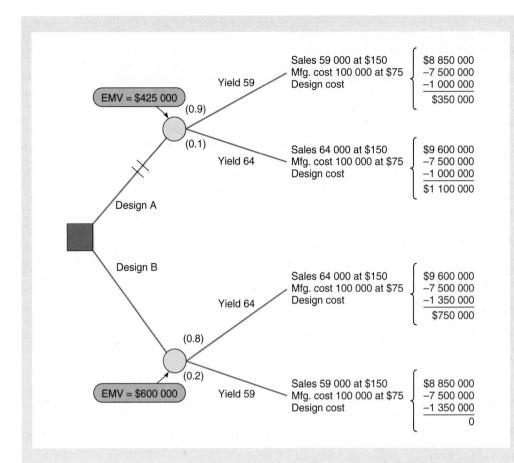

FIGURE 5.14
Decision Tree for Solved Problem 5.1

Problems*

•• **5.1** Construct a house of quality matrix for a wristwatch. Be sure to indicate specific customer wants that you think the general public desires. Then complete the matrix to show how an operations manager might identify specific attributes that can be measured and controlled to meet those customer desires.

•• **5.2** Using the house of quality, pick a real product (a good or service) and analyze how an existing organization satisfies customer requirements.

•• **5.3** Prepare a house of quality for a mousetrap.

•• **5.4** Conduct an interview with a prospective purchaser of a new bicycle and translate the customer's *wants* into the specific *hows* of the firm.

•• **5.5** Prepare a bill of material for (a) a pair of eyeglasses and its case or (b) a fast-food sandwich (visit a local sandwich shop like Subway, McDonald's, Mr. Submarine, Quiznos; perhaps a clerk or the manager will provide you with details on the quantity or weight of various ingredients—otherwise, estimate the quantities).

•• **5.6** Draw an assembly chart for a pair of eyeglasses and its case.

•• **5.7** Prepare a script for telephone callers at the university's annual "phone-a-thon" fund-raiser.

•• **5.8** Prepare an assembly chart for a table lamp.

•• **5.9** Prepare a product-by-value analysis for the following products, and given the position in its life cycle, identify the issues likely to confront the operations manager, and his or her possible actions. Product Alpha has annual sales of 1000 units and a contribution of $2500; it is in the introductory stage. Product Bravo has annual sales of 1500 units and a contribution of $3000; it is in the growth stage. Product Charlie has annual sales of 3500 units and a contribution of $1750; it is in the decline stage.

•• **5.10** Given the contribution made on each of the three products in the following table and their position in the life cycle, identify a reasonable operations strategy for each:

Product	Product Contribution (% of selling price)	Company Contribution (%: total annual contribution divided by total annual sales)	Position in Life Cycle
Kindle 2	30	40	Growth
Netbook computer	30	50	Introduction
Hand calculator	50	10	Decline

*Note: **PX** means the problem may be solved with POM for windows and/or Excel OM.

· · 5.11 The product design group of Flores Electric Supplies, Inc., has determined that it needs to design a new series of switches. It must decide on one of three design strategies. The market forecast is for 200 000 units. The better and more sophisticated the design strategy and the more time spent on value engineering, the less will be the variable cost. The chief of engineering design, Dr. W. L. Berry, has decided that the following costs are a good estimate of the initial and variable costs connected with each of the three strategies:

a) *Low-tech:* A low-technology, low-cost process consisting of hiring several new junior engineers. This option has a fixed cost of $45 000 and variable cost probabilities of 0.3 for $0.55 each, 0.4 for $0.50, and 0.3 for $0.45.

b) *Subcontract:* A medium-cost approach using a good outside design staff. This approach would have a fixed cost of $65 000 and variable cost probabilities of 0.7 of $0.45, 0.2 of $0.40, and 0.1 of $0.35.

c) *High-tech:* A high-technology approach using the very best of the inside staff and the latest computer-aided design technology. This approach has a fixed cost of $75 000 and variable cost probabilities of 0.9 of $0.40 and 0.1 of $0.35.

What is the best decision based on an expected monetary value (EMV) criterion? (*Note:* We want the lowest EMV, as we are dealing with costs in this problem.)

· · 5.12 Tremblay Products, Inc., of Quebec City, has the option of (a) proceeding immediately with production of a new top-of-the-line stereo TV that has just completed prototype testing or (b) having the value analysis team complete a study. If Ed Lusk, VP for operations, proceeds with the existing prototype (option (a)), the firm can expect sales to be 100 000 units at $550 each, with a probability of 0.6 and a 0.4 probability of 75 000 at $550. If, however, he uses the value analysis team (option (b)), the firm expects sales of 75 000 units at $750, with a probability of 0.7 and a 0.3 probability of 70 000 units at $750. Value analysis, at a cost of $100 000, is used only in option (b). Which option has the highest expected monetary value (EMV)? **Px**

· · 5.13 Residents of Mill River have fond memories of ice skating at a local park. An artist has captured the experience in a drawing and is hoping to reproduce it and sell framed copies to current and former residents. He thinks that if the market is good, he can sell 400 copies of the elegant version at $125 each. If the market is not good, he will sell only 300 at $90 each. He can make a deluxe version of the same drawing instead. He feels that if the market is good, he can sell 500 copies of the deluxe version at $100 each. If the market is not good, he will sell only 400 copies at $70 each. In either case, production costs will be approximately $35 000. He can also choose to do nothing. If he believes there is a 50% probability of a good market, what should he do? Why? **Px**

· · 5.14 Ritz Products's materials manager, Bruce Elwell, must determine whether to make or buy a new semiconductor for the wrist TV that the firm is about to produce. One million units are expected to be produced over the life cycle. If the product is made, start-up and production costs of the *make* decision total $1 million, with a probability of 0.4 that the product will be satisfactory and a 0.6 probability that it will not. If the product is not satisfactory, the firm will have to re-evaluate the decision. If the decision is re-evaluated, the choice will be whether to spend another $1 million to redesign the semiconductor or to purchase. Likelihood of success the second time that the make decision is made is 0.9. If the second *make* decision also fails, the firm must purchase. Regardless of when the purchase takes place, Elwell's best judgment of cost is that Ritz will pay $0.50 for each purchased semiconductor plus $1 million in vendor development cost.

a) Assuming that Ritz must have the semiconductor (stopping or doing without is not a viable option), what is the best decision?
b) What criteria did you use to make this decision?
c) What is the worst that can happen to Ritz as a result of this particular decision? What is the best that can happen? **Px**

· · 5.15 Page Engineering designs and constructs air conditioning and heating systems for hospitals and clinics. Currently, the company's staff is overloaded with design work. There is a major design project due in eight weeks. The penalty for completing the design late is $14 000 per week, since any delay will cause the facility to open later than anticipated, and cost the client significant revenue. If the company uses its inside engineers to complete the design, it will have to pay them overtime for all work. Page has estimated that it will cost $12 000 per week (wages and overhead), including late weeks, to have company engineers complete the design. Page is also considering having an outside engineering firm do the design. A bid of $92 000 has been received for the completed design. Yet another option for completing the design is to conduct a joint design by having a third engineering company complete all electromechanical components of the design at a cost of $56 000. Page would then complete the rest of the design and control systems at an estimated cost of $30 000.

Page has estimated the following probabilities of completing the project within various time frames when using each of the three options. Those estimates are shown in the following table:

| Option | Probability of Completing the Design | | | |
	On Time	1 Week Late	2 Weeks Late	3 Weeks Late
Internal engineers	0.4	0.5	0.1	—
External engineers	0.2	0.4	0.3	0.1
Joint design	0.1	0.3	0.4	0.2

What is the best decision based on an expected monetary value criterion? (*Note:* You want the lowest EMV because we are dealing with costs in this problem.) **Px**

· · · 5.16 Use the data in Solved Problem 5.1 to examine what happens to the decision if Sarah King can increase yields from 59 000 to 64 000 by applying an expensive phosphorus to the screen at an added cost of $250 000. Prepare the modified decision tree. What are the payoffs, and which branch has the greatest EMV?

· · · · 5.17 Using the house of quality sequence, as described in Figure 5.4, determine how you might deploy resources to achieve the desired quality for a product or service whose production process you understand.

· · · · 5.18 McBurger, Inc., wants to redesign its kitchens to improve productivity and quality. Three designs, called designs K1, K2, and K3, are under consideration. No matter which design is used, daily demand for sandwiches at a typical McBurger restaurant is for 500 sandwiches. A sandwich costs $1.30 to produce. Non-defective sandwiches sell, on the average, for $2.50 per sandwich. Defective sandwiches cannot be sold and are scrapped. The goal is to choose a design that maximizes the expected profit at a typical restaurant over a 300-day period. Designs K1, K2, and K3 cost $100 000, $130 000, and $180 000 respectively. Under design K1, there is a 0.80 chance that 90 out of each 100 sandwiches are nondefective and a 0.20 chance that 70 out of each 100 sandwiches are nondefective. Under design K2, there is a 0.85 chance that 90 out of each 100 sandwiches are non defective and a 0.15 chance that 75 out of each 100 sandwiches are nondefective. Under design K3, there is a 0.90 chance that 95 out of each 100 sandwiches are nondefective and a 0.10 chance that 80 out of each 100 sandwiches are nondefective. What is the expected profit level of the design that achieves the maximum expected 300-day profit level?

•• **5.19** Draw a two-participant PCN diagram (similar to Figure 5.12) for one of the following processes:
a) The process of having your computer repaired.
b) The process of pizza preparation.
c) The process of procuring tickets for a concert.

•• **5.20** Review strategic process positioning options for the regions in Figure 5.12, discussing the operational impact (in terms of the 10 strategic OM decisions) for:
a) Manufacturing the sandwiches.
b) Direct interaction.
c) Establishing a sandwich buffet.

••• **5.21** Select a service business that involves interaction between customers and service providers, and create a PCN diagram similar to Figure 5.12. Pick a key step that could be performed either by the service provider or by the customers. Show process positioning options for the step. Describe how the options compare in terms of efficiency, economies of scale, and opportunity for customization.

CASE STUDIES

StackTeck

With its headquarters and its largest manufacturing site based in Brampton, Ontario, StackTeck has become the largest plastics mould-maker in the world. In order to capitalize on global opportunities, the company has expanded its operations to include facilities in Hong Kong and Mexico.

To remain on the cutting edge, StackTeck is always seeking to challenge itself and its 250 employees with a process of constant improvement. Achieving both Six Sigma and ISO certification is testament to this fact.

Lou Dimaulo, VP of operations, suggests that one of their key strengths is in product development, design, and execution. Through extensive collaboration with internal and external stakeholders (including customers), solutions to complex product needs are created. This approach has garnered StackTeck a reputation for innovation, quality, and creativity.

In 1991, StackTeck pioneered the first four-level stack mould, a patented technology that has been proven in numerous applications. Stack moulds are opening new opportunities in flexible manufacturing as moulders turn to larger tonnage machines, more multi-material applications, and faster system automation. StackTeck has developed 70% of the four-level moulds that are in production today.

By virtually doubling, tripling, or quadrupling the output of a conventional single face moulding system, stack mould technology increases plant productivity while reducing manufacturing and capital investment costs.

Source: Based on **www.stackteck.com**.

Flexible manufacturing using larger tonnage injection machines has spurred development of four-level stack mould applications beyond traditional packaging. Delivering four times the output from a single machine has a tremendous impact on part production costs, machine productivity, and factory planning. High-volume moulders are developing new stack mould systems for multi-material applications and running multiple tools in the same stack mould to minimize inventories and product handling costs.

Stack moulds are only one area where StackTeck excels and has distinguished itself as a world leader. It is also a leader in flexible manufacturing, in-mould labelling (IML), quick product change (QPC) moulds, and alternative mould cooling technology. In each case, the product design was developed in consultation with customers and end users. StackTeck ensures that everyone wins when it ensures its customers' needs are met, such as improving productivity, better product design, reduced cycle time, etc. But the company won't stop here as the improvement process is never ending.

Discussion Questions

1. Name three Canadian companies in different industries that mirror StackTeck's approach to continuous improvement and innovation in product design.
2. Discuss why it is important for StackTeck never to stop designing and developing new products.

Product Strategy at Regal Marine

With hundreds of competitors in the boat business, Regal Marine must work to differentiate itself. As we saw in the *Global Company Profile* that opened this chapter, Regal continuously introduces innovative, high-quality new boats. Its differentiation strategy is reflected in a product line consisting of 22 models.

To maintain this stream of innovation, and with so many boats at varying stages of their life cycles, Regal constantly seeks design input from customers, dealers, and consultants. Design ideas rapidly find themselves in the styling studio, where they are placed onto CAD machines in order to speed the development process. Existing boat designs are always evolving as the company tries to stay stylish and competitive. Moreover, with life cycles as short as three years, a steady stream of new products is required. A few years ago, the new product was the three-passenger $11 000 Rush, a small but powerful boat capable of pulling a water-skier. This was followed with a 6-metre inboard–outboard performance boat with so many innovations that it won prize after prize in the industry. Another new boat is a redesigned 13-metre Commodore that sleeps six in luxury staterooms. With all these models and innovations, Regal designers and production personnel are under pressure to respond quickly.

By getting key suppliers on board early and urging them to participate at the design stage, Regal improves both innovations and quality while speeding product development. Regal finds that the sooner it brings suppliers on board, the faster it can bring new boats to the market. After a development stage that constitutes concept and styling, CAD designs yield product specifications. The first stage in actual production is the creation of the "plug," a foam-based carving used to make the moulds for fibreglass hulls and decks. Specifications from the CAD system drive the carving process. Once the plug is carved, the permanent moulds for each new hull and deck design are formed. Moulds take about four to eight weeks to produce and are all handmade. Similar moulds are made for many of the other features in Regal boats—from galley and stateroom components to lavatories and steps. Finished moulds can be joined and used to make thousands of boats.

Discussion Questions*

1. How does the concept of product life cycle apply to Regal Marine products?
2. What strategy does Regal use to stay competitive?
3. What kind of engineering savings is Regal achieving by using CAD technology rather than traditional drafting techniques?
4. What are the likely benefits of the CAD design technology?

---

* You may wish to view the video that accompanies this case before addressing these questions.

CHAPTER 5 | RAPID REVIEW

MyLab Operations Management

Main Heading	Review Material	
GOODS AND SERVICES SELECTION (pp. 152–155)	Although the term *products* may often refer to tangible goods, it also refers to offerings by service organizations. *The objective of the product decision is to develop and implement a product strategy that meets the demands of the marketplace with a competitive advantage.* • **Product decision**—The selection, definition, and design of products. The four phases of the product life cycle are introduction, growth, maturity, and decline. • **Product-by-value analysis**—A list of products, in descending order of their individual dollar contribution to the firm, as well as the *total annual dollar* contribution of the product.	Problem: 5.9 **VIDEO 5.1** Product Strategy at Regal Marine
GENERATING NEW PRODUCTS (pp. 155–156)	Product selection, definition, and design take place on a continuing basis. Changes in product opportunities, the products themselves, product volume, and product mix may arise due to understanding the customer, economic change, sociological and demographic change, technological change, political/legal change, market practice, professional standards, suppliers, or distributors.	
PRODUCT DEVELOPMENT (pp. 156–161)	• **Quality function deployment (QFD)**—A process for determining customer requirements (customer "wants") and translating them into attributes (the "hows") that each functional area can understand and act on. • **House of quality**—A part of the QFD process that utilizes a planning matrix to relate customer wants to how the firm is going to meet those wants. • **Product development teams**—Teams charged with moving from market requirements for a product to achieving product success. • **Concurrent engineering**—Use of participating teams in design and engineering activities. • **Manufacturability and value engineering**—Activities that help improve a product's design, production, maintainability, and use.	

MyLab Operations
Management

Main Heading	Review Material
ISSUES FOR PRODUCT DESIGN (pp. 162–164)	• **Robust design**—A design that can be produced to requirements even with unfavourable conditions in the production process. • **Modular designs**—Designs in which parts or components of a product are subdivided into modules that are easily interchanged or replaced. • **Computer-aided design (CAD)**—Interactive use of a computer to develop and document a product. • **Design for manufacture and assembly (DFMA)**—Software that allows designers to look at the effect of design on manufacturing of a product. • **3-D object modelling**—An extension of CAD that builds small prototypes. • **Standard for the exchange of product data (STEP)**—A standard that provides a format allowing the electronic transmission of three-dimensional data. • **Computer-aided manufacturing (CAM)**—The use of information technology to control machinery. • **Virtual reality**—A visual form of communication in which images substitute for reality and typically allow the user to respond interactively. • **Value analysis**—A review of successful products that takes place during the production process.
TIME-BASED COMPETITION (pp. 164–166)	• **Time-based competition**—Competition based on time; rapidly developing products and moving them to market. *Internal development strategies* include (1) new internally developed products, (2) enhancements to existing products, and (3) migrations of existing products. *External development strategies* include (1) purchase of the technology or expertise by acquiring the developer, (2) establishment of joint ventures, and (3) development of alliances. • **Joint ventures**—Firms establishing joint ownership to pursue new products or markets. • **Alliances**—Cooperative agreements that allow firms to remain independent but pursue strategies consistent with their individual missions.
DEFINING A PRODUCT (pp. 166–168)	• **Engineering drawing**—A drawing that shows the dimensions, tolerances, materials, and finishes of a component. • **Bill of material (BOM)**—A list of the components, their description, and the quantity of each required to make one unit of a product. • **Make-or-buy decision**—The choice between producing a component or a service and purchasing it from an outside source. • **Group technology**—A product and component coding system that specifies the type of processing and the parameters of the processing; it allows similar products to be grouped.
DOCUMENTS FOR PRODUCTION (pp. 169–170)	• **Assembly drawing**—An exploded view of a product. • **Assembly chart**—A graphic means of identifying how components flow into subassemblies and final products • **Route sheet**—A listing of the operations necessary to produce a component with the material specified in the bill of material. • **Work order**—An instruction to make a given quantity of a particular item. • **Engineering change notice (ECN)**—A correction or modification of an engineering drawing or bill of material. • **Configuration management**—A system by which a product's planned and changing components are accurately identified. • **Product life cycle management (PLM)**—Software programs that tie together many phases of product design and manufacture.

Main Heading	Review Material	
SERVICE DESIGN (pp. 170–173)	• **Process–chain–network (PCN) analysis**—Analysis that focuses on the ways in which processes can be designed to optimize interaction between firms and their customers. • **Process chain**—A sequence of steps that accomplishes an identifiable purpose (of providing value to process participants). Techniques to reduce costs and enhance the service offering include (1) limiting options, (2) delaying customization, (3) modularizing, (4) automating, and (5) designing for the "moment of truth".	
APPLICATION OF DECISION TREES TO PRODUCT DESIGN (pp. 173–175)	To form a decision tree, (1) include all possible alternatives (including "do nothing") and states of nature; (2) enter payoffs at the end of the appropriate branch; and (3) determine the expected value of each course of action by starting at the end of the tree and working towards the beginning, calculating values at each step and "pruning" inferior alternatives.	Problems: 5.10–5.15, 5.18 **ACTIVE MODEL 5.1** Virtual Office Hours for Solved Problem: 5.1
TRANSITION TO PRODUCTION (p. 175)	One of the arts of modern management is knowing when to move a product from development to production; this move is known as *transition to production*.	

Self-Test

■ **Before taking the self-test,** refer to the learning objectives listed at the beginning of the chapter and the key terms listed at the end of the chapter.

LO1 A product's life cycle is divided into four stages, including:
  a) introduction.
  b) growth.
  c) maturity.
  d) all of the above.

LO2 Product development systems include:
  a) bills of material.
  b) routing charts.
  c) functional specifications.
  d) product-by-value analysis.
  e) configuration management.

LO3 A house of quality is:
  a) a matrix relating customer "wants" to the firm's "hows".
  b) a schematic showing how a product is put together.
  c) list of the operations necessary to produce a component.
  d) an instruction to make a given quantity of a particular item.
  e) a set of detailed instructions about how to perform a task.

LO4 Time-based competition focuses on:
  a) moving new products to market more quickly.
  b) reducing the life cycle of a product.
  c) linking QFD to PLM.
  d) design database availability.
  e) value engineering.

LO5 Products are defined by:
  a) value analysis.
  b) value engineering.
  c) routing sheets.
  d) assembly charts.
  e) engineering drawings.

LO6 A route sheet:
  a) lists the operations necessary to produce a component.
  b) is an instruction to make a given quantity of a particular item.
  c) is a schematic showing how a product is assembled.
  d) is a document showing the flow of product components.
  e) all of the above.

LO7 Decision trees use:
  a) probabilities.
  b) payoffs.
  c) logic.
  d) options.
  e) all of the above.

LO8 The three process regions in a process–chain–network diagram are:
  a) manufacture, supplier, customer.
  b) direct and surrogate, customer, provider.
  c) independent, dependent, customer interaction.
  d) direct interaction, surrogate interaction, independent processing.

Answers: LO1. d; LO2. c; LO3. a; LO4. a; LO5. e; LO6. a; LO7. e; LO8. d.

MyLab Operations Management

Most of these questions can be found in MyLab Operations Management. Visit MyLab Operations Management to access cases, videos, downloadable software, and much more. MyLab Operations Management Management also features a personalized Study Plan that helps you identify which chapter concepts you've mastered and guides you towards study tools for additional practice.

Sustainability in the Supply Chain

Supplement

5

Alaska Airlines

Alaska Airlines

Airlines from around the world, including Air Canada, Air China, Virgin Atlantic Airways, KLM, Alaska, Air New Zealand, and Japan Airlines, are experimenting with alternative fuels to power their jets in an effort to reduce greenhouse gas emissions and to reduce their dependence on traditional petroleum-based jet fuel. Alternative biofuels are being developed from recycled cooking oil, sewage sludge, municipal waste, coconuts, sugar cane, and genetically modified algae that feed on plant waste.

Lex Van Lieshout/EPA/Newscom

Corporate Social Responsibility[1]

LO1 Describe corporate social responsibility

Managers must consider how the products and services they provide affect both people and the environment. Certainly, firms must provide products and services that are innovative and attractive to buyers. But today's technologies allow consumers, communities, public interest groups, and regulators to be well informed about all aspects of an organization's performance. As a result, stakeholders can have strong views about firms that fail to respect the environment or that engage in unethical conduct. Firms need to consider all the implications of a product—from design to disposal.

Many companies now realize that "doing what's right" and doing it properly can be beneficial to all stakeholders. Companies that practice **corporate social responsibility (CSR)** introduce policies that consider environmental, societal, and financial impacts in their decision making. As managers consider approaches to CSR, they find it helpful to consider the concept of creating **shared value**. *Shared value* suggests finding policies and practices that enhance the organization's competitiveness while simultaneously advancing the economic and social conditions in the communities in which it operates. For instance, note how automakers Tesla, Toyota, and Nissan find shared value in low-emission vehicles—vehicles that enhance their competiveness in a global market while meeting society's interest in low-emission vehicles. Similarly, Dow Chemical finds social benefits and profit in Nexera canola and sunflower seeds. These seeds yield twice as much cooking oil as soybeans, enhancing profitability to the grower. They also have a longer shelf life, which reduces operating costs throughout the supply chain. As an added bonus, the oils have lower levels of saturated fat than traditional products and contain no trans fats. A win–win for Dow and society.

Operations functions—from supply chain management to product design to production to packaging and logistics—provide an opportunity for finding shared value and meeting CSR goals.[2]

Corporate social responsibility (CSR)

Managerial decision making that considers environmental, societal, and financial impacts.

Shared value

Developing policies and practices that enhance the competitiveness of an organization while advancing the economic and social conditions in the communities in which it operates.

[1] The authors wish to thank Dr. Steve Leon, University of Central Florida, for his contributions to this supplement.

[2] See related discussions in M. E. Porter and M. R. Kramer, "Creating Shared Value," *Harvard Business Review* (Jan.–Feb. 2011) and M. Pfitzer, V. Bockstette, and M. Stamp, "Innovating for Shared Values," *Harvard Business Review* (Sept. 2013).

Sustainability

Sustainability is often associated with corporate social responsibility. The term **sustainability** refers to meeting the needs of the present without compromising the ability of future generations to meet their needs. Many people who hear of sustainability for the first time think of green products or "going green"—recycling, global warming, and saving rainforests. This is certainly part of it. However, it is more than this. True sustainability involves thinking not only about environmental resources but also about employees, customers, community, and the company's reputation. Three concepts may be helpful as managers consider sustainability decisions: a *systems* view, the *commons*, and the *triple bottom line*.

Sustainability
Meeting the needs of the present without compromising the ability of future generations to meet their needs.

LO2 Describe sustainability

SYSTEMS VIEW

Managers may find that their decisions regarding sustainability improve when they take a *systems* view. This means looking at a product's life from design to disposal, including all the resources required. Recognizing that both raw materials and human resources are subsystems of any production process may provide a helpful perspective. Similarly, the product or service itself is a small part of much larger social, economic, and environmental systems. Indeed, managers need to understand the inputs and interfaces between the interacting systems and identify how changes in one system affect others. For example, hiring or laying off employees can be expected to have morale implications for internal systems (within an organization), as well as socioeconomic implications for external systems. Similarly, dumping chemicals down the drain has implications on systems beyond the firm. Once managers understand that the systems immediately under their control have interactions with systems below them and above them, more informed judgments regarding sustainability can be made.

VIDEO S5.1
Building Sustainability at the Orlando Magic's Amway Center

COMMONS

Many inputs to a production system have market prices, but others do not. Those that do not are those held by the public, or in the *common*. Resources held in the *common* are often misallocated. Examples include depletion of fish in international waters and polluted air and waterways. The attitude seems to be that just a little more fishing or a little more pollution will not matter, or the adverse results may be perceived as someone else's problem. Society is still groping for solutions for use of those resources in the *common*. The answer is slowly being found in a number of ways: (1) moving some of the *common* to private property (e.g., selling radio frequency spectrum), (2) allocation of rights (e.g., establishing fishing boundaries), and (3) allocation of yield (e.g., only a given quantity of fish can be harvested). As managers understand the issues of the *commons*, they have further insight about sustainability and the obligation of caring for the *commons*.

TRIPLE BOTTOM LINE

Firms that do not consider the impact of their decisions on all their stakeholders see reduced sales and profits. Profit maximization is not the only measure of success. A one-dimensional bottom line, profit, will not suffice; the larger socioeconomic systems beyond the firm demand more. One way to think of sustainability is to consider the systems necessary to support the triple bottom line of the three *P*s: *people, planet*, and *profit* (see Figure S5.1), which we will now discuss.

STUDENT TIP
Profit is now just one of the three *P*s: people, planet, and profit.

PEOPLE Companies are becoming more aware of how their decisions affect people—not only their employees and customers but also those who live in the communities in which they operate. Most employers want to pay fair wages, offer educational opportunities, and provide a safe and healthy workplace. So do their suppliers. But globalization and the reliance on outsourcing to suppliers around the world complicate the task. This means companies must create policies that guide supplier selection and performance. Sustainability suggests that supplier selection and performance criteria evaluate safety in the work environment, whether living wages are paid, if child labour is used, and whether work hours are excessive. Apple, GE, Procter & Gamble, and Walmart are examples of companies that conduct supplier audits to uncover any harmful or exploitative business practices that are counter to their sustainability goals and objectives.

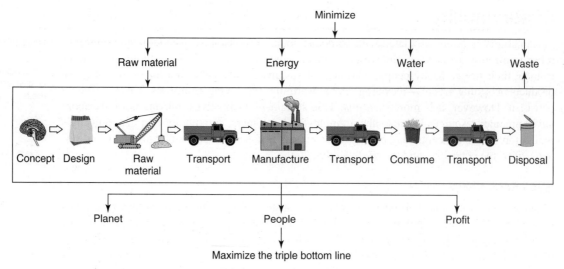

FIGURE S5.1
Improving the Triple Bottom Line with Sustainability

Recognizing that customers increasingly want to know that the materials in the products they buy are safe and produced in a responsible way, Walmart initiated the development of the world-wide sustainable product index for evaluating the sustainability of products. The goals of that initiative are to create a more transparent supply chain, accelerate the adoption of best practices, and drive product innovation.

Walmart found a correlation between supply chain transparency, positive labour practices, community involvement, *and* quality, efficiency, and cost. Walmart is committed to working with its suppliers to sell quality products that are safe, that create value for customers, and that are produced in a sustainable way. The firm is accomplishing this in four ways:

STUDENT **TIP**

Walmart has become a global leader in sustainability. Read *Force of Nature: The Unlikely Story of Walmart's Green Revolution.*

1. Improving livelihoods through the creation of productive, healthy, and safe workplaces and promoting quality of life
2. Building strong communities through access to affordable, high-quality services such as education and job training that support workers and their families
3. Preventing exposure to substances that are considered harmful or toxic to human health
4. Promoting health and wellness by increasing access to nutritious products, encouraging healthy lifestyles, and promoting access to healthcare

Walmart's CEO has said that companies that are unfair to their people are also likely to skimp on quality and that he will not continue to do business with those suppliers. Accordingly, operations managers must consider the working conditions in which they place their employees. This includes training and safety orientations, before-shift exercises, earplugs, safety goggles, and rest breaks to reduce the possibility of worker fatigue and injury. Operations managers must also make decisions regarding the disposal of material and chemical waste, including hazardous materials, so they don't harm employees or the community.

PLANET When discussing the subject of sustainability, our planet's environment is the first thing that comes to mind, so it understandably gets the most attention from managers. Operations managers look for ways to reduce the environmental impact of their operations, whether from raw material selection, process innovation, alternative product delivery methods, or disposal of products at their end-of-life. The overarching objective for operations managers is to conserve scarce resources, thereby reducing the negative impact on the environment. Here are a few examples of how organizations creatively make their operations more environmentally friendly:

- S.C. Johnson, the company that makes Windex, Saran Wrap, Pledge, Ziploc bags, and Raid, developed Greenlist, a classification system that evaluates the impact of raw materials on human and environmental health. By using Greenlist, S.C. Johnson has eliminated millions of kilograms of pollutants from its products.

- Thirty-one public school districts across the state of Kentucky operate hybrid electric school buses. They estimate fuel savings as high as 40%, relative to standard diesel buses.
- Levi's has started a campaign to save water in the creation of jeans, as seen in the *OM in Action* box "Blue Jeans and Sustainability."

To gauge their environmental impact on the planet, many companies are measuring their carbon footprint. **Carbon footprint** is a measure of the total greenhouse gas (GHG) emissions caused directly and indirectly by an organization, a product, an event, or a person. A substantial portion of greenhouse gases are released naturally by farming, cattle, and decaying forests and, to a lesser degree, by manufacturing and services. The most common greenhouse gas produced by human activities is carbon dioxide, primarily from burning fossil fuels for electricity generation, heating, and transport. Operations managers are being asked to do their part to reduce GHG emissions.

Industry leaders such as Frito-Lay have been able to break down the carbon emissions from various stages in the production process. For instance, in potato chip production, a 34.5-gram (1.2-ounce) bag of chips is responsible for about twice its weight in emissions—75 grams per bag (see Figure S5.2).

PROFIT   Social and environmental sustainability do not exist without economic sustainability. **Economic sustainability** refers to how companies remain in business. Staying in business requires making investments, and investments require making profits. Though profits may be relatively easy to determine, other measures can also be used to gauge economic sustainability. The alternative measures that point to a successful business include risk profile, intellectual property, employee morale, and company valuation. To support economic sustainability, firms may supplement standard financial accounting and reporting with some version of *social accounting*. Social accounting can include brand equity, management talent, human capital development and benefits, research and development, productivity, philanthropy, and taxes paid.

Carbon footprint

A measure of total greenhouse gas emissions caused directly or indirectly by an organization, a product, an event, or a person.

VIDEO S5.2
Green Manufacturing and Sustainability at Frito-Lay

Economic sustainability

Appropriately allocating scarce resources to make a profit.

OM in Action   Blue Jeans and Sustainability

The recent drought in California is hurting more than just farmers. It is also having a significant impact on the fashion industry and spurring changes in how jeans are made and how they should be laundered. Southern California is estimated to be the world's largest supplier of so-called premium denim, the $100- to $200-plus-a-pair of designer jeans. Water is a key component in the various steps of the processing and repeated washing with stones, or bleaching and dyeing that create that "distressed" vintage look. Southern California produces 75% of the high-end denim in the United States that is sold worldwide. The area employs about 200 000 people, making it the largest U.S. fashion manufacturing hub.

Now that water conservation is a global priority, major denim brands are working to cut water use. Levi's, with sales of $5 billion, is using ozone machines to replace the bleach traditionally used to lighten denim. It is also reducing the number of times it washes jeans. The company has saved more than a billion litres of water since 2011 with its Levi's Water Less campaign. By 2020, the company plans to have 80% of Levi's brand products made using the Water Less process, up from about 25% currently.

Traditionally, about 34 litres of water are used in the cutting, sewing, and finishing process to make a pair of Levi's signature 501 jeans. Nearly 3800 litres of water are used throughout the lifetime of a pair of Levi's 501. A study found cotton cultivation represents 68% of that and consumer washing another 23%. So Levi's is promoting

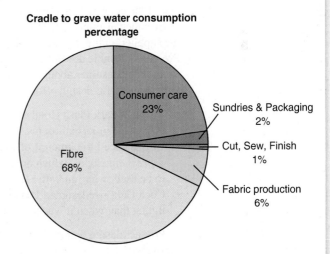

Cradle to grave water consumption percentage

- Fibre 68%
- Consumer care 23%
- Sundries & Packaging 2%
- Cut, Sew, Finish 1%
- Fabric production 6%

the idea that jeans only need washing after 10 *wears*. (The average North American consumer washes after two *wears*.) Levi's CEO recently urged people to stop washing their jeans, saying he hadn't washed his one-year-old jeans at the time. "You can air dry and spot clean instead," he said.

Sources: The Wall Street Journal (April 10, 2015) and *New York Times* (March 31, 2015).

FIGURE S5.2

Carbon Footprint of a 34.5-gram Bag of Frito-Lay Chips

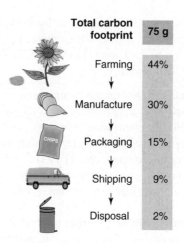

Total carbon footprint	75 g
Farming	44%
Manufacture	30%
Packaging	15%
Shipping	9%
Disposal	2%

Design and Production for Sustainability

Life cycle assessment

Analysis of environmental impacts of products from the design stage through end-of-life.

The operations manager's greatest opportunity to make substantial contributions to the company's environmental objectives occurs during product life cycle assessment. **Life cycle assessment** evaluates the environmental impact of a product, from raw material and energy inputs all the way to the disposal of the product at its end-of-life. The goal is to make decisions that help reduce the environmental impact of a product throughout its entire life. Focusing on the 3*R*s—*reduce, reuse,* and *recycle*— can help accomplish this goal. By incorporating the 3*R*s, product design teams, process managers, and supply chain personnel can make great strides towards reducing the environmental impact of products—to the benefit of all stakeholders.

PRODUCT DESIGN

LO3 Explain the 3*R*s for sustainability

Product design is the most critical phase in product life cycle assessment. The decisions that are made during this phase greatly affect materials, quality, cost, processes, related packaging and logistics, and ultimately how the product will be processed when discarded. During design, one of the goals is to incorporate a systems view in the product or service design that lowers the environmental impact. This is the first *R*. Such an approach reduces waste and energy costs at the supplier, in the logistics system, and for the end user. For instance, by taking a systems view, Procter & Gamble developed Tide Coldwater, a detergent that gets clothes clean with cold water, saving the consumer about three-fourths of the energy used in a typical wash.
Other successful design efforts include:

- Boston's Park Plaza Hotel eliminated bars of soap and bottles of shampoo by installing pump dispensers in its bathrooms, saving the need for 1 million plastic containers a year.
- UPS reduced the amount of materials it needs for its envelopes by developing its *reusable express envelopes,* which are made from 100% recycled fibre. These envelopes are designed to be used twice, and after the second use, the envelope can be recycled.
- Coca-Cola's redesigned Dasani bottle reduced the amount of plastic needed and is now 30% lighter than when it was introduced.

Product design teams also look for *alternative* materials from which to make their products. Innovating with alternative materials can be expensive, but it may make autos, trucks, and aircraft more environmentally friendly while improving payload and fuel efficiency. Aircraft and auto makers, for example, constantly seek lighter materials to use in their products. Lighter materials translate into better fuel economy, fewer carbon emissions, and reduced operating cost. For instance:

- Mercedes is building some car exteriors from a banana fibre that is both biodegradable and lightweight.
- Some Fords have seat upholstery made from recycled plastic soda bottles and old clothing.
- Boeing is using carbon fibre, epoxy composites, and titanium graphite laminate to reduce weight in its new 787 Dreamliner.

An excellent place for operations managers to begin the sustainability challenge is with good product design. Here Tom Malone, CEO of MicroGreen Polymers, discusses the company's new ultra-light cup with production personnel (left). The cup can be recycled over and over and never go to a landfill. Another new design is the "winglet" (right). These wing tip extensions increase climb speed, reduce noise by 6.5%, cut CO_2 emissions by 5%, and save 6% in fuel costs. Alaska Air has retrofitted its entire 737 fleet with winglets, saving $20 million annually.

Product designers often must decide between two or more environmentally friendly design alternatives. Example S1 deals with a *design for disassembly* cost–benefit analysis. This process focuses on the second and third *R*s: reuse and recycle. The design team analyzes the amount of revenue that might be reclaimed against the cost of disposing of the product at its end-of-life.

STUDENT **TIP**

A fourth *R, improved reputation,* follows the success of reduce, reuse, and recycle.

Sound Barrier, Inc., needs to decide which of two speaker designs is better environmentally.

APPROACH ▶ The design team collected the following information for two audio speaker designs, the Harmonizer and the Rocker:

1. Resale value of the components minus the cost of transportation to the disassembly facility
2. Revenue collected from recycling
3. Processing costs, which include disassembly, sorting, cleaning, and packaging
4. Disposal costs, including transportation, fees, taxes, and processing time

SOLUTION ▶ The design team developed the following revenue and cost information for the two speaker design alternatives:

Harmonizer

Part	Resale Revenue Per Unit	Recycling Revenue Per Unit	Processing Cost Per Unit	Disposal Cost Per Unit
Printed circuit board	$5.93	$1.54	$3.46	$0.00
Laminate back	0.00	0.00	4.53	1.74
Coil	8.56	5.65	6.22	0.00
Processor	9.17	2.65	3.12	0.00
Frame	0.00	0.00	2.02	1.23
Aluminum case	11.83	2.10	2.98	0.00
Total	$35.49	$11.94	$22.33	$2.97

EXAMPLE **S1**

Design for Disassembly

LO4 Calculate design for disassembly

Rocker

Part	Resale Revenue Per Unit	Recycling Revenue Per Unit	Processing Cost Per Unit	Disposal Cost Per Unit
Printed circuit board	$7.88	$3.54	$2.12	$0.00
Coil	6.67	4.56	3.32	0.00
Frame	0.00	0.00	4.87	1.97
Processor	8.45	4.65	3.43	0.00
Plastic case	0.00	0.00	4.65	3.98
Total	$23.00	$12.75	$18.39	$5.95

Using the Equation (S5-1), the design team can compare the two design alternatives:

Revenue retrieval =
Total resale revenue + Total recycling revenue − Total processing cost − Total disposal cost (S5-1)

Revenue retrieval for Harmonizer = $35.49 + $11.94 − $22.33 − $2.97 = $22.13

Revenue retrieval for Rocker = $23.00 + $12.75 − $18.39 − $5.95 = $11.41

INSIGHT ▶ After analyzing both environmental revenue and cost components of each speaker design, the design team finds that the Harmonizer is the better environmental design alternative as it achieves a higher revenue retrieval opportunity. Note that the team is assuming that both products have the same market acceptance, profitability, and environmental impact.

LEARNING EXERCISE ▶ What would happen if there was a change in the supply chain that caused the processing and disposal costs to triple for the laminate back part of the Harmonizer? [Answer: The revenue retrieval from the Harmonizer is $35.49 + $11.94 − $31.39 − $6.45 = $9.59. This is less than the Rocker's revenue retrieval of $11.41, so the Rocker becomes the better environmental design alternative, as it achieves a higher revenue retrieval opportunity.]

RELATED PROBLEMS ▶ S5.1, S5.2, S5.3, S5.9, S5.12, S5.13, S5.14

PRODUCTION PROCESS

Manufacturers look for ways to reduce the amount of resources in the production process. Opportunities to reduce environmental impact during production typically revolve around the themes of energy, water, and environmental contamination. Conservation of energy and improving energy efficiency come from the use of alternative energy and more energy-efficient machinery. For example:

- S.C. Johnson built its own power plant that runs on natural gas and methane piped in from a nearby landfill, cutting back its reliance on coal-fired power.
- PepsiCo developed Resource Conservation (ReCon), a diagnostic tool for understanding and reducing in-plant water and energy usage. In its first two years, ReCon helped sites across the world identify 2.2 billion litres of water savings, with a corresponding cost savings of nearly $2.7 million.
- Frito-Lay decided to extract water from potatoes, which are 80% water. Each year, a single factory processes 350 000 tonnes of potatoes, and as those potatoes are processed, the company reuses the extracted water for that factory's daily production.

STUDENT TIP

Las Vegas, always facing a water shortage, pays residents $40 000 an acre to take out lawns and replace them with rocks and native plants.

These and similar successes in the production process reduce both costs and environmental concerns. Less energy is consumed, and less material is going to landfills.

LOGISTICS

As products move along in the supply chain, managers strive to achieve efficient route and delivery networks, just as they seek to drive down operating cost. Doing so reduces environmental impact. Management analytics (such as linear programming, queuing, and vehicle routing software) help firms worldwide optimize elaborate supply chain and distribution networks. Networks of container ships, airplanes, trains, and trucks are being analyzed to reduce the number of kilometres traveled or the number of hours required to make deliveries. For example:

- UPS has found that making left turns increases the time it takes to make deliveries. This in turn increases fuel usage and carbon emissions. So UPS plans its delivery truck routes with

Three key success factors in the trucking industry are (1) getting shipments to customers promptly (rapid response), (2) keeping trucks busy (capacity utilization), and (3) buying inexpensive fuel (driving down costs). Many firms have now developed devices like the one shown on the right to track location of trucks and facilitate communication between drivers and dispatchers. Some systems use global positioning satellites (shown on the left), to speed shipment response, maximize utilization of the truck, and ensure purchase of fuel at the most economical location. Sensors are also being added inside trailers. These sensors communicate whether the trailer is empty or full and detect if the trailer is connected to a truck or riding on a railroad car.

the fewest possible left turns. Likewise, airplanes fly at different altitudes and routes to take advantage of favourable wind conditions in an effort to reduce fuel use and carbon emissions.

- Food distribution companies now have trucks with three temperature zones (frozen, cool, and nonrefrigerated) instead of using three different types of trucks.
- Whirlpool radically revised its packaging to reduce "dings and dents" of appliances during delivery, generating huge savings in transportation and warranty costs.

To further enhance logistic efficiency, operations managers also evaluate equipment alternatives, taking into account cost, payback period, and the firm's stated environmental objectives. Example S2 deals with decision making that takes into account life cycle ownership costs. A firm must decide whether to pay *more* up front for vehicles to further its sustainability goals or to pay *less* up front for vehicles that do not.

EXAMPLE S2

Life Cycle Ownership and Crossover Analysis

Blue Star is starting a new distribution service that delivers auto parts to the service departments of auto dealerships in the local area. Blue Star has found two light-duty trucks that would do the job well, so now it needs to pick one to perform this new service. The Ford TriVan costs $28 000 to buy and uses regular unleaded gasoline, with an average fuel efficiency of 24 kilometres per litre. The TriVan has an operating cost of $0.20 per kilometre. The Honda CityVan, a hybrid truck, costs $32 000 to buy and uses regular unleaded gasoline and battery power; it gets an average of 37 kilometres per litre. The CityVan has an operating cost of $0.22 per kilometre. The distance traveled annually is estimated to be 22 000 kilometres, with the life of either truck expected to be eight years. The average gas price is $4.25 per litre.

APPROACH ▶ Blue Star applies Equation (S5-2) to evaluate total life cycle cost for each vehicle:

Total life cycle cost = Cost of vehicle + Life cycle cost of fuel + Life cycle operating cost   (S5-2)

a) Based on life cycle cost, which model truck is the best choice?
b) How many kilometres does Blue Star need to put on a truck for the costs to be equal?
c) What is the crossover point in years?

SOLUTION ▶

a) Ford TriVan:

$$\text{Total life-cycle cost} = \$28\,000 + \left[\frac{22\,000\frac{kilometres}{year}}{24\frac{kilometres}{litre}} \right] (\$4.25/litre)(8\ years)$$

$$+ \left(22\,000\frac{kilometres}{year} \right)(\$0.20/kilometre)(8\ years)$$

$$= \$28\,000 + \$31\,167 + \$35\,200 = \$94\,367$$

Honda CityVan:

$$
\text{Total life-cycle cost} = \$32\,000 + \left[\dfrac{22\,000\dfrac{kilometres}{year}}{37\dfrac{kilometres}{litre}}\right](\$4.25/litre)(8\ years)
$$

$$
+ \left(22\,000\dfrac{kilometres}{year}\right)(\$0.22/kilometre)(8\ years)
$$

$$
= \$32\,000 + \$20\,216 + \$38\,720 = \$90\,936
$$

b) Blue Star lets M be the crossover (break-even) point in kilometres, sets the two life cycle cost equations equal to each other, and solves for M:

$$
\text{Total cost for Ford TriVan} = \text{Total cost for Honda CityVan}
$$

$$
\$28\,000 + \left[\dfrac{4.25\dfrac{\$}{litre}}{24\dfrac{kilometres}{litre}} + .20\dfrac{\$}{kilometre}\right](M\ kilometres) = \$32\,000
$$

$$
+ \left[\dfrac{4.25\dfrac{\$}{litre}}{37\dfrac{kilometres}{litre}} + .22\dfrac{\$}{kilometre}\right](M\ kilometres)
$$

or,

$$
\$28\,000 + \left(.3770\dfrac{\$}{kilometre}\right)(M) = \$32\,000 + \left(.3349\dfrac{\$}{kilometre}\right)(M)
$$

or,

$$
\left(.0421\dfrac{\$}{kilometre}\right)(M) = \$4\,000
$$

$$
M = \dfrac{\$4\,000}{.0421\dfrac{\$}{kilometre}} = 95\,012\ kilometres
$$

(Rounding to four decimal places was used in these calculations.)

c) The crossover point in years is:

$$
\text{Crossover point} = \dfrac{95\,012\ kilometres}{22\,000\dfrac{kilometres}{year}} = 4.32\ years
$$

INSIGHT ▶

a) Honda CityVan is the best choice, even though the initial fixed cost and variable operating cost per kilometre are higher. The savings comes from the better fuel mileage (more kilometres per litre) for the Honda CityVan.

b) The crossover (break-even) point is at 95 012 kilometres, which indicates that at this mileage point, the cost for either truck is the same.

c) It will take 4.32 years to recoup the cost of purchasing and operating either vehicle. It will cost Blue Star approximately $0.03 per kilometre less to operate the Honda CityVan than the Ford TriVan over the eight-year expected life.

LEARNING EXERCISE ▶ If the cost of gasoline drops to $3.25, what will be the total life cycle cost of each van, the break-even point in kilometres, and the crossover point in years? [Answer: The cost of the Ford TriVan is $87 033; the Honda CityVan costs $86 179; the break-even is 144 927 kilometres; and the crossover point is 6.59 years.]

RELATED PROBLEMS ▶ S5.4, S5.5, S5.6, S5.10, S5.11, S5.15, S5.16, S5.17, S5.18, S5.19

END-OF-LIFE PHASE

We noted earlier that during product design, managers need to consider what happens to a product or its materials after the product reaches its end-of-life stage. Products with less material, with recycled material, or with recyclable materials all contribute to sustainability efforts, reducing the need for the "burn or bury" decision and conserving scarce natural resources.

Innovative and sustainability-conscious companies are now designing **closed-loop supply chains**, also called *reverse logistics*. Firms can no longer sell a product and then forget about it. They need to design and implement end-of-life systems for the physical return of products that facilitate recycling or reuse.

Caterpillar, through its expertise in remanufacturing technology and processes, has devised *Cat Reman,* a remanufacturing initiative, in an effort to show its commitment to sustainability. Caterpillar remanufactures parts and components that provide same-as-new performance and reliability at a fraction of new cost, while reducing the impact on the environment. The remanufacturing program is based on an exchange system where customers return a used component in exchange for a remanufactured product. The result is lower operating costs for the customer, reduced material waste, and less need for raw material to make new products. In a one-year period, Caterpillar took back 2.1 million end-of-life units and remanufactured over 130 million pounds of material from recycled iron.

The *OM in Action* box "From Assembly Lines to Green Disassembly Lines" describes one automaker's car design philosophy to facilitate the disassembly, recycling, and reuse of its autos that have reached their end-of-life.

Closed-loop supply chains
Supply chains that consider forward and reverse product flows over the entire life cycle.

Regulations and Industry Standards

Government, industry standards, and company policies are all important factors in operational decisions. Failure to recognize these constraints can be costly. Over the last 100 years, we have seen development of regulations, standards, and policies to guide managers in product design, manufacturing/assembly, and disassembly/disposal.

To guide decisions in *product design* laws and regulations provide guidance and often explicit regulations.

LO5 Explain the impact of sustainable regulations on operations

---

OM in Action From Assembly Lines to Green Disassembly Lines

A century has passed since assembly lines were developed to make automobiles—and now we're developing *disassembly* lines to take them apart. So many automobiles are disassembled that recycling is the 16th-largest industry in the United States The motivation for this comes from many sources, including mandated industry recycling standards and a growing consumer interest in purchasing cars based on how "green" they are.

New car designs have traditionally been unfriendly to recyclers, with little thought given to disassembly. Some components, such as air bags, are hard to handle and dangerous, and they take time to disassemble. However, manufacturers now design in such a way that materials can be easily reused in the next generation of cars. The 2015 Mercedes S-class is 95% recyclable. BMW has disassembly plants in Europe, Japan, New York, Los Angeles, and Orlando.

A giant 200 000-square-foot facility in Baltimore (called CARS) can disassemble up to 30 000 vehicles per year. At CARS's initial "greening station," special tools puncture tanks and drain fluids and remove the battery and gas tank. Then wheels, doors, hood, and trunk are removed;

next come the interior items; plastic parts are removed and sorted for recycling; then glass and interior and trunk materials. Eventually the chassis is a bale and sold as a commodity to minimills that use scrap steel. Reusable parts are bar-coded and entered into a database. The photo shows an operator controlling the car recycling plant.

Sources: Wall Street Journal (April 29, 2008) and *Time* (February 4, 2010).

Manufacturing and assembly activities have their own set of regulatory agencies providing guidance and standards of operations. These include many federal, provincial, and local agencies that regulate workers' rights and employment standards.

As product life spans shorten due to ever-changing trends and innovation, product designers are under added pressure to *design for disassembly*. This encourages designers to create products that can be disassembled and whose components can be recovered, minimizing impact on the environment.

Organizations are obliged by society and regulators to reduce harm to consumers, employees, and the environment. The result is a proliferation of community, provincial, federal, and even international laws that often complicate compliance. The lack of coordination of regulations and reporting requirements between jurisdictions adds not just complexity but cost.

From the following examples it is apparent that nearly all industries must abide by regulations in some form or another:

- Commercial homebuilders are required not just to manage water runoff but to have a pollution prevention plan for each site.
- Hospitals are required to meet the terms of regulations that govern the storage and handling of hazardous material.

The consequences of ignoring regulations can be disastrous and even criminal. The government investigates environmental crimes in which companies and individuals are held accountable. Prison time and expensive fines can be handed down. (British Petroleum paid billions of dollars in fines in the past few years for breaking environmental and safety laws.) Even if a crime has not been committed, the financial impacts and customer upheaval can be disastrous to companies that do not comply with regulations. Due to lack of supplier oversight, Mattel, Inc., one of the world's largest toymakers, has recalled over 10 million toys in recent years because of consumer health hazards such as lead paint.

INTERNATIONAL ENVIRONMENTAL POLICIES AND STANDARDS

Organizations such as the U.N. Framework Convention on Climate Change (UNFCCC), International Organization for Standardization (ISO), and governments around the globe are guiding businesses to reduce environmental impacts from disposal of materials to reductions in greenhouse gas (GHG) emissions. Some governments are implementing laws that mandate the outright reduction of GHG emissions by forcing companies to pay taxes based on the amount of GHG emissions that are emitted. We now provide an overview of some of the international standards that apply to how businesses operate, manufacture, and distribute goods and services.

European Union Emissions Trading System   The European Union has developed and implemented the EU Emissions Trading System (EUETS) to combat climate change. This is the key tool for reducing industrial greenhouse gas emissions in the EU. The EUETS works on the "cap-and-trade" principle. This means there is a cap, or limit, on the total amount of certain greenhouse gases that can be emitted by factories, power plants, and airlines in EU airspace. Within this cap, companies receive emission allowances, which they can sell to, or buy from, one another as needed.

ISO 14000   The International Organization for Standardization (ISO) is widely known for its contributions in ISO 9000 quality assurance standards (discussed in Chapter 6). The **ISO 14000** family grew out of the ISO's commitment to support the 1992 U.N. objective of sustainable development. ISO 14000 is a series of environmental management standards that contain five core elements: (1) environmental management, (2) auditing, (3) performance evaluation, (4) labelling, and (5) life cycle assessment. Companies that demonstrate these elements may apply for certification. ISO 14000 has several advantages:

- Positive public image and reduced exposure to liability
- Good systematic approach to pollution prevention through minimization of ecological impact of products and activities
- Compliance with regulatory requirements and opportunities for competitive advantage
- Reduction in the need for multiple audits

OM in Action   Subaru's Clean, Green Set of Wheels with ISO 14001

"Going green" had humble beginnings. First, it was newspapers, soda cans and bottles, and corrugated packaging—the things you typically throw into your own recycling bins. Similarly, at Subaru's Lafayette, Indiana, plant, the process of becoming the first completely waste-free auto plant in North America began with employees dropping these items in containers throughout the plant. Then came employee empowerment. "We had 268 suggestions for different things to improve our recycling efforts," said Denise Coogan, plant ISO 14001 environmental compliance leader.

Some ideas were easy to handle. "With plastic shrink wrap, we found some (recyclers) wouldn't take colored shrink wrap. So we went back to our vendors and asked for only clear shrink wrap," Coogan said. Some suggestions were a lot dirtier. "We went dumpster diving to see what we were throwing away and see what we could do with it."

The last load of waste generated by Subaru made its way to a landfill seven years ago. Since then, everything that enters the plant eventually exits as a usable product. Coogan adds, "We didn't redefine 'zero.' Zero means zero. Nothing from our manufacturing process goes to the landfill."

Last year alone, the Subaru plant recycled 13 142 tonnes of steel, 1 448 tonnes of paper products, 194 tonnes

cnky Photography/Fotolia

of plastics, 10 tonnes of solvent-soaked rags, and 4 tonnes of lightbulbs. Doing so conserved 29 200 trees, 670 000 litres of oil, 34 700 litres of gas, 10 million litres of water, and 53 000 million watts of electricity. "Going green" isn't easy, but it can be done!

Sources: IndyStar (May 10, 2014) and *BusinessWeek* (June 6, 2011).

ISO 14000 standards have been implemented by more than 200 000 organizations in 155 countries. Companies that have implemented ISO 14000 standards report environmental and economic benefits such as reduced raw material/resource use, reduced energy consumption, lower distribution costs, improved corporate image, improved process efficiency, reduced waste generation and disposal costs, and better utilization of recoverable resources.

ISO 14001, which addresses environmental management systems, gives guidance to companies to minimize harmful effects on the environment caused by their activities. The *OM in Action* box "Subaru's Clean, Green Set of Wheels with ISO 14001" illustrates the growing application of the ISO 14000 standards.

SUPPLEMENT SUMMARY

If a firm wants to be viable and competitive, it must have a strategy for corporate social responsibility and sustainability. Operations and supply chain managers understand that they have a critical role in a firm's sustainability objectives. Their actions impact all the stakeholders. They must continually seek new and innovative ways to design, produce, deliver, and dispose of profitable, customer-satisfying products while adhering to many environmental regulations. Without the expertise and commitment of operations and supply chain managers, firms are unable to meet their sustainability obligations.

Discussion Questions

1. Why must companies practice corporate social responsibility?
2. Find statements of sustainability for a well-known company online and analyze that firm's policy.
3. Explain sustainability.
4. Discuss the 3*R*s.
5. Explain closed-loop supply chains.
6. How would you classify a company as green?
7. Why are sustainable business practices important?

Solved Problems Virtual Office Hours help is available in MyLab Operations Management.

▼ SOLVED PROBLEM S5.1

The design team for Superior Electronics is creating a mobile audio player and must choose between two design alternatives. Which is the better environmental design alternative, based on achieving a higher revenue retrieval opportunity?

▼ SOLUTION

Collecting the resale revenue per unit, recycling revenue per unit, processing cost per unit, and the disposal cost per unit, the design team computes the revenue retrieval for each design:

Design 1

Part	Resale Revenue Per Unit	Recycling Revenue Per Unit	Processing Cost Per Unit	Disposal Cost Per Unit
Tuner	$4.93	$2.08	$2.98	$0.56
Speaker	0.00	0.00	4.12	1.23
Case	6.43	7.87	4.73	0.00
Total	$11.36	$9.95	$11.83	$1.79

Design 2

Part	Resale Revenue Per Unit	Recycling Revenue Per Unit	Processing Cost Per Unit	Disposal Cost Per Unit
Tuner	$6.91	$4.92	$3.41	$2.13
Case	5.83	3.23	2.32	1.57
Amplifier	1.67	2.34	4.87	0.00
Speaker	0.00	0.00	3.43	1.97
Total	$14.41	$10.49	$14.03	$5.67

Using the following formula [Equation (S5-1)], compare the two design alternatives:

Revenue retrieval = Total resale revenue + Total recycling revenue − Total processing cost − Total disposal cost

Revenue retrieval Design 1 = $11.36 + $9.95 − $11.83 − $1.79 = $7.69

Revenue retrieval Design 2 = $14.41 + $10.49 − $14.03 − $5.67 = $5.20

Design 1 brings in the most revenue from its design when the product has reached its end-of-life.

▼ SOLVED PROBLEM S5.2

The City of High Point is buying new school buses for the local school system. High Point has found two models of school buses that it is interested in. Eagle Mover costs $80 000 to buy and uses diesel fuel, with an average fuel efficiency of 10 kilometres per litre. Eagle Mover has an operating cost of $0.28 per kilometre. Yellow Transport, a hybrid bus, costs $105 000 to buy and uses diesel fuel and battery power, getting an average of 22 kilometres per litre. Yellow Transport has an operating cost of $0.32 per kilometre. The distance traveled annually is determined to be 25 000 kilometres, with the expected life of either bus to be 10 years. The average diesel price is $3.50 per litre.

▼ SOLUTION

a) Based on life cycle cost, which bus is the better choice?

Eagle Mover:

$$\$80\,000 + \left[\frac{25\,000 \frac{kilometres}{year}}{10 \frac{kilometres}{litre}} \right] (\$3.50/litre)(10\,years) + \left(25\,000 \frac{kilometres}{year} \right)(\$0.28/kilometre)(10\,years)$$

$$= \$80\,000 + \$85\,500 + \$70\,000 = \$237\,500$$

Yellow Transport:

$$\$105\,000 + \left[\frac{25\,000 \frac{kilometres}{year}}{22 \frac{kilometres}{litre}} \right] (\$3.50/litre)(10\,years) + \left(25\,000 \frac{kilometres}{year} \right)(\$0.32/kilometre)(10\,years)$$

$$= \$105\,000 + \$39\,773 + \$80\,000 = \$224\,773$$

Yellow Transport is the better choice.

b) How many kilometres does the school district need to put on a bus for costs to be equal?

Let M be the break-even point in kilometres, set the equations equal to each other, and solve for M:

Total cost for Eagle Mover = Total cost for Yellow Transport

$$\$80\,000 + \left[\frac{3.50 \frac{\$}{litre}}{10 \frac{kilometres}{litre}} + 0.28 \frac{\$}{kilometre} \right] (M\,kilometres) = \$105\,000 + \left[\frac{3.50 \frac{\$}{litre}}{22 \frac{kilometres}{litre}} + 0.32 \frac{\$}{kilometre} \right] (M\,kilometres)$$

$$\$80\,000 + \left(0.630\frac{\$}{kilometre}\right)(M) = \$105\,000 + \left(0.479\frac{\$}{kilometre}\right)(M)$$

$$\left(0.151\frac{\$}{kilometre}\right)(M) = \$25\,000$$

$$M = \frac{\$25\,000}{0.151\dfrac{\$}{kilometre}} = 165\,563\ kilometres$$

(Rounding to three decimal places was used in these calculations.)

c) What is the crossover point in years?

$$Crossover\ point = \frac{165\,563\,kilometres}{25\,000\dfrac{kilometres}{year}} = 6.62\,years$$

Problems

Problems S5.1–S5.19 relate to *Design and Production for Sustainability*

•• **S5.1** The Brew House needs to decide which of two coffee maker designs is better environmentally. Using the following tables, determine which model is the better design alternative.

Brew Master

Part	Resale Revenue Per Unit	Recycling Revenue Per Unit	Processing Cost Per Unit	Disposal Cost Per Unit
Metal frame	$1.65	$2.87	$1.25	$0.75
Timer	0.50	0.00	1.53	1.45
Plug/cord	4.25	5.65	6.22	0.00
Coffee pot	2.50	2.54	2.10	1.35

Brew Mini

Part	Resale Revenue Per Unit	Recycling Revenue Per Unit	Processing Cost Per Unit	Disposal Cost Per Unit
Plastic frame	$1.32	$3.23	$0.95	$0.95
Plug/cord	3.95	4.35	5.22	0.00
Coffee pot	2.25	2.85	2.05	1.25

•• **S5.2** Using the information in Problem S5.1, which design alternative is the better environmental choice if the Brew House decided to add a timer to the Brew Mini model? The timer revenue and costs are identical to those of the Brew Master.

•• **S5.3** Using the information in Problem S5.1, which design alternative is the better environmental choice if the Brew House decided to remove the timer from the Brew Master model?

•• **S5.4** What is the total vehicle life cycle cost of this hybrid car, given the information provided in the following table?

Vehicle Purchase Cost	$17 000
Vehicle Operating Cost Per Kilometre	$0.12
Useful Life of Vehicle	15 years
Kilometres Per Year	14 000
Kilometres Per Litre	32
Average Fuel Price Per Litre	$3.75

•• **S5.5** What is the crossover point in kilometres between the hybrid vehicle in Problem S5.4 and this alternative vehicle from a competing auto manufacturer?

Vehicle Purchase Cost	$19 000
Vehicle Operating Cost Per Kilometre	$0.09
Useful Life of Vehicle	15 years
Kilometres Per Year	14 000
Kilometres Per Litre	35
Average Fuel Price Per Litre	$3.75

•• **S5.6** Given the crossover mileage in Problem S5.5, what is the crossover point in years?

•• **S5.7** In Problem S5.5, if gas prices rose to $4.00 per litre, what would be the new crossover point in kilometres?

•• **S5.8** Using the new crossover mileage in Problem S5.7, what is the crossover point in years?

•• **S5.9** Mercedes is assessing which of two windshield suppliers provides a better environmental design for disassembly. Using the tables below, select between PG Glass and Glass Unlimited.

PG Glass

Part	Resale Revenue Per Unit	Recycling Revenue Per Unit	Processing Cost Per Unit	Disposal Cost Per Unit
Glass	$12	$10	$6	$2
Steel frame	2	1	1	1
Rubber insulation	1	2	1	1

Glass Unlimited

Part	Resale Revenue Per Unit	Recycling Revenue Per Unit	Processing Cost Per Unit	Disposal Cost Per Unit
Reflective glass	$15	$12	$7	$3
Aluminium frame	4	3	2	2
Rubber insulation	2	2	1	1

•• **S5.10** Environmentally conscious Susan has been told that a new electric car will only generate 6 grams of greenhouse gases (GHG) per kilometre, but that a standard internal combustion car is double that at 12 grams per kilometre. However, the nature of electric cars is such that the new technology and electric batteries generate 30 000 lbs. of GHG to manufacture and another 10 000 lbs. to recycle. A standard car generates only 14 000 lbs. of GHG to manufacture, and recycling with established technology is only 1 000 lbs. Susan is interested in taking a systems approach that considers the life cycle impact of her decision. How many kilometres must she drive the electric car for it to be the preferable decision in terms of reducing greenhouse gases? Susan anticipates the vehicles will be in service for 16 years.

••• **S5.11** A Southern Georgia school district is considering ordering 53 propane-fuelled school buses. "They're healthier, they're cleaner burning, and they're much quieter than the diesel option," said a school administrator. Propane-powered buses also reduce greenhouse gasses by 22% compared to gasoline-powered buses and 6% compared to diesel ones. But they come at a premium—$103 000 for a propane model, $15 000 more than the diesel equivalent.

The propane bus operating cost (above and beyond fuel cost) is 30 cents/kilometre, compared to 40 cents for the diesel. Diesel fuel costs about $2/litre in Georgia, about $1 more than propane. Bus mileage is 12 kpl for the propane model vs. 10 kpl for diesel. The life of a school bus in the district averages nine years, and each bus travels an average of 30 000 kilometres per year because the district is so large and rural.

Which bus is the better choice based on a life cycle analysis?

•• **S5.12** Green Forever, a manufacturer of lawn equipment, has preliminary drawings for two grass trimmer designs. Charla Fraley's job is to determine which is better environmentally. Specifically, she is to use the following data to help the company determine:
a) The revenue retrieval for the GF Deluxe
b) The revenue retrieval for the Premium Mate
c) Which model is the better design alternative based on revenue retrieval

GF Deluxe

Part	Resale Revenue Per Unit	Recycling Revenue Per Unit	Processing Cost Per Unit	Disposal Cost Per Unit
Metal drive	$3.27	$4.78	$1.05	$0.85
Battery	0.00	3.68	6.18	3.05
Motor housing	3.93	2.95	2.05	1.25
Trimmer head	1.25	0.75	1.00	0.65

Premium Mate

Part	Resale Revenue Per Unit	Recycling Revenue Per Unit	Processing Cost Per Unit	Disposal Cost Per Unit
Metal drive	$3.18	$3.95	$1.15	$0.65
Battery	0.00	2.58	4.98	2.90
Motor housing	4.05	3.45	2.45	1.90
Trimmer head	1.05	0.85	1.10	0.75

•• **S5.13** Green Forever (see Problem S5.12) has decided to add an automatic string feeder system with cost and revenue estimates as shown below to the GF Deluxe model.
a) What is the new revenue retrieval value for each model?
b) Which model is the better environmental design alternative?

Part	Resale Revenue Per Unit	Recycling Revenue Per Unit	Processing Cost Per Unit	Disposal Cost Per Unit
String feeder system	$1.05	$1.25	$1.50	$1.40

•• **S5.14** Green Forever's challenge (see Problem S5.12) is to determine which design alternative is the better environmental choice if it uses a different battery for the Premium Mate. The alternate battery revenue and costs are as follows:

Part	Resale Revenue Per Unit	Recycling Revenue Per Unit	Processing Cost Per Unit	Disposal Cost Per Unit
Battery	$0.00	$3.68	$4.15	$3.00

a) What is the revenue retrieval for the GF Deluxe?
b) What is the revenue retrieval for the Premium Mate?
c) Which is the better environmental design alternative?

•• **S5.15** Hartley Auto Supply delivers parts to area auto service centres and is replacing its fleet of delivery vehicles. What is the total vehicle life cycle cost of this gasoline engine truck given the information provided in the following table?

Vehicle Purchase Cost	$25 000
Vehicle Operating Cost Per Kilometre	$0.13
Useful Life of Vehicle	10 years
Kilometres Per Year	18 000
Kilometres Per Litre	25
Average Fuel Price Per Litre	$2.55

•• **S5.16** Given the data in Problem S5.15 and an alternative hybrid vehicle with the specifications shown below:
a) What is the crossover point in kilometres?
b) Which vehicle is has the lowest cost until the crossover point is reached?

Vehicle Purchase Cost	$29 000
Vehicle Operating Cost Per Kilometre	$0.08
Useful Life of Vehicle	10 years
Kilometres Per Year	18 000
Kilometres Per Litre	40
Average Fuel Price Per Litre	$2.55

• **S5.17** Based the crossover point in kilometres found in Problem S5.16, what is this point in years?

•• **S5.18** Using the data from Problem S5.16, if gas prices rose to $3.00 per litre, what would be the new crossover point in kilometres?

• **S5.19** Using the new crossover point in Problem S5.18, how many years does it take to reach that point?

CASE STUDIES

Video Case ## Building Sustainability at the Orlando Magic's Amway Center

When the Amway Center opened in Orlando in 2011, it became the first LEED (Leadership in Energy and Environmental Design) gold–certified professional basketball arena in the country. It took 10 years for Orlando Magic's management to develop a plan for the new state-of-the-art sports and entertainment centre. The community received not only an entertainment centre but an environmentally sustainable building to showcase in its revitalized downtown location. "We wanted to make sure we brought the most sustainable measures to the construction, so in operation we can be a good partner to our community and our environment," states CEO Alex Martins. The new 875 000-square-foot facility—almost triple the size of the Amway Arena it replaced—is now the benchmark for other sports facilities.

Here are a few of the elements in the Amway Center project that helped earn the LEED certification:

- The roof of the building is designed to minimize daytime heat gain by using reflective and insulated materials.
- Rainwater and air-conditioning condensation are captured and used for irrigation.
- There is 40% less water usage than in similar arenas (saving millions of litres per year), mostly through use of high-efficiency restrooms, including low-flow, dual-flush toilets.
- There is 20% energy savings (about $750 000 per year) with the use of high-efficiency heating and cooling systems.
- The centre used environmentally friendly building materials and recycled 83% of the wood, steel, and concrete construction waste that would have ended up in a landfill.
- There is preferred parking for hybrids and other energy-efficient cars.
- The centre is maintained using green-friendly cleaning products.

LEED certification means five environmental measures and one design measure must be met when a facility is graded by the U.S. Green Building Council, which is a nationally accepted benchmark program. The categories are sustainability of site, water efficiency, energy, materials/resources, indoor environmental quality, and design innovation.

Courtesy of Barry Render

Other Amway Center design features include efficient receiving docks, food storage layouts, and venue change-over systems. Massive LED electronic signage controlled from a central control room also contributes to lower operating costs. From an operations management perspective, combining these savings with the significant ongoing savings from reduced water and energy usage will yield a major reduction in annual operating expenses. "We think the LEED certification is not only great for the environment but good business overall," says Martins.

Discussion Questions*

1. Find a LEED-certified building in your area and compare its features to those of the Amway Center.
2. What does a facility need to do to earn the gold LEED rating? What other ratings exist?
3. Why did the Orlando Magic decide to "go green" in its new building?

---

* You may wish to view the video that accompanies this case before answering these questions.

Video Case ## Green Manufacturing and Sustainability at Frito-Lay

Frito-Lay, the multibillion-dollar snack food giant, requires vast amounts of water, electricity, natural gas, and fuel to produce its 41 well-known brands. In keeping with growing environmental concerns, Frito-Lay has initiated ambitious plans to produce environmentally friendly snacks. But even environmentally friendly snacks require resources. Recognizing the environmental impact, the firm is an aggressive "green manufacturer," with major initiatives in resource reduction and sustainability.

For instance, the company's energy management program includes a variety of elements designed to engage employees in reducing energy consumption. These elements include scorecards and customized action plans that empower employees and recognize their achievements.

At Frito-Lay's factory in Casa Grande, Arizona, more than 200 000 kilograms of potatoes arrive every day to be washed, sliced, fried, seasoned, and portioned into bags of Lay's and Ruffles chips. The process consumes enormous amounts of energy and creates vast amounts of wastewater, starch, and potato peelings. Frito-Lay plans to take the plant off the power grid and run it almost entirely on renewable fuels and recycled water. The managers at the Casa Grande plant have also installed skylights in conference rooms, offices, and a finished goods warehouse to reduce the need for artificial light. More fuel-efficient ovens recapture heat from exhaust stacks. Vacuum hoses that pull moisture from potato slices to recapture the water and to reduce the amount of heat needed to cook the potato chips are also being used.

Frito-Lay has also built over 50 acres of solar concentrators behind its Modesto, California, plant to generate solar power. The solar power is being converted into heat and used to cook Sun Chips. A biomass boiler, which will burn agricultural waste, is also planned to provide additional renewable fuel.

Frito-Lay is installing high-tech filters that recycle most of the water used to rinse and wash potatoes. It also recycles corn by-products to make Doritos and other snacks; starch is reclaimed and sold, primarily as animal feed, and leftover sludge is burned to create methane gas to run the plant boiler.

There are benefits besides the potential energy savings. Like many other large corporations, Frito-Lay is striving to establish its green credentials as consumers become more focused on environmental issues. There are marketing opportunities, too. The company, for example, advertises that its popular Sun Chips snacks are made using solar energy.

At Frito-Lay's Florida plant, only 3.5% of the waste goes to landfills, but that is still almost a million kilograms annually. The goal is zero waste to landfills. The snack food maker earned its spot in the National Environmental Performance Task Program by maintaining a sustained environmental compliance record and making new commitments to reduce, reuse, and recycle at this facility.

Substantial resource reductions have been made in the production process, with an energy reduction of 21% across Frito-Lay's 34 U.S. plants. But the continuing battle for resource reduction continues. The company is also moving towards biodegradable packaging and seasoning bags and cans and bottles. Although these multiyear initiatives are expensive, they have the backing at the highest levels of Frito-Lay as well as corporate executives at PepsiCo, the parent company.

Discussion Questions*

1. What are the sources of pressure on firms such as Frito-Lay to reduce their environmental footprint?
2. Identify the specific techniques that Frito-Lay is using to become a "green manufacturer".
3. Select another company and compare its green policies to those of Frito-Lay.

---

* You might want to view the video that accompanies this case before answering these questions.

SUPPLEMENT 5 | RAPID REVIEW

MyLab Operations Management

Main Heading	Review Material
CORPORATE SOCIAL RESPONSIBILITY (p. 184)	Managers must consider how the products and services they make affect people and the environment in which they operate. ■ **Corporate social responsibility (CSR)**—Managerial decision making that considers environmental, societal, and financial impacts. ■ *Shared value*—Developing policies and practices that enhance the competitiveness of an organization, while advancing the economic and social conditions in the communities in which it operates.

OM in Action

ISO 14001 Certification Cherished by Canada's Military Training Centre in Goose Bay

When people think of ISO 14001 certification, a nation's military does not often spring to mind. However, Canada's Department of National Defence (DND) takes matters involving impact on the environment very seriously. The military training location in Goose Bay, Newfoundland, has achieved ISO 14001 certification due to its demonstrated commitment to safeguarding the environment through an ongoing mitigation program. In this context, the environmental impact at this DND location is unlike other industrial or commercial ventures. Much of the impact is a short-lived noise event resulting from an ultra-low over-flight and is in the range of 114–118 decibels, typically lasting only a few brief seconds. At a worst case, acoustic startle may result, with potential effects to sensitive wildlife, including:

- Abandonment of an animal's prime habitat;
- Auditory damage;
- Breaking the cow/calf bond; and
- Breaking or chilling of eggs.

The mitigation program is funded in large part by the revenues derived from the training that is offered for foreign air forces at Goose Bay. It relies on extensive observation and monitoring of the training area to identify sensitive human or wildlife locations on the ground and to restrict aircraft activity from those areas. Working closely with federal and provincial wildlife managers and the scientific community, the DND makes use of satellite telemetry and aerial surveys to detect and monitor caribou herds and bird nest sites. In addition, they sponsor field studies of migrating waterfowl and other species. Also, in order to independently conduct "effects research," the DND funds the operation of the Institute for Environmental Monitoring and Research (IEMR), a group whose board of directors includes a majority of Aboriginal voting members.

The DND has demonstrated a solid commitment to environmental "stewardship," and every reasonable effort is made to remain a "good neighbour."

Source: www.forces.gc.ca/en/training-establishments/foreign-military-training-goose-bay.page.

- Positive public image and reduced exposure to liability.
- Good systematic approach to pollution prevention through the minimization of ecological impact of products and activities.
- Compliance with regulatory requirements and opportunities for competitive advantage.
- Reduction in need for multiple audits.

This standard is being accepted worldwide, with ISO 14001, which addresses environmental impacts of activities systematically, receiving great attention. The *OM in Action* box "ISO 14001 Certification Cherished by Canada's Military Training Centre in Goose Bay" illustrates the growing application of the ISO 14000 series.

As a follow-on to ISO 14000, ISO 24700 reflects the business world's current approach to reusing recovered components from many products. These components must be "qualified as good as new" and meet all safety and environmental criteria. Xerox was one of the companies that helped write ISO 24700 and was an early applicant for certification.

COST OF QUALITY (COQ)

Four major categories of costs are associated with quality. Called the **cost of quality (COQ)**, they are:

- *Prevention costs:* costs associated with reducing the potential for defective parts or services (e.g., training, quality improvement programs).
- *Appraisal costs:* costs related to evaluating products, processes, parts, and services (e.g., testing, labs, inspectors).
- *Internal failure:* costs that result from production of defective parts or services before delivery to customers (e.g., rework, scrap, downtime).
- *External costs:* costs that occur after delivery of defective parts or services (e.g., rework, returned goods, liabilities, lost goodwill, costs to society).

The first three costs can be reasonably estimated, but external costs are very hard to quantify. When GE had to recall 3.1 million dishwashers recently (because of a defective switch alleged to have started seven fires), the cost of repairs exceeded the value of all the machines. This leads to the belief by many experts that the cost of poor quality is consistently underestimated.

Observers of quality management believe that, on balance, the cost of quality products is only a fraction of the benefits. They think the real losers are organizations that fail to work

Cost of quality (COQ)
The cost of doing things wrong—that is, the price of nonconformance.

Table 6.1

Leaders in the Field of Quality Management

Leader	Philosophy/Contribution
W. Edwards Deming	Deming insisted management accept responsibility for building good systems. The employee cannot produce products that on average exceed the quality of what the process is capable of producing. His 14 points for implementing quality improvement are presented in this chapter.
Joseph M. Juran	A pioneer in teaching the Japanese how to improve quality, Juran believed strongly in top management commitment, support, and involvement in the quality effort. He was also a believer in teams that continually seek to raise quality standards. Juran varies from Deming somewhat in focusing on the customer and defining quality as fitness for use, not necessarily the written specifications.
Armand Feigenbaum	His 1961 book, *Total Quality Control*, laid out 40 steps to quality improvement processes. He viewed quality not as a set of tools but as a total field that integrated the processes of a company. His work in how people learn from each other's successes led to the field of cross-functional teamwork.
Philip B. Crosby	*Quality Is Free* was Crosby's attention-getting book published in 1979. Crosby believed that in the traditional trade-off between the cost of improving quality and the cost of poor quality, the cost of poor quality is understated. The cost of poor quality should include all of the things that are involved in not doing the job right the first time. Crosby coined the term *zero defects* and stated, "There is absolutely no reason for having errors or defects in any product or service."

aggressively at quality. For instance, Philip Crosby stated that quality is free. "What costs money are the unquality things—all the actions that involve not doing it right the first time".[1]

LEADERS IN QUALITY Besides Crosby, there are several other giants in the field of quality management, including Deming, Feigenbaum, and Juran. Table 6.1 summarizes their philosophies and contributions.

ETHICS AND QUALITY MANAGEMENT

For operations managers, one of the most important jobs is to deliver healthy, safe, and quality products and services to customers. The development of poor-quality products, because of inadequate design and production processes, not only results in higher production costs but also leads to injuries, lawsuits, and increased government regulation.

If a firm believes that it has introduced a questionable product, ethical conduct must dictate the responsible action. This may be a worldwide recall, as conducted by both Johnson & Johnson (for Tylenol) and Perrier (for sparkling water) when each of their products was found to be contaminated. A manufacturer must accept responsibility for any poor-quality product released to the public.

There are many stakeholders involved in the production and marketing of poor-quality products, including shareholders, employees, customers, suppliers, distributors, and creditors. As a matter of ethics, management must ask if any of these stakeholders are being wronged. Every company needs to develop core values that become day-to-day guidelines for everyone from the CEO to production-line employees.

STUDENT TIP

The seven concepts that make up TQM are part of the lexicon of business.

Total quality management (TQM)

Management of an entire organization so that it excels in all aspects of products and services that are important to the customer.

Total Quality Management

Total quality management (TQM) refers to a quality emphasis that encompasses the entire organization, from supplier to customer. TQM stresses a commitment by management to have a continuing companywide drive towards excellence in all aspects of products and services that are important to the customer. Each of the 10 decisions made by operations managers deals with some aspect of identifying and meeting customer expectations.

---

[1] Philip B. Crosby, *Quality Is Free* (New York, NY: McGraw-Hill, 1979). Further, J. M. Juran states, in his book *Juran on Quality by Design* (The Free Press 1992, p. 119), that costs of poor quality "are huge, but the amounts are not known with precision. In most companies the accounting system provides only a minority of the information needed to quantify this cost of poor quality. It takes a great deal of time and effort to extend the accounting system so as to provide full coverage."

Table 6.2

Deming's 14 Points for Implementing Quality Improvement

1. Create consistency of purpose.
2. Lead to promote change.
3. Build quality into the product; stop depending on inspections to catch problems.
4. Build long-term relationships based on performance instead of awarding business on the basis of price.
5. Continuously improve product, quality, and service.
6. Start training.
7. Emphasize leadership.
8. Drive out fear.
9. Break down barriers between departments.
10. Stop haranguing workers.
11. Support, help, and improve.
12. Remove barriers to pride in work.
13. Institute a vigorous program of education and self-improvement.
14. Put everybody in the company to work on the transformation.

Source: Based on W. Edwards Deming, *Out of the Crisis*, pp. 23–24, © 2000 Massachusetts Institute of Technology.

Meeting those expectations requires an emphasis on TQM if a firm is to compete as a leader in world markets.

Quality expert W. Edwards Deming used 14 points (see Table 6.2) to indicate how he implemented TQM. We develop these into seven concepts for an effective TQM program: (1) continuous improvement, (2) Six Sigma, (3) employee empowerment, (4) benchmarking, (5) just-in-time (JIT), (6) Taguchi concepts, and (7) knowledge of TQM tools.

CONTINUOUS IMPROVEMENT

Total quality management requires a never-ending process of continuous improvement that covers people, equipment, suppliers, materials, and procedures. The basis of the philosophy is that every aspect of an operation can be improved. The end goal is perfection, which is never achieved but always sought.

PLAN–DO–CHECK–ACT Walter Shewhart, another pioneer in quality management, developed a circular model known as **PDCA** (plan, do, check, act) as his version of continuous improvement. Deming later took this concept to Japan during his work there after the Second World War.[2] The PDCA cycle is shown in Figure 6.3 as a circle to stress the continuous nature of the improvement process.

PDCA

A continuous improvement model that involves four stages: plan, do, check, and act.

The Japanese use the word *kaizen* to describe this ongoing process of unending improvement—the setting and achieving of ever-higher goals. In Canada and the United States, *TQM* and *zero defects* are also used to describe continuous improvement efforts. But whether it's PDCA, kaizen, TQM, or zero defects, the operations manager is a key player in building a work culture that endorses continuous improvement.

FIGURE 6.3

PDCA Cycle

---

[2] As a result, the Japanese refer to the PDCA cycle as a Deming circle, while others call it a Shewhart circle.

FIGURE 6.4

Defects per Million for ±3σ Versus ±6σ

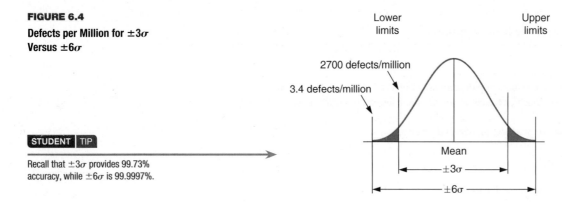

Six Sigma

A program to save time, improve quality, and lower costs.

LO3 Explain what Six Sigma is

SIX SIGMA

The term **Six Sigma**, popularized by Motorola, Honeywell, and General Electric, has two meanings in TQM. In a *statistical* sense, it describes a process, product, or service with an extremely high capability (99.9997% accuracy). For example, if 1 million passengers pass through the Kelowna International Airport with checked baggage each year, a Six Sigma program for baggage handling will result in only 3.4 passengers with misplaced luggage. The more common *three sigma* program (which we address in supplement 6) would result in 2700 passengers with misplaced bags every year (see Figure 6.4).

The second TQM definition of Six Sigma is a program designed to reduce defects to help lower costs, save time, and improve customer satisfaction. Six Sigma is a comprehensive system—a strategy, a discipline, and a set of tools—for achieving and sustaining business success:

- It is a *strategy* because it focuses on total customer satisfaction.
- It is a *discipline* because it follows the formal Six Sigma Improvement Model known as *DMAIC*. This five-step process improvement model (1) *Defines* the project's purpose, scope, and outputs and then identifies the required process information, keeping in mind the customer's definition of quality; (2) *Measures* the process and collects data; (3) *Analyzes* the data, ensuring repeatability (the results can be duplicated) and reproducibility (others get the same result); (4) *Improves*, by modifying or redesigning, existing processes and procedures; and (5) *Controls* the new process to make sure performance levels are maintained.
- It is a *set of seven tools* that we introduce shortly in this chapter: check sheets, scatter diagrams, cause-and-effect diagrams, Pareto charts, flowcharts, histograms, and statistical process control.

Motorola developed Six Sigma in the 1980s in response to customer complaints about its products and to stiff competition. The company first set a goal of reducing defects by 90%. Within one year, it had achieved such impressive results—through benchmarking competitors, soliciting new ideas from employees, changing reward plans, adding training, and revamping critical processes—that it documented the procedures into what it called Six Sigma. Although the concept was rooted in manufacturing, GE later expanded Six Sigma into services, including human resources, sales, customer services, and financial/credit services. The concept of wiping out defects turns out to be the same in both manufacturing and services.

IMPLEMENTING SIX SIGMA Implementing Six Sigma "is a big commitment," says the head of that program at Praxair, a major industrial gas company. "We're asking our executives to spend upward of 15% of their time on Six Sigma. If you don't spend the time, you don't get the results." Indeed, successful Six Sigma programs in every firm, from GE to Motorola to DuPont to Texas Instruments, require a major time commitment, especially from top management. These leaders have to formulate the plan, communicate their buy-in and the firm's objectives, and take a visible role in setting the example for others.

Successful Six Sigma projects are clearly related to the strategic direction of a company. It is a management-directed, team-based, and expert-led approach.[3]

---

[3] To train employees in quality improvement and its relationship to customers, there are three other key players in the Six Sigma program: Master Black Belts, Black Belts, and Green Belts. Master Black Belts are full-time teachers who have extensive training in statistics, quality tools, and leadership. They mentor Black Belts, who in turn are project team leaders, directing perhaps a half-dozen projects per year. Dow Chemical and DuPont have more than 1000 Black Belts each in their global operations. DuPont also has 160 Master Black Belts and introduces over 2000 Green Belts per year into its ranks.

EMPLOYEE EMPOWERMENT

Employee empowerment means involving employees in every step of the production process. Consistently, business literature suggests that some 85% of quality problems have to do with materials and processes, not with employee performance. Therefore, the task is to design equipment and processes that produce the desired quality. This is best done with a high degree of involvement by those who understand the shortcomings of the system. Those dealing with the system on a daily basis understand it better than anyone else. One study indicated that TQM programs that delegate responsibility for quality to shop-floor employees tend to be twice as likely to succeed as those implemented with "top-down" directives.[4]

When nonconformance occurs, the worker is seldom wrong. Either the product was designed wrong, the system that makes the product was designed wrong, or the employee was improperly trained. Although the employee may be able to help solve the problem, the employee rarely causes it.

Techniques for building employee empowerment include (1) building communication networks that involve employees; (2) developing open, supportive supervisors; (3) moving responsibility from both managers and staff to production employees; (4) building high-morale organizations; and (5) creating such formal organization structures as teams and quality circles.

Teams can be built to address a variety of issues. One popular focus of teams is quality. Such teams are often known as quality circles. A **quality circle** is a group of employees who meet regularly to solve work-related problems. The members receive training in group planning, problem solving, and statistical quality control. They generally meet once a week (usually after work but sometimes on company time). Although the members are not rewarded financially, they do receive recognition from the firm. A specially trained team member, called the *facilitator*, usually helps train the members and keeps the meetings running smoothly. Teams with a quality focus have proven to be a cost-effective way to increase productivity as well as quality.

Workers at this TRW airbag manufacturing plant in Marshall, Illinois, are their own inspectors. Empowerment is an essential part of TQM. This man is checking the quality of a crash sensor he built.

Employee empowerment
Enlarging employee jobs so that the added responsibility and authority is moved to the lowest level possible in the organization.

Quality circle
A group of employees meeting regularly with a facilitator to solve work-related problems in their work area.

BENCHMARKING

Benchmarking is another ingredient in an organization's TQM program. **Benchmarking** involves selecting a demonstrated standard of products, services, costs, or practices that represent the very best performance for processes or activities very similar to your own. The idea is to develop a target at which to shoot and then to develop a standard or benchmark against which to compare your performance. The steps for developing benchmarks are:

1. Determine what to benchmark.
2. Form a benchmark team.
3. Identify benchmarking partners.
4. Collect and analyze benchmarking information.
5. Take action to match or exceed the benchmark.

LO4 Explain how benchmarking is used in TQM

Benchmarking
Selecting a demonstrated standard of performance that represents the very best performance for a process or an activity.

Typical performance measures used in benchmarking include percentage of defects, cost per unit or per order, processing time per unit, service response time, return on investment, customer satisfaction rates, and customer retention rates.

In the ideal situation, you find one or more similar organizations that are leaders in the particular areas you want to study. Then you compare yourself (benchmark yourself) against them. The company need not be in your industry. Indeed, to establish world-class standards, it may be best to look outside your industry. If one industry has learned how to compete via rapid product development while yours has not, it does no good to study your industry.

This is exactly what Xerox and Mercedes Benz did when they went to L.L. Bean for order-filling and warehousing benchmarks. Xerox noticed that L.L. Bean was able to "pick" orders three times as fast as it could. After benchmarking, it was immediately able to pare warehouse costs by 10%. Mercedes Benz observed that L.L. Bean warehouse employees used flowcharts to spot

4 "The Straining of Quality," *The Economist* (January 14, 1995): 55. We also see that this is one of the strengths of Southwest Airlines, which offers bare-bones domestic service but whose friendly and humorous employees help it obtain number one ranking for quality. (See *Fortune* [March 6, 2006]: 65–69.)

Table 6.3

Best Practices for Resolving Customer Complaints

Best Practice	Justification
Make it easy for clients to complain.	It is free market research.
Respond quickly to complaints.	It adds customers and loyalty.
Resolve complaints on the first contact.	It reduces cost.
Use computers to manage complaints.	Discover trends, share them, and align your services.
Recruit the best for customer service jobs.	It should be part of formal training and career advancement.

Source: Based on Canadian Government Guide on Complaint Mechanism.

wasted motions. The auto giant followed suit and now relies more on problem solving at the worker level.

Benchmarks often take the form of "best practices" found in other firms or in other divisions. Table 6.3 illustrates best practices for resolving customer complaints.

Likewise, Britain's Great Ormond Street Hospital benchmarked the Ferrari Racing Team's pit stops to improve one aspect of medical care. (See the *OM in Action* box "A Hospital Benchmarks against the Ferrari Racing Team?")

INTERNAL BENCHMARKING When an organization is large enough to have many divisions or business units, a natural approach is the internal benchmark. Data are usually much more accessible than from outside firms. Typically, one internal unit has superior performance worth learning from.

OM in Action | **A Hospital Benchmarks Against the Ferrari Racing Team?**

After surgeons successfully completed a six-hour operation to fix a hole in a three-year-old boy's heart, Dr. Angus McEwan supervised one of the most dangerous phases of the procedure: the boy's transfer from surgery to the intensive care unit.

Thousands of such "handoffs" occur in hospitals every day, and devastating mistakes can happen during them. In fact, at least 35% of preventable hospital mishaps take place because of handoff problems. Risks come from many sources: using temporary nursing staff, frequent shift changes for interns, surgeons working in larger teams, and an ever-growing tangle of wires and tubes connected to patients.

In one of the most unlikely benchmarks in modern medicine, Britain's largest children's hospital turned to Italy's Formula One Ferrari racing team for help in revamping patient-handoff techniques. Armed with videos and slides, the racing team described how they analyze pit crew performance. They also explained how their system for recording errors stressed the small ones that go unnoticed in pit-stop handoffs.

To move forward, Ferrari invited a team of doctors to attend practice sessions at the British Grand Prix in order to get closer looks at pit stops. Ferrari's technical director, Nigel Stepney, then watched a video of a hospital handoff. Stepney was not impressed. "In fact, he was amazed at how clumsy, chaotic, and informal the process appeared," said one hospital official. At that meeting, Stepney

described how each Ferrari crew member is required to do a specific job, in a specific sequence, and in silence. The hospital handoff, in contrast, had several conversations going on at once, while different members of its team disconnected or reconnected patient equipment, but in no particular order.

Oliver Multhaup/AP Images

Results of the benchmarking process: Handoff errors fell 42% to 49%, with a bonus of faster handoff time.

Sources: The Wall Street Journal (December 3, 2007): B11 and (November 14, 2006): A1, A8.

Xerox's almost religious belief in benchmarking has paid off not only by looking outward to L.L. Bean but also by examining the operations of its various country divisions. For example, Xerox Europe, a $6 billion subsidiary of Xerox Corp., formed teams to see how better sales could result through internal benchmarking. Somehow, France sold five times as many colour copiers as did other divisions in Europe. By copying France's approach, namely, better sales training and use of dealer channels to supplement direct sales, Norway increased sales by 152%, the Netherlands by 300%, and Switzerland by 328%!

Benchmarks can and should be established in a variety of areas. Total quality management requires no less.[5]

JUST-IN-TIME (JIT)

The philosophy behind just-in-time (JIT) is one of continuing improvement and enforced problem solving. JIT systems are designed to produce or deliver goods just as they are needed. JIT is related to quality in three ways:

- *JIT cuts the cost of quality:* This occurs because scrap, rework, inventory investment, and damage costs are directly related to inventory on hand. Because there is less inventory on hand with JIT, costs are lower. In addition, inventory hides bad quality, whereas JIT immediately *exposes* bad quality.
- *JIT improves quality:* As JIT shrinks lead time, it keeps evidence of errors fresh and limits the number of potential sources of error. JIT creates, in effect, an early warning system for quality problems, both within the firm and with vendors.
- *Better quality means less inventory and a better, easier-to-employ JIT system:* Often, the purpose of keeping inventory is to protect against poor production performance resulting from unreliable quality. If consistent quality exists, JIT allows firms to reduce all the costs associated with inventory.

TAGUCHI CONCEPTS

Most quality problems are the result of poor product and process design. Genichi Taguchi has provided us with three concepts aimed at improving both product and process quality: *quality robustness*, *quality loss function*, and *target-oriented quality*.[6]

LO5 Explain quality robust products and Taguchi concepts

Quality robust products are ones that can be produced uniformly and consistently in adverse manufacturing and environmental conditions. Taguchi's idea is to remove the *effects* of adverse conditions instead of removing the causes. Taguchi suggests that removing the effects is often cheaper than removing the causes and more effective in producing a robust product. In this way, small variations in materials and process do not destroy product quality.

Quality robust

Products that are consistently built to meet customer needs in spite of adverse conditions in the production process.

A **quality loss function (QLF)** identifies all costs connected with poor quality and shows how these costs increase as the product moves away from being exactly what the customer wants. These costs include not only customer dissatisfaction but also warranty and service costs; internal inspection, repair, and scrap costs; and costs that can best be described as costs to society. Notice that Figure 6.5(a) shows the quality loss function as a curve that increases at an increasing rate. It takes the general form of a simple quadratic formula:

Quality loss function (QLF)

A mathematical function that identifies all costs connected with poor quality and shows how these costs increase as product quality moves from what the customer wants: $L = D^2C$.

$$L = D^2C$$

where L = loss to society
D^2 = square of the distance from the target value
C = cost of the deviation at the specification limit

All the losses to society due to poor performance are included in the loss function. The smaller the loss, the more desirable the product. The further the product is from the target value, the more severe the loss.

Taguchi observed that traditional conformance-oriented specifications (i.e., the product is good as long as it falls within the tolerance limits) are too simplistic. As shown in Figure 6.5(b),

---

[5] Note that benchmarking is good for evaluating how well you are doing the thing you are doing compared with the industry, but the more imaginative approach to process improvement is to ask, "Should we be doing this at all?" Comparing your warehousing operations to the marvellous job that L.L. Bean does is fine, but maybe you should be outsourcing the warehousing function (see Supplement 11).

[6] G. Taguchi, S. Chowdhury, and Y. Wu, *Taguchi's Quality Engineering Handbook* (New York, NY: Wiley, 2004).

FIGURE 6.5

(a) Quality Loss Function and (b) Distribution of Products Produced

Taguchi aims for the target because products produced near the upper and lower acceptable specifications result in higher quality loss function.

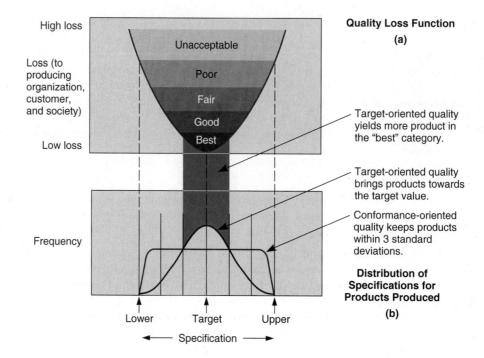

FIGURE 6.5

(a) Quality Loss Function and (b) Distribution of Products Produced

Taguchi aims for the target because products produced near the upper and lower acceptable specifications result in higher quality loss function.

conformance-oriented quality accepts all products that fall within the tolerance limits, producing more units further from the target. Therefore, the loss (cost) is higher in terms of customer satisfaction and benefits to society. Target-oriented quality, on the other hand, strives to keep the product at the desired specification, producing more (and better) units near the target. **Target-oriented quality** is a philosophy of continuous improvement to bring the product exactly on target.

Target-oriented quality

A philosophy of continuous improvement to bring a product exactly on target.

KNOWLEDGE OF TQM TOOLS

To empower employees and implement TQM as a continuing effort, everyone in the organization must be trained in the techniques of TQM. In the following section, we focus on some of the diverse and expanding tools that are used in the TQM crusade.

Tools of TQM

Seven tools that are particularly helpful in the TQM effort are shown in Figure 6.6. We will now introduce these tools.

LO6 Use the seven tools of TQM

CHECK SHEETS

A check sheet is any kind of form that is designed for recording data. In many cases, the recording is done so the patterns are easily seen while the data are being taken (see Figure 6.6[a]). Check sheets help analysts find the facts or patterns that may aid subsequent analysis. An example might be a drawing that shows a tally of the areas where defects are occurring or a check sheet showing the type of customer complaints.

SCATTER DIAGRAMS

Scatter diagrams show the relationship between two measurements. An example is the positive relationship between length of a service call and the number of trips a repair person makes back to the truck for parts. Another example might be a plot of productivity and absenteeism, as shown in Figure 6.6(b). If the two items are closely related, the data points will form a tight band. If a random pattern results, the items are unrelated.

Cause-and-effect diagram

A schematic technique used to discover possible locations of quality problems; also known as an *Ishikawa diagram* or a *fish-bone chart*.

CAUSE-AND-EFFECT DIAGRAMS

Another tool for identifying quality issues and inspection points is the **cause-and-effect diagram**, also known as an *Ishikawa diagram* or a *fish-bone chart*, as shown in Figure 6.6(c).

FIGURE 6.6 Seven Tools of TQM

Tools for Generating Ideas

(a) *Check Sheet:* An organized method of recording data

Defect	Hour							
	1	2	3	4	5	6	7	8
A	///	/		/	/	/	///	/
B	//	/	/	/			//	///
C	/	//					//	////

(b) *Scatter Diagram:* A graph of the value of one variable vs. another variable

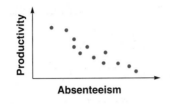

(c) *Cause-and-Effect Diagram:* A tool that identifies process elements (causes) that may affect an outcome

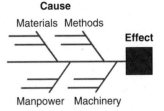

Tools for Organizing the Data

(d) *Pareto Chart:* A graph that identifies and plots problems or defects in descending order of frequency

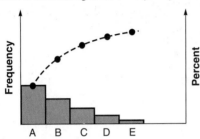

(e) *Flowchart (Process Diagram):* A chart that describes the steps in a process

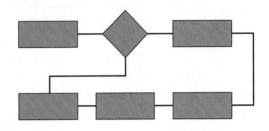

Tools for Identifying Problems

(f) *Histogram:* A distribution that shows the frequency of occurrences of a variable

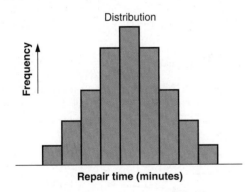

(g) *Statistical Process Control Chart:* A chart with time on the horizontal axis for plotting values of a statistic

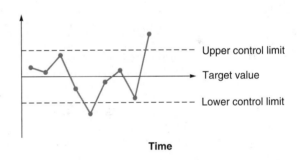

Figure 6.7 illustrates a chart (note the shape resembling the bones of a fish) for a basketball quality control problem—missed free throws. Each "bone" represents a possible source of error.

The operations manager starts with four categories: material, machinery/equipment, manpower, and methods. These four *M*s are the "causes". They provide a good checklist for initial analysis. Individual causes associated with each category are tied in as separate bones along that branch, often through a brainstorming process. For example, the method branch in Figure 6.7 has problems caused by hand position, follow-through, aiming point, bent knees, and balance. When a fish-bone chart is systematically developed, possible quality problems and inspection points are highlighted.

PARETO CHARTS

Pareto charts are a method of organizing errors, problems, or defects to help focus on problem-solving efforts, as shown in Figure 6.6(d). They are based on the work of Vilfredo Pareto, a 19th-century economist. Joseph M. Juran popularized Pareto's work when he suggested that 80% of a firm's problems are a result of only 20% of the causes.

Example 1 indicates that of the five types of complaints identified, the vast majority were of one type—poor room service.

Pareto charts

Graphics that identify the few critical items as opposed to many less important ones.

FIGURE 6.7   **Fish-Bone Chart (or Cause-and-Effect Diagram) for Problems With Missed Free Throws**

Material (ball)   Method (shooting process)

Grain/feel (grip)   Aiming point

Air pressure   Bend knees

Size of ball   Balance

Hand position

Lopsidedness

Follow-through

Missed free throws

Training

Conditioning   Motivation   Rim size   Rim height

Consistency   Concentration   Rim alignment

Backboard stability

Manpower (shooter)   **Machine (hoop and backboard)**

Source: Based on MoreSteam.com, 2007.

The Hard Rock Hotel in Bali has just collected the data from 75 complaint calls to the general manager during the month of October. The manager wants to prepare an analysis of the complaints. The data provided are room service, 54; check-in delays, 12; hours the pool is open, 4; minibar prices, 3; and miscellaneous, 2.

APPROACH ▶ A Pareto chart is an excellent choice for this analysis.

SOLUTION ▶ The Pareto chart shown below indicates that 72% of the calls were the result of one cause: room service. The majority of complaints will be eliminated when this one cause is corrected.

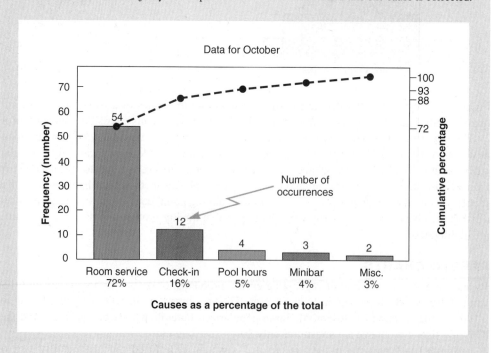

Data for October

Number of occurrences

INSIGHT ▶ This visual means of summarizing data is very helpful—particularly with large amounts of data, as in the Fast Creek Lightning case study at the end of this chapter. We can immediately spot the top problems and prepare a plan to address them.

LEARNING EXERCISE ▶ Hard Rock's bar manager decides to do a similar analysis on complaints she has collected over the past year: too expensive, 22; weak drinks, 15; slow service, 65; short hours, 8; unfriendly bartender, 12. Prepare a Pareto chart. [Answer: Slow service, 53%; too expensive, 18%; weak drinks, 12%; unfriendly bartender, 10%; short hours, 7%.]

RELATED PROBLEMS ▶ 6.1, 6.3, 6.7b, 6.12, 6.13, 6.16c

ACTIVE MODEL 6.1 This example is further illustrated in Active Model 6.1 at **MyLab Operations Management**.

Pareto analysis indicates which problems may yield the greatest payoff. A regional service division at Bell Canada discovered this when it tried to find a way to reduce damage to buried phone cable, the number one cause of phone outages. Pareto analysis showed that 69% of cable damage was caused by human error. Armed with this information, the regional service division at Bell Canada was able to devise a plan to reduce cable cuts by 28% in one year, saving millions of dollars on an annual basis.

Likewise, Japan's Ricoh Corp., a copier maker, used the Pareto principle to tackle the "callback" problem. Callbacks meant the job was not done right the first time and that a second visit, at Ricoh's expense, was needed. Identifying and retraining only the 11% of the customer engineers with the most callbacks resulted in a 19% drop in return visits.

FLOWCHARTS

Flowcharts graphically present a process or system using annotated boxes and interconnected lines, as shown in Figure 6.6(e). They are a simple but great tool for trying to make sense of a process or explain a process. Example 2 uses a flowchart to show the process of completing an MRI at a hospital.

Flowcharts
Block diagrams that graphically describe a process or system.

Port Owen Hospital has undertaken a series of process improvement initiatives. One of these is to make the MRI service efficient for patient, doctor, and hospital. The first step, the administrator believes, is to develop a flowchart for this process.

APPROACH ▶ A process improvement staffer observed a number of patients and followed them (and information flow) from start to end. Here are the 11 steps:

1. Physician schedules MRI after examining patient (START).
2. Patient taken to the MRI lab with test order and copy of medical records.
3. Patient signs in, completes required paperwork.
4. Patient is prepped by technician for scan.
5. Technician carries out the MRI scan.
6. Technician inspects film for clarity.
7. If MRI not satisfactory (20% of time), steps 5 and 6 are repeated.
8. Patient taken back to hospital room.
9. MRI is read by radiologist and report is prepared.
10. MRI and report are transferred electronically to physician.
11. Patient and physician discuss report (END).

SOLUTION ▶ Here is the flowchart:

EXAMPLE 2

A Flowchart for Hospital MRI Service

STUDENT TIP

Flowcharting any process is an excellent way to understand and then try to improve that process.

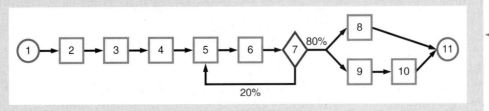

INSIGHT ▶ With the flowchart in hand, the hospital can analyze each step and identify value-added activities and activities that can be improved or eliminated.

LEARNING EXERCISE ▶ If the patient's blood pressure is over 200/120 when being prepped for the MRI, she is taken back to her room for two hours and the process returns to step 2. How does the flowchart change? Answer:

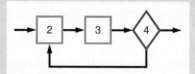

RELATED PROBLEMS ▶ 6.6, 6.15

HISTOGRAMS

Histograms show the range of values of a measurement and the frequency with which each value occurs (see Figure 6.6[f]). They show the most frequently occurring readings as well as the variations in the measurements. Descriptive statistics, such as the average and standard deviation, may be calculated to describe the distribution. However, the data should always be plotted so the shape of the distribution can be "seen". A visual presentation of the distribution may also provide insight into the cause of the variation.

STATISTICAL PROCESS CONTROL (SPC)

Statistical process control (SPC)

A process used to monitor standards, make measurements, and take corrective action as a product or service is being produced.

Statistical process control monitors standards, makes measurements, and takes corrective action as a product or service is being produced. Samples of process outputs are examined; if they are within acceptable limits, the process is permitted to continue. If they fall outside certain specific ranges, the process is stopped and, typically, the assignable cause located and removed.

Control charts

Graphic presentations of process data over time, with predetermined control limits.

Control charts are graphic presentations of data over time that show upper and lower limits for the process we want to control (see Figure 6.6[g]). Control charts are constructed in such a way that new data can be quickly compared with past performance data. We take samples of the process output and plot the average of each of these samples on a chart that has the limits on it. The upper and lower limits in a control chart can be in units of temperature, pressure, weight, length, and so on.

Figure 6.8 shows the plot of the average percentages of samples in a control chart. When the average of the samples falls within the upper and lower control limits and no discernible pattern is present, the process is said to be in control with only natural variation present. Otherwise, the process is out of control or out of adjustment.

Supplement 6 details how control charts of different types are developed. It also deals with the Statistical foundation underlying the use of this important tool.

FIGURE 6.8

Control Chart for Percentage of Free Throws Missed by the Chicago Bulls in Their First Nine Games of the New Season

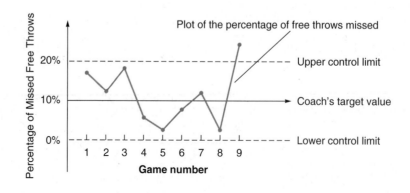

The Role of Inspection

To make sure a system is producing at the expected quality level, control of the process is needed. The best processes have little variation from the standard expected. The operations manager's task is to build such systems and to verify, often by inspection, that they are performing to standard. This **inspection** can involve measurement, tasting, touching, weighing, or testing of the product (sometimes even destroying it when doing so). Its goal is to detect a bad process immediately. Inspection does not correct deficiencies in the system or defects in the products; nor does it change a product or increase its value. Inspection finds only deficiencies and defects. Moreover, inspections are expensive and do not add value to the product.

One of the themes of quality is that "quality cannot be inspected into a product".

Inspection
A means of ensuring that an operation is producing at the quality level expected.

Inspection should be thought of as a vehicle for improving the system. Operations managers need to know critical points in the system: (1) *when to inspect* and (2) *where to inspect*.

WHEN AND WHERE TO INSPECT

Deciding when and where to inspect depends on the type of process and the value added at each stage. Inspections can take place at any of the following points:

1. At your supplier's plant while the supplier is producing.
2. At your facility upon receipt of goods from your supplier.
3. Before costly or irreversible processes.
4. During the step-by-step production process.
5. When production or service is complete.
6. Before delivery to your customer.
7. At the point of customer contact.

The seven tools of TQM discussed in the previous section aid in this "when and where to inspect" decision. However, inspection is not a substitute for a robust product produced by well-trained employees in a good process. In one well-known experiment conducted by an independent research firm, 100 defective pieces were added to a "perfect" lot of items and then subjected to 100% inspection.[7] The inspectors found only 68 of the defective pieces in their first inspection. It took another three passes by the inspectors to find the next 30 defects. The last two defects were never found. So the bottom line is that there is variability in the inspection process. Additionally, inspectors are only human: They become bored, they become tired, and the inspection equipment itself has variability. Even with 100% inspection, inspectors cannot guarantee perfection. (See *OM in Action* box "Maple Leaf Foods Inc.") Therefore, good processes, employee empowerment, and source control are a better solution than trying to find defects by inspection. You cannot inspect quality into the product.

OM in Action | Maple Leaf Foods Inc.

After many years with an excellent reputation for quality, Canada was shocked to learn of a listeriosis outbreak originating in a food processing location operated by Maple Leaf Foods in 2008. Regrettably, 22 Canadians died and many more became sick because of this. Because its meat products were linked to these deaths, the company stated that it was committed to "becoming a global leader in food safety to prevent this kind of a tragedy from ever happening again." Maple Leaf took out full-page ads in a number of Canadian newspapers to mark the one-year anniversary of the listeriosis outbreak. "On behalf of our 24 000 employees, we promise to never forget," said Michael McCain, Maple Leaf's chief executive officer, in a letter-style advertisement.

To prevent the situation from recurring, Maple Leaf recalled the meat, closed and cleaned the plant where it was packaged, and stepped up company-wide sanitary procedures. Moreover, the company hired a chief food safety officer whose role is to improve inspection procedures and policies within Maple Leaf to ensure there is no repeat of such an outbreak. Maple Leaf has since stated it has "zero tolerance" for listeria contamination, which occurs once in every 200 meat packages, a company spokesperson said. So, more testing—twice the level the company did previously—means that the company will be recalling more meat under the new quality-control regime.

Quality control is important in most, if not all, aspects of business. But when it comes to the food industry, it is vital.

Source: http://www.cbc.ca/news/story/2009/08/24/maple-leaf-anniversary-listeriosis.html.

---

[7] *Statistical Quality Control* (Springfield, MA: Monsanto Chemical Company, n.d.): 19.

For example, at Velcro Industries, as in many organizations, quality was viewed by machine operators as the job of "those quality people". Inspections were based on random sampling, and if a part showed up bad, it was thrown out. The company decided to pay more attention to the system (operators, machine repair and design, measurement methods, communications, and responsibilities), and to invest more money in training. Over time as defects declined, Velcro was able to pull half its quality control people out of the process.

SOURCE INSPECTION

Source inspection

Controlling or monitoring at the point of production or purchase—at the source.

The best inspection can be thought of as no inspection at all; this "inspection" is always done at the source—it is just doing the job properly with the operator ensuring that this is so. This may be called **source inspection** (or source control) and is consistent with the concept of employee empowerment, where individual employees self-check their own work. The idea is that each supplier, process, and employee *treats the next step in the process as the customer*, ensuring perfect product to the next "customer".

Poka-yoke

Literally translated, "foolproof"; it has come to mean a device or technique that ensures the production of a good unit every time.

This inspection may be assisted by the use of checklists and controls such as a fail-safe device called a *poka-yoke*, a name borrowed from the Japanese. A **poka-yoke** is a foolproof device or technique that ensures production of good units every time. These special devices avoid errors and provide quick feedback of problems. A simple example of a poka-yoke device is the diesel gas pump nozzle that will not fit into the "unleaded" gas tank opening on your car. In McDonald's, the French fry scoop and standard-size bag used to measure the correct quantity are poka-yokes. Similarly, in a hospital, the prepackaged surgical coverings that contain exactly the items needed for a medical procedure are poka-yokes. Checklists are another type of poka-yoke. The idea of source inspection and poka-yokes is to ensure that 100% good product or service is provided at each step in the process.

SERVICE INDUSTRY INSPECTION

In *service*-oriented organizations, inspection points can be assigned at a wide range of locations, as illustrated in Table 6.4. Again, the operations manager must decide where inspections are justified and may find the seven tools of TQM useful when making these judgments.

INSPECTION OF ATTRIBUTES VERSUS VARIABLES

Attribute inspection

An inspection that classifies items as being either good or defective.

Variable inspection

Classifications of inspected items as falling on a continuum scale, such as dimension or strength.

When inspections take place, quality characteristics may be measured as either *attributes* or *variables*. **Attribute inspection** classifies items as being either good or defective. It does not address the *degree* of failure. For example, the light bulb burns or it does not. **Variable inspection** measures such dimensions as weight, speed, size, or strength to see if an item falls within an acceptable range. If a piece of electrical wire is supposed to be 0.01 inch in diameter, a micrometer can be used to see if the product is close enough to pass inspection.

Knowing whether attributes or variables are being inspected helps us decide which statistical quality control approach to take, as we will see in supplement 6.

Good methods analysis and the proper tools can result in poka-yokes that improve both quality and speed. Here, two poka-yokes are demonstrated. First, the aluminum scoop automatically positions the French fries vertically, and second, the properly sized container ensures that the portion served is correct. McDonald's thrives by bringing rigour and consistency to the restaurant business.

Matthias Schrader/dpa picture alliance archive/Alamy Stock Photo

Organization	What Is Inspected	Standard
Torys Law Firm	Receptionist performance	Phone answered by the second ring
	Billing	Accurate, timely, and correct format
	Lawyer	Promptness in returning calls
Holiday Inn Express	Reception desk	Use customer's name
	Doorman	Greet guest in less than 30 seconds
	Room	All lights working, spotless bathroom
	Minibar	Restocked and charges accurately posted to bill
Mt. Sinai Hospital	Pharmacy	Prescription accuracy, inventory accuracy
	Lab	Audit for lab-test accuracy
	Nurses	Charts immediately updated
	Admissions	Data entered correctly and completely
Boston Pizza	Server	Serves water within one minute
	Busboy	Clears all entrée items and crumbs prior to dessert
	Server	Knows and suggests specials, desserts
Real Canadian Superstore	Display areas	Attractive, well organized, stocked, good lighting
	Stockrooms	Rotation of goods, organized, clean
	Salesclerks	Neat, courteous, very knowledgeable

Table 6.4

Examples of Inspection in Services

TQM in Services

The personal component of services is more difficult to measure than the quality of the tangible component. Generally, the user of a service, like the user of a good, has features in mind that form a basis for comparison among alternatives. Lack of any one feature may eliminate the service from further consideration. Quality also may be perceived as a bundle of attributes in which many lesser characteristics are superior to those of competitors. This approach to product comparison differs little between goods and services. However, what is very different about the selection of

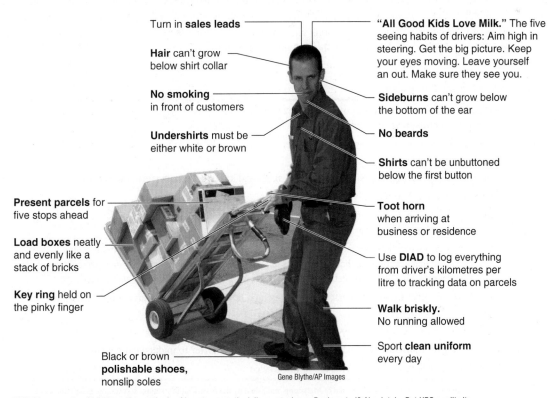

Turn in **sales leads**

Hair can't grow below shirt collar

No smoking in front of customers

Undershirts must be either white or brown

Present parcels for five stops ahead

Load boxes neatly and evenly like a stack of bricks

Key ring held on the pinky finger

Black or brown **polishable shoes,** nonslip soles

"All Good Kids Love Milk." The five seeing habits of drivers: Aim high in steering. Get the big picture. Keep your eyes moving. Leave yourself an out. Make sure they see you.

Sideburns can't grow below the bottom of the ear

No beards

Shirts can't be unbuttoned below the first button

Toot horn when arriving at business or residence

Use **DIAD** to log everything from driver's kilometres per litre to tracking data on parcels

Walk briskly. No running allowed

Sport **clean uniform** every day

Gene Blythe/AP Images

UPS drivers are taught 340 precise methods of how to correctly deliver a package. Regimented? Absolutely. But UPS credits its uniformity and efficiency with laying the foundation for its high-quality service.

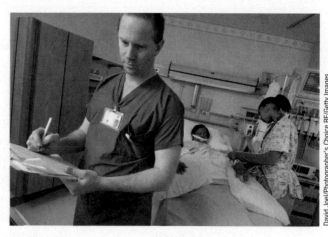

Checklists, simple as they are, provide a powerful way to improve quality. Everyone from airline pilots to physicians use them.

services is the poor definition of the (1) *intangible differences between products* and (2) *the intangible expectations customers have of those products.* Indeed, the intangible attributes may not be defined at all. They are often unspoken images in the purchaser's mind. This is why all of those marketing issues such as advertising, image, and promotion can make a difference.

The operations manager plays a significant role in addressing several major aspects of service quality. First, the *tangible component of many services is important.* How well the service is designed and produced does make a difference. This might be how accurate, clear, and complete your checkout bill at the hotel is, how warm the food is at Boston Pizza, or how well your car runs after you pick it up at the repair shop.

Second, another aspect of service and service quality is the process. Notice in Table 6.5 that nine out of 10 of the determinants of service quality are related to *the service process.* Such things as reliability and courtesy are part of the process. An operations manager can *design processes (service products) that have these attributes* and can ensure their quality through the TQM techniques discussed in this chapter.

Third, the operations manager should realize that the customer's expectations are the standard against which the service is judged. Customers' perceptions of service quality result from a comparison of their before-service expectations with their actual-service experience. In other words, service quality is judged on the basis of whether it meets expectations. The *manager may be able to influence both the quality of the service and the expectation.* Don't promise more than you can deliver.

Table 6.5
Determinants of Service Quality

Reliability involves consistency of performance and dependability. It means that the firm performs the service right the first time and that the firm honours its promises.

Responsiveness concerns the willingness or readiness of employees to provide service. It involves timeliness of service.

Competence means possession of the required skills and knowledge to perform the service.

Access involves approachability and ease of contact.

Courtesy involves politeness, respect, consideration, and friendliness of contact personnel (including receptionists, telephone operators, etc.).

Communication means keeping customers informed in language they can understand and listening to them. It may mean that the company has to adjust its language for different consumers—increasing the level of sophistication with a well-educated customer and speaking simply and plainly with a novice.

Credibility involves trustworthiness, believability, and honesty. It involves having the customer's best interests at heart.

Security is the freedom from danger, risk, or doubt.

Understanding/knowing the customer involves making the effort to understand the customer's needs.

Tangibles include the physical evidence of the service.

Source: Reprinted with permission from Journal of Marketing, published by the American Marketing Association, Determinants of Service Quality, Adapted from A. Parasuraman, Valarie A. Zeithaml, and Leonard L. Berry, "A Conceptual Model of Service Quality and Its Implications for Future Research," *Journal of Marketing* (Fall 1985): 44; *Journal of Marketing*, 58, no. 1.

OM in Action — Richey International's Spies

How do luxury hotels maintain quality? They inspect. But when the product is one-on-one service, largely dependent on personal behaviour, how do you inspect? You hire spies!

Richey International is the spy. Preferred Hotels and Resorts Worldwide and Intercontinental Hotels have both hired Richey to do quality evaluations via spying. Richey employees posing as customers perform the inspections. However, even then management must have established what the customer expects and specific services that yield customer satisfaction. Only then do managers know where and how to inspect. Aggressive training and objective inspections reinforce behaviour that will meet those customer expectations.

The hotels use Richey's undercover inspectors to ensure performance to exacting standards. The hotels do not know when the evaluators will arrive. Nor what aliases they will use. Over 50 different standards are evaluated before the inspectors even check in at a luxury hotel. Over the next 24 hours, using checklists, tape recordings, and photos, written reports are prepared. The reports include evaluation of standards such as:

- Does the doorman greet each guest in less than 30 seconds?
- Does the front-desk clerk use the guest's name during check-in?
- Is the bathroom tub and shower spotlessly clean?
- How many minutes does it take to get coffee after the guest sits down for breakfast?
- Did the server make eye contact?
- Were minibar charges posted correctly on the bill?

Established standards, aggressive training, and inspections are part of the TQM effort at these hotels. Quality does not happen by accident.

Sources: Hotel and Motel Management (August 2002): 128; *The Wall Street Journal* (May 12, 1999): B1, B12; and *Forbes* (October 5, 1998): 88–89.

Fourth, the manager must expect exceptions. There is a standard quality level at which the regular service is delivered, such as the bank teller's handling of a transaction. However, there are "exceptions" or "problems" initiated by the customer or by less-than-optimal operating conditions (e.g., the computer "crashed"). This implies that the quality control system must recognize and *have a set of alternative plans for less-than-optimal operating conditions*.

Well-run companies have **service recovery** strategies. This means they train and empower frontline employees to immediately solve a problem. For instance, staff at Marriott Hotels are drilled in the LEARN routine—*L*isten, *E*mpathize, *A*pologize, *R*eact, *N*otify—with the final step ensuring that the complaint is fed back into the system. And at the Ritz-Carlton, staff members are trained not to say merely "I'm sorry" but "Please accept my apology." The Ritz gives them a budget for reimbursing upset guests.

Managers of service firms may find **Servqual** useful when evaluating performance. SERVQUAL is a widely used instrument that provides direct comparisons between customer service expectations and the actual service provided. SERVQUAL focuses on the *gaps* between the customer service expectations and the service provided on 10 service quality determinants. The most common version of the scale collapses the 10 service quality determinants shown in Table 6.5 into five factors for measurement: reliability, assurance, tangibles, empathy, and responsiveness.

Designing the product, managing the service process, matching customer expectations to the product, and preparing for the exceptions are keys to quality services. The *OM in Action* box "Richey International's Spies" provides another glimpse of how OM managers improve quality in services.

Service recovery
Training and empowering frontline workers to solve a problem immediately.

Servqual
A popular measurement scale for service quality that compares service expectations with service performance.

VIDEO 6.3
TQM at Ritz-Carlton Hotels

CHAPTER SUMMARY

Quality is a term that means different things to different people. We define *quality* as "the totality of features and characteristics of a product or service that bears on its ability to satisfy stated or implied needs." Defining quality expectations is critical to effective and efficient operations.

Quality requires building a total quality management (TQM) environment because quality cannot be inspected into a product. The chapter also addresses seven TQM *concepts*: continuous improvement, Six Sigma, employee empowerment, benchmarking, just-in-time, Taguchi concepts, and knowledge of TQM tools. The seven TQM *tools* introduced in this chapter are check sheets, scatter diagrams, cause-and-effect diagrams, Pareto charts, flowcharts, histograms, and statistical process control (SPC).

ETHICAL | DILEMMA

A lawsuit a few years ago made headlines worldwide when a McDonald's drive-through customer spilled a cup of scalding hot coffee on herself. Claiming the coffee was too hot to be safely consumed in a car, the badly burned 80-year-old woman won U.S. $2.9 million in court. (The judge later reduced the award to U.S. $640 000.) McDonald's claimed the product was served to the correct specifications and was of proper quality. Further, the cup read "Caution—Contents May Be Hot." McDonald's coffee, at 31.5°C,

is substantially hotter (by corporate rule) than typical restaurant coffee, despite hundreds of coffee-scalding complaints in the past 10 years. Similar court cases, incidentally, resulted in smaller verdicts, but again in favour of the plaintiffs. For example, Motor City Bagel Shop was sued for a spilled cup of coffee by a drive-through patron, and Starbucks by a customer who spilled coffee on her own ankle.

Are McDonald's, Motor City, and Starbucks at fault in situations such as these? How do quality and ethics enter into these cases?

Discussion Questions

1. Explain how improving quality can lead to reduced costs.
2. As an internet exercise, determine the Baldrige Award Criteria. See the website **http://www.nist.gov/baldrige**.
3. Which three of Deming's 14 points do you think are most critical to the success of a TQM program? Why?
4. List the seven concepts that are necessary for an effective TQM program. How are these related to Deming's 14 points?
5. Name three of the important people associated with the quality concepts of this chapter. In each case, write a short sentence about each one summarizing their primary contribution to the field of quality management.
6. What are seven tools of TQM?
7. How does fear in the workplace (and in the classroom) inhibit learning?
8. How can a university control the quality of its output (i.e., its graduates)?
9. Philip Crosby said that quality is free. Why?
10. List the three concepts central to Taguchi's approach.
11. What is the purpose of using a Pareto chart for a given problem?

12. What are the four broad categories of "causes" to help initially structure an Ishikawa diagram or cause-and-effect diagram?
13. Of the several points where inspection may be necessary, which apply especially well to manufacturing?
14. What roles do operations managers play in addressing the major aspects of service quality?
15. Explain, in your own words, what is meant by *source inspection*.
16. What are 10 determinants of service quality?
17. Name several products that do not require high quality.
18. What does the formula $L = D^2C$ mean?
19. In this chapter, we have suggested that building quality into a process and its people is difficult. Inspections are also difficult. To indicate just how difficult inspections are, count the number of Es (both capital E and lowercase e) in the *OM in Action* box "Richey International's Spies" (include the title but not the footnote). How many did you find? If each student does this individually, you are very likely to find a distribution rather than a single number!

Problems

• **6.1** An avant-garde clothing manufacturer runs a series of high-profile, risqué ads on a billboard on the Trans-Canada Highway and regularly collects protest calls from people who are offended by them. The company has no idea how many people in total see the ads, but it has been collecting statistics on the number of phone calls from irate viewers:

Type	Description	Number of Complaints
R	Offensive racially/ethnically	10
M	Demeaning to men	4
W	Demeaning to women	14
I	Ad(s) is/are incomprehensible	6
O	Other	2

a) Depict this data with a Pareto chart. Also depict the cumulative complaint line.
b) What percent of the total complaints can be attributed to the most prevalent complaint?

• **6.2** Develop a scatter diagram for two variables of interest (say pages in the newspaper by day of the week; see example in Figure 6.6[b]).

• **6.3** Develop a Pareto chart of the following causes of poor grades on an exam:

Reason for Poor Grade	Frequency
Insufficient time to complete	15
Late arrival to exam	7
Difficulty understanding material	25
Insufficient preparation time	2
Studied wrong material	2
Distractions in exam room	9
Calculator batteries died during exam	1
Forgot exam was scheduled	3
Felt ill during exam	4

6.4 Develop a histogram of the time it took for you or your friends to receive six recent orders at a fast-food restaurant.

•• **6.5** A small family restaurant in Saskatoon has recorded the following data for eight recent customers:

Customer Number, i	Minutes From Time Food Ordered Until Food Arrived (y_i)	No. of Trips to Kitchen by Waitress (x_i)
1	10.50	4
2	12.75	5
3	9.25	3
4	8.00	2
5	9.75	3
6	11.00	4
7	14.00	6
8	10.75	5

a) The owner wants you to graph the eight points (x_i, y_i), $i = 1$, 2, ... 8. She has been concerned because customers have been waiting too long for their food, and this graph is intended to help her find possible causes of the problem.

b) This is an example of what type of graph?

•• **6.6** Develop a flowchart (as in Figure 6.6[e] and Example 2) showing all the steps involved in planning a party.

•• **6.7** Consider the types of poor driving habits that might occur at a traffic light. Make a list of the 10 you consider most likely to happen. Add the category of "other" to that list.

a) Compose a check sheet (like that in Figure 6.6[a]) to collect the frequency of occurrence of these habits. Using your check sheet, visit a busy traffic light intersection at four different times of the day, with two of these times being during high-traffic periods (rush hour, lunch hour). For 15 to 20 minutes each visit, observe the frequency with which the habits you listed occurred.

b) Construct a Pareto chart showing the relative frequency of occurrence of each habit.

•• **6.8** Draw a fish-bone chart detailing reasons why an airline customer might be dissatisfied.

•• **6.9** Consider the everyday task of getting to work on time or arriving at your first class on time in the morning. Draw a fish-bone chart showing reasons why you might arrive late in the morning.

•• **6.10** Construct a cause-and-effect diagram to reflect "student dissatisfied with university registration process". Use the "four Ms" or create your own organizing scheme. Include at least 12 causes.

•• **6.11** Draw a fish-bone chart depicting the reasons that might give rise to an incorrect fee statement at the time you go to pay for your registration at school.

••• **6.12** Mary Beth Marrs, the manager of an apartment complex, feels overwhelmed by the number of complaints she is receiving. Below is the check sheet she has kept for the past 12 weeks. Develop a Pareto chart using this information. What recommendations would you make?

Week	Grounds	Parking/ Drives	Pool	Tenant Issues	Electrical/ Plumbing
1	✓✓✓	✓✓	✓	✓✓✓	
2	✓	✓✓✓	✓✓	✓✓	✓
3	✓✓✓	✓✓✓	✓✓	✓	
4	✓	✓✓✓✓	✓	✓	✓✓
5	✓✓	✓✓✓	✓✓✓✓	✓✓	
6	✓	✓✓✓✓	✓✓		
7		✓✓✓	✓✓	✓✓	
8	✓	✓✓✓✓	✓✓	✓✓✓	✓
9	✓	✓✓	✓		
10	✓	✓✓✓✓	✓✓	✓✓	
11		✓✓✓	✓✓	✓	
12	✓✓	✓✓✓	✓✓✓	✓	

• **6.13** Use Pareto analysis to investigate the following data collected on a printed-circuit-board assembly line:

Defect	Number of Defect Occurrences
Components not adhering	143
Excess adhesive	71
Misplaced transistors	601
Defective board dimension	146
Mounting holes improperly positioned	12
Circuitry problems on final test	90
Wrong component	212

a) Prepare a graph of the data.

b) What conclusions do you reach?

•• **6.14** A list of 16 issues that led to incorrect formulations in Richard Dulski's jam manufacturing unit is provided below:

List of Issues	
1. Incorrect measurement	9. Variability
2. Antiquated scales	10. Equipment in disrepair
3. Lack of clear instructions	11. Technician calculation off
4. Damaged raw material	12. Jars mislabelled
5. Operator misreads display	13. Temperature controls off
6. Inadequate cleanup	14. Incorrect weights
7. Incorrect maintenance	15. Priority miscommunication
8. Inadequate flow controls	16. Inadequate instructions

Create a fish-bone diagram and categorize each of these issues correctly, using the "four Ms" method.

•• **6.15** Develop a flowchart for one of the following:

a) Filling up with gasoline at a self-serve station.

b) Determining your account balance and making a withdrawal at an ATM.

c) Getting a cone of yogurt or ice cream from an ice cream store.

•••• **6.16** Kenora Electric Generators has been getting many complaints from its major customer, Home Station, about the quality of its shipments of home generators. Daniel Magill, the plant manager, is alarmed that a customer is providing him with the only information the company has on shipment quality. He decides to collect information on defective shipments through a form he has asked his drivers to complete on arrival at customers' stores. The forms for the first 279 shipments have been turned in. They show the following over the past eight weeks:

Week	No. of Ship- ments	No. of Ship- ments With Defects	Incorrect Bill of Lading	Incorrect Truck- load	Damaged Product	Trucks Late
			Reason for Defective Shipment			
1	23	5	2	2	1	
2	31	8	1	4	1	2
3	28	6	2	3	1	
4	37	11	4	4	1	2
5	35	10	3	4	2	1
6	40	14	5	6	3	
7	41	12	3	5	3	1
8	44	15	4	7	2	2

Even though Daniel increased his capacity by adding more workers to his normal contingent of 30, he knew that for many weeks he exceeded his regular output of 30 shipments per week. A review of his turnover over the past eight weeks shows the following:

a) Develop a scatter diagram using total number of shipments and number of defective shipments. Does there appear to be any relationship?

Week	No. of New Hires	No. of Terminations	Total No. of Workers
1	1	0	30
2	2	1	31
3	3	2	32
4	2	0	34
5	2	2	34
6	2	4	32
7	4	1	35
8	3	2	36

b) Develop a scatter diagram using the variable "turnover" (number of new hires plus number of terminations) and the number of defective shipments. Does the diagram depict a relationship between the two variables?

c) Develop a Pareto chart for the type of defects that have occurred.

d) Draw a fish-bone chart showing the possible causes of the defective shipments.

••• **6.17** A Gallup poll of 519 adults who flew during a year (published in _The Economist_, June 16, 2007, p. 6) found the following their number one complaints about flying: cramped seats (45), cost (16), dislike or fear of flying (57), security measures (119), poor service (12), connecting flight problems (8), overcrowded planes (42), late planes/waits (57), food (7), lost luggage (7), and other (51).

a) What percentage of those surveyed found nothing they disliked?

b) Draw a Pareto chart summarizing these responses. Include the "no complaints" group.

c) Use the "four _M_s" method to create a fish-bone diagram for the 10 specific categories of dislikes (exclude "other" and "no complaints").

d) If you were managing an airline, what two or three specific issues would you tackle to improve customer service? Why?

CASE STUDIES

Fast Creek Lightning: (C)*

The popularity of the Fast Creek Lightning hockey team under its new coach, Scotty Beauchamp, has surged in each of the five years since his arrival in town. (See Fast Creek Lightning (A) in Chapter 3 and (B) in Chapter 4.) With an arena close to maxing out at 10 800 seats and a vocal coach pushing for a new facility, Fast Creek Lightning owner Keith MacLennan faced some difficult decisions. After a phenomenal upset victory over its archrival, the Walkerford Wolves, at the Holiday Classic in December, MacLennan was not as happy as one would think. Instead of ecstatic fans, all MacLennan heard were complaints. "The lines at the concession stands were too long"; "Parking was harder to find and farther away than in the old days"; "Seats were shabby"; "Traffic was backed up halfway to Saskatoon"; and on and on. "I just can't win," muttered MacLennan.

At his staff meeting the following Monday, MacLennan turned to his VP of operations, Leslie Gardner. "I wish you would take on these complaints, Leslie," he said. "See what the real problems are—let me know how you've resolved them." Gardner wasn't surprised at the request. "I've already got a handle on it, Keith," she replied. "We've been randomly surveying 50 fans per game for the past five games to see what's on their minds. It's all part of the organization-wide TQM effort. Let me tally things up and I'll get back to you in a week."

When she returned to her office, Gardner pulled out the file her assistant had compiled (see Table 6.6). "There's a lot of information here," she thought.

Discussion Questions

1. Using at least two different quality tools, analyze the data and present your conclusions.

2. How could the survey have been more useful?

3. What is the next step?

---

* This integrated case study runs throughout the text. Other issues facing Fast Creek's new arena include: (A) managing the renovation project (Chapter 3); (B) forecasting game attendance (Chapter 4); (D) break-even analysis of food services (Supplement 7 MyLab Operations Management); (E) locating the new arena (Chapter 8 MyLab Operations Management); (F) inventory planning of hockey programs (Chapter 12 MyLab Operations Management); and (G) scheduling of security officers/staff for game days (Chapter 13). Recurring cases are also available in a separate file for instructors using the PCL.

Table 6.6 Fan Satisfaction Survey Results (*N* = 250)

		Overall Grade				
		A	**B**	**C**	**D**	**E**
Game Day	A. Parking	90	105	45	5	5
	B. Traffic	50	85	48	52	15
	C. Seating	45	30	115	35	25
	D. Entertainment	160	35	26	10	19
	E. Printed Program	66	34	98	22	30
Tickets	A. Pricing	105	104	16	15	10
	B. Season Ticket Plans	75	80	54	41	0
Concessions	A. Prices	16	116	58	58	2
	B. Selection of Foods	155	60	24	11	0
	C. Speed of Service	35	45	46	48	76
Respondents	250					

Open-Ended Comments on Survey Cards:

Parking a mess	More hot dog stands	Put in bigger seats	Everything is great
Add a luxury box	Seats are all metal	Friendly ushers	Need boxes
Seats too narrow	Seats stink	Expand parking lots	Want softer seats
Everything is okay	Go Lightning!	Need better seats	Beat those Wolves!
Too crowded	Lines are awful	Hot dogs cold	I'll pay for a box
Programs overpriced	Seats are uncomfortable	$3 for a coffee? No way!	I will pay more for better view
Great food	Seats too small	Get some boxes	Music was terrific
Bigger parking lot	Get a new arena	Well done	Love Beauchamp
I smelled drugs being smoked	Double the parking attendants	Took an hour to park	My company will buy a box—build it!
Stadium is ancient	Not enough police	Coach is terrific	Build new arena
Scotty B. for prime minister	Not enough cops for traffic	More water fountains	Move games to Saskatoon
Seats are like rocks	Fans too rowdy	Better seats	No complaints
Game starts too late	Parking terrible	Seats not comfy	Dirty bathroom
Hire more traffic cops	Toilets weren't clean	I want cushioned seats	Love the new uniforms
Need new sound system	Not enough handicap spots in lot	I'm too old for these seats	Cold coffee served at game
Great!			

Video Case	**The Culture of Quality at Arnold Palmer Hospital**

Founded in 1989, Arnold Palmer Hospital is one of the largest hospitals for women and children in the United States, with 431 beds in two facilities totalling 62 800 square metres. Located in downtown Orlando, Florida, and named after its famed golf benefactor, the hospital, with more than 2000 employees, serves an 18-county area in central Florida and is the only Level 1 trauma centre for children in that region. Arnold Palmer Hospital provides a broad range of medical services, including neonatal and pediatric intensive care, pediatric oncology and cardiology, care for high-risk pregnancies, and maternal intensive care.

The Issue of Assessing Quality Healthcare

Quality healthcare is a goal all hospitals profess, but Arnold Palmer Hospital has actually developed comprehensive and scientific means of asking customers to judge the quality of care they receive. Participating in a national benchmark comparison against other hospitals, Arnold Palmer Hospital consistently scores in the top 10% in overall patient satisfaction. Executive director Kathy Swanson states, "Hospitals in this area will be distinguished largely on the basis of their customer satisfaction. We must have accurate information about how our patients and their families judge the quality of our care, so I follow the questionnaire results daily. The in-depth survey helps me and others on my team to gain quick knowledge from patient feedback." Arnold Palmer Hospital employees are empowered to provide gifts in value up to $200 to patients who find reason to complain about any hospital service such as food, courtesy, responsiveness, or cleanliness.

Swanson doesn't focus just on the customer surveys, which are mailed to patients one week after discharge, but also on a variety of internal measures. These measures usually start at the grassroots level, where the staff sees a problem and develops ways to track performance. The hospital's longstanding philosophy supports the concept that each patient is important and respected as a person. That patient has the right to comprehensive, compassionate family-centred healthcare provided by a knowledgeable physician-directed team.

Some of the measures Swanson carefully monitors for continuous improvement are morbidity, infection rates, readmission rates, costs per case, and length of stays. The tools she uses daily include Pareto charts, flowcharts, and process charts, in addition to benchmarking against hospitals both nationally and in the southeast region.

The result of all of these efforts has been a quality culture as manifested in Arnold Palmer's high ranking in patient satisfaction and one of the highest survival rates of critically ill babies.

Discussion Questions*

1. Why is it important for Arnold Palmer Hospital to get a patient's assessment of healthcare quality? Does the patient have the expertise to judge the healthcare she or he receives?
2. How would you build a culture of quality in an organization, such as Arnold Palmer Hospital?
3. What techniques does Arnold Palmer Hospital practise in its drive for quality and continuous improvement?
4. Develop a fish-bone diagram illustrating the quality variables for a patient who just gave birth at Arnold Palmer Hospital (or any other hospital).

---

* You may wish to view the video that accompanies this case before answering these questions.

Quality Counts at Alaska Airlines

Alaska Airlines, with nearly 100 destinations, including regular service to Alaska, Hawaii, Canada, and Mexico, is the seventh-largest U.S. carrier. Alaska Airlines has won the J.D. Power and Associates Award for highest customer satisfaction in the industry for eight years in a row while being the number one on-time airline for five years in a row.

Management's unwavering commitment to quality has driven much of the firm's success and generated an extremely loyal customer base. Executive VP Ben Minicucci exclaims, "We have rewritten our DNA." Building an organization that can achieve quality is a demanding task, and the management at Alaska Airlines accepted the challenge. This is a highly participative quality culture, reinforced by leadership training, constant process improvement, comprehensive metrics, and frequent review of those metrics. The usual training of flight crews and pilots is supplemented with classroom training in areas such as Six Sigma. Over 200 managers have obtained Six Sigma Green Belt certification.

Alaska collects more than 100 quality and performance metrics every day. For example, the accompanying picture tells the crew that it has six minutes to close the door and back away from the gate to meet the "time to pushback" target. Operations personnel review each airport hub's performance scorecard daily and the over-

all operations scorecard weekly. As Director of System Operations Control Wayne Newton proclaims, "If it is not measured, it is not managed." The focus is on identifying problem areas or trends, determining causes, and working on preventive measures.

Within the operations function there are numerous detailed input metrics for station operations (such as the percentage of time that hoses are free of twists, the ground power cord is stowed, and no vehicles are

Elements	Weighting	Performance	Score	Bonus Points	Total	Grade
Process Compliance	20		15		15	B
Staffing	15		15	5	20	A+
MAP Rate (for bags)	20		15		15	B
Delays	10		9		9	A
Time to Carousel (total weight = 10)			10		10	A
Percentage of flights scanned	2	98.7%				
Percentage of bags scanned	2	70.9%				
20 minutes all bags dropped (% compliance)	4	92.5%				
Outliers (>25mins)	2	2				
Safety Compliance	15		15	5	20	A+
Quality Compliance	10		10		10	A
Total - 100%	100		89	10	99	A+

Time to Carousel

Points	2	1.5	1	0
Percentage of flights scanned	95%–100%	90%–94.9%	89.9%–85%	< 84.9%

Points	2	0		
Percentage of bags scanned	60% or above	≤ 59.9%		

Points	0	4		
Last bag percent compliance	Below 89.9%	90%–100%		

Points	0	1	1.5	2
Last bag >25 min. (Outliers)	20	15	10	5

parked in prohibited zones). Management operates under the assumption that if all the detailed input metrics are acceptable, the major key performance indicators, such as Alaska's on-time performance and 20-minute luggage guarantee, will automatically score well.

The accompanying table displays a sample monthly scorecard for Alaska's ground crew provider in Seattle. The major evaluation categories include process compliance, staffing (degree that crew members are available when needed), MAP rate (minimum acceptable performance for mishandled bags), delays, time to carousel, safety compliance, and quality compliance. The quality compliance category alone tracks 64 detailed input metrics using approximately 30 000 monthly observations. Each of the major categories on the scorecard has an importance weight, and the provider is assigned a weighted average score at the end of each month. The contract with the supplier provides for up to a 3.7% bonus for outstanding performance and as much as a 5.0% penalty for poor performance. The provider's line workers receive a portion of the bonus when top scores are achieved.

As a company known for outstanding customer service, service recovery efforts represent a necessary area of emphasis. When things go wrong, employees mobilize to first communicate with, and in many cases compensate, affected customers. "It doesn't matter if it's not our fault," says Minicucci. Frontline workers are empowered with a "toolkit" of options to offer to inconvenienced customers, including the ability to provide up to 5000 frequent flyer miles and/or vouchers for meals, hotels, luggage, and tickets. When an Alaska flight had to make an emergency landing in Eugene, Oregon, due to a malfunctioning oven, passengers were immediately texted with information about what happened and why, and they were told that a replacement plane would be arriving within one hour. Within that hour, an apology letter along with a $450 ticket voucher were already in the mail to each passenger's home. No customer complaints subsequently appeared on Twitter or Facebook. It's no wonder why Alaska's customers return again and again.

Discussion Questions*

1. What are some ways that Alaska can ensure that quality and performance metric standards are met when the company outsources its ground operations to a contract provider?

2. Identify several quality metrics, in addition to those identified earlier, that you think Alaska tracks or should be tracking.

3. Think about a previous problem that you had when flying, for example, a late flight, a missed connection, or lost luggage. How, if at all, did the airline respond? Did the airline adequately address your situation? If not, what else should they have done? Did your experience affect your desire (positively or negative) to fly with that airline in the future?

4. See the accompanying table. The contractor received a perfect Time to Carousel score of 10 total points, even though its performance was not "perfect". How many total points would the contractor have received with the following performance scores: 93.2% of flights scanned, 63.5% of bags scanned, 89.6% of all bags dropped within 20 minutes, and 15 bags arriving longer than 25 minutes?

*You may wish to view the video that accompanies this case before addressing these questions.

Video Case — TQM at Ritz-Carlton Hotels

Ritz-Carlton. The name alone evokes images of luxury and quality. As the first hotel company to win the Malcolm Baldrige National Quality Award, the Ritz treats quality as if it is the heartbeat of the company. This means a daily commitment to meeting customer expectations and making sure that each hotel is free of any deficiency.

In the hotel industry, quality can be hard to quantify. Guests do not purchase a product when they stay at the Ritz: They buy an experience. Thus, creating the right combination of elements to make the experience stand out is the challenge and goal of every employee, from maintenance to management.

Before applying for the Baldrige Award, company management undertook a rigorous self-examination of its operations in an attempt to measure and quantify quality. Nineteen processes were studied, including room service delivery, guest reservation and registration, message delivery, and breakfast service. This period of self-study included statistical measurement of process work flows and cycle times for areas ranging from room service delivery times and reservations to valet parking and housekeeping efficiency. The results were used to develop performance benchmarks against which future activity could be measured.

With specific, quantifiable targets in place, Ritz-Carlton managers and employees now focus on continuous improvement. The goal is 100% customer satisfaction: If a guest's experience does not meet expectations, the Ritz-Carlton risks losing that guest to competition.

One way the company has put more meaning behind its quality efforts is to organize its employees into "self-directed" work teams. Employee teams determine work scheduling, what work needs to be done, and what to do about quality problems in their own areas. In order that they can see the relationship of their specific area to the overall goals, employees are also given the opportunity to take additional training in hotel operations. Ritz-Carlton believes that a more educated and informed employee is in a better position to make decisions in the best interest of the organization.

Discussion Questions*

1. In what ways could the Ritz-Carlton monitor its success in achieving quality?

2. Many companies say that their goal is to provide quality products or services. What actions might you expect from a company that intends quality to be more than a slogan or buzzword?

3. Why might it cost the Ritz-Carlton less to "do things right" the first time?

4. How could control charts, Pareto diagrams, and cause-and-effect diagrams be used to identify quality problems at a hotel?

5. What are some nonfinancial measures of customer satisfaction that might be used by the Ritz-Carlton?

* You may wish to view the video that accompanies this case before addressing these questions.

Source: Charles T. Horngren, George Foster, Srikant M. Dakar, Madhav Rajan, and Chris Ittner, *Cost Accounting: A Managerial Emphasis,* 13th edition © 2009, pp. 180–181. Reprinted by permission of Pearson Education, Inc. Upper Saddle River, NJ.

CHAPTER 6 | RAPID REVIEW

Main Heading	Review Material	
QUALITY AND STRATEGY (pp. 204–205)	Managing quality helps build successful strategies of differentiation, low cost, and *response*. Two ways that quality improves profitability are: • Sales gains via improved response, price flexibility, increased market share, and/or improved reputation • Reduced costs via increased productivity, lower rework and scrap costs, and/or lower warranty costs	**VIDEO 6.1** The Culture of Quality at Arnold Palmer Hospital
DEFINING QUALITY (pp. 205–208)	An operations manager's objective is to build a total quality management system that identifies and satisfies customer need. • **Quality**—The ability of a product or service to meet customer needs. The American Society for Quality (ASQ) defines *quality* as "the totality of features and characteristics of a product or service that bears on its ability to satisfy stated or implied needs." Well-known quality awards are: • *Canada*: Canada Awards for Excellence • *United States*: Malcolm Baldrige National Quality Award, named after a former secretary of commerce • *Japan*: Deming Prize, named after an American, Dr. W. Edwards Deming • **ISO 9000**—A set of quality standards developed by the International Organization for Standardization (ISO). ISO 9000 is the only quality standard with international recognition. To do business globally, being listed in the ISO directory is critical. • **ISO 14000**—A series of environmental management standards established by the ISO. ISO 14000 contains five core elements: (1) environmental management, (2) auditing, (3) performance evaluation, (4) labelling, and (5) life cycle assessment. As a follow-on to ISO 14000, ISO 24700 reflects the business world's current approach to reuse recovered components from many products. • **Cost of quality (COQ)**—The cost of doing things wrong—that is, the price of nonconformance. The four major categories of costs associated with quality are: *prevention costs, appraisal costs, internal failure*, and *external costs*. Four leaders in the field of quality management are W. Edwards Deming, Joseph M. Juran, Armand Feigenbaum, and Philip B. Crosby.	
TOTAL QUALITY MANAGEMENT (pp. 208–214)	• **Total quality management (TQM)**—Management of an entire organization so that it excels in all aspects of products and services that are important to the customer. Seven concepts for an effective TQM program are (1) continuous improvement, (2) Six Sigma, (3) employee empowerment, (4) benchmarking, (5) just-in-time (JIT), (6) Taguchi concepts, and (7) knowledge of TQM tools. • **PDCA**—A continuous improvement model that involves four stages: plan, do, check, and act. The Japanese use the word *kaizen* to describe the ongoing process of unending improvement—the setting and achieving of ever-higher goals. • **Six Sigma**—A program to save time, improve quality, and lower costs. In a statistical sense, Six Sigma describes a process, product, or service with an extremely high capability—99.9997% accuracy, or 3.4 defects per million.	Problems: 6.1, 6.3, 6.5, 6.13, 6.14, 6.16, and 6.17

Main Heading	Review Material	
	• **Employee empowerment**—Enlarging employee jobs so that the added responsibility and authority is moved to the lowest level possible in the organization.	
	Business literature suggests that some 85% of quality problems have to do with materials and processes, not with employee performance.	
	• **Quality circle**—A group of employees meeting regularly with a facilitator to solve work-related problems in their work area.	
	• **Benchmarking**—Selecting a demonstrated standard of performance that represents the very best performance for a process or an activity.	
	The philosophy behind just-in-time (JIT) involves continuing improvement and enforced problem solving. JIT systems are designed to produce or deliver goods just as they are needed.	
	• **Quality robust**—Products that are consistently built to meet customer needs, in spite of adverse conditions in the production process.	
	• **Quality loss function (QLF)**—A mathematical function that identifies all costs connected with poor quality and shows how these costs increase as product quality moves from what the customer wants: $L = D^2C$.	
	• **Target-oriented quality**—A philosophy of continuous improvement to bring a product exactly on target.	
TOOLS OF TQM (pp. 214–218)	TQM tools that generate ideas include the *check sheet* (organized method of recording data), *scatter diagram* (graph of the value of one variable vs. another variable), and *cause-and-effect diagram*. Tools for organizing the data are the *Pareto chart* and *flowchart*. Tools for identifying problems are the *histogram* (distribution showing the frequency of occurrences of a variable) and *statistical process control chart*.	**ACTIVE MODEL 6.1**
	• **Cause-and-effect diagram**—A schematic technique used to discover possible locations of quality problems; also known as an *Ishikawa diagram* or a *fish-bone chart*.	
	The four *Ms* (material, machinery/equipment, manpower, and methods) may be broad "causes".	
	• **Pareto charts**—Graphics that identify the few critical items as opposed to many less important ones.	
	• **Flowcharts**—Block diagrams that graphically describe a process or system.	
	• **Statistical process control (SPC)**—A process used to monitor standards, make measurements, and take corrective action as a product or service is being produced.	
	• **Control charts**—Graphic presentations of process data over time, with predetermined control limits.	
THE ROLE OF INSPECTION (pp. 219–221)	• **Inspection**—A means of ensuring that an operation is producing at the quality level expected.	
	• **Source inspection**—Controlling or monitoring at the point of production or purchase—at the source.	
	• **Poka-yoke**—Literally translated, "foolproof"; it has come to mean a device or technique that ensures the production of a good unit every time.	
	• **Attribute inspection**—An inspection that classifies items as being either good or defective.	
	• **Variable inspection**—Classifications of inspected items as falling on a continuum scale, such as dimension or strength.	
TQM IN SERVICES (pp. 221–223)	Determinants of service quality: reliability, responsiveness, competence, access, courtesy, communication, credibility, security, understanding/knowing the customer, and tangibles.	**VIDEO 6.2** TQM at Ritz-Carlton Hotels
	• **Service recovery**—Training and empowering frontline workers to solve a problem immediately.	
	• **SERVQUAL**—A popular measurement scale for service quality that compares service expectations with service performance.	

Self-Test

■ **Before taking the self-test,** refer to the learning objectives listed at the beginning of the chapter and the key terms listed at the end of the chapter.

LO1 In this chapter, *quality* is defined as:
   a) the degree of excellence at an acceptable price and the control of variability at an acceptable cost.
   b) how well a product fits patterns of consumer preferences.
   c) the totality of features and characteristics of a product or service that bears on its ability to satisfy stated or implied needs.
   d) being impossible to define, but you know what it is.

LO2 ISO 14000 is an international standard that addresses _____.

LO3 If 1 million passengers pass through the Kelowna International Airport with checked baggage each year, a successful Six Sigma program for baggage handling would result in how many passengers with misplaced luggage?
   a) 3.4   b) 6.0
   c) 34   d) 2700
   e) 6 times the monthly standard deviation of passengers

LO4 The process of identifying other organizations that are best at some facet of your operations and then modelling your organization after them is known as:
   a) continuous improvement.   b) employee empowerment.
   c) benchmarking.   d) copycatting.
   e) patent infringement.

LO5 The Taguchi method includes all except which of the following major concepts?
   a) Employee involvement
   b) Remove the effects of adverse conditions
   c) Quality loss function
   d) Target specifications

LO6 The seven tools of total quality management are _____, _____, _____ , _____, _____, _____, and _____.

Answers: LO1. c; LO2. environmental management; LO3. a; LO4. c; LO5. a; LO6. check sheets, scatter diagrams, cause-and-effect diagrams, Pareto charts, flowcharts, histograms, SPC charts.

MyLab Operations Management

Most of these questions can be found in MyLab Operations Management. Visit MyLab Operations Management to access cases, videos, downloadable software, and much more. MyLab Operations Management Management also features a personalized Study Plan that helps you identify which chapter concepts you've mastered and guides you towards study tools for additional practice.

Statistical Process Control

Learning Objectives

LO1 Explain the purpose of a control chart **235**

LO2 Explain the role of the central limit theorem in SPC **235**

LO3 Build $\bar{x}$-charts and R-charts **237**

LO4 List the five steps involved in building control charts **240**

LO5 Build p-charts and c-charts **242**

LO6 Explain process capability and compute C_p and C_{pk} **246**

LO7 Explain acceptance sampling **248**

LO8 Compute the AOQ **250**

Statistical Process Control (SPC)

In this supplement, we address statistical process control—the same techniques used at BetzDearborn, IBM, GE, and Motorola to achieve quality standards. We also introduce acceptance sampling. **Statistical process control** is the application of statistical techniques to the control of processes. *Acceptance sampling* is used to determine acceptance or rejection of material evaluated by a sample.

Statistical process control (SPC) is a statistical technique that is widely used to ensure that processes meet standards. All processes are subject to a certain degree of variability. While studying process data in the 1920s, Walter Shewhart of Bell Laboratories made the distinction between the common and special causes of variation. Many people now refer to these variations as *natural* and *assignable* causes. He developed a simple but powerful tool to separate the two—the **control chart**.

We use statistical process control to measure performance of a process. A process is said to be operating *in statistical control* when the only source of variation is common (natural) causes. The process must first be brought into statistical control by detecting and eliminating special (assignable) causes of variation.[1] Then its performance is predictable, and its ability to meet customer expectations can be assessed. The *objective* of a process control system is to *provide a statistical signal when assignable causes of variation are present*. Such a signal can quicken appropriate action to eliminate assignable causes.

NATURAL VARIATIONS

Natural variations affect almost every production process and are to be expected. **Natural variation** is the many sources of variation that occur within a process that is in statistical control. Natural variations behave like a constant system of chance causes. Although individual values

---

[1] Removing assignable causes is work. Quality expert W. Edwards Deming observed that a state of statistical control is not a natural state for a manufacturing process. Deming instead viewed it as an achievement, arrived at by elimination, one by one, by determined effort, of special causes of excessive variation. See J. R. Thompson and J. Koronacki, *Statistical Process Control, The Deming Paradigm and Beyond*. Boca Raton, FL: Chapman and Hall, 2002.

are all different, as a group they form a pattern that can be described as a *distribution*. When these distributions are *normal*, they are characterized by two parameters:

Mean, μ (the measure of central tendency—in this case, the average value)
Standard deviation, σ (the measure of dispersion)

As long as the distribution (output measurements) remains within specified limits, the process is said to be "in control," and natural variations are tolerated.

ASSIGNABLE VARIATIONS

Assignable variation

Variation in a production process that can be traced to specific causes.

Assignable variation in a process can be traced to a specific reason. Factors such as machine wear, misadjusted equipment, fatigued or untrained workers, or new batches of raw material are all potential sources of assignable variation.

Natural and assignable variations distinguish two tasks for the operations manager. The first is to *ensure that the process is capable* of operating under control with only natural variation. The second is, of course, to *identify and eliminate assignable variations* so that the processes will remain under control.

SAMPLES

Because of natural and assignable variation, statistical process control uses averages of small samples (often of four to eight items) as opposed to data on individual parts. Individual pieces tend to be too erratic to make trends quickly visible.

Figure S6.1 provides a detailed look at the important steps in determining process variation. The horizontal scale can be weight (as in the number of ounces in boxes of cereal) or length (as in fence posts) or any physical measure. The vertical scale is frequency. The samples of five boxes of cereal in Figure S6.1 (a) are weighed, (b) form a distribution, and

FIGURE S6.1

Natural and Assignable Variation

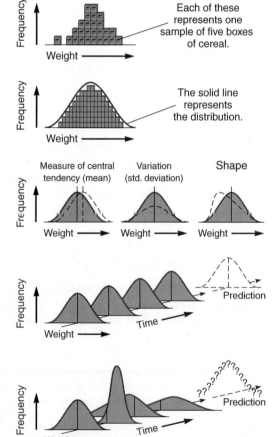

(a) Samples of the product, say five boxes of cereal taken off the filling machine line, vary from one another in weight.

Each of these represents one sample of five boxes of cereal.

(b) After enough sample means are taken from a stable process, they form a pattern called a *distribution*.

The solid line represents the distribution.

(c) There are many types of distributions, including the normal (bell-shaped) distribution, but distributions do differ in terms of central tendency (mean), standard deviation or variance, and shape.

Measure of central tendency (mean)   Variation (std. deviation)   Shape

(d) If only natural causes of variation are present, the output of a process forms a distribution that is stable over time and is predictable.

Prediction

(e) If assignable causes of variation are present, the process output is not stable over time and is not predictable. That is, when causes that are not an expected part of the process occur, the samples will yield unexpected distributions that vary by central tendency, standard deviation, and shape.

Prediction

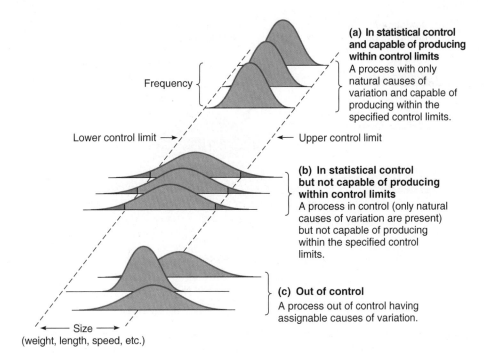

(c) can vary. The distributions formed in (b) and (c) will fall in a predictable pattern (d) if only natural variation is present. If assignable causes of variation are present, then we can expect either the mean to vary or the dispersion to vary, as is the case in (e).

CONTROL CHARTS

The process of building control charts is based on the concepts presented in Figure S6.2. This figure shows three distributions that are the result of outputs from three types of processes. We plot small samples and then examine characteristics of the resulting data to see if the process is within "control limits". The purpose of control charts is to help distinguish between natural variations and variations due to assignable causes. As seen in Figure S6.2, a process is (a) in control *and the process is capable of producing within established control limits*, (b) in control *but the process is not capable of producing within established limits*, or (c) out of control. We now look at ways to build control charts that help the operations manager keep a process under control.

CONTROL CHARTS FOR VARIABLES

The variables of interest here are those that have continuous dimensions. They have an infinite number of possibilities. Examples are weight, speed, length, or strength. Control charts for the mean, $\bar{x}$ or x-bar, and the range, R, are used to monitor processes that have continuous dimensions. The **$\bar{x}$-chart** tells us whether changes have occurred in the central tendency (the mean, in this case) of a process. These changes might be due to such factors as tool wear, a gradual increase in temperature, a different method used on the second shift, or new and stronger materials. The **R-chart** values indicate that a gain or loss in dispersion has occurred. Such a change may be due to worn bearings, a loose tool, an erratic flow of lubricants to a machine, or sloppiness on the part of a machine operator. The two types of charts go hand in hand when monitoring variables because they measure the two critical parameters: central tendency and dispersion.

THE CENTRAL LIMIT THEOREM

The theoretical foundation for $\bar{x}$-charts is the **central limit theorem**. This theorem states that regardless of the distribution of the population, the distribution of $\bar{x}$ (each of which is a mean of a sample drawn from the population) will tend to follow a normal curve as the number of samples increases. Fortunately, even if the sample (n) is fairly small (say, four or five items), the distributions of the averages will still roughly follow a normal curve. The theorem also states that (1) the mean of the distribution of the $\bar{x}s$ (called $\bar{\bar{x}}$) will equal the mean of the overall population

LO1 Explain the purpose of a control chart

$\bar{x}$-chart
A quality control chart for variables that indicates when changes occur in the central tendency of a production process.

R-chart
A control chart that tracks the "range" within a sample; it indicates that a gain or loss in uniformity has occurred in dispersion of a production process.

LO2 Explain the role of the central limit theorem in SPC

Central limit theorem
The theoretical foundation for $\bar{x}$-charts, which states that regardless of the distribution of the population of all parts or services, the $\bar{x}$ distribution tends to follow a normal curve as the number of samples increases.

FIGURE S6.3

The Relationship Between Population and Sampling Distributions

Even though the population distributions will differ (e.g., normal, beta, uniform), each with its own mean (μ) and standard deviation (σ), the distribution of sample means always approaches a normal distribution.

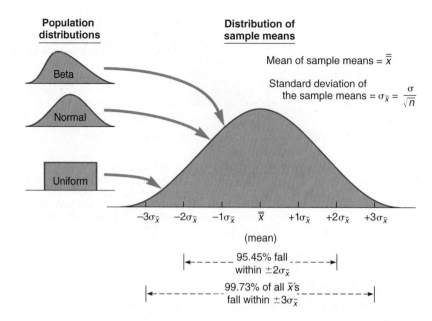

Population distributions

Distribution of sample means

Mean of sample means = $\bar{\bar{x}}$

Standard deviation of the sample means = $\sigma_{\bar{x}} = \dfrac{\sigma}{\sqrt{n}}$

Beta

Normal

Uniform

$-3\sigma_{\bar{x}}$ $-2\sigma_{\bar{x}}$ $-1\sigma_{\bar{x}}$ $\bar{\bar{x}}$ $+1\sigma_{\bar{x}}$ $+2\sigma_{\bar{x}}$ $+3\sigma_{\bar{x}}$

(mean)

95.45% fall within $\pm 2\sigma_{\bar{x}}$

99.73% of all $\bar{x}$'s fall within $\pm 3\sigma_{\bar{x}}$

(called μ), and (2) the standard deviation of the *sampling distribution*, $\sigma_{\bar{x}}$, will be the *population standard deviation*, divided by the square root of the sample size, n. In other words:[2]

$$\bar{\bar{x}} = \mu \tag{S6-1}$$

and

$$\sigma_{\bar{x}} = \frac{\sigma}{\sqrt{n}} \tag{S6-2}$$

Figure S6.3 shows three possible population distributions, each with its own mean, μ, and standard deviation, σ. If a series of random samples $\bar{x}_1, \bar{x}_2, \bar{x}_3, \bar{x}_4$, and so on, each of size n, is drawn from any population distribution (which could be normal, beta, uniform, and so on), the resulting distribution of $\bar{x}_i$s will appear as they do in Figure S6.3.

Moreover, the sampling distribution, as is shown in Figure S6.4, will have less variability than the process distribution. Because the sampling distribution is normal, we can state that:

- 95.45% of the time, the sample averages will fall within $\pm 2\sigma_{\bar{x}}$ if the process has only natural variations.
- 99.73% of the time, the sample averages will fall within $\pm 3\sigma_{\bar{x}}$ if the process has only natural variations.

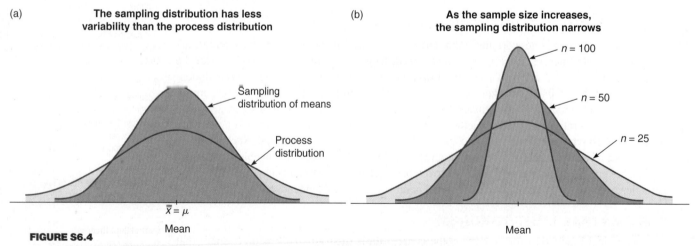

(a) **The sampling distribution has less variability than the process distribution**

Sampling distribution of means

Process distribution

$\bar{\bar{x}} = \mu$

Mean

(b) **As the sample size increases, the sampling distribution narrows**

$n = 100$

$n = 50$

$n = 25$

Mean

FIGURE S6.4

The Sampling Distribution of Means Is Normal and Has Less Variability Than the Process Distribution

In this figure, the process distribution from which the sample was drawn was also normal, but it could have been any distribution.

[2] The standard deviation is easily calculated as $\sigma = \sqrt{\dfrac{\displaystyle\sum_{i=1}^{n}(x_i - \bar{x})^2}{n - 1}}$.

If a point on the control chart falls outside of the $\pm 3\sigma_{\bar{x}}$ control limits, then we are 99.73% sure the process has changed. Figure S6.4(b) shows that as the sample size increases, the sampling distribution becomes narrower. So the sample statistic is closer to the true value of the population for larger sample sizes. This is the theory behind control charts.

LO3 Build $\bar{x}$-charts and R-charts

SETTING MEAN CHART LIMITS ($\bar{X}$-CHARTS)

If we know, through past data, the standard deviation of the process population, σ, we can set upper and lower control limits by using these formulas:

$$\text{Upper control limit (UCL)} = \bar{\bar{x}} + z\sigma_{\bar{x}} \qquad \text{(S6-3)}$$

$$\text{Lower control limit (LCL)} = \bar{\bar{x}} - z\sigma_{\bar{x}} \qquad \text{(S6-4)}$$

Where $\bar{\bar{x}}$ = mean of the sample means or a target value set for the process
  z = number of normal standard deviations (2 for 95.45% confidence, 3 for 99.73%)
  $\sigma_{\bar{x}}$ = standard deviation of the sample means $= \sigma/\sqrt{n}$
  σ = population (process) standard deviation
  n = sample size

Example S1 shows how to set control limits for sample means using standard deviations.

The weights of single-serving boxes of Oat Flakes within a large production lot are sampled each hour. Managers want to set control limits that include 99.73% of the sample means.

APPROACH ▶ Randomly select and weigh nine ($n = 9$) boxes each hour. Then find the overall mean and use Equations (S6-3) and (S6-4) to compute the control limits. Here are the nine boxes chosen for hour 1:

EXAMPLE S1

Setting Control Limits Using Samples

Oat Flakes	Oat Flakes	Oat Flakes	Oat Flakes	Oat Flakes	Oat Flakes	Oat Flakes	Oat Flakes	Oat Flakes
17 grams	13 grams	16 grams	18 grams	17 grams	16 grams	15 grams	17 grams	16 grams

STUDENT TIP

If you want to see an example of such variability in your supermarket, go to the soft drink section and line up a few 2-litre bottles of Coke, Pepsi, or any other brand. Notice that the liquids are not the same measurement.

SOLUTION ▶

$$\text{The average weight in the first sample} = \frac{17 + 13 + 16 + 18 + 17 + 16 + 15 + 17 + 16}{9}$$

$$= 16.1 \text{ grams.}$$

Also, the *population* standard deviation (σ) is known to be 1 gram. We do not show each of the boxes randomly selected in hours 2 through 12, but here are all 12 hourly samples:

	Weight of Sample		Weight of Sample		Weight of Sample
Hour	**(Avg. of 9 Boxes)**	**Hour**	**(Avg. of 9 Boxes)**	**Hour**	**(Avg. of 9 Boxes)**
1	16.1	5	16.5	9	16.3
2	16.8	6	16.4	10	14.8
3	15.5	7	15.2	11	14.2
4	16.5	8	16.4	12	17.3

The average mean of the 12 samples is calculated to be exactly 16 grams. We therefore have $\bar{\bar{x}} = 16$ grams, $\sigma = 1$ gram, $n = 9$, and $z = 3$. The control limits are:

$$\text{UCL}_{\bar{x}} = \bar{\bar{x}} + z\sigma_{\bar{x}} = 16 + 3\left(\frac{1}{\sqrt{9}}\right) = 16 + 3\left(\frac{1}{3}\right) = 17 \text{ grams}$$

$$\text{LCL}_{\bar{x}} = \bar{\bar{x}} - z\sigma_{\bar{x}} = 16 - 3\left(\frac{1}{\sqrt{9}}\right) = 16 - 3\left(\frac{1}{3}\right) = 15 \text{ grams}$$

The 12 samples are then plotted on the following control chart:

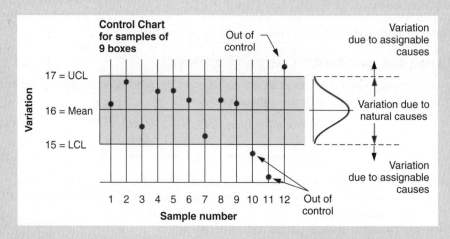

INSIGHT ▶ Because the means of recent sample averages fall outside the upper and lower control limits of 17 and 15, we can conclude that the process is becoming erratic and is *not* in control.

LEARNING EXERCISE ▶ If Oat Flakes's population standard deviation (σ) is 2 (instead of 1), what is your conclusion? [Answer: LCL = 14, UCL = 18; the process would be in control.]

RELATED PROBLEMS ▶ S6.1, S6.2, S6.4, S6.8, S6.10ab

EXCEL OM Data File **Ch06SExS1.xlsx** can be found at **MyLab Operations Management.**

ACTIVE MODEL S6.1 This example is further illustrated in Active Model S6.1 at **MyLab Operations Management**.

Because process standard deviations are either not available or difficult to compute, we usually calculate control limits based on the average *range* values rather than on standard deviations. Table S6.1 provides the necessary conversion for us to do so. The *range* is defined as the difference between the largest and smallest items in one sample. For example, the heaviest box of Oat Flakes in hour 1 of Example S1 was 18 grams and the lightest was 13 grams, so the range for that hour is 5 grams. We use Table S6.1 and the equations:

$$UCL_{\bar{x}} = \bar{\bar{x}} + A_2\bar{R} \tag{S6-5}$$

and:

$$LCL_{\bar{x}} = \bar{\bar{x}} - A_2\bar{R} \tag{S6-6}$$

where $\bar{R}$ = average range of the samples
A_2 = value found in Table S6.1
$\bar{\bar{x}}$ = mean of the sample means

Table S6.1

Factors for Computing Control Chart Limits (3 sigma)

Sample Size, n	Mean Factor, A_2	Upper Range, D_4	Lower Range, D_3
2	1.880	3.268	0
3	1.023	2.574	0
4	0.729	2.282	0
5	0.577	2.115	0
6	0.483	2.004	0
7	0.419	1.924	0.076
8	0.373	1.864	0.136
9	0.337	1.816	0.184
10	0.308	1.777	0.223
12	0.266	1.716	0.284

Source: Reprinted by permission of American Society for Testing Materials. Copyright 1951. Taken from Special Technical Publication 15–C, "Quality Control of Materials," pp. 63 and 72.

Example S2 shows how to set control limits for sample means by using Table S6.1 and the average range.

EXAMPLE S2

Setting Mean Limits Using Table Values

Super Cola cases of bottled soft drinks are labelled "net weight 12 litres". Indeed, an overall process average of 12 litres ($\bar{\bar{x}}$) has been found by taking many samples, in which each sample contained five cases. The average range of the process is 0.25 litre ($\bar{R}$). The OM team wants to determine the upper and lower control limits for averages in this process.

APPROACH ▶ Super Cola applies Equations (S6-5) and (S6-6) and uses the A_2 column of Table S6.1.

SOLUTION ▶ Looking in Table S6.1 for a sample size of 5 in the mean factor A_2 column, we find the value 0.577. Thus, the upper and lower control chart limits are:

$$UCL_{\bar{x}} = \bar{\bar{x}} + A_2\bar{R}$$
$$= 12 + (0.577)(0.25)$$
$$= 12 + 0.144$$
$$= 12.144 \text{ litres}$$
$$LCL_{\bar{x}} = \bar{\bar{x}} - A_2\bar{R}$$
$$= 12 - 0.144$$
$$= 11.856 \text{ litres}$$

INSIGHT ▶ The advantage of using this range approach, instead of the standard deviation, is that it is easy to apply and may be less confusing.

LEARNING EXERCISE ▶ If the sample size was $n = 4$ and the average range $= 0.20$ litres, what are the revised $UCL_{\bar{x}}$ and $LCL_{\bar{x}}$? [Answer: 12.146, 11.854.]

RELATED PROBLEMS ▶ S6.3a, S6.5, S6.6, S6.7, S6.9, S6.10bcd, S6.11, S6.34

EXCEL OM Data File Ch06SExS2.xlsx can be found at **MyLab Operations Management**.

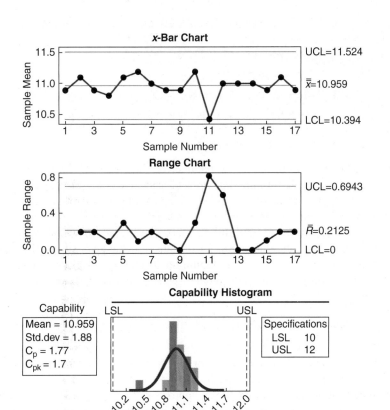

STUDENT TIP

Here, the restaurant chain uses *weight* (11 oz) as a measure of SPC for salmon fillets.

STUDENT TIP

The *range* here is the difference between the heaviest and the lightest salmon fillets weighed in each sample. A range chart shows changes in *dispersion*.

VIDEO S6.1

Farm to Fork: Quality at Darden Restaurants

Salmon fillets are monitored by Darden Restaurant's SPC software, which includes $\bar{x}$- and R-charts and a process capability histogram. The video case study "Farm to Fork: Quality at Darden Restaurants," at the end of this supplement, asks you to interpret these figures.

SETTING RANGE CHART LIMITS (*R*-CHARTS)

In Examples S1 and S2, we determined the upper and lower control limits for the process *average*. In addition to being concerned with the process average, operations managers are interested in the process *dispersion*, or *range*. Even though the process average is under control, the dispersion of the process may not be. For example, something may have worked itself loose in a piece of equipment that fills boxes of Oat Flakes. As a result, the average of the samples may remain the same, but the variation within the samples could be entirely too large. For this reason, operations managers use control charts for ranges to monitor the process variability, as well as control charts for averages, which monitor the process central tendency. The theory behind the control charts for ranges is the same as that for process average control charts. Limits are established that contain ± 3 standard deviations of the distribution for the average range $\overline{R}$. We can use the following equations to set the upper and lower control limits for ranges:

$$\text{UCL}_R = D_4 \overline{R} \tag{S6-7}$$

$$\text{LCL}_R = D_3 \overline{R} \tag{S6-8}$$

where UCL_R = upper control chart limit for the range
LCL_R = lower control chart limit for the range
D_4 and D_3 = values from Table S6.1

Example S3 shows how to set control limits for sample ranges using Table S6.1 and the average range.

EXAMPLE S3

Setting Range Limits Using Table Values

The average *range* of a product at Clinton Manufacturing is 5.3 kilograms. With a sample size of 5, owner Roy Clinton wants to determine the upper and lower control chart limits.

APPROACH ▶ Looking in Table S6.1 for a sample size of 5, he finds that $D_4 = 2.115$ and $D_3 = 0$.

SOLUTION ▶ The range control limits are:

$$\text{UCL}_R = D_4 \overline{R} = (2.115)(5.3 \text{ kilograms}) = 11.2 \text{ kilograms}$$
$$\text{LCL}_R = D_3 \overline{R} = (0)(5.3 \text{ kilograms}) = 0$$

INSIGHT ▶ Computing ranges with Table S6.1 is straightforward and an easy way to evaluate dispersion.

LEARNING EXERCISE ▶ Clinton decides to increase the sample size to $n = 7$. What are the new UCL_R and LCL_R values? [Answer: 10.197, 0.403.]

RELATED PROBLEMS ▶ S6.3b, S6.5, S6.6, S6.7, S6.9, S6.10c, S6.11, S6.12, S6.34

USING MEAN AND RANGE CHARTS

The normal distribution is defined by two parameters, the *mean* and *standard deviation*. The (mean) $\overline{x}$-chart and the *R*-chart mimic these two parameters. The $\overline{x}$-chart is sensitive to shifts in the process mean, whereas the *R*-chart is sensitive to shifts in the process standard deviation. Consequently, by using both charts we can track changes in the process distribution.

For instance, the samples and the resulting $\overline{x}$-chart in Figure S6.5(a) show the shift in the process mean, but because the dispersion is constant, no change is detected by the *R*-chart. Conversely, the samples and the $\overline{x}$-chart in Figure S6.5(b) detect no shift (because none is present), but the *R*-chart does detect the shift in the dispersion. Both charts are required to track the process accurately.

LO4 List the five steps involved in building control charts

STEPS TO FOLLOW WHEN USING CONTROL CHARTS Five steps are generally followed in using $\overline{x}$- and *R*-charts:

1. Collect 20 to 25 samples, often of $n = 4$ or $n = 5$ observations each, from a stable process and compute the mean and range of each.
2. Compute the overall means ($\overline{\overline{x}}$ and $\overline{R}$), set appropriate control limits, usually at the 99.73% level, and calculate the preliminary upper and lower control limits. Refer to Table S6.2 for other control limits. *If the process is not currently stable and in control*, use the desired mean, μ, instead of $\overline{\overline{x}}$ to calculate limits.

(a)

These sampling distributions result in the charts below.

(Sampling mean is shifting upward, but range is consistent.)

FIGURE S6.5

Mean and Range Charts Complement Each Other by Showing the Mean and Dispersion of the Normal Distribution

UCL

$\bar{x}$-chart

($\bar{x}$-chart detects shift in central tendency.)

LCL

UCL

R-chart

(R-chart does not detect change in mean.)

LCL

STUDENT **TIP**

Mean $\bar{x}$ charts are a measure of *central tendency*, while range (R) charts are a measure of *dispersion*. SPC requires both charts for a complete assessment because a sample mean could be out of control while the range is in control, and vice versa.

(b)

These sampling distributions result in the charts below.

(Sampling mean is constant, but dispersion is increasing.)

UCL

$\bar{x}$-chart

($\bar{x}$-chart does not detect the increase in dispersion.)

LCL

UCL

R-chart

(R-chart detects increase in dispersion.)

LCL

Table S6.2
Common z-Values

Desired Control Limit (%)	z-Value (standard deviation required for desired level of confidence)
90.0	1.65
95.0	1.96
95.45	2.00
99.0	2.58
99.73	3.00

3. Graph the sample means and ranges on their respective control charts and determine whether they fall outside the acceptable limits.
4. Investigate points or patterns that indicate the process is out of control. Try to assign causes for the variation, address the causes, and then resume the process.
5. Collect additional samples and, if necessary, revalidate the control limits using the new data.

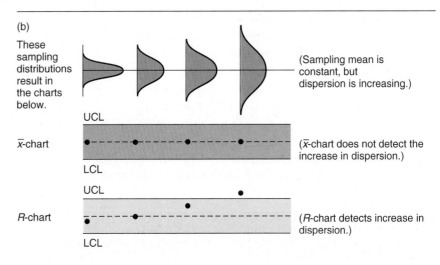

WEIGHTED SINGLE SAMPLE CENTERLINING CHART

FritoLay

FL-5885 (Rev. 11/03)

SHIFT	NUMBER OF CHECKS	MAX. TIME GAP BETWEEN CHECKS
1st SHIFT	10 Checks	40 min
2nd SHIFT		
3rd SHIFT		

INSTRUCTIONS

1. CURRENT VALUE MUST BE WITHIN SPECIFICATION LIMITS. IF NOT, FOLLOW PRESCRIBED PROCEDURES (ABORT, HOLD, ETC.). RECORD CORRECTIVE ACTION AT BOTTOM OF CHART.
2. PREDICTED VALUE = AVERAGE OF CURRENT VALUE AND PREVIOUS PREDICTED VALUE. THE PREDICTED VALUE IS ALWAYS PLOTTED ON THE CHART.
3. DECISION RULE: ANY PREDICTED VALUE IN THE YELLOW (RED TAKE ACTION) INDICATES IMMEDIATE CORRECTIVE ACTION IS REQUIRED. RECORD CORRECTIVE ACTION AT BOTTOM OF CHART.
4. AT START-UP OR AFTER MAJOR PROCESS ADJUSTMENTS THE CURRENT VALUE WILL ALSO BE USED AS THE PREDICTED VALUE.

RED ABORT SPECIFICATION LIMITS
1.70--2.50

TIME:	710	750	830	910	950	1000	1035	1115	1155	1235	115
CURRENT VALUE	218	182	210	215	194	Break	1.99	193	193	205	191
PREDICTED VALUE (PLOT ON CHART)	218	200	205	210	202	↓	201	197	193	199	195

ADJUST

UCL = 2.22

216

AIM = 2.10

204

LCL = 1.98

ADJUST

Frito-Lay uses $\bar{x}$-charts to control production quality at critical points in the process. About every 40 minutes, three batches of chips are taken from the conveyor (on the left) and analyzed electronically to get an average salt content, which is plotted on an $\bar{x}$-chart (on the right). Points plotted in the green zone are "in control," while those in the yellow zone are "out of control". The SPC chart is displayed where all production employees can monitor process stability.

LO5 Build *p*-charts and *c*-charts

CONTROL CHARTS FOR ATTRIBUTES

Control charts for $\bar{x}$ and R do not apply when we are sampling *attributes*, which are typically classified as *defective* or *nondefective*. Measuring defectives involves counting them (e.g., number of bad light bulbs in a given lot, or number of letters or data entry records typed with errors), whereas *variables* are usually measured for length or weight. There are two kinds of attribute control charts: (1) those that measure the *percent* defective in a sample—called *p*-charts—and (2) those that count the *number* of defects—called *c*-charts.

p-chart

A quality control chart that is used to control attributes.

P-CHARTS Using a **p-chart** is the chief way to control attributes. Although attributes that are either good or bad follow the binomial distribution, the normal distribution can be used to calculate *p*-chart limits when sample sizes are large. The procedure resembles the $\bar{x}$-chart approach, which is also based on the central limit theorem.

The formulas for *p*-chart upper and lower control limits follow:

$$UCL_p = \bar{p} + z\sigma_{\hat{p}} \tag{S6-9}$$

$$LCL_p = \bar{p} - z\sigma_{\hat{p}} \tag{S6-10}$$

VIDEO S6.2

Frito-Lay's Quality-Controlled Potato Chips

Where $\bar{p}$ = mean fraction defective in the samples
   z = number of standard deviations ($z = 2$ for 95.45% limits; $z = 3$ for 99.73% limits)
   $\sigma_{\hat{p}}$ = standard deviation of the sampling distribution

$\sigma_{\hat{p}}$ is estimated by the formula:

$$\sigma_{\hat{p}} = \sqrt{\frac{\bar{p}(1 - \bar{p})}{n}} \tag{S6-11}$$

where n = number of observations in *each* sample

Example S4 shows how to set control limits for *p*-charts for these standard deviations. The *OM in Action* box "Cutting Costs in the Life Insurance Business" provides a real-world follow-up to Example S4.

Clerks at Mosier Data Systems key in thousands of insurance records each day for a variety of client firms. CEO Donna Mosier wants to set control limits to include 99.73% of the random variation in the data entry process when it is in control.

APPROACH ▶ Samples of the work of 20 clerks are gathered (and shown in the table). Mosier carefully examines 100 records entered by each clerk and counts the number of errors. She also computes the fraction defective in each sample. Equations (S6-9), (S6-10), and (S6-11) are then used to set the control limits.

Sample Number	Number of Errors	Fraction Defective	Sample Number	Number of Errors	Fraction Defective
1	6	0.06	11	6	0.06
2	5	0.05	12	1	0.01
3	0	0.00	13	8	0.08
4	1	0.01	14	7	0.07
5	4	0.04	15	5	0.05
6	2	0.02	16	4	0.04
7	5	0.05	17	11	0.11
8	3	0.03	18	3	0.03
9	3	0.03	19	0	0.00
10	2	0.02	20	4	0.04
				80	

SOLUTION ▶

$$\bar{p} = \frac{\text{Total number of errors}}{\text{Total number of records examined}} = \frac{80}{(100)(20)} = 0.04$$

$$\sigma_{\hat{p}} = \sqrt{\frac{(0.04)(1 - 0.04)}{100}} = 0.02 \text{ (rounded up from 0.0196)}$$

(*Note:* 100 is the size of *each* sample = n.)

$$\text{UCL}_p = \bar{p} - z\sigma_{\hat{p}} = 0.04 + 3(0.02) = 0.10$$

$$\text{UCL}_p = \bar{p} - z\sigma_{\hat{p}} = 0.04 - 3(0.02) = 0$$

(because we cannot have a negative percentage defective)

INSIGHT ▶ When we plot the control limits and the sample fraction defectives, we find that only one data-entry clerk (number 17) is out of control. The firm may wish to examine that individual's work a bit more closely to see if a serious problem exists (see Figure S6.6).

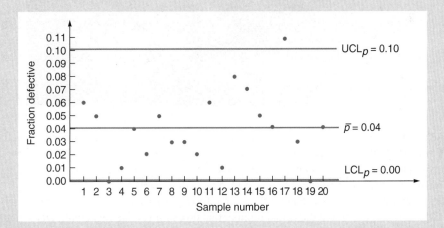

FIGURE S6.6

p-Chart for Data Entry for Example S4

STUDENT TIP

We are always pleased to be at zero or below the centre line in a *p*-chart.

LEARNING EXERCISE ▶ Mosier decides to set control limits at 95.45% instead. What are the new UCL_p and LCL_p? [Answer: 0.08, 0.]

RELATED PROBLEMS ▶ S6.13, S6.14, S6.15, S6.16, S6.17, S6.18, S6.19, S6.20, S6.25, S6.35

EXCEL OM Data File **Ch06SExS4.xlsx** can be found at **MyLab Operations Management**.

ACTIVE MODEL S6.2 This example is further illustrated in Active Model S6.2 at **MyLab Operations Management**.

OM in Action   Cutting Costs in the Life Insurance Business

Canada Bankers Life Assurance Company was looking to cut costs while simultaneously increasing revenue. New sources of sales revenues were explored through the use of aggressive marketing campaigns. Loyalty programs were also considered, and the first area being examined involved focusing on excellence in customer service. But management felt there were also opportunities to reduce expenditures in the area of distribution, particularly as it related to their sales and service call centre.

Several call centre companies were interviewed with the intent of outsourcing the function to the firm that could deliver the required services at the lowest cost. The firm winning the bid was Electro-tech, a company with a history of being a low-cost service provider. Electro-tech was ultimately successful in reducing costs in the distribution channel, but Canada Bankers Life Assurance discovered that this expense reduction exercise cost dearly in other areas. For example, although the call centre was successful in reducing payroll costs and lowering the cost per call, customer service levels plummeted and unhappy clients

cancelled their policies. Potential clients also felt the pinch of the austerity measures and noticed the difficulty in reaching an agent on the phone. Two important measures highlighted the dramatic drop in service:

1. Quality: the number of life insurance applications containing errors deviated from a baseline of 3% to 22%;
2. Wastage: the number of life insurance applications that were "not proceeded with" and not transferred into insurance policies because of improper sales handling, errors, missing information, etc., deviated from a baseline of 5% to 37%.

After lengthy negotiations and consideration, the insurance company determined it was best to cancel the outsourcing agreement and assume responsibility for its call centre. However, the company did accept much of the blame and realized it should have been more closely monitoring each of the key metrics in the distribution area, as well as observing the impact this change had on the other aspects of the business.

Sampling wine from these wooden barrels, to make sure it is aging properly, uses both SPC (for alcohol content and acidity) and subjective measures (for taste).

Charles O'Rear/Corbis/VCG/Corbis Documentary/Getty Images

c-chart

A quality control chart used to control the number of defects per unit of output.

C-CHARTS In Example S4, we counted the number of defective records entered. A defective record was one that was not exactly correct because it contained at least one defect. However, a bad record may contain more than one defect. We use a **c-chart** to control the *number* of defects per unit of output (or per insurance record, in the preceding case).

Control charts for defects are helpful for monitoring processes in which a large number of potential errors can occur, but the actual number that do occur is relatively small. Defects may be errors in newspaper words, bad circuits in a microchip, blemishes on a table, or missing pickles on a fast-food hamburger.

The Poisson probability distribution,[3] which has a variance equal to its mean, is the basis for c-charts. Because $\bar{c}$ is the mean number of defects per unit, the standard deviation is equal to $\sqrt{\bar{c}}$. To compute 99.73% control limits for $\bar{c}$, we use the formula:

$$\text{Control limits} = \bar{c} \pm 3\sqrt{\bar{c}} \tag{S6-12}$$

Example S5 shows how to set control limits for a $\bar{c}$-chart.

EXAMPLE S5

Setting Control Limits for Number Defective

Red Top Cab Company receives several complaints per day about the behaviour of its drivers. Over a nine-day period (where days are the units of measure), the owner, Gordon Hoft, received the following numbers of calls from irate passengers: 3, 0, 8, 9, 6, 7, 4, 9, 8, for a total of 54 complaints. Hoft wants to compute 99.73% control limits.

APPROACH ▶ He applies Equation (S6-12).

SOLUTION ▶ $\bar{c} = \dfrac{54}{9} = 6$ complaints per day

Thus:

$$\text{UCL}_c = \bar{c} + 3\sqrt{\bar{c}} = 6 + 3\sqrt{6} = 6 + 3(2.45) = 13.35, \text{ or } 13$$
$$\text{LCL}_c = \bar{c} - 3\sqrt{\bar{c}} = 6 - 3\sqrt{6} = 6 - 3(2.45) = 0 \leftarrow \text{(since it cannot be negative)}$$

INSIGHT ▶ After Hoft plotted a control chart summarizing these data and posted it prominently in the drivers' locker room, the number of calls received dropped to an average of three per day. Can you explain why this occurred?

LEARNING EXERCISE ▶ Hoft collects three more days' worth of complaints (10, 12, and 8 complaints) and wants to combine them with the original nine days to compute updated control limits. What are the revised UCL_c and LCL_c? [Answer: 14.94, 0.]

RELATED PROBLEMS ▶ S6.21, S6.22, S6.23, S6.24

EXCEL OM Data File **Ch06SExS5.xlsx** can be found at **MyLab Operations Management**.

---

[3] A Poisson probability distribution is a discrete distribution commonly used when the items of interest (in this case, defects) are infrequent or occur in time and space.

Variable Data	Attribute Data

Using an x̄-Chart and an R-Chart

1. Observations are *variables*, which are usually products measured for size or weight. Examples are the width or length of a wire being cut and the weight of a can of Campbell's soup.

2. Collect 20 to 25 samples, usually of $n = 4$, $n = 5$, or more, each from a stable process, and compute the means for an x̄-chart and the ranges for an R-chart

3. We track samples of n observations each, as in Example S1.

Using a p-Chart

1. Observations are *attributes* that can be categorized as good or bad (or pass–fail, or functional–broken), that is, in two states.

2. We deal with fraction, proportion, or percent defectives.

3. There are several samples, with many observations in each. For example, 20 samples of $n = 100$ observations in each, as in Example S4.

Using a c-Chart

4. Observations are *attributes* whose defects per unit of output can be counted.

5. We deal with the number counted, which is a small part of the possible occurrences.

6. Defects may be: number of blemishes on a desk; complaints in a day; crimes in a year; broken seats in a stadium; typos in a chapter of this text; or flaws in a bolt of cloth, as is shown in Example S5.

Table S6.3

Helping You Decide Which Control Chart to Use

STUDENT TIP

This is a really useful table. When you are not sure which control chart to use, turn here for clarification.

MANAGERIAL ISSUES AND CONTROL CHARTS

In an ideal world, there is no need for control charts. Quality is uniform and so high that employees need not waste time and money sampling and monitoring variables and attributes. But because most processes have not reached perfection, managers must make three major decisions regarding control charts.

- First, managers must select the points in their process that need SPC. They may ask, "Which parts of the job are critical to success?" or "Which parts of the job have a tendency to become out of control?"

- Second, operations managers need to decide if variable charts (i.e., x̄ and R) or attribute charts (i.e., p and c) are appropriate. Variable charts monitor weights or dimensions. Attribute charts are more of a "yes–no" or "go–no go" gauge and tend to be less costly to implement. Table S6.3 can help you understand when to use each of these types of control charts.

- Third, the company must set clear and specific SPC policies for employees to follow. For example, should the data-entry process be halted if a trend is appearing in percent defective records being keyed? Should an assembly line be stopped if the average length of five successive samples is above the centre line? Figure S6.7 illustrates some of the patterns to look for over time in a process.

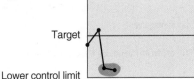

Normal behaviour. Process is "in control".

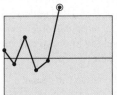

One point out above (or below). Investigate for cause. Process is "out of control".

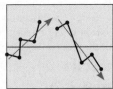

Trends in either direction, five points. Investigate for cause of progressive change. This could be the result of gradual tool wear.

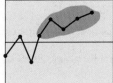

Two points very near lower (or upper) control. Investigate for cause.

Run of five points above (or below) central line. Investigate for cause.

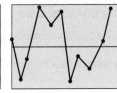

Erratic behaviour. Investigate.

FIGURE S6.7

Patterns to Look for on Control Charts

Source: Bertrand L. Hansen, *Quality Control: Theory and Applications*, 1st Edition. ©1964. Reprinted and electronically reproduced by permission of Pearson Education, Inc., Upper Saddle River, New Jersey.

STUDENT TIP

Workers in companies such as Frito-Lay are trained to follow rules like these.

Run test

A test used to examine the points in a control chart to see if nonrandom variation is present.

A tool called a **run test** is available to help identify the kind of abnormalities in a process that we see in Figure S6.7. In general, a run of five points above or below the target or centre line may suggest that an assignable, or nonrandom, variation is present. When this occurs, even though all the points may fall inside the control limits, a flag has been raised. This means the process may not be statistically in control. A variety of run tests are described in books on the subject of quality methods.[4]

STUDENT TIP

Here, we deal with whether a process meets the specification it was *designed* to yield.

Process Capability

LO6 Explain process capability and compute C_p and C_{pk}

Process capability

The ability to meet design specifications.

Statistical process control means keeping a process in control. This means that the natural variation of the process must be stable. But a process that is in statistical control may not yield goods or services that meet their *design specifications* (tolerances). The ability of a process to meet design specifications, which are set by engineering design or customer requirements, is called **process capability**. Even though that process may be statistically in control (stable), the output of that process may not conform to specifications.

For example, let's say the time a customer expects to wait for the completion of a lube job at Mr. Lube is 12 minutes, with an acceptable tolerance of ± 2 minutes. This tolerance gives an upper specification of 14 minutes and a lower specification of 10 minutes. The lube process has to be capable of operating within these design specifications—if not, some customers will not have their requirements met. As a manufacturing example, the tolerances for Harley-Davidson cam gears are extremely low, only 0.0127 mm—and a process must be designed that is capable of achieving this tolerance.

There are two popular measures for quantitatively determining if a process is capable: process capability ratio (C_p) and process capability index (C_{pk}).

PROCESS CAPABILITY RATIO (C_p)

C_p

A ratio for determining whether a process meets design specifications; a ratio of the specification to the process variation.

For a process to be capable, its values must fall within upper and lower specifications. This typically means the process capability is within ± 3 standard deviations from the process mean. Since this range of values is six standard deviations, a capable process tolerance, which is the difference between the upper and lower specifications, must be greater than or equal to six.

The process capability ratio, C_p is computed as:

$$C_p = \frac{\text{Upper specification} - \text{Lower specification}}{6\sigma} \qquad \textbf{(S6-13)}$$

Example S6 shows the computation of C_p.

EXAMPLE S6

Process Capability Ratio (C_p)

In a GE insurance claims process, $\bar{x} = 210.0$ minutes, and $\sigma = 0.516$ minutes.

The design specification to meet customer expectations is 210 ± 3 minutes. So the Upper Specification is 213 minutes and the lower specification is 207 minutes. The OM manager wants to compute the process capability ratio.

APPROACH ▶ GE applies Equation (S6-13).

SOLUTION ▶ $(213 - 207) / 6(0.516) = 6 / 3.096 = 1.938$.

INSIGHT ▶ Since a ratio of 1.00 means that 99.73% of a process's outputs are within specifications, this ratio suggests a very capable process, with nonconformance of less than four claims per million.

LEARNING EXERCISE ▶ If $\sigma = 0.60$ (instead of 0.516), what is the new C_p? [Answer: 1.667, a very capable process still.]

RELATED PROBLEMS ▶ S6.26, S6.27

EXCEL OM Data File **Ch06SExS6.xlsx** can be found at **MyLab Operations Management**.

ACTIVE MODEL S6.3 This example is further illustrated in Active Model S6.3 at **MyLab Operations Management**.

---

[4] See Gerald Smith, *Statistical Process Control and Process Improvement*, 7th ed. (Upper Saddle River, NJ: Prentice Hall, 2010).

A capable process has a C_p of at least 1.0. If the C_p is less than 1.0, the process yields products or services that are outside their allowable tolerance. With a C_p of 1.0, 2.7 parts in 1000 can be expected to be "out of spec".[5] The higher the process capability ratio, the greater the likelihood the process will be within design specifications. Many firms have chosen a C_p of 1.33 (a four-sigma standard) as a target for reducing process variability. This means that only 64 parts per million can be expected to be out of specification.

Recall that in Chapter 6 we mentioned the concept of *Six Sigma* quality, championed by GE and Motorola. This standard equates to a C_p of 2.0, with only 3.4 defective parts per million (very close to zero defects) instead of the 2.7 parts per 1000 with three-sigma limits.

Although C_p relates to the spread (dispersion) of the process output relative to its tolerance, it does not look at how well the process average is centred on the target value.

PROCESS CAPABILITY INDEX (C_{pk})

The process capability index, $\mathbf{C_{pk}}$, measures the difference between the desired and actual dimensions of goods or services produced.

The formula for C_{pk} is:

$$C_{pk} = \text{Minimum of} \left[\frac{\text{Upper specification limit} - \overline{X}}{3\sigma}, \frac{\overline{X} - \text{Lower specification limit}}{3\sigma} \right] \quad \text{(S6-14)}$$

where $\overline{X}$ = process mean

σ = standard deviation of the process population

When the C_{pk} index for both the upper and lower specification limits equals 1.0, the process variation is centred and the process is capable of producing within ± 3 standard deviations (fewer than 2700 defects per million). A C_{pk} of 2.0 means the process is capable of producing fewer than 3.4 defects per million. For C_{pk} to exceed 1, σ must be less than $\frac{1}{3}$ of the difference between the specification and the process mean ($\overline{X}$). Figure S6.8 shows the meaning of various measures of C_{pk}, and Example S7 shows an application of C_{pk}.

C_{pk}
A proportion of variation (3σ) between the centre of the process and the nearest specification limit.

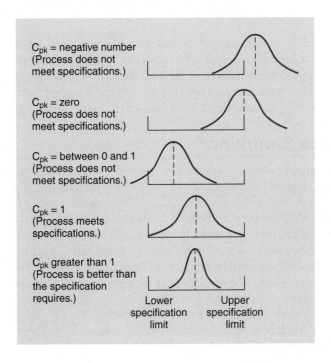

C_{pk} = negative number (Process does not meet specifications.)

C_{pk} = zero (Process does not meet specifications.)

C_{pk} = between 0 and 1 (Process does not meet specifications.)

C_{pk} = 1 (Process meets specifications.)

C_{pk} greater than 1 (Process is better than the specification requires.)

Lower specification limit

Upper specification limit

FIGURE S6.8

Meanings of C_{pk} Measures

A C_{pk} index of 1.0 for both the upper and lower control limits indicates that the process variation is within the upper and lower control limits. As the C_{pk} index goes above 1.0, the process becomes increasingly target-oriented, with fewer defects. If the C_{pk} is less than 1.0, the process will not produce within the specified tolerance. Because a process may not be centred, or may "drift," a C_{pk} above 1.0 is desired.

---

[5] This is because a C_p of 1.0 has 99.73% of outputs within specifications. So $1.00 - 0.9973 = 0.0027$; with 1000 parts, there are $0.0027 \times 1000 = 2.7$ defects. For a C_p of 2.0, 99.99966% of outputs are "within spec". So $1.00 - 0.9999966 = 0.0000034$; with 1 million parts, there are 3.4 defects.

EXAMPLE S7

Process Capability Index (C$_{pk}$)

You are the process improvement manager and have developed a new machine to cut insoles for the company's top-of-the-line running shoes. You are excited because the company's goal is no more than 3.4 defects per million, and this machine may be the innovation you need. The insoles cannot be more than ±0.001 of a centimetre from the required thickness of 0.250 cm. You want to know if you should replace the existing machine, which has a C$_{pk}$ of 1.0.

APPROACH ▶ You decide to determine the C$_{pk}$, using Equation (S6-14), for the new machine and make a decision on that basis.

SOLUTION ▶

$$\text{Upper specification limit} = 0.251 \text{ centimetre}$$
$$\text{Lower specification limit} = 0.249 \text{ centimetre}$$

Mean of the new process $\overline{X} = 0.250$ centimetre
Estimated standard deviation of the new process $= \sigma = 0.0005$ centimetre

$$C_{pk} = \text{Minimum of} \left[\frac{\text{Upper specification limit} - X}{3\sigma}, \frac{X - \text{Lower specification limit}}{3\sigma} \right]$$

$$C_{pk} = \text{Minimum of} \left[\frac{(0.251) - 0.250}{(3)0.0005}, \frac{0.250 - (0.249)}{(3)0.0005} \right]$$

Both calculations result in: $\dfrac{0.001}{0.0015} = 0.67$.

INSIGHT ▶ Because the new machine has a C$_{pk}$ of only 0.67, the new machine should *not* replace the existing machine.

LEARNING EXERCISE ▶ If the insoles can be ±0.002 cm (instead of 0.001 cm) from the required 0.250 cm, what is the new C$_{pk}$? [Answer: 1.33 and the new machine *should* replace the existing one.]

RELATED PROBLEMS ▶ S6.27, S6.28, S6.29, S6.30, S6.31

EXCEL OM Data File **Ch06SExS7.xlsx** can be found at **MyLab Operations Management.**

ACTIVE MODEL S6.3 This example is further illustrated in Active Model S6.3 at **MyLab Operations Management.**

Note that C$_p$ and C$_{pk}$ will be the same when the process is centred. However, if the mean of the process is not centred on the desired (specified) mean, then the smaller numerator in Equation (S6-14) is used (the minimum of the difference between the upper specification limit and the mean or the lower specification limit and the mean). This application of C$_{pk}$ is shown in Solved Problem S6.4. C$_{pk}$ is the standard criterion used to express process performance.

Acceptance Sampling[6]

LO7 Explain acceptance sampling

Acceptance sampling
A method of measuring random samples of lots or batches of products against predetermined standards.

Acceptance sampling is a form of testing that involves taking random samples of "lots," or batches, of finished products and measuring them against predetermined standards. Sampling is more economical than 100% inspection. The quality of the sample is used to judge the quality of all items in the lot. Although both attributes and variables can be inspected by acceptance sampling, attribute inspection is more commonly used, as illustrated in this section.

Acceptance sampling can be applied either when materials arrive at a plant or at final inspection, but it is usually used to control incoming lots of purchased products. A lot of items rejected, based on an unacceptable level of defects found in the sample, can (1) be returned to the supplier or (2) be 100% inspected to cull out all defects, with the cost of this screening usually billed to the supplier. However, acceptance sampling is not a substitute for adequate process controls. In fact, the current approach is to build statistical quality controls at suppliers' operations so that acceptance sampling can be eliminated.

OPERATING CHARACTERISTIC CURVE

Operating characteristic (OC) curve
A graph that describes how well an acceptance plan discriminates between good and bad lots.

The **operating characteristic (OC) curve** describes how well an acceptance plan discriminates between good and bad lots. A curve pertains to a specific plan—that is, to a combination of n

---

[6] Refer to Online Tutorial 2 on MyLab Operations Management for an extended discussion of acceptance sampling.

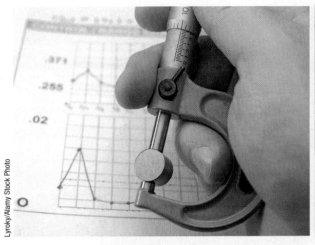

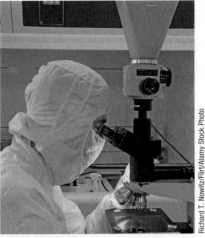

Raw data for statistical process control are collected in a wide variety of ways. Here physical measures using a micrometer (on the left) and a microscope (on the right) are being made.

(sample size) and *c* (acceptance level). It is intended to show the probability that the plan will accept lots of various quality levels.

With acceptance sampling, two parties are usually involved: the producer of the product and the consumer of the product. In specifying a sampling plan, each party wants to avoid costly mistakes in accepting or rejecting a lot. The producer usually has the responsibility of replacing all defects in the rejected lot or of paying for a new lot to be shipped to the customer. The producer, therefore, wants to avoid the mistake of having a good lot rejected (**producer's risk**). On the other hand, the customer or consumer wants to avoid the mistake of accepting a bad lot because defects found in a lot that has already been accepted are usually the responsibility of the customer (**consumer's risk**). The OC curve shows the features of a particular sampling plan, including the risks of making a wrong decision.[7]

Figure S6.9 can be used to illustrate one sampling plan in more detail. Four concepts are illustrated in this figure.

Producer's risk

The mistake of having a producer's good lot rejected through sampling.

Consumer's risk

The mistake of a customer's acceptance of a bad lot overlooked through sampling.

FIGURE S6.9

An Operating Characteristic (OC) Curve Showing Producer's and Consumer's Risks

A good lot for this particular acceptance plan has less than or equal to 2% defectives. A bad lot has 7% or more defectives.

STUDENT TIP

Figure S6.9 is further illustrated in Active Model S6.4 on our website, **MyLab Operations Management.**

---

[7] Note that sampling always runs the danger of leading to an erroneous conclusion. Let us say in one company that the total population under scrutiny is a load of 1000 computer chips, of which in reality only 30 (or 3%) are defective. This means that we would want to accept the shipment of chips, because for this particular firm, 4% is the allowable defect rate. However, if a random sample of $n = 50$ chips was drawn, we could conceivably end up with 0 defects and accept that shipment (i.e., it is okay), or we could find all 30 defects in the sample. If the latter happened, we could wrongly conclude that the whole population was 60% defective and reject them all.

This laser tracking device, by Faro Technologies, enables quality control personnel to measure and inspect parts and tools during production. The portable tracker can measure objects from 262 feet away and takes up to 1000 accurate readings per second.

Faro Technologies, Inc.

Acceptable quality level (AQL)

The quality level of a lot considered good.

Lot tolerance percentage defective (LTPD)

The quality level of a lot considered bad.

Type I error

Statistically, the probability of rejecting a good lot.

Type II error

Statistically, the probability of accepting a bad lot.

The **acceptable quality level (AQL)** is the poorest level of quality that we are willing to accept. In other words, we wish to accept lots that have this or a better level of quality, but no lower. If an acceptable quality level is 20 defects in a lot of 1000 items or parts, then AQL is $20/1000 = 2\%$ defectives.

The **lot tolerance percentage defective (LTPD)** is the quality level of a lot that we consider bad. We wish to reject lots that have this or a poorer level of quality. If it is agreed that an unacceptable quality level is 70 defects in a lot of 1000, then the LTPD is $70/1000 = 7\%$ defective.

To derive a sampling plan, producer and consumer must define not only "good lots" and "bad lots" through the AQL and LTPD, but they must also specify risk levels.

Producer's risk (α) is the probability that a "good" lot will be rejected. This is the risk that a random sample might result in a much higher proportion of defects than the population of all items. A lot with an acceptable quality level of AQL still has an α chance of being rejected. Sampling plans are often designed to have the producer's risk set at $\alpha = 0.05$, or 5%.

Consumer's risk (β) is the probability that a "bad" lot will be accepted. This is the risk that a random sample may result in a lower proportion of defects than the overall population of items. A common value for consumer's risk in sampling plans is $\beta = 0.10$, or 10%.

The probability of rejecting a good lot is called a **type I error**. The probability of accepting a bad lot is a **type II error**.

Sampling plans and OC curves may be developed by computer (as seen in the software available with this text), by published tables, or by calculation, using binomial or Poisson distributions.

AVERAGE OUTGOING QUALITY

LO8 Compute the AOQ

In most sampling plans, when a lot is rejected, the entire lot is inspected and all defective items replaced. Use of this replacement technique improves the average outgoing quality in terms of percent defective. In fact, given (1) any sampling plan that replaces all defective items encountered and (2) the true incoming percent defective for the lot, it is possible to determine the **average outgoing quality (AOQ)** in percentage defective. The equation for AOQ is:

Average outgoing quality (AOQ)

The percentage defective in an average lot of goods inspected through acceptance sampling.

$$\text{AOQ} = \frac{(P_d)(P_a)(N - n)}{N} \qquad \text{(S6-15)}$$

Where P_d = true percentage defective of the lot
  P_a = probability of accepting the lot for a given sample size and quantity defective
  N = number of items in the lot
  n = number of items in the sample

The maximum value of AOQ corresponds to the highest average percentage defective or the lowest average quality for the sampling plan. It is called the *average outgoing quality limit (AOQL)*.

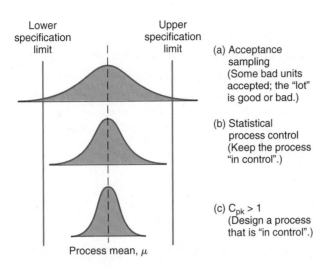

FIGURE S6.10

The Application of Statistical Process Techniques Contributes to the Identification and Systematic Reduction of Process Variability

Acceptance sampling is useful for screening incoming lots. When the defective parts are replaced with good parts, acceptance sampling helps to increase the quality of the lots by reducing the outgoing percent defective.

Figure S6.10 compares acceptance sampling, SPC, and C_{pk}. As Figure S6.10 shows, (a) acceptance sampling by definition accepts some bad units, (b) control charts try to keep the process in control, but (c) the C_{pk} index places the focus on improving the process. As operations managers, that is what we want to do—improve the process.

SUPPLEMENT SUMMARY

Statistical process control is a major statistical tool of quality control. Control charts for SPC help operations managers distinguish between natural and assignable variations. The $\bar{x}$-chart and the R-chart are used for variable sampling, and the p-chart and the c-chart for attribute sampling. The C_{pk} index is a way to express process capability. Operating characteristic (OC) curves facilitate acceptance sampling and provide the manager with tools to evaluate the quality of a production run or shipment.

Discussion Questions

1. List Shewhart's two types of variation. What are they also called?
2. Define "in statistical control".
3. Explain briefly what an $\bar{x}$-chart and an R-chart do.
4. What might cause a process to be out of control?
5. List five steps in developing and using $\bar{x}$-charts and R-charts.
6. List some possible causes of assignable variation.
7. Explain how a person using two-sigma control charts will more easily find samples "out of bounds" than three-sigma control charts. What are some possible consequences of this fact?
8. When is the desired mean, μ, used in establishing the centre line of a control chart instead of $\bar{\bar{x}}$?
9. Can a production process be labelled as "out of control" because it is too good? Explain.
10. In a control chart, what would be the effect on the control limits if the sample size varied from one sample to the next?
11. Define C_{pk} and explain what a C_{pk} of 1.0 means. What is C_p?
12. What does a run of five points above or below the centre line in a control chart imply?
13. What are the acceptable quality level (AQL) and the lot tolerance percentage defective (LTPD)? How are they used?
14. What is a run test and when is it used?
15. Discuss the managerial issues regarding the use of control charts.
16. What is an OC curve?
17. What is the purpose of acceptance sampling?
18. What two risks are present when acceptance sampling is used?
19. Is a *capable* process a *perfect* process? That is, does a capable process generate only output that meets specifications? Explain.

Using Software for SPC

Excel, Excel OM, and POM for Windows may be used to develop control charts for most of the problems in this chapter.

✗ CREATING EXCEL SPREADSHEETS TO DETERMINE CONTROL LIMITS FOR A C-CHART

Excel and other spreadsheets are extensively used in industry to maintain control charts. Program S6.1 is an example of how to use Excel to determine the control limits for a c-chart. These charts are used when the number of defects per unit of output is known. The data from Example S5 are used. In this example, 54 complaints occurred over nine days. Excel also contains a built-in graphing ability with Chart Wizard.

PROGRAM S6.1 An Excel Spreadsheet for Creating a *c*-Chart for Example S5

Source: Courtesy of Microsoft Corporation.

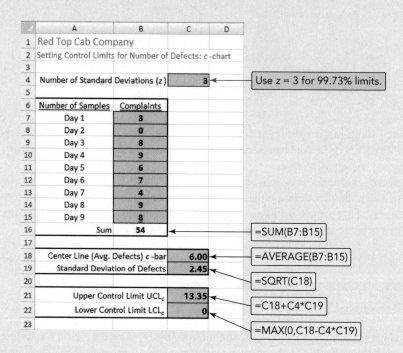

✗ USING EXCEL OM

Excel OM's Quality Control module has the ability to develop $\bar{x}$-charts, p-charts, and c-charts. It also handles OC curves, acceptance sampling, and process capability. Program S6.2 illustrates Excel OM's spreadsheet approach to computing the $\bar{x}$ control limits for the Oat Flakes company in Example S1.

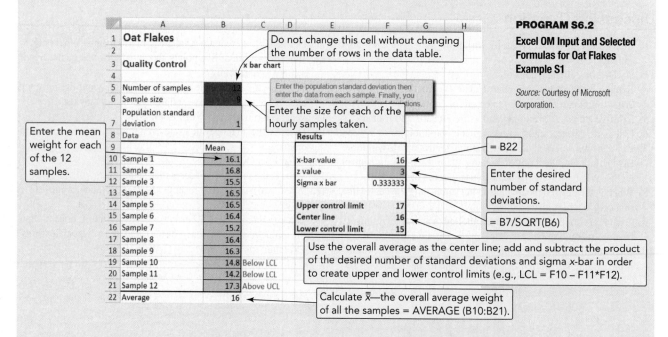

PROGRAM S6.2

Excel OM Input and Selected Formulas for Oat Flakes Example S1

Source: Courtesy of Microsoft Corporation.

P USING POM FOR WINDOWS

The POM for Windows Quality Control module has the ability to compute all the SPC control charts we introduced in this supplement, as well as OC curves, acceptance sampling, and process capability. See Appendix IV for further details.

Solved Problems Virtual Office Hours help is available at MyLab Operations Management.

▼ SOLVED PROBLEM S6.1

A manufacturer of precision machine parts produces round shafts for use in the construction of drill presses. The average diameter of a shaft is 0.56 centimetre. Inspection samples contain six shafts each. The average range of these samples is 0.006 centimetre. Determine the upper and lower $\bar{x}$ control chart limits.

▼ SOLUTION

The mean factor A_2 from Table S6.1, where the sample size is 6, is seen to be 0.483. With this factor, you can obtain the upper and lower control limits:

$$\text{UCL}_{\bar{x}} = 0.56 + (0.483)(0.006)$$
$$= 0.56 + 0.0029$$
$$= 0.5629 \text{ inch}$$
$$\text{LCL}_{\bar{x}} = 0.56 - 0.0029$$
$$= 0.5571 \text{ inch}$$

▼ SOLVED PROBLEM S6.2

Nocaf Drinks, Inc., a producer of decaffeinated coffee, bottles Nocaf in jugs for bulk distribution. Each jug should have a net weight of 4 kilograms. The machine that fills the jugs with coffee is new, and the operations manager wants to make sure that it is properly adjusted. Bonnie Crutcher, the operations manager, randomly selects and weighs $n = 8$ jugs and records the average and range in kilograms for each sample. The data for several samples are given in the following table. Note that every sample consists of eight jugs.

Sample	Sample Range	Sample Average	Sample	Sample Range	Sample Average
A	0.41	4.00	E	0.56	4.17
B	0.55	4.16	F	0.62	3.93
C	0.44	3.99	G	0.54	3.98
D	0.48	4.00	H	0.44	4.01

Is the machine properly adjusted and in control?

▼ SOLUTION

We first find that $\bar{\bar{x}} = 4.03$ and $\bar{R} = 0.505$. Then, using Table S6.1, we find:

$$\text{UCL}_x = \bar{\bar{x}} + A_2\bar{R} = 4.03 + (0.373)(0.505) = 4.22$$
$$\text{LCL}_x = \bar{\bar{x}} - A_2\bar{R} = 4.03 - (0.373)(0.505) = 3.84$$
$$\text{UCL}_R = D_4\bar{R} = (1.864)(0.505) = 0.94$$
$$\text{LCL}_R = D_3\bar{R} = (0.136)(0.505) = 0.07$$

It appears that the process average and range are both in statistical control.

The operations manager needs to determine if a process with a mean (4.03) slightly above the desired mean of 4.00 is satisfactory; if it is not, the process will need to be changed.

▼ SOLVED PROBLEM S6.3

Altman Distributors, Inc., fills catalogue orders. Samples of size $n = 100$ orders have been taken each day over the past six weeks. The average defect rate was 0.05. Determine the upper and lower limits for this process for 99.73% confidence.

▼ SOLUTION

$z = 3, \bar{p} = 0.05$. Using Equations (S6-9), (S6-10), and (S6-11),

$$\text{UCL}_p = \bar{p} + 3\sqrt{\frac{\bar{p}(1-\bar{p})}{n}} = 0.05 + 3\sqrt{\frac{(0.05)(1-0.05)}{100}}$$
$$= 0.05 + 3(0.0218) = 0.1154$$

$$\text{LCL}_p = \bar{p} - 3\sqrt{\frac{\bar{p}(1-\bar{p})}{n}} = 0.05 - 3(0.0218)$$
$$= 0.05 - 0.0654 = 0 \text{ (because percentage defective cannot be negative)}$$

▼ SOLVED PROBLEM S6.4

Ettlie Engineering has a new catalyst injection system for your countertop production line. Your process engineering department has conducted experiments and determined that the mean is 8.01 grams with a standard deviation of 0.03. Your specifications are: $\mu = 8.0$ and $\sigma = 0.04$, which means an upper specification limit of 8.12 [$= 8.0 + 3(0.04)$] and a lower specification limit of 7.88 [$= 8.0 - 3(0.04)$]. What is the C_{pk} performance of the injection system?

▼ SOLUTION

Using Equation (S6-14):

$$C_{pk} = \text{Minimum of} \left[\frac{\text{Upper specification limit} - \overline{X}}{3\sigma}, \frac{\overline{X} - \text{Lower specification limit}}{3\sigma} \right]$$

where $\overline{X}$ = process mean

σ = standard deviation of the process population

$$C_{pk} = \text{minimum of} \left[\frac{8.12 - 8.01}{(3)(0.03)}, \frac{8.01 - 7.88}{(3)(0.03)} \right]$$

$$\left[\frac{0.11}{0.09} = 1.22, \frac{0.13}{0.09} = 1.44 \right]$$

The minimum is 1.22, so the C_{pk} is within specifications and has an implied error rate of less than 2700 defects per million.

Problems*

• **S6.1** Boxes of Organic Flakes are produced to contain 14 grams, with a standard deviation of 0.1 gram. Set up the three-sigma $\bar{x}$-chart for a sample size of 36 boxes. **Px**

• **S6.2** The overall average on a process you are attempting to monitor is 50 units. The process standard deviation is 1.72. Determine the upper and lower control limits for a mean chart, if you choose to use a sample size of 5. **Px**
a) $z = 3$.
b) Now set $z = 2$. How do the control limits change?

• **S6.3** Thirty-five samples of size 7 each were taken from a fertilizer-bag-filling machine. The results were:
Overall mean = 57.75 kg; Average range = 1.78 kg.
a) Determine the upper and lower control limits of the $\bar{x}$-chart, where $\sigma = 3$.
b) Determine the upper and lower control limits of the R-chart, where $\sigma = 3$. **Px**

• **S6.4** Pioneer Chicken advertises "lite" chicken with 30% fewer calories than standard chicken. When the process for "lite" chicken breast production is in control, the average chicken breast contains 420 calories, and the standard deviation in caloric content of the chicken breast population is 25 calories.
   Pioneer wants to design an $\bar{x}$-chart to monitor the caloric content of chicken breasts, where 25 chicken breasts would be chosen at random to form each sample.
a) What are the lower and upper control limits for this chart if these limits are chosen to be *four* standard deviations from the target?
b) What are the limits with three standard deviations from the target? **Px**

• **S6.5** Cordelia Barrera is attempting to monitor a filling process that has an overall average of 705 cc. The average range is 6 cc. If you use a sample size of 10, what are the upper and lower control limits for the mean and range?

•• **S6.6** Sampling four pieces of precision-cut wire (to be used in computer assembly) every hour for the past 24 hours has produced the following results:

Hour	$\bar{x}$	R	Hour	$\bar{x}$	R
1	3.25 cm	0.71 cm	13	3.11 cm	0.85 cm
2	3.10	1.18	14	2.83	1.31
3	3.22	1.43	15	3.12	1.06
4	3.39	1.26	16	2.84	0.50
5	3.07	1.17	17	2.86	1.43
6	2.86	0.32	18	2.74	1.29
7	3.05	0.53	19	3.41	1.61
8	2.65	1.13	20	2.89	1.09
9	3.02	0.71	21	2.65	1.08
10	2.85	1.33	22	3.28	0.46
11	2.83	1.17	23	2.94	1.58
12	2.97	0.40	24	2.64	0.97

Develop appropriate control charts and determine whether there is any cause for concern in the cutting process. Plot the information and look for patterns. **Px**

•• **S6.7** Auto pistons at Yongpin Zhou's plant in Shanghai are produced in a forging process, and the diameter is a critical factor that must be controlled. From sample sizes of 10 pistons produced each day, the mean and the range of this diameter have been as follows:

Day	Mean (mm)	Range (mm)
1	156.9	4.2
2	153.2	4.6
3	153.6	4.1
4	155.5	5.0
5	156.6	4.5

a) What is the value of $\bar{\bar{x}}$?
b) What is the value of $\bar{R}$?

---

* *Note:* **Px** means the problem may be solved with POM for Windows and/or Excel OM/Excel.

c) What are the $UCL_{\bar{x}}$ and $LCL_{\bar{x}}$ using 3σ?

d) What are the UCL_R and LCL_R using 3σ?

e) If the true diameter mean should be 155 mm and you want this as your centre (nominal) line, what are the new $UCL_{\bar{x}}$ and $LCL_{\bar{x}}$? **PX**

•• **S6.8**   Bill Kime's bowling ball factory makes bowling balls of adult size and weight only. The standard deviation in the weight of a bowling ball produced at the factory is known to be 0.12 pounds. Each day for 24 days, the average weight, in pounds, of nine of the bowling balls produced that day has been assessed as follows:

Day	Average (lb)	Day	Average (lb)
1	16.3	13	16.3
2	15.9	14	15.9
3	15.8	15	16.3
4	15.5	16	16.2
5	16.3	17	16.1
6	16.2	18	15.9
7	16.0	19	16.2
8	16.1	20	15.9
9	15.9	21	15.9
10	16.2	22	16.0
11	15.9	23	15.5
12	15.9	24	15.8

a) Establish a control chart for monitoring the average weights of the bowling balls in which the upper and lower control limits are each two standard deviations from the mean. What are the values of the control limits?

b) If three standard deviations are used in the chart, how do these values change? Why? **PX**

•• **S6.9**   Whole Grains LLC uses statistical process control to ensure that its health-conscious, low-fat, multigrain sandwich loaves have the proper weight. Based on a previously stable and in-control process, the control limits of the $\bar{x}$- and R-charts are: $UCL_{\bar{x}} = 6.56$, $LCL_{\bar{x}} = 5.84$, $UCL_R = 1.141$, $LCL_R = 0$. Over the past few days, managers have taken five random samples of four loaves each and have found the following:

		Net Weight		
Sample	Loaf #1	Loaf #2	Loaf #3	Loaf #4
1	6.3	6.0	5.9	5.9
2	6.0	6.0	6.3	5.9
3	6.3	4.8	5.6	5.2
4	6.2	6.0	6.2	5.9
5	6.5	6.6	6.5	6.9

Is the process still in control? Explain why or why not. **PX**

••• **S6.10**   A process that is considered to be in control measures an ingredient in grams. Below are the last 10 samples (each of size $n = 5$) taken. The population standard deviation is 1.36.

				Samples					
1	2	3	4	5	6	7	8	9	10
10	9	13	10	12	10	10	13	8	10
9	9	9	10	10	10	11	10	8	12
10	11	10	11	9	8	10	8	12	9
9	11	10	10	11	12	8	10	12	8
12	10	9	10	10	9	9	8	9	12

a) What is the process standard deviation σ? What is $\sigma_{\bar{x}}$?

b) If $z = 3$, what are the control limits for the mean chart?

c) What are the control limits for the range chart?

d) Is the process in control? **PX**

••• **S6.11**   Twelve samples, each containing five parts, were taken from a process that produces steel rods. The length of each rod in the samples was determined. The results were tabulated and sample means and ranges were computed. The results were:

Sample	Sample Mean (cm)	Range (cm)
1	10.002	0.011
2	10.002	0.014
3	9.991	0.007
4	10.006	0.022
5	9.997	0.013
6	9.999	0.012
7	10.001	0.008
8	10.005	0.013
9	9.995	0.004
10	10.001	0.011
11	10.001	0.014
12	10.006	0.009

a) Determine the upper and lower control limits and the overall means for $\bar{x}$-charts and R-charts.

b) Draw the charts and plot the values of the sample means and ranges.

c) Do the data indicate a process that is in control?

d) Why or why not? **PX**

•• **S6.12**   Eagletrons are all-electric automobiles produced by Mogul Motors, Inc. One of the concerns of Mogul Motors is that the Eagletrons be capable of achieving appropriate maximum speeds. To monitor this, Mogul executives take samples of eight Eagletrons at a time. For each sample, they determine the average maximum speed and the range of the maximum speeds within the sample. They repeat this with 35 samples to obtain 35 sample means and 35 ranges. They find that the average sample mean is 88.50 kilometres per hour, and the average range is 3.25 kilometres per hour. Using these results, the executives decide to establish an R-chart. They would like this chart to be established so that when it shows that the range of a sample is not within the control limits, there is only approximately a 0.0027 probability that this is due to natural variation. What will be the upper control limit (UCL) and the lower control limit (LCL) in this chart? **PX**

•• **S6.13**   The defect rate for data entry of insurance claims has historically been about 1.5%.

a) What are the upper and lower control chart limits if you wish to use a sample size of 100 and three-sigma limits?

b) What if the sample size used were 50, with 3σ?

c) What if the sample size used were 100, with 2σ?

d) What if the sample size used were 50, with 2σ?

e) What happens to $\sigma_{\hat{p}}$ when the sample size is larger?

f) Explain why the lower control limit cannot be less than 0. **PX**

•• **S6.14**   You are attempting to develop a quality monitoring system for some parts purchased from Charles Sox Manufacturing Co. These parts are either good or defective. You have decided to take a sample of 100 units. Develop a table of the appropriate upper and lower control chart limits for various values of the average fraction defective in the samples taken. The values for $\bar{p}$ in this table should range from 0.02 to 0.10 in increments of 0.02. Develop the upper and lower control limits for a 99.73% confidence level.

$n = 100$		
$\bar{p}$	UCL	LCL
0.02		
0.04		
0.06		
0.08		
0.10		

•• **S6.15** The results of inspection of DNA samples taken over the past 10 days are given below. Sample size is 100.

Day	1	2	3	4	5	6	7	8	9	10
Defectives	7	6	6	9	5	6	0	8	9	1

a) Construct a three-sigma p-chart using this information.
b) If the number of defectives on the next three days are 12, 5, and 13, is the process in control? **Px**

• **S6.16** In the past, the defective rate for your product has been 1.5%. What are the upper and lower control chart limits if you wish to use a sample size of 500 and $z = 3$? **Px**

• **S6.17** Refer to Problem S6.16. If the defective rate was 3.5% instead of 1.5%, what would be the control limits ($z = 3$)? **Px**

•• **S6.18** Five data entry operators work at the data processing department of the Royal Bank. Each day for 30 days, the number of defective records in a sample of 250 records typed by these operators has been noted, as follows:

Sample No.	No. Defective	Sample No.	No. Defective	Sample No.	No. Defective
1	7	11	18	21	17
2	5	12	5	22	12
3	19	13	16	23	6
4	10	14	4	24	7
5	11	15	11	25	13
6	8	16	8	26	10
7	12	17	12	27	4
8	9	18	4	28	6
9	6	19	6	29	12
10	13	20	16	30	3

a) Establish 3σ upper and lower control limits.
b) Why can the lower control limit not be a negative number?
c) The industry standards for the upper and lower control limits are 0.10 and 0.01, respectively. What does this imply about Royal Bank's own standards? **Px**

•• **S6.19** Toronto General Hospital is trying to improve the patient experience by improving food services with tasty, inviting patient meals that are also healthful. A questionnaire accompanies each meal served, asking the patient, among other things, whether he or she is satisfied or unsatisfied with the meal. A 100-patient sample of the survey results over the past seven days yielded the following data:

Day	No. of Unsatisfied Patients	Sample Size
1	24	100
2	22	100
3	8	100
4	15	100
5	10	100
6	26	100
7	17	100

Construct a p-chart that plots the percentage of patients unsatisfied with their meals. Set the control limits to include 99.73% of the random variation in meal satisfaction. Comment on your results. **Px**

•• **S6.20** Winnipeg Office Supply Company manufactures paper clips and other office products. Although inexpensive, paper clips have provided the firm with a high margin of profitability. Sample size is 200. Results are given for the last 10 samples.

Sample	1	2	3	4	5	6	7	8	9	10
Defectives	5	7	4	4	6	3	5	6	2	8

a) Establish upper and lower control limits for the control chart and graph the data.
b) Is the process in control?
c) If the sample size were 100 instead, how would your limits and conclusions change? **Px**

• **S6.21** Peter Ittig's department store, Ittig Brothers, is Medicine Hat's largest independent clothier. The store receives an average of six returns per day. Using $z = 3$, would nine returns in a day warrant action? **Px**

•• **S6.22** An ad agency tracks the complaints, by week received, about the billboards in its city:

Week	No. of Complaints
1	4
2	5
3	4
4	11
5	3
6	9

a) What type of control chart would you use to monitor this process and why?
b) What are the three-sigma control limits for this process? Assume that the historical complaint rate is unknown.
c) Is the process mean in control, according to the control limits? Why or why not?
d) Assume now that the historical complaint rate has been four calls a week. What would the three-sigma control limits for this process be now? Is the process in control according to the control limits? **Px**

•• **S6.23** The school board is trying to evaluate a new math program introduced to second-graders in five elementary schools across the county this year. A sample of the student scores on standardized math tests in each elementary school yielded the following data:

School	No. of Test Errors
A	52
B	27
C	35
D	44
E	55

Construct a c-chart for test errors, and set the control limits to contain 99.73% of the random variation in test scores. What does the chart tell you? Has the new math program been effective? **PX**

•• **S6.24** Telephone inquiries of 100 CRA "customers" are monitored daily at random. Incidents of incorrect information or other nonconformities (such as impoliteness to customers) are recorded. The data for last week follow:

Day	No. of Nonconformities
1	5
2	10
3	23
4	20
5	15

a) Construct a 3-standard deviation c-chart of nonconformities.
b) What does the control chart tell you about the CRA telephone operators? **PX**

••• **S6.25** The accounts receivable department at Rick Wing Manufacturing has been having difficulty getting customers to pay the full amount of their bills. Many customers complain that the bills are not correct and do not reflect the materials that arrived at their receiving docks. The department has decided to implement SPC in its billing process. To set up control charts, 10 samples of 50 bills each were taken over a month's time and the items on the bills checked against the bill of lading sent by the company's shipping department to determine the number of bills that were not correct. The results were:

Sample No.	No. of Incorrect Bills	Sample No.	No. of Incorrect Bills
1	6	6	5
2	5	7	3
3	11	8	4
4	4	9	7
5	0	10	2

a) Determine the value of p-bar, the mean fraction defective. Then determine the control limits for the p-chart using a 99.73% confidence level (three standard deviations). Is this process in control? If not, which sample(s) was/were out of control?
b) How might you use the quality tools discussed in Chapter 6 to determine the source of the billing defects and where might you start your improvement efforts to eliminate the causes? **PX**

• **S6.26** The difference between the upper specification and the lower specification for a process is 0.6 cm. The standard deviation is 0.1 cm. What is the process capability ratio, C_p? Interpret this number. **PX**

•• **S6.27** Meena Chavan Corp.'s computer chip production process yields DRAM chips with an average life of 1800 hours and $\sigma = 100$ hours. The tolerance upper and lower specification limits are 2400 hours and 1600 hours, respectively. Is this process capable of producing DRAM chips to specification? **PX**

•• **S6.28** Blackburn, Inc., an equipment manufacturer, has submitted a sample cutoff valve to improve your manufacturing process. Your process engineering department has conducted experiments and found that the valve has a mean (μ) of 8.00 and a standard deviation (σ) of 0.04. Your desired performance is $\mu = 8.0$ and $\sigma = 0.045$. What is the C_{pk} of the Blackburn valve? **PX**

•• **S6.29** The specifications for a plastic liner for concrete highway projects call for a thickness of 3.0 mm ± 0.1 mm. The standard deviation of the process is estimated to be 0.02 mm. What are the upper and lower specification limits for this product? The process is known to operate at a mean thickness of 3.0 mm. What is the C_{pk} for this process? About what percentage of all units of this liner will meet specifications? **PX**

•• **S6.30** The manager of a food processing plant desires a quality specification with a mean of 16 grams, an upper specification limit of 16.5, and a lower specification limit of 15.5. The process has a mean of 16 grams and a standard deviation of 1 gram. Determine the C_{pk} of the process. **PX**

•• **S6.31** A process filling small bottles with baby formula has a target of 3 grams ± 0.150 gram. Two hundred bottles from the process were sampled. The results showed the average amount of formula placed in the bottles to be 3.042 grams. The standard deviation of the amounts was 0.034 gram. Determine the value of C_{pk}. Roughly what proportion of bottles meet the specifications? **PX**

••• **S6.32** As the supervisor in charge of shipping and receiving, you need to determine *the average outgoing quality* in a plant where the known incoming lots from your assembly line have an average defective rate of 3%. Your plan is to sample 80 units of every 1000 in a lot. The number of defects in the sample is not to exceed 3. Such a plan provides you with a probability of acceptance of each lot of 0.79 (79%). What is your average outgoing quality? **PX**

••• **S6.33** An acceptance sampling plan has lots of 500 pieces and a sample size of 60. The number of defects in the sample may not exceed 2. This plan, based on an OC curve, has a probability of 0.57 of accepting lots when the incoming lots have a defective rate of 4%, which is the historical average for this process. What do you tell your customer the average outgoing quality is? **PX**

••• **S6.34** West Battery Corp. has recently been receiving complaints from retailers that its 9-volt batteries are not lasting as long as other name brands. James West, head of the TQM program at West's Camrose plant, believes there is no problem because his batteries have had an average life of 50 hours, about 10% longer than competitors' models. To raise the lifetime above this level would require a new level of technology not available to West. Nevertheless, he is concerned enough to set up hourly assembly-line checks. Previously, after ensuring that the process was running properly, West took size $n = 5$ samples of 9-volt batteries for each of 25 hours to establish the standards for control chart limits. Those samples are shown in the following table:

West Battery Data—Battery Lifetimes (in hours)

Hour	1	2	3	4	5	$\bar{x}$	R
1	51	50	49	50	50	50.0	2
2	45	47	70	46	36	48.8	34
3	50	35	48	39	47	43.8	15
4	55	70	50	30	51	51.2	40
5	49	38	64	36	47	46.8	28
6	59	62	40	54	64	55.8	24
7	36	33	49	48	56	44.4	23
8	50	67	53	43	40	50.6	27
9	44	52	46	47	44	46.6	8
10	70	45	50	47	41	50.6	29
11	57	54	62	45	36	50.8	26
12	56	54	47	42	62	52.2	20
13	40	70	58	45	44	51.4	30
14	52	58	40	52	46	49.6	18
15	57	42	52	58	59	53.6	17
16	62	49	42	33	55	48.2	29
17	40	39	49	59	48	47.0	20
18	64	50	42	57	50	52.6	22
19	58	53	52	48	50	52.2	10
20	60	50	41	41	50	48.4	19
21	52	47	48	58	40	49.0	18
22	55	40	56	49	45	49.0	16
23	47	48	50	50	48	48.6	3
24	50	50	49	51	51	50.2	2
25	51	50	51	51	62	53.0	12

With these limits established, West now takes five more hours of data, which are shown in the following table:

	Sample				
Hour	1	2	3	4	5
26	48	52	39	57	61
27	45	53	48	46	66
28	63	49	50	45	53
29	57	70	45	52	61
30	45	38	46	54	52

a) Determine means and the upper and lower control limits for $\bar{x}$ and R (using the first 25 hours only).
b) Is the manufacturing process in control?
c) Comment on the lifetimes observed. **Px**

•••• **S6.35** One of Alberta Air's top competitive priorities is on-time arrivals. Quality VP Mike Hanna decided to personally monitor Alberta Air's performance. Each week for the past 30 weeks, Hanna checked a random sample of 100 flight arrivals for on-time performance. The table that follows contains the number of flights that did not meet Alberta Air's definition of "on time":

Sample (week)	Late Flights	Sample (week)	Late Flights
1	2	16	2
2	4	17	3
3	10	18	7
4	4	19	3
5	1	20	2
6	1	21	3
7	13	22	7
8	9	23	4
9	11	24	3
10	0	25	2
11	3	26	2
12	4	27	0
13	2	28	1
14	2	29	3
15	8	30	4

a) Using a 95% confidence level, plot the overall percentage of late flights ($\bar{p}$) and the upper and lower control limits on a control chart.
b) Assume that the airline industry's upper and lower control limits for flights that are not on time are 0.1000 and 0.0400, respectively. Draw them on your control chart.
c) Plot the percentage of late flights in each sample. Do all samples fall within Alberta Air's control limits? When one falls outside the control limits, what should be done?
d) What can Mike Hanna report about the quality of service? **Px**

CASE STUDIES

PEI Potato Purveyors

Throughout the year in 2018, Angus MacDonald had been receiving random complaints from various customers. Angus is the operations manager at PEI Potato Purveyors Inc. and the complaints he received surrounded the fact that the quantities of product delivered was inconsistently deviating from the amounts specified on the packaging. This would require Angus to fully investigate this matter.

Angus ordered the supervisors to undertake a random sample weight measurement of 50 containers, each of which historically held 50 kilograms of potatoes, with an acceptable standard deviation of 1.2 kilograms. Upon closer examination, Angus discovered that the potato containers in this random sample weighed on average 47.51 kilograms, well outside of the acceptable standard

Time	Average Weight Kilograms	Range Smallest	Range Largest	Time	Average Weight Kilograms	Range Smallest	Range Largest
6:00 a.m.	49.6	48.7	50.7	6:00	46.8	41.0	51.2
7:00	50.2	49.1	51.2	7:00	50.0	46.2	51.7
8:00	50.6	49.6	51.4	8:00	47.4	44.0	48.7
9:00	50.8	50.2	51.8	9:00	47.0	44.2	48.9
10:00	49.9	49.2	52.3	10:00	47.2	46.6	50.2
11:00	50.3	48.6	51.7	11:00	48.6	47.0	50.0
12 Noon	48.6	46.2	50.4	12 Midnight	49.8	48.2	50.4
1:00 p.m.	49.0	46.4	50.0	1:00 a.m.	49.6	48.4	51.7
2:00	49.0	46.0	50.6	2:00	50.0	49.0	52.2
3:00	49.8	48.2	50.8	3:00	50.0	49.2	50.0
4:00	50.3	49.2	52.7	4:00	47.2	46.3	50.5
5:00	51.4	50.0	55.3	5:00	47.0	44.1	49.7
6:00	51.6	49.2	54.7	6:00	48.4	45.0	49.0
7:00	51.8	50.0	55.6	7:00	48.8	44.8	49.7
8:00	51.0	48.6	53.2	8:00	49.6	48.0	51.8
9:00	50.5	49.4	52.4	9:00	50.0	48.1	52.7
10:00	49.2	46.1	50.7	10:00	51.0	48.1	55.2
11:00	49.0	46.3	50.8	11:00	50.4	49.5	54.1
12 Midnight	48.4	45.4	50.2	12 Noon	50.0	48.7	50.9
1:00 a.m.	47.6	44.3	49.7	1:00 p.m.	48.9	47.6	51.2
2:00	47.4	44.1	49.6	2:00	49.8	48.4	51.0
3:00	48.2	45.2	49.0	3:00	49.8	48.8	50.8
4:00	48.0	45.5	49.1	4:00	50.0	49.1	50.6
5:00	48.4	47.1	49.6	5:00	47.8	45.2	51.2
6:00	48.6	47.4	52.0	6:00	46.4	44.0	49.7
7:00	50.0	49.2	52.2	7:00	46.4	44.4	50.0
8:00	49.8	49.0	52.4	8:00	47.2	46.6	48.9
9:00	50.3	49.4	51.7	9:00	48.4	47.2	49.5
10:00	50.2	49.6	51.8	10:00	49.2	48.1	50.7
11:00	50.0	49.0	52.3	11:00	48.4	47.0	50.8
12 Noon	50.0	48.8	52.4	12 Midnight	47.2	46.4	49.2
1:00 p.m.	50.1	49.4	53.6	1:00 a.m.	47.4	46.8	49.0
2:00	49.7	48.6	51.0	2:00	48.8	47.2	51.4
3:00	48.4	47.2	51.7	3:00	49.6	49.0	50.6
4:00	47.2	45.3	50.9	4:00	51.0	50.5	51.5
5:00	46.8	44.1	49.0	5:00	50.5	50.0	51.9

deviation. Angus was deeply concerned for several reasons. Why did he receive only random and not consistent complaints? Did no one notice or was this an inconsistent problem? Why had the weight changed over the years while using the same container?

Further investigation informed Angus of several contributing factors. The PEI Potato Purveyors's typical customer would be a food processing company that makes large quantities of French fries, mashed potatoes, hash browns, etc. The container that is used is too heavy to lift and is normally loaded and unloaded by forklift, and in some cases the entire quantity is dumped into a processing machine. Some machines would process 50 kilograms

of potatoes at one time. If the input was short on quantity, so too would the output be, and this would be noticeable to the food processing firm. Angus discovered that the majority of complaints were generated by firms with this type of equipment, and he immediately ordered a credit for those that brought this situation to his attention.

But Angus still had to uncover the root cause and rectify it. What was different now than before that could affect the weight? It turned out that although they were using the same containers, they were using a different lid that dipped into the container somewhat. In order to fit the lid properly, employees would remove several potatoes from the container rather than push down and damage them. Also, it was discovered that they had a new supplier of potatoes added to their list, and this farm produced a new type of potato that was large and irregular in shape. This caused more air space in the container, thus less weight. Ultimately, a new container lid that resembled the original style would be required, and a new sorting mechanism for the large irregular shaped potatoes.

Angus wanted to determine if different shifts in the plant were dealing with these issues in a different way and arranged for six random weight measurements per hour to be taken throughout the day.

Discussion Questions

1. Comment on what you perceive as the contributing factors to the challenges with the weight of the containers.
2. What policies, procedures, and protocols would you implement to correct this quality issue?

Video Case Frito-Lay's Quality-Controlled Potato Chips

Frito-Lay, the multibillion-dollar snack food giant, produces billions of pounds of product every year at its dozens of U.S. and Canadian plants. From the farming of potatoes—in Florida, North Carolina, and Michigan—to factory and to retail stores, the ingredients and final product of Lay's chips, for example, are inspected at least 11 times: in the field, before unloading at the plant, after washing and peeling, at the sizing station, at the fryer, after seasoning, when bagged (for weight), at carton filling, in the warehouse, and as they are placed on the store shelf by Frito-Lay personnel. Similar inspections take place for its other famous products, including Cheetos, Fritos, Ruffles, and Tostitos.

In addition to these employee inspections, the firm uses proprietary vision systems to look for defective potato chips. Chips are pulled off the high-speed line and checked twice if the vision system senses them to be too brown.

The company follows the very strict standards of the American Institute of Baking (AIB), standards that are much tougher than those of the U.S. Food and Drug Administration. Two unannounced AIB site visits per year keep Frito-Lay's plants on their toes. Scores, consistently in the "excellent" range, are posted, and every employee knows exactly how the plant is doing.

There are two key metrics in Frito-Lay's continuous improvement quality program: (1) total customer complaints (measured on a complaints-per-million-bag basis) and (2) hourly or daily statistical process control scores (for oil, moisture, seasoning, and salt content, for chip thickness, for fryer temperature, and for weight).

In the Florida plant, Angela McCormack, who holds engineering and MBA degrees, oversees a 15-member quality assurance staff. They watch all aspects of quality, including training employees on the factory floor, monitoring automated processing equipment, and developing and updating statistical process control (SPC) charts. The upper and lower control limits for one checkpoint, salt content in Lay's chips, are 2.22% and 1.98%, respectively. To see exactly how these limits are created using SPC, watch the video that accompanies this case.

Discussion Questions*

1. Angela is now going to evaluate a new salt process delivery system and wants to know if the upper and lower control limits at 3 standard deviations for the new system will meet the upper and lower control specifications noted above.
   The data (in percents) from the initial trial samples are:
   Sample 1: 1.98, 2.11, 2.15, 2.06
   Sample 2: 1.99, 2.0, 2.08, 1.99
   Sample 3: 2.20, 2.10. 2.20, 2.05
   Sample 4: 2.18, 2.01, 2.23, 1.98
   Sample 5: 2.01, 2.08, 2.14, 2.16
   Provide the report to Angela.
2. What are the advantage and disadvantages of Frito-Lay drivers stocking their customers' shelves?
3. Why is quality a critical function at Frito-Lay?

---

* You may wish to view the video that accompanies this case before answering these questions.

Sources: Professors Barry Render, Rollins College; Jay Heizer, Texas Lutheran University; and Beverly Amer, Northern Arizona University.

Video Case Farm to Fork: Quality at Darden Restaurants

Darden Restaurants—the $5.2 billion owner of such popular brands as Olive Garden, Red Lobster, Seasons 52, and Bahama Breeze—serves more than 300 million meals annually in its 1700 restaurants across the United States and Canada. Before any one of these meals is placed before a guest, the ingredients for each recipe must pass quality control inspections from the source, ranging from measurement and weighing, to tasting, touching, or lab testing. Darden has differentiated itself from its restaurant peers by developing the gold standard in continuous improvement.

To assure both customers and the company that quality expectations are met, Darden uses a rigorous inspection process, employing statistical process control (SPC) as part of its "Farm to Fork" program.

More than 50 food scientists, microbiologists, and public health professionals report to Ana Hooper, vice-president of quality assurance.

As part of Darden's Point Source program, Hooper's team, based in Southeast Asia (in China, Thailand, and Singapore) and Latin America (in Ecuador, Honduras, and Chile), approves and inspects—and works with Darden buyers to purchase—more than 50 million pounds of seafood each year for restaurant use. Darden used to build quality in at the end by inspecting shipments as they reached U.S. distribution centres. Now, thanks to coaching and partnering with vendors abroad, Darden needs but a few domestic inspection labs to verify compliance to its exacting standards. Food vendors in source countries know that when supplying Darden, they are subject to regular audits that are stricter than U.S. Food and Drug Administration (FDA) standards.

Two Quality Success Stories

Quality specialists' jobs include raising the bar and improving quality and safety at all plants in their geographic area. The Thai quality representative, for example, worked closely with several of Darden's largest shrimp vendors to convert them to a production-line-integrated quality assurance program. The vendors were able to improve the quality of shrimp supplied and reduce the percentage of defects by 19%.

Likewise, when the Darden quality teams visited fields of growers/shippers in Mexico recently, they identified challenges such as low employee hygiene standards, field food safety problems, lack of portable toilets, child labour, and poor working conditions. Darden addressed these concerns and hired third party independent food safety verification firms to ensure continued compliance to standards.

SPC Charts

SPC charts are particularly important. These charts document pre-cooked food weights; meat, seafood, and poultry temperatures; blemishes on produce; and bacteria counts on shrimp—just to name a few. Quality assurance is part of a much bigger process that is key to Darden's success—its supply chain (see Chapter 11 and Supplement 11 for discussion and case studies on this topic). That's because quality comes from the source and flows through distribution to the restaurant and guests.

Discussion Questions*

1. How does Darden build quality into the supply chain?
2. Select two potential problems—one in the Darden supply chain and one in a restaurant—that can be analyzed with a fish-bone chart. Draw a complete chart to deal with each problem.
3. Darden applies SPC in many product attributes. Identify where these are probably used.
4. The SPC chart shown earlier in this chapter illustrates Darden's use of control charts to monitor the weight of salmon fillets. Given these data, what conclusion do you draw, as a Darden quality control inspector? What report do you issue to your supervisor? How do you respond to the salmon vendor?

---

* You might want to view the video that accompanies this case before answering these questions.

▶**Additional Case Study:** Visit **MyLab Operations Management** for this case study: **Green River Chemical Company:** Involves a company that needs to set up a control chart to monitor sulphate content because of customer complaints.

SUPPLEMENT 6 | RAPID REVIEW

MyLab Operations Management

Main Heading	Review Material	
STATISTICAL PROCESS CONTROL (SPC) (pp. 233–246)	• **Statistical process control (SPC)**—A process used to monitor standards by taking measurements and corrective action as a product or service is being produced. • **Control chart**—A graphical presentation of process data over time. A process is said to be operating *in statistical control* when the only source of variation is common (natural) causes. The process must first be brought into statistical control by detecting and eliminating special (assignable) causes of variation. *The objective of a process control system is to provide a statistical signal when assignable causes of variation are present.* • **Natural variation**—Variability that affects every production process to some degree and is to be expected; also known as *common cause*. When natural variations form a *normal distribution*, they are characterized by two parameters: • Mean, μ (the measure of central tendency—in this case, the average value) • Standard deviation, σ (the measure of dispersion) As long as the distribution (output measurements) remains within specified limits, the process is said to be "in control," and natural variations are tolerated. • **Assignable variation**—Variation in a production process that can be traced to specific causes. Control charts for the mean, $\bar{x}$, and the range, R, are used to monitor *variables* (outputs with continuous dimensions), such as weight, speed, length, or strength.	Problems: S6.1–S6.25, S6.34

Main Heading	Review Material	

- $\bar{x}$**-chart**—A quality control chart for variables that indicates when changes occur in the central tendency of a production process.
- R**-chart**—A control chart that tracks the range within a sample; it indicates that a gain or loss in uniformity has occurred in dispersion of a production process.
- **Central limit theorem**—The theoretical foundation for $\bar{x}$-charts, which states that regardless of the distribution of the population of all parts or services, the $\bar{x}$ distribution tends to follow a normal curve as the number of samples increases.

$$\bar{\bar{x}} = \mu \tag{S6-1}$$

$$\sigma_{\bar{x}} = \frac{\sigma}{\sqrt{n}} \tag{S6-2}$$

The $\bar{x}$-chart limits, if we know the true standard deviation σ of the process population, are:

$$\text{Upper control limit (UCL)} = \bar{\bar{x}} + z\sigma_{\bar{x}} \tag{S6-3}$$
$$\text{Lower control limit (LCL)} = \bar{\bar{x}} + z\sigma_{\bar{x}} \tag{S6-4}$$

where z = the confidence level selected (e.g., $z = 3$ is 99.73% confidence)

The *range*, R, of a sample is defined as the difference between the largest and smallest items. If we do not know the true standard deviation, σ, of the population, the $\bar{x}$-chart limits are:

$$\text{UCL}_{\bar{x}} = \bar{\bar{x}} + A_2\bar{R} \tag{S6-5}$$
$$\text{LCL}_{\bar{x}} = \bar{\bar{x}} - A_2\bar{R} \tag{S6-6}$$

In addition to being concerned with the process average, operations managers are interested in the process dispersion, or range. The R-chart control limits for the range of a process are:

$$\text{UCL}_R = D_4\bar{R} \tag{S6-7}$$
$$\text{LCL}_R = D_3\bar{R} \tag{S6-8}$$

Attributes are typically classified as *defective* or *nondefective*. The two attribute charts are (1) *p*-charts (which measure the *percent* defective in a sample), and (2) *c*-charts (which *count* the number of defects in a sample).

- *p*-**chart**—A quality control chart that is used to control attributes.

$$\text{UCL}_p = \bar{p} + z\sigma_{\hat{p}} \tag{S6-9}$$
$$\text{LCL}_p = \bar{p} + z\sigma_{\hat{p}} \tag{S6-10}$$

$$\sigma_{\hat{p}} = \sqrt{\frac{\bar{p}(1 - \bar{p})}{n}} \tag{S6-11}$$

- *c*-**chart**—A quality control chart used to control the number of defects per unit of output. The Poisson distribution is the basis for *c*-charts, whose 99.73% limits are computed as:

$$\text{Control limits} = \bar{c} \pm 3\sqrt{\bar{c}} \tag{S6-12}$$

- **Run test**—A test used to examine the points in a control chart to see if nonrandom variation is present.

PROCESS CAPABILITY
(pp. 246–248)

- **Process capability**—The ability to meet design specifications.
- C_p—A ratio for determining whether a process meets design specifications; a ratio of the specification to the process variation.

$$C_p = \frac{(\text{Upper specification} - \text{Lower specification})}{6\sigma} \tag{S6-13}$$

- C_{pk}—A proportion of variation (3σ) between the centre of the process and the nearest specification limit:

$$C_{pk} = \text{Minimum of} \left[\frac{\text{Upper spec limit} - \bar{X}}{3\sigma}, \frac{\bar{X} - \text{Lower spec limit}}{3\sigma} \right]$$
$$\tag{S6-14}$$

VIDEO S6.1

Farm to Fork: Quality at Darden Restaurants

VIDEO S6.2

Frito-Lay's Quality-Controlled Potato Chips

Virtual Office Hours for Solved Problems: S6.3

ACTIVE MODEL S6.1

ACTIVE MODEL S6.2

Problems: S6.26–S6.31

Virtual Office Hours for Solved Problem: S6.4

ACTIVE MODEL S6.3

MyLab Operations Management

Main Heading	Review Material	
ACCEPTANCE SAMPLING (pp. 248–251)	• **Acceptance sampling**—A method of measuring random samples of lots or batches of products against predetermined standards.	Problems: S6.32, S6.33
	• **Operating characteristic (OC) curve**—A graph that describes how well an acceptance plan discriminates between good and bad lots.	
	• **Producer's risk**—The mistake of having a producer's good lot rejected through sampling.	
	• **Consumer's risk**—The mistake of a customer's acceptance of a bad lot overlooked through sampling.	**ACTIVE** MODEL S6.4
	• **Acceptable quality level (AQL)**—The quality level of a lot considered good.	
	• **Lot tolerance percent defective (LTPD)**—The quality level of a lot considered bad.	
	• **Type I error**—Statistically, the probability of rejecting a good lot.	
	• **Type II error**—Statistically, the probability of accepting a bad lot.	
	• **Average outgoing quality (AOQ)**—The percentage defective in an average lot of goods inspected through acceptance sampling:	

$$\text{AOQ} = \frac{(P_d)(P_a)(N - n)}{N} \qquad \text{(S6-15)}$$

Self-Test

■ **Before taking the self-test,** refer to the learning objectives listed at the beginning of the supplement and the key terms listed at the end of the supplement.

LO1 If the mean of a particular sample is within control limits and the range of that sample is not within control limits:
a) the process is in control, with only assignable causes of variation.
b) the process is not producing within the established control limits.
c) the process is producing within the established control limits, with only natural causes of variation.
d) the process has both natural and assignable causes of variation.

LO2 The central limit theorem:
a) is the theoretical foundation of the c-chart.
b) states that the average of assignable variations is zero.
c) allows managers to use the normal distribution as the basis for building some control charts.
d) states that the average range can be used as a proxy for the standard deviation.
e) controls the steepness of an operating characteristic curve.

LO3 The type of chart used to control the central tendency of variables with continuous dimensions is:
a) $\bar{x}$-chart.   b) *R*-chart.   c) *p*-chart.
d) *c*-chart.   e) none of the above.

LO4 If parts in a sample are measured and the mean of the sample measurement is outside the tolerance limits:
a) the process is out of control, and the cause should be established.
b) the process is in control but not capable of producing within the established control limits.

c) the process is within the established control limits, with only natural causes of variation.
d) all of the above are true.

LO5 Control charts for attributes are:
a) *p*-charts.   b) *c*-charts.   c) *R*-charts.
d) $\bar{x}$-charts.   e) both a and b.

LO6 The ability of a process to meet design specifications is called:
a) Taguchi.
b) process capability.
c) capability index.
d) acceptance sampling.
e) average outgoing quality.

LO7 The ____ risk is the probability that a lot will be rejected despite the quality level exceeding or meeting the ____.

LO8 In most acceptance sampling plans, when a lot is rejected, the entire lot is inspected, and all defective items are replaced. When using this technique, the AOQ:
a) worsens (AOQ becomes a larger fraction).
b) improves (AOQ becomes a smaller fraction).
c) is not affected, but the AQL is improved.
d) is not affected.
e) falls to zero.

Answers: LO1. b; LO2. c; LO3. a; LO4. a; LO5. e; LO6. b; LO7. producer's risk, AQL; LO8. b.

MyLab Operations Management

Most of these questions can be found in MyLab Operations Management. Visit MyLab Operations Management to access cases, videos, downloadable software, and much more. MyLab Operations Management Management also features a personalized Study Plan that helps you identify which chapter concepts you've mastered and guides you towards study tools for additional practice.

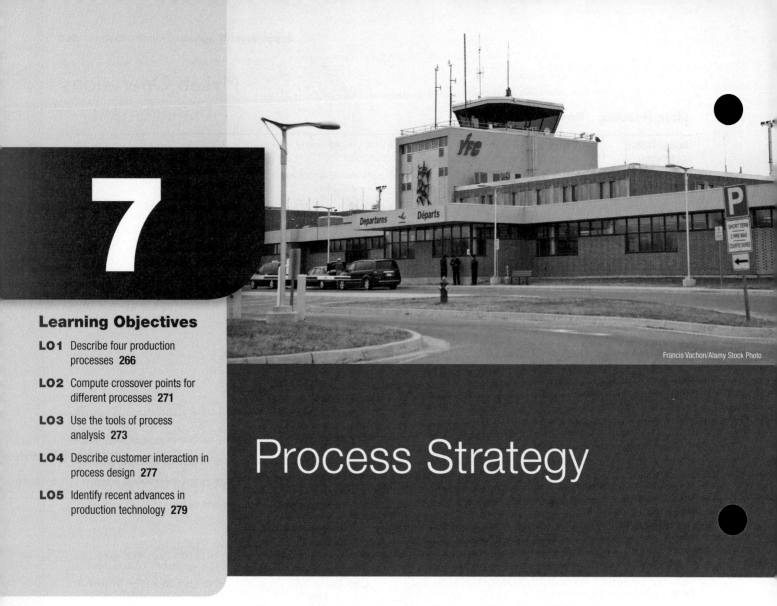
Francis Vachon/Alamy Stock Photo

7

Learning Objectives

LO1 Describe four production processes **266**

LO2 Compute crossover points for different processes **271**

LO3 Use the tools of process analysis **273**

LO4 Describe customer interaction in process design **277**

LO5 Identify recent advances in production technology **279**

Process Strategy

Global > Company Profile Harley-Davidson

Repetitive Manufacturing Works at Harley-Davidson

Since Harley-Davidson's founding in Milwaukee in 1903, it has competed with hundreds of manufacturers, foreign and domestic. The competition has been tough. Recent competitive battles have been with the Japanese, and earlier battles were with the German, English, and Italian manufacturers. But after over 100 years, Harley is the only major U.S. motorcycle company. The company now has five U.S. facilities and an assembly plant in Brazil. The Sportster Powertrain is manufactured in Wauwatosa, Wisconsin, and the sidecars, saddlebags, windshields, and other specialty items are produced in Tomahawk, Wisconsin. The families of Touring and Softail bikes are assembled in York, Pennsylvania, while the Sportster models, Dyna models, and VRSC models of motorcycles are produced in Kansas City, Missouri. The brand remains a sentimental favourite among Canadian motorcycle enthusiasts, and there are many Harley dealers coast to coast in Canada to meet the ongoing demand.

As a part of management's lean manufacturing effort, Harley groups together production of parts that require similar processes. The result is work cells. Using the latest technology, work cells perform in one location all the operations necessary for production of a specific module. Raw materials are moved to the work cells and then the modules proceed to the assembly line. As a double check on quality, Harley has also installed "light curtain" technology that uses an infrared sensor to verify the bin from which an operator is taking parts. Materials go to the assembly line on a just-in-time basis or, as Harley calls it, using a *materials as needed* (MAN) system.

The 12.5-million-square-foot York facility includes manufacturing cells that perform tube bending, frame building, machining, painting, and polishing. Innovative manufacturing techniques use robots to load machines and highly automated production to reduce machining time. Automation and precision sensors play a key role in maintaining tolerances and producing a quality product. Each day, the York facility produces up to 600 heavy-duty factory-custom

For manufacturers like Harley-Davidson, which produces a large number of end products from a relatively small number of options, modular bills of material provide an effective solution.

motorcycles. Bikes are assembled with different engine displacements, multiple wheel options, colours, and accessories. The result is a huge number of variations in the motorcycles available, which allows customers to individualize their purchase. The Harley-Davidson production system works because high-quality modules are brought together on a tightly scheduled repetitive production.

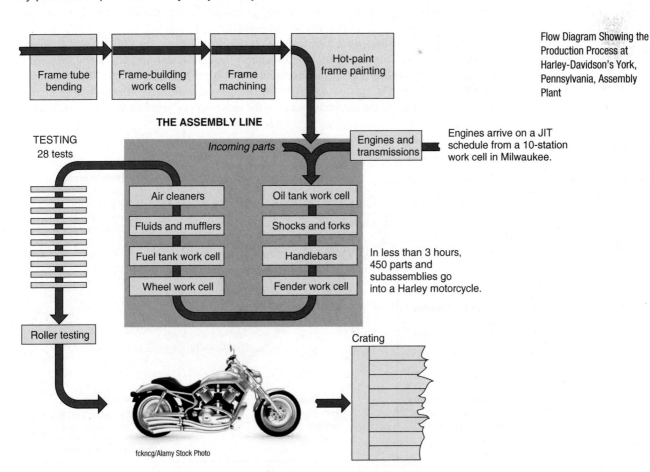

Flow Diagram Showing the Production Process at Harley-Davidson's York, Pennsylvania, Assembly Plant

Frame tube bending → Frame-building work cells → Frame machining → Hot-paint frame painting

THE ASSEMBLY LINE

TESTING 28 tests

Incoming parts

Engines and transmissions — Engines arrive on a JIT schedule from a 10-station work cell in Milwaukee.

Air cleaners · Oil tank work cell
Fluids and mufflers · Shocks and forks
Fuel tank work cell · Handlebars
Wheel work cell · Fender work cell

In less than 3 hours, 450 parts and subassemblies go into a Harley motorcycle.

Roller testing

Crating

fckncg/Alamy Stock Photo

Process (or transformation) strategy

An organization's approach to transforming resources into goods and services.

LO1 Describe four production processes

Process focus

A production facility organized around processes to facilitate low-volume, high-variety production.

Four Process Strategies

When offering goods and services, we must consider the need for their selection, definition, and design. Our purpose may be to create environmentally friendly designs that could be delivered in an ethical, sustainable manner. We now turn to their production. A major decision for an operations manager is finding the best way to produce so as not to waste our planet's resources. Let's look at ways to help managers design a process for achieving this goal.

A **process (or transformation) strategy** is an organization's approach to transforming resources into goods and services. *The objective of a process strategy is to build a production process that meets customer requirements and product specifications within cost and other managerial constraints.* The process selected will have a long-term effect on efficiency and flexibility of production, as well as on cost and quality of the goods produced. Therefore, the limitations of a firm's operations strategy are determined at the time of the process decision.

Virtually every good or service is made by using some variation of one of four process strategies: (1) process focus, (2) repetitive focus, (3) product focus, and (4) mass customization. The relationship of these four strategies to volume and variety is shown in Figure 7.1. We examine *Arnold Palmer Hospital* as an example of a process-focused firm, *Harley-Davidson* as a repetitive producer, *Frito-Lay* as a product-focused operation, and *Dell* as a mass customizer.

PROCESS FOCUS

The vast majority of global production is devoted to making *low-volume, high-variety* products in places called *job shops*. Such facilities are organized around specific activities or processes. In a factory, these processes might be departments devoted to welding, grinding, and painting. In an office, the processes might be accounts payable, sales, and payroll. In a restaurant, they might be bar, grill, and bakery. Such facilities have a **process focus** in terms of equipment, layout, and supervision. They provide a high degree of product flexibility as products move between processes. Each process is designed to perform a wide variety of activities and handle frequent changes. Consequently, they are also called *intermittent processes*.

Referring to Figure 7.2(a), imagine a diverse group of patients entering Arnold Palmer Hospital, a process-focused facility, to be routed to specialized departments, treated in a distinct way, and then exiting as uniquely cared for individuals.

Process-focused facilities have high variable costs with extremely low utilization of facilities, as low as 5%. This is the case for many restaurants, hospitals, and machine shops. However, some facilities that lend themselves to electronic controls do somewhat better. With computer-controlled machines, it is possible to program machine tools, piece movement, tool changing, placement of the parts on the machine, and even the movement of materials between machines.

FIGURE 7.1

Process Selected Must Fit With Volume and Variety

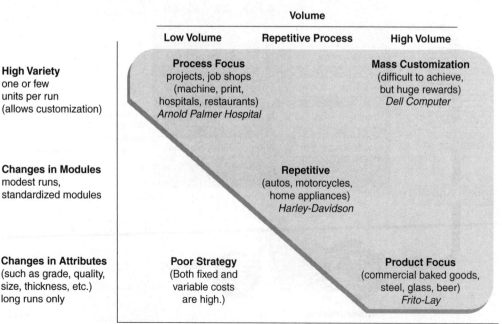

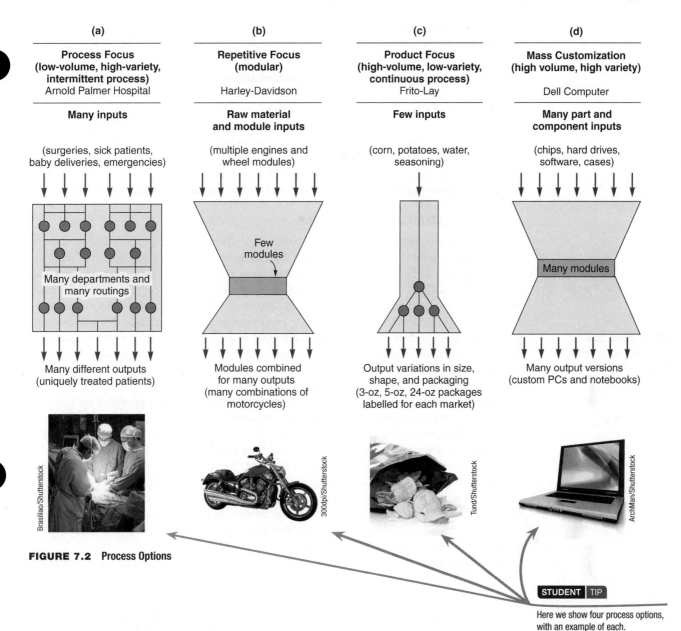

(a)	(b)	(c)	(d)

FIGURE 7.2 Process Options

REPETITIVE FOCUS

A repetitive process falls between the product and process focuses seen in Figures 7.1 and 7.2(b). Repetitive processes, as we saw in the *Global Company Profile* on Harley-Davidson, use modules. Modules are parts or components previously prepared, often in a continuous process.

The **repetitive process** is the classic assembly line. Widely used in the assembly of virtually all automobiles and household appliances, it has more structure and consequently less flexibility than a process-focused facility.

Fast-food firms are another example of a repetitive process using **modules**. This type of production allows more customizing than a product-focused facility; modules (e.g., meat, cheese, sauce, tomatoes, onions) are assembled to get a quasi-custom product, a cheeseburger. In this manner, the firm obtains both the economic advantages of the continuous model (where many of the modules are prepared) and the custom advantage of the low-volume, high-variety model.

Repetitive process

A product-oriented production process that uses modules.

Modules

Parts or components of a product previously prepared, often in a continuous process.

PRODUCT FOCUS

High-volume, low-variety processes have a **product focus**. The facilities are organized around *products*. They are also called *continuous processes*, because they have very long, continuous production runs. Products such as glass, paper, tin sheets, light bulbs, beer, and potato chips are made via a continuous process. Some products, such as light bulbs, are discrete; others, such as

Product focus

A facility organized around products; a product-oriented, high-volume, low-variety process.

rolls of paper, are nondiscrete. Still others, such as repaired hernias at Shouldice Hospital, are services. It is only with standardization and effective quality control that firms have established product-focused facilities. An organization producing the same light bulb or hot dog bun day after day can organize around a product. Such an organization has an inherent ability to set standards and maintain a given quality, as opposed to an organization that is producing unique products every day, such as a print shop or general-purpose hospital. For example, Frito-Lay's family of products is also produced in a product-focused facility (see Figure 7.2[c]). At Frito-Lay, corn, potatoes, water, and seasoning are the relatively few inputs, but outputs (like Cheetos, Ruffles, Tostitos, and Fritos) vary in seasoning and packaging within the product family.

A product-focused facility produces high volume and low variety. The specialized nature of the facility requires high fixed cost, but low variable costs reward high facility utilization.

MASS CUSTOMIZATION FOCUS

Our increasingly wealthy and sophisticated world demands individualized goods and services. A peek at the rich variety of goods and services that operations managers are called on to supply is shown in Table 7.1. The explosion of variety has taken place in automobiles, movies, breakfast cereals, and thousands of other areas. In spite of this proliferation of products, operations managers have improved product quality while reducing costs. Consequently, the variety of products continues to grow. Operations managers use *mass customization* to produce this vast array of goods and services. **Mass customization** is the rapid, low-cost production of goods and services that fulfill increasingly unique customer desires. But mass customization (see the upper right section of Figure 7.1) is not just about variety; it is about making precisely *what* the customer wants *when* the customer wants it economically.

Mass customization

Rapid, low-cost production that caters to constantly changing unique customer desires.

Mass customization brings us the variety of products traditionally provided by low-volume manufacture (a process focus) at the cost of standardized high-volume (product-focused) production. However, achieving mass customization is a challenge that requires sophisticated operational capabilities. Building agile processes that rapidly and inexpensively produce custom products requires imaginative and aggressive use of organizational resources. And the link between sales, design, production, supply chain, and logistics must be tight.

Dell Computer (see Figure 7.2[d]) has demonstrated that the payoff for mass customization can be substantial. More traditional manufacturers include Toyota, which recently announced delivery of custom-ordered cars in five days. Similarly, electronic controls allow designers in the textile industry to rapidly revamp their lines and respond to changes.

The service industry is also moving towards mass customization. For instance, not very many years ago, most people had the same telephone service. Now, not only is the phone service full

Table 7.1

Mass Customization Provides More Choices Than Ever

Sources: Various; however, many of the data are from the Federal Reserve Bank of Dallas.

Item	Number of Choices[a]	
	1970s	**21st Century**
Vehicle models	140	286
Vehicle styles	18	1 212
Bicycle types	8	211 000[c]
Software titles	0	400 000
Websites	0	634,000,000[d]
Movie releases per year	267	765[e]
New book titles	40 530	300 000+
Typical local TV channels	5	185
Breakfast cereals	160	340
Items (SKUs) in supermarkets	14 000[b]	150 000[f]
LCD TVs	0	102

[a]Variety available in the United States; worldwide, the variety increases even more.
[b]1989.
[c]Possible combinations for one manufacturer.
[d]Royal Pingdom Estimate (2008).
[e]www.movieweb.com (2009).
[f]SKUs managed by H. E. Butts grocery chain.

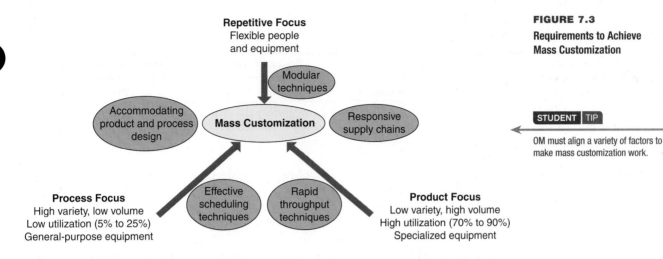

FIGURE 7.3
Requirements to Achieve Mass Customization

STUDENT TIP

OM must align a variety of factors to make mass customization work.

of options, from caller ID to voice mail, but contemporary phones are hardly phones. They may also be part camera, computer, game player, GPS, and web browser. Insurance companies are adding and tailoring new products with shortened development times to meet the unique needs of their customers. And firms like iTunes and emusic maintain a music inventory on the internet that allows customers to select a dozen songs of their choosing and have them made into a custom CD. Similarly, the number of new books and movies increases each year. Mass customization places new demands on operations managers who must build the processes that provide this expanding variety of goods and services.

One of the essential ingredients in mass customization is a reliance on modular design. However, as Figure 7.3 shows, very effective scheduling, personnel and facility flexibility, supportive supply chains, and rapid throughput are also required. These items influence all 10 of the OM decisions and therefore require excellent operations management.

MAKING MASS CUSTOMIZATION WORK Mass customization suggests a high-volume system in which products are built-to-order.[1] **Build-to-order (BTO)** means producing to customer orders, not forecasts. Build-to-order can be a successful order-winning strategy when executed successfully. But high-volume build-to-order is difficult. Some major challenges are:

Build-to-order (BTO)
Produce to customer order rather than to a forecast.

- Product design must be imaginative and fast. Successful build-to-order designs often use modules. Ping Inc., the premier golf club manufacturer, uses different combinations of club heads, grips, shafts, and angles to make 20 000 variations of its golf clubs.
- Process design must be flexible and able to accommodate changes in both design and technology. For instance, **postponement** allows for customization late in the production process. Toyota installs unique interior modules very late in production for certain models, a process also typical with customized vans. Postponement is further discussed in Chapter 11.
- Inventory management requires tight control. To be successful with build-to-order, a firm must avoid being stuck with unpopular or obsolete components. With virtually no raw material, Dell puts custom computers together in less than a day.
- Tight schedules that track orders and material from design through delivery are another requirement of mass customization. Align Technology, a well-known name in orthodontics, figured out how to achieve competitive advantage by delivering custom-made clear plastic aligners within three weeks of your first visit to the dentist's office.
- Responsive partners in the supply chain can yield effective collaboration. Forecasting, inventory management, and ordering for many Loblaw products are all handled for the retailer by its various suppliers that can be in distant locations.

Postponement
The delay of any modifications or customization to a product as long as possible in the production process.

Mass customization/build-to-order is difficult, but it is the new imperative for operations. There are advantages to mass customization and building to order: First, by meeting the demands

---

[1] Build-to-order (BTO) may be referred to and refined as engineer-to-order (ETO) and design-to-order (DTO), depending on the extent of the customization.

Table 7.2

Comparison of the Characteristics of Four Types of Processes

Process Focus (low volume, high variety) (e.g., Arnold Palmer Hospital)	Repetitive Focus (modular) (e.g., Harley-Davidson)	Product Focus (high volume, low variety) (e.g., Frito-Lay)	Mass Customization (high volume, high variety) (e.g., Dell Computer)
1. Small quantity and large variety of products are produced.	1. Long runs, usually a standardized product with options, are produced from modules.	1. Large quantity and small variety of products are produced.	1. Large quantity and large variety of products are produced.
2. Equipment used is general purpose.	2. Special equipment aids in use of an assembly line.	2. Equipment used is special purpose.	2. Rapid changeover on flexible equipment.
3. Operators are broadly skilled.	3. Employees are modestly trained.	3. Operators are less broadly skilled.	3. Flexible operators are trained for the necessary customization.
4. There are many job instructions because each job changes.	4. Repetitive operations reduce training and changes in job instructions.	4. Work orders and job instructions are few because they are standardized.	4. Custom orders require many job instructions.
5. Raw material inventories are high relative to the value of the product.	5. Just-in-time procurement techniques are used.	5. Raw material inventories are low relative to the value of the product.	5. Raw material inventories are low relative to the value of the product.
6. Work-in-process is high compared to output.	6. Just-in-time inventory techniques are used.	6. Work-in-process inventory is low compared to output.	6. Work-in-process inventory is driven down by JIT, kanban, lean production.
7. Units move slowly through the facility.	7. Assembly is measured in hours and days.	7. Swift movement of units through the facility is typical.	7. Goods move swiftly through the facility.
8. Finished goods are usually made to order and not stored.	8. Finished goods are made to frequent forecasts.	8. Finished goods are usually made to a forecast and stored.	8. Finished goods are often build-to-order (BTO).
9. Scheduling is complex and concerned with the trade-off between inventory availability, capacity, and customer service.	9. Scheduling is based on building various models from a variety of modules to forecasts.	9. Scheduling is relatively simple and concerned with establishing a rate of output sufficient to meet sales forecasts.	9. Sophisticated scheduling is required to accommodate custom orders.
10. Fixed costs tend to be low and variable costs high.	10. Fixed costs are dependent on flexibility of the facility.	10. Fixed costs tend to be high and variable costs low.	10. Fixed costs tend to be high, but variable costs must be low.

of the marketplace, firms win orders and stay in business; in addition, they trim costs (from personnel to inventory to facilities) that exist because of inaccurate sales forecasting.

COMPARISON OF PROCESS CHOICES

The characteristics of the four processes are shown in Table 7.2 and Figure 7.2. Advantages exist across the continuum of processes, and firms may find strategic advantage in any process. Each of the processes, when properly matched to volume and variety, can produce a low-cost advantage. For instance, unit costs will be less in the continuous-process case when high volume (and high utilization) exists. However, we do not always use the continuous process (i.e., specialized equipment and facilities) because it is too expensive when volumes are low or flexibility is required. A low-volume, unique, highly differentiated good or service is more economical when produced under process focus; this is the way fine-dining restaurants and general-purpose hospitals are organized. Just as all four processes, when appropriately selected and well managed, can yield low cost, so too can all four be responsive and produce differentiated products.

Figure 7.3 indicates that equipment utilization in a process-focused facility is often in the range of 5% to 25%. When utilization goes above 15%, moving towards a repetitive or product focus, or even mass customization, may be advantageous. A cost advantage usually exists by improving utilization, provided the necessary flexibility is maintained. McDonald's started an entirely new industry by moving its limited menu from process focus to repetitive focus. McDonald's is now trying to add more variety and move towards mass customization.

Much of what is produced in the world is still produced in very small lots—often as small as one. This is true for most legal services, medical services, dental services, and restaurants. An X-ray machine in a dentist's office and much of the equipment in a fine-dining restaurant have low utilization. Hospitals, too, have low utilization, which suggests why their costs are considered high. Why is utilization low? In part it is low because excess capacity for peak loads is desirable. Hospital administrators, as well as managers of other service facilities and their patients and customers, expect equipment to be available as needed. Another reason is poor scheduling (although substantial efforts have been made to forecast demand in the service industry) and the resulting imbalance in the use of facilities.

CROSSOVER CHARTS The comparison of processes can be further enhanced by looking at the point where the total cost of the processes changes. For instance, Figure 7.4 shows three alternative processes compared on a single chart. Such a chart is sometimes called a **crossover chart**. Process A has the lowest cost for volumes below V_1, process B has the lowest cost between V_1 and V_2, and process C has the lowest cost at volumes above V_2.

Example 1 illustrates how to determine the exact volume where one process becomes more expensive than another.

Crossover chart
A chart of costs at the possible volumes for more than one process.

LO2 Compute crossover points for different processes

Kleber Enterprises would like to evaluate three accounting software products (A, B, and C) to support changes in its internal accounting processes. The resulting processes will have cost structures similar to those shown in Figure 7.4. The costs of the software for these processes are:

EXAMPLE 1

Crossover Chart

	Total Fixed Cost	Dollars Required per Accounting Report
Software A	$200 000	$60
Software B	$300 000	$25
Software C	$400 000	$10

APPROACH ▶ Solve for the crossover point for software A and B and then the crossover point for software B and C.

SOLUTION ▶ Software A yields a process that is most economical up to V_1 but to exactly what number of reports (volume)? To determine the volume at V_1, we set the cost of software A equal to the cost of software B. V_1 is the unknown volume:

$$200\,000 + (60)V_1 = 300\,000 + (25)V_1$$
$$35V_1 = 100\,000$$
$$V_1 \approx 2857$$

This means that software A is most economical from 0 reports to 2857 reports (V_1).

Similarly, to determine the crossover point for V_2, we set the cost of software B equal to the cost of software C:

$$300\,000 + (25)V_2 = 400\,000 + (10)V_2$$
$$15V_2 = 100\,000$$
$$V_2 \approx 6666$$

This means that software B is most economical if the number of reports is between 2857 (V_1) and 6666 (V_2) and that software C is most economical if reports exceed 6666 (V_2).

INSIGHT ▶ As you can see, the software and related process chosen are highly dependent on the forecasted volume.

LEARNING EXERCISE ▶ If the vendor of software A reduces the fixed cost to $150 000, what is the new crossover point between A and B? [Answer: 4286.]

RELATED PROBLEMS ▶ 7.5, 7.6, 7.7, 7.8, 7.9, 7.10, 7.11, 7.12, 7.14

EXCEL OM Data File **Ch07Ex1.xlsx** can be found at **MyLab Operations Management.**

ACTIVE MODEL 7.1 This example is further illustrated in Active Model 7.1 at **MyLab Operations Management.**

FIGURE 7.4
Crossover Charts

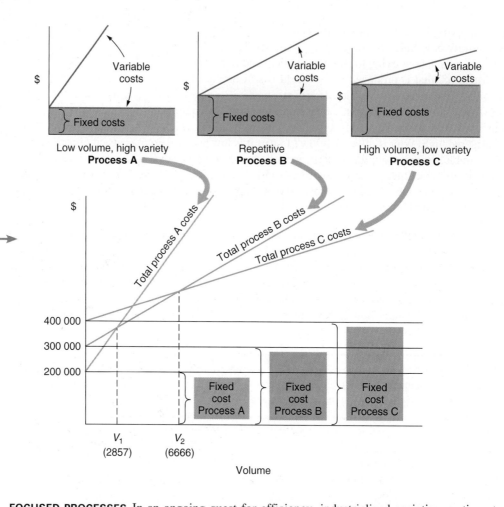

Low volume, high variety
Process A

Repetitive
Process B

High volume, low variety
Process C

STUDENT | TIP

Different processes can be expected to have different costs. However, at any given volume, only one will have the lowest cost.

VIDEO 7.1
Process Strategy at Wheeled
Coach Ambulance

FOCUSED PROCESSES In an ongoing quest for efficiency, industrialized societies continue to move towards specialization. The focus that comes with specialization contributes to efficiency. Managers who focus on a limited number of activities, products, and technologies do better. As the variety of products in a facility increases, overhead costs increase even faster. Similarly, as the variety of products, customers, and technology increases, so does complexity. The resources necessary to cope with the complexity expand disproportionately. A focus on depth of product line as opposed to breadth is typical of outstanding firms, of which Intel, Motorola, L.M. Ericsson, Nokia, and Bosch are world-class examples. Specialization, simplification, concentration, and *focus* yield efficiency. They also contribute to building a core competence that yields market and financial success. The focus can be:

- Customers (such as WestJet Airlines, a company whose primary focus is on the "guest").
- Products with similar attributes (such as those of Canada's mining industry, which is the largest in the world; and Gallagher, a New Zealand company, which has 45% of the world market in electric fences).
- Service (such as Orlando's Arnold Palmer Hospital, with a focus on children and women; or Shouldice Hospital, in Canada, with a focus on hernia repair).
- Technology (such as Texas Instruments, with a focus on only certain specialized kinds of semiconductors; and SAP, which, in spite of a world of opportunities, remains focused on software).

The key for the operations manager is to move continuously towards specialization, focusing on the products, technology, customers, processes, and talents necessary to excel in that specialty.

STUDENT | TIP

A process that is going to win orders often depends on the selection of the proper equipment.

Selection of Equipment and Technology

Ultimately, selection of a particular process strategy requires decisions about equipment and technology. These decisions can be complex, as alternative methods of production are present in virtually all operations functions, from hospitals, to restaurants, to manufacturing facilities. Picking the best equipment requires understanding the specific industry and available

OM in Action — The iPad Menu ... a New Process

Mass customization begins with the order. And at restaurants from California to Boston, the order now starts with an iPad. Stacked Restaurants lets customers choose ingredients for their sandwiches using an iPad on the table. Diners also get a great photo of the menu item (which stimulates sales), a list of ingredients and nutritional information (a plus for those with allergies or watching their diet), and an opportunity to build their own meal (mass customization).

Some restaurants, in addition to having the enticing photo of the meal, find that they can add a description and photo of just what a medium-rare steak looks like. They can further enrich the dining experience by adding a "recipe" tab or "history" tab with descriptions of the item's origins and tradition. Steakhouses—a chain in San Francisco, Atlanta, and Chicago—finds the tabs great

for its lengthy wine lists. Other restaurants find that the customer's ability to order immediately and the instantaneous placement of the order to the kitchen is a significant advantage as it reinforces their response strategy.

Using iPads means developing a new process. iPads are not cheap, but they are accurate and fast, with lots of options; you can even pay at the table via the iPad. And they are fun to use.

Stacked Restaurants

Sources: USA Today (February 16, 2011 and July 25, 2012); and *Commercial Integrator* (March 28, 2011).

processes and technology. The choice of equipment—be it an X-ray machine for a hospital, a computer-controlled lathe for a factory, or a new computer for an office—requires considering cost, cash flow, market stability, quality, capacity, and flexibility. To make this decision, operations managers develop documentation that indicates the capacity, size, tolerances, and maintenance requirements of each option.

In this age of rapid technological change and short product life cycles, adding flexibility to the production process can be a major competitive advantage. **Flexibility** is the ability to respond with little penalty in time, cost, or customer value. This may mean modular, movable, or digitally controlled equipment. Honda's process flexibility, for example, has allowed it to become the industry leader at responding to market dynamics by modifying production volume and product mix.

Flexibility

The ability to respond with little penalty in time, cost, or customer value.

Building flexibility into a production process can be difficult and expensive, but if it is not present, change may mean starting over. Consider what would be required for a rather simple change—such as McDonald's adding the flexibility necessary to serve you a charbroiled hamburger. What appears to be rather straightforward would require changes in many of the 10 OM decisions. For instance, changes may be necessary in (1) purchasing (a different quality of meat, perhaps with more fat content, and supplies such as charcoal), (2) quality standards (how long and at what temperature the patty will cook), (3) equipment (the charbroiler), (4) layout (space for the new process and for new exhaust vents), (5) training, and (6) maintenance. You may want to consider the implications of another simple change, such as a change from paper menus to iPad menus as discussed in the *OM in Action* box "The iPad Menu ... A New Process".

Changing processes or equipment can be difficult and expensive. It is best to get this critical decision right the first time.

Process Analysis and Design

STUDENT TIP

When analyzing and designing processes, we ask questions such as the following:

Here we look at five tools that help in understanding processes.

- Is the process designed to achieve competitive advantage in terms of differentiation, response, or low cost?
- Does the process eliminate steps that do not add value?
- Does the process maximize customer value as perceived by the customer?
- Will the process win orders?

LO3 Use the tools of process analysis

A number of tools help us understand the complexities of process design and redesign. They are simply ways of making sense of what happens or must happen in a process. Let's look at five of them: flowcharts, time-function mapping, value-stream mapping, process charts, and service blueprinting.

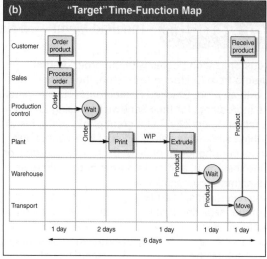
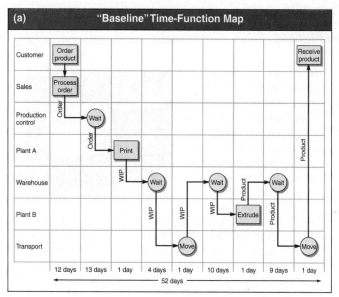

FIGURE 7.5 Time-Function Mapping (Process Mapping) for a Product Requiring Printing and Extruding Operations at American National Can Company

This technique clearly shows that waiting and order processing contributed substantially to the 46 days that can be eliminated in this operation.

Source: Excerpted from Elaine J. Labach, "Faster, Better, and Cheaper," *Target* no. 5: 43 with permission of the Association for Manufacturing Excellence, 380 West Palatine Road, Wheeling, IL 60090-5863, 847/520-3282, www.ame.org. Reprinted with permission of *Target Magazine.*

FLOWCHART

Flowchart

A drawing used to analyze movement of people or material.

The first tool is the **flowchart**, which is a schematic or drawing of the movement of material, product, or people. For instance, the flowchart in the *Global Company Profile* for this chapter shows the assembly processes for Harley-Davidson. Such charts can help understanding, analysis, and communication of a process.

TIME-FUNCTION MAPPING

Time-function mapping (or process mapping)

A flowchart with time added on the horizontal axis.

A second tool for process analysis and design is a flowchart, but with time added on the horizontal axis. Such charts are sometimes called **time-function mapping** (or **process mapping**). With time-function mapping, nodes indicate the activities and the arrows indicate the flow direction, with time on the horizontal axis. This type of analysis allows users to identify and eliminate waste such as extra steps, duplication, and delay. Figure 7.5 shows the use of process mapping before and after process improvement at American National Can Company. In this example, substantial reduction in waiting time and process improvement in order processing contributed to a savings of 46 days.

VALUE-STREAM MAPPING

Value-stream mapping (VSM)

A process that helps managers understand how to add value in the flow of material and information through the entire production process.

A variation of time-function mapping is **value-stream mapping (VSM)**; however, value-stream mapping takes an expanded look at where value is added (and not added) in the entire production process, including the supply chain. As with time-function mapping, the idea is to start with the customer and understand the production process, but value-stream mapping extends the analysis back to suppliers.

Value-stream mapping takes into account not only the process but, as shown in Example 2, also the management decisions and information systems that support the process.

Value-Stream Mapping

BlackBerry has received an order for 11 000 smartphones per month and wants to understand how the order will be processed through manufacturing.

APPROACH ▶ To fully understand the process from customer to supplier, BlackBerry prepares a value-stream map.

SOLUTION ▶ Although value-stream maps appear complex, their construction is easy. Here are the steps needed to complete the value-stream map shown in Figure 7.6.

1. Begin with symbols for customer, supplier, and production to ensure the big picture.
2. Enter customer order requirements.
3. Calculate the daily production requirements.
4. Enter the outbound shipping requirements and delivery frequency.
5. Determine inbound shipping method and delivery frequency.
6. Add the process steps (i.e., machine, assemble) in sequence, left to right.
7. Add communication methods, add their frequency, and show the direction with arrows.
8. Add inventory quantities (shown with ▲ℹ) between all steps of the entire flow.
9. Determine total working time (value-added time) and delay (non-value-added time).

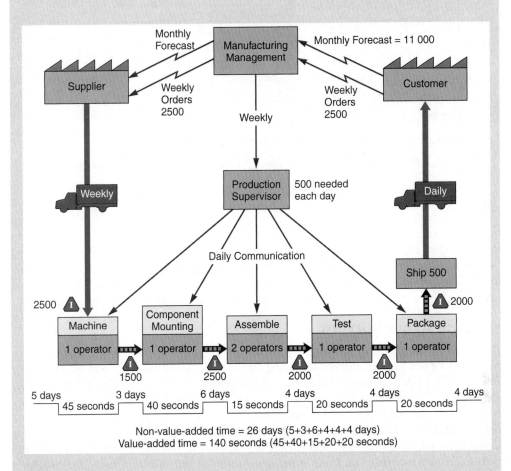

FIGURE 7.6 **Value-Stream Mapping (VSM)**

INSIGHT ▶ From Figure 7.6, we note that large inventories exist in incoming raw material and between processing steps, and that the value-added time is low as a proportion of the entire process.

LEARNING EXERCISE ▶ How might raw material inventory be reduced? [Answer: Have deliveries twice per week rather than once per week.]

RELATED PROBLEMS ▶ 7.13

PROCESS CHARTS

The fourth tool is the *process chart*. **Process charts** use symbols, time, and distance to provide an objective and structured way to analyze and record the activities that make up a process.[2] They allow us to focus on value-added activities. For instance, the process chart shown in Figure 7.7, which includes the present method of hamburger assembly at a fast-food restaurant, includes a value-added line to help us distinguish between value-added activities and waste. Identifying all value-added operations (as opposed to inspection, storage, delay, and transportation, which add

Process charts

Charts that use symbols to analyze the movement of people or material.

---

[2] An additional example of a process chart is shown in Chapter 10.

FIGURE 7.7

Process Chart Showing a Hamburger Assembly Process at a Fast-Food Restaurant

Present Method ☒		PROCESS CHART		Proposed Method ☐
SUBJECT CHARTED _Hamburger Assembly Process_			DATE _8/1/15_	
DEPARTMENT _____		CHART BY _KH_	SHEET NO. _1_ OF _1_	

DIST. IN METRES	TIME IN MINS.	CHART SYMBOLS	PROCESS DESCRIPTION
—	—	○ ⇨ ☐ D ▽	Meat Patty in Storage
1.5	0.05	○ ⇨ ☐ D ▽	Transfer to Broiler
	2.50	○ ⇨ ☐ D ▽	Broiler
	0.05	○ ⇨ ☐ D ▽	Visual Inspection
1.0	0.05	○ ⇨ ☐ D ▽	Transfer to Rack
	0.15	○ ⇨ ☐ D ▽	Temporary Storage
0.5	0.10	○ ⇨ ☐ D ▽	Obtain Buns, Lettuce, etc.
	0.20	○ ⇨ ☐ D ▽	Assemble Order
0.5	0.05	○ ⇨ ☐ D ▽	Place in Finish Rack
		○ ⇨ ☐ D ▽	
3.5	3.15	2 4 1 – 2	TOTALS

Value-added time = Operation time/Total time = (2.50+0.20)/3.15 = 85.7%

○ = operation; ⇨ = transportation; ☐ = inspection; D = delay; ▽ = storage.

no value) allows us to determine the percent of value added to total activities.[3] We can see from the computation at the bottom of Figure 7.7 that the value added in this case is 85.7%. The operations manager's job is to reduce waste and increase the percent of value added. The non-value-added items are a waste; they are resources lost to the firm and to society forever.

SERVICE BLUEPRINTING

Service blueprinting

A process analysis technique that lends itself to a focus on the customer and the provider's interaction with the customer.

Products with a high service content may warrant use of yet a fifth process technique. **Service blueprinting** is a process analysis technique that focuses on the customer and the provider's interaction with the customer. For instance, the activities at level one of Figure 7.8 are under the control of the customer. In the second level are activities of the service provider interacting with the customer. The third level includes those activities that are performed away from, and not immediately visible to, the customer. Each level suggests different management issues. For instance, the top level may suggest educating the customer or modifying expectations, whereas the second level may require a focus on personnel selection and training. Finally, the third level lends itself to more typical process innovations. The service blueprint shown in Figure 7.8 also notes potential failure points and shows how poka-yoke techniques can be added to improve quality. The consequences of these failure points can be greatly reduced if identified at the design stage when modifications or appropriate poka-yokes can be included. A time dimension is included in Figure 7.8 to aid understanding, extend insight, and provide a focus on customer service.

Each of these five process analysis tools has its strengths and variations. Flowcharts are a quick way to view the big picture and try to make sense of the entire system. Time-function mapping adds some rigour and a time element to the macro analysis. Value-stream mapping extends beyond the immediate organization to customers and suppliers. Process charts are designed to provide a much more detailed view of the process, adding items such as value-added time, delay, distance, storage, and so forth. Service blueprinting, on the other hand, is designed to help us focus on the customer interaction part of the process. Because customer interaction is often an important variable in process design, we now examine some additional aspects of service process design.

---

[3] Waste includes *inspection* (if the task is done properly, then inspection is unnecessary); *transportation* (movement of material within a process may be a necessary evil, but it adds no value); *delay* (an asset sitting idle and taking up space is waste); *storage* (unless part of a "curing" process, storage is waste).

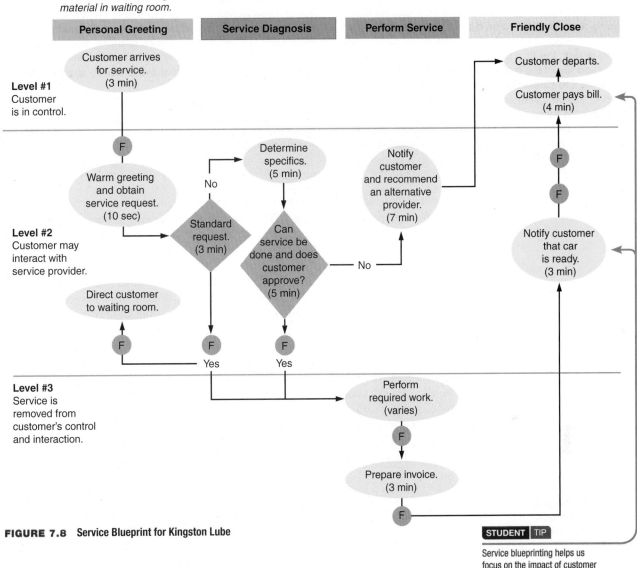

FIGURE 7.8 Service Blueprint for Kingston Lube

STUDENT TIP

Service blueprinting helps us focus on the impact of customer interaction with the process.

Special Considerations for Service Process Design

STUDENT TIP

Customer interaction with service processes increases the design challenge.

Interaction with the customer often affects process performance adversely. But a service, by its very nature, implies that some interaction and customization is needed. Recognizing that the customer's unique desires tend to play havoc with a process, the more the manager designs the process to accommodate these special requirements, the more effective and efficient the process will be. Notice how well Align Technology has managed the interface between the customer and the process by using the internet (see the *OM in Action* box "Mass Customization for Straight Teeth"). The trick is to find the right combination of cost and customer interaction.

CUSTOMER INTERACTION AND PROCESS DESIGN

LO4 Describe customer interaction in process design

The four quadrants of Figure 7.9 provide additional insight on how operations managers design service processes to find the best level of specialization and focus while maintaining the necessary customer interaction and customization. The 10 operations decisions we introduced in Chapters 1 and 2 are used with a different emphasis in each quadrant. For instance:

OM in Action — Mass Customization for Straight Teeth

Align Technology wants to straighten your teeth with a clear plastic removable aligner. The company is a mass customizer for orthodontic treatments. Each patient is *very* custom, requiring a truly unique product; no two patients are alike. Based on dental impressions, X-rays, and photos taken at the dentist's office and sent to Align headquarters, the firm builds a precise 3-D computer model and file of the patient's mouth. This digitized file is then sent to Costa Rica, where technicians develop a comprehensive treatment plan, which is then returned to the dentist for approval. After approval, data from the 3-D virtual models and treatment plan are used to program stereolithography equipment to form moulds.

The moulds are then shipped to Juárez, Mexico, where a series of customized tooth aligners—usually about 19 pairs—are made. The time required for this process: about three weeks from start to finish. The clear aligners take the place of the traditional "wire and brackets." Align calls the product "complex to make, easy to use." With good OM, mass customization works, even for a very complex, very individualized product, such as tooth aligners.

Sources: Laura Rock Kopezak and M. Eric Johnson, "Aligning the Supply Chain," Case #6-0024, Dartmouth College, 2006; and www.invisalign.com, Annual Report, 2007.

- In the upper sections (quadrants) of *mass service* and *professional service*, where *labour content is high*, we expect the manager to focus extensively on human resources. This is often done with personalized services, requiring high labour involvement and therefore significant selection and training issues in the human resources area. This is particularly true in the professional service quadrant.
- The quadrants with *low customization* tend to (1) standardize or restrict some offerings, as do fast-food restaurants; (2) automate, as do airlines with ticket vending machines; or (3) remove some services, such as seat assignments, as in the case of some airlines. Offloading some aspect of the service through automation may require innovations in process design as well as capital investment. Such is the case with airline ticket vending and bank ATMs. This move to standardization and automation may require added capital expenditure, as well as putting operations managers under pressure to develop new skills for the purchase and maintenance of such equipment. A reduction in a customization capability will require added strength in other areas.
- Because customer feedback is lower in the quadrants with *low customization*, tight control may be required to maintain quality standards.
- Operations with *low labour intensity* may lend themselves particularly well to innovations in process technology and scheduling.

FIGURE 7.9

Services Moving Towards Specialization and Focus Within the Service Process Matrix

Source: Based on work by Roger Schmenner, "Service Business and Productivity," *Decision Sciences* 35, no. 3 (Summer 2004): 333–347.

STUDENT TIP

Notice how services find a competitive opportunity by moving from the rectangles to the ovals.

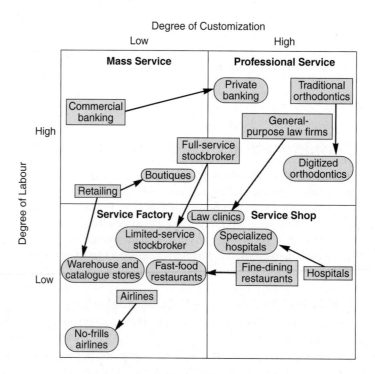

Table 7.3
Techniques for Improving
Service Productivity

Strategy	Technique	Example
Separation	Structuring service so customers must go where the service is offered	Bank customers go to a manager to open a new account, to loan officers for loans, and to tellers for deposits
Self-service	Self-service so customers examine, compare, and evaluate at their own pace	Supermarkets and department stores using internet ordering
Postponement	Customizing at delivery	Customizing vans at delivery rather than at production
Focus	Restricting the offerings	Limited-menu restaurant
Modules	Modular selection of service Modular production	Investment and insurance selection Prepackaged food modules in restaurants
Automation	Separating services that may lend themselves to some type of automation	Automated teller machines
Scheduling	Precise personnel scheduling	Scheduling ticket counter personnel at 15-minute intervals at airlines
Training	Clarifying the service options Explaining how to avoid problems	Investment counsellor, funeral director After-sale maintenance personnel

Table 7.3 shows some additional techniques for innovative process design in services. Managers focus on designing innovative processes that enhance the service. For instance, super-market *self-service* reduces cost while it allows customers to check for the specific features they want, such as freshness or colour. Dell Computer provides another version of self-service by allowing customers to design their own product on the web. Customers seem to like this, and it is cheaper and faster for Dell.

MORE OPPORTUNITIES TO IMPROVE SERVICE PROCESSES

LAYOUT Layout design is an integral part of many service processes, particularly in retailing, dining, and banking. In retailing, layout can provide not only product exposure but also customer education and product enhancement. In restaurants, layout can enhance the dining experience as well as provide an effective flow between bar, kitchen, and dining area. In banks, layout provides security as well as work flow and personal comfort. Because layout is such an integral part of many services, it provides continuing opportunity for winning orders.

HUMAN RESOURCES Because so many services involve direct interaction with the customer (as the upper quadrants of Figure 7.9 suggest), the human resource issues of recruiting and training can be particularly important ingredients in service processes. Additionally, a committed workforce that exhibits flexibility when schedules are made, and is cross-trained to fill in when the process requires less than a full-time person, can have a tremendous impact on overall process performance.

VIDEO 7.2
Process Analysis at
Arnold Palmer Hospital

Production Technology

STUDENT TIP

Here are nine technologies that can improve employee safety, product quality, and productivity.

LO5 Identify recent advances in production technology

Advances in technology that enhance production and productivity have a wide range of applications in both manufacturing and services. In this section, we introduce nine areas of technology: (1) machine technology, (2) automatic identification systems (AIS), (3) process control, (4) vision systems, (5) robots, (6) automated storage and retrieval systems (ASRSs), (7) automated guided vehicles (AGVs), (8) flexible manufacturing systems (FMSs), and (9) computer-integrated manufacturing (CIM).

MACHINE TECHNOLOGY

Most of the world's machinery that performs operations such as cutting, drilling, boring, and milling is undergoing tremendous progress in both precision and control. New machinery turns out metal components that vary less than a micron—$\frac{1}{76}$ the width of a human hair. They can accelerate water to three times the speed of sound to cut titanium for surgical tools. Machinery of the 21st century is often five times more productive than that of previous generations while being smaller and using less power. And continuing advances in lubricants now allow the use of water-based lubricants rather than oil-based. Using water-based lubricants eliminates hazardous waste and allows shavings to be easily recovered and recycled.

The intelligence now available for the control of new machinery via computer chips allows more complex and precise items to be made faster. Electronic controls increase speed by reducing changeover time, reducing waste (because of fewer mistakes), and enhancing flexibility. Machinery with its own computer and memory is called **computer numerical control (CNC)** machinery.

Computer numerical control (CNC)

Machinery with its own computer and memory.

Advanced versions of such technology are used at Bombardier's Thunder Bay location. The new machinery has contributed to process improvements, reducing some of their processing times from days down to hours.

New advances in machinery suggest that rather than removing material as has traditionally been done, *adding* material may in many cases be more efficient. **Additive manufacturing** or, as it is commonly called, 3-D printing, is frequently used for design testing, prototypes, and custom products. The technology continues to advance and now supports innovative product design (variety and complexity), minimal custom tooling (little tooling is needed), minimal assembly (integrated assemblies can be "printed"), low inventory (make-to-order systems), and reduced time to market. As a result, additive manufacturing is being increasingly used to enhance production efficiency for high-volume products. In addition, production processes using numerous materials including plastics, ceramics, and even a paste of living cells are being developed. The convergence of software advances, computer technology, worldwide communication, and 3-D printing seems to be putting us on the cusp of true mass customization. We can expect personalized mass markets via additive manufacturing to bring enormous changes to operations.

Additive manufacturing

The production of physical items by adding layer upon layer, much in the same way an inkjet printer lays down ink.

Automatic identification system (AIS)

A system for transforming data into electronic form; for example, barcodes.

AUTOMATIC IDENTIFICATION SYSTEMS (AISs) AND RFID

New equipment, from numerically controlled manufacturing machinery to ATM machines, is controlled by digital electronic signals. Electrons are a great vehicle for transmitting information, but they have a major limitation—most OM data do not start out in bits and bytes. Therefore, operations managers must get the data into an electronic form. Making data digital is done via computer keyboards, barcodes, radio frequencies, optical characters, and so forth. An **automatic identification system (AIS)** helps us move data into electronic form, where it is easily manipulated.

Because of its decreasing cost and increasing pervasiveness, **radio frequency identification (RFID)** warrants special note. RFID is integrated circuitry with its own tiny antennas that use radio waves to send signals a limited range—usually a matter of metres. These RFID tags (sometimes called RFID circuits) provide unique identification that enables the tracking and monitoring of parts, pallets, people, and pets—virtually everything that moves. RFID requires no line of sight between tag and reader.

Radio frequency identification (RFID)

A wireless system in which integrated circuits with antennas send radio waves.

Process control

The use of information technology to control a physical process.

PROCESS CONTROL

Process control is the use of information technology to monitor and control a physical process. For instance, process control is used to measure the moisture content and thickness of paper as it travels over a paper machine at thousands of metres per minute. Process control is also used to determine and control temperatures, pressures, and quantities in petroleum refineries, petrochemical processes, cement plants, steel mills, nuclear reactors, and other product-focused facilities.

Sophisticated process control is required to monitor complex processes that vary from beer at Anheuser-Busch, to steel at Nucor, to nuclear reactors at Dominion Resources (shown here).

Process control systems operate in a number of ways, but the following is typical:

- Sensors collect data.
- Devices read data on some periodic basis, perhaps once a minute or once every second.
- Measurements are translated into digital signals, which are transmitted to a computer.
- Computer programs read the file (the digital data) and analyze the data.
- The resulting output may take numerous forms. These include messages on computer consoles or printers, signals to motors to change valve settings, warning lights or horns, or statistical process control charts.

VISION SYSTEMS

Vision systems combine video cameras and computer technology and are often used in inspection roles. Visual inspection is an important task in most food processing and manufacturing organizations. Moreover, in many applications, visual inspection performed by humans is tedious, mind-numbing, and error prone. Thus, vision systems are widely used when the items being inspected are very similar. For instance, vision systems are used to inspect Frito-Lay's potato chips so that imperfections can be identified as the chips proceed down the production line. Vision systems are used to ensure that sealant is present and in the proper amount on Whirlpool's washing machine transmissions, and to inspect and reject bottles containing glass chip defects at Labatt Breweries, even during peak bottling speeds. Vision systems are consistently accurate, do not become bored, and are of modest cost. These systems are vastly superior to individuals trying to perform these tasks.

Vision systems
Systems that use video cameras and computer technology in inspection roles.

ROBOTS

When a machine is flexible and has the ability to hold, move, and perhaps "grab" items, we tend to use the word *robot*. A **robot** is a mechanical device that uses electronic impulses to activate motors and switches. Robots may be used effectively to perform tasks that are especially monotonous or dangerous or those that can be improved by the substitution of mechanical for human effort. Such is the case when consistency, accuracy, speed, strength, or power can be enhanced by the substitution of machines for people. Ford, for example, uses robots to do 98% of the welding and most of the painting on some automobiles.

Robot
A flexible machine with the ability to hold, move, or grab items. It functions through electronic impulses that activate motors and switches.

AUTOMATED STORAGE AND RETRIEVAL SYSTEMS (ASRSs)

Because of the tremendous labour involved in error-prone warehousing, computer-controlled warehouses have been developed. Known as an **automated storage and retrieval system (ASRS)**, it provides for the automatic placement and withdrawal of parts and products into and from designated places in a warehouse. Such systems are commonly used in distribution facilities of retailers such as Walmart, Tupperware, and Benetton. These systems are also found in inventory and test areas of manufacturing firms.

Automated storage and retrieval system (ASRS)
Computer-controlled warehouses that provide for the automatic placement of parts into and from designated places within a warehouse.

AUTOMATED GUIDED VEHICLES (AGVs)

Automated material handling can take the form of monorails, conveyors, robots, or automated guided vehicles. An **automated guided vehicle (AGV)** is an electronically guided and controlled cart used in manufacturing to move parts and equipment. They are also used in offices to move mail and in hospitals and in jails to deliver meals.

Automated guided vehicle (AGV)
Electronically guided and controlled cart used to move materials.

FLEXIBLE MANUFACTURING SYSTEMS (FMSs)

When a central computer provides instructions to each workstation *and* to the material-handling equipment (which moves material to that station), the system is known as an automated work cell or, more commonly, a **flexible manufacturing system (FMS)**. An FMS is flexible because both the material-handling devices and the machines themselves are controlled by easily changed electronic signals (computer programs). Operators simply load new programs, as necessary, to produce different products. The result is a system that can economically produce low volume but high variety. For example, Streit Manufacturing Inc., an Ontario-based manufacturer of armoured vehicles and limousines, efficiently builds these custom products for clients. The

Flexible manufacturing system (FMS)
A system that uses an automated work cell controlled by electronic signals from a common centralized computer facility.

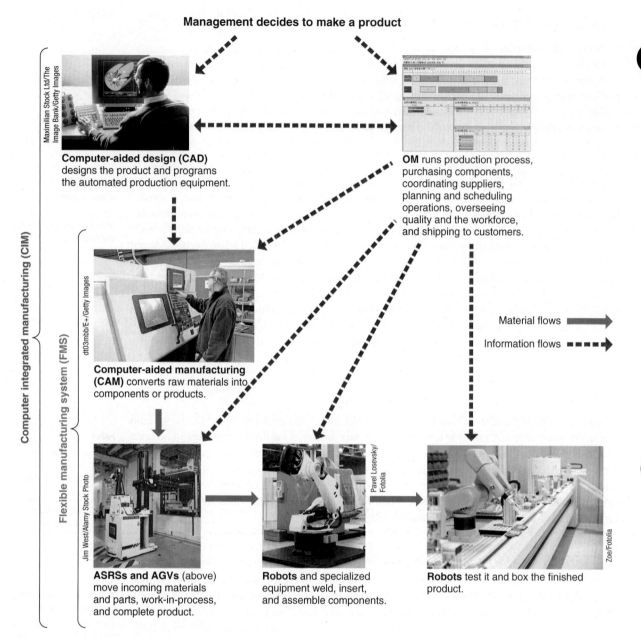

Management decides to make a product

Computer-aided design (CAD) designs the product and programs the automated production equipment.

OM runs production process, purchasing components, coordinating suppliers, planning and scheduling operations, overseeing quality and the workforce, and shipping to customers.

Computer-aided manufacturing (CAM) converts raw materials into components or products.

Material flows

Information flows

ASRSs and AGVs (above) move incoming materials and parts, work-in-process, and complete product.

Robots and specialized equipment weld, insert, and assemble components.

Robots test it and box the finished product.

FIGURE 7.10 Computer-Integrated Manufacturing (CIM)

CIM includes computer-aided design (CAD), computer-aided manufacturing (CAM), flexible manufacturing systems (FMSs), automated storage and retrieval systems (ASRSs), automated guided vehicles (AGVs), and robots to provide an integrated and flexible manufacturing process.

costs associated with changeover and low utilization have been reduced substantially. FMSs bridge the gap between product-focused and process-focused facilities.

COMPUTER-INTEGRATED MANUFACTURING (CIM)

Computer-integrated manufacturing (CIM)

A manufacturing system in which CAD, FMSs, inventory control, warehousing, and shipping are integrated.

Flexible manufacturing systems can be extended backward electronically into the engineering and inventory control departments and forward to the warehousing and shipping departments. In this way, computer-aided design (CAD) generates the necessary electronic instructions to run a numerically controlled machine. In a computer-integrated manufacturing environment, a design change initiated at a CAD terminal can result in that change being made in the part produced on the shop floor in a matter of minutes. When this capability is integrated with inventory control, warehousing, and shipping as a part of a flexible manufacturing system, the entire system is called **computer-integrated manufacturing (CIM)** (see Figure 7.10).

> ### OM in Action ▸ Technology Changes the Hotel Industry
>
> Technology is introducing "intelligent rooms" to the hotel industry. Hotel management can now precisely track a maid's time through the use of a security system. When a maid enters a room, a card is inserted that notifies the front-desk computer of the maid's location. "We can show her a printout of how long she takes to do a room," says one manager.
>
> Security systems also enable guests to use their own credit cards as keys to unlock their doors. There are also other uses for the system. The computer can bar a guest's access to the room after checkout time and automatically control the air conditioning or heat, turning it on at check-in and off at checkout.
>
> Minibars are now equipped with sensors that alert the central computer system at the hotel when an item is removed. Such items are immediately billed to the room. And now, with a handheld infrared unit, housekeeping staff can check, from the hallway, to see if a room is physically occupied. This both eliminates the embarrassment of having a hotel staffer walk in on a guest *and* improves security for housekeepers.
>
> At Loew's Portofino Bay Hotel at Universal Studios, Orlando, guest smart cards act as credit cards in both the theme park and the hotel, and staff smart cards (programmed for different levels of security access) create an audit trail of employee movement. Starwood Hotels, which runs such properties under the Sheraton and Westin names, use Casio Pocket PCs to communicate with a hotel wireless network. Now guests can check in and out from any place on the property, such as at their restaurant table after breakfast or lunch.
>
> *Sources: Hotel and Motel Management* (November 5, 2007): 16; *Hotels* (April 2004): 51–54; and *Newsweek* (international ed.) (September 27, 2004): 73.

Flexible manufacturing systems and computer-integrated manufacturing are reducing the distinction between low-volume/high-variety and high-volume/low-variety production. Information technology is allowing FMSs and CIM to handle increasing variety while expanding to include a growing range of volumes.

Technology in Services

Just as we have seen rapid advances in technology in the manufacturing sector, so we also find dramatic changes in the service sector. These range from electronic diagnostic equipment at auto repair shops, to blood- and urine-testing equipment in hospitals, to retinal security scanners at airports and high-security facilities. The hospitality industry provides other examples, as discussed in the *OM in Action* box "Technology Changes the Hotel Industry". The McDonald's approach is to use self-serve kiosks. The labour savings when ordering and speedier checkout service provide valuable productivity increases for both the restaurant and the customer.

Similarly, IKEA has developed user-friendly computer software that enables customers to design their own kitchens. The customer calls up a product information guide, promotion mate-

Pharmaceutical companies are counting on RFID to aid the tracking and tracing of drugs in the distribution system to reduce losses that total over U.S. $30 billion a year.

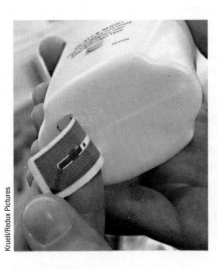

Kruell/Redux Pictures

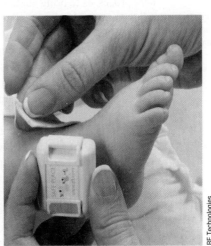

RF Technologies

Hospitals use RFID sensors to track patients, staff, and equipment.

Table 7.4

Examples of Technology's Impact on Services

Service Industry	Example
Financial services	Debit cards, electronic funds transfer, automated teller machines, internet stock trading, online banking via cell phone.
Education	Online newspapers, online journals, interactive assignments via Web CT, Blackboard, and smartphones.
Utilities and government	Automated one-man garbage trucks, optical mail scanners, flood-warning systems, meters allowing homeowners to control energy usage and costs.
Restaurants and foods	Wireless orders from waiters to the kitchen, robot butchering, transponders on cars that track sales at drive-throughs.
Communications	Interactive TV, ebooks via Kindle 2.
Hotels	Electronic check-in/checkout, electronic key/lock systems, mobile web bookings.
Wholesale/retail trade	Point-of-sale (POS) terminals, ecommerce, electronic communication between store and supplier, barcoded data, RFID.
Transportation	Automatic toll booths, satellite-directed navigation systems, Wi-Fi in automobiles.
Healthcare	Online patient-monitoring systems, online medical information systems, robotic surgery.
Airlines	Ticketless travel, scheduling, internet purchases, boarding passes downloaded as two-dimensional barcodes on smartphones.

rial, a gallery of designs, and a sketch pad to create the designs desired. The software also allows the customer to determine the associated costs and see a graphic view of the kitchen fitted with the new cabinets and fixtures.

In retail stores, POS terminals download prices quickly to reflect changing costs or market conditions, and sales are tracked in 15-minute segments to aid scheduling. Pharmacies such as Shoppers Drug Mart are considering the policy and privacy implications of tracking critical medications with radio frequency identification (RFID) tags in order to reduce counterfeiting and theft.

Table 7.4 provides a glimpse of the impact of technology on services. Operations managers in services, as in manufacturing, must be able to evaluate the impact of technology on their firm. This ability requires particular skill when evaluating reliability, investment analysis, human resource requirements, and maintenance/service. (See Video Case "Alaska Airlines: 20-Minute Baggage Process—Guaranteed!")

VIDEO 7.1
Alaska Airlines: 20-Minute Baggage Process—Guaranteed!

Process Redesign

Often a firm finds that the initial assumptions of its process are no longer valid. The world is a dynamic place, and customer desires, product technology, and product mix change. Consequently, processes are redesigned. **Process redesign** is the fundamental rethinking of business processes to bring about dramatic improvements in performance. Effective process redesign relies on re evaluating the purpose of the process and questioning both purpose and underlying assumptions. It works only if the basic process and its objectives are re examined.

Process redesign also focuses on those activities that cross functional lines. Because managers are often in charge of specific "functions" or specialized areas of responsibility, those activities (processes) that cross from one function or specialty to another may be neglected. Redesign casts aside all notions of how the process is currently being done and focuses on dramatic improvements in cost, time, and customer value. Any process is a candidate for radical redesign. The process can be a factory layout, a purchasing procedure, a new way of processing credit applications, or a new order-fulfillment process.

Shell Lubricants, for example, reinvented its order-fulfillment process by replacing a group of people who handled different parts of an order with one individual who does it all. As a result, Shell has cut the cycle time of turning an order into cash by 75%, reduced operating expenses by 45%, and boosted customer satisfaction 105%—all by introducing a new way of handling orders. Time, cost, and customer satisfaction—the dimensions of performance shaped by operations—get major boosts from operational innovation.

CHAPTER | SUMMARY

Effective operations managers understand how to use process strategy as a competitive weapon. They select a production process with the necessary quality, flexibility, and cost structure to meet product and volume requirements. They also seek creative ways to combine the low unit cost of high-volume, low-variety manufacturing with the customization available through low-volume, high-variety facilities. Managers use the techniques of lean production and employee participation to encourage the development of efficient equipment and processes. They design their equipment and processes to have capabilities beyond the tolerance required by their customers, while ensuring the flexibility needed for adjustments in technology, features, and volumes.

ETHICAL | DILEMMA

For the sake of efficiency and lower costs, Premium Standard Farms has turned pig production into a standardized product-focused process. Slaughterhouses have done this for hundreds of years—but after the animal was dead. Doing it while the animal is alive is a relatively recent innovation. Here is how it works.

Impregnated females (sows) wait for 40 days in metal stalls so small that they cannot turn around. After an ultrasound test, they wait 67 days in a similar stall until they give birth. Two weeks after delivering 10 or 11 piglets, the sows are moved back to breeding rooms for another cycle. After three years, the sows are slaughtered. Animal welfare advocates say such confinement drives pigs crazy. Premium Standard replies that its hogs are in fact comfortable, arguing that only 1% die before Premium Standard wants them to and that its system helps reduce the cost of pork products.

Discuss the productivity and ethical implications of this industry and these two divergent opinions.

glenda/Shutterstock

Discussion Questions

1. What is process strategy?
2. What type of process is used for making each of the following products?
   (a) beer
   (b) wedding invitations
   (c) automobiles
   (d) paper
   (e) Big Macs
   (f) custom homes
   (g) motorcycles
3. What is service blueprinting?
4. What is process redesign?
5. What are the techniques for improving service productivity?
6. Name the four quadrants of the service process matrix. Discuss how the matrix is used to classify services into categories.
7. What is CIM?
8. What do we mean by a process control system, and what are the typical elements in such systems?
9. Identify *manufacturing* firms that compete on each of the four processes shown in Figure 7.1.
10. Identify the competitive advantage of each of the firms identified in Question 9.
11. Identify *service* firms that compete on each of the four processes shown in Figure 7.1.
12. Identify the competitive advantage of each of the firms identified in Question 11.
13. What are numerically controlled machines?
14. Describe briefly what an automatic identification system (AIS) is and how service organizations could use AISs to increase productivity and at the same time increase the variety of services offered.
15. Name some of the advances being made in technology that enhance production and productivity.
16. Explain what a flexible manufacturing system (FMS) is.
17. In what ways do CAD and FMS connect?
18. What is additive manufacturing?
19. Discuss the advantages and disadvantages of 3-D printing.

Solved Problem Virtual Office Hours help is available at MyLab Operations Management.

▼ SOLVED PROBLEM 7.1

Bagot Copy Shop has a volume of 125 000 black-and-white copies per month. Two salespersons have made presentations to Gordon Bagot for machines of equal quality and reliability. The Print Shop 5 has a cost of $2000 per month and a variable cost of $0.03 per copy. The other machine (a Speed Copy 100) will cost only $1500 per month but the toner is more expensive, driving the cost per copy up to $0.035. If cost and volume are the only considerations, which machine should Bagot purchase?

▼ SOLUTION

$$2000 + 0.03X = 1500 + 0.035X$$
$$2000 - 1500 = 0.035X - 0.03X$$
$$500 = 0.005X$$
$$100\,000 = X$$

Because Bagot expects his volume to exceed 100 000 units, he should choose the Print Shop 5.

Problems*

• **7.1** Prepare a flowchart for one of the following:
a) the registration process at a school
b) the process at the local car wash
c) a shoe shine
d) some other process with the approval of the instructor

• **7.2** Prepare a process chart for one of the activities in Problem 7.1.

•• **7.3** Prepare a time-function map for one of the activities in Problem 7.1.

•• **7.4** Prepare a service blueprint for one of the activities in Problem 7.1.

• **7.5** Meile Machine Shop, Inc., has a one-year contract for the production of 200 000 gear housings for a new off-road vehicle. Owner Larry Meile hopes the contract will be extended and the volume increased next year. Meile has developed costs for three alternatives. They are general-purpose equipment (GPE), flexible manufacturing system (FMS), and expensive, but efficient, dedicated machine (DM). The cost data follow:

	General-Purpose Equipment (GPE)	Flexible Manufacturing System (FMS)	Dedicated Machine (DM)
Annual contracted units	200 000	200 000	200 000
Annual fixed cost	$100 000	$200 000	$500 000
Per unit variable cost	$15.00	$14.00	$13.00

Which process is best for this contract? **Px**

• **7.6** Using the data in Problem 7.5, determine the economical volume for each process. **Px**

• **7.7** Using the data in Problem 7.5, determine the best process for each of the following volumes: (1) 75 000, (2) 275 000, and (3) 375 000.

• **7.8** Refer to Problem 7.5. If a contract for the second and third years is pending, what are the implications for process selection?

•• **7.9** Oscar Lee's company is considering producing a gear assembly that it now purchases from Okanagan Supply, Inc.

Okanagan Supply charges $4 per unit with a minimum order of 3000 units. Stan estimates that it will cost $15 000 to set up the process and then $1.82 per unit for labour and materials.
a) Draw a graph illustrating the crossover (or indifference) point.
b) Determine the number of units where either choice has the same cost. **Px**

•• **7.10** Ski Boards, Inc., wants to enter the market quickly with a new finish on its ski boards. It has three choices: (a) refurbish the old equipment at a cost of $800, (b) make major modifications at the cost of $1100, or (c) purchase new equipment at a net cost of $1800. If the firm chooses to refurbish the equipment, materials and labour will be $1.10 per board. If it chooses to make modifications, materials and labour will be $0.70 per board. If it buys new equipment, variable costs are estimated to be $0.40 per board.
a) Graph the three total cost lines on the same chart.
b) Which alternative should Ski Boards, Inc., choose if it thinks it can sell more than 3000 boards?
c) Which alternative should the firm use if it thinks the market for boards will be between 1000 and 2000? **Px**

•• **7.11** Susan Meyer, owner/manager of Meyer's Motor Court in Wasaga Beach, Ontario, is considering outsourcing the daily room cleanup for her motel to Duffy's Maid Service. Susan rents an average of 50 rooms for each of 365 nights (365 × 50 equals the total rooms rented for the year). Susan's cost to clean a room is $12.50. The Duffy's Maid Service quote is $18.50 per room plus a fixed cost of $25 000 for sundry items such as uniforms with the motel's name. Susan's annual fixed cost for space, equipment, and supplies is $61 000. Which is the preferred process for Susan, and why? **Px**

•• **7.12** Keith Whittingham, as manager of Designs by Whittingham, is upgrading his CAD software. The high-performance (HP) software rents for $3000 per month per workstation. The standard-performance (SP) software rents for $2000 per month per workstation. The productivity figures that he has available suggest that the HP software is faster for his kind of design. Therefore, with the HP software he will need five engineers and with the SP software he will need six. This translates into a variable cost of $200 per drawing for the HP system and $240 per drawing for the SP system. At his projected volume of 80 drawings per month, which system should he rent? **Px**

•• **7.13** Using Figure 7.6 in the discussion of value-stream mapping as a starting point, analyze an opportunity for improvement in a process with which you are familiar and develop an improved process.

••• **7.14** Creative Cabinets, Inc., needs to choose a production method for its new office shelf, the Maxistand. To help accomplish this, the firm has gathered the following production cost data:

* *Note:* **Px** means the problem may be solved with POM for windows and/or Excel OM.

Process Type	Annualized Fixed Cost of Plant & Equip.	Variable Costs (per unit) ($)		
		Labour	Material	Energy
Mass Customization	$1 260 000	30	18	12
Intermittent	$1 000 000	24	26	20
Repetitive	$1 625 000	28	15	12
Continuous	$1 960 000	25	15	10

Creative Cabinets projects an annual demand of 24 000 units for the Maxistand. The Maxistand will sell for $120 per unit.

a) Which process type will maximize the annual profit from producing the Maxistand?

b) What is the value of this annual profit? **Px**

•• **7.15** California Gardens, Inc., prewashes, shreds, and distributes a variety of salad mixes in 2-pound bags. Doug Voss, Operations VP, is considering a new Hi-Speed shredder to replace the old machine, referred to in the shop as "Clunker". Hi-Speed will have a fixed cost of $85 000 per month and a variable cost of $1.25 per bag. Clunker has a fixed cost of only $44 000 per month, but a variable cost of $1.75. Selling price is $2.50 per bag.

a) What is the crossover point in units (point of indifference) for the processes?

b) What is the monthly profit or loss if the company changes to the Hi-Speed shredder and sells 60 000 bags per month?

c) What is the monthly profit or loss if the company stays with Clunker and sells 60 000 bags per month?

•• **7.16** Nagle Electric, Inc., of Lincoln, Nebraska, must replace a robotic Mig welder and is evaluating two alternatives. Machine A has a fixed cost for the first year of $75 000 and a variable cost of $16, with a capacity of 18 000 units per year. Machine B is slower, with a speed of one-half of A's, but the fixed cost is only $60 000. The variable cost will be higher, at $20 per unit. Each unit is expected to sell for $28.

a) What is the crossover point (point of indifference) in units for the two machines?

b) What is the range of units for which machine A is preferable?

c) What is the range of units for which machine B is preferable?

•• **7.17** Stapleton Manufacturing intends to increase capacity through the addition of new equipment. Two vendors have presented proposals. The fixed cost for proposal A is $65 000, and for proposal B, $34 000. The variable cost for A is $10, and for B, $14. The revenue generated by each unit is $18.

a) What is the crossover point in units for the two options?

b) At an expected volume of 8 300 units, which alternative should be chosen?

CASE STUDIES

Regina Manufacturing's Process Decision

Regina Manufacturing Corporation (RMC) is considering moving some of its production from traditional numerically controlled machines to a flexible manufacturing system (FMS). Its computer numerical control machines have been operating in a high-variety, low-volume manner. Machine utilization, as near as it can determine, is hovering around 10%. The machine tool salespeople and a consulting firm want to put the machines together in an FMS. They believe that a $3 million expenditure on machinery and the transfer machines will handle about 30% of RMC's work. There will, of course, be transition and start-up costs in addition to this.

The firm has not yet entered all its parts into a comprehensive group technology system but believes that the 30% is a good estimate of products suitable for the FMS. This 30% should fit very nicely into a "family". A reduction, because of higher utilization, should take place in the number of pieces of machinery. The firm should be able to go from 15 to about 4 machines and personnel should go from 15 to perhaps as low as 3. Similarly, floor space reduction will go from 1860 square metres to about 560.

Throughput of orders should also improve with processing of this family of parts in 1 to 2 days rather than 7 to 10. Inventory reduction is estimated to yield a one-time $750 000 savings, and annual labour savings should be in the neighbourhood of $300 000.

Although the projections all look very positive, an analysis of the project's return on investment showed it to be between 10% and 15% per year. The company has traditionally had an expectation that projects should yield well over 15% and have payback periods of substantially less than five years.

Discussion Questions

1. As a production manager for RMC, what do you recommend? Why?

2. Prepare a case by a conservative plant manager for maintaining the status quo until the returns are more obvious.

3. Prepare the case for an optimistic sales manager that you should move ahead with the FMS now.

Environmental Sustainability at Walmart

Walmart views "environmental sustainability as one of the most important opportunities for both the future of our business, and the future of our world."* Its environmental vision is clear: "... to be supplied 100 percent by renewable energy; to create zero waste; and

to sell products that sustain our natural resources and the environment." Its specific goals in the three areas are as follows:

• *Renewable energy:* existing stores are to be 20% more efficient in seven years, new stores are to be 30% more efficient in four years, and the trucking fleet is to be 25% more efficient in three years and twice as efficient in 10 years.

* See **http://walmartstores.com/sustainability**.

- *Zero waste:* 25% reduction in solid waste in three years and improved brand packaging through right-sized packaging that uses reusable material.
- *Sustain resources and the environment:* 20% of its 61 000 suppliers will abide by the program within three years.

The three above goals make up what Walmart refers to as its Sustainable Value Network. Renewable energy includes global logistics, greenhouse gas (GHG) emissions, and sustainable buildings, in addition to alternative fuels. Waste refers to packaging, operations, and procurement.

Walmart has also launched various experiments and innovations, including the following:

- Building high-efficiency stores using recycled building material and lighting that conserves energy. These new facilities are 25% more energy efficient than the firm's 2005 baseline.
- Purchasing solar-powered equipment at a rate that could put it in the top 10 largest-ever solar-power purchasers in the United States Solar power is to be used at 22 locations in Hawaii and California.
- Reducing packaging. For example, changes to packaging for patio sets resulted in 400 fewer shipping containers. And the company used 230 fewer shipping containers to distribute toys.

- Selling reusable bags to reduce the use of disposable plastic bags; encouraging schools to collect plastic bags, for which the schools are paid.
- Adopting a series of aerodynamic innovations for its trucking fleet. It even developed a power unit to warm or cool drivers at night without turning on the truck's engine.

With these policies and initiatives, Walmart hopes to blunt criticism and as a major worldwide employer lead the way in environmental sustainability. As one critic admitted begrudgingly, "Walmart has more green clout than anyone."

Discussion Questions

1. How is Walmart doing in terms of environmental sustainability?
2. Based on library and internet research, report on other Walmart sustainability efforts.
3. Compare the firm's sustainability plan to those of Rona, Target, or other big-box retailers.
4. How much of Walmart's sustainability effort is (a) resource focused, (b) recycling focused, (c) regulation focused, and (d) reputation focused?

Source: Based on material by Professor Asbjorn Osland, San Jose State University.

Process Strategy at Wheeled Coach Ambulance

Wheeled Coach, based in Winter Park, Florida, is the world's largest manufacturer of ambulances. Working four 10-hour days each week, 350 employees make only custom-made ambulances: Virtually every vehicle is unique. Wheeled Coach accommodates the marketplace by providing a wide variety of options and an engineering staff accustomed to innovation and custom design. Continuing growth, which now requires that more than 20 ambulances roll off the assembly line each week, makes process design a continuing challenge. Wheeled Coach's response has been to build a focused factory: Wheeled Coach builds nothing but ambulances. Within the focused factory, Wheeled Coach established work cells for every major module feeding an assembly line, including aluminum bodies, electrical wiring harnesses, interior cabinets, windows, painting, and upholstery.

Labour standards drive the schedule so that every work cell feeds the assembly line on schedule, just in time for installations. The chassis, usually that of a Ford truck, moves to a station at which the aluminum body is mounted. Then the vehicle is moved to painting. Following a custom paint job, it moves to the assembly line, where it will spend seven days. During each of these seven workdays, each work cell delivers its respective module to the appropriate position on the assembly line. During the first day, electrical

wiring is installed; on the second day, the unit moves forward to the station at which cabinetry is delivered and installed, then to a window and lighting station, on to upholstery, to fit and finish, to further customizing, and finally to inspection and road testing. The *Global Company Profile* featuring Wheeled Coach, which opens Chapter 14, provides further details about this process.

Discussion Questions*

1. Why do you think major auto manufacturers do not build ambulances?
2. What is an alternative process strategy to the assembly line that Wheeled Coach currently uses?
3. Why is it more efficient for the work cells to prepare "modules" and deliver them to the assembly line than it would be to produce the component (e.g., interior upholstery) on the line?
4. How does Wheeled Coach manage the tasks to be performed at each work station?

---

*You may wish to view the video that accompanies this case before addressing these questions.

Process Analysis at Arnold Palmer Hospital

The Arnold Palmer Hospital (APH) in Orlando, Florida, is one of the busiest and most respected hospitals for the medical treatment of children and women in the United States. Since its opening on golfing legend Arnold Palmer's birthday—September 10, 1989— more than 1.6 million children and women have passed through its doors. It is the fourth busiest labour and delivery hospital in the United States and one of the largest neonatal intensive care units in the Southeast. APH ranks in the top 10% of hospitals nationwide in patient satisfaction.

"Part of the reason for APH's success," says executive director Kathy Swanson, "is our continuous improvement process. Our goal is 100% patient satisfaction. But getting there means constantly examining and reexamining everything we do, from patient flow, to cleanliness, to layout space, to a work-friendly environment, to speed of medication delivery from the pharmacy to a patient. Continuous improvement is a huge and never-ending task."

One of the tools the hospital uses consistently is the process flowchart (like those in Figures 7.1 to 7.3 in this chapter and

Figure 6.6e in Chapter 6). Staffer Diane Bowles, who carries the title "Clinical Practice Improvement Consultant," charts scores of processes. Bowles's flowcharts help study ways to improve the turnaround of a vacated room (especially important in a hospital that has pushed capacity for years), speed up the admission process, and deliver warm meals warm.

Lately, APH has been examining the flow of maternity patients (and their paperwork) from the moment they enter the hospital until they are discharged, hopefully with their healthy baby, a day or two later. The flow of maternity patients follows these steps:

1. Enter APH's Labour & Delivery (L&D) check-in desk entrance.

2. If the baby is born en route or if birth is imminent, the mother and baby are taken directly to Labour & Delivery on the second floor and registered and admitted directly at the bedside. If there are no complications, the mother and baby go to step 6.

3. If the baby is *not* yet born, the front desk asks if the mother is preregistered. (Most do preregister at the 28- to 30-week pregnancy mark). If she is not, she goes to the registration office on the first floor.

4. The pregnant woman is then taken to L&D Triage on the eighth floor for assessment. If she is in active labour, she is taken to an L&D room on the second floor until the baby is born. If she is not ready, she goes to step 5.

5. Pregnant women not ready to deliver (i.e., no contractions or false alarm) are either sent home to return on a later date and re enter the system at that time, or if contractions are not yet close enough, they are sent to walk around the hospital grounds (to encourage progress) and then return to L&D Triage at a prescribed time.

6. When the baby is born, if there are no complications, after two hours, the mother and baby are transferred to a "mother–baby care unit" room on the third, fourth, or fifth floors for an average of 40–44 hours.

7. If there *are* complications with the mother, she goes to an operating room and/or intensive care unit. From there, she goes back to a mother–baby care room upon stabilization—or is discharged at another time if not stabilized. Complications for the baby may result in a stay in the neonatal intensive care unit (NICU) before transfer to the baby nursery near the mother's room. If the baby is not stable enough for discharge with the mother, the baby is discharged later.

8. Mother and/or baby, when ready, are discharged and taken by wheelchair to the discharge exit for pickup to travel home.

Discussion Questions*

1. As Diane's new assistant, you need to flowchart this process. Explain how the process might be improved once you have completed the chart.

2. If a mother is scheduled for a Caesarean-section birth (i.e., the baby is removed from the womb surgically), how would this flowchart change?

3. If *all* mothers were electronically (or manually) preregistered, how would the flowchart change? Redraw the chart to show your changes.

4. Describe in detail a process that the hospital could analyze, besides the ones mentioned in this case.

---

* You may wish to view the video that accompanies this case before addressing these questions.

Video Case | **Alaska Airlines: 20-Minute Baggage Process—Guaranteed!**

Alaska Airlines is unique among the nine major U.S. carriers not only for its extensive flight coverage of remote towns throughout Alaska (it also covers the United States, Hawaii, and Mexico from its primary hub in Seattle). It is also one of the smallest independent airlines, with 10 300 employees, including 3 000 flight attendants and 1 500 pilots. What makes it really unique, though, is its ability to build state-of-the-art processes, using the latest technology, that yield high customer satisfaction. Indeed, J.D. Power and Associates has ranked Alaska Airlines highest in North America for seven years in a row for customer satisfaction.

Alaska Airlines was the first to sell tickets via the internet, first to offer web check-in and print boarding passes online, and first with kiosk check-in. As Wayne Newton, Director of System Operation Control, states, "We are passionate about our processes. If it's not measured, it's not managed."

One of the processes Alaska is most proud of is its baggage handling system. Passengers can check in at kiosks, tag their own bags with barcode stickers, and deliver them to a customer service agent at the carousel, which carries the bags through the vast underground system that eventually delivers the bags to a baggage handler. En route, each bag passes through TSA automated screening and is manually opened or inspected if it appears suspicious. With the help of barcode readers, conveyer belts automatically sort and transfer bags to their location (called a "pier") at the tarmac level. A baggage handler then loads the bags onto a cart and takes it to the plane for loading by the ramp team waiting inside the cargo hold. There are different procedures for "hot bags" (bags that have less than 30 minutes between plane transfer) and for "cold bags" (bags with over 60 minutes between plane transfers). Hot bags are delivered directly from one plane to another (called "tail-to-tail"). Cold bags are sent back into the normal conveyer system.

The process continues on the destination side with Alaska's unique guarantee that customer luggage will be delivered to the terminal's carousel within 20 minutes of the plane's arrival at the gate. If not, Alaska grants each passenger a 2 000 frequent-flier mile bonus!

The airline's use of technology includes barcode scanners to check in the bag when a passenger arrives, and again before it is placed on the cart to the plane. Similarly, on arrival, the time the passenger door opens is electronically noted and bags are again scanned as they are placed on the baggage carousel at the destination—tracking this metric means that the "time to carousel" (TTC) deadline is seldom missed. And the process almost guarantees that the lost bag rate approaches zero. On a recent day, only one out of 100 flights missed the TTC mark. The baggage process relies not just on technology, though. There are detailed, documented procedures to ensure that bags hit the 20-minute timeframe. Within one minute of the plane door opening at the gate, baggage handlers must begin the unloading. The first bag must be out of the plane within three minutes of parking the plane. This means the ground crew must be in the proper location—with their trucks and ramps in place and ready to go.

Largely because of technology, flying on Alaska Airlines is remarkably reliable—even in the dead of an Alaska winter with only two hours of daylight, 50 mph winds, slippery runways, and low visibility. Alaska Airlines has had the industry's best on-time performance, with 87% if its flights landing on time.

Discussion Questions*

1. Prepare a flowchart of the process a passenger's bag follows from kiosk to destination carousel. (See Example 2 in Chapter 6 for a sample flowchart.) Include the exception process for the TSA opening of selected bags.

2. What other processes can an airline examine? Why is each important?
3. How does the kiosk alter the check-in process?
4. What metrics (quantifiable measures) are needed to track baggage?
5. What is the role of scanners in the baggage process?

_____

*You may wish to view the video that accompanies this case before addressing these questions.

CHAPTER 7 | RAPID REVIEW

MyLab Operations Management

Main Heading	Review Material	
FOUR PROCESS STRATEGIES (pp. 266–272)	• **Process (or transformation) strategy**—An organization's approach to transforming resources into goods and services.	Problems: 7.5–7.14
	The objective of a process strategy is to build a production process that meets customer requirements and product specifications within cost and other managerial constraints.	
	Virtually every good or service is made by using some variation of one of four process strategies.	
	Process focus—A production facility organized around processes to facilitate low-volume, high-variety production.	
	The vast majority of global production is devoted to making low-volume, high-variety products in process-focused facilities, also known as job shops or *intermittent process* facilities.	
	Process-focused facilities have high variable costs with extremely low utilization (5% to 25%) of facilities.	**VIDEO 7.1** Process Strategy at Wheeled Coach Ambulance
	• **Repetitive process**—A product-oriented production process that uses modules.	
	• **Modules**—Parts or components of a product previously prepared, often in a continuous process.	**ACTIVE MODEL 7.1**
	The repetitive process is the classic assembly line. It allows the firm to use modules and combine the economic advantages of the product-focused model with the customization advantages of the process-focused model.	
	• **Product focus**—A facility organized around products; a product-oriented, high-volume, low-variety process.	
	Product-focused facilities are also called *continuous processes,* because they have very long, continuous production runs.	
	The specialized nature of a product-focused facility requires high fixed cost; however, low variable costs reward high facility utilization.	
	• **Mass customization**—Rapid, low-cost production that caters to constantly changing unique customer desires.	
	• **Build-to-order (BTO)**—Produce to customer order rather than to a forecast.	
	Major challenges of a build-to-order system include: *product design, process design, inventory management, tight schedules,* and *responsive partners.*	Virtual Office Hours for Solved Problem: 7.1
	• **Postponement**—The delay of any modifications or customization to a product as long as possible in the production process.	
	• **Crossover chart**—A chart of costs at the possible volumes for more than one process.	

MyLab Operations Management

Main Heading	Review Material	
SELECTION OF EQUIPMENT AND TECHNOLOGY (pp. 272–273)	Picking the best equipment involves understanding the specific industry and available processes and technology. The choice requires considering cost, quality, capacity, and flexibility. • **Flexibility**—The ability to respond with little penalty in time, cost, or customer value.	
PROCESS ANALYSIS AND DESIGN (pp. 273–277)	Five tools of process analysis are (1) flowcharts, (2) time-function mapping, (3) value-stream mapping, (4) process charts, and (5) service blueprinting. • **Flowchart**—A drawing used to analyze movement of people or material. • **Time-function mapping (or process mapping)**—A flowchart with time added on the horizontal axis. • **Value-stream mapping (VSM)**—A process that helps managers understand how to add value in the flow of material and information through the entire production process. • **Process charts**—Charts that use symbols to analyze the movement of people or material. Process charts allow managers to focus on value-added activities and to compute the percentage of value-added time (= operation time/total time). • **Service blueprinting**—A process analysis technique that lends itself to a focus on the customer and the provider's interaction with the customer.	Problems: 7.2, 7.3
SPECIAL CONSIDERATIONS FOR SERVICE PROCESS DESIGN (pp. 277–279)	Services can be classified into one of four quadrants, based on relative degrees of labour and customization: 1 *Service factory;* 2 *Service shop;* 3 *Mass service;* 4 *Professional service* Techniques for improving service productivity include: • *Separation*—Structuring service so customers must go where the service is offered • *Self-service*—Customers examining, comparing, and evaluating at their own pace • *Postponement*—Customizing at delivery • *Focus*—Restricting the offerings • *Modules*—Modular selection of service; modular production • *Automation*—Separating services that may lend themselves to a type of automation • *Scheduling*—Precise personnel scheduling • *Training*—Clarifying the service options; explaining how to avoid problems	**VIDEO 7.2** Process Analysis at Arnold Palmer Hospital
PRODUCTION TECHNOLOGY (pp. 279–283)	• **Computer numerical control (CNC)**—Machinery with its own computer and memory. • **Automatic identification system (AIS)**—A system for transforming data into electronic form (e.g., barcodes). • **Radio frequency identification (RFID)**—A wireless system in which integrated circuits with antennas send radio waves. • **Process control**—The use of information technology to control a physical process. • **Vision systems**—Systems that use video cameras and computer technology in inspection roles. • **Robot**—A flexible machine with the ability to hold, move, or grab items. It functions through electronic impulses that activate motors and switches. • **Automated storage and retrieval systems (ASRSs)**—Computer-controlled warehouses that provide for the automatic placement of parts into and from designated places within a warehouse. • **Automated guided vehicle (AGV)**—Electronically guided and controlled cart used to move materials. • **Flexible manufacturing system (FMS)**—A system that uses an automated work cell controlled by electronic signals from a common centralized computer facility. • **Computer-integrated manufacturing (CIM)**—A manufacturing system in which CAD, FMS, inventory control, warehousing, and shipping are integrated.	

Main Heading	Review Material
TECHNOLOGY IN SERVICES (pp. 283–284)	Many rapid technological developments have occurred in the service sector. These range from POS terminals and RFID to online newspapers and ebooks.
PROCESS REDESIGN (p. 284)	• **Process redesign**—The fundamental rethinking of business processes to bring about dramatic improvements in performance. Process redesign often focuses on activities that cross functional lines.

Self-Test

■ **Before taking the self-test,** refer to the learning objectives listed at the beginning of the chapter.

LO1 Low-volume, high-variety processes are also known as:
   a) continuous processes.
   b) process focused.
   c) repetitive processes.
   d) product focused.

LO2 A crossover chart for process selection focuses on:
   a) labour costs.
   b) material cost.
   c) both labour and material costs.
   d) fixed and variable costs.
   e) fixed costs.

LO3 Tools for process analysis include all of the following except:
   a) flowchart.
   b) vision systems.
   c) service blueprinting.
   d) time-function mapping.
   e) value-stream mapping.

LO4 Customer feedback in process design is lower as:
   a) the degree of customization is increased.
   b) the degree of labour is increased.
   c) the degree of customization is lowered.
   d) both a and b.
   e) both b and c.

LO5 Computer-integrated manufacturing (CIM) includes manufacturing systems that have:
   a) computer-aided design, direct numerical control machines, and material handling equipment controlled by automation.
   b) transaction processing, a management information system, and decision support systems.
   c) automated guided vehicles, robots, and process control.
   d) robots, automated guided vehicles, and transfer equipment.

Answers: LO1. b; LO2. d; LO3. b; LO4. c; LO5. a.

MyLab Operations Management

Most of these questions can be found in MyLab Operations Management. Visit MyLab Operations Management to access cases, videos, downloadable software, and much more. MyLab Operations Management Management also features a personalized Study Plan that helps you identify which chapter concepts you've mastered and guides you towards study tools for additional practice.

Capacity and Constraint Management

Supplement

7

Learning Objectives

LO1 Define *capacity* 293

LO2 Determine design capacity, effective capacity, and utilization 295

LO3 Perform bottleneck analysis 300

LO4 Compute break-even 304

LO5 Determine expected monetary value of a capacity decision 309

LO6 Compute net present value 309

Capacity

What should be the seating capacity of a concert hall? How many customers per day should an Olive Garden or a Hard Rock Cafe be able to serve? How large should a Frito-Lay plant be to produce 75 000 bags of Ruffles in an eight-hour shift? In this supplement, we look at tools that help a manager make these decisions.

After selection of a production process (see Chapter 7), managers need to determine capacity. **Capacity** is the *throughput*, or the number of units, a facility can hold, receive, store, or produce in a given time. Capacity decisions often determine capital requirements and therefore a large portion of fixed cost. Capacity also determines whether demand will be satisfied or whether facilities will be idle. If a facility is too large, portions of it will sit unused and add cost to existing production. If a facility is too small, customers—and perhaps entire markets—will be lost. Determining facility size, with an objective of achieving high levels of utilization and a high return on investment, is critical.

Capacity planning can be viewed in three time horizons. In Figure S7.1 we note that long-range capacity (greater than one year) is a function of adding facilities and equipment that have a long lead time. In the intermediate range (three to 18 months), we can add equipment, personnel, and shifts; we can subcontract; and we can build or use inventory. This is the "aggregate planning" task. In the short run (usually up to three months), we are primarily concerned with scheduling jobs and people, as well as allocating machinery. Modifying capacity in the short run is difficult, as we are usually constrained by existing capacity.

LO1 Define *capacity*

Capacity
The *throughput*, or number of units a facility can hold, receive, store, or produce in a period of time.

DESIGN AND EFFECTIVE CAPACITY

Design capacity is the maximum theoretical output of a system in a given period under ideal conditions. It is normally expressed as a rate, such as the number of tonnes of steel that can be produced per week, per month, or per year. For many companies, measuring capacity can be straightforward: It is the maximum number of units the company is capable of producing in a specific time. However, for some organizations, determining capacity can be more difficult. Capacity can be measured in terms of beds (a hospital), active members (a church), or classroom size (a school). Other organizations use total work time available as a measure of overall capacity.

Design capacity
The theoretical maximum output of a system in a given period under ideal conditions.

When designing a concert hall, management hopes that the forecasted capacity (the product mix—opera, symphony, and special events—and the technology needed for these events) is accurate and adequate for operation above the break-even point. However, many concert halls, even when operating at full capacity, are unable to reach the break-even point, and supplemental funding must be obtained.

Klaus Lang/All Canada Photos/Alamy Stock Photo

Most organizations operate their facilities at a rate less than the design capacity. They do so because they have found that they can operate more efficiently when their resources are not stretched to the limit. For example, Ian's Bistro has tables set with two or four chairs seating a total of 270 guests. But the tables are never filled that way. Some tables will have one or three guests; tables can be pulled together for parties of six or eight. There are always unused chairs. Design capacity is 270, but *effective capacity* is often closer to 220, which is 81% of design capacity.

Effective capacity

The capacity a firm can expect to achieve, given its product mix, methods of scheduling, maintenance, and standards of quality.

Utilization

Actual output as a percent of design capacity.

Efficiency

Actual output as a percent of effective capacity.

Effective capacity is the capacity a firm *expects* to achieve given the current operating constraints. Effective capacity is often lower than design capacity because the facility may have been designed for an earlier version of the product or a different product mix than is currently being produced.

Two measures of system performance are particularly useful: utilization and efficiency. **Utilization** is simply the percent of *design capacity* actually achieved. **Efficiency** is the percent of *effective capacity* actually achieved. Depending on how facilities are used and managed, it may be difficult or impossible to reach 100% efficiency. Operations managers tend to be evaluated on

FIGURE S7.1

Time Horizons and Capacity Options

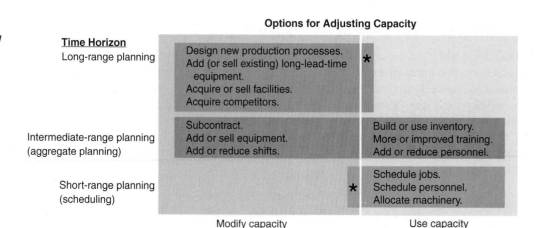

Options for Adjusting Capacity

Time Horizon	Modify capacity	Use capacity
Long-range planning	Design new production processes. Add (or sell existing) long-lead-time equipment. Acquire or sell facilities. Acquire competitors. *	
Intermediate-range planning (aggregate planning)	Subcontract. Add or sell equipment. Add or reduce shifts.	Build or use inventory. More or improved training. Add or reduce personnel.
Short-range planning (scheduling)	*	Schedule jobs. Schedule personnel. Allocate machinery.

* Difficult to adjust capacity, as limited options exist

efficiency. The key to improving efficiency is often found in correcting quality problems and in effective scheduling, training, and maintenance. Utilization and efficiency are computed below:

$$\text{Utilization} = \text{Actual output}/\text{Design capacity} \qquad \text{(S7-1)}$$

$$\text{Efficiency} = \text{Actual output}/\text{Effective capacity} \qquad \text{(S7-2)}$$

In Example S1, we determine these values.

Sara James Bakery has a plant for processing *Deluxe* breakfast rolls and wants to better understand its capability. Determine the design capacity, utilization, and efficiency for this plant when producing this *Deluxe* roll.

APPROACH ▶ Last week, the facility produced 148 000 rolls. The effective capacity is 175 000 rolls. The production line operates seven days per week, with three 8-hour shifts per day. The line was designed to process the nut-filled, cinnamon-flavoured *Deluxe* roll at a rate of 1200 per hour. The firm first computes the design capacity and then uses Equation (S7-1) to determine utilization and Equation (S7-2) to determine efficiency.

SOLUTION ▶

$$\text{Design capacity} = (7 \text{ days} \times 3 \text{ shifts} \times 8 \text{ hours}) \times (1200 \text{ rolls per hour}) = 201\,600 \text{ rolls}$$

$$\text{Utilization} = \text{Actual output}/\text{Design capacity} = 148\,000/201\,600 = 73.4\%$$

$$\text{Efficiency} = \text{Actual output}/\text{Effective capacity} = 148\,000/175\,000 = 84.6\%$$

INSIGHT ▶ The bakery now has the information necessary to evaluate efficiency.

LEARNING EXERCISE ▶ If the actual output is 150 000, what is the efficiency? [Answer: 85.7%.]

RELATED PROBLEMS ▶ S7.1, S7.2, S7.4, S7.5, S7.7

ACTIVE MODEL S7.1 This example is further illustrated in Active Model S7.1 at **MyLab Operations Management.**

EXAMPLE S1

Determining Capacity Utilization and Efficiency

Design capacity, utilization, and efficiency are all important measures for an operations manager. But managers often need to know the expected output of a facility or process. To do this, we solve for actual (or in this case, future or expected) output as shown in Equation (S7-3):

$$\text{Actual (or Expected) output} = (\text{Effective capacity})(\text{Efficiency}) \qquad \text{(S7-3)}$$

Expected output is sometimes referred to as *rated capacity*. With a knowledge of effective capacity and efficiency, a manager can find the expected output of a facility. We do so in Example S2.

LO2 Determine design capacity, effective capacity, and utilization

---

The manager of Sara James Bakery (see Example S1) now needs to increase production of the increasingly popular *Deluxe* roll. To meet this demand, she will be adding a second production line.

APPROACH ▶ The manager must determine the expected output of this second line for the sales department. Effective capacity on the second line is the same as on the first line, which is 175 000 *Deluxe* rolls. The first line is operating at an efficiency of 84.6%, as computed in Example S1. But output on the second line will be less than the first line because the crew will be primarily new hires; the efficiency can be expected to be no more than 75%. What is the expected output?

SOLUTION ▶ Use Equation (S7-3) to determine the expected output:

$$\text{Expected output} = (\text{Effective capacity})(\text{Efficiency}) = (175\,000)(0.75) = 131\,250 \text{ rolls}$$

INSIGHT ▶ The sales department can now be told the expected output is 131 250 *Deluxe* rolls.

LEARNING EXERCISE ▶ After one month of training, the crew on the second production line is expected to perform at 80% efficiency. What is the revised expected output of *Deluxe* rolls? [Answer: 140 000.]

RELATED PROBLEMS ▶ S7.3, S7.6, S7.8

EXAMPLE S2

Determining Expected Output

OM in Action Matching Airline Capacity to Demand

Airlines constantly struggle to control their capital expenditures and to adapt to unstable demand patterns.

Southwest and Lufthansa have each taken their own approach to increasing capacity while holding down capital investment. To manage capacity constraints on the cheap, Southwest squeezes seven flight segments out of its typical plane schedule per day—one more than most competitors. Its operations personnel find that quick ground turnaround, long a Southwest strength, is a key to this capital-saving technique.

Lufthansa has cut hundreds of millions of dollars in new jet purchases by squashing rows of seats 2 inches closer together. On the A320, for example, Lufthansa added two rows of seats, giving the plane 174 seats instead of 162. For its European fleet, this is the equivalent of having 12 more Airbus A320 jets. But Lufthansa will tell you that squeezing in more seats is not quite as bad as it sounds, as the new generation of ultra-thin seats provides passengers with more leg room. Using a strong mesh, similar to that in fancy office chairs (instead of inches of foam padding), and moving magazine pockets to the top of seat backs, there is actually more knee room than with the old chairs.

Unstable demands in the airline industry provide another capacity challenge. Seasonal patterns (e.g., fewer people fly in the winter), compounded by spikes in demand during major holidays and summer vacations, play havoc with efficient use of capacity. Airlines attack costly seasonality in several ways. First, they schedule more planes for maintenance and renovations during slow winter months, curtailing winter capacity; second, they seek out contra-seasonal routes. And when capacity is substantially above demand, placing planes in storage (as shown in the photo) may be the most economical answer.

Airlines also use revenue management (see Chapter 13) to maximize perseat pricing of available capacity, regardless of current demand patterns.

Sources: The Wall Street Journal (February 29, 2012) and (October 6, 2011).

If the expected output is inadequate, additional capacity may be needed. Much of the remainder of this supplement addresses how to effectively and efficiently add that capacity.

CAPACITY AND STRATEGY

Sustained profits come from building competitive advantage, not just from a good financial return on a specific process. Capacity decisions must be integrated into the organization's mission and strategy. Investments are not to be made as isolated expenditures but as part of a coordinated plan that will place the firm in an advantageous position. The questions to be asked are, "Will these investments eventually win profitable customers?" and "What competitive advantage (such as process flexibility, speed of delivery, improved quality, and so on) do we obtain?"

All 10 decisions of operations management we discuss in this text, as well as other organizational elements such as marketing and finance, are affected by changes in capacity. Change in capacity will have sales and cash flow implications, just as capacity changes have quality, supply chain, human resource, and maintenance implications. All must be considered. See *OM in Action Box*, "Matching Airline Capacity to Demand".

CAPACITY CONSIDERATIONS

In addition to tight integration of strategy and investments, there are four special considerations for a good capacity decision:

1. *Forecast demand accurately:* An accurate forecast is paramount to the capacity decision. The new product may be Olive Garden's veal scampi, a dish that places added demands on the restaurant's food service, or the product may be a new maternity capability at Arnold Palmer Hospital, or the new hybrid Lexus. Whatever the new product, its prospects and the life cycle of existing products must be determined. Management must know which products are being added and which are being dropped, as well as their expected volumes.

2. *Understand the technology and capacity increments:* The number of initial alternatives may be large, but once the volume is determined, technology decisions may be aided by analysis of cost, human resources required, quality, and reliability. Such a review often reduces the number of alternatives to a few. The technology may dictate the capacity increment. Meeting added demand with a few extra tables in an Olive Garden may not be difficult, but meeting increased demand for a new automobile by adding a new assembly line at BMW may be very difficult—and expensive. The operations manager is held responsible for the technology and the correct capacity increment.

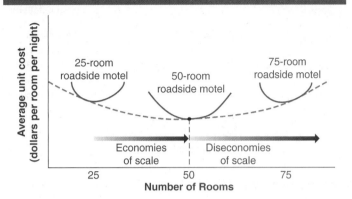

FIGURE S7.2
Economies and Diseconomies of Scale

STUDENT TIP

Each industry and technology has an optimum size.

3. *Find the optimum operating size (volume):* Technology and capacity increments often dictate an optimal size for a facility. A roadside motel may require 50 rooms to be viable: If smaller, the fixed cost is too burdensome; if larger, the facility becomes more than one manager can supervise. A hypothetical optimum for the motel is shown in Figure S7.2. This issue is known as *economies and diseconomies of scale.* For decades, very large integrated steel mills were considered optimal. Then along came Nucor, CMC, and other mini-mills with a new process and a new business model that changed the optimum size of a steel mill.

4. *Build for change:* In our fast-paced world, change is inevitable. So operations managers build flexibility into the facility and equipment. They evaluate the sensitivity of the decision by testing several revenue projections on both the upside and downside for potential risks. Buildings can often be built in phases; and buildings and equipment can be designed with modifications in mind to accommodate future changes in product, product mix, and processes.

Rather than strategically manage capacity, managers may tactically manage demand.

MANAGING DEMAND

Even with good forecasting and facilities built to that forecast, there may be a poor match between the actual demand that occurs and available capacity. A poor match may mean demand exceeds capacity or capacity exceeds demand. However, in both cases, firms have options.

Tim Hortons does considerable research before determining the optimum size for each location.

FIGURE S7.3

By Combining Products that Have Complementary Seasonal Patterns, Capacity Can Be Better Utilized

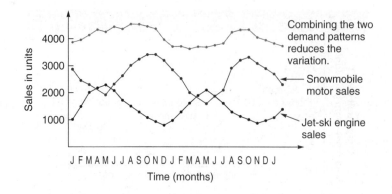

Combining the two demand patterns reduces the variation.

← Snowmobile motor sales

← Jet-ski engine sales

J F M A M J J A S O N D J F M A M J J A S O N D J

Time (months)

DEMAND EXCEEDS CAPACITY When *demand exceeds capacity*, the firm may be able to curtail demand simply by raising prices, scheduling long lead times (which may be inevitable), and discouraging marginally profitable business. However, because inadequate facilities reduce revenue below what is possible, the long-term solution is usually to increase capacity.

CAPACITY EXCEEDS DEMAND When *capacity exceeds demand*, the firm may want to stimulate demand through price reductions or aggressive marketing, or it may accommodate the market through product changes. When decreasing customer demand is combined with old and inflexible processes, layoffs and plant closings may be necessary to bring capacity in line with demand.

ADJUSTING TO SEASONAL DEMANDS A seasonal or cyclical pattern of demand is another capacity challenge. In such cases, management may find it helpful to offer products with complementary demand patterns—that is, products for which the demand is high for one when low for the other. For example, in Figure S7.3, the firm is adding a line of snowmobile motors to its line of jet-skis to smooth demand. With appropriate complementing of products, perhaps the utilization of facility, equipment, and personnel can be smoothed.

TACTICS FOR MATCHING CAPACITY TO DEMAND Various tactics for matching capacity to demand exist. Options for adjusting capacity include:

1. Making staffing changes (increasing or decreasing the number of employees or shifts).
2. Adjusting equipment (purchasing additional machinery or selling or leasing out existing equipment).
3. Improving processes to increase throughput.
4. Redesigning products to facilitate more throughput.
5. Adding process flexibility to better meet changing product preferences.
6. Closing facilities.

Recessions (e.g., 2008—2010) and terrorist attacks (e.g., September 11, 2001) can make even the best capacity decision for an airline look bad. And excess capacity for an airline can be very expensive, with storage costs running as high as $60 000 per month per aircraft. Here, as a testimonial to excess capacity, aircraft sit idle in the Mojave Desert.

Matching capacity and demand can be a challenge. When market share is declining, the mismatch between demand and capacity means empty plants and laid-off employees (left). On the other hand, when demand exceeds capacity, as at this opening of the Apple store on the outskirts of Rome, Italy, the mismatch may mean frustrated customers and lost revenue (right).

The foregoing tactics can be used to adjust demand to existing facilities. The strategic issue is, of course, how to have a facility of the correct size.

DEMAND AND CAPACITY MANAGEMENT IN THE SERVICE SECTOR

In the service sector, scheduling customers is *demand management*, and scheduling the work-force is *capacity management*.

DEMAND MANAGEMENT When demand and capacity are fairly well matched, demand management can often be handled with appointments, reservations, or a first-come, first-served rule. In some businesses, such as doctors' and lawyers' offices, an *appointment system* is the schedule and is adequate. *Reservations systems* work well in rental car agencies, hotels, and some restaurants as a means of minimizing customer waiting time and avoiding disappointment over unfilled service. In retail shops, a post office, or a fast-food restaurant, a *first-come, first-served* rule for serving customers may suffice. Each industry develops its own approaches to matching demand and capacity. Other more aggressive approaches to demand management include many variations of discounts: "early bird" specials in restaurants, discounts for matinee performances or for seats at odd hours on an airline, and cheap weekend phone calls.

CAPACITY MANAGEMENT When managing demand is not feasible, then managing capacity through changes in full-time, temporary, or part-time staff may be an option. This is the approach in many services. Getting fast and reliable radiology readings can be the difference between life and death for an emergency room patient. To smooth out the demand, Canadian hospitals are striving to offer more night-time services, and those patients who cannot or choose not to wait could have the ability to move up the queue and have their scan or MRI done sooner, perhaps at 3:00 a.m.

Bottleneck Analysis and the Theory of Constraints

As managers seek to match capacity to demand, decisions must be made about the size of specific operations or work areas in the larger system. Each of the interdependent work areas can be expected to have its own unique capacity. **Capacity analysis** involves determining the through-put capacity of workstations in a system and ultimately the capacity of the entire system.

A key concept in capacity analysis is the role of a constraint or **bottleneck**. A bottleneck is an operation that is the limiting factor or constraint. The term *bottleneck* refers to the literal neck of a bottle that constrains flow or, in the case of a production system, constrains throughput. A bottleneck has the lowest effective capacity of any operation in the system and thus limits the system's output. Bottlenecks occur in all facets of life—from job shops where a machine is constraining the work flow to highway traffic where two lanes converge into one inadequate lane, resulting in traffic congestion.

We define the **process time** of a station as the time to produce a unit (or a specified batch size of units) at that workstation. For example, if 16 customers can be checked out in a super-

Capacity analysis
A means of determining through-put capacity of workstations or an entire production system.

Bottleneck
The limiting factor or constraint in a system.

Process time
The time to produce a unit (or specified batch of units) at a workstation.

market line every 60 minutes, then the process time at that station is 3.75 minutes per customer (= 60/16). (Process time is simply the inverse of capacity, which in this case is 60 minutes per hour/3.75 minutes per customer 5 16 customers per hour.)

To determine the bottleneck in a production system, simply identify the station with the slowest process time. The **bottleneck time** is the process time of the slowest workstation (the one that takes the longest) in a production system. For example, the flowchart in Figure S7.4 shows a simple assembly line. Individual station process times are 2, 4, and 3 minutes, respectively. The bottleneck time is 4 minutes. This is because station B is the slowest station. Even if we were to speed up station A, the entire production process would not be faster. Inventory would simply pile up in front of station B even more than now. Likewise, if station C could work faster, we could not tap its excess capacity because station B will not be able to feed products to it any faster than 1 every 4 minutes.

Bottleneck time

The process time of the longest (slowest) process, that is, the bottleneck.

FIGURE S7.4

Three-Station Assembly Line

A box represents an operation, a triangle represents inventory, and arrows represent precedence relationships.

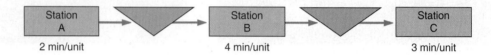

Throughput time

The time it takes for a product to go through the production process *with no waiting*. It is the time of the longest path through the system.

The **throughput time**, on the other hand, is the time it takes a unit to go through production from start to end, *with no waiting*. (Throughput time describes the behaviour in an empty system. In contrast, flow time describes the time to go through a production process from beginning to end, including idle time waiting for stations to finish working on other units.) The throughput time to produce a new completed unit in Figure S7.4 is 9 minutes (= 2 minutes + 4 minutes + 3 minutes).

Bottleneck time and throughput time may be quite different. For example, a Ford assembly line may roll out a new car every minute (bottleneck time), but it may take 25 hours to actually make a car from start to finish (throughput time). This is because the assembly line has many workstations, with each station contributing to the completed car. Thus, bottleneck time determines the system's capacity (one car per minute), while its throughput time determines potential ability to produce a newly ordered product from scratch in 25 hours.

The following two examples illustrate capacity analysis for slightly more complex systems. Example S3 introduces the concept of parallel processes, and Example S4 introduces the concept of simultaneous processing.

EXAMPLE **S3**

Capacity Analysis with Parallel Processes

LO3 Perform bottleneck analysis

Howard Kraye's sandwich shop provides healthy sandwiches for customers. Howard has two identical sandwich assembly lines. A customer first places an order, which takes 30 seconds. The order is then sent to one of the two assembly lines. Each assembly line has two workers and three operations: (1) assembly worker 1 retrieves and cuts the bread (15 seconds/sandwich), (2) assembly worker 2 adds ingredients and places the sandwich onto the toaster conveyor belt (20 seconds/sandwich), and (3) the toaster heats the sandwich (40 seconds/sandwich). Finally, another employee wraps the heated sandwich coming out of the toaster and delivers it to the customer (37.5 seconds/sandwich). A flowchart of the process is shown below. Howard wants to determine the bottleneck time and throughput time of this process.

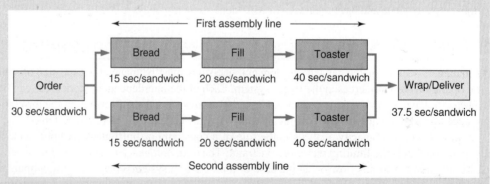

APPROACH ▶ Clearly the toaster is the single-slowest resource in the five-step process, but is it the bottleneck? Howard should first determine the bottleneck time of each of the two assembly lines separately, then the bottleneck time of the combined assembly lines, and finally the bottleneck time of the entire operation. For throughput time, each assembly line is identical, so Howard should just sum the process times for all five operations.

SOLUTION ▶ Because each of the three assembly-line operations uses a separate resource (worker or machine), different partially completed sandwiches can be worked on simultaneously at each station. Thus, the bottleneck time of each assembly line is the longest process time of each of the three operations. In this case, the 40-second toasting time represents the bottleneck time of each assembly line. Next, the bottleneck time of the *combined* assembly-line operations is 40 seconds per *two* sandwiches, or 20 seconds per sandwich. Therefore, the wrapping and delivering operation, with a process time of 37.5 seconds, appears to be the bottleneck for the entire operation. The capacity per hour equals 3 600 seconds per hour/37.5 seconds per sandwich = 96 sandwiches per hour. The throughput time equals 30 + 15 + 20 + 40 + 37.5 = 142.5 seconds (or 2 minutes and 22.5 seconds), assuming no wait time in line to begin with.

INSIGHT ▶ Doubling the resources at a workstation effectively cuts the time at that station in half. (If n parallel [redundant] operations are added, the process time of the combined workstation operation will equal $1/n$ times the original process time.)

LEARNING EXERCISE ▶ If Howard hires an additional wrapper, what will be the new hourly capacity? [Answer: The new bottleneck is now the order-taking station: Capacity = 3600 seconds per hour/30 seconds per sandwich = 120 sandwiches per hour.]

RELATED PROBLEMS ▶ S7.9, S7.10, S7.11, S7.12, S7.13

In Example S3, how could we claim that the process time of the toaster was 20 seconds per sandwich when it takes 40 seconds to toast a sandwich? The reason is that we had two toasters; thus, two sandwiches could be toasted every 40 seconds, for an average of one sandwich every 20 seconds. And that time for a toaster can actually be achieved if the start times for the two are *staggered* (i.e., a new sandwich is placed in a toaster every 20 seconds). In that case, even though each sandwich will sit in the toaster for 40 seconds, a sandwich could emerge from one of the two toasters every 20 seconds. As we see, doubling the number of resources effectively cuts the process time at that station in half, resulting in a doubling of the capacity of those resources.

Dr. Cynthia Knott's dentistry practice has been cleaning customers' teeth for decades. The process for a basic dental cleaning is relatively straightforward: (1) the customer checks in (2 minutes); (2) a lab technician takes and develops X-rays (2 and 4 minutes, respectively); (3) the dentist processes and examines the X-rays (5 minutes) *while* the hygienist cleans the teeth (24 minutes); (4) the dentist meets with the patient to poke at a few teeth, explain the X-ray results, and tell the patient to floss more often (8 minutes); and (5) the customer pays and books her next appointment (6 minutes). A flowchart of the customer visit is shown below. Dr. Knott wants to determine the bottleneck time and throughput time of this process.

EXAMPLE S4

Capacity Analysis with Simultaneous Processes

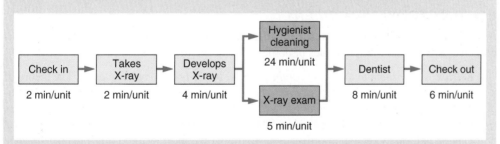

APPROACH ▶ With simultaneous processes, an order or a product is essentially *split* into different paths to be rejoined later on. To find the bottleneck time, each operation is treated separately, just as though all operations were on a sequential path. To find the throughput time, the time over *all* paths must be computed, and the throughput time is the time of the *longest* path.

SOLUTION ▶ The bottleneck in this system is the hygienist cleaning operation at 24 minutes per patient, resulting in an hourly system capacity of 60 minutes/24 minutes per patient = 2.5 patients. The throughput time is the maximum of the two paths through the system. The path through the X-ray exam is 2 + 2 + 4 + 5 + 8 + 6 = 27 minutes, while the path through the hygienist cleaning operation is 2 + 2 + 4 + 24 + 8 + 6 = 46 minutes. Thus a patient should be out the door after 46 minutes (i.e., the maximum of 27 and 46).

INSIGHT ▶ With simultaneous processing, all operation times in the entire system are not simply added together to compute throughput time because some operations are occurring simultaneously. Instead, the time of the longest path through the system is deemed the throughput time.

LEARNING EXERCISE ▶ Suppose that the same technician now has the hygienist start immediately after the X-rays are taken (allowing the hygienist to start 4 minutes sooner). The technician then develops the X-rays while the hygienist is cleaning teeth. The dentist still examines the X-rays while the teeth cleaning is occurring. What would be the new system capacity and throughput time? [Answer: The X-ray development operation is now on the parallel path with cleaning and X-ray exam, reducing the total patient visit duration by 4 minutes, for a throughput time of 42 minutes (the maximum of 27 and 42). However, the hygienist cleaning operation is still the bottleneck, so the capacity remains 2.5 patients per hour.]

RELATED PROBLEMS ▶ S7.14, S7.15

To summarize: (1) the *bottleneck* is the operation with the longest (slowest) process time, after dividing by the number of parallel (redundant) operations, (2) the *system capacity* is the inverse of the *bottleneck time* , and (3) the *throughput time* is the total time through the longest path in the system, assuming no waiting.

THEORY OF CONSTRAINTS

Theory of constraints (TOC)
A body of knowledge that deals with anything that limits an organization's ability to achieve its goals.

The **theory of constraints (TOC)** has been popularized by the book *The Goal: A Process of Ongoing Improvement,* by Goldratt and Cox.[1] TOC is a body of knowledge that deals with anything that limits or constrains an organization's ability to achieve its goals. Constraints can be physical (e.g., process or personnel availability, raw materials, or supplies) or nonphysical (e.g., procedures, morale, and training). Recognizing and managing these limitations through a five-step process is the basis of TOC.

Step 1: Identify the constraints.
Step 2: Develop a plan for overcoming the identified constraints.
Step 3: Focus resources on accomplishing Step 2.
Step 4: Reduce the effects of the constraints by offloading work or by expanding capability. Make sure that the constraints are recognized by all those who can have an impact on them.
Step 5: When one set of constraints is overcome, go back to Step 1 and identify new constraints.

The *OM in Action* box "Overcoming the Constraints" shows that TOC is used in services as well as manufacturing.

BOTTLENECK MANAGEMENT

A crucial constraint in any system is the bottleneck, and managers must focus significant attention on it. We present four principles of bottleneck management:

1. *Release work orders to the system at the pace set by the bottleneck's capacity:* The theory of constraints utilizes the concept of *drum, buffer, rope* to aid in the implementation of bottleneck and non-bottleneck scheduling. In brief, the *drum* is the beat of the system. It provides the schedule—the pace of production. The *buffer* is the resource, usually inventory, which may be helpful to keep the bottleneck operating at the pace of the drum. Finally, the *rope* provides the synchronization or communication necessary to pull units through the system. The rope can be thought of as signals between workstations.
2. *Lost time at the bottleneck represents lost capacity for the whole system:* This principle implies that the bottleneck should always be kept busy with work. Well-trained and cross-trained employees and inspections prior to the bottleneck can reduce lost capacity at a bottleneck.
3. *Increasing the capacity of a non-bottleneck station is a mirage:* Increasing the capacity of *non-bottleneck* stations has no impact on the system's overall capacity. Working faster

---

[1] See E. M. Goldratt and J. Cox, *The Goal: A Process of Ongoing Improvement*, 3rd rev. ed., Great Barrington, MA: North River Press (2004).

OM in Action   Overcoming the Constraints

The Fredericton International Airport Authority Inc. (FIAA) has operated the Fredericton International Airport in New Brunswick since 2001. The facility that was inherited from the Government of Canada at that time was deficient in many respects and was obstructed by many strategic and tactical constraints. It had enjoyed little investment and was incapable of meeting the needs of even the traffic that was using it at that time.

The early years of the airport authority were marked by a number of important investments in the runway, terminal, and many other aspects of the airport facility. All of these investments resulted in a significant expansion of the capabilities of the airport to facilitate a broader range of services that reflected the needs of the community. There resulted an expansion of the use of the airport and a substantial growth in both aircraft and passenger traffic.

Management has learned much about the challenges of operating an airport since 2001. As a smaller scale airport, they are challenged to meet the needs of the community within the context of a National Airport System mandate. They do not serve a large population, and they operate in a highly competitive market with two other airports operating in New Brunswick.

Within this environment, they must define a strategy that meets these challenges. They must fulfill their mandate responsibly, be good managers of the facility, meet their obligations for safety and security, and develop services needed by their population.

Since privatization, they have refined the operation and are effective in meeting their challenges. They have developed an organization and structures necessary for operational efficiency and integrity. They have developed a strong team of people, better trained and able to respond to the challenges of their jobs. They have demonstrated an ability to be capable, efficient, and entrepreneurial. They are becoming a model small airport organization, an organization that others look up to.

Strategies and Sustainability

The Fredericton International Airport Authority Inc. must be competitive with other New Brunswick National Airport System airports as well as others in the Canadian marketplace. Its costs cannot become disincentives for air carriers and customers to do business there. The second major financial imperative is the need to be financially sustainable in the long term, a considerable challenge given the scale of the operations. In meeting these overall needs, CEO and president David Innes

indicated that the following strategic objectives are important:

- FIAA must strive to increase all types of traffic at the airport, and, in particular, airline passenger traffic. To do this, it will support current air carriers in the delivery of their operations at the airport and encourage them to expand services at this airport. It will also more aggressively pursue new air carriers to add new routes to the service network.
- FIAA intends to grow its operating and administration expenses at a rate less than the rate at which traffic growth occurs and pass this increased productivity on to customers.
- FIAA will work to increase its discretionary revenue at the airport by selling additional services to customers. The target growth rate of discretionary revenue stream will be 120% of the traffic growth rate.
- FIAA will budget to establish a "Capital and Emergency Fund" of $2 million to be used in financial emergencies. It will budget to add $100 000 per year in this fund and will also place all unused budgeted capital and operating contingency monies in that fund.
- FIAA will seek long-term and ongoing financial assistance arrangements with all levels of government for capital projects.

While operating in a vital and unique industry such as this, it is imperative that organizations such as the FIAA continuously define and redefine their strategies in order to remain viable and relevant. This approach has been a key factor in its current and ongoing success.

Discussion Questions

1. Using the five steps of the theory of constraints process as a guide, explain how the FIAA has been advancing its operational effectiveness.
2. Discuss the value that a good process strategy provides in order to overcome operational constraints in an operation such as the Fredericton International Airport.
3. What are the implications of poor processes in this type of business?
4. What would be the linkages between process strategy and sustainability in the Fredericton International Airport?

Sources: yfcmobile.ca; www.frederictonairport.ca/images/stories/about_yfc/2009strategicplanfinal.pdf.

---

on a non-bottleneck station may just create extra inventory, with all of its adverse effects. This implies that non-bottlenecks should have planned idle time. Extra work or setups at non-bottleneck stations will not cause delay, which allows for smaller batch sizes and more frequent product changeovers at non-bottleneck stations.

4. *Increasing the capacity of the bottleneck increases capacity for the whole system:* Managers should focus improvement efforts on the bottleneck. Bottleneck capacity may be improved by various means, including offloading some of the bottleneck operations to another workstation (e.g., let the beer foam settle next to the tap at the bar, not under it, so the next beer

can be poured), increasing capacity of the bottleneck (adding resources, working longer or working faster), subcontracting, developing alternative routings, and reducing setup times.

Even when managers have process and quality variability under control, changing technology, personnel, products, product mixes, and volumes can create multiple and shifting bottlenecks. Identifying and managing bottlenecks is a required operations task, but by definition, bottlenecks cannot be "eliminated". A system will always have at least one.

STUDENT TIP

Failure to operate above break-even can be devastating.

Break-Even Analysis

LO4 Compute break-even

Break-even analysis

A means of finding the point, in dollars and units, at which costs equal revenues.

Break-even analysis is the critical tool for determining the capacity a facility must have to achieve profitability. The objective of **break-even analysis** is to find the point, in dollars and units, at which costs equal revenue. This point is the break-even point. Firms must operate above this level to achieve profitability. As shown in Figure S7.5, break-even analysis requires an estimation of fixed costs, variable costs, and revenue.

Fixed costs are costs that continue even if no units are produced. Examples include depreciation, taxes, debt, and mortgage payments. *Variable costs* are those that vary with the volume of units produced. The major components of variable costs are labour and materials. However, other costs, such as the portion of the utilities that varies with volume, are also variable costs. The difference between selling price and variable cost is *contribution*. Only when total contribution exceeds total fixed cost will there be profit.

Another element in break-even analysis is the *revenue function*. In Figure S7.5, revenue begins at the origin and proceeds upward to the right, increasing by the selling price of each unit. Where the revenue function crosses the total cost line (the sum of fixed and variable costs), is the break-even point, with a profit corridor to the right and a loss corridor to the left.

ASSUMPTIONS

A number of assumptions underlie the basic break-even model. Notably, costs and revenue are shown as straight lines. They are shown to increase linearly—that is, in direct proportion to the volume of units being produced. However, neither fixed costs nor variable costs (nor, for that matter, the revenue function) needs be a straight line. For example, fixed costs change as more capital equipment or warehouse space is used; labour costs change with overtime or as marginally skilled workers are employed; the revenue function may change with such factors as volume discounts.

GRAPHIC APPROACH

The first step in the graphic approach to break-even analysis is to define those costs that are fixed and sum them. The fixed costs are drawn as a horizontal line beginning at that dollar

FIGURE S7.5
Basic Break-Even Point

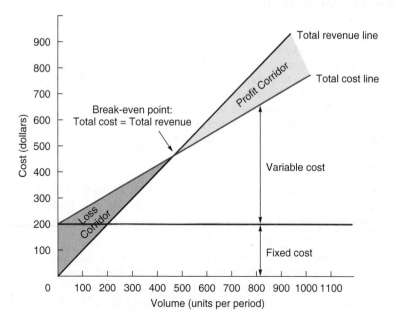

amount on the vertical axis. The variable costs are then estimated by an analysis of labour, materials, and other costs connected with the production of each unit. The variable costs are shown as an incrementally increasing cost, originating at the intersection of the fixed cost on the vertical axis and increasing with each change in volume as we move to the right on the volume (or horizontal) axis.

ALGEBRAIC APPROACH

The formulas for the break-even point in units and dollars are shown below. Let:

BEP_x = break-even point in units TR = total revenue = Px

$BEP_\$$ = break-even point in dollars F = fixed costs

P = price per unit (after all discounts) V = variable costs per unit

x = number of units produced TC = total costs = $F + Vx$

The break-even point occurs where total revenue equals total costs. Therefore:

$$TR = TC \quad \text{or} \quad Px = F + Vx$$

Solving for x, we get

$$\text{Break-even point in units } (BEP_x) = \frac{F}{P - V}$$

and:

$$\text{Break-even point in dollars } (BEP_\$) = BEP_x P = \frac{F}{P - V} P = \frac{F}{(P - V)/P} = \frac{F}{1 - V/P}$$

$$\text{Profit} = TR - TC = Px - (F + Vx) = Px - F - Vx = (P - V)x - F$$

Using these equations, we can solve directly for break-even point and profitability. The two break-even formulas of particular interest are:

$$\text{Break-even in units} = \frac{\text{Total fixed cost}}{\text{Price} - \text{Variable cost}} \tag{S7-4}$$

$$\text{Break-even in dollars} = \frac{\text{Total fixed cost}}{1 - \dfrac{\text{Variable cost}}{\text{Selling price}}} \tag{S7-5}$$

SINGLE-PRODUCT CASE

In Example S5, we determine the break-even point in dollars and units for one product.

EXAMPLE S5

Single Product Break-Even Analysis

Stephens, Inc., wants to determine the minimum dollar volume and unit volume needed at its new facility to break even.

APPROACH ▶ The firm first determines that it has fixed costs of $10 000 this period. Direct labour is $1.50 per unit, and material is $0.75 per unit. The selling price is $4.00 per unit.

SOLUTION ▶ The break-even point in dollars is computed as follows:

$$BEP_\$ = \frac{F}{1 - (V/P)} = \frac{\$10\,000}{1 - [(1.50 + 0.75)/(4.00)]} = \frac{\$10\,000}{0.4375} = \$22\,857.14$$

The break-even point in units is:

$$BEP_x = \frac{F}{P - V} = \frac{\$10\,000}{4.00 - (1.50 + 0.75)} \approx 5714$$

Note that we use total variable costs (i.e., both labour and material).

INSIGHT ▶ The management of Stephens, Inc., now has an estimate in both units and dollars of the volume necessary for the new facility.

LEARNING EXERCISE ▶ If Stephens finds that fixed cost will increase to $12 000, what happens to the break-even in units and dollars? [Answer: The break-even in units increases to ~6857, and break-even in dollars increases to $27 428.57.]

RELATED PROBLEMS ▶ S7.16, S7.17, S7.18, S7.19, S7.20, S7.21, S7.22, S7.23, S7.24, S7.25

EXCEL OM Data File **Ch07SExS5.xlsx** can be found at **MyLab Operations Management.**

ACTIVE MODEL S7.2 This example is further illustrated in Active Model S7.2 at **MyLab Operations Management.**

MULTIPRODUCT CASE

Most firms, from manufacturers to restaurants (even fast-food restaurants), have a variety of offerings. Each offering may have a different selling price and variable cost. Utilizing break-even analysis, we modify Equation (S7-5) to reflect the proportion of sales for each product.

We do this by "weighting" each product's contribution by its proportion of sales. The formula is then:

$$\text{Break-even point in dollars } (BEP_\$) = \frac{F}{\sum\left[\left(1 - \frac{V_i}{P_i}\right) \times (W_i)\right]} \tag{S7-6}$$

where

V = variable cost per unit
P = price per unit
F = fixed cost
W = percent each product is of total dollar sales
i = each product

Paper machines such as the one shown here require a high capital investment. This investment results in a high fixed cost but allows production of paper at a very low variable cost. The production manager's job is to maintain utilization above the break-even point to achieve profitability.

Image Ideas/Stockbyte/Getty Images

Example S6 shows how to determine the break-even point for the multiproduct case at the Le Bistro restaurant.

EXAMPLE S6

Multiproduct Break-Even Analysis

Le Bistro, like most other restaurants, makes more than one product and would like to know its break-even point in dollars.

APPROACH ▶ Information for Le Bistro follows. Fixed costs are $3000 per month.

Item	Price	Cost	Annual Forecasted Sales Units
Sandwich	$5.00	$3.00	9000
Drinks	1.50	0.50	9000
Baked potato	2.00	1.00	7000

With a variety of offerings, we proceed with break-even analysis just as in a single-product case, except that we weight each of the products by its proportion of total sales using Equation (S7-6).

SOLUTION ▶ Multiproduct Break-Even: Determining Contribution

1	2	3	4	5	6	7	8
Item (*i*)	Selling Price (*P*)	Variable Cost (*V*)	(*V/P*)	1 − (*V/P*)	Annual Forecasted Sales $	% of Sales	Weighted Contribution (col. 5 × col. 7)
Sandwich	$5.00	$3.00	0.60	0.40	$45 000	0.621	0.248
Drinks	1.50	0.50	0.33	0.67	13 500	0.186	0.125
Baked potato	2.00	1.00	0.50	0.50	14 000	0.193	0.096
					$72 500	1.000	0.469

Note: Revenue for sandwiches is $45 000 (= $5.00 × 9000), which is 62.1% of the total revenue of $72 500. Therefore, the contribution for sandwiches is "weighted" by 0.621. The weighted contribution is 0.621 × 0.40 = 0.248. In this manner, its *relative* contribution is properly reflected.

Using this approach for each product, we find that the total weighted contribution is $0.469 for each dollar of sales, and the break-even point in dollars is $76 759.

$$BEP_\$ = \frac{F}{\sum\left[\left(1 - \frac{V_i}{P_i}\right) \times (W_i)\right]} = \frac{\$3000 \times 12}{0.469} = \frac{\$36\,000}{0.469} = \$76\,759.06$$

The information given in this example implies total daily sales (52 weeks at six days each) of:

$$\frac{\$76\,759}{312 \text{ days}} = \$246.02$$

INSIGHT ▶ The management of Le Bistro now knows that it must generate average sales of $246.02 each day to break even. Management also knows that if the forecasted sales of $72 500 are correct, Le Bistro will lose money, as break-even is $76 759.

LEARNING EXERCISE ▶ If the manager of Le Bistro wants to make an additional $1000 per month in salary, and considers this a fixed cost, what is the new break-even point in average sales per day? [Answer: $328.03.]

RELATED PROBLEMS ▶ S7.26, S7.27

Break-even figures by product provide the manager with added insight as to the realism of the sales forecast. They indicate exactly what must be sold each day, as we illustrate in Example S7.

Le Bistro also wants to know the break-even for the number of sandwiches that must be sold every day.

APPROACH ▶ Using the data in Example S6, we take the forecast sandwich sales of 62.1% times the daily break-even of $246.02 divided by the selling price of each sandwich ($5.00).

SOLUTION ▶ At break-even, sandwich sales must then be:

$$\frac{0.621 \times \$246.02}{\$5.00} = \text{Number of sandwiches} = 30.6 \approx 31 \text{ sandwiches each day}$$

INSIGHT ▶ With knowledge of individual product sales, the manager has a basis for determining material and labour requirements.

LEARNING EXERCISE ▶ At a dollar break-even of $328.03 per day, how many sandwiches must Le Bistro sell each day? [Answer: ~40.74 or 41 sandwiches.]

RELATED PROBLEMS ▶ S7.26b, S7.27b

EXAMPLE S7

Unit Sales at Break-Even

Once break-even analysis has been prepared, analyzed, and judged to be reasonable, decisions can be made about the type and capacity of equipment needed. Indeed, a better judgment of the likelihood of success of the enterprise can now be made.

Reducing Risk with Incremental Changes

When demand for goods and services can be forecast with a reasonable degree of precision, determining a break-even point and capacity requirements can be rather straightforward. But, more likely, determining the capacity and how to achieve it will be complicated, as many factors are difficult to measure and quantify. Factors such as technology, competitors, building restrictions, cost of capital, human resource options, and regulations make the decision interesting. To complicate matters further, demand growth is usually in small units, while capacity additions are likely to be both instantaneous and in large units. This contradiction adds to the capacity decision risk. To reduce risk, incremental changes that hedge demand forecasts may be a good option. Figure S7.6 illustrates three approaches to new capacity.

Alternative Figure S7.6(a) *leads* capacity—that is, acquires capacity to stay ahead of demand, with new capacity being acquired at the beginning of Period 1. This capacity handles increased demand, until the beginning of Period 2. At the beginning of Period 2, new capacity is again acquired, which will allow the organization to stay ahead of demand until the beginning of Period 3. This process can be continued indefinitely into the future. Here capacity is acquired *incrementally*—at the beginning of Period 1 *and* at the beginning of Period 2. But managers can also elect to make a larger increase at the beginning of Period 1—an increase that may satisfy expected demand until the beginning of Period 3.

Excess capacity gives operations managers flexibility. For instance, in the hotel industry, added (extra) capacity in the form of rooms can allow a wider variety of room options and perhaps flexibility in room cleanup schedules. In manufacturing, excess capacity can be used to do more setups, shorten production runs, and drive down inventory costs.

But Figure S7.6(b) shows an option that *lags* capacity, perhaps using overtime or subcontracting to accommodate excess demand. Figure S7.6(c) *straddles* demand by building capacity that is "average," sometimes lagging demand and sometimes leading it. Both the lag and straddle option have the advantage of delaying capital expenditure.

In cases where the business climate is stable, deciding between alternatives can be relatively easy. The total cost of each alternative can be computed, and the alternative with the least total cost can be selected. However, when capacity requirements are subject to significant unknowns, "probabilistic" models may be appropriate. One technique for making successful capacity planning decisions with an uncertain demand is decision theory, including the use of expected monetary value.

(a) Leading Strategy
Management leads capacity in periodic increments. Management could also add enough capacity in one period to handle expected demand for multiple periods.

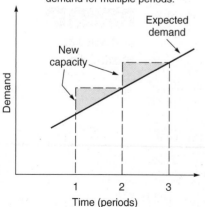

(b) Lag Strategy
Here management lags (chases) demand.

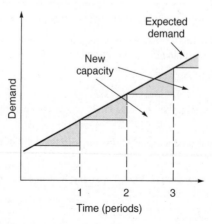

(c) Straddle Strategy
Here management uses average capacity increments to straddle demand.

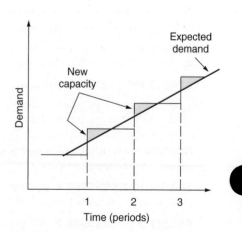

FIGURE S7.6 **Approaches to Capacity Expansion**

Applying Expected Monetary Value (EMV) to Capacity Decisions

STUDENT TIP

Uncertainty in capacity decisions makes EMV a helpful tool.

Determining expected monetary value (EMV) requires specifying alternatives and various states of nature. For capacity planning situations, the state of nature usually is future demand or market favourability. By assigning probability values to the various states of nature, we can make decisions that maximize the expected value of the alternatives. Example S8 shows how to apply EMV to a capacity decision.

LO5 Determine expected monetary value of a capacity decision

Northern Hospital Supplies, a company that makes hospital gowns, is considering capacity expansion.

APPROACH ▶ Northern's major alternatives are to do nothing, build a small plant, build a medium plant, or build a large plant. The new facility would produce a new type of gown, and currently the potential or marketability for this product is unknown. If a large plant is built and a favourable market exists, a profit of $100 000 could be realized. An unfavourable market would yield a $90 000 loss. However, a medium plant would earn a $60 000 profit with a favourable market. A $10 000 loss would result from an unfavourable market. A small plant, on the other hand, would return $40 000 with favourable market conditions and lose only $5000 in an unfavourable market. Of course, there is always the option of doing nothing.

Recent market research indicates that there is a 0.4 probability of a favourable market, which means that there is also a 0.6 probability of an unfavourable market. With this information, the alternative that will result in the highest expected monetary value (EMV) can be selected.

SOLUTION ▶ Compute the EMV for each alternative:

$$\text{EMV (large plant)} = (0.4)(\$100\ 000) + (0.6)(-\$90\ 000) = -\$14\ 000$$

$$\text{EMV (medium plant)} = (0.4)(\$60\ 000) + (0.6)(-\$10\ 000) = +\$18\ 000$$

$$\text{EMV (small plant)} = (0.4)(\$40\ 000) + (0.6)(-\$5000) = +\$13\ 000$$

$$\text{EMV (do nothing)} = \$0$$

Based on EMV criteria, Northern should build a medium plant.

INSIGHT ▶ If Northern makes many decisions like this, then determining the EMV for each alternative and selecting the highest EMV is a good decision criterion.

LEARNING EXERCISE ▶ If a new estimate of the loss from a medium plant in an unfavourable market increases to −$20 000 what is the new EMV for this alternative? [Answer: $12 000, which changes the decision because the small plant EMV is now higher.]

RELATED PROBLEMS ▶ S7.28, S7.29

EXAMPLE S8

EMV Applied to Capacity Decision

Applying Investment Analysis to Strategy-Driven Investments

STUDENT TIP

An operations manager may be held responsible for return on investment (ROI).

Once the strategy implications of potential investments have been considered, traditional investment analysis is appropriate. We introduce the investment aspects of capacity next.

INVESTMENT, VARIABLE COST, AND CASH FLOW

Because capacity and process alternatives exist, so do options regarding capital investment and variable cost. Managers must choose from among different financial options as well as capacity and process alternatives. Analysis should show the capital investment, variable cost, and cash flows as well as net present value for each alternative.

LO6 Compute net present value

NET PRESENT VALUE

Determining the discount value of a series of future cash receipts is known as the **net present value** technique. By way of introduction, let us consider the time value of money. Say you invest $100.00 in a bank at 5% for one year. Your investment will be worth $100.00 + ($100.00)(0.05) = $105.00.

Net present value
A means of determining the discounted value of a series of future cash receipts.

If you invest the $105.00 for a second year, it will be worth $105.00 + ($105.00)(0.05) = $110.25 at the end of the second year. Of course, we could calculate the future value of $100.00 at 5% for as many years as we wanted by simply extending this analysis. However, there is an easier way to express this relationship mathematically. For the first year:

$$\$105 = \$100(1 + 0.05)$$

For the second year:

$$\$110.25 = \$105(1 + 0.05) = \$100(1 + 0.05)^2$$

In general:

$$F = P(1 + i)^N \tag{S7-7}$$

where F = future value (such as $110.25 or $105)
   P = present value (such as $100.00)
   i = interest rate (such as 0.05)
   N = number of years (such as one year or two years)

In most investment decisions, however, we are interested in calculating the present value of a series of future cash receipts. Solving for P, we get:

$$P = \frac{F}{(1 + i)^N} \tag{S7-8}$$

When the number of years is not too large, the preceding equation is effective. However, when the number of years, N, is large, the formula is cumbersome. For 20 years, you would have to compute $(1 + i)^{20}$. Without a sophisticated calculator, this computation would be difficult. Interest-rate tables, such as Table S7.1, alleviate this situation. First, let us restate the present value equation:

$$P = \frac{F}{(1 + i)^N} = FX \tag{S7-9}$$

where X = a factor from Table S7.1 defined as = $1/(1 + i)^N$ and F = future value

Thus, all we have to do is find the factor X and multiply it by F to calculate the present value, P. The factors, of course, are a function of the interest rate, i, and the number of years, N. Table S7.1 lists some of these factors.

Table S7.1
Present Value of $1

Year	5%	6%	7%	8%	9%	10%	12%	14%
1	0.952	0.943	0.935	0.926	0.917	0.909	0.893	0.877
2	0.907	0.890	0.873	0.857	0.842	0.826	0.797	0.769
3	0.864	0.840	0.816	0.794	0.772	0.751	0.712	0.675
4	0.823	0.792	0.763	0.735	0.708	0.683	0.636	0.592
5	0.784	0.747	0.713	0.681	0.650	0.621	0.567	0.519
6	0.746	0.705	0.666	0.630	0.596	0.564	0.507	0.456
7	0.711	0.665	0.623	0.583	0.547	0.513	0.452	0.400
8	0.677	0.627	0.582	0.540	0.502	0.467	0.404	0.351
9	0.645	0.592	0.544	0.500	0.460	0.424	0.361	0.308
10	0.614	0.558	0.508	0.463	0.422	0.386	0.322	0.270
15	0.481	0.417	0.362	0.315	0.275	0.239	0.183	0.140
20	0.377	0.312	0.258	0.215	0.178	0.149	0.104	0.073

Equations (S7-8) and (S7-9) are used to determine the present value of one future cash amount, but there are situations in which an investment generates a series of uniform and equal cash amounts. This type of investment is called an *annuity*. For example, an investment might yield $300 per year for three years. Easy-to-use factors have been developed for the present value of annuities. These factors are shown in Table S7.2. The basic relationship is

$$S = RX$$

where X = factor from Table S7.2
S = present value of a series of uniform annual receipts
R = receipts that are received every year for the life of the investment (the annuity)

Year	5%	6%	7%	8%	9%	10%	12%	14%
1	0.952	0.943	0.935	0.926	0.917	0.909	0.893	0.877
2	1.859	1.833	1.808	1.783	1.759	1.736	1.690	1.647
3	2.723	2.673	2.624	2.577	2.531	2.487	2.402	2.322
4	3.546	3.465	3.387	3.312	3.240	3.170	3.037	2.914
5	4.329	4.212	4.100	3.993	3.890	3.791	3.605	3.433
6	5.076	4.917	4.766	4.623	4.486	4.355	4.111	3.889
7	5.786	5.582	5.389	5.206	5.033	4.868	4.564	4.288
8	6.463	6.210	5.971	5.747	5.535	5.335	4.968	4.639
9	7.108	6.802	6.515	6.247	5.985	5.759	5.328	4.946
10	7.722	7.360	7.024	6.710	6.418	6.145	5.650	5.216
15	10.380	9.712	9.108	8.559	8.060	7.606	6.811	6.142
20	12.462	11.470	10.594	9.818	9.128	8.514	7.469	6.623

Table S7.2
Present Value of an Annuity of $1

The present value of a uniform annual series of amounts is an extension of the present value of a single amount, and thus Table S7.2 can be directly developed from Table S7.1. The factors for any given interest rate in Table S7.2 are the cumulative sum of the values in Table S7.1. In Table S7.1, for example, 0.943, 0.890, and 0.840 are the factors for years 1, 2, and 3 when the interest rate is 6%. The cumulative sum of these factors is 2.673. Now look at the point in Table S7.2 where the interest rate is 6% and the number of years is 3. The factor for the present value of an annuity is 2.673, as you would expect.

Example S9 shows how to determine the present value of an annuity.

River Road Medical Clinic is thinking of investing in a sophisticated new piece of medical equipment. It will generate $7000 per year in receipts for five years.

APPROACH ▶ Determine the present value of this cash flow; assume an interest rate of 6%.

SOLUTION ▶ The factor from Table S7.2 (4.212) is obtained by finding that value when the interest rate is 6% and the number of years is 5:

$$S = RX = \$7000(4.212) = \$29\,484$$

INSIGHT ▶ There is another way of looking at this example. If you went to a bank and took a loan for $29 484 today, your payments would be $7000 per year for five years if the bank used an interest rate of 6% compounded yearly. Thus, $29 484 is the present value.

LEARNING EXERCISE ▶ If the interest rate is 8%, what is the present value? [Answer: $27 951.]

RELATED PROBLEMS ▶ S7.30, S7.31, S7.32, S7.33, S7.34, S7.35

EXCEL OM Data File Ch07SExS9.xlsx can be found at **MyLab Operations Management.**

EXAMPLE S9

Determining Net Present Value of Future Receipts of Equal Value

The net present value method is straightforward: You simply compute the present value of all cash flows for each investment alternative. When deciding among investment alternatives, you pick the investment with the highest net present value. Similarly, when making several investments, those with higher net present values are preferable to investments with lower net present values.

Solved Problem S7.4 shows how to use the net present value to choose between investment alternatives.

Although net present value is one of the best approaches to evaluating investment alternatives, it does have its faults. Limitations of the net present value approach include the following:

1. Investments with the same net present value may have significantly different projected lives and different salvage values.
2. Investments with the same net present value may have different cash flows. Different cash flows may make substantial differences in the company's ability to pay its bills.
3. The assumption is that we know future interest rates, which we do not.
4. Payments are always made at the end of the period (week, month, or year), which is not always the case.

SUPPLEMENT SUMMARY

Managers tie equipment selection and capacity decisions to the organization's missions and strategy. Four additional considerations are critical: (1) accurately forecasting demand; (2) understanding the equipment, processes, and capacity increments; (3) finding the optimum operating size; and (4) ensuring the flexibility needed for adjustments in technology, product features and mix, and volumes.

Techniques that are particularly useful to operations managers when making capacity decisions include good forecasting, bottleneck analysis, break-even analysis, expected monetary value, cash flow, and net present value (NPV).

The single most important criterion for investment decisions is the contribution to the overall strategic plan and the winning of profitable orders. Successful firms select the correct process and capacity.

Discussion Questions

1. Distinguish between design capacity and effective capacity.
2. What is effective capacity?
3. What is efficiency?
4. How is actual, or expected, output computed?
5. Explain why doubling the capacity of a bottleneck may not double the system capacity.
6. Distinguish between bottleneck time and throughput time.
7. What is the theory of constraints?
8. What are the assumptions of break-even analysis?
9. What keeps plotted revenue data from falling on a straight line in a break-even analysis?
10. Under what conditions would a firm want its capacity to lag demand? To lead demand?
11. Explain how net present value is an appropriate tool for comparing investments.
12. Describe the five-step process that serves as the basis of the theory of constraints.
13. What are the techniques available to operations managers to deal with a bottleneck operation? Which of these does not decrease throughput time?

Using Software for Break-Even Analysis

Excel, Excel OM, and POM for Windows all handle break-even and cost–volume analysis problems.

X Using Excel

It is a straightforward task to develop the formulas to do a break-even analysis in Excel. Although we do not demonstrate the basics here, Active Model S7.2 provides a working example. You can see similar spreadsheet analysis in the Excel OM preprogrammed software that accompanies this text.

X USING EXCEL OM

Excel OM's Break-Even Analysis module provides the Excel formulas needed to compute the break-even points, and the solution and graphical output.

P USING POM FOR WINDOWS

Similar to Excel OM, POM for Windows also contains a break-even/cost–volume analysis module.

Solved Problems Virtual Office Hours help is available at MyLab Operations Management.

▼ SOLVED PROBLEM S7.1

Sara James Bakery, described in Examples S1 and S2, has decided to increase its facilities by adding one additional process line. The firm will have two process lines, each working seven days a week, three shifts per day, eight hours per shift, with effective capacity of 300 000 rolls. This addition, however, will reduce overall system efficiency to 85%. Compute the expected production with this new effective capacity.

▼ SOLUTION

Expected production = (Effective capacity)(Efficiency)

$$= 300\ 000(0.85)$$

$$= 255\ 000 \text{ rolls per week}$$

▼ SOLVED PROBLEM S7.2

Marty McDonald has a business packaging software in Regina. His annual fixed cost is $10 000, direct labour is $3.50 per package, and material is $4.50 per package. The selling price will be $12.50 per package. What is the break-even point in dollars? What is break-even in units?

▼ SOLUTION

$$BEP_\$ = \frac{F}{1 - (V/P)} = \frac{\$10\ 000}{1 - (\$8.00/\$12.50)} = \frac{\$10\ 000}{0.36} = \$27\ 777.78$$

$$BEP_x = \frac{F}{P - V} = \frac{\$10\ 000}{\$12.50 - \$8.00} = \frac{\$10\ 000}{\$4.50}$$

$$= {\sim}2222.22 \text{ or } 2222 \text{ units}$$

▼ SOLVED PROBLEM S7.3

John has been asked to determine whether the $22.50 cost of tickets for the community dinner theatre will allow the group to achieve break-even and whether the 175 seating capacity is adequate. The cost for each performance of a 10-performance run is $2500. The facility rental cost for the entire 10 performances is $10 000. Drinks and parking are extra charges and have their own price and variable costs, as shown below:

1	2	3	4	5	6	7	8	9
	Selling Price (P)	Variable Cost (V)	Percent Variable Cost (V/P)	Contribution 1 = (V/P)	Estimated Quantity of Sales Units (sales)	Dollar Sales (Sales × P)	Percent of Sales	Contribution Weighted by Percent Sales (col. 5 × col. 8)
Tickets with dinner	$22.50	$10.50	0.467	0.533	175	$ 3938	0.741	0.395
Drinks	$ 5.00	$ 1.75	0.350	0.650	175	$ 875	0.165	0.107
Parking	$ 5.00	$ 2.00	0.400	0.600	100	$ 500	0.094	0.056
					450	$ 5313	1.000	0.558

▼ SOLUTION

$$BEP_\$ = \frac{F}{\sum\left[\left(1 - \frac{V_i}{P_i}\right) \times (W_i)\right]} = \frac{\$(10 \times 2500) + \$10\ 000}{0.558} = \frac{\$35\ 000}{0.558} = \$62\ 724$$

Revenue for each performance (from column 7) = $5313
Total forecasted revenue for the 10 performances = (10 × $5313) = $53 130
Forecasted revenue with this mix of sales shows a break-even of $62 724.01.

Thus, given this mix of costs, sales, and capacity, John determines that the theatre will not break even.

▼ SOLVED PROBLEM S7.4

Your boss has told you to evaluate the cost of two machines. After some questioning, you are assured that they have the costs shown. Assume:

a. The life of each machine is three years, and
b. The company thinks it knows how to make 14% on investments no riskier than this one.

Determine via the present value method which machine to purchase.

	Machine A	Machine B
Original cost	$13 000	$20 000
Labour cost per year	2 000	3 000
Floor space per year	500	600
Energy (electricity) per year	1 000	900
Maintenance per year	2 500	500
Total annual cost	$ 6 000	$ 5 000
Salvage value	$ 2 000	$ 7 000

▼ SOLUTION

		Machine A			Machine B		
		Column 1	Column 2	Column 3	Column 4	Column 5	Column 6
Now	Expense	1.000	$13 000	$13 000	1.000	$20 000	$20 000
1 yr.	Expense	0.877	6 000	5 262	0.877	5 000	4 385
2 yr.	Expense	0.769	6 000	4 614	0.769	5 000	3 845
3 yr.	Expense	0.675	6 000	4 050	0.675	5 000	3 375
				$26 926			$31 605
3 yr.	Salvage Revenue	0.675	$ 2 000	–1 350	0.675	$ 7 000	–4 725
				$25 576			$26 880

We use 1.0 for payments with no discount applied against them (i.e., when payments are made now, there is no need for a discount). The other values in columns 1 and 4 are from the 14% column and the respective year in Table S7.1 (e.g., the intersection of 14% and one year is 0.877, etc.). Columns 3 and 6 are the products of the present value figures times the combined costs. This computation is made for each year and for the salvage value.

The calculation for machine A for the first year is:

$$0.877 \times (\$2000 + \$500 + \$1000 + \$2500) = \$5262$$

The salvage value of the product is *subtracted* from the summed costs, because it is a receipt of cash. Since the sum of the net costs for machine B is larger than the sum of the net costs for machine A, machine A is the low-cost purchase, and your boss should be so informed.

▼ **SOLVED PROBLEM S7.5**

T. Smunt Manufacturing Corp. has the process displayed below. The drilling operation occurs separately from and simultaneously with the sawing and sanding operations. The product only needs to go through one of the three assembly operations (the assembly operations are "parallel").

a. Which operation is the bottleneck?
b. What is the system's process time?
c. What is the throughput time for the overall system?

d. If the firm operates eight hours per day, 22 days per month, what is the monthly capacity of the manufacturing process?
e. Suppose that a second drilling machine is added, and it has the same process time as the original drilling machine. What is the new bottleneck time?
f. Suppose that a second drilling machine is added, and it has the same process time as the original drilling machine. What is the new throughput time?

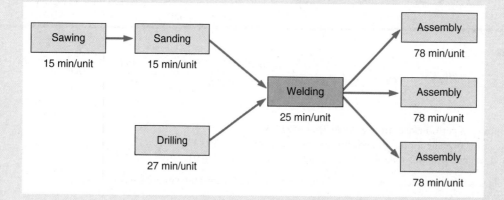

▼ SOLUTION

a. The process time of assembly is 78 minutes/3 operators = 26 minutes per unit, so the station with the longest process time, hence the bottleneck, is drilling, at 27 minutes.
b. The system's process time is 27 minutes per unit (the longest process, drilling).
c. System throughput time is the maximum of (15 + 15 + 25 + 78), (27 + 25 + 78) = maximum of (133, 130) = 133 minutes.

d. Monthly capacity = (60 minutes)(8 hours)(22 days)/27 minutes per unit = 10 560 minutes per month/27 minutes per unit = 391.11 units/month.
e. The bottleneck shifts to assembly, with a process time of 26 minutes per unit.
f. Redundancy does not affect throughput time. It is still 133 minutes.

Problems*

•   **S7.1**   If a plant were designed to produce 7000 hammers per day but is limited to making 6000 hammers per day because of the time needed to change equipment between styles of hammers, what is the utilization?

•   **S7.2**   For the past month, the plant in Problem S7.1, which has an effective capacity of 6500, has made only 4500 hammers per day because of material delay, employee absences, and other problems. What is its efficiency?

•   **S7.3**   If a plant has an effective capacity of 6500 and an efficiency of 88%, what is the actual (planned) output?

•   **S7.4**   A plant has an effective capacity of 900 units per day and produces 800 units per day with its product mix; what is its efficiency?

•   **S7.5**   Material delays have routinely limited production of household sinks to 400 units per day. If the plant efficiency is 80%, what is the effective capacity?

•   **S7.6**   The effective capacity and efficiency for the next quarter at MMU Mfg. in Burlington, Ontario, for each of three departments are shown:

Department	Effective Capacity	Recent Efficiency
Design	93 600	0.95
Fabrication	156 000	1.03
Finishing	62 400	1.05

Compute the expected production for next quarter for each department.

•• **S7.7**   A Canadian university's business program has the facilities and faculty to handle an enrolment of 2000 new students per semester. However, in an effort to limit class sizes to a "reasonable" level (under 200, generally), the university's registrar, Tom Choi, placed a ceiling on enrolment of 1500 new students. Although there was ample demand for business courses last semester, conflicting schedules allowed only 1450 new students to take business courses. What are the utilization and efficiency of this system?

•• **S7.8**   Under ideal conditions, a service bay at a Fast Lube can serve six cars per hour. The effective capacity and efficiency of a Fast Lube service bay are known to be 5.5 and 0.880, respectively. What is the minimum number of service bays Fast Lube needs to achieve an anticipated production of 200 cars per eight-hour day?

•   **S7.9**   A production line at V. J. Sugumaran's machine shop has three stations. The first station can process a unit in 10 minutes. The second station has two identical machines, each of which can process a unit in 12 minutes (each unit needs only to be processed on one of the two machines). The third station can process a unit in 8 minutes. Which station is the bottleneck station?

•• **S7.10**   A work cell at Chris Ellis Commercial Laundry has a workstation with two machines, and each unit produced at the station needs to be processed by both of the machines. (The same unit cannot be worked on by both machines simultaneously.) Each machine has a production capacity of four units per hour. What is the throughput time of the work cell?

•• **S7.11**   The three-station work cell illustrated in Figure S7.7 has a product that must go through one of the two machines at Station 1 (they are parallel) before proceeding to Station 2.

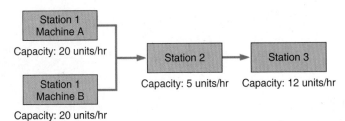

FIGURE S7.7

a) What is the bottleneck time of the system?
b) What is the bottleneck station of this work cell?
c) What is the throughput time?
d) If the firm operates 10 hours per day, five days per week, what is the weekly capacity of this work cell?

•• **S7.12**   The three-station work cell at Pullman Mfg., Inc. is illustrated in Figure S7.8. It has two machines at station 1 in parallel (i.e., the product needs to go through only one of the two machines before proceeding to Station 2).
a) What is the throughput time of this work cell?
b) What is the bottleneck time of this work cell?
c) If the firm operates eight hours per day, six days per week, what is the weekly capacity of this work cell?

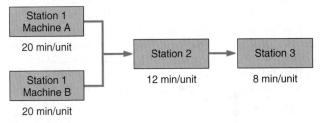

FIGURE S7.8

•• **S7.13**   The Pullman Mfg., Inc. three-station work cell illustrated in Figure S7.8 has two machines at station 1 in parallel. (The product needs to go through only one of the two machines before proceeding to Station 2.) The manager, Ms. Hartley, has asked you to evaluate the system if she adds a parallel machine at Station 2.
a) What is the throughput time of the new work cell?
b) What is the bottleneck time of the new work cell?
c) If the firm operates eight hours per day, six days per week, what is the weekly capacity of this work cell?
d) How did the addition of the second machine at Station 2 affect the performance of the work cell from Problem S7.12?

•   **S7.14**   Klassen Toy Company, Inc. assembles two parts (Parts 1 and 2): Part 1 is first processed at workstation A for 15 minutes per unit and then processed at workstation B for 10 minutes per unit. Part 2 is simultaneously processed at workstation C for 20 minutes per unit. Workstations B and C feed the parts to an assembler at workstation D, where the two parts are assembled. The time at workstation D is 15 minutes.
a) What is the bottleneck of this process?
b) What is the hourly capacity of the process?

•• **S7.15**   A production process at Kenneth Day Manufacturing is shown in Figure S7.9. The drilling operation occurs separately from, and simultaneously with, the sawing and sanding operations.

---

*Note: ⨍means the problem may be solved with POM for Windows and/or Excel OM.

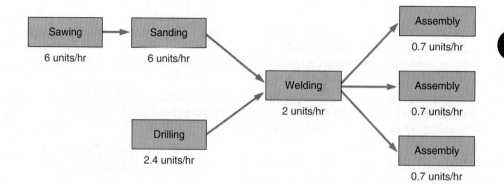

FIGURE S7.9

A product needs to go through only one of the three assembly operations (the operations are in parallel).
a) Which operation is the bottleneck?
b) What is the bottleneck time?
c) What is the throughput time of the overall system?
d) If the firm operates eight hours per day, 20 days per month, what is the monthly capacity of the manufacturing process?

•   **S7.16** Smithson Cutting is opening a new line of scissors for supermarket distribution. It estimates its fixed cost to be $500.00 and its variable cost to be $0.50 per unit. Selling price is expected to average $0.75 per unit.
a) What is Smithson's break-even point in units?
b) What is the break-even point in dollars? **Px**

•   **S7.17** Markland Manufacturing intends to increase capacity by overcoming a bottleneck operation by adding new equipment. Two vendors have presented proposals. The fixed costs for proposal A are $50 000, and for proposal B, $70 000. The variable cost for A is $12.00, and for B, $10.00. The revenue generated by each unit is $20.00.
a) What is the break-even point in units for proposal A?
b) What is the break-even point in units for proposal B? **Px**

•   **S7.18** Using the data in Problem S7.17:
a) What is the break-even point in dollars for proposal A if you add $10 000 installation to the fixed cost?
b) What is the break-even point in dollars for proposal B if you add $10 000 installation to the fixed cost? **Px**

•   **S7.19** Given the data in Problem S7.17, at what volume (units) of output would the two alternatives yield the same profit? **Px**

••   **S7.20** Janelle Heinke, the owner of Ha'Peppas!, is considering a new oven in which to bake the firm's signature dish, vegetarian pizza. Oven type A can handle 20 pizzas an hour. The fixed costs associated with oven A are $20 000 and the variable costs are $2.00 per pizza. Oven B is larger and can handle 40 pizzas an hour. The fixed costs associated with oven B are $30 000 and the variable costs are $1.25 per pizza. The pizzas sell for $14 each.
a) What is the break-even point for each oven?
b) If the owner expects to sell 9000 pizzas, which oven should she purchase?
c) If the owner expects to sell 12 000 pizzas, which oven should she purchase?
d) At what volume should Janelle switch ovens? **Px**

•   **S7.21** Given the following data, calculate: a) BEP_x; b) $BEP_\$$; and c) the profit at 100 000 units:

$$P = \$8/\text{unit} \quad V = \$4/\text{unit} \quad F = \$50\ 000 \text{ **Px**}$$

••   **S7.22** You are considering opening a copy service in the student union. You estimate your fixed cost at $15 000 and the variable

cost of each copy sold at $0.01. You expect the selling price to average $0.05.
a) What is the break-even point in dollars?
b) What is the break-even point in units? **Px**

••   **S7.23** An electronics firm is currently manufacturing an item that has a variable cost of $0.50 per unit and a selling price of $1.00 per unit. Fixed costs are $14 000. Current volume is 30 000 units. The firm can substantially improve the product quality by adding a new piece of equipment at an additional fixed cost of $6000. Variable cost would increase to $0.60, but volume should jump to 50 000 units due to a higher-quality product. Should the company buy the new equipment? **Px**

••   **S7.24** The electronics firm in Problem S7.23 is now considering the new equipment and increasing the selling price to $1.10 per unit. With the higher-quality product, the new volume is expected to be 45 000 units. Under these circumstances, should the company purchase the new equipment and increase the selling price? **Px**

••••**S7.25** Zan Azlett and Angela Zesiger have joined forces to start A&Z Lettuce Products, a processor of packaged shredded lettuce for institutional use. Zan has years of food processing experience, and Angela has extensive commercial food preparation experience. The process will consist of opening crates of lettuce and then sorting, washing, slicing, preserving, and finally packaging the prepared lettuce. Together, with help from vendors, they feel they can adequately estimate demand, fixed costs, revenues, and variable cost per 5-pound bag of lettuce. They think a largely manual process will have monthly fixed costs of $37 500 and variable costs of $1.75 per bag. A more mechanized process will have fixed costs of $75 000 per month with variable costs of $1.25 per 5-pound bag. They expect to sell the shredded lettuce for $2.50 per 5-pound bag.
a) What is the break-even quantity for the manual process?
b) What is the revenue at the break-even quantity for the manual process?
c) What is the break-even quantity for the mechanized process?
d) What is the revenue at the break-even quantity for the mechanized process?
e) What is the monthly profit or loss of the *manual* process if they expect to sell 60 000 bags of lettuce per month?
f) What is the monthly profit or loss of the *mechanized* process if they expect to sell 60 000 bags of lettuce per month?
g) At what quantity would Zan and Angela be indifferent to the process selected?
h) Over what range of demand would the *manual* process be preferred over the mechanized process? Over what range of demand would the *mechanized* process be preferred over the manual process? **Px**

•••• **S7.26** As a prospective owner of a club known as the Red Rose, you are interested in determining the volume of sales dollars necessary for the coming year to reach the break-even point. You have decided to break down the sales for the club into four categories, the first category being beer. Your estimate of the beer sales is that 30 000 drinks will be served. The selling price for each unit will average $1.50; the cost is $0.75. The second major category is meals, which you expect to be 10 000 units with an average price of $10.00 and a cost of $5.00. The third major category is desserts and wine, of which you also expect to sell 10 000 units, but with an average price of $2.50 per unit sold and a cost of $1.00 per unit. The final category is lunches and inexpensive sandwiches, which you expect to total 20 000 units at an average price of $6.25 with a food cost of $3.25. Your fixed cost (i.e., rent, utilities, and so on) is $1800 per month plus $2000 per month for entertainment.

a) What is your break-even point in dollars per month?

b) What is the expected number of meals each day if you are open 30 days a month?

••• **S7.27** As manager of the St. Cloud Theatre Company, you have decided that concession sales will support themselves. The following table provides the information you have been able to put together thus far:

Item	Selling Price	Variable Cost	% of Revenue
Soft drink	$1.00	$0.65	25
Wine	1.75	0.95	25
Coffee	1.00	0.30	30
Candy	1.00	0.30	20

Last year's manager, Jim Freeland, has advised you to be sure to add 10% of variable cost as a waste allowance for all categories.

You estimate labour cost to be $250.00 (five booths with two people each). Even if nothing is sold, your labour cost will be $250.00, so you decide to consider this a fixed cost. Booth rental, which is a contractual cost at $50.00 for *each* booth per night, is also a fixed cost.

a) What is break-even volume per evening performance?

b) How much wine would you expect to sell at the break-even point?

•• **S7.28** James Lawson's Bed and Breakfast, in a small historic Newfoundland town, must decide how to subdivide (remodel) the large old home that will become its inn. There are three alternatives: Option A would modernize all baths and combine rooms, leaving the inn with four suites, each suitable for two to four adults. Option B would modernize only the second floor; the results would be six suites, four for two to four adults, two for two adults only. Option C (the status quo option) leaves all walls intact. In this case, there are eight rooms available, but only two are suitable for four adults, and four rooms will not have private baths. Below are the details of profit and demand patterns that will accompany each option:

Alternatives	Annual Profit Under Various Demand Patterns			
	High	*p*	Average	*p*
A (modernize all)	$90 000	0.5	$25 000	0.5
B (modernize 2nd)	$80 000	0.4	$70 000	0.6
C (status quo)	$60 000	0.3	$55 000	0.7

Which option has the highest expected monetary value? **Px**

•••• **S7.29** As operations manager of Holz Furniture, you must make a decision about adding a line of rustic furniture. In discussing the possibilities with your sales manager, Steve Gilbert, you decide that there will definitely be a market and that your firm should enter that market. However, because rustic furniture has a different finish from your standard offering, you decide you need another process line. There is no doubt in your mind about the decision, and you are sure that you should have a second process. But you do question how large to make it. A large process line is going to cost $400 000; a small process line will cost $300 000. The question, therefore, is the demand for rustic furniture. After extensive discussion with Mr. Gilbert and Tim Ireland of Ireland Market Research, Inc., you determine that the best estimate you can make is that there is a two-out-of-three chance of profit from sales as large as $600 000 and a one-out-of-three chance as low as $300 000.

With a large process line, you could handle the high figure of $600 000. However, with a small process line you could not and would be forced to expand (at a cost of $150 000), after which time your profit from sales would be $500 000 rather than the $600 000 because of the lost time in expanding the process. If you do not expand the small process, your profit from sales would be held to $400 000. If you build a small process and the demand is low, you can handle all of the demand.

Should you open a large or small process line?

•• **S7.30** What is the net present value of an investment that costs $75 000 and has a salvage value of $45 000? The annual profit from the investment is $15 000 each year for five years. The cost of capital at this risk level is 12%. **Px**

• **S7.31** The initial cost of an investment is $65 000 and the cost of capital is 10%. The return is $16 000 per year for eight years. What is the net present value? **Px**

• **S7.32** What is the present value of $5600 when the interest rate is 8% and the return of $5600 will not be received for 15 years? **Px**

•• **S7.33** Tim Smunt has been asked to evaluate two machines. After some investigation, he determines that they have the costs shown in the following table. He is told to assume that:

a) the life of each machine is three years, and

b) the company thinks it knows how to make 12% on investments no more risky than this one.

	Machine A	Machine B
Original cost	$10 000	$20 000
Labour per year	2 000	4 000
Maintenance per year	4 000	1 000
Salvage value	2 000	7 000

Determine, via the present value method, which machine Tim should recommend.

•••• **S7.34** Your boss has told you to evaluate two ovens for Tink-the-Tinkers, a gourmet sandwich shop. After some questioning of vendors and receipt of specifications, you are assured that the ovens have the attributes and costs shown in the following table. The following two assumptions are appropriate:

1. The life of each machine is five years.

2. The company thinks it knows how to make 14% on investments no more risky than this one.

	Three Small Ovens at $1250 Each	Two Large Ovens at $2500 Each
Original cost	$3750	$5000
Labour per year in excess of larger models	$750 (total)	
Cleaning/ maintenance	$750 (= $250 each)	$400 (= $200 each)
Salvage value	$750 (= $250 each)	$1000 (= $500 each)

a) Determine via the present value method which machine to tell your boss to purchase.

b) What assumption are you making about the ovens?

c) What assumptions are you making in your methodology?

•••• **S7.35** Bold's Gym, a health club chain, is considering expanding into a new location: the initial investment would be $1 million in equipment, renovation, and a six-year lease, and its annual upkeep and expenses would be $75 000. Its planning horizon is six years out, and at the end, it can sell the equipment for $50 000. Club capacity is 500 members who would pay an annual fee of $600. Bold's expects to have no problems filling membership slots. Assume that the interest rate is 10% (see Table S7.1).

a) What is the present value profit/loss of the deal?

b) The club is considering offering a special deal to the members in the first year. For $3000 upfront, they get a full six-year membership (i.e., one year free). Would it make financial sense to offer this deal?

CASE STUDY

Video Case — Capacity Planning at Arnold Palmer Hospital

Since opening day, the Arnold Palmer Hospital has experienced an explosive growth in demand for its services. One of only six hospitals in the United States to specialize in healthcare for women and children, Arnold Palmer Hospital has cared for over 1 500 000 patients who came to the Orlando facility from all 50 states and more than 100 countries. With patient satisfaction scores in the top 10% of U.S. hospitals surveyed (over 95% of patients would recommend the hospital to others), one of Arnold Palmer Hospital's main focuses is delivery of babies. Originally built with 281 beds and a

Table S7.3
Births at Arnold Palmer Hospital

Year	Births
1995	6 144
1996	6 230
1997	6 432
1998	6 950
1999	7 377
2000	8 655
2001	9 536
2002	9 825
2003	10 253
2004	10 555
2005	12 316
2006	13 070
2007	14 028
2008	14 241
2009	13 050
2010	12 571
2011	12 978
2012	13 529
2013	13 576
2014	13 994

capacity for 6500 births per year, the hospital steadily approached and then passed 10 000 births. Looking at Table S7.3, executive director Kathy Swanson knew an expansion was necessary.

With continuing population growth in its market area serving 18 central Florida counties, Arnold Palmer Hospital was delivering the equivalent of a kindergarten class of babies every day and still not meeting demand. Supported with substantial additional demographic analysis, the hospital was ready to move ahead with a capacity expansion plan and a new 11-storey hospital building across the street from the existing facility.

Thirty-five planning teams were established to study such issues as (1) specific forecasts, (2) services that would transfer to the new facility, (3) services that would remain in the existing facility, (4) staffing needs, (5) capital equipment, (6) pro forma accounting data, and (7) regulatory requirements. Ultimately, Arnold Palmer Hospital was ready to move ahead with a budget of $100 million and a commitment to an additional 150 beds. But given the growth of the central Florida region, Swanson decided to expand the hospital in stages: the top two floors would be empty interiors ("shell") to be completed at a later date, and the fourth-floor operating room could be doubled in size when needed. "With the new facility in place, we are now able to handle up to 16 000 births per year," says Swanson.

Discussion Questions*

1. Given the capacity planning discussion in the text (see Figure S7.6) what approach is being taken by Arnold Palmer Hospital towards matching capacity to demand?

2. What kinds of major changes could take place in Arnold Palmer Hospital's demand forecast that would leave the hospital with an underutilized facility (namely, what are the risks connected with this capacity decision)?

3. Use regression analysis to forecast the point at which Swanson needs to "build out" the top two floors of the new building, namely, when demand will exceed 16 000 births.

---

* You may wish to view the video accompanying this case before addressing these questions.

▶ **Additional Case Study:** Visit **MyLab Operations Management** for this case study:
Fast Creek Lightning Requires the development of a multiproduct break-even solution.

SUPPLEMENT 7 | RAPID REVIEW

MyLab Operations
Management

Main Heading	Review Material
CAPACITY (pp. 293–299)	• **Capacity**—The *throughput*, or number of units a facility can hold, receive, store, or produce in a period of time. Capacity decisions often determine capital requirements and, therefore, a large portion of fixed cost. Capacity also determines whether demand will be satisfied or whether facilities will be idle. *Determining facility size, with an objective of achieving high levels of utilization and a high return on investment, is critical.* Capacity planning can be viewed in three time horizons: 1. *Long-range* (>1 year)—Adding facilities and long lead-time equipment 2. *Intermediate-range* (3–18 months)—"Aggregate planning" tasks, including adding equipment, personnel, and shifts; subcontracting; and building or using inventory 3. *Short-range* (<3 months)—Scheduling jobs and people, and allocating machinery • **Design capacity**—The theoretical maximum output of a system in a given period under ideal conditions. Most organizations operate their facilities at a rate less than the design capacity. • **Effective capacity**—The capacity a firm can expect to achieve, given its product mix, methods of scheduling, maintenance, and standards of quality. • **Utilization**—Actual output as a percent of design capacity. • **Efficiency**—Actual output as a percent of effective capacity. $$\text{Utilization} = \text{Actual output}/\text{Design capacity} \quad (S7\text{-}1)$$ $$\text{Efficiency} = \text{Actual output}/\text{Effective capacity} \quad (S7\text{-}2)$$ $$\text{Actual (or Expected) output} = (\text{Effective capacity})(\text{Efficiency}) \quad (S7\text{-}3)$$ Expected output is sometimes referred to as *rated capacity*. When demand exceeds capacity, a firm may be able to curtail demand simply by raising prices, increasing lead times (which may be inevitable), and discouraging marginally profitable business. When capacity exceeds demand, a firm may want to stimulate demand through price reductions or aggressive marketing, or it may accommodate the market via product changes. In the service sector, scheduling customers is *demand management,* and scheduling the workforce is *capacity management.* When demand and capacity are fairly well matched, demand management in services can often be handled with appointments, reservations, or a first-come, first-served rule. Otherwise, discounts based on time of day may be used (e.g., "early bird" specials, matinee pricing). When managing demand in services is not feasible, managing capacity through changes in full-time, temporary, or part-time staff may be an option.

Main Heading	Review Material	
BOTTLENECK ANALYSIS AND THE THEORY OF CONSTRAINTS (pp. 299–304)	• **Capacity analysis**—A means of determining throughput capacity of workstations or an entire production system. • **Bottleneck**—The limiting factor or constraint in a system. • **Process time**—The time to produce units at a single workstation. • **Bottleneck time**—The time of the longest (slowest) process; that is, the bottleneck. • **Throughput time**—The time it takes for a product to go through the production process with no waiting. A system's process time determines its capacity (e.g., one car per minute), while its process cycle time determines potential ability to build product (e.g., 30 hours). If n parallel (redundant) operations are added, the process time of the combined operations will equal $1/n$ times the process time of the original. With simultaneous processing, an order or product is essentially *split* into different paths to be rejoined later on. The longest path through the system is deemed the throughput time. • **Theory of constraints (TOC)**—A body of knowledge that deals with anything that limits an organization's ability to achieve its goals.	Problems: S7.9–S7.15
BREAK-EVEN ANALYSIS (pp. 304–308)	• **Break-even analysis**—A means of finding the point, in dollars and units, at which costs equal revenues. *Fixed costs* are costs that exist even if no units are produced. Variable costs are those that vary with the volume of units produced. In the break-even model, costs and revenue are assumed to increase linearly. $$\text{Break-even in units} = \frac{\text{Total Fixed cost}}{\text{Price} - \text{Variable cost}} \quad (S7\text{-}4)$$ $$\text{Break-even in dollars} = \frac{\text{Total Fixed cost}}{1 - \dfrac{\text{Variable cost}}{\text{Selling price}}} \quad (S7\text{-}5)$$ $$\text{Break-even point in dollars } (BEP_\$) = \frac{F}{\sum\left[\left(1 - \dfrac{V_i}{P_i}\right) \times (W_i)\right]} \quad (S7\text{-}6)$$	Problems: S7.16–S7.27 Virtual Office Hours for Solved Problem: S7.3 **ACTIVE MODEL S7.2**
REDUCING RISK WITH INCREMENTAL CHANGES (p. 308)	Demand growth is usually in small units, while capacity additions are likely to be both instantaneous and in large units. To reduce risk, incremental changes that hedge demand forecasts may be a good option. Three approaches to capacity expansion are (1) *leading* strategy, (2) *lag* strategy, and (3) *straddle* strategy. Both lag strategy and straddle strategy delay capital expenditure.	**VIDEO S7.1** Capacity Planning at Arnold Palmer Hospital
APPLYING EXPECTED MONETARY VALUE (EMV) TO CAPACITY DECISIONS (p. 309)	Determining expected monetary value requires specifying alternatives and various states of nature (e.g., demand or market favourability). By assigning probability values to the various states of nature, we can make decisions that maximize the expected value of the alternatives.	Problems: S7.28–S7.29
APPLYING INVESTMENT ANALYSIS TO STRATEGY-DRIVEN INVESTMENTS (pp. 309–312)	• **Net present value**—A means of determining the discounted value of a series of future cash receipts. $$F = P(1 + i)^N \quad (S7\text{-}7)$$ $$P = \frac{F}{(1 + i)^N} \quad (S7\text{-}8)$$ $$P = \frac{F}{(1 + i)^N} = FX \quad (S7\text{-}9)$$ When making several investments, those with higher net present values are preferable to investments with lower net present values.	Problems: S7.30–S7.35 Virtual Office Hours for Solved Problem: S7.4

Self-Test

■ **Before taking the self-test,** refer to the learning objectives listed at the beginning of the chapter.

LO1 Capacity decisions should be made on the basis of:
a) building sustained competitive advantage.
b) good financial returns.
c) a coordinated plan.
d) integration into the company's strategy.
e) all of the above.

LO2 Effective capacity is:
a) the capacity a firm expects to achieve, given the current operating constraints.
b) the percent of design capacity actually achieved.
c) the percent of capacity actually achieved.
d) actual output.
e) efficiency.

LO3 System capacity is based on:
a) the bottleneck.
b) throughput time.
c) time of the fastest station.
d) throughput time plus waiting time.
e) none of the above.

LO4 The break-even point is:
a) adding processes to meet the point of changing product demands.
b) improving processes to increase throughput.
c) the point in dollars or units at which cost equals revenue.
d) adding or removing capacity to meet demand.
e) the total cost of a process alternative.

LO5 Expected monetary value is most appropriate:
a) when the payoffs are equal.
b) when the probability of each decision alternative is known.
c) when probabilities are the same.
d) when both revenue and cost are known.
e) when probabilities of each state of nature are known.

LO6 Net present value (NPV):
a) is greater if cash receipts occur later rather than earlier.
b) is greater if cash receipts occur earlier rather than later.
c) is revenue minus fixed cost.
d) is preferred over break-even analysis.
e) is greater if $100 monthly payments are received in a lump sum ($1200) at the end of the year.

Answers: LO1. e; LO2. a; LO3. a; LO4. c; LO5. e; LO6. b.

B. O'Kane/Alamy Stock Photo

Location Strategies

Global > Company Profile FedEx

Location Provides Competitive Advantage for FedEx

Overnight-delivery powerhouse FedEx has believed in the hub concept throughout its 40-year existence. Even though Fred Smith, founder and CEO, got a C on his college paper proposing a hub for small-package delivery, the idea has proven extremely successful. Starting with a hub in Memphis, Tennessee (now called its *superhub*), the U.S. $45 billion firm has added a European hub in Paris, an Asian hub in Guangzhou, China, a Latin American hub in Miami, and a Canadian hub in Toronto. FedEx's fleet of 667 planes flies into 375 airports worldwide, then delivers to the door with more than 80 000 vans and trucks.

Why was Memphis picked as FedEx's central location? (1) It is located in the middle of the United States. (2) It has very few hours of bad weather closures, perhaps contributing to the firm's excellent flight-safety record. (3) It provided FedEx with generous tax incentives.

At the preliminary sorting area, packages and documents are sorted and sent to a secondary sorting area. The Memphis facility covers 1.5 million square feet; it is big enough to hold 33 football fields. Packages are sorted and exchanged until 4:00 a.m.

Each night, except Sunday, FedEx brings to Memphis packages from throughout the world that are going to cities for which FedEx does not have direct flights. The central hub permits service to a far greater number of points with fewer aircraft than the traditional City A–to–City B system. It also allows FedEx to match aircraft flights with package loads each night and to reroute flights when load volume requires it, a major cost savings. Moreover, FedEx also believes that the central hub system helps reduce mishandling and delay in transit because there is total control over the packages from pickup point through delivery.

The Strategic Importance of Location

STUDENT TIP

This chapter illustrates techniques organizations use to locate plants, warehouses, stores, or offices.

VIDEO 8.1
Hard Rock's Location Selection

World markets continue to expand, and the global nature of business is accelerating. Indeed, one of the most important strategic decisions made by many companies—including FedEx, Mercedes-Benz, and Hard Rock—is where to locate their operations. When FedEx opened its Asian hub in Guangzhou, China, in 2009, it set the stage for "round-the-world" flights linking its Paris and Memphis package hubs to Asia. When Mercedes-Benz announced its plans to build its first major overseas plant in Vance, Alabama, it completed a year of competition among 170 sites in 30 states and two countries. When Hard Rock Cafe opened in Moscow, it ended three years of advance preparation of a Russian food supply chain. The strategic impact, cost, and international aspect of these decisions indicate how significant location decisions are.

Firms throughout the world are using the concepts and techniques of this chapter to address the location decision because location greatly affects both fixed and variable costs. Location has a major impact on the overall risk and profit of the company. For instance, depending on the product and type of production or service taking place, transportation costs alone can total as much as 25% of the product's selling price. That is, one-fourth of a firm's total revenue may be needed just to cover freight expenses of the raw materials coming in and finished products going

From Dubai to Chongqing to Honduras, location decisions are often taking shape in urban developments based on airport hubs. The ideal "aerotropolis" is an amalgam of office parks, cargo complexes, convention hotels, and even factories that sometimes line the runway. Welcome to the new global city.

out. Other costs that may be influenced by location include taxes, wages, raw material costs, and rents. When all costs are considered, location may alter total operating expenses as much as 50%.

The economics of transportation are so significant that companies—and even cities—have coalesced around a transportation advantage. For centuries, rivers and ports (and, more recently, rail hubs and then highways) have been a major factor in the location decision. Today airports are often the deciding factor, providing fast, low-cost transportation of goods and people. The book *Aerotropolis* defines an "airport–integration region, extending as far as 60 miles from the inner cluster of hotel, office, distribution, and logistics facilities."[1] The airport is not just a piece of the city but becomes an "airport city".

Companies make location decisions relatively infrequently, usually because demand has outgrown the current plant's capacity or because of changes in labour productivity, exchange rates, costs, or local attitudes. Companies may also relocate their manufacturing or service facilities because of shifts in demographics and customer demand.

Location options include (1) expanding an existing facility instead of moving, (2) maintaining current sites while adding another facility elsewhere, or (3) closing the existing facility and moving to another location.

The location decision often depends on the type of business. For industrial location decisions, the strategy is usually minimizing costs, although innovation and creativity may also be critical. For retail and professional service organizations, the strategy focuses on maximizing revenue. Warehouse location strategy, however, may be driven by a combination of cost and speed of delivery. *The objective of location strategy is to maximize the benefit of location to the firm.*

LOCATION AND COSTS

Because location is such a significant cost and revenue driver, location often has the power to make (or break) a company's business strategy. Key multinationals in every major industry, from automobiles to cellular phones, now have or are planning a presence in each of their major markets. Location decisions to support a low-cost strategy require particularly careful consideration.

Once management is committed to a specific location, many costs are firmly in place and difficult to reduce. For instance, if a new factory location is in a region with high energy costs, even good management with an outstanding energy strategy is starting at a disadvantage. Management is in a similar bind with its human resource strategy if labour in the selected location is expensive, is ill-trained, or has a poor work ethic. Consequently, hard work to determine an optimal facility location is a good investment.

STUDENT TIP

We now look at major location issues.

LO1 Identify and explain seven major factors that affect location decisions

Factors that Affect Location Decisions

Selecting a facility location is becoming much more complex with the globalization of the workplace. As we saw in Chapter 2, globalization has taken place because of the development of (1) market economics; (2) better international communications; (3) more rapid, reliable travel and shipping; (4) ease of capital flow between countries; and (5) high differences in labour costs. Many firms now consider opening new offices, factories, retail stores, or banks outside their home country. Location decisions transcend national borders. In fact, as Figure 8.1 shows, the sequence of location decisions often begins with choosing a country in which to operate.

One approach to selecting a country is to identify what the parent organization believes are key success factors (KSFs) needed to achieve competitive advantage. Six possible country KSFs are listed at the top of Figure 8.1. Using such factors (including some negative ones, such as crime), the World Economic Forum biannually ranks the global competitiveness of 144 countries (see Table 8.1) using a weighted index of 12 criteria: (1) institutions, (2) infrastructure, (3) macroeconomic environment, (4) health and primary education, (5) higher education and training, (6) goods market efficiency, (7) labour market efficiency, (8) financial market development, (9) technological readiness, (10) market size, (11) business sophistication, and (12) innovation.[2]

Once a firm decides which country is best for its location, it focuses on a region of the chosen country and a community. The final step in the location decision process is choosing a specific site within a community. The company must pick the one location that is best suited for shipping

[1] John D. Kasarda and Greg Lindsay. *Aerotropolis*. New York, NY: Farrar, Straus, and Giroux, 2011.

[2] **http://reports.weforum.org/global-competitiveness-report-2014-2015/view/methodology/**.

Country Decision

Key Success Factors

1. Political risks, government rules, attitudes, incentives
2. Cultural and economic issues
3. Location of markets
4. Labour talent, attitudes, productivity, costs
5. Availability of supplies, communications, energy
6. Exchange rates and currency risk

FIGURE 8.1

Some Considerations and Factors that Affect Location Decisions

Region/Community Decision

1. Corporate desires
2. Attractiveness of region (culture, taxes, climate, etc.)
3. Labour availability, costs, attitudes towards unions
4. Cost and availability of utilities
5. Environmental regulations of state and town
6. Government incentives and fiscal policies
7. Proximity to raw materials and customers
8. Land/construction costs

Site Decision

1. Site size and cost
2. Air, rail, highway, and waterway systems
3. Zoning restrictions
4. Proximity of services/supplies needed
5. Environmental impact issues
6. Customer density and demographics

and receiving, zoning, utilities, size, and cost. Again, Figure 8.1 summarizes this series of decisions and the factors that affect them.

Besides globalization, a number of other factors affect the location decision. Among these are labour productivity, foreign exchange, culture, changing attitudes towards the industry, and proximity to markets, suppliers, and competitors.

Table 8.1

2014–2015 Competitiveness of Selected Countries

Country	2014–2015 Ranking	Country	2014–2015 Ranking
Switzerland	1	China	28
Singapore	2	…	
United States	3	Italy	49
Finland	4	…	
Germany	5	Russian Federation	53
Japan	6		
Hong Kong SAR	7		
Netherlands	8	Mexico	61
United Kingdom	9	…	
Sweden	10	Vietnam	68
…		…	
Canada	15	India	71
…		…	
Australia	22	Iran	83
France	23		
…		Chad	143
Israel	27	Guinea	144

Source: Based on **http://reports.weforum.org/global-competitiveness-report-2014-2015/rankings/**.

OM in Action | Quality Coils Pulls the Plug on Mexico

Keith Gibson, president of Quality Coils, Inc., saw the savings of low Mexican wages and headed south. He shut down a factory in Connecticut and opened one in Juárez, where he could pay Mexicans one-third the wage rates he was paying back home. "All the figures pointed out we should make a killing," says Gibson.

Instead, his company was nearly destroyed. The electromagnetic coil maker regularly lost money during four years in Mexico. High absenteeism, low productivity, and problems of long-distance management wore Gibson down until he finally pulled the plug on Juárez.

Moving back home and rehiring some of his original workers, Gibson learned, "I can hire one person in Connecticut for what three were doing in Juárez."

When unions complain that they cannot compete against the low wages in other countries and when the

Teamster rallies chant "$4 a day/No way!" they overlook several factors. First, productivity in low-wage countries often erases a wage advantage that is not nearly as great as people believe. Second, a host of problems, from poor roads to corrupt governments, run up operating costs. Third, although labour costs in many underdeveloped countries are only one-third of those in North America, they may represent less than 10% of total manufacturing costs. Thus, the difference may not overcome other disadvantages. And, most importantly, the cost of labour for most North American manufacturers is less important than such factors as the skill of the workforce, the quality of transportation, and access to technology.

Sources: Global Information Network (January 8, 2004): 1; and *The Wall Street Journal* (January 13, 2004): A12 and (September 15, 1993): A1.

LABOUR PRODUCTIVITY

LO2 Compute labour productivity

When deciding on a location, management may be tempted by an area's low wage rates. However, wage rates cannot be considered by themselves, as Quality Coils, Inc., discovered when it opened its plant in Mexico (see the *OM in Action* box "Quality Coils Pulls the Plug on Mexico"). Management must also consider productivity.

As discussed in Chapter 1, differences exist in productivity in various countries. What management is really interested in is the combination of production and the wage rate. For example, if Quality Coils pays $70 per day with 60 units produced per day in Connecticut, it will spend less on labour than at a Mexican plant that pays $25 per day with production of 20 units per day:

$$\frac{\text{Labour cost per day}}{\text{Production (i.e., units per day)}} = \text{Labour cost per unit}$$

Case 1: Connecticut plant:

$$\frac{\$70 \text{ wages per day}}{60 \text{ units produced per day}} = \frac{\$70}{60} = \$1.17 \text{ per unit}$$

Case 2: Juárez, Mexico, plant:

$$\frac{\$25 \text{ wages per day}}{20 \text{ units produced per day}} = \frac{\$25}{20} = \$1.25 \text{ per unit}$$

STUDENT TIP

Final cost is the critical factor, and low productivity can negate low cost.

Employees with poor training, poor education, or poor work habits may not be a good buy even at low wages. By the same token, employees who cannot or will not always reach their places of work are not much good to the organization, even at low wages. (Labour cost per unit is sometimes called the *labour content* of the product.)

EXCHANGE RATES AND CURRENCY RISK

Although wage rates and productivity may make a country seem economical, unfavourable exchange rates may negate any savings. Sometimes, though, firms can take advantage of a particularly favourable exchange rate by relocating or exporting to a foreign country. However, the values of foreign currencies continually rise and fall in most countries. Such changes could well make what was a good location in 2010 a disastrous one in 2017.

COSTS

We can divide location costs into two categories, tangible and intangible. **Tangible costs** are those costs that are readily identifiable and precisely measured. They include utilities, labour, material, taxes, depreciation, and other costs that the accounting department and management can identify. In addition, such costs as transportation of raw materials, transportation of finished goods, and site construction are all factored into the overall cost of a location.

Intangible costs are less easily quantified. They include quality of education, public transportation facilities, community attitudes towards the industry and the company, and quality and attitude of prospective employees. They also include quality-of-life variables, such as climate and sports teams, that may influence personnel recruiting. See *OM in Action* Box, "Tim Hortons is Winning New Friends Abroad".

Tangible costs
Readily identifiable costs that can be measured with some precision.

Intangible costs
A category of location costs that cannot be easily quantified, such as quality of life and government.

POLITICAL RISK, VALUES, AND CULTURE

The political risk associated with national, provincial, and local governments' attitudes towards private and intellectual property, zoning, pollution, and employment stability may be in flux. Governmental positions at the time a location decision is made may not be lasting ones. However, management may find that these attitudes can be influenced by their own leadership.

Worker values may also differ from country to country, region to region, and small town to city. Worker views regarding turnover, unions, and absenteeism are all relevant factors. In turn, these values can affect a company's decision whether to make offers to current workers if the firm relocates to a new location.

One of the greatest challenges in a global operations decision is dealing with another country's culture. Cultural variations in punctuality by employees and suppliers make a marked difference in production and delivery schedules. Bribery likewise creates substantial economic inefficiency, as well as ethical and legal problems in the global arena. As a result, operations managers face significant challenges when building effective supply chains across cultures. Table 8.2 provides one ranking of public sector corruption in countries around the world.

PROXIMITY TO MARKETS

For many firms, locating near customers is extremely important. Particularly, service organizations—such as drugstores, restaurants, post offices, or barbers—find that proximity to market is *the* primary location factor. Manufacturing firms find it useful to be close to customers when transporting finished goods is expensive or difficult (perhaps because they are bulky, heavy, or fragile). Foreign-owned auto giants such as Mercedes, Honda, Toyota, and Hyundai build millions of cars each year in the United States and Canada.

In addition, with just-in-time production, suppliers want to locate near users. For a firm like Coca-Cola, whose product's primary ingredient is water, it makes sense to have bottling plants in many cities rather than shipping heavy (and sometimes fragile glass) containers cross-country.

OM in Action   Tim Hortons Is Winning New Friends Abroad

It would be difficult to travel through a Canadian city or town and not see a Tim Hortons coffee outlet. But their placement is not random and is part of a larger location strategy. Initially concentrated in Ontario and the Atlantic provinces, the company has since expanded its presence in Quebec and also in the western provinces. An important aspect of the company's location strategy is to situate the outlet in a high pedestrian or automobile traffic area. This is due to the reality that the average customer purchase is relatively small in terms of dollars, thus making high volume and turnover crucial.

Tim Hortons has been expanding this successful strategy into the United States as well as the United Kingdom, among other places. Similar to the Canadian strategy of placing some smaller outlets in gas stations, stores, and offices, it has located outlets in the United Kingdom in some SPAR convenience stores and Tesco supermarkets. Similarly, in the United States, locations have been opening in Tops Market stores, and the company also recently ventured into New York City in former Dunkin' Donuts locations. One of its stores can be found in Madison Square Garden, a somewhat sentimental spot, as it is the home of the New York Rangers National Hockey League team for which Tim Horton played for a few years as a professional hockey player.

It is quite evident that this location strategy is working for Tim Hortons. Further expansion is planned for hundreds of new outlets over the next few years.

Source: **www.timhortons.com.**

Table 8.2

2014 Ranking Public Sector Corruption in Selected Countries: Scores Range from 0 (Highly Corrupt) to 100 (Very Clean).

Rank	Country	Score	Rank	Country	Score
1	Denmark	92	...		
2	New Zealand	91	85	India	38
3	Finland	89	...		
...			100	China	36
10	Canada	81	...		
11	Australia	80	136 (tied)	Iran	27
12	Germany	79	136 (tied)	Russia	27
...			...		
37	Israel	60	170	Iraq	16
...			...		
43	South Korea	55	173	Sudan	11
...			174 (tied)	North Korea	8
69	Italy	43	174 (tied)	Somalia	8

Source: Based on Transparency International, Corruption Perceptions Index 2014, **http://www.transparency.org/cpi2014/results.**

PROXIMITY TO SUPPLIERS

Firms locate near their raw materials and suppliers because of (1) perishability, (2) transportation costs, or (3) bulk. Bakeries, dairy plants, and frozen seafood processors deal with *perishable* raw materials, so they often locate close to suppliers. Companies dependent on inputs of heavy or bulky raw materials (such as steel producers using coal and iron ore) face expensive inbound *transportation costs*, so transportation costs become a major factor. And goods for which there is a *reduction in bulk* during production (such as lumber mills locating in British Columbia near timber resources) typically need to be near the raw material. See *OM in Action* Box, "Denmark's Meat Cluster".

OM in Action   Denmark's Meat Cluster

Every day, 20 000 pigs are delivered to the Danish Crown company's slaughterhouse in central Denmark. The pigs trot into the stunning room, guided by workers armed with giant fly swats. The animals are hung upside down, divided in two, shaved, and scalded clean. A machine cuts them into pieces, which are then cooled, boned, and packed.

The slaughterhouse is enormous: 10 football fields long with over 10 kilometres of conveyor belts. Its managers attend to the tiniest detail. The workers wear green rather than white because this puts the pigs in a better mood. The cutting machine photographs a carcass before adjusting its blades to the exact carcass contours. The company calibrates not only how to carve the flesh, but also where the various parts will fetch the highest prices.

Denmark is a tiny country, with 5.6 million people and wallet-draining labour costs. But it is an agricultural giant, home to 30 million pigs and numerous global brands. Farm products make up over 20% of its goods exports—and the value of these exports is expected to grow from $5.5 billion in 2001 to $31 billion by 2020.

How is this meat-processing cluster still thriving? It is because clustering can be applied to ancient industries like slaughtering as well as to new ones. The cluster includes several big companies: Danish Crown, Arla, Rose Poultry,

and DuPont Danisco, as well as plenty of smaller firms, which act as indicators of nascent trends and incubators of new ideas. Other firms are contributing information technology tools for the cluster. Among these are LetFarm for fields, Bovisoft for stables, Agrosoft for pigs, Webstech for grain, and InOMEGA for food.

The cluster also has a collection of productivity-spurring institutions (the Cattle Research Center, for example, creates ways to boost pork productivity through robotics) and Danish Tech University, where 1500 people work on food-related subjects.

Sources: *The Economist* (Jan. 4, 2014); and GlobalMeatNews.com (Nov. 1, 2013).

Table 8.3
Clustering of Companies

Industry	Locations	Reason for Clustering
Wine making	Niagara-on-the-Lake (ON), Okanagan Valley (BC), Bordeaux region (France)	Natural resources of land and climate
Software firms	Kanata (ON), Silicon Valley, Boston, Bangalore (India)	Talent resources of bright graduates in scientific/technical areas, venture capitalists nearby
Race car building	Huntington/North Hampton region (England)	Critical mass of talent and information
Theme parks (including Disney World, Universal Studios, and Sea World)	Orlando, Florida	A hot spot for entertainment, warm weather, tourists, and inexpensive labour
Electronics firms (such as Sony, IBM, HP, Motorola, and Panasonic)	Northern Mexico	USMCA, duty-free export to United States (24% of all TVs are built here)
Computer hardware manufacturing	Singapore, Taiwan	High technological penetration rates and per capita GDP, skilled/educated workforce with large pool of engineers
Fast-food chains (such as Wendy's, McDonald's, Burger King, and Pizza Hut)	Sites within 1 kilometre of one another	Stimulate food sales, high traffic flows
General aviation aircraft (including Cessna, Learjet, Boeing, and Raytheon)	Wichita, Kansas	Mass of aviation skills (60–70% of world's small planes/jets built here)
Orthopaedic device manufacturing	Warsaw, Indiana	Ready supply of skilled workers, strong U.S. market

Table 8.3
Clustering of Companies

PROXIMITY TO COMPETITORS (CLUSTERING)

Both manufacturing and service organizations also like to locate, somewhat surprisingly, near competitors. This tendency, called **clustering**, often occurs when a major resource is found in that region. Such resources include natural resources, information resources, venture capital resources, and talent resources. Table 8.3 presents nine examples of industries that exhibit clustering, and the reasons why.

Italy may be the true leader when it comes to clustering, however, with northern zones of that country holding world leadership in such specialties as ceramic tile (Modena), gold jewellery (Vicenza), machine tools (Busto Arsizio), cashmere and wool (Biella), designer eyeglasses (Belluma), and pasta machines (Parma).

Clustering

The location of competing companies near each other, often because of a critical mass of information, talent, venture capital, or natural resources.

Methods of Evaluating Location Alternatives

Four major methods are used for solving location problems: the factor rating method, locational break-even analysis, the centre-of-gravity method, and the transportation model. This section describes these approaches.

STUDENT TIP

Here are four techniques that help in making good location decisions.

THE FACTOR RATING METHOD

There are many factors, both qualitative and quantitative, to consider in choosing a location. Some of these factors are more important than others, so managers can use weightings to make the decision process more objective. The **factor rating method** is popular because a wide variety of factors, from education to recreation to labour skills, can be objectively included. Figure 8.1 listed a few of the many factors that affect location decisions.

The factor rating method has six steps:

1. Develop a list of relevant factors called *key success factors* (such as those in Figure 8.1).
2. Assign a weight to each factor to reflect its relative importance in the company's objectives.

LO3 Apply the factor rating method

Factor rating method

A location method that instils objectivity into the process of identifying hard-to-evaluate costs.

3. Develop a scale for each factor (e.g., 1 to 10 or 1 to 100 points).
4. Have management score each location for each factor, using the scale in step 3.
5. Multiply the score by the weights for each factor and total the score for each location.
6. Make a recommendation based on the maximum point score, considering the results of other quantitative approaches as well.

When a decision is sensitive to minor changes, further analysis of the weighting and the points assigned may be appropriate. Alternatively, management may conclude that these intangible factors are not the proper criteria on which to base a location decision. Managers therefore place primary weight on the more quantitative aspects of the decision.

EXAMPLE 1

Factor Rating Method for an Expanding Theme Park

Five Flags, a chain of 10 family-oriented theme parks in North America, has decided to expand overseas by opening its first park in Europe. It wishes to select between France and Denmark.

APPROACH ▶ The ratings sheet in Table 8.4 lists key success factors that management has decided are important; their weightings and their rating for two possible sites—Dijon, France, and Copenhagen, Denmark—are shown.

SOLUTION ▶ Table 8.4 uses weights and scores to evaluate alternative site locations. Given the option of 100 points assigned to each factor, the French location is preferable.

INSIGHT ▶ By changing the points or weights slightly for those factors about which there is some doubt, we can analyze the sensitivity of the decision. For instance, we can see that changing the scores for "labour availability and attitude" by 10 points can change the decision. The numbers used in factor weighting can be subjective, and the model's results are not "exact" even though this is a quantitative approach.

LEARNING EXERCISE ▶ If the weight for "tax structure" drops to 0.20 and the weight for "education and health" increases to 0.40, what is the new result? [Answer: Denmark is now chosen, with a 68.0 versus a 67.5 score for France.]

Table 8.4
Weights, Scores, and Solution

STUDENT TIP
These weights do not need to be on a 0–1 scale or total to 1. We can use a 1–10 scale, 1–100 scale, or any other scale we prefer.

Key Success Factor	Weight	Scores (out of 100) France	Scores (out of 100) Denmark	Weighted Scores France	Weighted Scores Denmark
Labour availability and attitude	0.25	70	60	$(0.25)(70) = 17.5$	$(0.25)(60) = 15.0$
People-to-car ratio	0.05	50	60	$(0.05)(50) = 2.5$	$(0.05)(60) = 3.0$
Per capita income	0.10	85	80	$(0.10)(85) = 8.5$	$(0.10)(80) = 8.0$
Tax structure	0.39	75	70	$(0.39)(75) = 29.3$	$(0.39)(70) = 27.3$
Education and health	0.21	60	70	$(0.21)(60) = 12.6$	$(0.21)(70) = 14.7$
Totals	1.00			70.4	68.0

RELATED PROBLEMS ▶ 8.5, 8.6, 8.7, 8.8, 8.9, 8.10, 8.11, 8.12, 8.13, 8.14, 8.15, 8.24, 8.25

EXCEL OM Data File **Ch08Ex1.xlsx** can be found at **MyLab Operations Management.**

LO4 Complete a locational break-even analysis graphically and mathematically

---

LOCATIONAL BREAK-EVEN ANALYSIS

Locational break-even analysis
A cost–volume analysis to make an economic comparison of location alternatives.

Locational break-even analysis is the use of cost–volume analysis to make an economic comparison of location alternatives. By identifying fixed and variable costs and graphing them for each location, we can determine which one provides the lowest cost. Locational break-even analysis can be done mathematically or graphically. The graphic approach has the advantage of providing the range of volume over which each location is preferable.

The three steps to locational break-even analysis are as follows:

1. Determine the fixed and variable cost for each location.
2. Plot the costs for each location, with costs on the vertical axis of the graph and annual volume on the horizontal axis.
3. Select the location that has the lowest total cost for the expected production volume.

John Kros, owner of Sudbury Ignitions Manufacturing, needs to expand his capacity. He is considering three locations—Timmins, Sault Ste. Marie, and North Bay—for a new plant. The company wishes to find the most economical location for an expected volume of 2000 units per year.

EXAMPLE 2

Locational Break-Even for a Parts Manufacturer

APPROACH ▶ Kros conducts locational break-even analysis. To do so, he determines that fixed costs per year at the sites are $30 000, $60 000, and $110 000, respectively; and variable costs are $75 per unit, $45 per unit, and $25 per unit, respectively. The expected selling price of each ignition system produced is $120.

SOLUTION ▶ For each of the three locations, Kros can plot the fixed costs (those at a volume of zero units) and the total cost (fixed costs + variable costs) at the expected volume of output. These lines have been plotted in Figure 8.2.

For Timmins:

$$\text{Total cost} = \$30\,000 + \$75(2000) = \$180\,000$$

For Sault Ste. Marie:

$$\text{Total cost} = \$60\,000 + \$45(2000) = \$150\,000$$

For North Bay:

$$\text{Total cost} = \$110\,000 + \$25(2000) = \$160\,000$$

With an expected volume of 2000 units per year, Sault Ste. Marie provides the lowest cost location. The expected profit is:

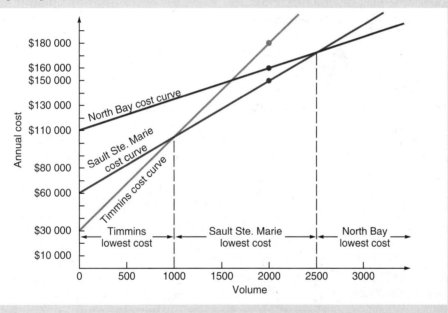

FIGURE 8.2
Crossover Chart for Locational Break-Even Analysis

$$\text{Total revenue} - \text{Total cost} = \$120(2000) - \$150\,000 = \$90\,000 \text{ per year}$$

The crossover point for Timmins and Sault Ste. Marie is:

$$30\,000 + 75(x) = 60\,000 + 45(x)$$
$$30(x) = 30\,000$$
$$x = 1000$$

and the crossover point for Sault Ste. Marie and North Bay is:

$$60\,000 + 45(x) = 110\,000 + 25(x)$$
$$20(x) = 50\,000$$
$$x = 2500$$

INSIGHT ▶ As with every other OM model, locational break-even results can be sensitive to input data. For example, for a volume of less than 1000, Timmins would be preferred. For a volume greater than 2500, North Bay would yield the greatest profit.

LEARNING EXERCISE ▶ The variable cost for North Bay is now expected to be $22 per unit. What is the new crossover point between Sault Ste. Marie and North Bay? [Answer: ~2173.9 or 2174 units.]

RELATED PROBLEMS ▶ 8.16, 8.17, 8.18, 8.19

LO5 Use the centre-of-gravity method

EXCEL **OM** Data File **Ch08Ex2.xlsx** can be found at **MyLab Operations Management**.

CENTRE-OF-GRAVITY METHOD

Centre-of-gravity method

A mathematical technique used for finding the best location for a single distribution point that services several stores or areas.

The **centre-of-gravity method** is a mathematical technique used for finding the location of a distribution centre that will minimize distribution costs. The method takes into account the location of markets, the volume of goods shipped to those markets, and shipping costs in finding the best location for a distribution centre.

The first step in the centre-of-gravity method is to place the locations on a coordinate system. This will be illustrated in Example 3. The origin of the coordinate system and the scale used are arbitrary, just as long as the relative distances are correctly represented. This can easily be done by placing a grid over an ordinary map. The centre of gravity is determined using Equations (8-1) and (8-2):

$$x\text{-coordinate of the centre of gravity} = \frac{\sum_i d_{ix} Q_i}{\sum_i Q_i} \tag{8-1}$$

$$y\text{-coordinate of the centre of gravity} = \frac{\sum_i d_{iy} Q_i}{\sum_i Q_i} \tag{8-2}$$

where
d_{ix} = x-coordinate of location i
d_{iy} = y-coordinate of location i
Q_i = quantity of goods moved to or from location i

Note that Equations (8-1) and (8-2) include the term Q_i, the quantity of supplies transferred to or from location i.

Since the number of containers shipped each month affects cost, distance alone should not be the principal criterion. The centre-of-gravity method assumes that cost is directly proportional to both distance and volume shipped. The ideal location is that which minimizes the weighted distance between the warehouse and its retail outlets, where the distance is weighted by the number of containers shipped.[3]

EXAMPLE 3

Centre of Gravity

Quain's Discount Department Stores, a chain of four large Walmart-type outlets, has store locations in the vicinity of Owen Sound, Kingston, Oshawa, and Erie, PA. They are currently being supplied out of an old and inadequate warehouse in Kingston, the site of the chain's first store. The firm wants to find some "central" location in which to build a new warehouse.

APPROACH ▶ Quain's will apply the centre-of-gravity method. It gathers data on demand rates at each outlet (see Table 8.5).

Table 8.5

Demand for Quain's Discount Department Stores

Store Location	Number of Containers Shipped per Month
Owen Sound	2000
Oshawa	1000
Kingston	1000
Erie, PA	2000

Its current store locations are shown in Figure 8.3. For example, location 1 is Owen Sound, and from Table 8.5 and Figure 8.3, we have:

$$d_{1x} = 30$$
$$d_{1y} = 120$$
$$Q_1 = 2000$$

---

[3] Equations (8-1) and (8-2) compute a centre of gravity (COG) under "squared Euclidean" distances and may actually result in transportation costs slightly (less than 2%) higher than an *optimal* COG computed using "Euclidean" (straight-line) distances. The latter, however, is a more complex and involved procedure mathematically, so the formulas we present are generally used as an attractive substitute. See C. Kuo and R. E. White, "A Note on the Treatment of the Center-of-Gravity Method in Operations Management Textbooks," *Decision Sciences Journal of Innovative Education* 2 (Fall 2004): 219–227.

SOLUTION ▶ Using the data in Table 8.5 and Figure 8.3 for each of the other cities, and Equations (8-1) and (8-2), we find:

x-coordinate of the centre of gravity:

$$= \frac{(30)(2000) + (90)(1000) + (130)(1000) + (60)(2000)}{2000 + 1000 + 1000 + 2000} = \frac{400\,000}{6000}$$

$$= 66.7$$

y-coordinate of the centre of gravity:

$$= \frac{(120)(2000) + (110)(1000) + (130)(1000) + (40)(2000)}{2000 + 1000 + 1000 + 2000} = \frac{560\,000}{6000}$$

$$= 93.3$$

This location (66.7, 93.3) is shown by the crosshairs in Figure 8.3.

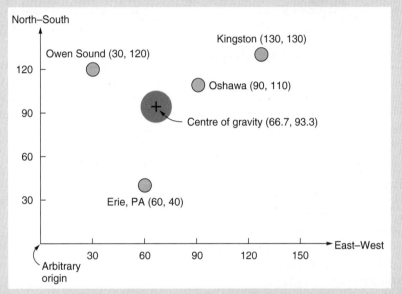

FIGURE 8.3
Coordinate Locations of Four Quain's Department Stores and Centre of Gravity

INSIGHT ▶ By overlaying a map on this exhibit, we find this location is near Toronto. The firm may well wish to consider Mississauga or a nearby city as an appropriate location. It is important to have both North–South and East–West highways near the city selected to make delivery times quicker.

LEARNING EXERCISE ▶ The number of containers shipped per month to Erie is expected to grow quickly to 3000. How does this change the centre of gravity, and where should the new warehouse be located? [Answer: 65.7, 85.7.]

RELATED PROBLEMS ▶ 8.20, 8.21, 8.22, 8.23

EXCEL OM Data File **ch08ex3.xlsx** can be found at **MyLab Operations Management**.

ACTIVE MODEL 8.1 This example is further illustrated in Active Model 8.1 at **MyLab Operations Management**.

TRANSPORTATION MODEL

The objective of the **transportation model** is to determine the best pattern of shipments from several points of supply (sources) to several points of demand (destinations) so as to minimize total production and transportation costs. Every firm with a network of supply-and-demand points faces such a problem. The complex Volkswagen supply network (shown in Figure 8.4) provides one such illustration. We note in Figure 8.4, for example, that VW de Mexico ships vehicles for assembly and parts to VW of Nigeria, sends assemblies to VW do Brasil, and receives parts and assemblies from headquarters in Germany.

Although the linear programming (LP) technique can be used to solve this type of problem, more efficient, special-purpose algorithms have been developed for the transportation application. The transportation model finds an initial feasible solution and then makes step-by-step improvements until an optimal solution is reached.

Transportation model
A technique for solving a class of linear programming problems.

FIGURE 8.4
Worldwide Distribution of Volkswagens and Parts

Source: Reprinted with permission from "The Economist Newspaper Limited, London. Distributed by *The New York Times/Special Edition*".

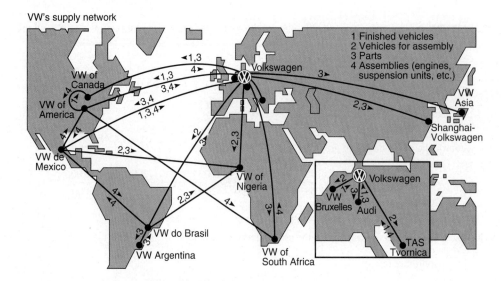

VW's supply network

1 Finished vehicles
2 Vehicles for assembly
3 Parts
4 Assemblies (engines, suspension units, etc.)

Service Location Strategy

While the focus in industrial-sector location analysis is on minimizing cost, the focus in the service sector is on maximizing revenue. This is because manufacturing firms find that costs tend to vary substantially among locations, while service firms find that location often has more impact on revenue than cost. This means that the location focus for service firms should be on determining the volume of business and revenue.

There are eight major determinants of volume and revenue for the service firm:

LO6 Understand the differences between service- and industrial-sector location analysis

1. Purchasing power of the customer-drawing area.
2. Service and image compatibility with demographics of the customer-drawing area.
3. Competition in the area.
4. Quality of the competition.
5. Uniqueness of the firm's and competitors' locations.
6. Physical qualities of facilities and neighbouring businesses.
7. Operating policies of the firm.
8. Quality of management.

Realistic analysis of these factors can provide a reasonable picture of the revenue expected. The techniques used in the service sector include correlation analysis, traffic counts, demographic analysis, purchasing power analysis, the factor rating method, the centre-of-gravity method, and geographic information systems. Table 8.6 provides a summary of location strategies for both service and goods-producing organizations.

GEOGRAPHIC INFORMATION SYSTEMS

Geographic information system (GIS)

A system that stores and displays information that can be linked to a geographic location.

Geographic information systems are an important tool to help firms make successful analytical decisions with regard to location. A **geographic information system (GIS)** stores and displays information that can be linked to a geographical location. For instance, retailers, banks, food chains, gas stations, and print shop franchises can all use geographically coded files from a GIS to conduct demographic analyses. By combining population, age, income, traffic flow, and density figures with geography, a retailer can pinpoint the best location for a new store or restaurant.

Here are some of the geographic databases available in many GISs:

- Census data by block, tract, city, region, metropolitan area, province, postal code.
- Maps of every street, highway, bridge, and tunnel in Canada.
- Utilities such as electrical, water, and gas lines.
- All rivers, mountains, lakes, forests.
- All major airports, universities, hospitals.

For example, airlines use GISs to identify airports where ground services are the most effective. This information is then used to help schedule and to decide where to purchase fuel, meals, and other services.

Commercial office building developers use GISs in the selection of cities for future construction. Building new office space takes several years, so developers value the database approach

SERVICE/RETAIL/PROFESSIONAL	GOODS-PRODUCING
Revenue Focus	**Cost Focus**
Volume/revenue	**Tangible costs**
Drawing area; purchasing power	Transportation cost of raw material
Competition; advertising/pricing	Shipment cost of finished goods
Physical quality	Energy and utility cost; labour; raw material; taxes, and so on
Parking/access; security/lighting; appearance/image	**Intangible and future costs**
Cost determinants	Attitude towards union
Rent	Quality of life
Management calibre	Education expenditures by province
Operation policies (hours, wage rates)	Quality of provincial and local government
Techniques	**Techniques**
Regression models to determine importance of various factors	Transportation method
Factor rating method	Factor rating method
Traffic counts	Locational break-even analysis
Demographic analysis of drawing area	Crossover charts
Purchasing power analysis of area	
Centre-of-gravity method	
Geographic information systems	
Assumptions	**Assumptions**
Location is a major determinant of revenue	Location is a major determinant of cost
High customer-contact issues are critical	Most major costs can be identified explicitly for each site
Costs are relatively constant for a given area; therefore, the revenue function is critical	Low customer contact allows focus on the identifiable costs
	Intangible costs can be evaluated

STUDENT TIP

This table helps differentiate between service- and manufacturing-sector decisions. Almost every aspect of the decision is different.

that a GIS can offer. GIS is used to analyze factors that influence the location decisions by addressing five elements for each city: (1) residential areas, (2) retail shops, (3) cultural and entertainment centres, (4) crime incidence, and (5) transportation options.

Here are five more examples of how location-scouting GIS software is turning commercial real estate into a science:[4]

- *Tim Hortons:* This large chain of coffee shops uses GIS to create a demographic profile of what a typically successful neighbourhood for a Tim Hortons looks like—income, ages, and spending patterns.
- *Saber Roofing:* Rather than send workers out to estimate the costs for reroofing jobs, this firm pulls up aerial shots of the building via Google Earth. The owner can measure roofs, eye-ball the conditions, and email the client an estimate, saving hundreds of kilometres of driving daily. In one case, while on the phone, a potential client was told her roof was too steep for the company to tackle after the Saber employee quickly looked up the home on Google Earth.
- *Arby's:* As this fast-food chain learned, specific products can affect behaviour. Using MapInfo, Arby's discovered that diners drove up to 20% farther for their roast beef sandwich (which they consider a "destination" product) than for its chicken sandwich.
- *Home Depot:* Wanting a store in a large urban metropolis, even though Home Depot demographics are usually for customers who own big homes, the company took a chance when GIS software predicted a particular location would do well. Although most people in that vicinity live in apartments and very small homes, the store has become one of the chain's highest-volume outlets.
- *Toys "R" Us:* Toys "R" Us (Canada) used GIS to aid in the decision to open a new outlet in Sherwood Park, Alberta. This positions them well to capture the local young family market.

Other packages similar to MapInfo are Hemisphere Solutions (by Unisys Corp.), Atlas GIS (from Strategic Mapping, Inc.), Arc/Info (by ESRI), SAS/GIS (by SAS Institute, Inc.), Market Base (by National Decision Systems, Inc.), and MapPoint 2009 (by Microsoft).

---

[4] *The Wall Street Journal* (July 3, 2007): B1 and (July 18, 2005): R-7; and *Business 2.0* (May 2004): 76–77.

To illustrate how extensive some of these GISs can be, consider Microsoft's MapPoint 2009, which includes a comprehensive set of map and demographic data. Its North American maps have more than 11 million kilometres of streets and 1.9 million points of interest to allow users to locate restaurants, airports, hotels, gas stations, ATMs, museums, campgrounds, and highway exits. Demographic data includes statistics for population, age, income, education, and housing for 1980, 1990, 2000, and 2005. These data can be mapped by state, county, city, postal code, or census tract. MapPoint 2009 produces maps that identify business trends; pinpoint market graphics; locate clients, customers, and competitors; and visualize sales performance and product distribution. The European version of MapPoint includes 7.8 million kilometres of roads as well as 400 000 points of interest (see **www.mapapps.net**).

VIDEO 8.2
Locating the Next Red Lobster
Restaurant

The Video Case Study, "Locating the Next Red Lobster Restaurant," that appears at the end of this chapter describes how that chain uses its GIS to define trade areas based on market size and population density.

CHAPTER SUMMARY

Location may determine up to 50% of operating expense. Location is also a critical element in determining revenue for the service, retail, or professional firm. Industrial firms need to consider both tangible and intangible costs. Industrial location problems are typically addressed via a factor rating method, locational break-even analysis, the centre-of-gravity method, and the transportation method of linear programming.

For service, retail, and professional organizations, analysis is typically made of a variety of variables, including purchasing power of a drawing area, competition, advertising and promotion, physical qualities of the location, and operating policies of the organization.

ETHICAL DILEMMA

In this chapter, we have discussed a number of location decisions. Consider another: United Airlines announced its competition to select a town for a new billion-dollar aircraft-repair base. The bidding for the prize of 7500 jobs paying at least $25 per hour was fast and furious, with Edmonton offering $154 million in incentives and Hamilton more than twice that amount. One government official angrily rescinded their offer of $300 million, likening the bidding to "squeezing every drop of blood out of a turnip".

When United finally selected from among the 93 cities bidding on the base, the winner was Indianapolis and its $320 million offer of taxpayers' money.

But in 2003, with United near bankruptcy and having fulfilled its legal obligation, the company walked away from the massive aircraft-repair centre. This left the government out all that money, with no new tenant in sight. The city now even owns the tools, neatly arranged in each of the 12 elaborately equipped hangar bays. United outsourced its maintenance to mechanics at a rival firm (which pays one-third of what United gave out in salary and benefits in Indianapolis).

What are the ethical, legal, and economic implications of such location bidding wars? Who pays for such giveaways? Are local citizens allowed to vote on offers made by their cities, regions, or provinces? Should there be limits on these incentives?

Discussion Questions

1. How is FedEx's location a competitive advantage? Discuss.
2. Why do so many North American firms build facilities in other countries?
3. Why do so many foreign companies build facilities in North America?
4. What is clustering?
5. How does factor weighting incorporate personal preference in location choices?
6. What are the advantages and disadvantages of a qualitative (as opposed to a quantitative) approach to location decision making?
7. Provide two examples of clustering in the service sector.
8. What are the major factors that firms consider when choosing a country in which to locate?
9. What factors affect region/community location decisions?
10. Although most organizations may make the location decision infrequently, there are some organizations that make the

decision quite regularly and often. Provide one or two examples. How might their approach to the location decision differ from the norm?
11. List factors, other than globalization, that affect the location decision.
12. Explain the assumptions behind the centre-of-gravity method. How can the model be used in a service facility location?
13. What are the three steps to locational break-even analysis?
14. "Manufacturers locate near their resources, retailers locate near their customers." Discuss this statement, with reference to the proximity-to-markets arguments covered in the text. Can you think of a counter example in each case? Support your choices.
15. Why shouldn't low wage rates alone be sufficient to select a location?
16. List the techniques used by service organizations to select locations.

17. Contrast the location of a food distributor and a supermarket. (The distributor sends truckloads of food, meat, produce, etc., to the supermarket.) Show the relevant considerations (factors) they share; show those where they differ.

18. Elmer's Fudge Factory is planning to open 10 retail outlets in New Brunswick over the next two years. Identify (and weight) those factors relevant to the decision. Provide this list of factors and weights.

Using Software to Solve Location Problems

This section presents three ways to solve location problems with computer software. First, you can create your own spreadsheets to compute factor ratings, the centre of gravity, and break-even analysis. Second, Excel OM (free with your text and found at our website) is programmed to solve all three models. Third, POM for Windows is also found at MyLab Operations Management and can solve all problems labelled with a **P**.

Creating Your Own Excel Spreadsheets

Excel (and other spreadsheets) are easily developed to solve most of the problems in this chapter. We do not provide an example here, but you can see from Program 8.1 how the formulas are created.

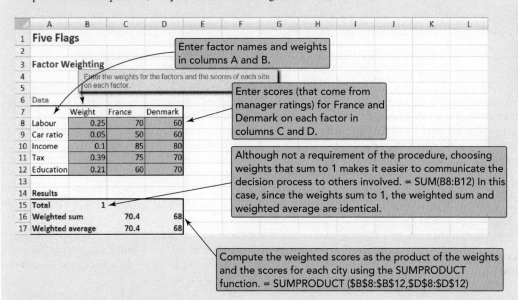

PROGRAM 8.1
Excel OM's Factor Rating Module, Including Inputs, Selected Formulas, and Outputs Using Five Flags Data in Example 1

Source: Courtesy of Microsoft Corporation.

✗ USING EXCEL OM

Excel OM may be used to solve Example 1 (with the Factor Rating module), Example 2 (with the Break-Even Analysis module), and Example 3 (with the Centre-of-Gravity module), as well as other location problems. To illustrate the factor rating method, consider the case of Five Flags (Example 1), which wishes to expand its corporate presence to Europe. Program 8.1 provides the data inputs for five important factors, including their weights, and ratings on a 1–100 scale (where 100 is the highest rating) for each country. As we see, France is more highly rated, with a 70.4 score versus 68.0 for Denmark.

𝑷 USING POM FOR WINDOWS

POM for Windows also includes three different facility location models: the factor rating method, the centre-of-gravity model, and locational break-even analysis. For details, refer to Appendix IV.

Solved Problems Virtual Office Hours help is available at MyLab Operations Management.

▼ SOLVED PROBLEM 8.1

Just as cities and communities can be compared for location selection by the weighted approach model, as we saw earlier in this chapter, so can actual site decisions within those cities. Table 8.7 illustrates four factors of importance to Washington, DC, and the health officials charged with opening that city's first public drug treatment clinic. Of primary concern (and given a weight of 5) was location of the clinic so it would be as accessible as possible to the largest number of patients. Due to a tight budget, the annual lease cost was also of some concern. A suite in the city hall, at 14th and U Streets, was highly rated because its rent would be free. An old office building near the downtown bus station received a much lower rating because of its cost. Equally important as lease cost was the need for confidentiality of patients and, therefore, for a relatively inconspicuous clinic. Finally, because so many of the staff at the clinic would be donating their time, the safety, parking, and accessibility of each site were of concern as well.

Using the factor rating method, which site is preferred?

Table 8.7
Potential Clinic Sites in Washington, DC

Factor	Importance Weight	Potential Locations[a]			Weighted Scores		
		Homeless Shelter (2nd and D, SE)	City Hall (14th and U, NW)	Bus Terminal Area (7th and H, NW)	Home-less Shelter	City Hall	Bus Terminal Area
Accessibility for addicts	5	9	7	7	45	35	35
Annual lease cost	3	6	10	3	18	30	9
Inconspicuous	3	5	2	7	15	6	21
Accessibility for health staff	2	3	6	2	6	12	4
Total scores:					84	83	69

[a]All sites are rated on a 1 to 10 basis, with 10 as the highest score and 1 as the lowest.

Source: From *Service Management and Operations*, 2/e, by Haksever/Render/Russell/Murdick, p. 266. Copyright © 2000. Reprinted by permission of Prentice Hall, Inc., Upper Saddle River, NJ.

▼ SOLUTION

From the three rightmost columns in Table 8.7, the weighted scores are summed. The bus terminal area has a low score and can be excluded from further consideration. The other two sites are virtually identical in total score. The city may now want to consider other factors, including political ones, in selecting between the two remaining sites.

▼ SOLVED PROBLEM 8.2

Ching-Chang Kau is considering opening a new foundry in Digby, Nova Scotia; Edmonton, Alberta; or Gatineau, Quebec, to produce high-quality rifle sights. He has assembled the following fixed cost and variable cost data:

Location	Fixed Cost per Year	Per-Unit Costs		
		Material	Labour	Overhead
Digby	$200 000	$0.20	$0.40	$0.40
Edmonton	$180 000	$0.25	$0.75	$0.75
Gatineau	$170 000	$1.00	$1.00	$1.00

(a) Graph the total cost lines.
(b) Over what range of annual volume is each facility going to have a competitive advantage?
(c) What is the volume at the intersection of the Edmonton and Gatineau cost lines?

▼ SOLUTION

(a) A graph of the total cost lines is shown in Figure 8.5.
(b) Below 8000 units, the Gatineau facility will have a competitive advantage (lowest cost); between 8000 units and 26 666 units, Edmonton has an advantage; and above 26 666, Digby has the advantage. (We have made the assumption in this problem that other costs—that is, delivery and intangible factors—are constant regardless of the decision.)
(c) From Figure 8.5, we see that the cost line for Gatineau and the cost line for Edmonton cross at about 8000. We can also determine this point with a little algebra:

$$\$180\ 000 + 1.75Q = 170\ 000 + 3.00Q$$
$$\$10\ 000 = 1.25Q$$
$$8000 = Q$$

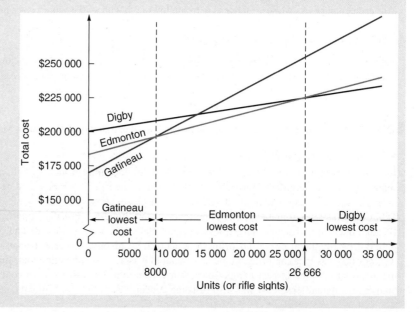

FIGURE 8.5
Graph of Total Cost Lines for Ching-Chang Kau

Problems*

• **8.1** In Cambodia, six labourers, each making the equivalent of $3 per day, can produce 40 units per day. In China, 10 labourers, each making the equivalent of $2 per day, can produce 45 units. In Winnipeg, two labourers, each making $60 per day, can make 100 units. Based on labour costs only, which location would be most economical to produce the item?

• **8.2** Refer to Problem 8.1. Shipping cost from Cambodia to Halifax, the final destination, is $1.50 per unit. Shipping cost from China to Halifax is $1 per unit, while the shipping cost from Winnipeg to Halifax is $0.25 per unit. Considering both labour and transportation costs, which is the most favourable production location?

•• **8.3** You have been asked to analyze the bids for 200 polished disks used in solar panels. These bids have been submitted by three suppliers: Thailand Polishing, India Shine, and Sacramento Glow. Thailand Polishing has submitted a bid of 2000 baht. India Shine has submitted a bid of 2000 rupee. Sacramento Glow has submitted a bid of $200. You check with your local bank and find that $1 = 10 baht and $1 = 8 rupee. Which company should you choose?

• **8.4** Refer to Problem 8.3. If the final destination is New Delhi, India, and there is a 30% import tax, which firm should you choose?

•• **8.5** Subway, with more than 3000 outlets in Canada, is planning for a new restaurant in Brampton, Ontario. Three locations are being considered. The following table gives the factors for each site.

Factor	Weight	Maitland	Baptist Church	Northside Mall
Space	0.30	60	70	80
Costs	0.25	40	80	30
Traffic density	0.20	50	80	60
Neighbourhood income	0.15	50	70	40
Zoning laws	0.10	80	20	90

a) At which site should Subway open the new restaurant?
b) If the weights for space and traffic density were reversed, how would this affect the decision? **Px**

• **8.6** Gayla Delong owns the Alberta Warriors, a minor league hockey team in northwest Alberta. She wishes to move the Warriors east, to either Red Deer or Camrose. The table below gives the factors that Gayla thinks are important, their weights, and the scores for Red Deer and Camrose.

Factor	Weight	Red Deer	Camrose
Incentive	0.4	80	60
Player satisfaction	0.3	20	50
Sports interest	0.2	40	90
Size of city	0.1	70	30

a) Which site should she select?
b) Camrose just raised its incentive package, and the new score is 75. Why doesn't this impact your decision in part (a)? **Px**

•• **8.7** Insurance Company of Latin America (ILA) is considering opening an office in the United States. The two cities under consideration are Philadelphia and New York. The factor ratings (higher scores are better) for the two cities are given in the following table. In which city should ILA locate?

Factor	Weight	Philadelphia	New York
Customer convenience	0.25	70	80
Bank accessibility	0.20	40	90
Computer support	0.20	85	75
Rental costs	0.15	90	55
Labour costs	0.10	80	50
Taxes	0.10	90	50

•• **8.8** Marilyn Helm Retailers is attempting to decide on a location for a new retail outlet. At the moment, the firm has three alternatives—stay where it is but enlarge the facility; locate along the main street in nearby Newbury; or locate in a new shopping mall in Hyde Park. The company has selected the four factors listed in the following table as the basis for evaluation and has assigned weights as shown:

Factor	Factor Description	Weight
1	Average community income	0.30
2	Community growth potential	0.15
3	Availability of public transportation	0.20
4	Labour availability, attitude, and cost	0.35

Helm has rated each location for each factor, on a 100-point basis. These ratings are given below:

	Location		
Factor	Present Location	Newbury	Hyde Park
1	40	60	50
2	20	20	80
3	30	60	50
4	80	50	50

a) What should Helm do?
b) A new subway station is scheduled to open across the street from the present location in about a month, so its third factor score should be raised to 40. How does this change your answer? **Px**

•• **8.9** A location analysis for Temponi Controls, a small manufacturer of parts for high-technology cable systems, has been narrowed down to four locations. Temponi will need to train assemblers, testers, and robotics maintainers in local training centres. Cecilia Temponi, the president, has asked each potential site to offer training programs, tax breaks, and other industrial incentives. The critical factors, their weights, and the ratings for each location are shown in the following table. High scores represent favourable values.

		Location			
Factor	Weight	Akron, OH	Biloxi, MS	Carthage, TX	Denver, CO
Labour availability	0.15	90	80	90	80
Technical school quality	0.10	95	75	65	85
Operating cost	0.30	80	85	95	85

Note: **Px** means the problem may be solved with POM for Windows and/or Excel OM.

Factor	Weight	Akron, OH	Biloxi, MS	Carthage, TX	Denver, CO
				Location	
Land and construction cost	0.15	60	80	90	70
Industrial incentives	0.20	90	75	85	60
Labour cost	0.10	75	80	85	75

a) Compute the composite (weighted average) rating for each location.

b) Which site would you choose?

c) Would you reach the same conclusion if the weights for operating cost and labour cost were reversed? Recompute as necessary and explain. **Px**

••• **8.10** Consolidated Refineries, headquartered in Calgary, must decide among three sites for the construction of a new oil-processing centre. The firm has selected the six factors listed below as a basis for evaluation and has assigned rating weights from 1 to 5 on each factor:

Factor	Factor Name	Rating Weight
1	Proximity to port facilities	5
2	Power-source availability and cost	3
3	Workforce attitude and cost	4
4	Distance from Calgary	2
5	Community desirability	2
6	Equipment suppliers in area	3

Management has rated each location for each factor on a 1- to 100-point basis.

Factor	Location A	Location B	Location C
1	100	80	80
2	80	70	100
3	30	60	70
4	10	80	60
5	90	60	80
6	50	60	90

a) Which site will be recommended based on *total* weighted scores?

b) If location B's score for proximity to port facilities were reset at 90, how would the result change?

c) What score would location B need on proximity to port facilities to change its ranking? **Px**

•• **8.11** A company is planning on expanding and building a new plant in one of three Southeast Asian countries. Chris Ellis, the manager charged with making the decision, has determined that five key success factors can be used to evaluate the prospective countries. Ellis used a rating system of 1 (least desirable country) to 5 (most desirable) to evaluate each factor.

Key Success Factors	Weight	Taiwan	Thailand	Singapore
			Candidate Country Ratings	
Technology	0.2	4	5	1
Level of education	0.1	4	1	5
Political and legal aspects	0.4	1	3	3
Social and cultural aspects	0.1	4	2	3
Economic factors	0.2	3	3	2

a) Which country should be selected for the new plant?

b) Political unrest in Thailand results in a lower score, 2, for political and legal aspects. Does your conclusion change?

c) What if Thailand's score drops even further, to a 1, for political and legal aspects? **Px**

• **8.12** Gander University is contemplating opening a European campus where students from the main campus could go to take courses for one of the four college years. At the moment, it is considering five countries: the Netherlands, Britain, Italy, Belgium, and Greece. The university wishes to consider eight factors in its decision. All the factors have equal weight. The following table illustrates its assessment of each factor for each country (5 is best).

Factor	Factor Description	Netherlands	Britain	Italy	Belgium	Greece
1	Stability of government	5	5	3	5	4
2	Degree to which the population can converse in English	4	5	3	4	3
3	Stability of the monetary system	5	4	3	4	3
4	Communications infrastructure	4	5	3	4	3
5	Transportation infrastructure	5	5	3	5	3
6	Availability of historic/cultural sites	3	4	5	3	5
7	Import restrictions	4	4	3	4	4
8	Availability of suitable quarters	4	4	3	4	3

a) In which country should Gander University choose to set up its European campus?

b) How would the decision change if the "degree to which the population can converse in English" was not an issue? **Px**

·· 8.13 Daniel Tracy, owner of Martin Manufacturing, must expand by building a new factory. The search for a location for this factory has been narrowed to four sites: A, B, C, or D. The following table shows the results thus far obtained by Tracy by using the factor rating method to analyze the problem. The scale used for each factor scoring is 1 through 5.

Factor	Weight	Site Scores			
		A	B	C	D
Quality of labour	10	5	4	4	5
Construction cost	8	2	3	4	1
Transportation costs	8	3	4	3	2
Proximity to markets	7	5	3	4	4
Taxes	6	2	3	3	4
Weather	6	2	5	5	4
Energy costs	5	5	4	3	3

a) Which site should Tracy choose?
b) If site D's score for energy costs increases from a 3 to a 5, do results change?
c) If site A's weather score is adjusted to a 4, what is the impact? What should Tracy do at this point? **Px**

··· 8.14 A Canadian consulting firm is planning to expand globally by opening a new office in one of four countries: Germany, Italy, Spain, or Greece. The chief partner entrusted with the decision, L. Wayne Shell, has identified eight key success factors that he views as essential for the success of any consultancy. He used a rating system of 1 (least desirable country) to 5 (most desirable) to evaluate each factor.

Key Success Factors	Candidate Country Ratings			
	Weight	Germany	Italy	Spain	Greece
Level of education					
Number of consultants	0.05	5	5	5	2
National literacy rate	0.05	4	2	1	1
Political aspects					
Stability of government	0.2	5	5	5	2
Product liability laws	0.2	5	2	3	5
Environmental regulations	0.2	1	4	1	3
Social and cultural aspects					
Similarity in language	0.1	4	2	1	1
Acceptability of consultants	0.1	1	4	4	3
Economic factors					
Incentives	0.1	2	3	1	5

a) Which country should be selected for the new office?
b) If Spain's score were lowered in the stability of government factor to a 4, how would its overall score change? On this factor, at what score for Spain *would* the rankings change? **Px**

·· 8.15 A British pharmaceutical chain wishes to make its first entry into the Canadian market by building a facility in southern Ontario, a region with which its director, Doug Moodie, is comfortable because he got his medical degree at McMaster University. After a preliminary analysis, four cities are chosen for further consideration. They are rated and weighted according to the factors shown below:

Factor	City				
	Weight	Hamilton	Fort Erie	Mississauga	Barrie
Costs	2.0	8	5	6	7
Need for a facility	1.5	4	9	8	4
Staff availability	1.0	7	6	4	7
Local incentives	0.5	8	6	5	9

a) Which city should Moodie select?
b) Assume a minimum score of 5 is now required for all factors. Which city should be chosen? **Px**

·· 8.16 The fixed and variable costs for three potential manufacturing plant sites for a rattan chair weaver are shown:

Site	Fixed Cost per Year	Variable Cost per Unit
1	$ 500	$11
2	1000	7
3	1700	4

a) Over what range of production is each location optimal?
b) For a production of 200 units, which site is best? **Px**

· 8.17 Peter Billington Stereo, Inc., supplies car radios to auto manufacturers and is going to open a new plant. The company is undecided between Vancouver and Victoria as the site. The fixed costs in Victoria are lower due to cheaper land costs, but the variable costs in Victoria are higher because shipping distances would increase. Given the following costs:

	Victoria	Vancouver
Fixed costs	$600 000	$800 000
Variable costs	$28/radio	$22/radio

a) Perform an analysis of the volume over which each location is preferable.
b) How does your answer change if Victoria's fixed costs increase by 10%? **Px**

··· 8.18 Audi Motors is considering three sites—A, B, and C—at which to locate a factory to build its new-model automobile, the Audi SUV XL500. The goal is to locate at a minimum-cost site, where cost is measured by the annual fixed plus variable costs of production. Audi Motors has gathered the following data:

Site	Annualized Fixed Cost	Variable Cost per Auto Produced
A	$10 000 000	$2500
B	$20 000 000	$2000
C	$25 000 000	$1000

The firm knows it will produce between 0 and 60 000 SUV XL500s at the new plant each year, but, thus far, that is the extent of its knowledge about production plans.

a) For what values of volume, V, of production, if any, is site C a recommended site?

b) What volume indicates site A is optimal?

c) Over what range of volume is site B optimal? Why? **Px**

8.19 Hugh Leach Corp., a producer of machine tools, wants to move to a larger site. Two alternative locations have been identified: Bonham and McKinney. Bonham would have fixed costs of $800 000 per year and variable costs of $14 000 per standard unit produced. McKinney would have annual fixed costs of $920 000 and variable costs of $13 000 per standard unit. The finished items sell for $29 000 each.

a) At what volume of output would the two locations have the same profit?

b) For what range of output would Bonham be superior (have higher profits)?

c) For what range would McKinney be superior?

d) What is the relevance of break-even points for these cities? **Px**

8.20 The following table gives the map coordinates and the shipping loads for a set of cities that we wish to connect through a central hub.

City	Map Coordinate (x, y)	Shipping Load
A	(5, 10)	5
B	(6, 8)	10
C	(4, 9)	15
D	(9, 5)	5
E	(7, 9)	15
F	(3, 2)	10
G	(2, 6)	5

a) Near which map coordinates should the hub be located?

b) If the shipments from city A triple, how does this change the coordinates? **Px**

8.21 A chain of home healthcare firms in Ontario needs to locate a central office from which to conduct internal audits and other periodic reviews of its facilities. These facilities are scattered throughout the province, as detailed in the following table. Each site, except for Toronto, will be visited three times each year by a team of workers, who will drive from the central office to the site. Toronto will be visited five times a year. Which coordinates represent a good central location for this office? What other factors might influence the office location decision? Where would you place this office? Explain.

City	Map Coordinates X	Y
Oshawa	9.2	3.5
Richmond Hill	7.3	2.5
Toronto	7.8	1.4
North Bay	5.0	8.4
Tobermory	2.8	6.5
Guelph	5.5	2.4
Waterloo	5.0	3.6
Sudbury	3.8	8.5

Px

8.22 A small rural county has experienced unprecedented growth over the past six years, and as a result, the local school district built the new 500-student North Park Elementary School. The district has three older and smaller elementary schools: Laurier, Pearson, and Borden. Now the growth pressure is being felt at the secondary level. The school district would like to build a centrally located middle school to accommodate students and reduce bussing costs. The older middle school is adjacent to the high school and will become part of the high school campus.

a) What are the coordinates of the central location?

b) What other factors should be considered before building a school? **Px**

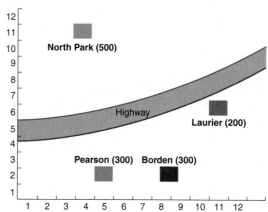

8.23 Todd's Video, a major video rental and TV sales chain headquartered in Fredericton, is about to open its first outlet in Moncton and wants to select a site that will place the new outlet in the centre of Moncton's population base. Todd examines the seven census tracts in Moncton, plots the coordinates of the centre of each from a map, and looks up the population base in each to use as a weighting. The information gathered appears in the following table.

Census Tract	Population in Census Tract	X, Y Map Coordinates
101	2000	(25, 45)
102	5000	(25, 25)
103	10 000	(55, 45)
104	7000	(50, 20)
105	10 000	(80, 50)
106	20 000	(70, 20)
107	14 000	(90, 25)

a) At what centre-of-gravity coordinates should the new store be located?

b) Census tracts 103 and 105 are each projected to grow by 20% in the next year. How will this influence the new store's coordinates? **Px**

•••• **8.24** Eagle Electronics must expand by building a second facility. The search has been narrowed down to locating the new facility in one of four cities: Ajax (A), Burlington (B), Canmore (C), or Dalhousie (D). The factors, scores, and weights follow:

a) Using the factor rating method, what is the recommended site for Eagle Electronics's new facility?

b) For what range of values for the weight (currently $w_7 = 10$) does the site given as the answer to part (a) remain a recommended site?

		Weight	Scores by Site			
i	Factor	(W_i)	A	B	C	D
1	Labour quality	20	5	4	4	5
2	Quality of life	16	2	3	4	1
3	Transportation	16	3	4	3	2
4	Proximity to markets	14	5	3	4	4
5	Proximity to suppliers	12	2	3	3	4
6	Taxes	12	2	5	5	4
7	Energy supplies	10	5	4	3	3

•••• **8.25** The EU has made changes in airline regulation that dramatically affect major European carriers such as British International Air (BIA), KLM, Air France, Alitalia, and Swiss International Air. With ambitious expansion plans, BIA has decided it needs a second service hub on the continent to complement its large Heathrow (London) repair facility. The location selection is critical, and with the potential for 4000 new skilled blue-collar jobs on the line, virtually every city in western Europe is actively bidding for BIA's business.

		Italy			France			Germany		
Factor	Importance Weight	Milan	Rome	Genoa	Paris	Lyon	Nice	Munich	Bonn	Berlin
Financial incentives	85	8	8	8	7	7	7	7	7	7
Skilled labour pool	80	4	6	5	9	9	7	10	8	9
Existing facility	70	5	3	2	9	6	5	9	9	2
Wage rates	70	9	8	9	4	6	6	4	5	5
Competition for jobs	70	7	3	8	2	8	7	4	8	9
Ease of air traffic access	65	5	4	6	2	8	8	4	8	9
Real estate cost	40	6	4	7	4	6	6	3	4	5
Communication links	25	6	7	6	9	9	9	10	9	8
Attractiveness to relocating executives	15	4	8	3	9	6	6	2	3	3
Political considerations	10	6	6	6	8	8	8	8	8	8
Expansion possibilities	10	10	2	8	1	5	4	4	5	6
Union strength	10	1	1	1	5	5	5	6	6	6

After initial investigations by Holmes Miller, head of operations, BIA has narrowed the list to nine cities. Each is then rated on 12 factors, as shown in the table.

a) Help Miller rank the top three cities that BIA should consider as its new site for servicing aircraft.

b) After further investigation, Miller decides that an existing set of hangar facilities for repairs is not nearly as important as earlier thought. If he lowers the weight of that factor to 30, does the ranking change?

c) After Miller makes the change in part (b), Germany announces it has reconsidered its offer of financial incentives, with an additional 200-million-euro package to entice BIA. Accordingly, BIA has raised Germany's rating to 10 on that factor. Is there any change in top rankings in part (b)? **Px**

CASE STUDIES

Atlantic Assembly Services

Starting from humble beginnings in 1984, Joe Hobbs successfully built a mid-sized assembly plant in Mississauga, Ontario. His company (Atlantic Assembly Services) gained a reputation among those manufacturers that outsourced to him as a reliable and flexible assembler of goods. But early in 2012, the economy was changing, and so too were the expectations placed upon his firm. Quicker turnaround, faster delivery, and lower costs were all in demand. Competition was fierce, and Atlantic found itself with diminishing market share and revenues, along with increasing costs. In order to save the company, Joe and his management team were forced to make some difficult decisions.

It was abundantly clear to Joe that he could operate from a somewhat distant location because his customers were spread all over southern Ontario. Mississauga was becoming too expensive for his business. General facility and overhead costs were high, as were wages in the area. Thus the hunt began for a new location, and contact was made with the Economic Development offices in certain targeted cities throughout southern Ontario in order to ascertain the types of incentives that might be available.

Ultimately, Atlantic Assembly Services decided upon Midland, Ontario. Midland offered property tax breaks for five years, reductions in utility costs, financial support for training costs when hiring local residents, and other considerations and minor relief on moving expenses. In addition to this, real estate costs were substantially lower in Midland versus Mississauga, and so too was the wage rate for comparable work. Overall, the reduction in capital and operating costs plus the municipal incentives contributed to making the decision to move to Midland justifiable.

On July 20, 2015, Joe Hobbs advised his staff of the decision. He provided each of them with the following letter:

> To: Employees of Atlantic Assembly Services
> From: Joe Hobbs, President
> Thank you for your dedication and service over the years. I sincerely appreciate your hard work and loyalty. It is with regret that I announce Atlantic Assembly Services will discontinue operations at the Mississauga location after November 1, 2015. Reduced revenues coupled with increased costs and unreasonable demands on the part of the union have forced us to make this decision. I extend to you best wishes for your future endeavours.

Discussion Questions

1. Comment on the incentives offered by the municipality of Midland. Is this type of practice ethical?
2. Do you feel there may be challenges in relocating Atlantic's senior management team to a smaller town such as Midland as opposed to remaining in Mississauga (a much larger city)?
3. Assess the notification made by Joe Hobbs to his employees. Are there aspects of this letter that are inappropriate? How would you rewrite this notice?
4. Does a company in Atlantic's position have a legal, moral, or ethical responsibility to the staff?

 Video Case ## Locating the Next Red Lobster Restaurant

From its first Red Lobster in 1968, Darden Restaurants has grown the chain to 690 locations, with over $2.6 billion in U.S. sales annually. The casual dining market may be crowded—with competitors such as Chili's, Ruby Tuesday, Applebee's, TGI Friday's, and Outback—but Darden's continuing success means the chain thinks there is still plenty of room to grow. Robert Reiner, director of market development, is charged with identifying the sites that will maximize new store sales without cannibalizing sales at the existing Red Lobster locations.

Characteristics for identifying a good site have not changed in 40 years; they still include real estate prices, customer age, competition, ethnicity, income, family size, population density, nearby hotels, and buying behaviour, to name just a few. What *has* changed is the powerful software that allows Reiner to analyze a new site in five minutes, as opposed to the eight hours he spent just a few years ago.

Darden has partnered with MapInfo Corp., whose geographic information system (GIS) contains a powerful module for analyzing a trade area (see the discussion of GIS in the chapter). With the U.S. geocoded down to the individual block, MapInfo allows Reiner to create a psychographic profile of existing and potential Red Lobster trade areas. "We can now target areas with greatest sales potential," says Reiner.

The United States is segmented into 72 "clusters" of customer profiles by MapInfo. If, for example, cluster 7, Equestrian Heights (see the MapInfo description on the right), represents 1.7% of a household base within a Red Lobster trade area, but this segment also accounts for 2.4% of sales, Reiner computes that this segment is effectively spending 1.39 times more than average (Index = 2.4/1.7) and adjusts his analysis of a new site to reflect this added weight.

Cluster	PSYTE 2003	Snap Shot Description
7	Equestrian Heights	They may not have a stallion in the barn, but they likely pass a corral on the way home. These families with teens live in older, larger homes adjacent to, or between, suburbs but not usually tract housing. Most are married with teenagers, but 40% are empty nesters. They use their graduate and professional school education—56% are dual earners. Over 90% are white, non-Hispanic. Their mean family income is $99 000, and they live within commuting distance of central cities. They have white-collar jobs during the week but require a riding lawn mower to keep the place up on weekends.

When Reiner maps the United States, a state, or a region for a new site, he wants one that is at least 5 kilometres from the nearest Red Lobster and won't negatively impact its sales by more than 8%;

MapInfo pinpoints the best spot. The software also recognizes the nearness of non-Darden competition and assigns a probability of success (as measured by reaching sales potential).

The specific spot selected depends on Darden's seven real estate brokers, whose list of considerations include proximity to a vibrant retail area, proximity to a freeway, road visibility, nearby hotels, and a corner location at a primary intersection.

"Picking a new Red Lobster location is one of the most critical functions we can do at Darden," says Reiner. "And the software we use serves as an independent voice in assessing the quality of an existing or proposed location."

Discussion Questions*

1. Visit the website for PSYTE 2003 (www.gemapping.com /downloads/targetpro_brochure.pdf). Describe the psychological profiling (PSYTE) clustering system. Select an industry, other than restaurants, and explain how the software can be used for that industry.

2. What are the major differences in site location for a restaurant versus a retail store versus a manufacturing plant?

3. Red Lobster also defines its trade areas based on market size and population density. Here are its seven density classes:

Density Class	Description	Households per Sq. Kilometre
1	Super Urban	8000+
2	Urban	4000–7999
3	Light Urban	2000–3999
4	First Tier Suburban	1000–1999
5	Second Tier Suburban	600–999
6	Exurban/Small	100–599
7	Rural	0–99

Note: Density classes are based on the households and land area within 5 kilometres of the geography (e.g., census tract) using population-weighted centroids.

Ninety-two percent of the Red Lobster restaurants fall into three of these classes. In which three classes do you think the chain has the most restaurants? Why?

Video Case

Hard Rock's Location Selection

Some people would say that Oliver Munday, Hard Rock's vice-president for cafe development, has the best job in the world. Travel the world to pick a country for Hard Rock's next cafe, select a city, and find the ideal site. It's true that selecting a site involves lots of incognito walking around, visiting nice restaurants, and drinking in bars. But that is not where Munday's work begins, or where it ends. At the front end, selecting the country and city first involves a great deal of research. At the back end, Munday not only picks the final site and negotiates the deal but then also works with architects and planners and stays with the project through the opening and first year's sales.

Munday is currently looking heavily into global expansion in Europe, Latin America, and Asia. "We've got to look at political risk, currency, and social norms—how does our brand fit into the country," he says. Once the country is selected, Munday focuses on the region and city. His research checklist is extensive:

Hard Rock's Standard Market Report (for offshore sites)

A. Demographics (local, city, region, SMSA), with trend analysis
　1. Population of area
　2. Economic indicators
B. Visitor market, with trend analysis
　1. Tourists/business visitors
　2. Hotels
　3. Convention center
　4. Entertainment
　5. Sports
　6. Retail
C. Transportation
　1. Airport　← subcategories include: (a) age of airport, (b) no. of passengers, (c) airlines, (d) direct flights, (e) hubs
　2. Rail
　3. Road
　4. Sea/river
D. Restaurants and nightclubs (a selection in key target market areas)
E. Political risk
F. Real estate market
G. Hard Rock Cafe comparable market analysis

Site location now tends to focus on the tremendous resurgence of "city centres," where nightlife tends to concentrate. That's what Munday selected in Moscow and Bogotá, although in both locations he chose to find a local partner and franchise the operation. In these two political environments, "Hard Rock wouldn't dream of operating by ourselves," says Munday. The location decision also is at least a 10- to 15-year commitment by Hard Rock, which employs tools such as break-even analysis to help decide whether to purchase land and build, or to remodel an existing facility.

Currently, Munday is considering four European cities for Hard Rock's next expansion. Although he could not provide the names, for competitive reasons, the following is known:

Factor	European City Under Consideration				Importance of this Factor at This Time
	A	B	C	D	
A. Demographics	70	70	60	90	20
B. Visitor market	80	60	90	75	20
C. Transportation	100	50	75	90	20
D. Restaurants/ nightclubs	80	90	65	65	10
E. Low political risk	90	60	50	70	10
F. Real estate market	65	75	85	70	10
G. Comparable market analysis	70	60	65	80	10

Discussion Questions*

1. From Munday's standard market report checklist, select any other four categories, such as population (A1), hotels (B2), or

---

*You may wish to view the video that accompanies this case before answering the questions.

restaurants/nightclubs (D), and provide three subcategories that should be evaluated. (See item C1 (airport) for a guide.)

2. Which is the highest rated of the four European cities under consideration, using the table above?

3. Why does Hard Rock put such serious effort into its location analysis?

4. Under what conditions do you think Hard Rock prefers to franchise a cafe?

▶**Additional Case Study:** Visit **MyLab Operations Management** for this case study:

Fast Creek Lightning (E): The town faces three choices where to locate its arena.

CHAPTER 8 | RAPID REVIEW

MyLab Operations Management

Main Heading	Review Material	
THE STRATEGIC IMPORTANCE OF LOCATION (pp. 323–324)	Location has a major impact on the overall risk and profit of the company. Transportation costs alone can total as much as 25% of the product's selling price. When all costs are considered, location may alter total operating expenses as much as 50%. Companies make location decisions relatively infrequently, usually because demand has outgrown the current plant's capacity or because of changes in labour productivity, exchange rates, costs, or local attitudes. Companies may also relocate their manufacturing or service facilities because of shifts in demographics and customer demand. Location options include (1) expanding an existing facility instead of moving, (2) maintaining current sites while adding another facility elsewhere, and (3) closing the existing facility and moving to another location.	**VIDEO 8.1** Hard Rock's Location Selection
	For industrial location decisions, the location strategy is usually minimizing costs. For retail and professional service organizations, the strategy focuses on maximizing revenue. Warehouse location strategy may be driven by a combination of cost and speed of delivery.	
	The objective of location strategy is to maximize the benefit of location to the firm.	
	When innovation is the focus, overall competitiveness and innovation are affected by (1) the presence of high-quality and specialized inputs such as scientific and technical talent, (2) an environment that encourages investment and intense local rivalry, (3) pressure and insight gained from a sophisticated local market, and (4) local presence of related and supporting industries.	
FACTORS THAT AFFECT LOCATION DECISIONS (pp. 324–329)	Globalization has taken place because of the development of (1) market economics; (2) better international communications; (3) more rapid, reliable travel and shipping; (4) ease of capital flow between countries; and (5) large differences in labour costs.	Problems: 8.1–8.4
	Labour cost per unit is sometimes called the *labour content* of the product:	
	Labour cost per unit = Labour cost per day ÷ Production (i.e., units per day)	
	Sometimes firms can take advantage of a particularly favourable exchange rate by relocating or exporting to (or importing from) a foreign country.	
	• **Tangible costs**—Readily identifiable costs that can be measured with some precision.	
	• **Intangible costs**—A category of location costs that cannot be easily quantified, such as quality of life and government.	
	• Many service organizations find that proximity to market is *the* primary location factor.	
	Firms locate near their raw materials and suppliers because of (1) perishability, (2) transportation costs, or (3) bulk.	
	• **Clustering**—The location of competing companies near each other, often because of a critical mass of information, talent, venture capital, or natural resources.	

Main Heading	Review Material	
METHODS OF EVALUATING LOCATION ALTERNATIVES (pp. 329–334)	• **Factor rating method**—A location method that instils objectivity into the process of identifying hard-to-evaluate costs. The six steps of the factor rating method are: 1. Develop a list of relevant factors called *key success factors*. 2. Assign a weight to each factor to reflect its relative importance in the company's objectives. 3. Develop a scale for each factor (e.g., 1 to 10 or 1 to 100 points). 4. Have management score each location for each factor, using the scale in step 3. 5. Multiply the score by the weight for each factor and total the score for each location. 6. Make a recommendation based on the maximum point score, considering the results of other quantitative approaches as well. • **Locational break-even analysis**—A cost–volume analysis used to make an economic comparison of location alternatives. The three steps to locational break-even analysis are: 1. Determine the fixed and variable cost for each location. 2. Plot the costs for each location, with costs on the vertical axis of the graph and annual volume on the horizontal axis. 3. Select the location that has the lowest total cost for the expected production volume. • **Centre-of-gravity method**—A mathematical technique used for finding the best location for a single distribution point that services several stores or areas. The centre-of-gravity method chooses the ideal location that minimizes the *weighted* distance between itself and the locations it serves, where the distance is weighted by the number of containers shipped Q_i: $$x\text{-coordinate of the centre of gravity} = \frac{\sum_i d_{ix}Q_i}{\sum_i Q_i} \quad \textbf{(8-1)}$$ $$y\text{-coordinate of the centre of gravity} = \frac{\sum_i d_{iy}Q_i}{\sum_i Q_i} \quad \textbf{(8-2)}$$ where d_{ix} = x-coordinate of location i d_{iy} = y-coordinate of location i Q_i = quantity of goods moved to or from location i • **Transportation model**—A technique for solving a class of linear programming problems. The transportation model determines the best pattern of shipments from several points of supply to several points of demand in order to minimize total production and transportation costs.	Problems: 8.5–8.25 Virtual Office Hours for Solved Problems: 8.1 **ACTIVE MODEL 8.1**
SERVICE LOCATION STRATEGY (pp. 334–336)	The eight major determinants of volume and revenue for the service firm are: 1. Purchasing power of the customer-drawing area 2. Service and image compatibility with demographics of the customer-drawing area 3. Competition in the area 4. Quality of the competition 5. Uniqueness of the firm's and competitors' locations 6. Physical qualities of facilities and neighbouring businesses 7. Operating policies of the firm 8. Quality of management • **Geographic information system (GIS)**—A system that stores and displays information that can be linked to a geographic location. Some of the geographic databases available in many GISs include (1) census data by block, tract, city, county, metropolitan area, province, and postal code; (2) maps of every street, highway, bridge, and tunnel in Canada; (3) utilities such as electrical, water, and gas lines; (4) all rivers, mountains, lakes, and forests; and (5) all major airports, schools, and hospitals.	**VIDEO 8.2** Locating the Next Red Lobster Restaurant

Self-Test

■ **Before taking the self-test,** refer to the learning objectives listed at the beginning of the chapter.

LO1 The factors involved in location decisions include:
   a) foreign exchange.
   b) attitudes.
   c) labour productivity.
   d) all of the above.

LO2 If Fender Guitar pays $30 per day to a worker in its Ensenada, Mexico, plant, and the employee completes four instruments per eight-hour day, the labour cost/unit is:
   a) $30.00.
   b) $3.75.
   c) $7.50.
   d) $4.00.
   e) $8.00.

LO3 Evaluating location alternatives by comparing their composite (weighted-average) scores involves:
   a) factor rating analysis.
   b) cost–volume analysis.
   c) transportation model analysis.
   d) linear regression analysis.
   e) crossover analysis.

LO4 On the crossover chart where the costs of two or more location alternatives have been plotted, the quantity at which two cost curves cross is the quantity at which:

   a) fixed costs are equal for two alternative locations.
   b) variable costs are equal for two alternative locations.
   c) total costs are equal for all alternative locations.
   d) fixed costs equal variable costs for one location.
   e) total costs are equal for two alternative locations.

LO5 A regional bookstore chain is about to build a distribution centre that is centrally located for its eight retail outlets. It will most likely employ which of the following tools of analysis?
   a) Assembly-line balancing
   b) Load–distance analysis
   c) Centre-of-gravity model
   d) Linear programming
   e) All of the above.

LO6 What is the major difference in focus between location decisions in the service sector and in the manufacturing sector?
   a) There is no difference in focus.
   b) The focus in manufacturing is revenue maximization, while the focus in service is cost minimization.
   c) The focus in service is revenue maximization, while the focus in manufacturing is cost minimization.
   d) The focus in manufacturing is on raw materials, while the focus in service is on labour.

Answers: LO1. d; LO2. c; LO3. a; LO4. e; LO5. c; LO6. c.

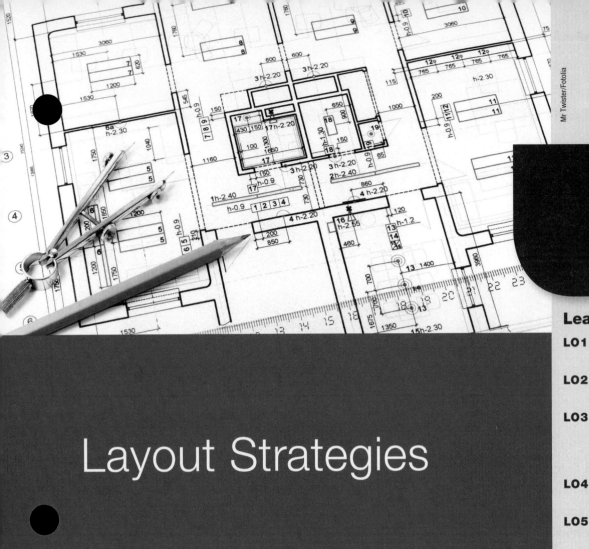

Mr Twister/Fotolia

9

Layout Strategies

McDonald's Looks for Competitive Advantage Through Layout

In its half-century of existence, McDonald's has revolutionized the restaurant industry by inventing the limited-menu fast-food restaurant. It has also made seven major innovations. The first, the introduction of *indoor seating* (1950s), was a layout issue, as was the second, *drive-through windows* (1970s). The third, adding *breakfasts* to the menu (1980s), was a product strategy. The fourth, *adding play areas* (late 1980s), was again a layout decision.

In the 1990s, McDonald's completed its fifth innovation, a radically new *redesign of the kitchens* in its 14 000 North American outlets to facilitate a mass customization process. Dubbed the "Made by You" kitchen system, sandwiches were assembled to order with the revamped layout.

In 2004, the chain began the rollout of its sixth innovation, a new food ordering layout: the *self-service kiosk.* Self-service kiosks have been infiltrating the service sector since the introduction of automated teller machines (ATMs) in 1985 (there are over 1.5 million ATMs in banking). Alaska Airlines was the first airline to provide self-service airport check-in, in 1996.

< Global Company Profile McDonald's

Chris Urso/ZUMA Press/Newscom

McDonald's finds that kiosks reduce both space requirements and waiting; order taking is faster. An added benefit is that customers like them. Also, kiosks are reliable—they don't call in sick. And, most importantly, sales are up 10%–15% (an average of $1) when a customer orders from a kiosk, which consistently recommends the larger size and other extras.

Most passengers of the major airlines now check themselves in for flights. Kiosks take up less space than an employee and reduce waiting line time.

Now, McDonald's is working on its seventh innovation, and not surprisingly, it also deals with restaurant layout. The company, on an unprecedented scale, is redesigning all 30 000 eateries around the globe to take on a *21st-century look*. The dining area will be separated into three sections with distinct personalities: (1) the "linger" zone focuses on young adults and offers comfortable furniture and Wi-Fi connections; (2) the "grab and go" zone features tall counters, bar stools, and flat-screen TVs; and (3) the "flexible" zone has colourful family booths, flexible seating, and kid-oriented music. The cost per outlet: a whopping $300 000–$400 000 renovation fee.

As McDonald's has discovered, facility layout is indeed a source of competitive advantage.

The Strategic Importance of Layout Decisions

Layout is one of the key decisions that determines the long-run efficiency of operations. Layout has numerous strategic implications because it establishes an organization's competitive priorities in regard to capacity, processes, flexibility, and cost, as well as quality of work life, customer contact, and image. An effective layout can help an organization achieve a strategy that supports differentiation, low cost, or response. Benetton, for example, supports a *differentiation* strategy by heavy investment in warehouse layouts that contribute to fast, accurate sorting and shipping to its 5000 outlets. Walmart store layouts support a strategy of *low cost*, as do its warehouse layouts. Hallmark's office layouts, where many professionals operate with open communication in work cells, support *rapid development* of greeting cards. *The objective of layout strategy is to develop an effective and efficient layout that will meet the firm's competitive requirements.*

In all cases, layout design must consider how to achieve the following:

- Higher utilization of space, equipment, and people.
- Improved flow of information, materials, or people.
- Improved employee morale and safer working conditions.
- Improved customer/client interaction.
- Flexibility (whatever the layout is now, it will need to change).

In our increasingly short-life-cycle, mass-customized world, layout designs need to be viewed as dynamic. This means considering small, movable, and flexible equipment. Store displays need to be movable, office desks and partitions modular, and warehouse racks prefabricated. To make quick and easy changes in product models and in production rates, operations managers must design flexibility into layouts. To obtain flexibility in layout, managers cross-train their workers, maintain equipment, keep investments low, place workstations close together, and use small, movable equipment. In some cases, equipment on wheels is appropriate, in anticipation of the next change in product, process, or volume.

Types of Layout

Layout decisions include the best placement of machines (in production settings), offices and desks (in office settings), or service centres (in settings such as hospitals or department stores). An effective layout facilitates the flow of materials, people, and information within and between areas. To achieve these objectives, a variety of approaches has been developed. We will discuss seven of them in this chapter:

1. *Office layout:* Positions workers, their equipment, and spaces/offices to provide for movement of information.
2. *Retail layout:* Allocates shelf space and responds to customer behaviour.
3. *Warehouse layout:* Addresses trade-offs between space and material handling.
4. *Fixed-position layout:* Addresses the layout requirements of large, bulky projects such as ships and buildings.
5. *Process-oriented layout:* Deals with low-volume, high-variety production (also called *job shop* or intermittent production).
6. *Work-cell layout:* Arranges machinery and equipment to focus on production of a single product or group of related products.
7. *Product-oriented layout:* Seeks the best personnel and machine utilization in repetitive or continuous production.

Examples for each of these classes of layouts are noted in Table 9.1.

Because only a few of these seven classes can be modelled mathematically, layout and design of physical facilities are still something of an art. However, we do know that a good layout requires determining the following:

- *Material handling equipment:* Managers must decide about equipment to be used, including conveyors, cranes, automated storage and retrieval systems, and automatic carts to deliver and store material.
- *Capacity and space requirements:* Only when personnel, machines, and equipment requirements are known can managers proceed with layout and provide space for each component.

Table 9.1
Layout Strategies

	Objectives	Examples
Office	Locate workers requiring frequent contact close to one another	Intact Insurance Microsoft Corp.
Retail	Expose customers to high-margin items	Loblaws Supercentre Joe Fresh Harry Rosen Menswear
Warehouse (storage)	Balance low-cost storage with low-cost material handling	Federal-Mogul's warehouse The Gap's distribution centre
Project (fixed position)	Move material to the limited storage areas around the site	Ingall Ship Building Corp. Trump Plaza Fredericton Airport
Job shop (process-oriented)	Manage varied material flow for each product	Arnold Palmer Hospital Hard Rock Cafe Olive Garden
Work cell (product families)	Identify a product family, build teams, cross-train team members	Hallmark Cards Wheeled Coach Standard Aero
Repetitive/continuous (product-oriented)	Equalize the task time at each workstation	Sony's TV assembly line Toyota Scion

In the case of office work, operations managers must make judgments about the space requirements for each employee. It may be a 6 × 6-foot cubicle plus allowance for hallways, aisles, restrooms, cafeterias, stairwells, elevators, and so forth, or it may be spacious executive offices and conference rooms. Management must also consider allowances for requirements that address safety, noise, dust, fumes, temperature, and space around equipment and machines.

- *Environment and aesthetics:* Layout concerns often require decisions about windows, planters, and height of partitions to facilitate air flow, reduce noise, provide privacy, and so forth.
- *Flows of information:* Communication is important to any organization and must be facilitated by the layout. This issue may require decisions about proximity as well as decisions about open spaces versus half-height dividers versus private offices.
- *Cost of moving between various work areas:* There may be unique considerations related to moving materials or to the importance of having certain areas next to each other. For example, moving molten steel is more difficult than moving cold steel.

Office Layout

Office layout

The grouping of workers, their equipment, and spaces/offices to provide for comfort, safety, and movement of information.

LO1 Discuss important issues in office layout

An **office layout** requires the grouping of workers, their equipment, and spaces to provide for comfort, safety, and movement of information. The main distinction of office layouts is the importance placed on the flow of information. Office layouts are in constant flux as the technological change sweeping society alters the way offices function.

Even though the movement of information is increasingly electronic, analysis of office layouts still requires a task-based approach. Paper correspondence, contracts, legal documents, confidential patient records, and hard-copy scripts, artwork, and designs still play a major role in many offices. Managers therefore examine both electronic and conventional communication patterns, separation needs, and other conditions affecting employee effectiveness. A useful tool for such an analysis is the *relationship chart* shown in Figure 9.1. This chart, prepared for an office of product designers, indicates that the chief marketing officer must be (1) near the designers' area, (2) less near the secretary and central files, and (3) not at all near the copy centre or accounting department.

General office-area guidelines allot an average of about 100 square feet per person (including corridors). A major executive is allotted about 400 square feet, and a conference room area is based on 25 square feet per person.

On the other hand, some layout considerations are universal (many of which apply to factories as well as to offices). They have to do with working conditions, teamwork, authority, and status. Should offices be private or open cubicles, have low file cabinets to foster informal communication or high cabinets to reduce noise and contribute to privacy? (See the *OM in Action* box "Layout and the Shrinking Office"). Should all employees use the same entrance, restrooms, lockers, and cafeteria? As mentioned earlier, layout decisions are part art and part science.

FIGURE 9.1

Office Relationship Chart

Source: Based on Richard Muther, *Simplified Systematic Layout Planning*, 3rd ed. (Kansas City, MO: Management & Industrial Research Publications.)

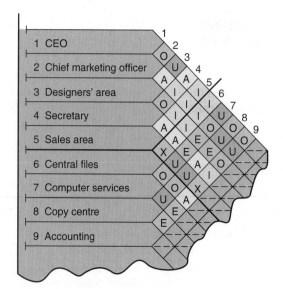

Value	CLOSENESS
A	Absolutely necessary
E	Especially important
I	Important
O	Ordinary OK
U	Unimportant
X	Not desirable

OM in Action   Layout and the Shrinking Office

Your future office may be a lot smaller than you had planned. But that's not all bad. As employees become more mobile and less tied to their desks, the workspace per employee nationwide (across all industries) has dropped from 400 square feet in 1985 to 250 square feet today. And it's heading toward 150 square feet within 10 years.

"A lot of thinking about the office has changed," says the president of Steelcase, the leading office furniture maker. "The work setting was a reflection of your status. A job focuses more on collaboration than on the individual now."

Intel, for example, was known for decades for its endless rows of grey cubicles, low ceilings, and fluorescent lighting. Never one of those tech companies to offer beanbag chairs, designer desks, or pinball machines, Intel has just completed a major re-layout of over 1 million square feet of office space. Grey walls are now yellow, purple, and white; cubicle walls are low enough to see other employees; and lounges have been equipped with flat-screen TVs, comfy chairs, and sleek kitchens. The whole idea was to get people to work more in groups rather than be isolated at their desks.

This also saves money. With less space needed per person, one newly laid-out floor at Intel holds 1000 employees, up from 600. In some departments where

employees are on the road a lot, two people may be assigned to one desk. Even tradition-bound firms in accounting and banking are embracing open-floor layouts. The thinking is that downsizing makes people interact more and become more productive.

Nyul/Fotolia

Sources: The New York Times (January 19, 2011); and *The Wall Street Journal* (January 4, 2012).

As a final comment on office layout, we note two major trends. First, technology, such as cell phones, iPads, faxes, the internet, laptop computers, and smartphones allows increasing layout flexibility by moving information electronically and allowing employees to work offsite. Second, modern firms create dynamic needs for space and services.

Here are two examples:[1]

- When Deloitte & Touche found that 30% to 40% of desks were empty at any given time, the firm developed its "hotelling programs". Consultants lost their permanent offices; anyone who plans to be in the building (rather than out with clients) books an office through a "concierge," who hangs that consultant's name on the door for the day and stocks the space with requested supplies.
- Cisco Systems cut rent and workplace service costs by 37% and saw productivity benefits of U.S. $2.4 billion per year by reducing square footage; reconfiguring space; creating movable, everything-on-wheels offices; and designing "get away from it all" innovation areas.

Retail Layout

Retail layout is based on the idea that sales and profitability vary directly with customer exposure to products. Thus, most retail operations managers try to expose customers to as many products as possible. Studies do show that the greater the rate of exposure, the greater the sales and the higher the return on investment. The operations manager can change exposure with store arrangement and the allocation of space to various products within that arrangement.

Five ideas are helpful for determining the overall arrangement of many stores:

1. Locate the high-draw items around the periphery of the store. Thus, we tend to find dairy products on one side of a supermarket and bread and bakery products on another. An example of this tactic is shown in Figure 9.2.

STUDENT TIP

The goal in a retail layout is to maximize profit per square foot of store space.

Retail layout

An approach that addresses flow, allocates space, and responds to customer behaviour.

LO2 Define the objectives of retail layout

---

[1] "Square Feet. Oh, How Square!" *Business Week* (July 3, 2006): 100–101.

Trying to penetrate urban areas that have lofty land prices and strong antidevelopment movements, Walmart is changing its layout to up, not out. A new generation of multilevel stores takes only one-third the space of the traditional 25-acre swaths. In this store, Walmart trained workers to help shoppers confused by the device next to the escalator that carries shopping carts from one floor to another.

Zuma /Alamy Stock photo

2. Use prominent locations for high-impulse and high-margin items. Best Buy puts fast-growing, high-margin digital goods—such as cameras and DVDs—in the front and centre of its stores.
3. Distribute what are known in the trade as "power items"—items that may dominate a purchasing trip—to both sides of an aisle, and disperse them to increase the viewing of other items.
4. Use end-aisle locations because they have a very high exposure rate.
5. Convey the mission of the store by carefully selecting the position of the lead-off department. For instance, if prepared foods are part of a supermarket's mission, position the bakery and deli up front to appeal to convenience-oriented customers. Walmart's push to increase sales of clothes means those departments are in broad view upon entering a store.

FIGURE 9.2

Store Layout With Dairy and Bakery, High-Draw Items, in Different Areas of the Store

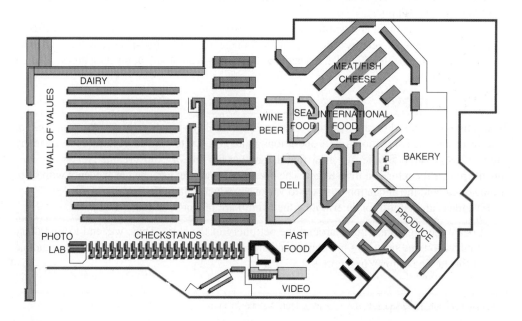

Once the overall layout of a retail store has been decided, products need to be arranged for sale. Many considerations go into this arrangement. However, the main *objective of retail layout is to maximize profitability per square foot of floor space* (or, in some stores, on linear foot of shelf space). Big-ticket, or expensive, items may yield greater dollar sales, but the profit per square foot may be lower. Computerized programs are available to assist managers in evaluating the profitability of various merchandising plans for hundreds of categories. This technique is known as category management.

An additional, and somewhat controversial, issue in retail layout is called slotting. **Slotting fees** are fees manufacturers pay to get their goods on the shelf in a retail store or supermarket chain. The result of massive new product introductions, retailers can now demand up to $25 000 to place an item in their chain. During the last decade, marketplace economics, consolidations, and technology have provided retailers with this leverage. The competition for shelf space is advanced by POS systems and scanner technology, which improve supply chain management and inventory control. Many small firms question the legality and ethics of slotting fees, claiming the fees stifle new products, limit their ability to expand, and cost consumers money. Walmart is one of the few major retailers that does not demand slotting fees. This removes the barrier to entry that small companies usually face. (See the *Ethical Dilemma* near the end of this chapter.)

Slotting fees
Fees manufacturers pay to get shelf space for their products.

SERVICESCAPES

Although the main objective of retail layout is to maximize profit through product exposure, there are other aspects of the service that managers consider (see the *OM in Action* box "Loblaw Companies Limited"). The term **servicescape** describes the physical surroundings in which the service is delivered and how the surroundings have a humanistic effect on customers and employees. To provide a good service layout, a firm considers three elements:

Servicescape
The physical surroundings in which a service takes place, and how they affect customers and employees.

1. *Ambient conditions*, which are background characteristics such as lighting, sound, smell, and temperature. All these affect workers *and* customers and can affect how much money is spent and how long a person stays in the building.
2. *Spatial layout and functionality*, which involve customer circulation path planning, aisle characteristics (such as width, direction, angle, and shelf spacing), and product grouping.
3. *Signs, symbols, and artifacts*, which are characteristics of building design that carry social significance (such as carpeted areas of a department store that encourage shoppers to slow down and browse).

Examples of each of these three elements of servicescape are:

- *Ambient conditions:* Fine-dining restaurants with linen tablecloths and candlelit atmosphere; Mrs. Fields's cookie bakery smells permeating the shopping mall; leather chairs at Starbucks.
- *Layout/functionality:* Canadian Tire's clustering of products by household need; Future Shop's spacious and bright stores.
- *Signs, symbols, and artifacts:* Walmart's greeter at the door; Hard Rock Cafe's wall of guitars; Disneyland's entrance looking like hometown heaven.

OM in Action — Loblaw Companies Limited

Optimizing real estate and space layout has been vital to the success of Loblaw. Loblaw Companies Limited (Loblaw) enjoys the enviable position of being Canada's largest food retailer. It is also a leading provider of general merchandise, pharmacy, and financial services. The company has a diverse portfolio of store formats and a proven track record of providing Canadians with a wide, growing, and successful range of products and services to meet their ongoing household needs. But in addition to being recognized for the quality, innovation, and value of its food offering, it is also important to note how these products and services are made available. The various store layouts are designed to enhance the shopping experience for the customer while making the diverse products and services visible and easy to access. Naturally, larger outlets offer

greater availability of products and services, but smaller locations also aim to optimize their square footage, and the layout of each store is designed to permit the customer the ability to move easily and seamlessly from area to area.

Loblaw has a strong control label program, including the unique President's Choice, No Name, and Joe Fresh brands. It also offers customers access to President's Choice Financial services and to the PC Points loyalty program. There are not many competitors that offer a location where you can acquire a mortgage, merchandise, and groceries all under one roof. But availability in itself is not enough; that is, the layout and flow of how and where the products and services are made available is just as important.

Source: www.loblaw.ca.

A critical element contributing to the bottom line at Hard Rock Cafe is the layout of each cafe's retail shop space. The retail space, from 600 to 1300 square feet in size, is laid out in conjunction with the restaurant area to create the maximum traffic flow before and after eating. The payoffs for cafes like this one in London are huge. Almost half of a cafe's annual sales are generated from these small shops, which have very high retail sales per square foot.

Michael Weber/imageBROKER/Alamy Stock Photo

Warehouse layout

A design that attempts to minimize total cost by addressing trade-offs between space and material handling.

LO3 Discuss modern warehouse management and terms such as ASRSs, cross-docking, and random stocking

Warehousing and Storage Layouts

The objective of **warehouse layout** *is to find the optimum trade-off between handling costs and costs associated with warehouse space.* Consequently, management's task is to maximize the utilization of the total "cube" of the warehouse—that is, utilize its full volume while maintaining low material handling costs. We define *material handling costs* as all the costs related to the transaction. This consists of incoming transport, storage, and outgoing transport of the materials to be warehoused. These costs include equipment, people, material, supervision, insurance, and depreciation. Effective warehouse layouts do, of course, also minimize the damage and spoilage of material within the warehouse.

Management minimizes the sum of the resources spent on finding and moving material plus the deterioration and damage to the material itself. The variety of items stored and the number of items "picked" has direct bearing on the optimum layout. A warehouse storing a few unique items lends itself to higher density than a warehouse storing a variety of items. Modern warehouse management is, in many instances, an automated procedure using *automated storage and retrieval systems* (ASRSs).

In 2009, Sobey's Inc. opened the most automated and technologically advanced ASRS facility of its kind. Located in Vaughan, Ontario, it is a dry grocery distribution centre that is 65 feet high and has an area of 500 000 square feet. By all accounts it has been a huge success, thus giving Sobey's the desire to open another similar facility. The *OM in Action* box, "Amazon Lets Loose the Robots," shows another way that technology can help minimize warehouse costs.

An important component of warehouse layout is the relationship between the receiving/unloading area and the shipping/loading area. Facility design depends on the type of supplies unloaded, what they are unloaded from (trucks, rail cars, barges, and so on), and where they are unloaded. In some companies, the receiving and shipping facilities, or *docks*, as they are called, are even in the same area; sometimes they are receiving docks in the morning and shipping docks in the afternoon.

CROSS-DOCKING

Cross-docking

Avoiding the placement of materials or supplies in storage by processing them as they are received for shipment.

Cross-docking means to avoid placing materials or supplies in storage by processing them as they are received. In a manufacturing facility, product is received directly to the assembly line. In a distribution centre, labelled and presorted loads arrive at the shipping dock for immediate rerouting, thereby avoiding formal receiving, stocking/storing, and order-selection activities. Because these activities add no value to the product, their elimination is 100% cost savings.

OM in Action — Amazon Lets Loose the Robots

Amazon's robot army is falling into place. The Seattle online retailer has outfitted several U.S. warehouses with over 10 000 short, orange, wheeled Kiva robots that move stocked shelves to workers, instead of having employees seek items amid long aisles of merchandise. This is similar to the introduction of the moving assembly line with cars moving down the line, rather than the employee moving from workstation to workstation.

At a 1.2-million-square-foot warehouse in Tracy, California, Amazon has replaced four floors of fixed shelving with the robots. Now, "pickers" at the facility stand in one place, and robots bring 4-foot-by-6-foot shelving units to them, sparing them what amounted to as much as 30 kilometres a day of walking through the warehouse. Employees at robot-equipped warehouses are now expected to pick and scan at least 300 items an hour, compared with 100 under the old system.

At the heart of the robot rollout is Amazon's relentless drive to compete with the immediacy of shopping at brick-and-mortar retailers by improving the efficiency of its logistics. If Amazon can shrink the time it takes to sort and pack goods at its 80 U.S. warehouses, it can guarantee same-day or overnight delivery for more products to more customers.

Noah Berger/Reuters

The robots save Amazon $400–$900 million a year in fulfillment costs by reducing the number of times a product is "touched." The Kiva robots pare 20% to 40% from the average $3.50-to-$3.75 cost of sorting, picking, and boxing an order.

Source: The Wall Street Journal (Nov. 20, 2014) and (Dec. 9, 2013).

Walmart, an early advocate of cross-docking, uses the technique as a major component of its continuing low-cost strategy. With cross-docking, Walmart reduces distribution costs and speeds restocking of stores, thereby improving customer service. Although cross-docking reduces product handling, inventory, and facility costs, it requires both (1) tight scheduling and (2) accurate inbound product identification.

RANDOM STOCKING

Automatic identification systems (AISs), usually in the form of barcodes or RFIDs, allow accurate and rapid item identification. When automatic identification systems are combined with effective management information systems, operations managers know the quantity and location of every unit. This information can be used with human

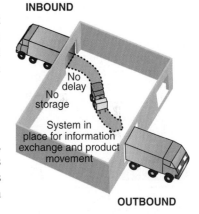

INBOUND

No delay

No storage

System in place for information exchange and product movement

OUTBOUND

Agencja Fotograficzna Caro/Dueselder/Alamy Stock Photo

Automated storage and retrieval systems are not found only in traditional warehouses, and they can take many forms. This parking garage in Wolfsburg, Germany, occupies only 20% of the space of a traditionally designed garage. The ASRS "retrieves" autos in less time, without the potential of the cars being damaged by an attendant.

operators or with automatic storage and retrieval systems to load units anywhere in the warehouse—randomly. Accurate inventory quantities and locations mean the potential utilization of the whole facility because space does not need to be reserved for certain stock-keeping units (SKUs) or part families. Computerized **random stocking** systems often include the following tasks:

1. Maintaining a list of "open" locations.
2. Maintaining accurate records of existing inventory and its locations.
3. Sequencing items to minimize the travel time required to "pick" orders.
4. Combining orders to reduce picking time.
5. Assigning certain items or classes of items, such as high-usage items, to particular warehouse areas so that the total distance travelled within the warehouse is minimized.

Random stocking systems can increase facility utilization and decrease labour cost, but they require accurate records.

CUSTOMIZING

Although we expect warehouses to store as little product as possible and hold it for as short a time as possible, we are now asking warehouses to customize products. Warehouses can be places where value is added through **customizing**. Warehouse customization is a particularly useful way to generate competitive advantage in markets where products have multiple configurations. For instance, a warehouse can be a place where computer components are put together, software loaded, and repairs made. Warehouses may also provide customized labelling and packaging for retailers so items arrive ready for display.

Increasingly, this type of work goes on adjacent to major airports, in facilities such as the FedEx terminal in Memphis. Adding value at warehouses adjacent to major airports also facilitates overnight delivery. For example, if your computer has failed, the replacement may be sent to you from such a warehouse for delivery the next morning. When your old machine arrives back at the warehouse, it is repaired and sent to someone else. These value-added activities at "quasi-warehouses" contribute to strategies of differentiation, low cost, and rapid response.

Fixed-Position Layout

In a **fixed-position layout**, the project remains in one place, and workers and equipment come to that one work area. Examples of this type of project are a ship, a highway, a bridge, a house, and an operating table in a hospital operating room.

The techniques for addressing the fixed-position layout are complicated by three factors. First, there is limited space at virtually all sites. Second, at different stages of a project, different materials are needed; therefore, different items become critical as the project develops. Third, the volume of materials needed is dynamic. For example, the rate of use of steel panels for the hull of a ship changes as the project progresses.

Because problems with fixed-position layouts are so difficult to solve well onsite, an alternative strategy is to complete as much of the project as possible offsite. This approach is used in the shipbuilding industry when standard units—say, pipe-holding brackets—are assembled on a nearby assembly line (a product-oriented facility). In an attempt to add efficiency to shipbuilding, Ingall Ship Building Corporation has moved towards product-oriented production when sections of a ship (modules) are similar or when it has a contract to build the same section of several similar ships. Also, as the top photo shows, many home builders are moving from a fixed-position layout strategy to one that is more product-oriented. An increasing number of new homes built in Canada are constructed using this approach. In addition, many houses that are built onsite (fixed position) have the majority of components such as doors, windows, fixtures, trusses, stairs, and wallboard built as modules with more efficient offsite processes.

Craig Ruttle/AP Images

Syracuse Newspapers/Dick Blume/The Image Works

U.S. Navy/Getty Images

Here are three versions of the fixed-position layout.

A house built via traditional fixed-position layout would be constructed onsite, with equipment, materials, and workers brought to the site. Then a "meeting of the trades" would assign space for various time periods. However, the home pictured here can be built at a much lower cost. The house is built in two movable modules in a factory. Scaffolding and hoists make the job easier, quicker, and cheaper, and the indoor work environment aids labour productivity.

A service example of a fixed-position layout is an operating room; the patient remains stationary on the table, and medical personnel and equipment are brought to the site.

In shipbuilding, there is limited space next to the fixed-position layout. Shipyards call these loading areas *platens*, and they are assigned for various time periods to each contractor.

Process-Oriented Layout

A **process-oriented layout** can simultaneously handle a wide variety of products or services. This is the traditional way to support a product differentiation strategy. It is most efficient when making products with different requirements or when handling customers, patients, or clients with different needs. A process-oriented layout is typically a low-volume, high-variety strategy as discussed in Chapter 7. In this job-shop environment, each product or each small group of products undergoes a different sequence of operations. A product or small order is produced by moving it from one department to another in the sequence required for that product. A good example of the process-oriented layout is a hospital or clinic. Figure 9.3 illustrates the process for two patients, A and B, at an emergency clinic in Toronto. An inflow of patients, each with his or her own needs, requires routing through admissions, laboratories, operating rooms, radiology, pharmacies, nursing beds, and so on. Equipment, skills, and supervision are organized around these processes.

A big advantage of process-oriented layout is its flexibility in equipment and labour assignments. The breakdown of one machine, for example, need not halt an entire process; work can be transferred to other machines in the department. Process-oriented layout is also especially good for handling the manufacture of parts in small batches, or **job lots**, and for the production of a wide variety of parts in different sizes or forms.

Process-oriented layout
A layout that deals with low-volume, high-variety production in which like machines and equipment are grouped together.

LO5 Explain how to achieve a good process-oriented facility layout

VIDEO 9.1
Layout at Arnold Palmer Hospital

Job lots
Groups or batches of parts processed together.

FIGURE 9.3

An Emergency Room Process Layout Showing the Routing of Two Patients

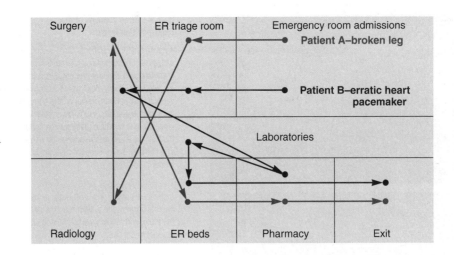

Patient A (broken leg) proceeds (blue arrow) to ER triage, to radiology, to surgery, to a bed, to pharmacy, to exit. Patient B (pacemaker problem) moves (red arrow) to ER triage, to surgery, to pharmacy, to lab, to a bed, to exit.

The disadvantages of process-oriented layout come from the general-purpose use of the equipment. Orders take more time to move through the system because of difficult scheduling, changing setups, and unique material handling. In addition, general-purpose equipment requires high labour skills, and work-in-process inventories are higher because of imbalances in the production process. High labour-skill needs also increase the required level of training and experience, and high work-in-process levels increase capital investment.

When designing a process layout, the most common tactic is to arrange departments or work centres so as to minimize the costs of material handling. In other words, departments with large flows of parts or people between them should be placed next to one another. Material handling costs in this approach depend on (1) the number of loads (or people) to be moved between two departments during some period of time and (2) the distance-related costs of moving loads (or people) between departments. Cost is assumed to be a function of distance between departments. The objective can be expressed as shown in Equation 9-1:

$$\text{Minimize cost} = \sum_{i=1}^{n}\sum_{j=1}^{n} X_{ij}\, C_{ij} \qquad \text{(9-1)}$$

where n = total number of work centres or departments

i, j = individual departments

X_{ij} = number of loads moved from department i to department j

C_{ij} = cost to move a load between department i and department j

Process-oriented facilities (and fixed-position layouts as well) try to minimize loads, or trips, times distance-related costs. The term C_{ij} combines distance and other costs into one factor. We thereby assume not only that the difficulty of movement is equal but also that the pickup and setdown costs are constant. Although they are not always constant, for simplicity's sake we summarize these data (i.e., distance, difficulty, and pickup and setdown costs) in this one variable, cost. The best way to understand the steps involved in designing a process layout is to look at an example.

EXAMPLE **1**

Designing a Process Layout

Walters Company management wants to arrange the six departments of its factory in a way that will minimize interdepartmental material handling costs. Managers make an initial assumption (to simplify the problem) that each department is 20 × 20 feet and that the building is 60 feet long and 40 feet wide.

APPROACH AND SOLUTION ▶ The process layout procedure that they follow involves six steps:

STEP 1: *Construct a "from–to matrix"* showing the flow of parts or materials from department to department (see Figure 9.4).

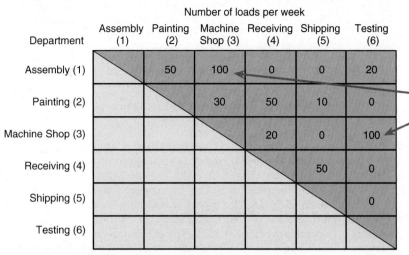

FIGURE 9.4
Interdepartmental Flow of Parts

Number of loads per week

Department	Assembly (1)	Painting (2)	Machine Shop (3)	Receiving (4)	Shipping (5)	Testing (6)
Assembly (1)		50	100	0	0	20
Painting (2)			30	50	10	0
Machine Shop (3)				20	0	100
Receiving (4)					50	0
Shipping (5)						0
Testing (6)						

STUDENT TIP
The high flows between 1 and 3 and between 3 and 6 are immediately apparent. Departments 1, 3, and 6, therefore, should be close together.

STEP 2: *Determine the space requirements* for each department. (Figure 9.5 shows available plant space.)

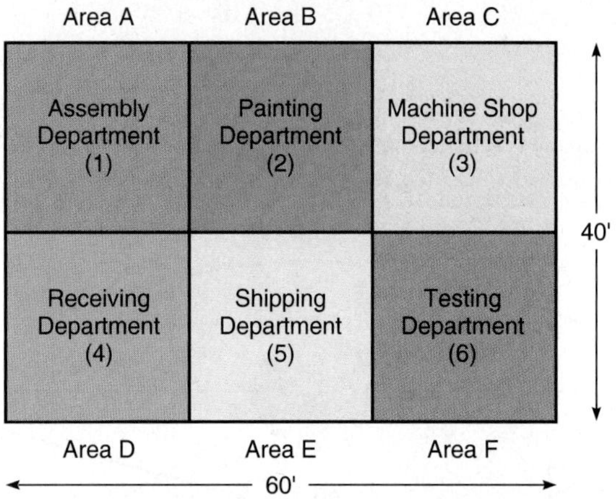

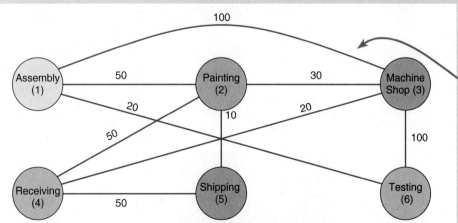

FIGURE 9.5
Building Dimensions and One Possible Department Layout

STUDENT TIP
Think of this as a starting, initial layout. Our goal is to improve it, if possible.

STEP 3: *Develop an initial schematic diagram* showing the sequence of departments through which parts must move. Try to place departments with a heavy flow of materials or parts next to one another (see Figure 9.6).

FIGURE 9.6
Interdepartmental Flow Graph Showing Number of Weekly Loads

STUDENT TIP
This shows that 100 loads also move weekly between assembly and the machine shop. We will probably want to move these two departments closer to one another to minimize the flow of parts through the factory.

STEP 4: *Determine the cost of this layout* by using the material handling cost equation:

$$\text{Cost} = \sum_{i=1}^{n}\sum_{j=1}^{n} X_{ij}C_{ij}$$

For this problem, Walters Company assumes that a forklift carries all interdepartmental loads. The cost of moving one load between adjacent departments is estimated to be \$1. Moving a load between nonadjacent departments costs \$2. Looking at Figures 9.4 and 9.5, we thus see that the handling cost between departments 1 and 2 is $50 (= $ 1 × 50 loads), $200 between departments 1 and 3 (= $ 2 × 100 loads), $40 between departments 1 and 6 (= $ 2 × 20 loads), and so on. Work areas that are diagonal to one another, such as 2 and 4, are treated as adjacent. The total cost for the layout shown in Figure 9.6 is:

$$\text{Cost} = \$50 + \$200 + \$40 + \$30 + \$50$$

(1 and 2) (1 and 3) (1 and 6) (2 and 3) (2 and 4)

$$+ \$10 + \$40 + \$100 + \$50$$

(2 and 5) (3 and 4) (3 and 6) (4 and 5)

$$= \$570$$

STEP 5: By trial and error (or by a more sophisticated computer program approach that we discuss shortly), *try to improve the layout* pictured in Figure 9.5 to establish a better arrangement of departments.

By looking at both the flow graph (Figure 9.6) and the cost calculations, we see that placing departments 1 and 3 closer together appears desirable. They currently are nonadjacent, and the high volume of flow between them causes a large handling expense. Looking the situation over, we need to check the effect of shifting departments and possibly raising, instead of lowering, overall costs.

One possibility is to switch departments 1 and 2. This exchange produces a second departmental flow graph (Figure 9.7), which shows a reduction in cost to $480, a savings in material handling of $90:

$$\text{Cost} = \$50 + \$100 + \$20 + \$60 + \$50$$

(1 and 2) (1 and 3) (1 and 6) (2 and 3) (2 and 4)

$$+ \$10 + \$40 + \$100 + \$50$$

(2 and 5) (3 and 4) (3 and 6) (4 and 5)

$$= \$480$$

Suppose Walters Company is satisfied with the cost figure of $480 and the flow graph of Figure 9.7. The problem may not be solved yet. Often, a sixth step is necessary:

FIGURE 9.7

Second Interdepartmental Flow Graph

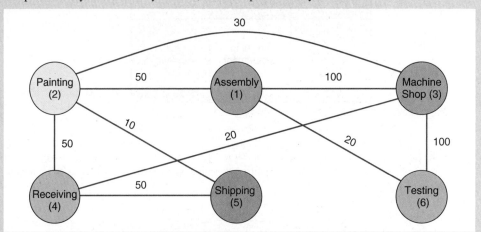

STEP 6: *Prepare a detailed plan* arranging the departments to fit the shape of the building and its nonmovable areas (such as the loading dock, washrooms, and stairways). Often this step involves ensuring that the final plan can be accommodated by the electrical system, floor loads, aesthetics, and other factors.

In the case of Walters Company, space requirements are a simple matter (see Figure 9.8).

FIGURE 9.8

A Feasible Layout for Walters Company

Area A	Area B	Area C
Painting Department (2)	Assembly Department (1)	Machine Shop Department (3)
Receiving Department (4)	Shipping Department (5)	Testing Department (6)
Area D	Area E	Area F

INSIGHT ▶ This switch of departments is only one of a large number of possible changes. For a six-department problem, there are actually 720 (or 6! = 6 × 5 × 4 × 3 × 2× 1) potential arrangements! In layout problems, we may not find the optimal solution and may have to be satisfied with a "reasonable" one.

LEARNING EXERCISE ▶ Can you improve on the layout in Figures 9.7 and 9.8? [Answer: Yes, it can be lowered to $430 by placing shipping in area A, painting in area B, assembly in area C, receiving in area D (no change), machine shop in area E, and testing in area F (no change).]

RELATED PROBLEMS ▶ 9.1, 9.2, 9.3, 9.4, 9.5, 9.6, 9.7, 9.8, 9.9

EXCEL OM Data File **Ch09Ex1.xlsx** can be found at **MyLab Operations Management**.

ACTIVE MODEL 9.1 Example 1 is further illustrated in Active Model 9.1 at **MyLab Operations Management**.

COMPUTER SOFTWARE FOR PROCESS-ORIENTED LAYOUTS

The graphic approach in Example 1 is fine for small problems. It does not, however, suffice for larger problems. When 20 departments are involved in a layout problem, more than 600 *trillion* different department configurations are possible. Fortunately, computer programs have been written to handle large layouts. These programs often add sophistication with flowcharts, multiple-storey capability, storage and container placement, material volumes, time analysis, and cost comparisons. These programs tend to be interactive—that is, require participation by the user. And most only claim to provide "good," not "optimal," solutions.

Proplanner Software for Process-Oriented Layouts

With the click of a mouse, material flow diagrams, such as this one from Proplanner, can manipulate layouts to show the cost saving from an improved layout. In this example, pump housings are received and stored nearer to the point of use reducing total in-plant travel distance from over 3.5 million feet to 2.2 million feet, a 38% saving. See www.proplanner.com for video demonstrations of this and other related tools.

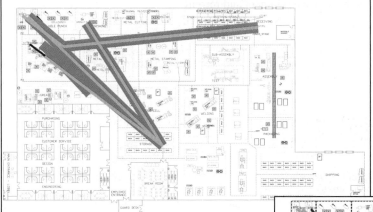

Before

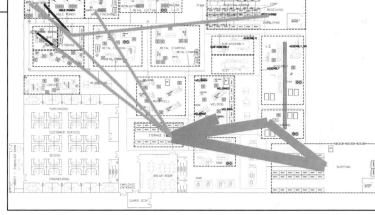

After

Work cell

An arrangement of machines and personnel that focuses on making a single product or family of related products.

LO6 Define *work cell* and the requirements of a work cell

Work Cells

A **work cell** reorganizes people and machines that would ordinarily be dispersed in various departments into a group so that they can focus on making a single product or a group of related products (see Figure 9.9). Cellular work arrangements are used when volume warrants a special arrangement of machinery and equipment. In a manufacturing environment, *group technology* (see Chapter 5) identifies products that have similar characteristics and lend themselves to being processed in a particular work cell. These work cells are reconfigured as product designs change or volume fluctuates. Although the idea of work cells was first presented by R. E. Flanders in 1925, only with the increasing use of group technology has the technique reasserted itself. The advantages of work cells are:

1. *Reduced work-in-process inventory* because the work cell is set up to provide one-piece flow from machine to machine.
2. *Less floor space* required because less space is needed between machines to accommodate work-in-process inventory.
3. *Reduced raw material and finished goods inventories* because less work-in-process allows more rapid movement of materials through the work cell.
4. *Reduced direct labour cost* because of improved communication among employees, better material flow, and improved scheduling.
5. *Heightened sense of employee participation* in the organization and the product: employees accept the added responsibility of product quality because it is directly associated with them and their work cell.
6. *Increased equipment and machinery utilization* because of better scheduling and faster material flow.
7. *Reduced investment in machinery and equipment* because good utilization reduces the number of machines and the amount of equipment and tooling.

REQUIREMENTS OF WORK CELLS

The requirements of cellular production include:

- Identification of families of products, often through the use of group technology codes or equivalents.
- A high level of training, flexibility, and empowerment of employees.
- Being self-contained, with its own equipment and resources.
- Conducting of tests (poka-yoke) at each station in the cell.

FIGURE 9.9

Improving Layouts by Moving to the Work Cell Concept

Note in both (a) and (b) that U-shaped work cells can reduce material and employee movement. The U shape may also reduce space requirements, enhance communication, cut the number of workers, and make inspection easier.

(a)

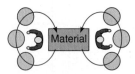

Current layout–workers in small closed areas.

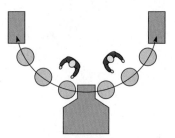

Improved layout—cross-trained workers can assist each other. May be able to add a third worker as added output is needed.

(b)

Current layout—straight lines make it hard to balance tasks because work may not be divided evenly.

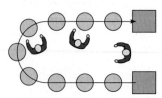

Improved layout—in U shape, workers have better access. Four cross-trained workers were reduced to three.

Siemens Corp. software such as this allows operations managers to quickly place and connect symbols for factory equipment for a full three-dimensional view of the layout. Such presentations provide added insight into the issues of facility layout in terms of process, material handling, efficiency, and safety. (Images created with Tecnomatix Plant Simulation software, courtesy of Siemens PLM Software)

Work cells have at least five advantages over assembly lines and process facilities: (1) Because tasks are grouped, inspection is often immediate; (2) fewer workers are needed; (3) workers can reach more of the work area; (4) the work area can be more efficiently balanced; and (5) communication is enhanced. Work cells are sometimes organized in a U shape, as shown on the right side of Figure 9.9.

About half of North American plants with fewer than 100 employees use some sort of cellular system, whereas 75% of larger plants have adopted cellular production methods. StackTeck Matrix of Brampton, Ontario, has incorporated pre-engineered work cells with notable success in its plastics mould-making facility. As noted in the *OM in Action* box "Work Cells Increase Productivity at Canon," Canon has had similar success with work cells.

STAFFING AND BALANCING WORK CELLS

Once the work cell has the appropriate equipment located in the proper sequence, the next task is to staff and balance the cell. Efficient production in a work cell requires appropriate staffing.

This involves two steps. First, determine the **takt time**,[2] which is the pace (frequency) of production units necessary to meet customer orders:

$$\text{Takt time} = \text{Total work time available}/\text{Units required} \qquad (9\text{-}2)$$

Second, determine the number of operators required. This requires dividing the total operation time in the work cell by the takt time:

$$\text{Workers required} = \text{Total operation time required}/\text{Takt time} \qquad (9\text{-}3)$$

Takt time
Pace of production to meet customer demands.

OM in Action | Work Cells Increase Productivity at Canon

Look quickly at Canon's factory near Tokyo, and you might think you had stepped back a few decades. Instead of the swiftly moving assembly lines you might expect to see in a high-cost, sophisticated digital camera and photocopier giant, you see workers gathered in small groups called *work cells*. Each cell is responsible for one product or a small family of products. The product focus encourages employees to exchange ideas about how to improve the assembly process. They also accept more responsibility for their work.

Canon's work cells have increased productivity by 30%. But how?

First, conveyor belts and their spare parts take up space, an expensive commodity in Japan. The shift to the cell system has freed 20 kilometres of conveyor-belt space at 54 plants and allowed Canon to close 29 parts warehouses, saving US $280 million in real estate costs.

Employees are encouraged to work in ever-tighter cells, with prizes given to those who free up the most space.

Second, the cells enable Canon to change the product mix more quickly to meet market demands for innovative products—a big advantage as product life cycles become shorter and shorter.

Third, staff morale has increased because instead of performing a single task over and over, employees are trained to put together whole machines. Some of Canon's fastest workers are so admired that they have become TV celebrities.

A layout change that improves morale while increasing productivity is a win–win for Canon.

Sources: The Wall Street Journal (September 27, 2004): R11; and *Financial Times* (September 23, 2003): 14.

---

[2] *Takt* is German for "time," "measure," or "beat" and is used in this context as the rate at which completed units must be produced to satisfy customer demand.

Example 2 considers these two steps when staffing work cells.

EXAMPLE 2

Staffing Work Cells

Mario Hebert's company in Sherbrooke makes auto mirrors. The major customer is the Honda plant nearby. Honda expects 600 mirrors delivered daily, and the work cell producing the mirrors is scheduled for eight hours. Mario wants to determine the takt time and the number of workers required.

APPROACH ▶ Mario uses Equations (9-2) and (9-3) and develops a work balance chart to help determine the time for each operation in the work cell, as well as total time.

SOLUTION ▶

Takt time = (8 hours × 60 minutes)/600 units = 480/600 = 0.8 minute = 48 seconds

Therefore, the customer requirement is one mirror every 48 seconds.

The *work balance chart* in Figure 9.10 shows that five operations are necessary, for a total operation time of 140 seconds:

$$\text{Workers required} = \text{Total operation time required}/\text{Takt time}$$
$$= (50 + 45 + 10 + 20 + 15)/48$$
$$= 140/48 = 2.92$$

FIGURE 9.10

Work Balance Chart for Mirror Production

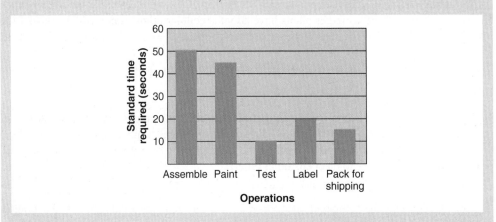

INSIGHT ▶ To produce one unit every 48 seconds will require 2.92 people. With three operators this work cell will be producing one unit each 46.67 seconds (140 seconds/3 employees = 46.67) and 617 units per day (480 minutes available × 60 seconds/46.67 seconds for each unit = 617).

LEARNING EXERCISE ▶ If testing time is expanded to 20 seconds, what is the staffing requirement? [Answer: 3.125 employees.]

RELATED PROBLEM ▶ 9.10

A *work balance chart* (like the one in Example 2) is also valuable for evaluating the operation times in work cells. Some consideration must be given to determining the bottleneck operation. Bottleneck operations can constrain the flow through the cell. Imbalance in a work cell is seldom an issue if the operation is manual, as cell members by definition are part of a cross-trained team. Consequently, the inherent flexibility of work cells typically overcomes modest imbalance issues within a cell. However, if the imbalance is a machine constraint, then an adjustment in machinery, process, or operations may be necessary. In such situations the use of traditional assembly-line-balancing analysis, the topic of our next section, may be helpful.

In many arrangements, without cells and without cross training, if one operation is halted for whatever reason (reading a drawing, getting a tool, maintaining a machine, etc.), the entire flow stops. Multiple-operator cells are therefore preferred. However, we should note that the increasing capability of multitasking machines can complicate work cell design and staffing.

The success of work cells is not limited to manufacturing. Hallmark, which has approximately half of the North American greeting card market and produces some 40 000 different cards, has modified its offices into a cellular design. In the past, its 700 creative professionals would take up to two years to develop a new card. Hallmark's decision to create work cells consisting of artists, writers, lithographers, merchandisers, and accountants, all located in

Table 9.2
Work Cell, Focused Work Centre, and Focused Factory

	Work Cell	Focused Work Centre	Focused Factory
Description	A work cell is a temporary product-oriented arrangement of machines and personnel in what is ordinarily a process-oriented facility.	A focused work centre is a permanent product-oriented arrangement of machines and personnel in what is ordinarily a process-oriented facility.	A focused factory is a permanent facility to produce a product or component in a product-oriented facility. Many of the focused factories currently being built were originally part of a process-oriented facility.
Example	A job shop with machinery and personnel rearranged to produce 300 unique control panels	Pipe bracket manufacturing at a shipyard	A plant to produce window mechanisms or seat belts for automobiles

the same area, has resulted in card preparation in a fraction of the time that the old layout required.

Commercial software, such as Proplanner and Factory Flow, is available to aid managers in their move to work cells. These programs typically require information that includes AutoCAD layout drawings; part routing data; and cost, times, and speeds of material handling systems.

THE FOCUSED WORK CENTRE AND THE FOCUSED FACTORY

When a firm has *identified a family of similar products that have a large and stable demand*, it may organize a focused work centre. A **focused work centre** moves production from a general-purpose, process-oriented facility to a large work cell that remains part of the present plant. If the focused work centre is in a separate facility, it is often called a **focused factory**. A fast-food restaurant is a focused factory—most are easily reconfigured for adjustments to product mix and volume. Burger King, for example, changes the number of personnel and task assignments rather than moving machines and equipment. In this manner, Burger King balances the assembly line to meet changing production demands. In effect, the "layout" changes numerous times each day.

The term *focused factories* may also refer to facilities that are focused in ways other than by product line or layout. For instance, facilities may be focused in regard to meeting quality, new product introduction, or flexibility requirements.

Focused facilities in both manufacturing and services appear to be better able to stay in tune with their customers, to produce quality products, and to operate at higher margins. This is true whether they are steel mills like Dofasco, CMC, Nucor, or Chaparral; restaurants like Harvey's, McDonald's, and Burger King; or a hospital like Arnold Palmer.

Table 9.2 summarizes our discussion of work cells, focused work centres, and focused factories.

Focused work centre
A permanent or semi-permanent product-oriented arrangement of machines and personnel.

Focused factory
A facility designed to produce similar products or components.

Repetitive and Product-Oriented Layout

Product-oriented layouts are organized around products or families of similar high-volume, low-variety products. Repetitive production and continuous production, which are discussed in Chapter 7, use product layouts. The assumptions are that:

1. Volume is adequate for high equipment utilization.
2. Product demand is stable enough to justify high investment in specialized equipment.
3. Product is standardized or approaching a phase of its life cycle that justifies investment in specialized equipment.
4. Supplies of raw materials and components are adequate and of uniform quality (adequately standardized) to ensure that they will work with the specialized equipment.

Two types of product-oriented layout are fabrication and assembly lines. The **fabrication line** builds components, such as automobile tires or metal parts for a refrigerator, on a series of machines, while an **assembly line** puts the fabricated parts together at a series of workstations. However, both are repetitive processes, and in both cases, the line must be "balanced": That is, the time spent to

STUDENT TIP

The traditional assembly line handles repetitive production.

LO7 Define *product-oriented layout*

Fabrication line
A machine-paced, product-oriented facility for building components.

Assembly line
An approach that puts fabricated parts together at a series of workstations; used in repetitive processes.

perform work on one machine must equal or "balance" the time spent to perform work on the next machine in the fabrication line, just as the time spent at one workstation by one assembly-line employee must "balance" the time spent at the next workstation by the next employee. The same issues arise when designing the *disassembly lines* of slaughterhouses and automobile recyclers.

Fabrication lines tend to be machine-paced and require mechanical and engineering changes to facilitate balancing. Assembly lines, on the other hand, tend to be paced by work tasks assigned to individuals or to workstations. Assembly lines, therefore, can be balanced by moving tasks from one individual to another. The central problem, then, in product-oriented layout planning is to balance the tasks at each workstation on the production line so that they are nearly the same while obtaining the desired amount of output.

Management's goal is to create a smooth, continuing flow along the assembly line with a minimum of idle time at each workstation. A well-balanced assembly line has the advantage of high personnel and facility utilization and equity among employees' workloads. Some union contracts require that workloads be nearly equal among those on the same assembly line. The term most often used to describe this process is **assembly-line balancing**. Indeed, the *objective of the product-oriented layout is to minimize imbalance in the fabrication or assembly line.*

Assembly-line balancing

Obtaining output at each workstation on a production line so delay is minimized.

The main advantages of product-oriented layout are:

1. The low variable cost per unit usually associated with high-volume, standardized products.
2. Low material handling costs.
3. Reduced work-in-process inventories.
4. Easier training and supervision.
5. Rapid throughput.

The disadvantages of product layout are:

1. The high volume required because of the large investment needed to establish the process.
2. Work stoppage at any one point ties up the whole operation.
3. A lack of flexibility when handling a variety of products or production rates.

VIDEO 9.2
Facility Layout at Wheeled Coach Ambulance

Because the problems of fabrication lines and assembly lines are similar, we focus our discussion on assembly lines. On an assembly line, the product typically moves via automated means, such as a conveyor, through a series of workstations until completed. This is the way fast-food hamburgers are made (see Figure 9.11), automobiles and some planes (such as the Boeing 737) are assembled, and television sets and ovens are produced. Product-oriented layouts use more automated and specially designed equipment than do process layouts.

ASSEMBLY-LINE BALANCING

Line balancing is usually undertaken to minimize imbalance between machines or personnel while meeting a required output from the line. To produce at a specified rate, management must know the tools, equipment, and work methods used. Then the time requirements for each assembly task (e.g., drilling a hole, tightening a nut, or spray-painting a part) must be determined. Management also needs to know the *precedence relationship* among the activities—that is, the sequence in which various tasks must be performed. Example 3 shows how to turn these task data into a precedence diagram.

LO8 Explain how to balance production flow in a repetitive or product-oriented facility

The Boeing 737, the world's most popular commercial airplane, is produced on a moving production line, travelling at 5 centimetres per minute through the final assembly process. The moving line, one of several lean manufacturing innovations, has enhanced quality, reduced flow time, slashed inventory levels, and cut space requirements. Final assembly is only 11 days—a time savings of 50%—and inventory is down more than 55%. Boeing has expanded the moving line concept to its 747 jumbo jet.

Boeing

Elapsed time	0:00	0:11	0:31	0:45		1:30
Task time (seconds)		11	20	14	0	45
Task	1. Order	2. Bun toasting	3. Assembly with condiments	4. Wrapping of patty with bun	5. Order picked up immediately to keep it fresh	6. Customer service (order and payment)

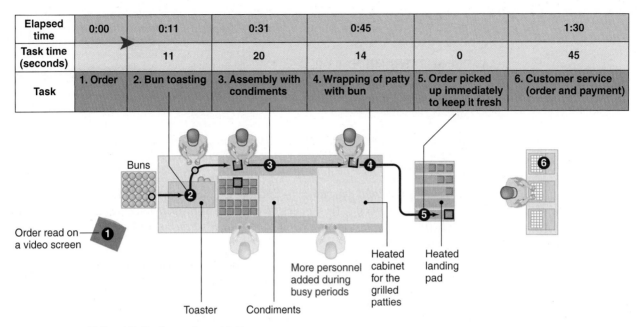

FIGURE 9.11 McDonald's Hamburger Assembly Line

Boeing wants to develop a precedence diagram for an electrostatic wing component that requires a total assembly time of 66 minutes.

APPROACH ▶ Staff gather tasks, assembly times, and sequence requirements for the component in Table 9.3.

EXAMPLE 3

Developing a Precedence Diagram for an Assembly Line

Table 9.3
Precedence Data for Wing Component

Task	Assembly Time (minutes)	Task Must Follow Task(s) Listed Below	
A	10	—	
B	11	A	This means that tasks B and E cannot be done until task A has been completed.
C	5	B	
D	4	B	
E	12	A	
F	3	C, D	
G	7	F	
H	11	E	
I	3	G, H	
	Total time 66		

SOLUTION ▶ Figure 9.12 shows the precedence diagram.

FIGURE 9.12
Precedence Diagram

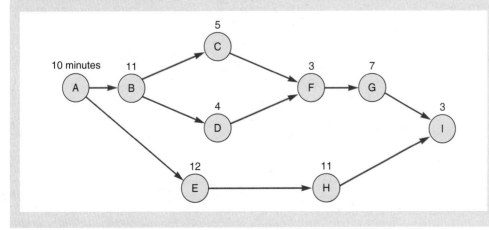

INSIGHT ▶ The diagram helps structure an assembly line and workstations, and it makes it easier to visualize the sequence of tasks.

LEARNING EXERCISE ▶ If task D had a second preceding task (C), how would Figure 9.12 change? [Answer: There would also be an arrow pointing from C to D.]

RELATED PROBLEMS ▶ 9.12a, 9.14a, 9.15a, 9.16a, 9.19a

Once we have constructed a precedence chart summarizing the sequences and performance times, we turn to the job of grouping tasks into job stations so that we can meet the specified production rate. This process involves three steps:

1. Take the units required (demand or production rate) per day and divide it into the productive time available per day (in minutes or seconds). This operation gives us what is called the **cycle time**[3]—namely, the maximum time allowed at each workstation if the production rate is to be achieved:

$$\text{Cycle time} = \frac{\text{Production time available per day}}{\text{Units required per day}} \quad \text{(9-4)}$$

2. Calculate the theoretical minimum number of workstations. This is the total task-duration time (the time it takes to make the product) divided by the cycle time. Fractions are rounded to the next higher whole number:

$$\text{Minimum number of workstations} = \frac{\sum_{i=1}^{n}\text{Time for task } i}{\text{Cycle time}} \quad \text{(9-5)}$$

where n is the number of assembly tasks.

3. Balance the line by assigning specific assembly tasks to each workstation. An efficient balance is one that will complete the required assembly, follow the specified sequence, and keep the idle time at each workstation to a minimum. A formal procedure for doing this is the following:
   a. Identify a master list of tasks.
   b. Eliminate those tasks that have been assigned.
   c. Eliminate those tasks whose precedence relationship has not been satisfied.
   d. Eliminate those tasks for which inadequate time is available at the workstation.
   e. Use one of the line-balancing *heuristics* described in Table 9.4. The five choices are (1) longest task time, (2) most following tasks, (3) ranked positional weight, (4) shortest task time, and (5) least number of following tasks. You may wish to test several of these **heuristics** to see which generates the "best" solution—that is, the smallest number of workstations and highest efficiency. Remember, however, that although heuristics provide solutions, they do not guarantee an optimal solution.

Cycle time

The maximum time that a product is allowed at each workstation.

Heuristics

Problem solving using procedures and rules rather than mathematical optimization.

Table 9.4

Layout Heuristics That May Be Used to Assign Tasks to Workstations in Assembly-Line Balancing

1. *Longest task (operation) time*	From the available tasks, choose the task with the largest (longest) time.
2. *Most following tasks*	From the available tasks, choose the task with the largest number of following tasks.
3. *Ranked positional weight*	From the available tasks, choose the task for which the sum of the times for each following task is longest. (In Example 4, we see that the ranked positional weight of task C = 5(C) + 3(F) + 7(G) + 3(I) = 18, whereas the ranked positional weight of task D = 4(D) + 3(F) + 7(G) + 3(I) =17; therefore, C would be chosen first, using this heuristic.)
4. *Shortest task (operations) time*	From the available tasks, choose the task with the shortest task time.
5. *Least number of following tasks*	From the available tasks, choose the task with the least number of subsequent tasks.

[3] *Cycle time* is the actual time to accomplish a task or process step. Several process steps may be necessary to complete the product. *Takt time*, discussed earlier, is determined by the customer and is the speed at which completed units must be produced to satisfy customer demand.

Example 4 illustrates a simple line-balancing procedure.

EXAMPLE 4

Balancing the Assembly Line

On the basis of the precedence diagram and activity times given in Example 3, Boeing determines that there are 480 productive minutes of work available per day. Furthermore, the production schedule requires that 40 units of the wing component be completed as output from the assembly line each day. It now wants to group the tasks into workstations.

APPROACH ▶ Following the three steps above, we compute the cycle time using Equation (9-4) and minimum number of workstations using Equation (9-5), and we assign tasks to workstations—in this case using the *most following tasks* heuristic.

SOLUTION ▶

$$\text{Cycle time (in minutes)} = \frac{480 \text{ minutes}}{40 \text{ units}}$$

$$= 12 \text{ minutes/unit}$$

$$\text{Minimum number of workstations} = \frac{\text{Total task time}}{\text{Cycle time}} = 0+11+5+4+12+3+7+11+\frac{3}{12} = \frac{66}{12}$$

$$= 5.5 \text{ or 6 stations}$$

Figure 9.13 shows one solution that does not violate the sequence requirements and that groups tasks into six one-person stations. To obtain this solution, activities with the most following tasks were moved into workstations to use as much of the available cycle time of 12 minutes as possible. The first workstation consumes 10 minutes and has an idle time of 2 minutes.

FIGURE 9.13
A Six-Station Solution to the Line-Balancing Problem

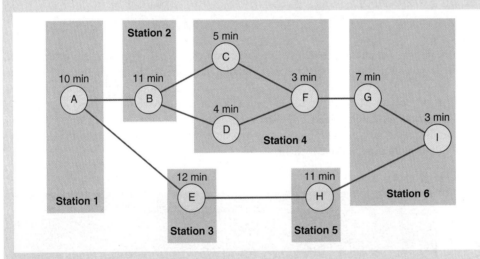

STUDENT TIP

Tasks C, D, and F can be grouped together in one workstation, provided that the physical facilities and skill levels meet the work requirements.

INSIGHT ▶ This is a reasonably well-balanced assembly line. The second workstation uses 11 minutes, and the third consumes the full 12 minutes. The fourth workstation groups three small tasks and balances perfectly at 12 minutes. The fifth has 1 minute of idle time, and the sixth (consisting of tasks G and I) has 2 minutes of idle time per cycle. Total idle time for this solution is 6 minutes per cycle.

LEARNING EXERCISE ▶ If task I required 6 minutes (instead of 3 minutes), how would this change the solution? [Answer: The cycle time would not change, and the *theoretical* minimum number of workstations would still be 6 (rounded up from 5.75), but it would take 7 stations to balance the line.]

RELATED PROBLEMS ▶ 9.11, 9.12, 9.13, 9.14, 9.15, 9.16, 9.17, 9.18, 9.19, 9.20, 9.21, 9.22, 9.23

We can compute the efficiency of a line balance by dividing the total task time by the product of the number of workstations required times the assigned (actual) cycle time of the longest workstation:

$$\text{Efficiency} = \frac{\sum \text{Task times}}{(\text{Actual number of workstations}) \times (\text{Largest assigned cycle time})} \quad \text{(9-6)}$$

Operations managers compare different levels of efficiency for various numbers of workstations. In this way, a firm can determine the sensitivity of the line to changes in the production rate and workstation assignments.

Example 5 illustrates how to determine line efficiency.

EXAMPLE 5

Determining Line Efficiency

Boeing needs to calculate the balance efficiency for Example 4.

APPROACH ▶ Equation (9-6) is applied.

SOLUTION ▶

$$\text{Efficiency} = \frac{66 \text{ minutes}}{(6 \text{ stations}) \times (12 \text{ minutes})} = \frac{66}{72} = 91.7\%$$

Note that opening a seventh workstation, for whatever reason, would decrease the efficiency of the balance to 78.6% (assuming that at least one of the workstations still required 12 minutes):

$$\text{Efficiency} = \frac{66 \text{ minutes}}{(7 \text{ stations}) \times (12 \text{ minutes})} = 78.6\%$$

INSIGHT ▶ Increasing efficiency may require that some tasks be divided into smaller elements and reassigned to other tasks. This facilitates a better balance between workstations and means higher efficiency.

LEARNING EXERCISE ▶ What is the efficiency if an eighth workstation is opened? [Answer: Efficiency = 68.75%.]

RELATED PROBLEMS ▶ 9.12f, 9.13c, 9.14f, 9.16c, 9.17b, 9.18b, 9.19e–g

---

Large-scale line-balancing problems, like large process layout problems, are often solved by computers. Several computer programs are available to handle the assignment of workstations on assembly lines with 100 (or more) individual work activities. Two computer routines, COMSOAL (Computer Method for Sequencing Operations for Assembly Lines) and ASYBL (General Electric's Assembly Line Configuration program), are widely used in larger problems to evaluate the thousands, or even millions, of possible workstation combinations much more efficiently than could ever be done by hand.

In the case of slaughtering operations, the assembly line is actually a disassembly line. The line-balancing procedures described in this chapter are the same as for an assembly/disassembly line. The chicken-processing plant shown here must balance the work of several hundred employees. The total labour content in each of the chickens processed is a few minutes.

Jens Wolf/dpa/picture alliance/Newscom

CHAPTER | SUMMARY

Layouts make a substantial difference in operating efficiency. The seven layout situations discussed in this chapter are (1) office, (2) retail, (3) warehouse, (4) fixed position, (5) process-oriented, (6) work cells, and (7) product-oriented. A variety of techniques have been developed to solve these layout problems. Office layouts often seek to maximize information flows, retail firms focus on product exposure, and warehouses attempt to optimize the trade-off between storage space and material handling cost.

The fixed-position layout problem attempts to minimize material handling costs within the constraint of limited space at the site. Process layouts minimize travel distances times the number of trips. Product layouts focus on reducing waste and the imbalance in an assembly line. Work cells are the result of identifying a family of products that justify a special configuration of machinery and equipment that reduces material travel and adjusts imbalances with cross-trained personnel.

Often, the issues in a layout problem are so wide-ranging that finding an optimal solution is not possible. For this reason, layout decisions, although the subject of substantial research effort, remain something of an art.

ETHICAL | DILEMMA

Although buried by mass customization and a proliferation of new products of numerous sizes and variations, grocery chains continue to seek to maximize payoff from their layout. Their layout includes a marketable commodity—shelf space—and they charge for it. This charge is known as a *slotting fee*.[4] Recent estimates are that food manufacturers now spend some 13% of sales on trade promotions, which is paid to grocers to get them to promote and discount the manufacturer's products. A portion of these fees is for slotting; but slotting fees drive up the manufacturer's cost. They also put the small company with a new product at a disadvantage, because small companies with limited resources are squeezed out of the marketplace. Slotting fees may also mean that customers may no longer be able to find the special local brand. How ethical are slotting fees?

---

[4]For an interesting discussion of slotting fees, see J. G. Kaikati and A. M. Kaikati, "Slotting and Promotional Allowances," *Supply Chain Management* 11, no. 2 (2006): 140–147; or J. L. Stanton and K. C. Herbst, "Slotting Allowances," *International Journal of Retail & Distribution Management* 34, no. 2/3 (2006): 187–197.

Discussion Questions

1. What are the seven layout strategies presented in this chapter?
2. What are the three factors that complicate a fixed-position layout?
3. What are the advantages and disadvantages of process layout?
4. How would an analyst obtain data and determine the number of trips in:
   (a) a hospital?
   (b) a machine shop?
   (c) an auto repair shop?
5. What are the advantages and disadvantages of product layout?
6. What are the four assumptions (or preconditions) of establishing layout for high-volume, low-variety products?
7. What are the three forms of work cells discussed in the textbook?
8. What are the advantages and disadvantages of work cells?
9. What are the requirements for a focused work centre or focused factory to be appropriate?
10. What are the two major trends influencing office layout?
11. What layout variables would you consider particularly important in an office layout where computer programs are written?
12. What layout innovations have you noticed recently in retail establishments?
13. What are the variables that a manager can manipulate in a retail layout?
14. Visit a local supermarket and sketch its layout. What are your observations regarding departments and their locations?
15. What is random stocking?
16. What information is necessary for random stocking to work?
17. Explain the concept of cross-docking.
18. What is a heuristic? Name several that can be used in assembly-line balancing.

Using Software to Solve Layout Problems

In addition to the many commercial software packages available for addressing layout problems, Excel OM and POM for Windows, both of which accompany this text, contain modules for the process problem and the assembly-line-balancing problem.

✘ USING EXCEL OM

Excel OM can assist in evaluating a series of department work assignments like the one we saw for the Walters Company in Example 1. The layout module can generate an optimal solution by enumeration or by computing the "total movement" cost for each layout you wish to examine. As such, it provides a speedy calculator for each flow–distance pairing.

Program 9.1 illustrates our inputs in the top two tables. We first enter department flows, then provide distances between work areas. Entering area assignments on a trial-and-error basis in the upper left of the top

PROGRAM 9.1   Using Excel OM's Process Layout Module to Solve the Walters Company Problem in Example 1

Source: Courtesy of Microsoft Corporation.

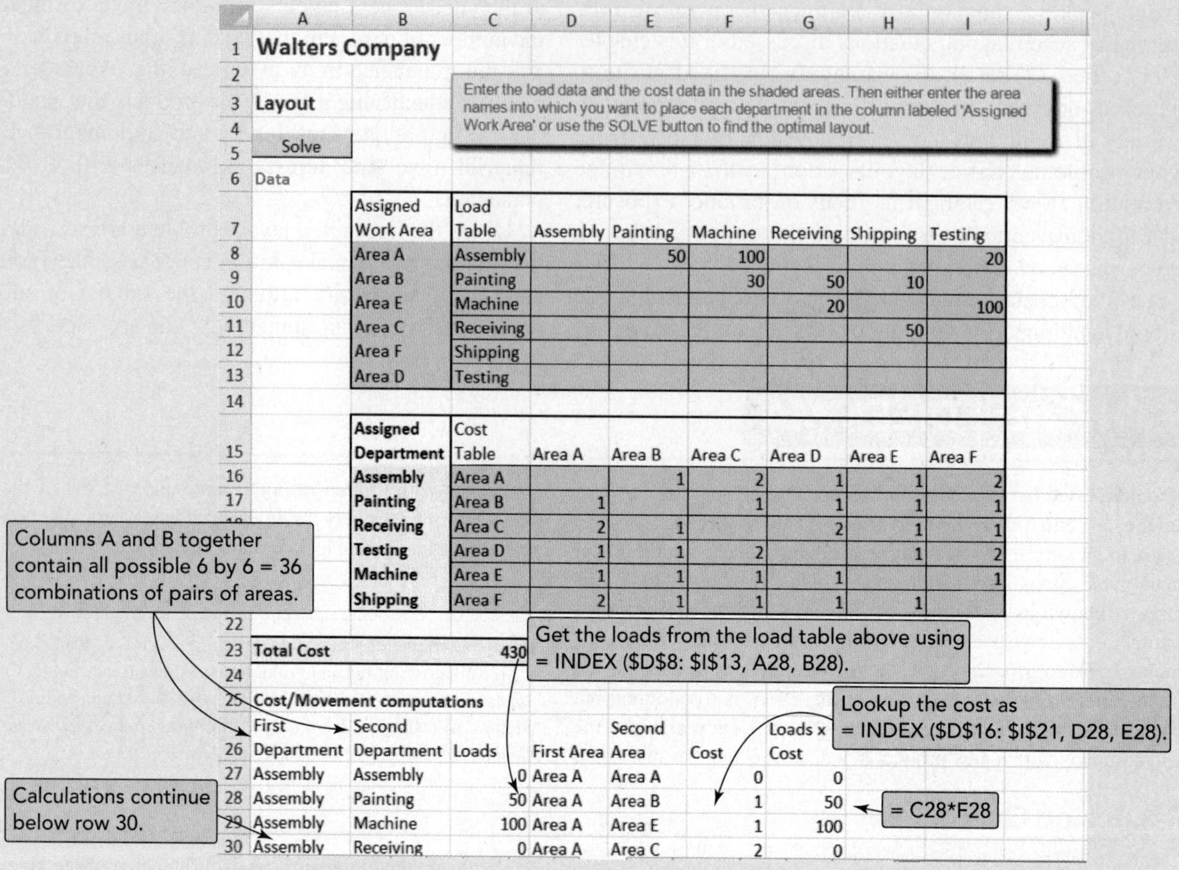

	A	B	C	D	E	F	G	H	I	J
1	**Walters Company**									
2										
3	**Layout**			Enter the load data and the cost data in the shaded areas. Then either enter the area names into which you want to place each department in the column labeled 'Assigned Work Area' or use the SOLVE button to find the optimal layout.						
4										
5	Solve									
6	Data									
7		Assigned Work Area	Load Table	Assembly	Painting	Machine	Receiving	Shipping	Testing	
8		Area A	Assembly		50	100			20	
9		Area B	Painting			30	50	10		
10		Area E	Machine				20		100	
11		Area C	Receiving					50		
12		Area F	Shipping							
13		Area D	Testing							
14										
15		Assigned Department	Cost Table	Area A	Area B	Area C	Area D	Area E	Area F	
16		**Assembly**	Area A		1	2	1	1	2	
17		**Painting**	Area B	1		1	1	1	1	
18		**Receiving**	Area C	2	1		2	1	1	
19		**Testing**	Area D	1	1	2		1	2	
20		**Machine**	Area E	1	1	1	1		1	
21		**Shipping**	Area F	2	1	1	1	1		
22										
23	Total Cost		430							
24										
25	Cost/Movement computations									
26	First Department	Second Department	Loads	First Area	Second Area	Cost	Loads x Cost			
27	Assembly	Assembly	0	Area A	Area A	0	0			
28	Assembly	Painting	50	Area A	Area B	1	50			
29	Assembly	Machine	100	Area A	Area E	1	100			
30	Assembly	Receiving	0	Area A	Area C	2	0			

Annotations:
- Columns A and B together contain all possible 6 by 6 = 36 combinations of pairs of areas.
- Get the loads from the load table above using = INDEX ($D$8: $I$13, A28, B28).
- Lookup the cost as = INDEX ($D$16: $I$21, D28, E28).
- = C28*F28
- Calculations continue below row 30.

table generates movement computations at the bottom of the screen. Total movement is recalculated each time we try a new area assignment. It turns out that the assignment shown is optimal at 430 feet of movement.

P USING POM FOR WINDOWS

The POM for Windows facility layout module can be used to place up to 10 departments in 10 rooms to minimize the total distance travelled as a function of the distances between the rooms and the flow between departments. The program exchanges departments until no exchange will reduce the total amount of movement, meaning an optimal solution has been reached.

The POM for Windows and Excel OM modules for line balancing can handle a line with up to 99 tasks, each with up to six immediate predecessors. In this program, cycle time can be entered either (1) *given*, if known, or (2) the *demand* rate can be entered with time available as shown. All five "heuristic rules" are used: (1) longest operation (task) time, (2) most following tasks, (3) ranked positional weight, (4) shortest operation (task) time, and (5) least number of following tasks. No one rule can guarantee an optimal solution, but POM for Windows displays the number of stations needed for each rule.

Appendix IV discusses further details regarding POM for Windows.

Solved Problems Virtual Office Hours help is available at MyLab Operations Management.

▼ SOLVED PROBLEM 9.1

Aero Maintenance is a small aircraft engine maintenance facility located in Yellowknife. Its new administrator, Ann Daniel, decides to improve material flow in the facility, using the process layout method she studied at university. The current layout of Aero Maintenance's eight departments is shown in Figure 9.14.

The only physical restriction perceived by Daniel is the need to keep the entrance in its current location. All other departments can be moved to a different work area (each 10 feet square) if layout analysis indicates a move would be beneficial.

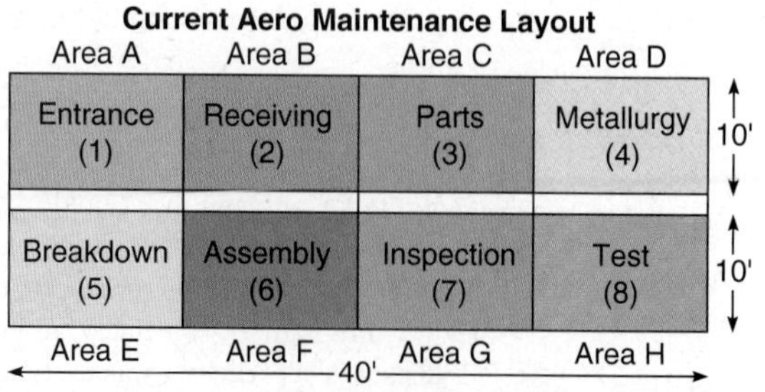

Current Aero Maintenance Layout

Area A	Area B	Area C	Area D
Entrance (1)	Receiving (2)	Parts (3)	Metallurgy (4)
Breakdown (5)	Assembly (6)	Inspection (7)	Test (8)
Area E	Area F	Area G	Area H

FIGURE 9.14   Aero Maintenance Layout

First, Daniel analyzes records to determine the number of material movements among departments in an average month. These data are shown in Figure 9.15. Her objective, Daniel decides, is to lay out the departments so as to minimize the total movement (distance travelled) of material in the facility. She writes her objective as:

$$\text{Minimize material movement} = \sum_{i=1}^{8}\sum_{j=1}^{8} X_{ij}C_{ij}$$

where X_{ij} = number of material movements per month (loads or trips) moving from department i to department j

C_{ij} = distance in feet between departments i and j (which, in this case, is the equivalent of cost per load to move between departments)

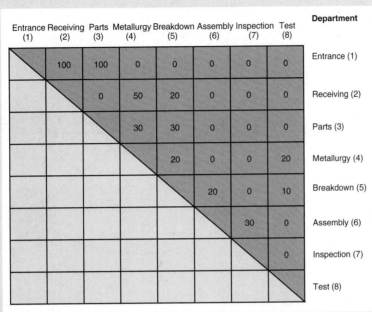

FIGURE 9.15
Number of Material Movements (Loads) Between Departments in One Month

Note that this is only a slight modification of the cost-objective equation shown earlier in the chapter.

Daniel assumes that adjacent departments, such as entrance (now in work area A) and receiving (now in work area B), have a walking distance of 10 feet. Diagonal departments are also considered adjacent and assigned a distance of 10 feet. Nonadjacent departments, such as the entrance and parts (now in area C) or the entrance and inspection (area G) are 20 feet apart, and nonadjacent rooms, such as entrance and metallurgy (area D), are 30 feet apart. (Hence,

10 feet is considered 10 units of cost, 20 feet is 20 units of cost, and 30 feet is 30 units of cost.)

Given the above information, redesign Aero Maintenance's layout to improve its material flow efficiency.

▼ **SOLUTION**
First, establish Aero Maintenance's current layout, as shown in Figure 9.16. Then, by analyzing the current layout, compute material movement:

$$\begin{array}{llll}
\text{Total movement} = & (100 \times 10') & + & (100 \times 20') & + & (50 \times 20') & + & (20 \times 10') \\
& \text{1 to 2} & & \text{1 to 3} & & \text{2 to 4} & & \text{2 to 5} \\
+ & (30 \times 10') & + & (30 \times 20') & + & (20 \times 30') & + & (20 \times 10') \\
& \text{3 to 4} & & \text{3 to 5} & & \text{4 to 5} & & \text{4 to 8} \\
+ & (20 \times 10') & + & (10 \times 30') & + & (30 \times 10') \\
& \text{5 to 6} & & \text{5 to 8} & & \text{6 to 7}
\end{array}$$

$= 1000 + 2000 + 1000 + 200 + 300 + 600 + 600$
$+ 200 + 200 + 300 + 300$
$= 6700 \text{ feet}$

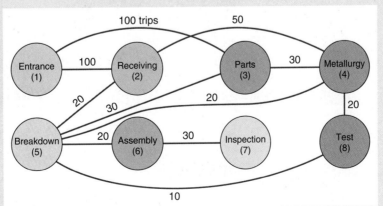

FIGURE 9.16
Current Material Flow

Propose a new layout that will reduce the current figure of 6700 feet. Two useful changes, for example, are to switch departments 3 and 5 and to interchange departments 4 and 6. This change would result in the schematic shown in Figure 9.17:

$$
\begin{aligned}
\text{Total movement} = \quad & \underset{\text{1 to 2}}{(100 \times 10')} \quad + \quad \underset{\text{1 to 3}}{(100 \times 10')} \quad + \quad \underset{\text{2 to 4}}{(50 \times 10')} \quad + \underset{\text{2 to 5}}{(20 \times 10')} \\
+ \; & \underset{\text{3 to 4}}{(30 \times 10')} \quad + \quad \underset{\text{3 to 5}}{(30 \times 20')} \quad + \quad \underset{\text{4 to 5}}{(20 \times 10')} \quad + \underset{\text{4 to 8}}{(20 \times 20')} \\
+ \; & \underset{\text{5 to 6}}{(20 \times 10')} \quad + \quad \underset{\text{5 to 8}}{(10 \times 10')} \quad + \quad \underset{\text{6 to 7}}{(30 \times 10')} \\
= \; & 1000 + 1000 + 500 + 200 + 300 + 600 + 200 \\
+ \; & 400 + 200 + 100 + 300 \\
= \; & 4800 \text{ feet}
\end{aligned}
$$

Do you see any room for further improvement?

FIGURE 9.17

Improved Layout

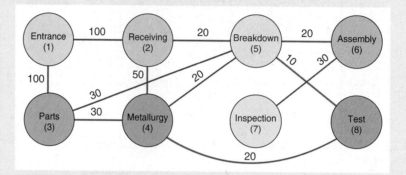

▼ SOLVED PROBLEM 9.2

The assembly line whose activities are shown in Figure 9.18 has an eight-minute cycle time. Draw the precedence graph and find the minimum possible number of one-person workstations. Then arrange the work activities into workstations so as to balance the line. What is the efficiency of your line balance?

Task	Performance Time (minutes)	Task Must Follow This Task
A	5	—
B	3	A
C	4	B
D	3	B
E	6	C
F	1	C
G	4	D, E, F
H	2	G
	28	

FIGURE 9.18

Four-Station Solution to the Line-Balancing Problem

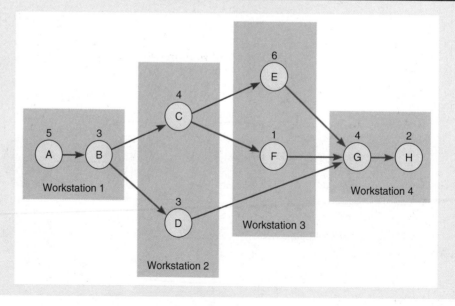

▼ SOLUTION

The theoretical minimum number of workstations is:

$$\frac{\sum t_i}{\text{Cycle time}} = \frac{28 \text{ minutes}}{8 \text{ minutes}} = 3.5, \text{ or } 4 \text{ stations}$$

The precedence graph and one good layout are shown in Figure 9.18.

$$\text{Efficiency} = \frac{\text{Total task time}}{(\text{Number of workstations}) \times (\text{Largest cycle time})} = \frac{28}{(4)(8)} = 87.5\%$$

Problems*

•• 9.1 Michael Plumb's job shop has four work areas: A, B, C, and D. Distances in metres between centres of the work areas are:

	A	B	C	D
A	—	4	9	7
B	—	—	6	8
C	—	—	—	10
D	—	—	—	—

Workpieces moved, in hundreds of workpieces per week, between pairs of work areas, are:

	A	B	C	D
A	—	8	7	4
B	—	—	3	2
C	—	—	—	6
D	—	—	—	—

It costs Michael $1 to move one workpiece 1 metre. What is the weekly total material handling cost of the layout? **Px**

•• 9.2 A Saskatoon job shop has four departments—machining (M), dipping in a chemical bath (D), finishing (F), and plating (P)—assigned to four work areas. The operations manager, Mary Marrs, has gathered the following data for this job shop as it is currently laid out (Plan A).

Hundreds of Workpieces Moved Between Work Areas Each Year

Plan A

	M	D	F	P
M	—	6	18	2
D	—	—	4	2
F	—	—	—	18
P	—	—	—	—

Distances Between Work Areas (Departments) in Metres

	M	D	F	P
M	—	20	12	8
D	—	—	6	10
F	—	—	—	4
P	—	—	—	—

It costs $0.50 to move one workpiece 1 metre in the job shop. Marrs's goal is to find a layout that has the lowest material handling cost.

a) Determine cost of the current layout, Plan A, from the data above.

b) One alternative is to switch those departments with the high loads, namely, finishing (F) and plating (P), which alters the distance between them and machining (M) and dipping (D), as follows:

Distances Between Work Areas (Departments) in Metres

Plan B

	M	D	F	P
M	—	20	8	12
D	—	—	10	6
F	—	—	—	4
P	—	—	—	—

What is the cost of *this* layout?

c) Marrs now wants you to evaluate Plan C, which also switches milling (M) and drilling (D), below.

Distance Between Work Areas (Departments) in Metres

Plan C

	M	D	F	P
M	—	20	10	6
D	—	—	8	12
F	—	—	—	4
P	—	—	—	—

What is the cost of *this* layout?

d) Which layout is best from a cost perspective? **Px**

• 9.3 Three departments—milling (M), drilling (D), and sawing (S)—are assigned to three work areas in Samuel Smith's machine shop in Summerside, PEI. The number of workpieces moved per day and the distances between the centres of the work areas, in metres, are shown in the next column.

---

* *Note:* **Px** means the problem may be solved with POM for Windows and/or Excel OM.

Pieces Moved Between Work Areas Each Day

	M	D	S
M	—	23	32
D	—	—	20
S	—	—	—

Distances Between Centres of Work Areas (Departments) in Metres

	M	D	S
M	—	10	5
D	—	—	8
S	—	—	—

It costs $2 to move one workpiece 1 metre.

What is the cost? **Px**

•• **9.4**   Roy Creasey Enterprises, a machine shop, is planning to move to a new, larger location. The new building will be 60 metres long by 40 metres wide. Creasey envisions the building as having six distinct production areas, roughly equal in size. He feels strongly about safety and intends to have marked pathways throughout the building to facilitate the movement of people and materials. See the following building schematic.

Building Schematic (with work areas 1–6)

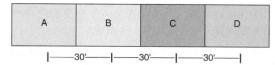

His foreman has completed a month-long study of the number of loads of material that have moved from one process to another in the current building. This information is contained in the following flow matrix.

Flow Matrix Between Production Processes

From \ To	Materials	Welding	Drills	Lathes	Grinders	Benders
Materials	0	100	50	0	0	50
Welding	25	0	0	50	0	0
Drills	25	0	0	0	50	0
Lathes	0	25	0	0	20	0
Grinders	50	0	100	0	0	0
Benders	10	0	20	0	0	0

Finally, Creasey has developed a matrix to indicate distances between the work areas shown in the building schematic.

Distance between Work Areas

	1	2	3	4	5	6
1		20	40	20	40	60
2			20	40	20	40
3				60	40	20
4					20	40
5						20
6						

What is the appropriate layout of the new building?

•• **9.5**   Registration at Dalhousie University has always been a time of emotion, commotion, and lines. Students must move among four stations to complete the trying semiannual process. Last semester's registration, held in the fieldhouse, is described in Figure 9.19. You can see, for example, that 450 students moved from the paperwork station (A) to advising (B), and 550 went directly from A to picking up their class cards (C). Graduate students, who for the most part had preregistered, proceeded directly from A to the station where registration is verified and payment collected (D). The layout used last semester is also shown in Figure 9.19. The registrar is preparing to set up this semester's stations and is anticipating similar numbers.

Interstation Activity Mix

	Pick up paperwork and forms (A)	Advising station (B)	Pick up class cards (C)	Verification of status and payment (D)
Paperwork/forms (A)	—	450	550	50
Advising (B)	350	—	200	0
Class cards (C)	0	0	—	750
Verification/payment (D)	0	0	0	—

Existing Layout

A	B	C	D

|—— 30' ——|—— 30' ——|—— 30' ——|

FIGURE 9.19   Registration Flow of Students

a) What is the "load × distance," or "movement cost," of the layout shown?

b) Provide an improved layout and compute its movement cost. **Px**

••• **9.6**   You have just been hired as the director of operations for Reid Chocolates, a purveyor of exceptionally fine candies. Reid Chocolates has two kitchen layouts under consideration for its recipe making and testing department. The strategy is to provide the best kitchen layout possible so that food scientists can devote their time and energy to product improvement, not wasted effort in the kitchen. You have been asked to evaluate these two kitchen layouts and to prepare a recommendation for your boss, Mr. Reid, so that he can proceed to place the contract for building the kitchens. (See Figure 9.20(a) and Figure 9.20(b).) **Px**

FIGURE 9.20(A) Reid Chocolates Data

Number of trips between work centres:

From: \ To:	Refrigerator 1	Counter 2	Sink 3	Storage 4	Stove 5
Refrig. 1	0	8	13	0	0
Counter 2	5	0	3	3	8
Sink 3	3	12	0	4	0
Storage 4	3	0	0	0	5
Stove 5	0	8	4	10	0

FIGURE 9.20(B) Layout Options

Kitchen layout #1

Walking distance in metres

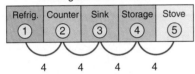

Kitchen layout #2

Walking distance in metres

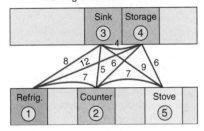

•• **9.7** Reid Chocolates (see Problem 9.6) is considering a third layout, as shown below. Evaluate its effectiveness in trip-distance metres. **Px**

Kitchen layout #3

Walking distance in metres

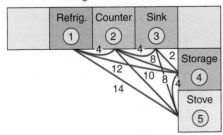

•• **9.8** Reid Chocolates (see Problems 9.6 and 9.7) has yet two more layouts to consider.
a) Layout 4 is shown below. What is the total trip distance?
b) Layout 5, which also follows, has what total trip distance?

Kitchen layout #4

Walking distance in metres

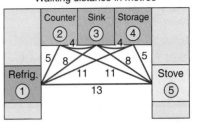

Kitchen layout #5

Walking distance in metres

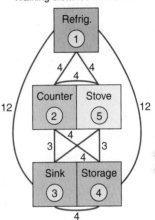

•• **9.9** Six processes are to be laid out in six areas along a long corridor at Linda Babat Accounting Services. The distance between adjacent work centres is 40 metres. The number of trips between work centres is given in the following table:

	Trips Between Processes					
			To			
From	A	B	C	D	E	F
A		18	25	73	12	54
B			96	23	31	45
C				41	22	20
D					19	57
E						48
F						

a) Assign the processes to the work areas in a way that minimizes the total flow, using a method that places processes with highest flow adjacent to each other.
b) What assignment minimizes the total traffic flow? **Px**

•• **9.10** After an extensive product analysis using group technology, Bob Buerlein has identified a product he believes should be pulled out of his process facility and handled in a work cell. Bob has identified the following operations as necessary for the work cell. The customer expects delivery of 250 units per day, and the workday is 420 minutes.
a) What is the takt time?
b) How many employees should be cross-trained for the cell?
c) Which operations may warrant special consideration?

Operation	Standard Time (min)
Shear	1.1
Bend	1.1
Weld	1.7
Clean	3.1
Paint	1.0

•• **9.11** Stanford Rosenberg Electronics wants to establish an assembly line for producing a new product, the Personal Little Assistant (PLA). The tasks, task times, and immediate predecessors for the tasks are as follows:

Task	Time (sec)	Immediate Predecessors
A	12	—
B	15	A
C	8	A
D	5	B, C
E	20	D

Rosenberg's goal is to produce 180 PLAs per hour.
a) What is the cycle time?
b) What is the theoretical minimum for the number of workstations that Rosenberg can achieve in this assembly line?
c) Can the theoretical minimum actually be reached when workstations are assigned? **Px**

••• **9.12** Quebec Urban Furniture, Inc. produces all types of office furniture. The "Executive Secretary" is a chair that has been designed using ergonomics to provide comfort during long work hours. The chair sells for $130. There are 480 minutes available during the day, and the average daily demand has been 50 chairs. There are eight tasks:

Task	Performance Time (min)	Task Must Follow Task Listed Below
A	4	—
B	7	—
C	6	A, B
D	5	C
E	6	D
F	7	E
G	8	E
H	6	F, G

Draw a precedence diagram of this operation.
a) What is the cycle time for this operation?
b) What is the theoretical minimum number of workstations?
c) Assign tasks to workstations.
d) What is the idle time per cycle?
e) How much total idle time is present each day?
f) What is the overall efficiency of the assembly line? **Px**

•• **9.13** Rita Gibson Appliances wants to establish an assembly line to manufacture its new product, the Mini-Me Microwave Oven. The goal is to produce five Mini-Me Microwave Ovens per hour.

The tasks, task times, and immediate predecessors for producing one Mini-Me Microwave Oven are as follows:

Task	Time (min)	Immediate Predecessors
A	10	—
B	12	A
C	8	A, B
D	6	B, C
E	6	C
F	6	D, E

a) What is the *theoretical* minimum for the smallest number of workstations that Gibson can achieve in this assembly line?
b) Graph the assembly line and assign workers to workstations. Can you assign them with the theoretical minimum?
c) What is the efficiency of *your* assignment? **Px**

•• **9.14** The Temple Toy Company has decided to manufacture a new toy tractor, the production of which is broken into six steps. The demand for the tractor is 4800 units per 40-hour workweek:

Task	Performance Time (sec)	Predecessors
A	20	None
B	30	A
C	15	A
D	15	A
E	10	B, C
F	30	D, E

a) Draw a precedence diagram of this operation.
b) Given the demand, what is the cycle time for this operation?
c) What is the *theoretical* minimum number of workstations?
d) Assign tasks to workstations.
e) How much total idle time is present each cycle?
f) What is the overall efficiency of the assembly line with five stations; and with six stations? **Px**

•• **9.15** The following table details the tasks required for Kelowna-based T. Liscio Industries to manufacture a fully portable industrial vacuum cleaner. The times in the table are in minutes. Demand forecasts indicate a need to operate with a cycle time of 10 minutes.

Activity	Activity Description	Immediate Predecessors	Time
A	Attach wheels to tub	—	5
B	Attach motor to lid	—	1.5
C	Attach battery pack	B	3
D	Attach safety cutoff	C	4
E	Attach filters	B	3
F	Attach lid to tub	A, E	2
G	Assemble attachments	—	3
H	Function test	D, F, G	3.5
I	Final inspection	H	2
J	Packing	I	2

a) Draw the appropriate precedence diagram for this production line.
b) Assign tasks to workstations and determine how much idle time is present each cycle?
c) Discuss how this balance could be improved to 100%.
d) What is the *theoretical* minimum number of workstations? **Px**

•• 9.16 Tailwind, Inc., produces high-quality but expensive training shoes for runners. The Tailwind shoe, which sells for $210, contains both gas- and liquid-filled compartments to provide more stability and better protection against knee, foot, and back injuries. Manufacturing the shoes requires 10 separate tasks. There are 400 minutes available for manufacturing the shoes in the plant each day. Daily demand is 60. The information for the tasks is as follows:

Task	Performance Time (min)	Task Must Follow Task Listed Below
A	1	—
B	3	A
C	2	B
D	4	B
E	1	C, D
F	3	A
G	2	F
H	5	G
I	1	E, H
J	3	I

a) Draw the precedence diagram.
b) Assign tasks to the minimum feasible number of workstations according to the "ranked positioned weight" decision rule.
c) What is the efficiency of the process?
d) What is the idle time per cycle? **Px**

•• 9.17 The Mach 10 is a one-person sailboat manufactured by Creative Leisure. The final assembly plant is in Victoria, British Columbia. The assembly area is available for production of the Mach 10 for 200 minutes per day. (The rest of the time it is busy making other products.) The daily demand is 60 boats. Given the following information,
a) Draw the precedence diagram and assign tasks using five workstations.
b) What is the efficiency of the assembly line, using your answer to part (a)?
c) What is the *theoretical* minimum number of workstations?
d) What is the idle time per boat produced? **Px**

Task	Performance Time (min)	Task Must Follow Task Listed Below
A	1	—
B	1	A
C	2	A
D	1	C
E	3	C
F	1	C
G	1	D, E, F
H	2	B
I	1	G, H

•• 9.18 Because of the expected high demand for Mach 10, Creative Leisure has decided to increase manufacturing time available to produce the Mach 10 (see Problem 9.17).
a) If demand remained the same but 300 minutes were available each day on the assembly line, how many workstations would be needed?
b) What would be the efficiency of the new system?
c) What would be the impact on the system if 400 minutes were available? **Px**

••• 9.19 Dr. Lori Baker, operations manager at Nesa Electronics, prides herself on excellent assembly-line balancing. She has been told that the firm needs to complete 96 instruments per 24-hour day. The assembly-line activities are:

Task	Time (min)	Predecessors
A	3	—
B	6	—
C	7	A
D	5	A, B
E	2	B
F	4	C
G	5	F
H	7	D, E
I	1	H
J	6	E
K	4	G, I, J
	50	

a) Draw the precedence diagram.
b) If the daily (24-hour) production rate is 96 units, what is the highest allowable cycle time?
c) If the cycle time after allowances is given as 10 minutes, what is the daily (24-hour) production rate?
d) With a 10-minute cycle time, what is the theoretical minimum number of stations with which the line can be balanced?
e) With a 10-minute cycle time and six workstations, what is the efficiency?
f) What is the total idle time per cycle with a 10-minute cycle time and six workstations?
g) What is the best workstation assignment you can make without exceeding a 10-minute cycle time and what is its efficiency? **Px**

•• 9.20 Suppose production requirements in Solved Problem 9.2 increase and require a reduction in cycle time from eight minutes to seven minutes. Balance the line once again, using the new cycle time. Note that it is not possible to combine task times so as to group tasks into the minimum number of workstations. This condition occurs in actual balancing problems fairly often.

•• 9.21 The mandatory pre-hire physical examination given to prospective pilots and navigators by the physicians at Yukon Airlines involves the following seven activities:

Activity	Average Time (min)
Medical history	10
Blood tests	8
Eye examination	5
Measurements (i.e., weight, height, blood pressure)	7
Medical examination	16
Psychological interview	12
Exit medical evaluation	10

These activities can be performed in any order, with two exceptions: medical history must be taken first, and exit medical evaluation is last. At present, there are three paramedics and two physicians on duty during each shift. Only physicians can perform exit evaluations and conduct psychological interviews. Other activities can be carried out by either physicians or paramedics.

a) Develop a layout and balance the line.
b) How many people can be processed per hour?
c) Which activity accounts for the current bottleneck?
d) What is the total idle time per cycle?
e) If one more physician and one more paramedic can be placed on duty, how would you redraw the layout? What is the new throughput?

• • •   9.22 Frank Pianki's company wants to establish an assembly line to manufacture its new product, the iScan phone. Frank's goal is to produce 60 iScans per hour. Tasks, task times, and immediate predecessors are as follows:

Task	Time (sec)	Immediate Predecessors	Task	Time (sec)	Immediate Predecessors
A	40	—	F	25	C
B	30	A	G	15	C
C	50	A	H	20	D, E
D	40	B	I	18	F, G
E	6	B	J	30	H, I

a) What is the theoretical minimum for the number of workstations that Frank can achieve in this assembly line?
b) Use the *most following tasks* heuristic to balance an assembly line for the iScan phone.
e) How many workstations are in your answer to part (b)?
d) What is the efficiency of your answer to part (b)?

• • • •   9.23 As the Cottrell Bicycle Co. of Regina completes plans for its new assembly line, it identifies 25 different tasks in the production process. Jonathan Cottrell, operations VP, now faces the job of balancing the line. He lists precedences and provides time estimates for each step based on work-sampling techniques. His goal is to produce 1000 bicycles per standard 40-hour workweek.

Task	Time (sec)	Precedence Tasks	Task	Time (sec)	Precedence Tasks
K3	60	—	E3	109	F3
K4	24	K3	D6	53	F4
K9	27	K3	D7	72	F9, E2, E3
J1	66	K3	D8	78	E3, D6
J2	22	K3	D9	37	D6
J3	3	—	C1	78	F7
G4	79	K4, K9	B3	72	D7, D8, D9, C1
G5	29	K9, J1	B5	108	C1
F3	32	J2	B7	18	B3
F4	92	J2	A1	52	B5
F7	21	J3	A2	72	B5
F9	126	G4	A3	114	B7, A1, A2
E2	18	G5, F3			

a) Balance this operation, using various heuristics. Which is best and why?
b) What happens if the firm can change to a 41-hour workweek? **Px**

CASE STUDIES

Automobile Licence Renewals

Manuel DeSousa, the manager of a metropolitan branch office of the Ministry of Transportation, attempted to analyze the driver's licence–renewal operations. He had to perform several steps. After examining the licence-renewal process, he identified those steps and associated times required to perform each step, as shown in the following table:

Automobile Licence–Renewal Process Times

Step	Average Time to Perform (seconds)
1. Review renewal application for correctness	15
2. Process and record payment	30
3. Check file for violations and restrictions	60
4. Conduct eye test	40
5. Photograph applicant	20
6. Issue temporary licence	30

DeSousa found that each step was assigned to a different person. Each application was a separate process in the sequence shown. He determined that his office should be prepared to accommodate a maximum demand of processing 120 renewal applicants per hour.

He observed that work was unevenly divided among clerks and that the clerk responsible for checking violations tended to shortcut her task to keep up with the others. Long lines built up during the maximum-demand periods.

DeSousa also found that Steps 1 to 4 were handled by general clerks who were each paid $12 per hour. Step 5 was performed by a photographer paid $16 per hour. (Branch offices were charged $10 per hour for each camera to perform photography.) Step 6, issuing temporary licences, was required by provincial policy to be handled by uniformed motor vehicle officers. Officers were paid $18 per hour but could be assigned to any job except photography.

A review of the jobs indicated that Step 1, reviewing applications for correctness, had to be performed before any other step could be taken. Similarly, Step 6, issuing temporary licences, could not be performed until all the other steps were completed.

Manuel DeSousa was under severe pressure to increase productivity and reduce costs, but he was also told by the regional director that he must accommodate the demand for renewals. Otherwise, "heads would roll".

Discussion Questions

1. What is the maximum number of applications per hour that can be handled by the present configuration of the process?
2. How many applications can be processed per hour if a second clerk is added to check for violations?
3. If the second clerk could be added *anywhere* you choose (and not necessarily to check for violations, as in Question 2), what is the maximum number of applications the process can handle? What is the new configuration?
4. How would you suggest modifying the process to accommodate 120 applications per hour? What is the cost per application of this new configuration?

Source: Modified from a case by W. Earl Sasser, Paul R. Olson, and D. Daryl Wyckoff, *Management of Services Operations: Text, Cases, and Readings* (Boston: Allyn & Bacon).

Layout at Arnold Palmer Hospital

When Orlando's Arnold Palmer Hospital began plans to create a new 273-bed, 11-storey hospital across the street from its existing facility, which was bursting at the seams in terms of capacity, a massive planning process began. The $100 million building, opened in 2006, was long overdue, according to the executive director Kathy Swanson: "We started Arnold Palmer Hospital in 1989, with a mission to provide quality services for children and women in a comforting, family-friendly environment. Since then we have served well over 1.5 million women and children and now deliver more than 12 000 babies a year. By 2001, we simply ran out of room, and it was time for us to grow."

The new hospital's unique, circular pod design provides a maximally efficient layout in all areas of the hospital, creating a patient-centred environment. *Servicescape* design features include a serene environment created through the use of warm colours, private rooms with pull-down Murphy beds for family members, 14-foot ceilings, and natural lighting with oversized windows in patient rooms. But these radical new features did not come easily. "This pod concept with a central nursing area and pie-shaped rooms resulted from over 1000 planning meetings of 35 user groups, extensive motion and time studies, and computer simulations of the daily movements of nurses," says Swanson.

In a traditional linear hospital layout, called the *racetrack* design, patient rooms line long hallways, and a nurse might walk 2.7 miles per day serving patient needs at Arnold Palmer. "Some nurses spent 30% of their time simply walking. With the nursing shortage and the high cost of healthcare professionals, efficiency is a major concern," added Swanson. With the nursing station in the centre of 10- or 12-bed circular pods, no patient room is more than 14 feet from a station. The time savings are in the 20% range. Swanson pointed to Figures 9.21 and 9.22 as examples of the old and new walking and trip distances.*

"We have also totally redesigned our neonatal rooms," says Swanson. "In the old system, there were 16 neonatal beds in a large and often noisy rectangular room. The new building features semi-private rooms for these tiny babies. The rooms are much improved, with added privacy and a quiet, simulated night atmosphere, in addition to pull-down beds for parents to use. Our research shows that babies improve and develop much more quickly with this layout design. Layout and environment indeed impact patient care!"

Discussion Questions*

1. Identify the many variables that a hospital needs to consider in layout design.
2. What are the advantages of the circular pod design over the traditional linear hallway layout found in most hospitals?
3. Figure 9.21 illustrates a sample linear hallway layout. During a period of random observation, nurse Thomas Smith's day includes 6 trips from the nursing station to each of the 12 patient rooms (back and forth), 20 trips to the medical supply room, 5 trips to the break room, and 12 trips to the linen supply room. What is his total distance travelled in miles?

---

* Layout and walking distances, including some of the numbers in Figures 9.21 and 9.22, have been simplified for purposes of this case.

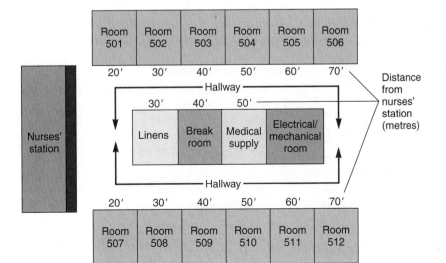

FIGURE 9.21

Traditional Hospital Layout

Patient rooms are on two linear hallways with exterior windows. Supply rooms are on interior corridors. This layout is called a "racetrack" design.

FIGURE 9.22

New Pod Design for Hospital Layout

Note that each room is 14 feet from the pod's *local* nursing station. The *break rooms* and the *central medical station* are each about 60 feet from the local nursing pod. Pod *linen supply* rooms are also 14 feet from the local nursing station.

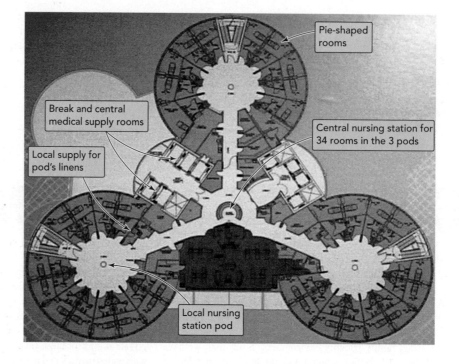

Pie-shaped rooms

Break and central medical supply rooms

Local supply for pod's linens

Central nursing station for 34 rooms in the 3 pods

Local nursing station pod

4. Figure 9.22 illustrates an architect's drawing of Arnold Palmer Hospital's new circular pod system. If nurse Susan Jones's day includes 7 trips from the nursing pod to each of the 12 rooms (back and forth), 20 trips to central medical supply, 6 trips to the break room, and 12 trips to the pod linen supply, how many miles does she walk during her shift? What are the differences in the travel times between the two nurses for this random day?

5. The concept of *servicescapes* is discussed in this chapter. Describe why this is so important at Arnold Palmer Hospital and give examples of its use in layout design.

---

* You may wish to view the video that accompanies this case before addressing these questions.

Facility Layout at Wheeled Coach Ambulance

When President Bob Collins began his career at Wheeled Coach, the world's largest manufacturer of ambulances, there were only a handful of employees. Now the firm's Florida plant has a workforce of 350. The physical plant has also expanded, with offices, R&D, final assembly, and wiring, cabinetry, and upholstery work cells in one large building. Growth has forced the painting work cell into a separate building, aluminum fabrication and body installation into another, inspection and shipping into a fourth, and warehousing into yet another.

Like many other growing companies, Wheeled Coach was not able to design its facility from scratch. And although management realizes that material handling costs are a little higher than an ideal layout would provide, Collins is pleased with the way the facility has evolved and employees have adapted. The aluminum cutting work cell lies adjacent to body fabrication, which, in turn, is located next to the body-installation work cell. And while the vehicle must be driven across a street to one building for painting and then to another for final assembly, at least the ambulance is on wheels. Collins is also satisfied with the flexibility shown in design of the work cells. Cell construction is flexible and can accommodate changes in product mix and volume. In addition, work cells are typically small and movable, with many work benches and staging racks borne on wheels so that they can be easily rearranged and products transported to the assembly line.

Assembly-line balancing is one key problem facing Wheeled Coach and every other repetitive manufacturer. Produced on a schedule calling for four 10-hour workdays per week, once an ambulance is on one of the six final assembly lines, it *must* move forward each day to the next workstation. Balancing just enough workers and tasks at each of the seven workstations is a never-ending challenge. Too many workers end up running into each other; too few can't finish an ambulance in seven days. Constant shifting of design and mix and improved analysis has led to frequent changes.

Discussion Questions*

1. What analytical techniques are available to help a company like Wheeled Coach deal with layout problems?
2. What suggestions would you make to Bob Collins about his layout?
3. How would you measure the "efficiency" of this layout?

---

* You may wish to view the video that accompanies this case before addressing these questions.

▶**Additional Case Study:** Visit **MyLab Operations Management** for this case study:

Microfix, Inc.: This company needs to balance its PC manufacturing assembly line and deal with sensitivity analysis of time estimates.

CHAPTER 9 | RAPID REVIEW

MyLab
Operations
Management

Main Heading	Review Material	
THE STRATEGIC IMPORTANCE OF LAYOUT DECISIONS (pp. 350–351)	Layout has numerous strategic implications because it establishes an organization's competitive priorities in regard to capacity, processes, flexibility, and cost, as well as quality of work life, customer contact, and image. *The objective of layout strategy is to develop an effective and efficient layout that will meet the firm's competitive requirements.*	
TYPES OF LAYOUT (pp. 351–352)	Types of layout and examples of their typical objectives include: 1. *Office layout:* Locate workers requiring frequent contact close to one another. 2. *Retail layout:* Expose customers to high-margin items. 3. *Warehouse layout:* Balance low-cost storage with low-cost material handling. 4. *Fixed-position layout:* Move material to the limited storage areas around the site. 5. *Process-oriented layout:* Manage varied material flow for each product. 6. *Work-cell layout:* Identify a product family, build teams, and cross-train team members. 7. *Product-oriented layout:* Equalize the task time at each workstation.	
OFFICE LAYOUT (pp. 352–353)	• **Office layout**—The grouping of workers, their equipment, and spaces/offices to provide for comfort, safety, and movement of information. A *relationship chart* displays a "closeness value" between each pair of people and/or departments that need to be placed in the office layout.	
RETAIL LAYOUT (pp. 353–355)	• **Retail layout**—An approach that addresses flow, allocates space, and responds to customer behaviour. Retail layouts are based on the idea that sales and profitability vary directly with customer exposure to products. The main *objective of retail layout is to maximize profitability per square foot of floor space* (or, in some stores, per linear foot of shelf space). • **Slotting fees**—Fees manufacturers pay to get shelf space for their products. • **Servicescape**—The physical surroundings in which a service takes place, and how they affect customers and employees.	
WAREHOUSING AND STORAGE LAYOUTS (pp. 356–357)	• **Warehouse layout**—A design that attempts to minimize total cost by addressing trade-offs between space and material handling. The variety of items stored and the number of items "picked" has direct bearing on the optimal layout. Modern warehouse management is often an automated procedure using *automated storage and retrieval systems* (ASRSs). • **Cross-docking**—Avoiding the placement of materials or supplies in storage by processing them as they are received for shipment. Cross-docking requires both tight scheduling and accurate inbound product identification. • **Random stocking**—Used in warehousing to locate stock wherever there is an open location. • **Customizing**—Using warehousing to add value to a product through component modification, repair, labelling, and packaging.	
FIXED-POSITION LAYOUT (pp. 358–359)	• **Fixed-position layout**—A system that addresses the layout requirements of stationary projects. Fixed-position layouts involve three complications: (1) There is limited space at virtually all sites, (2) different materials are needed at different stages of a project, and (3) the volume of materials needed is dynamic.	
PROCESS-ORIENTED LAYOUT (pp. 359–363)	• **Process-oriented layout**—A layout that deals with low-volume, high-variety production in which like machines and equipment are grouped together. • **Job lots**—Groups or batches of parts processed together. $$\text{Material handling cost minimization} = \sum_{i=1}^{n}\sum_{j=1}^{n} X_{ij}C_{ij} \quad \textbf{(9-1)}$$	Problems: 9.1–9.9 **VIDEO 9.1** Layout at Arnold Palmer Hospital **ACTIVE MODEL 9.1**
WORK CELLS (pp. 364–366)	• **Work cell**—An arrangement of machines and personnel that focuses on making a single product or family of related products. • **Takt time**—Pace of production to meet customer demands. $$\text{Takt time} = \text{Total work time available/Units required} \quad \textbf{(9-2)}$$ $$\text{Workers required} = \text{Total operation time required/Takt time} \quad \textbf{(9-3)}$$	Problem: 9.10

Main Heading	Review Material	
	• **Focused work centre**—A permanent or semi-permanent product-oriented arrangement of machines and personnel. • **Focused factory**—A facility designed to produce similar products or components.	
REPETITIVE AND PRODUCT-ORIENTED LAYOUT (pp. 367–372)	• **Fabrication line**—A machine-paced, product-oriented facility for building components. • **Assembly line**—An approach that puts fabricated parts together at a series of workstations; a repetitive process. • **Assembly-line balancing**—Obtaining output at each workstation on a production line so delay is minimized. • **Cycle time**—The maximum time that a product is allowed at each workstation. Cycle time = Production time available per day ÷ Units required per day **(9-4)** $$\text{Minimum number of workstations} = \sum_{i=1}^{n} \text{Time for task } i \div \text{Cycle time} \quad \textbf{(9-5)}$$ • **Heuristics**—Problem solving using procedures and rules rather than mathematical optimization. Line-balancing heuristics include *longest task (operation) time, most following tasks, ranked positional weight, shortest task (operation) time, and least number of following tasks.* $$\text{Efficiency} = \frac{\sum \text{Task times}}{(\text{Actual number of workstations}) \times (\text{Largest assigned cycle time})} \quad \textbf{(9-6)}$$	Problems: 9.11–9.22 **VIDEO 9.2** Facility Layout at Wheeled Coach Ambulance Virtual Office Hours for Solved Problem: 9.2

Self-Test

■ **Before taking the self-test,** refer to the learning objectives listed at the beginning of the chapter.

LO1 Which of the statements below best describes *office layout*?
a) Groups workers, their equipment, and spaces/offices to provide for movement of information.
b) Addresses the layout requirements of large, bulky projects such as ships and buildings.
c) Seeks the best personnel and machine utilization in repetitive or continuous production.
d) Allocates shelf space and responds to customer behaviour.
e) Deals with low-volume, high-variety production.

LO2 Which of the following does *not* support the retail layout objective of maximizing customer exposure to products?
a) Locate high-draw items around the periphery of the store.
b) Use prominent locations for high-impulse and high-margin items.
c) Maximize exposure to expensive items.
d) Use end-aisle locations.
e) Convey the store's mission with the careful positioning of the lead-off department.

LO3 The major problem addressed by the warehouse layout strategy is:
a) minimizing difficulties caused by material flow varying with each product.
b) requiring frequent contact close to one another.
c) addressing trade-offs between space and material handling.
d) balancing product flow from one workstation to the next.
e) none of the above.

LO4 A fixed-position layout:
a) groups workers to provide for movement of information.
b) addresses the layout requirements of large, bulky projects such as ships and buildings.
c) seeks the best machine utilization in continuous production.

d) allocates shelf space based on customer behaviour.
e) deals with low-volume, high-variety production.

LO5 A process-oriented layout:
a) groups workers to provide for movement of information.
b) addresses the layout requirements of large, bulky projects such as ships and buildings.
c) seeks the best machine utilization in continuous production.
d) allocates shelf space based on customer behaviour.
e) deals with low-volume, high-variety production.

LO6 For a focused work centre or focused factory to be appropriate, the following three factors are required:
a) _____
b) _____
c) _____

LO7 Before considering a product-oriented layout, it is important to be certain that:
a) _____
b) _____
c) _____
d) _____

LO8 An assembly line is to be designed for a product whose completion requires 21 minutes of work. The factory works 400 minutes per day. Can a production line with five workstations make 100 units per day?
a) Yes, with exactly 100 minutes to spare.
b) No, but four workstations would be sufficient.
c) No, it will fall short even with a perfectly balanced line.
d) Yes, but the line's efficiency is very low.
e) Cannot be determined from the information given.

Answers: LO1. a; LO2. c; LO3. c; LO4. b; LO5. e; LO6. family of products, stable forecast (demand), volume; LO7. adequate volume, stable demand, standardized product, adequate/quality supplies; LO8. c.

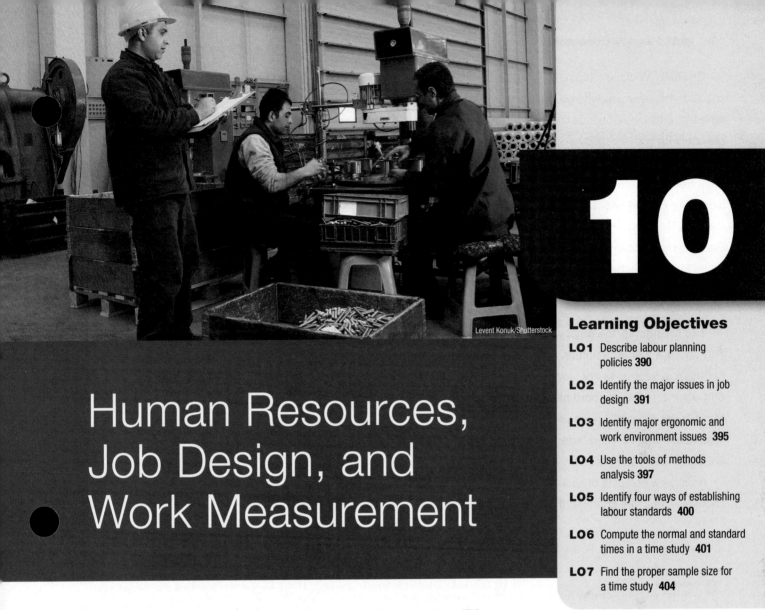

Levent Konuk/Shutterstock

10

Human Resources, Job Design, and Work Measurement

High-Performance Teamwork From the Pit Crew Makes the Difference Between Winning and Losing

In the 1990s, the popularity of NASCAR (National Association for Stock Car Auto Racing) exploded, bringing hundreds of millions of TV and sponsorship dollars into the sport. With more money, competition increased, as did the rewards for winning on Sunday. The teams—headed by such names as Rusty Wallace, Jeff Gordon, Dale Earnhardt Jr., and Tony Stewart—are as famous as the Montreal Canadiens, Toronto Blue Jays, or Vancouver Canucks.

The race car drivers may be famous, but it's the pit crews who often determine the outcome of a race. Twenty years ago, crews were auto mechanics during the week who simply did double duty on Sundays in the pits. They did pretty well to change four tires in less than 30 seconds. Today, because NASCAR teams find competitive advantage wherever they can, taking more than 16 seconds can be disastrous. A botched pit stop is the equivalent of ramming your car against the wall—crushing all hopes for the day.

< **Global Company Profile Rusty Wallace's NASCAR Racing Team**

On Rusty Wallace's team, as on all the top NASCAR squads, the crewmen who go "over the wall" are now athletes, usually ex-college football or basketball players with proven agility and strength. The Evernham team, for example, includes a former defensive back from Fairleigh Dickinson (who is now a professional tire carrier) and a 300-pound lineman from East Carolina University (who handles the jack). The Chip Ganassi racing team includes baseball players from Wake Forest, football players from University of Kentucky and North Carolina, and a hockey player from Dartmouth.

Tire changers—the guys who wrench lug nuts off and on—are a scarce human resource and average $100 000 a year in salary. Jeff Gordon was reminded of the importance of coordinated teamwork when five of his "over-the-wall" guys jumped to Dale Jarrett's organization a few years ago; it was believed to be a $500 000-per-year deal.

A pit crew consists of seven men: a front-tire changer; a rear-tire changer; front- and rear-tire carriers;

This Goodyear tire comes off Rusty Wallace's car and is no longer needed after going around the track for more than 40 laps in a Michigan International Speedway race.

John Raoux/The Orlando Sentinel

a man who jacks the car up; and two gas men with a 44-litre can.

Every sport has its core competencies and key metrics—for example, the speed of a pitcher's fastball, a running back's time on the 40-yard dash. In NASCAR, a tire changer should get five lug nuts off in 1.2 seconds. The jackman should haul his 25-pound aluminum jack from the car's right side to

1 Wallace's car pulls into the pit; the crew rushes to the right side of the car to begin service.

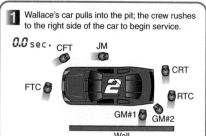

2 Right side is jacked up, tire starts to come off; gas man is emptying his first can.

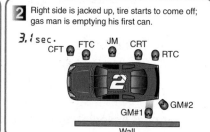

3 Action shifts to driver's side of the car; gas man carries second can of gas in.

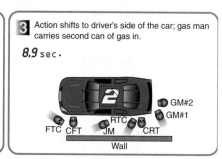

4 The second can of gas is being emptied; driver's side tires are being changed.

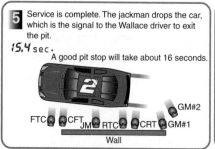

5 Service is complete. The jackman drops the car, which is the signal to the Wallace driver to exit the pit.

A good pit stop will take about 16 seconds.

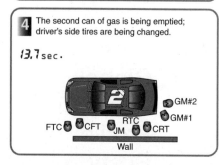

Movement of the pit crew members who go over the wall...

JM = Jackman
FTC = Front tire carrier
CFT = Changer front tire
RTC = Rear tire carrier
CRT = Changer rear tire
GM#1 = Gas man #1
GM#2 = Gas man #2

JM (Jackman) The jackman carries the hydraulic jack from the pit wall to raise the car's right side. After new tires are bolted on, he drops the car to the ground and repeats the process on the left side. His timing is crucial during this left side change, because when he drops the car again, it's the signal for the driver to go. The jackman has the most dangerous job of all the crew members; during the right-side change, he is exposed to oncoming traffic down pit row. ***FTC (Front tire carrier)*** Each tire carrier hauls a new 34-kilogram tire to the car's right side, places it on the wheel studs and removes the old tire after the tire change. They repeat this process on the left side of the car with a new tire rolled to them by crew members behind the pit wall. ***CFT (Changer front tire)*** Tire changers run to the car's right side and, using an air impact wrench, remove five lug nuts off the old tire and bolt on a new tire. They repeat the process on the left side. ***RTC (Rear tire carrier)*** Same as front tire carrier, except RTC may also adjust the rear jack bolt to alter the car's handling. ***CRT (Changer rear tire)*** Same as FT but on two rear tires. ***Gas man #1*** This gas man is usually the biggest and strongest person on the team. He goes over the wall carrying a 75-pound, 44-litre "dump can" whose nozzle he jams into the car's fuel cell receptacle. He is then handed (or tossed) another can, and the process is repeated. ***Gas man #2*** Gets second gas can to gas man #1 and catches excess fuel that spills out.

left in 3.8 seconds. For tire carriers, it should take 0.7 seconds to get a tire from the ground to mounted on the car.

The seven men who go over the wall are coached and orchestrated. Coaches use the tools of OM and watch "game tape" of pit stops and make intricate adjustments to the choreography.

"There's a lot of pressure," says D. J. Richardson, a Rusty Wallace team tire changer—and one of the best in the business. Richardson trains daily with the rest of the crew in the shop of the team owner. They focus on cardiovascular work and two muscle groups daily. Twice a week, they simulate pit stops—there can be from 12 to 14 variations—to work on their timing.

In a recent race in Michigan, Richardson and the rest of the Rusty Wallace team, with ergonomically designed gas cans, tools, and special safety gear,

were ready. On lap 43, the split-second frenzy began, with Richardson—air gun in hand—jumping over a half-metre white wall and sprinting to the right side of the team's Dodge. A teammate grabbed the tire and set it in place while Richardson secured it to the car. The process was repeated on the left side while the front crew followed the same procedure. Coupled with refuelling, the pit stop took 12.734 seconds.

After catching their breath for a minute, Richardson and the other pit crew guys reviewed a video, looking for split-second flaws.

The same process was repeated on lap 91. The Wallace driver made a late charge on Jeff Burton and Kurt Busch on the last lap and went from 14th place to a 10th-place finish.

Sources: The Wall Street Journal (June 15, 2005): A1; and *Orlando Sentinel* (June 26, 2005): C10–C12 and (February 11, 2001): M10–M11.

Human Resource Strategy for Competitive Advantage

STUDENT TIP

Mutual trust and commitment are key to a successful human resource strategy.

Good human resource strategies are expensive, difficult to achieve, and hard to sustain. But, like a NASCAR team, many organizations, from Hard Rock Cafe to Frito-Lay to WestJet Airlines, have demonstrated that sustainable competitive advantage can be built through a human resource strategy. The payoff can be significant and difficult for others to duplicate. In this chapter, we will examine some of the tools available to operations managers for achieving competitive advantage via human resource management.

The objective of a human resource strategy is to manage labour and design jobs so people are effectively and efficiently utilized. As we focus on a human resource strategy, we want to ensure that people:

VIDEO 10.1
Human Resources at Hard Rock Cafe

1. Are efficiently utilized within the constraints of other operations management decisions.
2. Have a reasonable quality of work life in an atmosphere of mutual commitment and trust.

By reasonable *quality of work life,* we mean a job that is not only reasonably safe and for which the pay is equitable but that also achieves an appropriate level of both physical and psychological requirements. *Mutual commitment* means that both management and employee strive to meet common objectives. *Mutual trust* is reflected in reasonable, documented employment policies that are honestly and equitably implemented to the satisfaction of both management and employee.[1] When management has a genuine respect for its employees and their contributions to the firm, establishing a reasonable quality of work life and mutual trust is not particularly difficult.

VIDEO 10.2
The "People" Focus: Human Resources at Alaska Airlines

CONSTRAINTS ON HUMAN RESOURCE STRATEGY

As Figure 10.1 suggests, many decisions made about people are constrained by other decisions. First, the product mix may determine seasonality and stability of employment. Second, technology, equipment, and processes may have implications for safety and job content. Third, the location decision may have an impact on the ambient environment in which the employees work. Finally, layout decisions, such as assembly line versus work cell, influence job content.

---

[1] We find many companies calling their employees *associates, individual contributors,* or *members* of a particular team.

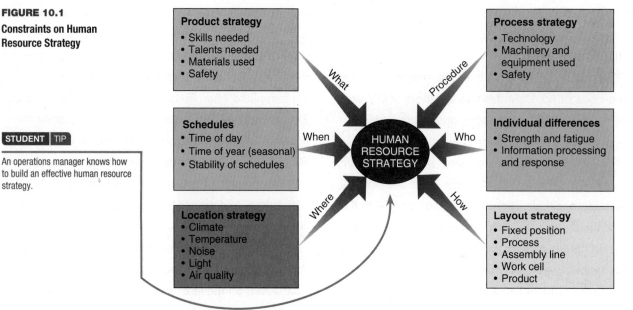

Technology decisions impose substantial constraints. For instance, some of the jobs in steel mills are dirty, noisy, and dangerous; slaughterhouse jobs may be stressful and subject workers to stomach-crunching stench; assembly-line jobs are often boring and mind numbing; and high capital investments such as those required for manufacturing semiconductor chips may require 24-hour, seven-day-a-week operation in restrictive clothing.

We are not going to change these jobs without making changes in our other strategic decisions. So, the trade-offs necessary to reach a tolerable quality of work life are difficult. Effective managers consider such decisions simultaneously. The result: an effective, efficient system in which both individual and team performance are enhanced through optimum job design.

Acknowledging the constraints imposed on human resource strategy, we now look at three distinct decision areas of human resource strategy: *labour planning*, *job design*, and *labour standards*.

Labour Planning

Labour planning is determining staffing policies that deal with (1) employment stability, (2) work schedules, and (3) work rules.

EMPLOYMENT-STABILITY POLICIES

Employment stability deals with the number of employees maintained by an organization at any given time. There are two very basic policies for dealing with stability:

1. *Follow demand exactly:* Following demand exactly keeps direct labour costs tied to production but incurs other costs. These other costs include (a) hiring and layoff costs, (b) unemployment insurance, and (c) premium wages to entice personnel to accept unstable employment. This policy tends to treat labour as a variable cost.
2. *Hold employment constant:* Holding employment levels constant maintains a trained workforce and keeps hiring, layoff, and unemployment costs to a minimum. However, with employment held constant, employees may not be utilized fully when demand is low, and the firm may not have the human resources it needs when demand is high. This policy tends to treat labour as a fixed cost.

The above policies are only two of many that can be efficient *and* provide a reasonable quality of work life. Firms must determine policies about employment stability.

WORK SCHEDULES

Although the standard work schedule in Canada is still five eight-hour days, many variations exist. A currently popular variation is a work schedule called flextime. *Flextime* allows employees, within limits, to determine their own schedules. A flextime policy might allow an employee (with proper notification) to be at work at 8:00 a.m. plus or minus two hours. This policy allows more autonomy and independence on the part of the employee. Some firms have found flextime a low-cost fringe benefit that enhances job satisfaction. The problem from the OM perspective is that much production work requires full staffing for efficient operations. A machine that requires three people cannot run at all if only two show up. Having a waiter show up to serve lunch at 1:30 p.m. rather than 11:30 a.m. is not much help either.

Similarly, some industries find that their process strategies severely constrain their human resource scheduling options. For instance, paper manufacturing, petroleum refining, and power stations require around-the-clock staffing except for maintenance and repair shutdown.

Another option is the *flexible workweek*. This plan often calls for fewer but longer days, such as four 10-hour days or, as in the case of light assembly plants, 12-hour shifts. Working 12-hour shifts usually means working three days one week and four the next. Such shifts are sometimes called *compressed workweeks*. These schedules are viable for many operations functions—as long as suppliers and customers can be accommodated.

Another option is shorter days rather than longer days. This plan often moves employees to *part-time status*. Such an option is particularly attractive in service industries, where staffing for peak loads is necessary. Banks and restaurants often hire part-time workers. Also, many firms reduce labour costs by reducing fringe benefits for part-time employees.

JOB CLASSIFICATIONS AND WORK RULES

Many organizations have strict job classifications and work rules that specify who can do what, when they can do it, and under what conditions they can do it, often as a result of union pressure. These job classifications and work rules restrict employee flexibility on the job, which in turn reduces the flexibility of the operations function. Yet part of an operations manager's task is to manage the unexpected. Therefore, the more flexibility a firm has when staffing and establishing work schedules, the more efficient and responsive it *can* be. This is particularly true in service organizations, where extra capacity often resides in extra or flexible staff. Building morale and meeting staffing requirements that result in an efficient, responsive operation are easier if managers have fewer job classifications and work-rule constraints. If the strategy is to achieve a competitive advantage by responding rapidly to the customer, a flexible workforce may be a prerequisite.

Job Design

Job design specifies the tasks that constitute a job for an individual or a group. We examine five components of job design: (1) job specialization, (2) job expansion, (3) psychological components, (4) self-directed teams, and (5) motivation and incentive systems.

LABOUR SPECIALIZATION

The importance of job design as a management variable is credited to the 18th-century economist Adam Smith. Smith suggested that a division of labour, also known as **labour specialization (or job specialization)**, would assist in reducing labour costs of multiskilled artisans. This is accomplished in several ways:

1. *Development of dexterity* and faster learning by the employee because of repetition.
2. *Less loss of time* because the employee need not change jobs or tools.
3. *Development of specialized tools* and the reduction of investment because each employee has only a few tools needed for a particular task.

The 19th-century British mathematician Charles Babbage determined that a fourth consideration was also important for labour efficiency. Because pay tends to follow skill with a rather high correlation, Babbage suggested *paying exactly the wage needed for the particular skill required*. If the entire job consists of only one skill, then we would pay for only that skill. Otherwise, we would tend to pay for the highest skill contributed by the employee. These four advantages of labour specialization are still valid today.

A classic example of labour specialization is the assembly line. Such a system is often very efficient, although it may require employees to do short, repetitive, mind-numbing jobs. The wage rate for many of these jobs, however, is very good. Given the relatively high wage rate for

STUDENT TIP

Job design is a key ingredient of a motivated workforce.

Job design
An approach that specifies the tasks that constitute a job for an individual or a group.

Labour specialization (or job specialization)
The division of labour into unique ("special") tasks.

LO2 Identify the major issues in job design

the modest skills required in many of these jobs, there is often a large pool of employees from which to choose.

From the manager's point of view, a major limitation of specialized jobs is their failure to bring the whole person to the job. Job specialization tends to bring only the employee's manual skills to work. In an increasingly sophisticated knowledge-based society, managers may want employees to bring their mind to work as well.

JOB EXPANSION

Moving from labour specialization towards more varied job design may improve the quality of work life. The theory is that variety makes the job "better" and that the employee therefore enjoys a higher quality of work life. This flexibility thus benefits the employee and the organization.

We modify jobs in a variety of ways. The first approach is **job enlargement**, which occurs when we add tasks requiring similar skill to an existing job. **Job rotation** is a version of job enlargement that occurs when the employee is allowed to move from one specialized job to another. Variety has been added to the employee's perspective of the job. Another approach is **job enrichment**, which adds planning and control to the job. An example is to have department store salespeople responsible for ordering, as well as selling, their goods. Job enrichment can be thought of as *vertical expansion*, as opposed to job enlargement, which is *horizontal*. These ideas are shown in Figure 10.2.

A popular extension of job enrichment, **employee empowerment** is the practice of enriching jobs so employees accept responsibility for a variety of decisions normally associated with staff specialists. Empowering employees helps them take "ownership" of their jobs so they have a personal interest in improving performance.

PSYCHOLOGICAL COMPONENTS OF JOB DESIGN

An effective human resources strategy also requires consideration of the psychological components of job design. These components focus on how to design jobs that meet some minimum psychological requirements.

HAWTHORNE STUDIES The Hawthorne studies introduced psychology to the workplace. They were conducted in the late 1920s at Western Electric's Hawthorne plant near Chicago. These studies were initiated to determine the impact of lighting on productivity. Instead, they found the dynamic social system and distinct roles played by employees to be more important than the intensity of the lighting. They also found that individual differences may be dominant in what an employee expects from the job and what the employee thinks her or his contribution to the job should be.

CORE JOB CHARACTERISTICS In the decades since the Hawthorne studies, substantial research regarding the psychological components of job design has taken place. Hackman and Oldham

Margin definitions

Job enlargement

The grouping of a variety of tasks about the same skill level; horizontal enlargement.

Job rotation

A system in which an employee is moved from one specialized job to another.

Job enrichment

A method of giving an employee more responsibility that includes some of the planning and control necessary for job accomplishment; vertical expansion.

Employee empowerment

Enlarging employee jobs so that the added responsibility and authority is moved to the lowest level possible.

FIGURE 10.2

An Example of Job Enlargement (*Horizontal*** Job Expansion) and Job Enrichment (***Vertical*** Job Expansion)**

STUDENT TIP

Job enrichment, expanding the job vertically, can occur by adding other types of tasks, such as participation in a quality team (planning) and testing tasks (control).

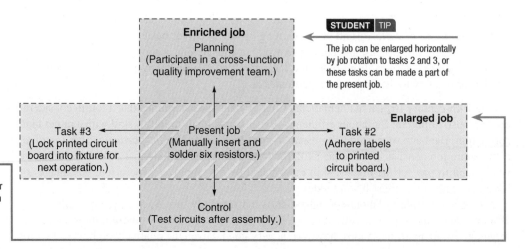

STUDENT TIP

The job can be enlarged horizontally by job rotation to tasks 2 and 3, or these tasks can be made a part of the present job.

have incorporated much of that work into five desirable characteristics of job design.[2] They suggest that jobs should include the following characteristics:

1. *Skill variety*, requiring the worker to use a variety of skills and talents.
2. *Job identity*, allowing the worker to perceive the job as a whole and recognize a start and a finish.
3. *Job significance*, providing a sense that the job has an impact on the organization and society.
4. *Autonomy*, offering freedom, independence, and discretion.
5. *Feedback*, providing clear, timely information about performance.

Including these five ingredients in job design is consistent with job enlargement, job enrichment, and employee empowerment. We now want to look at some of the ways in which teams can be used to expand jobs and achieve these five job characteristics.

SELF-DIRECTED TEAMS

Many world-class organizations have adopted teams to foster mutual trust and commitment, and provide the core job characteristics. One team concept of particular note is the **self-directed team**: a group of empowered individuals working together to reach a common goal. These teams may be organized for long- or short-term objectives. Teams are effective primarily because they can easily provide employee empowerment, ensure core job characteristics, and satisfy many of the psychological needs of individual team members. A job-design continuum is shown in Figure 10.3.

Self-directed team

A group of empowered individuals working together to reach a common goal.

LIMITATIONS OF JOB EXPANSION If job designs that enlarge, enrich, empower, and use teams are so good, why are they not universally used? Mostly it is because of costs. Here are a few limitations of expanded job designs:

- *Higher capital cost:* Job expansion may require additional equipment and facilities.
- *Individual differences:* Some employees opt for the less complex jobs.
- *Higher wage rates:* Expanded jobs may well require a higher average wage.
- *Smaller labour pool:* Because expanded jobs require more skill and acceptance of more responsibility, job requirements have increased.
- *Higher training costs:* Job expansion requires training and cross-training. Therefore, training budgets need to increase.

Despite these limitations, firms are finding a substantial payoff in job expansion.

MOTIVATION AND INCENTIVE SYSTEMS

Our discussion of the psychological components of job design provides insight into the factors that contribute to job satisfaction and motivation. In addition to these psychological factors, there are monetary factors. Money often serves as a psychological as well as financial motivator. Monetary rewards take the form of bonuses, profit and gain sharing, and incentive systems.

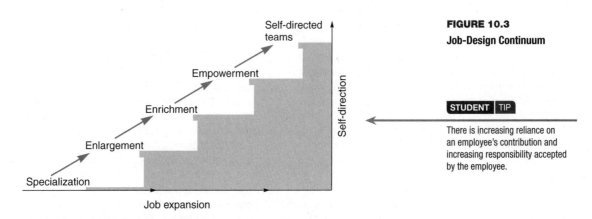

FIGURE 10.3
Job-Design Continuum

STUDENT TIP

There is increasing reliance on an employee's contribution and increasing responsibility accepted by the employee.

---

[2] See "Motivation Through the Design of Work," in Jay Richard Hackman and Greg R. Oldham, eds., *Work Redesign* (Reading, MA: Addison-Wesley, 1980), and A. Thomas, W. C. Buboltz, and C. Winkelspecht, "Job Characteristics and Personality as Predictors of Job Satisfaction," *Organizational Analysis*, 12, no. 2 (2004): 205–219.

WestJet employees fully comprehend the concept that a happy customer is a repeat customer, thus passengers are referred to and treated as guests. Customers are amazed that WestJet employees sincerely appear to be enjoying their jobs.

Bonuses, typically in cash or stock options, are often used at executive levels to reward management. Profit-sharing systems provide some part of the profit for distribution to employees. A variation of profit sharing is gain sharing, which rewards employees for improvements made in an organization's performance. The most popular of these is the Scanlon plan, in which any reduction in the cost of labour is shared between management and labour.

Incentive systems based on individual or group productivity are used throughout the world in a wide variety of applications, including nearly half of the manufacturing firms in North America. Production incentives often require employees or crews to produce at or above a predetermined standard. The standard can be based on a "standard time" per task or number of pieces made. Both systems typically guarantee the employee at least a base rate. Incentives, of course, need not be monetary. Awards, recognition, and other kinds of preferences such as a preferred work schedule can be effective. (See the *OM in Action* box "Using Incentives to Smooth Out Demand in Hospitals.") Hard Rock Cafe has successfully reduced its turnover by giving every employee—from the CEO to the busboys—a $10 000 gold Rolex watch on their 10th anniversary with the firm.

OM in Action   Using Incentives to Smooth Out Demand in Hospitals

Critical to the success of any service operation is the ability to meet customer demand in a timely fashion. Canadian hospitals are certainly not exempt from this requirement and are continually seeking new ways to meet the growing demand while containing costs. Two examples of how this can be achieved include the Shouldice Hospital in Thornhill and the Queensway Surgicentre in Toronto. Shouldice is a private hospital that specializes in hernia operations and Queensway is a division of the Trillium Health Centre, which is a public hospital.

Shouldice has been successful in smoothing out patient demand through the maximization of surgeons' time and talent, including tight scheduling of operations throughout the day. Typically, the surgeons would have the ability to earn higher pay in their own practice. But the reward of relatively routine surgeries performed during the week during daylight hours is an incentive for them and also for the patients. Surgeries are performed on a scheduled basis and unscheduled emergencies are not typically handled at that hospital.

Queensway also has been successful in transforming itself into a different type of healthcare facility. It is now the largest not-for-admission surgical centre in North America. Many non-emergency, elective-type surgeries are performed at Queensway, such as knee and hip replacements. These are pre-scheduled, thus maximizing the use of staff and patients' time. Due to the large number of procedures that are performed during the day on weekdays, the medical staff perceived this to be a valuable nonmonetary incentive while simultaneously smoothing out patient demand.

With the increasing use of teams, various forms of team-based pay are also being developed. Many are based on traditional pay systems supplemented with some form of bonus or incentive system. However, because many team environments require cross-training of enlarged jobs, *knowledge-based* pay systems have also been developed. Under knowledge-based (or skill-based) pay systems, a portion of the employee's pay depends on demonstrated knowledge or skills. There is a growing trend in Canada in which companies are amending their compensation policies such that employees receive pay raises *only* by mastering new skills such as scheduling, budgeting, and quality control.

Ergonomics and the Work Environment

STUDENT TIP

Ergonomics becomes more critical as technologies become more complex.

With the foundation provided by Frederick W. Taylor, the father of the era of scientific management, we have developed a body of knowledge about people's capabilities and limitations. This knowledge is necessary because humans are hand/eye animals possessing exceptional capabilities and some limitations. Because managers must design jobs that can be done, we now introduce a few of the issues related to people's capabilities and limitations.

LO3 Identify major ergonomic and work environment issues

ERGONOMICS

The operations manager is interested in building a good interface between humans, the environment, and machines. Studies of this interface are known as **ergonomics**. Ergonomics means "the study of work". (*Ergon* is the Greek word for "work".) The term *human factors* is often substituted for the word *ergonomics*. Understanding ergonomic issues helps to improve human performance.

Ergonomics

The study of the human interface with the environment and machines.

Male and female adults come in limited configurations. Therefore, design of tools and the workplace depends on the study of people to determine what they can and cannot do. Substantial data have been collected that provide basic strength and measurement data needed to design tools and the workplace. The design of the workplace can make the job easier or impossible. Additionally, we now have the ability, through the use of computer modelling, to analyze human motions and efforts.

OPERATOR INPUT TO MACHINES

Operator response to machines—be they hand tools, pedals, levers, or buttons—needs to be evaluated. Operations managers need to be sure that operators have the strength, reflexes, perception, and mental capacity to provide necessary control. Such problems as *carpal tunnel syndrome* may result when a tool as simple as a keyboard is poorly designed. The photo of the Champ race car steering wheel below shows one innovative approach to critical operator input.

FEEDBACK TO OPERATORS

Feedback to operators is provided by sight, sound, and feel; it should not be left to chance. In August 2001, due to a faulty fuel line, an Air Transat flight travelling from Toronto to Lisbon ran

Drivers of race cars have no time to grasp for controls or to look for small hidden gauges. Controls and instrumentation for modern race cars have migrated to the steering wheel itself—the critical interface between man and machine.

Inacio pires/Shutterstock

An important human factor/ ergonomic issue in the aircraft industry is cockpit design. Newer "glass cockpits" (on the right) display information in more concise form than the traditional rows of round analogue dials and gauges (on the left). New displays reduce the chance of human error, which is a factor in about two-thirds of commercial air accidents. Fractions of a second in the cockpit can literally mean the difference between life and death.

out of fuel over the Atlantic Ocean. Leading up to this near-disaster, the instruments were providing confusing and ambiguous signals to the pilots. Fortunately, the skilled pilots were able to guide the gliding plane onto a runway at an inactive airport. Such relatively simple issues make a difference in operator response and, therefore, performance. The photos above show changes in aircraft cockpits from recent efforts to improve feedback to operators.

THE WORK ENVIRONMENT

The physical environment in which employees work affects their performance, safety, and quality of work life. Illumination, noise and vibration, temperature, humidity, and air quality are work-environment factors under the control of the organization and the operations manager. The manager must approach them as controllable.

Illumination is necessary, but the proper level depends on the work being performed. Figure 10.4a provides some guidelines. However, other lighting factors are important. These include reflective ability, contrast of the work surface with surroundings, glare, and shadows.

Noise of some form is usually present in the work area, and most employees seem to adjust well. However, high levels of sound will damage hearing. Figure 10.4b provides indications of the sound generated by various activities. Extended periods of exposure to decibel levels above 85 dB are permanently damaging. Canada's Occupational Health and Safety Regulations require ear protection above this level if exposure equals or exceeds eight hours. Even at low levels, noise and vibration can be distracting and can raise a person's blood pressure, so managers make

FIGURE 10.4A

Recommended Levels of Illumination (using foot-candles [ft-c] as the measure of illumination)

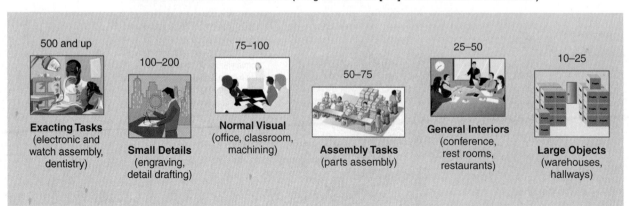

FIGURE 10.4B

Decibel (dB) Levels for Various Sounds

Source: Reprinted with permission from A. P. G. Peterson and E. E. Gross, Jr., *Handbook of Noise Measurement*, 7th ed. (New Concord, MA: General Radio Co.). GENRAD LLC Copyright 2012.

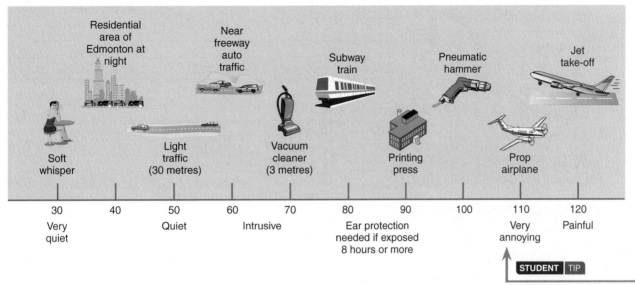

STUDENT TIP

Noise in the work environment can increase the risk of a heart attack by 50% or more.

substantial effort to reduce noise and vibration through good machine design, enclosures, or insulation.

Temperature and humidity parameters have also been well established. Managers with activities operating outside the established comfort zone should expect adverse effect on performance.

Methods Analysis

Methods analysis focuses on *how* a task is accomplished. Whether controlling a machine or making or assembling components, how a task is done makes a difference in performance, safety, and quality. Using knowledge from ergonomics and methods analysis, methods engineers are charged with ensuring that quality and quantity standards are achieved efficiently and safely. Methods analysis and related techniques are useful in office environments as well as in the factory. Methods techniques are used to analyze:

1. *Movement of individuals or material.* The analysis is performed using *flow diagrams* and *process charts* with varying amounts of detail.
2. *Activity of human and machine and crew activity.* This analysis is performed using *activity charts* (also known as man–machine charts and crew charts).
3. *Body movement* (primarily arms and hands). This analysis is performed using *operations charts.*

A **flow diagram** is a schematic (drawing) used to investigate movement of people or material. Britain's Paddy Hopkirk Factory in Figure 10.5 shows one version of a flow diagram, and the *OM in Action* box "Saving Steps on the B–2 Bomber" provides another way to analyze long-cycle repetitive tasks. Hopkirk's old method is shown in Figure 10.5(a), and a new method, with improved work flow and requiring less storage and space, is shown in Figure 10.5(b). A **process chart** uses symbols, as in Figure 10.5(c), to help us understand the movement of people or material. In this way non–value-added activities can be recognized and operations made more efficient. Figure 10.5(c) is a process chart used to supplement the flow diagrams shown in Figure 10.5(b).

An **activity chart** is used to study and improve the utilization of an operator and a machine or some combination of operators (a "crew") and machines. The typical approach is for the analyst to record the present method through direct observation and then propose the improvement on a

Methods analysis
A system that involves developing work procedures that are safe and produce quality products efficiently.

LO4 Use the tools of methods analysis

Flow diagram
A drawing used to analyze movement of people or material.

Process chart
Graphic representation that depicts a sequence of steps for a process.

Activity chart
A way of improving utilization of an operator and a machine or some combination of operators (a crew) and machines.

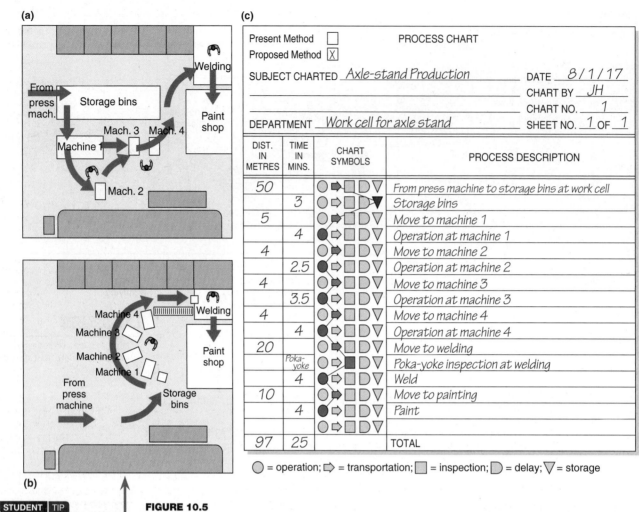

(a)

(b)

(c)

PROCESS CHART

Present Method ☐
Proposed Method ☒

SUBJECT CHARTED _Axle-stand Production_   DATE _8 / 1 / 17_
CHART BY _JH_
CHART NO. _1_
DEPARTMENT _Work cell for axle stand_   SHEET NO. _1_ OF _1_

DIST. IN METRES	TIME IN MINS.	CHART SYMBOLS	PROCESS DESCRIPTION
50			From press machine to storage bins at work cell
	3		Storage bins
5			Move to machine 1
	4		Operation at machine 1
4			Move to machine 2
	2.5		Operation at machine 2
4			Move to machine 3
	3.5		Operation at machine 3
4			Move to machine 4
	4		Operation at machine 4
20			Move to welding
	Poka-yoke		Poka-yoke inspection at welding
	4		Weld
10			Move to painting
	4		Paint
97	25		TOTAL

◯ = operation; ⇨ = transportation; ☐ = inspection; ◻ = delay; ▽ = storage

FIGURE 10.5

Flow Diagrams and Process Chart of Axle-Stand Production at Paddy Hopkirk Factory

(a) Old method; (b) new method; (c) process chart of axle-stand production using Paddy Hopkirk's new method shown in part (b).

OM in Action   Saving Steps on the B–2 Bomber

The aerospace industry is noted for making exotic products, but it is also known for doing so in a very expensive way. The historical batch-based processes used in the industry have left a lot of room for improvement. In leading the way, Northrop Grumman analyzed the work flow of a mechanic whose job in the plant was to apply about 20 metres of tape to the B–2 stealth bomber. The mechanic walked away from the plane 26 times and took

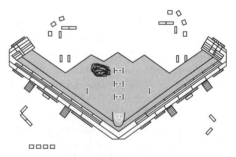

The mechanic's work path is reduced to the small area of blue lines shown here.

three hours just to gather chemicals, hoses, gauges, and other material needed just to get ready for the job. By making prepackaged kits for the job, Northrop Grumman cut preparation time to zero and the time to complete the job dropped from 8.4 hours to 1.6 hours.

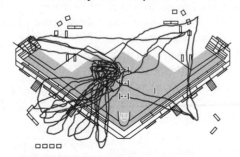

The 26 trips to various workstations to gather the tools and equipment to apply tape to the B–2 bomber are shown as blue lines above.

Sources: BusinessWeek (May 28, 2001): 14; *Aviation Week & Space Technology* (January 17, 2000): 44; and *The New York Times* (March 9, 1999): C1, C9.

FIGURE 10.6 Activity Chart for Two-Person Crew Doing an Oil Change in 12 Minutes at Quick Car Lube

FIGURE 10.7 Operations Chart (Right-Hand/Left-Hand Chart) for Bolt–Washer Assembly

ACTIVITY CHART

	OPERATOR #1		OPERATOR #2	
	TIME	%	TIME	%
WORK	12	100	12	100
IDLE	0	0	0	0

OPERATION: Oil change & fluid check
EQUIPMENT: One bay/pit
OPERATOR: Two-person crew
STUDY NO.: _____ ANALYST: NG

SUBJECT Quick Car Lube
PRESENT (PROPOSED) DEPT.
DATE 8-1-17
SHEET 1 OF 1 CHART BY LSA

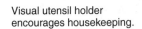

TIME	Operator #1	TIME	Operator #2	TIME
2	Take order		Move car to pit	
4	Vacuum car		Drain oil	
6	Clean windows		Check transmission	
8	Check under hood		Change oil filter	
10	Fill with oil		Replace oil plug	
12	Complete bill		Move car to front for customer	
14	Greet next customer		Move next car to pit	
16	Vacuum car		Drain oil	
18	Clean windows		Check transmission	

Repeat cycle

OPERATIONS CHART

SYMBOLS	PRESENT		PROPOSED	
	LH	RH	LH	RH
○ OPERATION	2	3		
⇨ TRANSPORT	1	1		
▢ INSPECTION				
D DELAY	4	3		
▽ STORAGE				

PROCESS: Bolt–washer assembly
EQUIPMENT: _____
OPERATOR: KJH
STUDY NO: _____ ANALYST: _____
DATE: 8 /1 /17 SHEET NO. 1 of 1
METHOD (PRESENT) PROPOSED)
REMARKS:

LEFT-HAND ACTIVITY Present METHOD	DIST.	SYMBOLS	SYMBOLS	DIST.	RIGHT-HAND ACTIVITY Present METHOD
1 Reach for bolt		●⇨▢D▽	○⇨▢D▽		Idle
2 Grasp bolt		●⇨▢D▽	○⇨▢D▽		Idle
3 Move bolt	15 cm	○➡▢D▽	○⇨▢D▽		Idle
4 Hold bolt		○⇨▢D▽	●⇨▢D▽		Reach for washer
5 Hold bolt		○⇨▢D▽	●⇨▢D▽		Grasp washer
6 Hold bolt		○⇨▢D▽	○➡▢D▽	20 cm	Move washer to bolt
7 Hold bolt		○⇨▢D▽	●⇨▢D▽		Place washer on bolt

STUDENT TIP

Activity charts are helpful for understanding crew or man–machine interaction.

second chart. Figure 10.6 is an activity chart to show a proposed improvement for a two-person crew at Quick Car Lube.

Body movement is analyzed by an **operations chart**. It is designed to show economy of motion by pointing out wasted motion and idle time (delay). The operations chart (also known as a *right-hand/left-hand chart*) is shown in Figure 10.7.

Operations chart
A chart depicting right- and left-hand motions.

The Visual Workplace

A **visual workplace** uses low-cost visual devices to share information quickly and accurately. Well-designed displays and graphs root out confusion and replace difficult-to-understand printouts and paperwork. Because workplace data change quickly and often, operations managers

Visual workplace
Uses a variety of visual communication techniques to rapidly communicate information to stakeholders.

Visual utensil holder encourages housekeeping.

A "3-minute service" clock reminds employees of the goal.

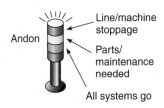

Visual signals at the machine notify support personnel.

Andon — Line/machine stoppage
— Parts/ maintenance needed
All systems go

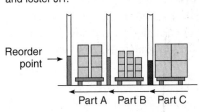

Visual kanbans reduce inventory and foster JIT.

Reorder point →

Part A   Part B   Part C

Quantities in bins indicate ongoing daily requirements and clipboards provide information on schedule changes.

Process specifications and operating procedures are posted in each work area.

FIGURE 10.8
The Visual Workplace

need to share accurate and up-to-date information. Changing customer requirements, specifications, schedules, and other details must be rapidly communicated to those who can make things happen.

The visual workplace can eliminate non–value-added activities by making standards, problems, and abnormalities visual (see Figure 10.8). The visual workplace needs less supervision because employees understand the standard, see the results, and know what to do.

Labour Standards

Labour standards

The amount of time required to perform a job or part of a job.

LO5 Identify four ways of establishing labour standards

So far in this chapter, we have discussed labour planning and job design. The third requirement of an effective human resource strategy is the establishment of labour standards. **Labour standards** are the amount of time required to perform a job or part of a job. Effective manpower planning is dependent on a knowledge of the labour required.

Modern labour standards originated with the works of Frederick W. Taylor and Frank and Lillian Gilbreth at the beginning of the 20th century. At that time, a large proportion of work was manual, and the resulting labour content of products was high. Little was known about what constituted a fair day's work, so managers initiated studies to improve work methods and understand human effort. These efforts continue to this day. Although labour costs are often less than 10% of sales, labour standards remain important and continue to play a major role in both service and manufacturing organizations. They are often a beginning point for determining staffing requirements. With over half of the manufacturing plants in North America using some form of labour incentive system, good labour standards are a requirement.

Effective operations management requires meaningful standards that help a firm determine:

1. Labour content of items produced (the labour cost).
2. Staffing needs (how many people it will take to meet required production).
3. Cost and time estimates prior to production (to assist in a variety of decisions, from cost estimates to make-or-buy decisions).
4. Crew size and work balance (who does what in a group activity or on an assembly line).
5. Expected production (so that both manager and worker know what constitutes a fair day's work).
6. Basis of wage-incentive plans (what provides a reasonable incentive).
7. Efficiency of employees and supervision (a standard is necessary against which to determine efficiency).

Properly set labour standards represent the amount of time that it should take an average employee to perform specific job activities under normal working conditions. Labour standards are set in four ways:

1. Historical experience.
2. Time studies.
3. Predetermined time standards.
4. Work sampling.

HISTORICAL EXPERIENCE

Labour standards can be estimated based on *historical experience*—that is, how many labour-hours were required to do a task the last time it was performed. Historical standards have the advantage of being relatively easy and inexpensive to obtain. They are usually available from employee time cards or production records. However, they are not objective, and we do not know their accuracy, whether they represent a reasonable or a poor work pace, and whether unusual occurrences are included. Because these variables are unknown, their use is not recommended. Instead, time studies, predetermined time standards, and work sampling are preferred.

Time study

Timing a sample of a worker's performance and using it as a basis for setting a standard time.

TIME STUDIES

The classical stopwatch study, or **time study**, originally proposed by Frederick W. Taylor in 1881, involves timing a sample of a worker's performance and using it to set a standard. (See the

OM in Action — Efficiency at WestJet Makes Customers Happy

Operating a business model similar to its U.S. counterpart Southwest Airlines, WestJet Airlines is known for maintaining a positive and collegial corporate culture. This culture has contributed to WestJet's durability during difficult times and may be the company's most valuable competitive advantage. As with any corporate culture, it can either drive or constrain productivity, safety, and customer service. Due to WestJet's reputation for excellence in each of these areas, it is not hard to see the linkage to how this airline nurtures and cherishes its corporate culture.

WestJet employees play the role of part-owner of the company and are given profit-sharing cheques twice per year. This contributes to the positive way they manage corporate assets, their demeanour, and delivery of excellent customer service. They recognize that efficiency in terms of saving time during the process is valuable to both the company and the customers. Employees readily understand the connection between happy and repeat customers, thus passengers are referred to and treated as guests. People are amazed that WestJet employees sincerely appear to be enjoying their jobs. This is not something that can be trained into people, but is a result of maintaining a positive corporate culture. This culture has contributed in a significant way to WestJet being placed at the top of the list of Waterstone Human Capital's top-10 ranking.

Source: www.canada.com/calgaryherald/news.

OM in Action box "Efficiency at WestJet Makes Customers Happy.") A trained and experienced person can establish a standard by following these eight steps:

1. Define the task to be studied (after methods analysis has been conducted).
2. Divide the task into precise elements (parts of a task that often take no more than a few seconds).
3. Decide how many times to measure the task (the number of job cycles or samples needed).
4. Time and record elemental times and ratings of performance.
5. Compute the average observed (actual) time. The **average observed time** is the arithmetic mean of the times for *each* element measured, adjusted for unusual influence for each element:

$$\text{Average observed time} = \frac{(\text{Sum of the times recorded to perform each element})}{\text{Number of observations}} \quad \text{(10-1)}$$

> **Average observed time**
> The arithmetic mean of the times for each element measured, adjusted for unusual influence for each element.

6. Determine performance rating (work pace) and then compute the **normal time** for each element.

$$\text{Normal time} = (\text{Average observed time}) \times (\text{Performance rating factor}) \quad \text{(10-2)}$$

> **Normal time**
> The average observed time, adjusted for pace.

The performance rating adjusts the average observed time to what a trained worker could expect to accomplish working at a normal pace. For example, a worker should be able to walk 5 kilometres per hour. He or she should also be able to deal a deck of 52 cards into four equal piles in 30 seconds. A performance rating of 1.05 would indicate that the observed worker performs the task slightly faster than average. Numerous videos specify work pace on which professionals agree, and benchmarks have been established by the Society for the Advancement of Management. Performance rating, however, is still something of an art.

> **LO6** Compute the normal and standard times in a time study

7. Add the normal times for each element to develop a total normal time for the task.
8. Compute the **standard time**. This adjustment to the total normal time provides for allowances such as *personal* needs, unavoidable work *delays*, and worker *fatigue*:

$$\text{Standard time} = \frac{\text{Total normal time}}{1 - \text{Allowance factor}} \quad \text{(10-3)}$$

> **Standard time**
> An adjustment to the total normal time; the adjustment provides allowances for personal needs, unavoidable work delays, and fatigue.

Personal time allowances are often established in the range of 4% to 7% of total time, depending on nearness to restrooms, water fountains, and other facilities. *Delay allowances* are often set as a result of the actual studies of the delay that occurs. *Fatigue allowances* are based on our growing knowledge of human energy expenditure under various physical and environmental conditions. A sample set of personal and fatigue allowances is shown in Table 10.1. Example 1 illustrates the computation of standard time.

Table 10.1

Allowance Factors (in Percentage) for Various Classes of Work

1. Constant allowances:	Weight lifted (pounds):
(A) Personal allowance 5	20 3
(B) Basic fatigue allowance 4	40 9
2. Variable allowances:	60 17
(A) Standing allowance 2	(D) Bad light:
(B) Abnormal position allowance:	(i) Well below recommended 2
(i) Awkward (bending) 2	(ii) Quite inadequate 5
(ii) Very awkward (lying, stretching) 7	(E) Noise level:
(C) Use of force or muscular energy in	(i) Intermittent—loud 2
lifting, pulling, pushing	(ii) Intermittent—very loud or high pitched 5

EXAMPLE 1

Determining Normal and Standard Time

The time study of a work operation at a Red Lobster restaurant yielded an average observed time of 4.0 minutes. The analyst rated the observed worker at 85%. This means the worker performed at 85% of normal when the study was made. The firm uses a 13% allowance factor. Red Lobster wants to compute the normal time and the standard time for this operation.

APPROACH ▶ The firm needs to apply Equations (10–2) and (10–3).

SOLUTION ▶ Average observed time = 4.0 min

$$\text{Normal time} = (\text{Average observed time}) \times (\text{Performance rating factor})$$
$$= (4.0)(0.85)$$
$$= 3.4 \text{ min}$$
$$\text{Standard time} = \frac{\text{Normal time}}{1 - \text{Allowance factor}} = \frac{3.4}{1 - 0.13} = \frac{3.4}{0.87}$$
$$= 3.9 \text{ min}$$

INSIGHT ▶ Because the observed worker was rated at 85% (slower than average), the normal time is less than the worker's 4.0 minute average time.

LEARNING EXERCISE ▶ If the observed worker is rated at 115% (faster than average), what are the new normal and standard times? [Answer: 4.6 min, 5.287 min.]

RELATED PROBLEMS ▶ 10.13, 10.14, 10.15, 10.16, 10.17, 10.18, 10.19, 10.20, 10.21, 10.33

EXCEL OM Data File **Ch10Ex1.xlsx** can be found at **MyLab Operations Management.**

Example 2 uses a series of actual stopwatch times for each element.

EXAMPLE 2

Using Time Studies to Compute Standard Time

Management Science Associates promotes its management development seminars by mailing thousands of individually composed and typed letters to various firms. A time study has been conducted on the task of preparing letters for mailing. On the basis of the following observations, Management Science Associates wants to develop a time standard for this task. The firm's personal, delay, and fatigue allowance factor is 15%.

	Observations (minutes)					
Job Element	**1**	**2**	**3**	**4**	**5**	**Performance Rating**
(A) Compose and type letter	8	10	9	21*	11	120%
(B) Type envelope address	2	3	2	1	3	105%
(C) Stuff, stamp, seal, and sort envelopes	2	1	5*	2	1	110%

APPROACH ▶ Once the data have been collected, the procedure is to:
1. Delete unusual or nonrecurring observations.
2. Compute the *average time* for each element, using Equation (10-1).
3. Compute the *normal time* for each element, using Equation (10-2).
4. Find the total normal time.
5. Compute the *standard time*, using Equation (10-3).

SOLUTION ▶

1. Delete observations such as those marked with an asterisk (*). (These may be due to business interruptions, conferences with the boss, or mistakes of an unusual nature; they are not part of the job element, but may be personal or delay time.)

2. Average time for each job element:

$$\text{Average time for A} = \frac{8 + 10 + 9 + 11}{4}$$
$$= 9.5 \text{ min}$$

$$\text{Average time for B} = \frac{2 + 3 + 2 + 1 + 3}{5}$$
$$= 2.2 \text{ min}$$

$$\text{Average time for C} = \frac{2 + 1 + 2 + 1}{4}$$
$$= 1.5 \text{ min}$$

3. Normal time for each job element:

$$\text{Normal time for A} = (\text{Average observed time}) \times (\text{Performance rating})$$
$$= (9.5)(1.2)$$
$$= 11.4 \text{ min}$$
$$\text{Normal time for B} = (2.2)(1.05)$$
$$= 2.31 \text{ min}$$
$$\text{Normal time for C} = (1.5)(1.10)$$
$$= 1.65 \text{ min}$$

Note: Normal times are computed for each element because the performance rating factor (work pace) may vary for each element, as it did in this case.

4. Add the normal times for each element to find the total normal time (the normal time for the whole job):

$$\text{Total normal time} = 11.40 + 2.31 + 1.65$$
$$= 15.36 \text{ min}$$

5. Standard time for the job:

$$\text{Standard time} = \frac{\text{Total normal time}}{1 - \text{Allowance factor}} = \frac{15.36}{1 - 0.15}$$
$$= 18.07 \text{ min}$$

Thus, 18.07 minutes is the time standard for this job.

INSIGHT ▶ When observed times are not consistent, they need to be reviewed. Abnormally short times may be the result of an observational error and are usually discarded. Abnormally long times need to be analyzed to determine if they, too, are an error. However, they may *include* a seldom occurring but legitimate activity for the element (such as a machine adjustment) or may be personal, delay, or fatigue time.

LEARNING EXERCISE ▶ If the two observations marked with an asterisk were *not* deleted, what would be the total normal time and the standard time? [Answer: 18.89 min, 22.22 min.]

RELATED PROBLEMS ▶ 10.22, 10.23, 10.24, 10.25, 10.28ab, 10.29a, 10.30a

Time study requires a sampling process; so the question of sampling error in the average observed time naturally arises. In statistics, error varies inversely with sample size. Thus, to determine just how many cycles we should time, we must consider the variability of each element in the study.

To determine an adequate sample size, three items must be considered:

1. How accurate we want to be (e.g., is ±5% of observed time close enough?).
2. The desired level of confidence (e.g., the *z*-value; is 95% adequate or is 99% required?).
3. How much variation exists within the job elements (e.g., if the variation is large, a larger sample will be required).

Table 10.2

Common z-Values

Desired Confidence (%)	z-Value (standard deviation required for desired level of confidence)
90.0	1.65
95.0	1.96
95.45	2.00
99.0	2.58
99.73	3.00

The formula for finding the appropriate sample size, given these three variables, is:

$$\text{Required sample size} = n = \left(\frac{zs}{h\bar{x}}\right)^2 \tag{10-4}$$

where h = accuracy level (acceptable error) desired in percent of the job element, expressed as a decimal (5% = 0.05)

z = number of standard deviations required for desired level of confidence (90% confidence = 1.65; see Table 10.2 or Appendix I for more z-values)

s = standard deviation of the initial sample

$\bar{x}$ = mean of the initial sample

n = required sample size

We demonstrate with Example 3.

EXAMPLE 3

Computing Sample Size

Thomas W. Jones Manufacturing Co. has asked you to check a labour standard prepared by a recently terminated analyst. Your first task is to determine the correct sample size. Your accuracy is to be within 5% and your confidence level at 95%. The standard deviation of the sample is 1.0 and the mean 3.00.

APPROACH ▶ You apply Equation (10–4).

SOLUTION ▶ $h = 0.05$ $\bar{x} = 3.00$ $s = 1.0$

$z = 1.96$ (from Table 10.2 or Appendix I)

$$n = \left(\frac{zs}{h\bar{x}}\right)^2$$

$$n = \left(\frac{1.96 \times 1.0}{0.05 \times 3}\right)^2 = 170.74 \approx 171$$

Therefore, you recommend a sample size of 171.

INSIGHT ▶ Notice that as the confidence level required increases, the sample size also increases. Similarly, as the desired accuracy level increases (say, from 5% to 1%), the sample size increases.

LEARNING EXERCISE ▶ The confidence level for Jones Manufacturing Co. can be set lower, at 90%, while retaining the same ±5% accuracy levels ($z = 1.645$). What sample size is needed now? [Answer: $n = 121$.]

RELATED PROBLEMS ▶ 10.26, 10.27, 10.28c, 10.29b, 10.30b

EXCEL OM Data File Ch10Ex3.xlsx can be found at **MyLab Operations Management.**

LO7 Find the proper sample size for a time study

Now let's look at two variations of Example 3.

First, if h, the desired accuracy, is expressed as an absolute amount of error (say, one minute of error is acceptable), then substitute e for $h\bar{x}$, and the appropriate formula is Equation 10-4:

$$n = \left(\frac{zs}{e}\right)^2 \tag{10-5}$$

where e is the absolute time amount of acceptable error.

Second, for those cases when s, the standard deviation of the sample, is not provided (which is typically the case outside the classroom), it must be computed. The formula for doing so is given in Equation (10-6):

$$s = \sqrt{\frac{\sum(x_i - \bar{x})^2}{n - 1}} = \sqrt{\frac{\sum(\text{Each sample observation} - \bar{x})^2}{\text{Number in sample} - 1}} \tag{10-6}$$

where x_i = value of each observation

$\bar{x}$ = mean of the observations

n = number of observations in the sample

An example of this computation is provided in Solved Problem 10.4.

Although time studies provide accuracy in setting labour standards (see the *OM in Action* box "UPS: The Tightest Ship in the Shipping Business"), they have two disadvantages. First, they

OM in Action   UPS: The Tightest Ship in the Shipping Business

United Parcel Service (UPS) employs 425 000 people and delivers an average of 16 million packages a day to locations throughout Canada and the United States and 220 other countries. To achieve its claim of "running the tightest ship in the shipping business," UPS methodically trains its delivery drivers in how to do their jobs as efficiently as possible.

Industrial engineers at UPS have time-studied each driver's route and set standards for each delivery, stop, and pickup. These engineers have recorded every second taken up by stoplights, traffic volume, detours, doorbells, walkways, stairways, and coffee breaks. Even bathroom stops are factored into the standards. All this information is then fed into company computers to provide detailed time standards for every driver, every day.

To meet their objective of 200 deliveries and pickups each day (versus only 80 at FedEx), UPS drivers must follow procedures exactly. As they approach a delivery stop, drivers unbuckle their seat belts, honk their horns,

and cut their engines. Ignition keys have been dispensed with and replaced by a digital remote fob that turns off the engine and unlocks the bulkhead door that leads to the packages. In one seamless motion, drivers are required to yank up their emergency brakes and push their gearshifts into first. Then they slide to the ground with their electronic clipboards under their right arm and their packages in their left hand. They walk to the customer's door at the prescribed 3 feet per second and knock first to avoid lost seconds searching for the doorbell. After making the delivery, they do the paperwork on the way back to the truck.

Productivity experts describe UPS as one of the most efficient companies anywhere in applying effective labour standards.

Sources: Wall Street Journal (February 19, 2015), (December 26, 2011), and (September 19, 2011); and G.Niemann, Big Brown : The Untold Story of UPS, New York: Wiley, 2007.

require a trained staff of analysts. Second, these standards cannot be set before tasks are actually performed. This leads us to two alternative work-measurement techniques that we discuss next.

PREDETERMINED TIME STANDARDS

In addition to historical experience and time studies, we can set production standards by using predetermined time standards. **Predetermined time standards** divide manual work into small basic elements that already have established times (based on very large samples of workers). To estimate the time for a particular task, the time factors for each basic element of that task are added together. Developing a comprehensive system of predetermined time standards would be prohibitively expensive for any given firm. Consequently, a number of systems are commercially available. The most common predetermined time standard is *methods time measurement* (MTM), which is a product of the Methods Time Measurement Association.[3]

Predetermined time standards are an outgrowth of basic motions called therbligs. The term *therblig* was coined by Frank Gilbreth (*Gilbreth* spelled backward, with the *t* and *h* reversed). **Therbligs** include such activities as *select*, *grasp*, *position*, *assemble*, *reach*, *hold*, *rest*, and *inspect*. These activities are stated in terms of **time measurement units** (**TMUs**), which are equal to only 0.00001 hour, or 0.0006 minute each. MTM values for various therbligs are specified in very detailed tables. Figure 10.9, for example, provides the set of time standards for the motion GET and PLACE. To use GET and PLACE, one must know what is "gotten," its approximate weight, and where and how far it is supposed to be placed.

Example 4 shows a use of predetermined time standards in setting service labour standards.

Families of predetermined time standards have been developed for many occupations.

Predetermined time standards
A division of manual work into small basic elements that have established and widely accepted times.

Therbligs
Basic physical elements of motion.

Time measurement units (TMUs)
Units for very basic micromotions in which 1 TMU = 0.0006 min or 100 000 TMUs = 1 hr.

General Hospital wants to set the standard time for lab technicians to pour a tube specimen using MTM.[4]

APPROACH ▶ This is a repetitive task for which the MTM data in Table 10.3 may be used to develop standard times. The sample tube is in a rack and the centrifuge tubes in a nearby box. A technician

EXAMPLE 4

Using Predetermined Time (MTM Analysis) to Determine Standard Time

---

[3] MTM is really a family of products available from the Methods Time Measurement Association. For example, MTM-HC deals with the healthcare industry, MTM-C handles clerical activities, MTM-M involves microscope activities, MTM-V deals with machine shop tasks, and so on.

[4] A. S. Helms, B. W. Shaw, and C. A. Lindner, "The Development of Laboratory Workload Standards Through Computer-Based Work Measurement Technique, Part I," *Journal of Methods–Time Measurement* 12: 43. Used with permission of MTM Association for Standards and Research.

FIGURE 10.9

Sample MTM Table for GET and PLACE Motion

Time values are in TMUs.

Source: Copyrighted by the MTM Association for Standards and Research. No reprint permission without consent from the MTM Association, 16–01 Broadway, Fair Lawn, NJ 07410. Used with permission of MTM Association for Standards Research.

GET and PLACE			DISTANCE RANGE IN CM	<8	>8 <20	>20 <32
WEIGHT	CONDITIONS OF GET	PLACE ACCURACY	MTM CODE	1	2	3
<1 KG	EASY	APPROXIMATE	AA	20	35	50
		LOOSE	AB	30	45	60
		TIGHT	AC	40	55	70
	DIFFICULT	APPROXIMATE	AD	20	45	60
		LOOSE	AE	30	55	70
		TIGHT	AF	40	65	80
	HANDFUL	APPROXIMATE	AG	40	65	80
>1 KG <8 KG		APPROXIMATE	AH	25	45	55
		LOOSE	AJ	40	65	75
		TIGHT	AK	50	75	85
>8 KG <20 KG		APPROXIMATE	AL	90	106	115
		LOOSE	AM	95	120	130
		TIGHT	AN	120	145	160

Table 10.3

MTM-HC Analysis: Pouring Tube Specimen

Element Description (1 TMU = 0.0006 minutes)	Element	Time
Get tube from rack	AA2	35
Uncap, place on counter	AA2	35
Get centrifuge tube, place at sample tube	AD2	45
Pour (3 sec)	PT	83
Place tubes in rack (simo)	PC2	40
	Total TMU	238

0.0006×238 = Total standard minutes = 0.143 or about 8.6 seconds

removes the sample tube from the rack, uncaps it, gets the centrifuge tube, pours, and places both tubes in the rack.

SOLUTION ▶ The first work element involves getting the tube from the rack. The conditions for GETTING the tube and PLACING it in front of the technician are:

- *Weight:* (less than 1 kilogram)
- *Conditions of GET:* (easy)
- *Place accuracy:* (approximate)
- *Distance range:* (20 to 50 centimetres)

Then the MTM element for this activity is AA2 (as seen in Figure 10.9). The rest of Table 10.3 is developed from similar MTM tables.

INSIGHT ▶ Most MTM calculations are computerized, so the user need only key in the appropriate MTM codes, such as AA2 in this example.

LEARNING EXERCISE ▶ General Hospital decides that the first step in this process really involves a distance range of 10 centimetres (getting the tube from the rack). The other work elements are unchanged. What is the new standard time? [Answer: 0.134 min. or just over 8 seconds]

RELATED PROBLEM ▶ 10.36

Predetermined time standards have several advantages over direct time studies. First, they may be established in a laboratory environment, where the procedure will not upset actual production activities (which time studies tend to do). Second, because the standard can be set *before* a task is actually performed, it can be used for planning. Third, no performance ratings are necessary. Fourth, unions tend to accept this method as a fair means of setting standards. Finally, predetermined time standards are particularly effective in firms that do substantial numbers of studies of similar tasks. To ensure accurate labour standards, some firms use both time studies and predetermined time standards.

WORK SAMPLING

The fourth method of developing labour or production standards, work sampling, was developed in England by L. Tippet in the 1930s. **Work sampling** estimates the percent of the time that a worker spends on various tasks. Random observations are used to record the activity that a worker is performing. The results are primarily used to determine how employees allocate their time among various activities. Knowledge of this allocation may lead to staffing changes, reassignment of duties, estimates of activity cost, and the setting of delay allowances for labour standards. When work sampling is done to establish delay allowances, it is sometimes called a *ratio delay study*.

Work sampling
An estimate, via sampling, of the percent of the time that a worker spends on various tasks.

The work-sampling procedure can be summarized in five steps:

1. Take a preliminary sample to obtain an estimate of the parameter value (e.g., percent of time a worker is busy).
2. Compute the sample size required.
3. Prepare a schedule for observing the worker at appropriate times. The concept of random numbers is used to provide for random observation. For example, let's say we draw the following five random numbers from a table: 07, 12, 22, 25, and 49. These can then be used to create an observation schedule of 9:07 a.m., 9:12 a.m., 9:22 a.m., 9:25 a.m., 9:49 a.m.
4. Observe and record worker activities.
5. Determine how workers spend their time (usually as a percentage).

To determine the number of observations required, management must decide on the desired confidence level and accuracy. First, however, the analyst must select a preliminary value for the parameter under study (Step 1 above). The choice is usually based on a small sample of perhaps 50 observations. The following formula then gives the sample size for a desired confidence and accuracy:

$$n = \frac{z^2 p(1 - p)}{h^2}$$

(10-7)

where n = required sample size
   z = number of standard deviations for the desired confidence level ($z = 1$ for 68.27% confidence, $z = 2$ for 95.45% confidence, and $z = 3$ for 99.73% confidence— these values are obtained from Table 10.2 or the normal table in Appendix I)
   p = estimated value of sample proportion (of time worker is observed busy or idle)
   h = acceptable error level, in percent

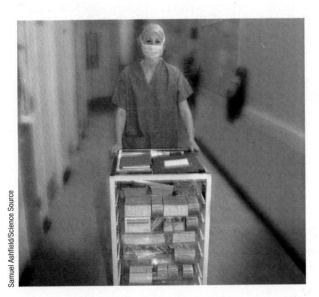

Using the techniques of this chapter to develop labour standards, operations managers at Orlando's Arnold Palmer Hospital determined that nurses walked an average of 2.7 miles per day. This constitutes up to 30% of the nurse's time, a terrible waste of critical talent. Analysis resulted in a new layout design that has reduced walking distances by 20%.

Samuel Ashfield/Science Source

Example 5 shows how to apply this formula.

EXAMPLE 5

Determining the Number of Work Sample Observations Needed

The manager of East Canadian Assurance Company's benefits office, Dana Johnson, estimates that her employees are idle 25% of the time. She would like to take a work sample that is accurate within 3% and wants to have 95.45% confidence in the results.

APPROACH ▶ Dana applies Equation (10-7) to determine how many observations should be taken.

SOLUTION ▶ Dana computes n:

$$n = \frac{z^2 p(1 - p)}{h^2}$$

where n = required sample size
z = 2 for 95.45% confidence level
p = estimate of idle proportion = 25% = 0.25
h = acceptable error of 3% = 0.03

She finds that

$$n = \frac{(2)^2(0.25)(0.75)}{(0.03)^2} \approx 833 \text{ observations}$$

INSIGHT ▶ Thus, 833 observations should be taken. If the percent of idle time observed is not close to 25% as the study progresses, then the number of observations may have to be recalculated and increased or decreased as appropriate.

LEARNING EXERCISE ▶ If the confidence level increases to 99.73%, how does the sample size change (z = 3)? [Answer: n = 1875.]

RELATED PROBLEMS ▶ 10.31, 10.32, 10.35, 10.37

ACTIVE MODEL 10.1 This example is further illustrated in Active Model 10.1 at **MyLab Operations Management.**

The focus of work sampling is to determine how workers allocate their time among various activities. This is accomplished by establishing the percent of time individuals spend on these activities rather than the exact amount of time spent on specific tasks. The analyst simply records in a random, nonbiased way the occurrence of each activity. Example 6 shows the procedure for evaluating employees at the insurance office introduced in Example 5.

EXAMPLE 6

Determining Employee Time Allocation With Work Sampling

Dana Johnson, the manager of East Canadian Assurance Company's benefits office, wants to be sure her employees have adequate time to provide prompt, helpful service. She believes that service to clients who phone or walk in without an appointment deteriorates rapidly when employees are busy more than 75% of the time. Consequently, she does not want her employees to be occupied with client service activities more than 75% of the time.

APPROACH ▶ The study requires several things: First, based on the calculations in Example 5, 833 observations are needed. Second, observations are to be made in a random, nonbiased way over a period of two weeks to ensure a true sample. Third, the analyst must define the activities that are "work". In this case, work is defined as all the activities necessary to take care of the client (filing, meetings, data entry, discussions with the supervisor, etc.). Fourth, personal time is to be included in the 25% of non-work time. Fifth, the observations are made in a nonintrusive way so as not to distort the normal work patterns. At the end of the two weeks, the 833 observations yield the following results:

No. of Observations	Activity
485	On the phone or meeting with a client
126	Idle
62	Personal time
23	Discussions with supervisor
137	Filing, meeting, and computer data entry
833	

SOLUTION ▶ The analyst concludes that all but 188 observations (126 idle and 62 personal) are work related. Since 22.6% (= 188/833) is less idle time than Dana believes necessary to ensure a high

Salespeople

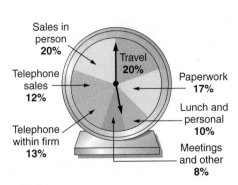

Assembly-Line Employees

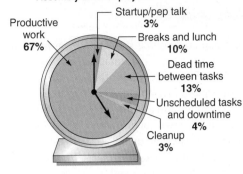

FIGURE 10.10
Work-Sampling Time Studies
These two work-sampling time studies were done to determine what salespeople do at a wholesale electronics distributor (left) and a composite of several auto assembly-line employees (right).

client service level, she needs to find a way to reduce current workloads. This could be done through a reassignment of duties or the hiring of additional personnel.

INSIGHT ▶ Work sampling is particularly helpful when determining staffing needs or the reallocation of duties (see Figure 10.10).

LEARNING EXERCISE ▶ The analyst working for Dana recategorizes several observations. There are now 450 "on the phone/meeting with client" observations, 156 "idle," and 67 "personal time" observations. The last two categories saw no changes. Do the conclusions change? [Answer: Yes; now about 27% of employee time is not work related—over the 25% Dana desires.]

RELATED PROBLEM ▶ 10.34

The results of similar studies of salespeople and assembly-line employees are shown in Figure 10.10.

Work sampling offers several advantages over time-study methods. First, because a single person can observe several workers simultaneously, it is less expensive. Second, observers usually do not require much training, and no timing devices are needed. Third, the study can be temporarily delayed at any time with little impact on the results. Fourth, because work sampling uses instantaneous observations over a long period, the worker has little chance of affecting the study's outcome. Fifth, the procedure is less intrusive and therefore less likely to generate objections.

The disadvantages of work sampling are (1) it does not divide work elements as completely as time studies, (2) it can yield biased or incorrect results if the observer does not follow random routes of travel and observation, and (3) because it is less intrusive, it tends to be less accurate; this is particularly true when job-content times are short.

Ethics

Ethics in the workplace presents some interesting challenges. As we have suggested in this chapter, many constraints influence job design. The issues of fairness, equity, and ethics are pervasive. Whether the issue is equal opportunity or safe working conditions, an operations manager is often the one responsible. Managers do have some guidelines. By knowing the law; by complying with Canada Occupational Health and Safety Regulations and Health Canada's Workplace Hazardous Materials Information System (WHMIS); and by considering the requirements of government agencies, unions, trade associations, insurers, and employees, managers can often determine the parameters of their decisions. Human resource and legal departments are also available for help and guidance through the labyrinth of laws and regulations.

Management's role is to educate employees; specify the necessary equipment, work rules, and work environment; and then enforce those requirements, even when employees think it is not necessary to wear safety equipment. We began this chapter with a discussion of mutual trust and commitment, and that is the environment that managers should foster. Ethical management requires no less.

Mutual trust and commitment cannot be achieved without ethical behaviour.

CHAPTER SUMMARY

Outstanding firms know that their human resource strategy can yield a competitive advantage. Often, a large percentage of employees and a large part of labour costs are under the direction of OM. Consequently, an operations manager usually has a major role to play in achieving human resource objectives. A requirement is to build an environment with mutual respect and commitment and a reasonable quality of work life. Successful organizations have designed jobs that use both the mental and physical capabilities of their employees. Regardless of the strategy chosen, the skill with which a firm manages its human resources ultimately determines its success.

Labour standards are required for an efficient operations system. They are needed for production planning, labour planning, costing, and evaluating performance. They are used throughout industry—from the factory to finance, sales, and the office. They can also be used as a basis for incentive systems. Standards may be established via historical data, time studies, predetermined time standards, and work sampling.

ETHICAL DILEMMA

Birmingham's McWane Inc., with 10 major foundries, is one of the world's largest makers of cast-iron water and sewer pipes. In one of the nation's most dangerous industries, McWane is perhaps the most unsafe, with four times the injury rate of its six competitors combined. Its worker death rate is six times that of its industry's. McWane plants were also found in violation of pollution and emission limits 450 times in a recent seven-year period.

Workers who protest dangerous work conditions claim they are "bull's-eyed"—marked for termination. Supervisors have bullied injured workers and intimidated union leaders. Line workers who fail to make daily quotas get disciplinary actions. Managers have put up safety signs *after* a worker was injured to make it appear the worker ignored posted policies. They alter safety records and doctor machines to cover up hazards. When the government investigated one worker's death in 2000, inspectors found the McWane policy "was not to correct anything until OSHA found it".

McWane plants have also been repeatedly fined for failing to stop production to repair broken pollution controls. Five plants have been designated "high priority" violators by the EPA. Inside the plants, workers have repeatedly complained of blurred vision, severe headaches, and respiratory problems after being exposed, without training or protection, to chemicals used to make pipes. Near one plant in Phillipsburg, New Jersey, school crossing guards have had to wear gas masks—that location alone received 150 violations between 1995 and 2002. McWane's "standard procedure" (according to a former plant manager) is to illegally dump industrial contaminants into local rivers and creeks. Workers wait for night or heavy rainstorms before flushing thousands of litres from their sump pumps.

Given the following fictional scenarios: What is your position, and what action should you take?

a) On your spouse's recent move to Birmingham, you accepted a job, perhaps somewhat naively, as a company nurse in one of the McWane plants. After two weeks on the job you became aware of the work environment noted above.

b) You are a contractor who has traditionally used McWane's products, which meet specifications. McWane is consistently the low bidder. Your customers are happy with the product.

c) You are McWane's banker.

d) You are a supplier to McWane.

Sources: The New York Times (January 9, 2003: E5, May 26, 2004: A19, and August 30, 2005: A16); and the *Wall Street Journal* (May 27, 2004: A8).

Discussion Questions

1. How would you define a good *quality of work life*?
2. What are some of the worst jobs you know about? Why are they bad jobs? Why do people want these jobs?
3. If you were redesigning the jobs described in Question 2, what changes would you make? Are your changes realistic? Would they improve productivity (not just *production* but *productivity*)?
4. Can you think of any jobs that push the human–machine interface to the limits of human capabilities?
5. What are the five core characteristics of a good job design?
6. What are the differences among job enrichment, job enlargement, job rotation, job specialization, and employee empowerment?
7. Define *ergonomics*. Discuss the role of ergonomics in job design.
8. List the techniques available for carrying out methods analysis.
9. Identify four ways in which labour standards are set.
10. What are some of the uses to which labour standards are put?
11. How would you classify the following job elements? Are they personal, fatigue, or delay?
    a) The operator stops to talk to you.
    b) The operator lights up a cigarette.
    c) The operator opens his lunch pail (it is not lunch time), removes an apple, and takes an occasional bite.
12. How do you classify the time for a drill press operator who is idle for a few minutes at the beginning of every job waiting for the setup person to complete the setup? Some of the setup time is used in going for stock, but the operator typically returns with stock before the setup person is finished with the setup.
13. How do you classify the time for a machine operator who, after every job and sometimes in the middle of jobs, turns off the machine and goes for stock?
14. The operator drops a part, which you pick up and hand to him. Does this make any difference in a time study? If so, how?

Solved Problems Virtual Office Hours help is available at MyLab Operations Management.

▼ SOLVED PROBLEM 10.1

As pit crew manager for Rusty Wallace's NASCAR team (see the *Global Company Profile* that opens this chapter), you would like to evaluate how your "Jackman" (JM) and "Gas Man #1" (GM #1) are utilized. Recent stopwatch studies have verified the following times:

Pit crew	Activity	Time (seconds)
JM	Move to right side of car and raise car	4.0
GM #1	Move to rear gas filler	2.5
JM	Move to left side of car and raise car	3.8
JM	Wait for tire	1.0
GM #1	Load fuel (per litre)	0.5
JM	Wait for tire	1.2
JM	Move back over wall from left side	2.5
GM #1	Move back over the wall from gas filler	2.5

Use an activity chart similar to the one in Figure 10.6 as an aid.

▼ SOLUTION

▼ SOLVED PROBLEM 10.2

A work operation consisting of three elements has been subjected to a stopwatch time study. The recorded observations are shown in the following table. By union contract, the allowance time for the operation is personal time 5%, delay 5%, and fatigue 10%. Determine the standard time for the work operation.

Job Element	Observations (minutes)						Performance Rating (%)
	1	2	3	4	5	6	
A	0.1	0.3	0.2	0.9	0.2	0.1	90
B	0.8	0.6	0.8	0.5	3.2	0.7	110
C	0.5	0.5	0.4	0.5	0.6	0.5	80

▼ SOLUTION

First, delete the two observations that appear to be very unusual (0.9 minute for job element A and 3.2 minutes for job element B). Then:

$$\text{A's average observed time} = \frac{0.1 + 0.3 + 0.2 + 0.2 + 0.1}{5}$$
$$= 0.18 \text{ min}$$

$$\text{B's average observed time} = \frac{0.8 + 0.6 + 0.8 + 0.5 + 0.7}{5}$$
$$= 0.68 \text{ min}$$

$$\text{C's average observed time} = \frac{0.5 + 0.5 + 0.4 + 0.5 + 0.6 + 0.5}{6}$$
$$= 0.50 \text{ min}$$

A's normal time = $(0.18)(0.90) = 0.16$ min

B's normal time = $(0.68)(1.10) = 0.75$ min

C's normal time = $(0.50)(0.80) = 0.40$ min

Normal time for job = $0.16 + 0.75 + 0.40 = 1.31$ min

Note, the total allowance factor = $0.05 + 0.05 + 0.10 = 0.20$

Then: Standard time = $\dfrac{1.31}{1-0.20} = 1.64$ min

▼ SOLVED PROBLEM 10.3

The preliminary work sample of an operation indicates the following:

Number of times operator working	60
Number of times operator idle	40
Total number of preliminary observations	100

What is the required sample size for a 99.73% confidence level with ±4 precision?

▼ SOLUTION

$z = 3$ for 99.73% confidence; $p = \dfrac{60}{100} = 0.6$; $h = 0.04$

So:

$$n = \frac{z^2 p(1-p)}{h^2} = \frac{(3)^2(0.6)(0.4)}{(0.04)^2} = 1350 \text{ sample size}$$

▼ SOLVED PROBLEM 10.4

Amor Manufacturing Co. of Geneva, Switzerland, has just observed a job in its laboratory in anticipation of releasing the job to the factory for production. The firm wants rather good accuracy for costing and labour forecasting. Specifically, it wants to provide a 99% confidence level and a cycle time that is within 3% of the true value. How many observations should it make? The data collected so far are as follows:

Observation	Time
1	1.7
2	1.6
3	1.4
4	1.4
5	1.4

▼ SOLUTION

First, solve for the mean, $\bar{x}$, and the sample standard deviation, s:

$$s = \sqrt{\frac{\sum(\text{Each sample observation} - \bar{x})^2}{\text{Number in sample} - 1}}$$

Observation	x_i	$\bar{x}$	$x_i - \bar{x}$	$(x_i - \bar{x})^2$
1	1.7	1.5	0.2	0.04
2	1.6	1.5	0.1	0.01
3	1.4	1.5	−0.1	0.01
4	1.4	1.5	−0.1	0.01
5	1.4	1.5	−0.1	0.01

$\bar{x} = 1.5$ $\qquad$ $0.08 = \sum(x_i - \bar{x})^2$

$$s = \sqrt{\frac{0.08}{n-1}} = \sqrt{\frac{0.08}{4}} = 0.141$$

Then, solve for $n = \left(\dfrac{zs}{h\bar{x}}\right)^2 = \left[\dfrac{(2.58)(0.141)}{(0.03)(1.5)}\right]^2 = 65.3$

where $\bar{x} = 1.5$

$s = 0.141$

$z = 2.58$ (from Table 10.2)

$h = 0.03$

Therefore, you round up to 66 observations.

▼ SOLVED PROBLEM 10.5

At Maggard Micro Manufacturing, Inc., workers press semiconductors into predrilled slots on printed circuit boards. The elemental motions for normal time used by the company are as follows:

Reach 15 centimetres for semiconductors	40 TMU
Grasp the semiconductor	10 TMU
Move semiconductor to printed circuit board	30 TMU
Position semiconductor	35 TMU
Press semiconductor into slots	65 TMU
Move board aside	20 TMU

(Each time measurement unit is equal to 0.0006 min.) Determine the normal time for this operation in minutes and in seconds.

▼ SOLUTION

Add the time measurement units:

$$40 + 10 + 30 + 35 + 65 + 20 = 200$$

Time in minutes $= (200)(0.0006 \text{ min.}) = 0.12 \text{ min}$

Time in seconds $= (0.12)(60 \text{ sec}) = 7.2 \text{ sec}$

▼ SOLVED PROBLEM 10.6

To obtain the estimate of time a worker is busy for a work-sampling study, a manager divides a typical workday into 480 minutes. Using a random-number table to decide what time to go to an area to sample work occurrences, the manager records observations on a tally sheet like the following:

Status	Tally
Productively working	✚✚ ✚✚ ✚✚ I
Idle	IIII

▼ SOLUTION

In this case, the supervisor made 20 observations and found that employees were working 80% of the time. So, out of 480 minutes in an office workday, 20%, or 96 minutes, was idle time, and 384 minutes were productive. Note that this procedure describes that a worker is busy, not necessarily what he or she *should* be doing.

Problems*

• **10.1** Make a process chart for changing the right rear tire on an automobile.

• **10.2** Draw an activity chart for a machine operator with the following operation. The relevant times are as follows:

Prepare mill for loading (cleaning, oiling, and so on)	0.50 min
Load mill	1.75 min
Mill operating (cutting material)	2.25 min
Unload mill	0.75 min

••• **10.3** Draw an activity chart (a crew chart similar to Figure 10.6) for a concert and determine how to put together the concert so the star has reasonable breaks. For instance, at what point is there an instrumental number, a visual effect, a duet, a dance moment, that allows the star to pause and rest physically or at least rest his or her voice? Do other members of the show have moments of pause or rest?

•• **10.4** Make an operations chart of one of the following:
a) Putting a new eraser in (or on) a pencil
b) Putting a paper clip on two pieces of paper
c) Putting paper in a printer

• **10.5** Develop a process chart for installing a new memory board in your personal computer.

• **10.6** Rate a job you have had using Hackman and Oldham's core job characteristics (see the section "Psychological Components of Job Design") on a scale from 1 to 10. What is your total score? What about the job could have been changed to make you give it a higher score?

•• **10.7** Using the data in Solved Problem 10.1, prepare an activity chart like the one in the solved problem, but a second gas man also delivers 44 litres.

•• **10.8** Prepare a process chart for the Jackman in Solved Problem 10.1.

•• **10.9** Draw an activity chart for changing the right rear tire on an automobile with:
a) Only one person working
b) Two people working

••• **10.10** Draw an activity chart for washing the dishes in a double-sided sink. Two people participate, one washing, the other rinsing and drying. The rinser dries a batch of dishes from the drip rack as the washer fills the right sink with clean but unrinsed dishes. Then the rinser rinses the clean batch and places them on the drip rack. All dishes are stacked before being placed in the cabinets.

••• **10.11** Your campus club is hosting a car wash. Due to demand, three people are going to be scheduled per wash line. (Three people have to wash each vehicle.) Design an activity chart for washing and drying a typical sedan. You must wash the wheels but ignore the cleaning of the interior, because this part of the operation will be done at a separate vacuum station.

---

* *Note:* **Px** means the problem may be solved with POM for Windows and/or Excel.

••••**10.12** Design a process chart for printing a short document on a laser printer at an office. Unknown to you, the printer in the hallway is out of paper. The paper is located in a supply room at the other end of the hall. You wish to make five stapled copies of the document once it is printed. The copier, located next to the printer, has a sorter but no stapler. How could you make the task more efficient with the existing equipment?

• **10.13** If Charlene Brewster has times of 8.4, 8.6, 8.3, 8.5, 8.7, and 8.5 and a performance rating of 110%, what is the normal time for this operation? Is she faster or slower than normal? **Px**

• **10.14** If Charlene, the worker in Problem 10.13, has a performance rating of 90%, what is the normal time for the operation? Is she faster or slower than normal? **Px**

•• **10.15** Refer to Problem 10.13.
a) If the allowance factor is 15%, what is the standard time for this operation?
b) If the allowance factor is 18% and the performance rating is now 90%, what is the standard time for this operation? **Px**

•• **10.16** Maurice Browne recorded the following times assembling a watch. Determine (a) the average time, (b) the normal time, and (c) the standard time taken by him, using a performance rating of 95% and a personal allowance of 8%.

Assembly Times Recorded

Observation No.	Time (minutes)	Observation No.	Time (minutes)
1	0.11	9	0.12
2	0.10	10	0.09
3	0.11	11	0.12
4	0.10	12	0.11
5	0.14	13	0.10
6	0.10	14	0.12
7	0.10	15	0.14
8	0.09	16	0.09

• **10.17** An Air Canada gate agent, Chip Gilliken, gives out seat assignments to ticketed passengers. He takes an average of 50 seconds per passenger and is rated 110% in performance. How long should a *typical* agent be expected to take to make seat assignments? **Px**

• **10.18** After being observed many times, Marilyn Jones, a hospital lab analyst, had an average observed time for blood tests of 12 minutes. Marilyn's performance rating is 105%. The hospital has a personal, fatigue, and delay allowance of 16%.
a) Find the normal time for this process.
b) Find the standard time for this blood test. **Px**

• **10.19** Jell Lee Beans is famous for its boxed candies, which are sold primarily to businesses. One operator had the following observed times for gift wrapping in minutes: 2.2, 2.6, 2.3, 2.5, 2.4. The operator has a performance rating of 105% and an allowance factor of 10%. What is the standard time for gift wrapping? **Px**

• **10.20** After training, Mary Fernandez, a computer technician, had an average observed time for memory-chip tests of 12 seconds. Mary's performance rating is 100%. The firm has a personal fatigue and delay allowance of 15%.
a) Find the normal time for this process.
b) Find the standard time for this process. **Px**

•• **10.21** Susan Cottenden clocked the observed time for welding a part onto truck doors at 5.3 minutes. The performance rating of the worker timed was estimated at 105%. Find the normal time for this operation.

Note: According to the local union contract, each welder is allowed 3 minutes of personal time per hour and 2 minutes of fatigue time per hour. Further, there should be an average delay allowance of 1 minute per hour. Compute the allowance factor and then find the standard time for the welding activity. **Px**

•• **10.22** A hotel housekeeper, Alison Harvey, was observed five times on each of four task elements, as shown in the following table. On the basis of these observations, find the standard time for the process. Assume a 10% allowance factor.

Element	Performance Rating (%)	Observations (minutes per cycle) 1	2	3	4	5
Check minibar	100	1.5	1.6	1.4	1.5	1.5
Make one bed	90	2.3	2.5	2.1	2.2	2.4
Vacuum floor	120	1.7	1.9	1.9	1.4	1.6
Clean bath	100	3.5	3.6	3.6	3.6	3.2

•• **10.23** Red Deer College promotes a wide variety of executive training courses for firms in the Red Deer area. Director Marilyn Helms believes that individually typed letters add a personal touch to marketing. To prepare letters for mailing, she conducts a time study of her secretaries. On the basis of the observations shown in the following table, she wishes to develop a time standard for the whole job.

The college uses a total allowance factor of 12%. Helms decides to delete all unusual observations from the time study. What is the standard time?

Element	Observations (minutes) 1	2	3	4	5	6	Performance Rating (%)
Typing letter	2.5	3.5	2.8	2.1	2.6	3.3	85
Typing envelope	0.8	0.8	0.6	0.8	3.1[a]	0.7	100
Stuffing envelope	0.4	0.5	1.9[a]	0.3	0.6	0.5	95
Sealing, sorting	1.0	2.9[b]	0.9	1.0	4.4[b]	0.9	125

[a] Disregard—secretary stopped to answer the phone.
[b] Disregard—interruption by supervisor. **Px**

• **10.24** The results of a time study to perform a quality control test are shown in the following table. On the basis of these observations, determine the normal and standard time for the test, assuming a 23% allowance factor. **Px**

Task Element	Performance Rating (%)	Observations (minutes) 1	2	3	4	5
1	97	1.5	1.8	2.0	1.7	1.5
2	105	0.6	0.4	0.7	3.7[a]	0.5
3	86	0.5	0.4	0.6	0.4	0.4
4	90	0.6	0.8	0.7	0.6	0.7

[a] Disregard—employee is smoking a cigarette (included in personal time).

•• **10.25** Peter Rourke, a loan processor at Royal Bank, has been timed performing four work elements, with the results shown in the following table. The allowances for tasks such as this are personal, 7%; fatigue, 10%; and delay, 3%.

Task Element	Performance Rating (%)	Observations (minutes) 1	2	3	4	5
1	110	0.5	0.4	0.6	0.4	0.4
2	95	0.6	0.8	0.7	0.6	0.7
3	90	0.6	0.4	0.7	0.5	0.5
4	85	1.5	1.8	2.0	1.7	1.5

a) What is the normal time?
b) What is the standard time? **Px**

•• **10.26** Each year, Hudson's Bay Company sets up a gift-wrapping station to assist its customers with holiday shopping. Preliminary observations of one worker at the station produced the following sample time (in minutes per package): 3.5, 3.2, 4.1, 3.6, 3.9. Based on this small sample, what number of observations would be necessary to determine the true cycle time with a 95% confidence level and an accuracy of 5%? **Px**

•• **10.27** A time study of a factory worker has revealed an average observed time of 3.20 minutes, with a standard deviation of 1.28 minutes. These figures were based on a sample of 45 observations. Is this sample adequate in size for the firm to be 99% confident that the standard time is within 5% of the true value? If not, what should be the proper number of observations? **Px**

•• **10.28** Based on a careful work study in the Richard Dulski Corp., the results shown in the following table have been observed:

Element	Observations (minutes) 1	2	3	4	5	Performance Rating (%)
Prepare daily reports	35	40	33	42	39	120
Photocopy results	12	10	36[a]	15	13	110
Label and package reports	3	3	5	5	4	90
Distribute reports	15	18	21	17	45[b]	85

[a] Photocopying machine broken; included as delay in the allowance factor.
[b] Power outage; included as delay in the allowance factor.

a) Compute the normal time for each work element.
b) If the allowance for this type of work is 15%, what is the standard time?
c) How many observations are needed for a 95% confidence level within 5% accuracy? (*Hint:* Calculate the sample size of each element.)

•• 10.29 The St. Lawrence Cement Company packs 36-kilogram bags of concrete mix. Time-study data for the filling activity are shown in the following table. Because of the high physical demands of the job, the company's policy is a 23% allowance for workers.
a) Compute the standard time for the bag-packing task.
b) How many observations are necessary for 99% confidence, within 5% accuracy?

Element	Observations (seconds) 1	2	3	4	5	Performance Rating (%)
Grasp and place bag	8	9	8	11	7	110
Fill bag	36	41	39	35	112[a]	85
Seal bag	15	17	13	20	18	105
Place bag on conveyor	8	6	9	30[b]	35[b]	90

[a] Bag breaks open; included as delay in the allowance factor.

[b] Conveyor jams; included as delay in the allowance factor.

•• 10.30 Installing mufflers at the Stanley Garage in Brandon, Manitoba, involves five work elements. Linda Stanley has timed workers performing these tasks seven times, with the results shown in the following table.

Job Element	Observations (minutes) 1	2	3	4	5	6	7	Performance Rating (%)
1. Select correct mufflers	4	5	4	6	4	15[a]	4	110
2. Remove old muffler	6	5	7	6	7	6	7	90
3. Weld/install new muffler	15	14	14	12	15	16	13	105
4. Check/inspect work	3	4	24[a]	5	4	3	18[a]	100
5. Complete paperwork	5	6	8	—	7	6	7	130

[a]Employee has lengthy conversations with boss (not job related).

By agreement with her workers, Stanley allows a 10% fatigue factor and a 10% personal-time factor but no time for delay. To compute standard time for the work operation, Stanley excludes all observations that appear to be unusual or nonrecurring. She does not want an error of more than 5%.
a) What is the standard time for the task?
b) How many observations are needed to assure a 95% confidence level? **Px**

• 10.31 Bank manager Art Hill wants to determine the percentage of time that tellers are working and idle. He decides to use work sampling, and his initial estimate is that the tellers are idle 15% of the time. How many observations should Hill take to be 95.45% confident that the results will not be more than 4% from the true result? **Px**

•• 10.32 Supervisor Robert Hall wants to determine the percent of time a machine in his area is idle. He decides to use work sampling, and his initial estimate is that the machine is idle 20% of the time. How many observations should Hall take to be 98% confident that the results will be less than 5% from the true results?

••• 10.33 Tim Nelson, a quality assurance product inspector, is expected to inspect 130 ornaments per day.
a) If he works an eight-hour day, how many minutes is he allowed for each inspection (i.e., what is his *standard time*)?
b) If he is allowed a 6% fatigue allowance, a 6% delay allowance, and 6% for personal time, what is the normal time that he is assumed to take to perform each inspection?

••• 10.34 A random work sample of operators taken over a 160-hour work month at Tele-Marketing, Inc., has produced the following results. What is the percent of time spent working?

On phone with customer	858
Idle time	220
Personal time	85

•• 10.35 A total of 300 observations of Bob Ramos, an assembly-line worker, were made over a 40-hour work week. The sample also showed that Bob was busy working (assembling the parts) during 250 observations.
a) Find the percentage of time Bob was working.
b) If you want a confidence level of 95%, and if 3% is an acceptable error, what size should the sample be?
c) Was the sample size adequate? **Px**

• 10.36 Sharpening your pencil is an operation that may be divided into eight small elemental motions. In MTM terms, each element may be assigned a certain number of TMUs:

Reach 10 centimetres for the pencil	6 TMU
Grasp the pencil	2 TMU
Move the pencil 15 centimetres	10 TMU
Position the pencil	20 TMU
Insert the pencil into the sharpener	4 TMU
Sharpen the pencil	120 TMU
Disengage the pencil	10 TMU
Move the pencil 10 centimetres	10 TMU

What is the total normal time for sharpening one pencil? Convert your answer into minutes and seconds.

•• 10.37 Supervisor Vic Sower at Huntsville Equipment Company is concerned that material is not arriving as promptly as needed at work cells. A new kanban system has been installed, but there seems to be some delay in getting the material moved to the work cells so that the job can begin promptly. Sower is interested in determining how much delay there is on the part of his highly paid machinists. Ideally, the delay would be close to zero. He has asked his assistant to determine the delay factor among his 10 work cells. The assistant collects the data on a random basis over the next two weeks and determines that of the 1200 observations, 105 were made while the operators were waiting for materials. Use a 95% confidence level and a 3% acceptable error. What report does he give to Sower? **Px**

•••• 10.38 The Winter Garden Hotel has 400 rooms. Every day, the housekeepers clean any room that was occupied the night before. If a guest is checking out of the hotel, the housekeepers give the room a thorough cleaning to get it ready for the next guest. This takes about 30 minutes. If a guest is staying another night, the housekeeper only "refreshes" the room, which takes 15 minutes.

Each day, each housekeeper reports for her six-hour shift, then prepares her cart. She pushes the cart to her floor and begins work. She usually has to restock the cart once per day; then she pushes it back to the storeroom at the end of the day and puts the things away. Here is a timetable:

1) Arrive at work and stock cart (10 minutes).
2) Push cart to floor (10 minutes).
3) Take morning break (15 minutes).
4) Stop for lunch (30 minutes).
5) Restock cart (20 minutes).
6) Take afternoon break (15 minutes).
7) Push cart back to laundry and store items (20 minutes).

Last night, the hotel was full (all 400 rooms were occupied). People are checking out of 200 rooms. Their rooms will need to be thoroughly cleaned. The other 200 rooms will need to be refreshed.

a) How many minutes per day of actual room cleaning can each housekeeper do?
b) How many minutes of room cleaning will the Winter Garden Hotel need today?
c) How many housekeepers will be needed to clean the hotel today?
d) If *all* the guests checked out this morning, how many housekeepers would be needed to clean the 400 rooms?

CASE STUDIES

Jackson Manufacturing Company

Kathleen McFadden, vice-president of operations at Jackson Manufacturing Company, has just received a request for quote (RFQ) from DeKalb Electric Supply for 400 units per week of a motor armature. The components are standard and either easy to work into the existing production schedule or readily available from established suppliers on a JIT basis. But there is some difference in assembly. Kathleen has identified eight tasks that Jackson must perform to assemble the armature. Seven of these tasks are very similar to ones performed by Jackson in the past; therefore, the average time and resulting labour standard of those tasks is known.

The eighth task, an *overload* test, requires performing a task that is very different from any performed previously, however. Kathleen has asked you to conduct a time study on the task to determine the standard time. Then an estimate can be made of the cost to assemble the armature. This information, combined with other cost data, will allow the firm to put together the information needed for the RFQ.

To determine a standard time for the task, an employee from an existing assembly station was trained in the new assembly process. Once proficient, the employee was then asked to perform the task 17 times so a standard could be determined. The actual times observed (in minutes) were as follows:

The worker had a 115% performance rating. The task can be performed in a sitting position at a well-designed ergonomic workstation in an air-conditioned facility. Although the armature itself weighs 4 kilograms, there is a carrier that holds it so that the operator need only rotate the armature. But the detail work remains high; therefore, the fatigue allowance should be 8%. The company has an established personal allowance of 6%. Delay should be very low. Previous studies of delay in this department average 2%. This standard is to use the same figure.

The workday is 7.5 hours, but operators are paid for 8 hours at an average of $12.50 per hour.

Discussion Questions

In your report to Ms. McFadden, you realize you will want to address several factors:

1. How big should the sample be for a statistically accurate standard (at, say, the 99.73% confidence level and accuracy of 5%)?
2. Is the sample size adequate?
3. How many units should be produced at this workstation per day?
4. What is the cost per unit for this task in direct labour cost?

1	2	3	4	5	6	7	8	9	10	11	12	13	14	15	16	17
2.05	1.92	2.01	1.89	1.77	1.80	1.86	1.83	1.93	1.96	1.95	2.05	1.79	1.82	1.85	1.85	1.99

Source: Based on material by Professor Hank Maddux, Sam Houston State University.

Video Case | The "People" Focus: Human Resources at Alaska Airlines

With thousands of employees spread across nearly 100 locations in the United States, Mexico, and Canada, building a committed and cohesive workforce is a challenge. Yet Alaska Airlines is making it work. The company's "people" focus states:

> While airplanes and technology enable us to do what we do, we recognize this is fundamentally a people business, and our future depends on how we work together to win in this extremely competitive

> environment. As we grow, we want to strengthen our small company feel . . . We will succeed where others fail because of our pride and passion, and because of the way we treat our customers, our suppliers and partners, and each other.

Managerial excellence requires a committed workforce. Alaska Airlines's pledge of respect for people is one of the key elements of a world-class operation.

Effective organizations require talented, committed, and trained personnel. Alaska Airlines conducts comprehensive training at all levels. Its "Flight Path" leadership training for all 10 000 employees is now being followed by "Gear Up" training for 800 frontline managers. In addition, training programs have been developed for Lean and Six Sigma as well as for the unique requirements for pilots, flight attendants, baggage, and ramp personnel. Because the company only hires pilots into first officer positions—the right seat in the cockpit, it offers a program called the "Fourth Stripe" to train for promotion into the captain's seat on the left side, along with all the additional responsibility that entails.

Customer service agents receive specific training on the company's "Empowerment Toolkit". Like the Ritz-Carlton's famous customer service philosophy, agents have the option of awarding customers hotel and meal vouchers or frequent flier miles when the customer has experienced a service problem.

Because many managers are cross-trained in operational duties outside the scope of their daily positions, they have the ability to pitch in to ensure that customer-oriented processes go smoothly. Even John Ladner, Director of Seattle Airport Operations, who is a fully licensed pilot, has left his desk to cover a flight at the last minute for a sick colleague.

Along with providing development and training at all levels, managers recognize that inherent personal traits can make a huge difference. For example, when flight attendants are hired, the ones who are still engaged, smiling, and fresh at the end of a very long interview day are the ones Alaska wants on the team. Why? The job requires these behaviours and attitudes to fit with the Alaska

Airlines team—and smiling and friendly flight attendants are particularly important at the end of a long flight.

Visual workplace tools also complement and close the loop that matches training to performance. Alaska Airlines makes full use of colour-coded graphs and charts to report performance against key metrics to employees. Twenty top managers gather weekly in an operations leadership meeting, run by Executive VP of Operations Ben Minicucci, to review activity consolidated into visual summaries. Key metrics are colour-coded and posted prominently in every work area.

Alaska's training approach results in empowered employees who are willing to assume added responsibility and accept the unknowns that come with that added responsibility.

Discussion Questions*

1. Summarize Alaska Airlines's human resources focus in your own words.
2. Why is employee empowerment useful to companies such as Alaska Airlines?
3. What tools discussed in the chapter might be employed to enhance the company's training and performance efforts? Why?

---

* Before answering these questions, you may wish to view the video that accompanies this case.

Video Case — Human Resources at Hard Rock Cafe

Everyone—managers and hourly employees alike—who goes to work for Hard Rock Cafe takes Rock 101, an initial two-day training class. There they receive their wallet-sized "Hard Rock Values" card, which they carry at all times. The Hard Rock values system is to bring a fun, healthy, nurturing environment into the Hard Rock Cafe culture.* This initial course and many other courses help employees develop both personally and professionally. The human resource department plays a critical role in any service organization, but at Hard Rock, with its "experience strategy," the human resource department takes on added importance.

Long before Jim Knight, manager of corporate training, begins the class, the human resource strategy of Hard Rock has had an impact. Hard Rock's strategic plan includes building a culture that allows for acceptance of substantial diversity and individuality. From a human resource perspective, this has the benefit of enlarging the pool of applicants as well as contributing to the Hard Rock culture. Creating a work environment above and beyond a paycheque is a unique challenge. Outstanding pay and benefits are a start, but the key is to provide an environment that works for the employees. This includes benefits that start for part-timers who work at least 19 hours per week (while others in the industry start at 35 hours per week); a unique respect for individuality; continuing training; and a high level of internal promotions—

some 60% of the managers are promoted from hourly employee ranks. The company's training is very specific, with job-oriented interactive CDs covering kitchen, retail, and front-of-the-house service. Outside volunteer work is especially encouraged to foster a bond between the workers, their community, and issues of importance to them.

Applicants also are screened on their interest in music and their ability to tell a story. Hard Rock builds on a hiring criterion of bright, positive-attitude, self-motivated individuals with an employee bill of rights and substantial employee empowerment. The result is a unique culture and work environment that, no doubt, contributes to the low turnover of hourly people—one-half the industry average.

The layout, memorabilia, music, and videos are important elements in the Hard Rock "experience," but it falls on the servers to make the experience come alive. They are particularly focused on providing an authentic and memorable dining experience. Like WestJet Airlines, Hard Rock is looking for people with a cause—people who like to serve. By succeeding with its human resource strategy, Hard Rock obtains a competitive advantage.

---

* Hard Rock Cafe's mission, mottos, and operating values are available at **www.hardrock.com/corporate/careers**.

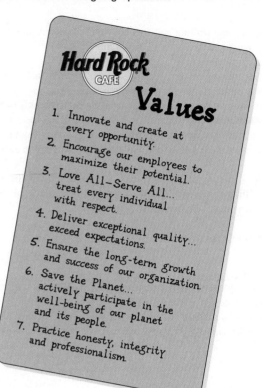

Hard Rock CAFE Values

1. Innovate and create at every opportunity.
2. Encourage our employees to maximize their potential.
3. Love All-Serve All... treat every individual with respect.
4. Deliver exceptional quality... exceed expectations.
5. Ensure the long-term growth and success of our organization.
6. Save the Planet... actively participate in the well-being of our planet and its people.
7. Practice honesty, integrity and professionalism.

Discussion Questions*

1. What has Hard Rock done to lower employee turnover to half the industry average?
2. How does Hard Rock's human resource department support the company's overall strategy?
3. How would Hard Rock's value system work for automobile assembly-line workers? (*Hint:* Consider Hackman and Oldham's core job characteristics.)
4. How might you adjust a traditional assembly line to address more "core job characteristics"?

---

* Before answering these questions, you may wish to view the video that accompanies this case.

▶**Additional Case Studies:** Visit **MyLab Operations Management** for these case studies:

Chicago Southern Hospital: Examines the requirements for a work-sampling plan for nurses.

Karstadt Versus JCPenney: Compares the work culture in retailing in the United States to Germany.

The Fleet That Wanders: Requires a look at ergonomic issues for truck drivers.

CHAPTER 10 | RAPID REVIEW

MyLab Operations Management

Main Heading	Review Material	
HUMAN RESOURCE STRATEGY FOR COMPETITIVE ADVANTAGE (pp. 389–390)	*The objective of a human resource strategy is to manage labour and design jobs so people are effectively and efficiently utilized* *Quality of work life* refers to a job that is not only reasonably safe with equitable pay but that also achieves an appropriate level of both physical and psychological requirements. *Mutual commitment* means that both management and employees strive to meet common objectives. *Mutual trust* is reflected in reasonable, documented employment policies that are honestly and equitably implemented to the satisfaction of both management and employees.	**VIDEO 10.1** Human Resources at Hard Rock Cafe
LABOUR PLANNING (pp. 390–391)	• **Labour planning**—A means of determining staffing policies dealing with employment stability, work schedules, and work rules. *Flextime* allows employees, within limits, to determine their own schedules. *Flexible* (or *compressed*) *workweeks* often call for fewer but longer workdays. *Part-time status* is particularly attractive in service industries with fluctuating demand loads.	

Main Heading	Review Material	
JOB DESIGN (pp. 391–395)	• **Job design**—An approach that specifies the tasks that constitute a job for an individual or group. • **Labour specialization (or job specialization)**—The division of labour into unique ("special") tasks. • **Job enlargement**—The grouping of a variety of tasks about the same skill level; horizontal enlargement. • **Job rotation**—A system in which an employee is moved from one specialized job to another. • **Job enrichment**—A method of giving an employee more responsibility that includes some of the planning and control necessary for job accomplishment; vertical expansion. • **Employee empowerment**—Enlarging employee jobs so that the added responsibility and authority is moved to the lowest level possible. • **Self-directed team**—A group of empowered individuals working together to reach a common goal.	
ERGONOMICS AND THE WORK ENVIRONMENT (pp. 395–397)	• **Ergonomics**—The study of the human interface with the environment and machines. The physical environment affects performance, safety, and quality of work life. Illumination, noise and vibration, temperature, humidity, and air quality are controllable by management.	
METHODS ANALYSIS (pp. 397–399)	• **Methods analysis**—A system that involves developing work procedures that are safe and produce quality products efficiently. • **Flow diagram**—A drawing used to analyze movement of people or material. • **Process chart**—Graphic representation that depicts a sequence of steps for a process. • **Activity chart**—A way of improving utilization of an operator and a machine or some combination of operators (a crew) and machines. • **Operations chart**—A chart depicting right- and left-hand motions.	
THE VISUAL WORKPLACE (pp. 399–400)	• **Visual workplace**—Uses a variety of visual communication techniques to rapidly communicate information to stakeholders.	
LABOUR STANDARDS (pp. 400–409)	• **Labour standards**—The amount of time required to perform a job or part of a job. Labour standards are set in four ways: (1) historical experience, (2) time studies, (3) predetermined time standards, and (4) work sampling. • **Time study**—Timing a sample of a worker's performance and using it as a basis for setting a standard time • **Average observed time**—The arithmetic mean of the times for each element measured, adjusted for unusual influence for each element. $$\text{Average observed time} = \frac{(\text{Sum of the times recorded to perform each element})}{\text{Number of observations}} \quad (10\text{-}1)$$ • **Normal time**—The average observed time, adjusted for paces: $$\text{Normal time} = (\text{Average observed time}) \times (\text{Performance rating factor}) \quad (10\text{-}2)$$ • **Standard time**—An adjustment to the total normal time; the adjustment provides allowances for personal needs, unavoidable work delays, and fatigue: $$\text{Standard time} = \frac{\text{Total normal time}}{1 - \text{Allowance factor}} \quad (10\text{-}3)$$ *Personal time allowances* are often established in the range of 4% to 7% of total time. $$\text{Required sample size} = n = \left(\frac{zs}{h\bar{x}}\right)^2 \quad (10\text{-}4)$$ $$n = \left(\frac{zs}{e}\right)^2 \quad (10\text{-}5)$$ $$s = \sqrt{\frac{\sum(x_i - \bar{x})^2}{n-1}} = \sqrt{\frac{\sum(\text{each sample observation} - \bar{x})^2}{\text{Number in sample} - 1}} \quad (10\text{-}6)$$ where x_i = value of each observation $\bar{x}$ = mean of the observations n = number of observations in the sample	Virtual Office Hours for Solved Problems: 10.2–10.6 Problems 10.13–10.37

foods; a third for other food items, like baked goods; and a fourth for restaurant supplies (everything from dishes to ovens to uniforms). Over U.S. $2 billion is spent in these supply chains annually. (See the Video Case Study at the end of this chapter for details.)

Darden's four supply channels have some common characteristics. They all require *supplier qualification*, have *product tracking*, are subject to *independent audits*, and employ *just-in-time delivery*. With best-in-class techniques and processes, Darden creates worldwide supply chain partnerships and alliances that are rapid, transparent, and efficient. Darden achieves competitive advantage through its superior supply chain.

Barry Render

Qualifying Worldwide Sources: Part of Darden's supply chain begins with a crab harvest in the frigid waters off the coast of Alaska. But long before a supplier is qualified to sell to Darden, a total quality team is appointed. The team provides guidance, assistance, support, and training to the suppliers to ensure that overall objectives are understood and desired results accomplished.

STUDENT TIP

Competition today is not between companies; it is between supply chains.

LO1 Explain the strategic importance of the supply chain

Supply chain management

Management of activities that procure materials and services, transform them into intermediate goods and final products, and deliver them through a distribution system.

The Supply Chain's Strategic Importance

Most firms, like Darden, spend a huge portion of their sales dollars on purchases. Because an increasing percentage of an organization's costs are determined by purchasing, relationships with suppliers are increasingly integrated and long term. Joint efforts that improve innovation, speed design, and reduce costs are common. Such efforts, when part of a corporate-wide strategy, can dramatically improve both partners' competitiveness. This integrated focus places added emphasis on managing supplier relationships.

Supply chain management is the integration of the activities that procure materials and services, transform them into intermediate goods and final products, and deliver them to customers. These activities include purchasing and outsourcing activities, plus many other functions that are important to the relationship with suppliers and distributors. As Figure 11.1 suggests,

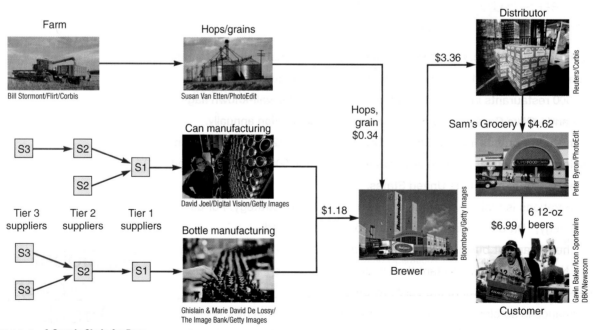

FIGURE 11.1 A Supply Chain for Beer

The supply chain includes all the interactions among suppliers, manufacturers, distributors, and customers. The chain includes transportation, scheduling information, cash and credit transfers, as well as ideas, designs, and material transfers. Even can and bottle manufacturers have their own tiers of suppliers providing components such as lids, labels, packing containers, etc. (Costs are approximate and include substantial taxes.)

Table 11.1
How Supply Chain Decisions Affect Strategy*

	Low-Cost Strategy	**Response Strategy**	**Differentiation Strategy**
Supplier's goal	Supply demand at lowest possible cost (e.g., Emerson Electric, Taco Bell)	Respond quickly to changing requirements and demand to minimize stockouts (e.g., Dell Computer)	Share market research; jointly develop products and options (e.g., Benetton)
Primary selection criteria	Select primarily for cost	Select primarily for capacity, speed, and flexibility	Select primarily for product development skills
Process characteristics	Maintain high average utilization	Invest in excess capacity and flexible processes	Use modular processes that lend themselves to mass customization
Inventory characteristics	Minimize inventory throughout the chain to hold down costs	Develop responsive system, with buffer stocks positioned to ensure supply	Minimize inventory in the chain to avoid obsolescence
Lead-time characteristics	Shorten lead time as long as it does not increase costs	Invest aggressively to reduce production lead time	Invest aggressively to reduce development lead time
Product design characteristics	Maximize performance and minimize cost	Use product designs that lead to low setup time and rapid production ramp-up	Use modular design to postpone product differentiation for as long as possible

*See related table and discussion in Marshall L. Fisher, "What Is the Right Supply Chain for Your Product?" *Harvard Business Review* (March–April 1997): 105.

supply chain management includes determining (1) transportation vendors, (2) credit and cash transfers, (3) suppliers, (4) distributors, (5) accounts payable and receivable, (6) warehousing and inventory, (7) order fulfillment, and (8) sharing customer, forecasting, and production information. *The objective is to build a chain of suppliers that focuses on maximizing value to the ultimate customer.*

As firms strive to increase their competitiveness via product customization, high quality, cost reductions, and speed to market, added emphasis is placed on the supply chain. Effective supply chain management makes suppliers "partners" in the firm's strategy to satisfy an ever-changing marketplace. A competitive advantage may depend on a close long-term strategic relationship with a few suppliers.

To ensure that the supply chain supports the firm's strategy, managers need to consider the supply chain issues shown in Table 11.1. Activities of supply chain managers cut across accounting, finance, marketing, and the operations discipline. Just as the OM function supports the firm's overall strategy, the supply chain must support the OM strategy. Strategies of low cost or rapid response demand different things from a supply chain than a strategy of differentiation. For instance, a low-cost strategy, as Table 11.1 indicates, requires suppliers be selected based primarily on cost. Such suppliers should have the ability to design low-cost products that meet the functional requirements, minimize inventory, and drive down lead times. However, if you want roses that are fresh, build a supply chain that focuses on response (see the *OM in Action* box "A Rose Is a Rose, but Only if It Is Fresh").

As supply chain management grows in prominence in Canada and globally, new advances and developments are visible on a regular basis. So too is the need for organizations, research, and education within the field. Several organizations in Canada are striving to increase awareness and expertise within this area. Most notably among them are:

VIDEO 11.1
Darden's Global Supply Chain

- Canadian Supply Chain Sector Council (CSCSC) (**www.supplychaincanada.org**)
- Supply Chain Management Association (**www.scmanational.ca**)
- APICS (**www.apics.org**)

Each organization has its own mandate and constituents. It is prudent for students, industry professionals, and companies to remain up to date on the activities of each of these organizations. A wealth of evolving information is available on their websites.

Firms must achieve integration of strategy up and down the supply chain, and must expect that strategy to be different for different products and to change as products move through their life cycle. Darden Restaurants, as noted in the opening *Global Company Profile*, has mastered

OM in Action A Rose Is a Rose, but Only if It Is Fresh

Supply chains for food and flowers must be fast, and they must be good. When the food supply chain has a problem, the best that can happen is the customer does not get fed on time; the worst that happens is the customer gets food poisoning and dies. In the floral industry, the timing and temperature are also critical. Indeed, flowers are the most perishable agricultural item—even more so than fish. Flowers not only need to move fast, but they must also be kept cool, at a constant temperature of 1 to 3 degrees Celsius. And they must be provided preservative-treated water while in transit. Roses are especially delicate, fragile, and perishable.

Roughly three-quarters of the roses sold in the Canadian market arrive by air from rural Colombia and Ecuador. Roses move through this supply chain via an intricate but fast transportation network. This network stretches from growers who cut, grade, bundle, pack, and ship, to importers who make the deal, to the Agriculture and Agri-Food Canada personnel who quarantine and inspect for insects, diseases, and parasites, to Canada Border Services Agency staff who inspect and approve, to facilitators who provide clearance and labelling, to wholesalers who distribute, to retailers who arrange and sell, and finally to the customer. Each and every minute the product is deteriorating. The time and temperature sensitivity of perishables like

Africa Studio/Fotolia

roses requires sophistication and refined standards in the supply chain. Success yields quality and low losses. After all, when it's Valentine's Day, what good is a shipment of roses that arrives wilted or late? This is a difficult supply chain; only an excellent one will get the job done.

Sources: IIE Solutions (February 2002): 26–32; and *World Trade* (June 2004): 22–25.

worldwide product and service complexity by segmenting its supply chain and at the same time integrating four unique supply chains into its overall strategy.

SUPPLY CHAIN RISK

In this age of increasing specialization, low communication cost, and fast transportation, companies are making less and buying more. This means more reliance on supply chains and more risk. Managing the new integrated supply chain is a strategic challenge. Having fewer suppliers makes the supplier and customer more dependent on each other, increasing risk for both. This risk is compounded by globalization and logistical complexity. In any supply chain, vendor reliability and quality may be challenging, but the new paradigm of a tight, fast, low-inventory supply chain, operating across political and cultural boundaries, adds a new dimension to risk. As organizations go global, shipping time may increase, logistics may be less reliable, and tariffs and quotas may block companies from doing business. In addition, international supply chains complicate information flows and increase political and currency risks.

Thus, the development of a successful strategic plan for supply chain management requires careful research, an understanding of the risk involved, and innovative planning. Reducing risk in this increasingly global environment suggests that management must be able to mitigate and react to disruptions in:

1. *Processes* (raw material and component availability, quality, and logistics)
2. *Controls* (management metrics and reliable secure communication for financial transactions, product designs, and logistics scheduling)
3. *Environment* (customs duties, tariffs, security screening, natural disaster, currency fluctuations, terrorist attacks, and political issues)

Let's look at how several organizations address these risks in their supply chains:

- To reduce *process risk*, McDonald's planned its supply chain six years in advance of its opening in Russia. Creating a $60 million "food town," it developed independently owned supply plants in Moscow to keep its transportation costs and handling times low and its quality and customer-service levels high. Every component in this food chain—meat plant, chicken plant, bakery, fish plant, and lettuce plant—is closely monitored to make sure that all the system's links are strong.

- Ford's *process risk* reduction strategy is to develop a global network of *few but exceptional* suppliers who will provide the lowest cost and highest quality. This has driven one division's supplier base down to only 227 suppliers worldwide, compared with 700 previously.
- Darden Restaurants has placed extensive *controls*, including third-party audits, on supplier processes and logistics to ensure constant monitoring and reduction of risk.
- Boeing is reducing *control* risk through its state-of-the-art international communication system that transmits engineering, scheduling, and logistics data not only to Boeing facilities but to the suppliers of the 75% to 80% of the 787 Dreamliner that is built by non-Boeing companies.
- Hard Rock Cafe is reducing *environmental* (political) risk by franchising and licensing, rather than owning, when the political and cultural barriers seem significant.
- Toyota, after its experience with both fire and earthquakes, has moved to reduce *environmental* (natural disaster) risk with a policy of having at least two suppliers for each component.

Tight integration of the supply chain can have significant benefits, but the risks can and must be managed.

Ethics and Sustainability

Let's look at three aspects of ethics in the supply chain: personal ethics, ethics within the supply chain, and ethical behaviour regarding the environment.

STUDENT TIP

Because so much money passes through the supply chain, the opportunity for ethical lapses is significant.

PERSONAL ETHICS

Ethical decisions are critical to the long-term success of any organization. However, the supply chain is particularly susceptible to ethical lapses, as the opportunities for unethical behaviour are enormous. With sales personnel anxious to sell and purchasing agents spending huge sums, temptations abound. Many salespeople become friends with customers, do favours for them, take them to lunch, or present small (or large) gifts. Determining when tokens of friendship become bribes can be challenging. Many companies have strict rules and codes of conduct that limit what is acceptable. Recognizing these issues, the Institute for Supply Management—Canada has developed principles and standards to be used as guidelines for ethical behaviour (as shown in Table 11.2). As the supply chain becomes international, operations managers need to expect an additional set of ethical issues to manifest themselves as they deal with new cultural values.

ETHICS WITHIN THE SUPPLY CHAIN

In this age of hyper-specialization, much of any organization's resources are purchased, putting great stress on ethics in the supply chain. Managers may be tempted to ignore ethical lapses by suppliers or offload pollution to suppliers. But firms must establish standards for their suppliers, just as they have established standards for themselves. Society expects ethical performance throughout the supply chain. For instance, Gap Inc. reported that of its 3000-plus factories worldwide, about 90% failed their initial evaluation.[1] The report indicated that 10% to 25% of its Chinese factories engaged in psychological or verbal abuse, and more than 50% of the factories visited in sub-Saharan Africa operate without proper safety devices. The challenge of enforcing ethical standards is significant, but responsible firms such as Gap are finding ways to deal with this difficult issue.

ETHICAL BEHAVIOUR REGARDING THE ENVIRONMENT

While ethics on both a personal basis and in the supply chain are important, so is ethical behaviour in regard to the environment. Good ethics extends to doing business in a way that supports

---

[1] Amy Merrick, "Gap Offers Unusual Look at Factory Conditions," *The Wall Street Journal* (May 12, 2004): A1, A12.

Table 11.2

Principles and Standards of Ethical Supply Management Conduct

INTEGRITY IN YOUR DECISIONS AND ACTIONS; VALUE FOR YOUR EMPLOYER; LOYALTY TO YOUR PROFESSION

1. **PERCEIVED IMPROPRIETY** Prevent the intent and appearance of unethical or compromising conduct in relationships, actions and communications.

2. **CONFLICTS OF INTEREST** Ensure that any personal, business, or other activity does not conflict with the lawful interests of your employer.

3. **ISSUES OF INFLUENCE** Avoid behaviours or actions that may negatively influence, or appear to influence, supply management decisions.

4. **RESPONSIBILITIES TO YOUR EMPLOYER** Uphold fiduciary and other responsibilities using reasonable care and granted authority to deliver value to your employer.

5. **SUPPLIER AND CUSTOMER RELATIONSHIPS** Promote positive supplier and customer relationships.

6. **SUSTAINABILITY AND SOCIAL RESPONSIBILITY** Champion social responsibility and sustainability practices in supply management.

7. **CONFIDENTIAL AND PROPRIETARY INFORMATION** Protect confidential and proprietary information.

8. **RECIPROCITY** Avoid improper reciprocal agreements.

9. **APPLICABLE LAWS, REGULATIONS, AND TRADE AGREEMENTS** Know and obey the letter and spirit of laws, regulations, and trade agreements applicable to supply management.

10. **PROFESSIONAL COMPETENCE** Develop skills, expand knowledge, and conduct business that demonstrate competence and promote the supply management profession.

Source: Reprinted with permission from Principles and Standards of Ethical Supply Management Conduct. www.instituteforsupplymanagement.org.

conservation and renewal of resources. This requires evaluation of the entire environmental impact, from raw material, to manufacture, through use, and final disposal. For instance, Darden and Walmart require their shrimp and fish suppliers in Southeast Asia to abide by the standards of the Global Aquaculture Alliance. These standards must be met if suppliers want to maintain the business relationship. Operations managers also ensure that sustainability is reflected in the performance of second- and third-tier suppliers. Enforcement can be done by in-house inspectors, third-party auditors, governmental agencies, or nongovernmental watchdog organizations. All four approaches are used.

The incoming supply chain garners most of the attention, but it is only part of the ethical challenge of sustainability. The "return" supply chain is also significant. Returned products can only be burned, buried, or reused. And the first two options have adverse consequences. Once viewed in this manner, the need for operations managers to evaluate the entire product life cycle is apparent.

While 84% of an automobile and 90% of an airplane are recycled, these levels are not easily achieved. Recycling efforts began at product and process design. Then special end-of-product-life processes were developed. Oil, lead, gasoline, explosives in air bags, acid in batteries, and the many components (axles, differentials, jet engines, hydraulic valves) that still have many years of service all demand their own unique recovery, remanufacturing, or recycling process. This complexity places significant demands on the producer as well as return and reuse supply chains in the quest for sustainability. But pursuing this quest is the ethical thing to do. Saving the earth is a challenging task.

Supply Chain Economics

The supply chain receives such attention because it is an integral part of a firm's strategy and the most costly activity in most firms. For both goods and services, supply chain costs as a percentage of sales are often substantial (see Table 11.3). Because such a huge portion of revenue is devoted to the supply chain, an effective strategy is vital. The supply chain provides a major opportunity to reduce costs and increase contribution margins.

Table 11.4 and Example 1 illustrate the amount of leverage available to the operations manager through the supply chain.

These numbers indicate the strong role that supply chains play in profitability.

STUDENT | TIP

A huge part of a firm's revenue is typically spent on purchases, so this is a good place to look for savings.

Table 11.3

Supply Chain Costs as a Percentage of Sales

Industry	% Purchased
Automobile	67
Beverages	52
Chemical	62
Food	60
Lumber	61
Metals	65
Paper	55
Petroleum	79
Transportation	62

Hau Lee Furniture Inc. spends 50% of its sales dollar in the supply chain and has a net profit of 4%. Hau wants to know how many dollars of sales are equivalent to supply chain savings of $1.

APPROACH ▶ Table 11.4 (given Hau's assumptions) can be used to make the analysis.

SOLUTION ▶ Table 11.4 indicates that every $1 Hau can save in the supply chain results in the same profit that would be generated by $3.70 in sales.

Percentage Net Profit of Firm	Percentage of Sales Spent in the Supply Chain						
	30%	40%	50%	60%	70%	80%	90%
2	$2.78	$3.23	$3.85	$4.76	$6.25	$9.09	$16.67
4	$2.70	$3.13	$3.70	$4.55	$5.88	$8.33	$14.29
6	$2.63	$3.03	$3.57	$4.35	$5.56	$7.69	$12.50
8	$2.56	$2.94	$3.45	$4.17	$5.26	$7.14	$11.11
10	$2.50	$2.86	$3.33	$4.00	$5.00	$6.67	$10.00

ªThe required increase in sales assumes that 50% of the costs other than purchases are variable and that half the remaining costs (less profit) are fixed. Therefore, at sales of $100 (50% purchases and 2% margin), $50 are purchases, $24 are other variable costs, $24 are fixed costs, and $2 are profit. Increasing sales by $3.85 yields the following:

Purchases at 50%	$ 51.93 (50% of $103.85)
Other Variable Costs	24.92 (24% of $103.85)
Fixed Cost	24.00 (fixed)
Profit	3.00 (from $2 to $3 profit)
	$103.85

Through $3.85 of additional sales, we have increased profit by $1, from $2 to $3. The same increase in margin could have been obtained by reducing supply chain costs by $1.

INSIGHT ▶ Effective management of the supply chain can generate substantial benefits.

LEARNING EXERCISE ▶ If Hau increases his profit to 6%, how much of an increase in sales is necessary to equal $1 savings? [Answer: $3.57.]

RELATED PROBLEMS ▶ 11.6, 11.7

MAKE-OR-BUY DECISIONS

A wholesaler or retailer buys everything that it sells; a manufacturing operation hardly ever does. Manufacturers, restaurants, and assemblers of products buy components and subassemblies that go into final products. As we saw in Chapter 5, choosing products and services that can be advantageously obtained *externally* as opposed to produced *internally* is known as the **make-or-buy decision**. Supply chain personnel evaluate alternative suppliers and provide current, accurate, and complete data relevant to the buy alternative. Increasingly, firms focus not on an analytical make-or-buy decision but on identifying their core competencies.

Make-or-buy decision
A choice between producing a component or service in-house or purchasing it from an outside source.

OUTSOURCING

Outsourcing transfers some of what are traditional internal activities and resources of a firm to outside vendors, making it slightly different from the traditional make-or-buy decision. Outsourcing is part of the continuing trend towards utilizing the efficiency that comes with specialization. The vendor performing the outsourced service is an expert in that particular specialty. This leaves the outsourcing firm to focus on its critical success factors, that is, its core competencies that yield a competitive advantage. Outsourcing is the focus of Supplement 11.

Outsourcing
Transferring a firm's activities that have traditionally been internal to external suppliers.

Supply Chain Strategies

For goods and services to be obtained from outside sources, the firm must decide on a supply chain strategy. One such strategy is the approach of *negotiating with many suppliers* and playing one supplier against another. A second strategy is to develop *long-term "partnering"* relationships with a few suppliers to satisfy the end customer. A third strategy is *vertical integration*, in which a firm decides to use vertical backward integration by actually buying the supplier. A fourth approach is some type of collaboration that allows two or more firms to combine

STUDENT TIP
Supply chain strategies come in many varieties; choosing the correct one is the trick.

LO2 Identify six sourcing strategies

resources—typically in what is called a *joint venture*—to produce a component. A fifth variation is a combination of few suppliers and vertical integration, known as a *keiretsu*. In a *keiretsu*, *suppliers become part of a company coalition*. Finally, a sixth strategy is to develop *virtual companies that use suppliers on an as-needed basis*. We will now discuss each of these strategies.

MANY SUPPLIERS

With the many-suppliers strategy, a supplier responds to the demands and specifications of a "request for quotation," with the order usually going to the low bidder. This is a common strategy when products are commodities. This strategy plays one supplier against another and places the burden of meeting the buyer's demands on the supplier. Suppliers aggressively compete with one another. Although many approaches to negotiations can be used with this strategy, long-term "partnering" relationships are not the goal. This approach holds the supplier responsible for maintaining the necessary technology, expertise, and forecasting abilities, as well as cost, quality, and delivery competencies.

FEW SUPPLIERS

A strategy of few suppliers implies that rather than looking for short-term attributes, such as low cost, a buyer is better off forming a long-term relationship with a few dedicated suppliers. Long-term suppliers are more likely to understand the broad objectives of the procuring firm and the end customer. Using few suppliers can create value by allowing suppliers to have economies of scale and a learning curve that yields both lower transaction costs and lower production costs.

Few suppliers, each with a large commitment to the buyer, may also be more willing to participate in JIT systems as well as provide design innovations and technological expertise. Many firms have moved aggressively to incorporate suppliers into their supply systems. Ford, for one, now seeks to choose suppliers even before parts are designed. Motorola also evaluates suppliers on rigorous criteria, but in many instances has eliminated traditional supplier bidding, placing added emphasis on quality and reliability. On occasion, these relationships yield contracts that extend through the product's life cycle. The expectation is that both the purchaser and supplier collaborate, becoming more efficient and reducing prices over time. The natural outcome of such relationships is fewer suppliers, but those that remain have long-term relationships.

Service companies like Marks & Spencer, a British retailer, have also demonstrated that cooperation with suppliers can yield cost savings for customers and suppliers alike. This strategy has resulted in suppliers that develop new products, winning customers for Marks & Spencer and the supplier. The move towards tight integration of the suppliers and purchasers is occurring in both manufacturing and services.

Like all strategies, a downside exists. With few suppliers, the cost of changing partners is huge, so both buyer and supplier run the risk of becoming captives of the other. Poor supplier performance is only one risk the purchaser faces. The purchaser must also be concerned about trade secrets and suppliers that make other alliances or venture out on their own. This happened when the Schwinn Bicycle Co., needing additional capacity, taught Taiwan's Giant Manufacturing Company to make and sell bicycles. Giant Manufacturing is now the largest bicycle manufacturer in the world, and Schwinn was acquired out of bankruptcy by Pacific Cycle LLC.

VIDEO 11.2
Supply Chain Management at
Regal Marine

VERTICAL INTEGRATION

Vertical integration

Developing the ability to produce goods or services previously purchased or actually buying a supplier or a distributor.

Purchasing can be extended to take the form of vertical integration. By **vertical integration**, we mean developing the ability to produce goods or services previously purchased or to actually buy a supplier or a distributor. As shown in Figure 11.2, vertical integration can take the form of *forward* or *backward integration*.

Backward integration suggests a firm purchase its suppliers, as in the case of Ford Motor Company deciding to manufacture its own car radios. Forward integration, on the other hand, suggests that a manufacturer of components make the finished product. An example is Texas Instruments, a manufacturer of integrated circuits that also makes calculators and flat-screens containing integrated circuits for TVs.

Vertical integration can offer a strategic opportunity for the operations manager. For firms with the capital, managerial talent, and required demand, vertical integration may provide substantial opportunities for cost reduction, quality adherence, and timely delivery. Other advantages, such as inventory reduction and scheduling, can accrue to the company that effectively manages vertical integration or close, mutually beneficial relationships with suppliers.

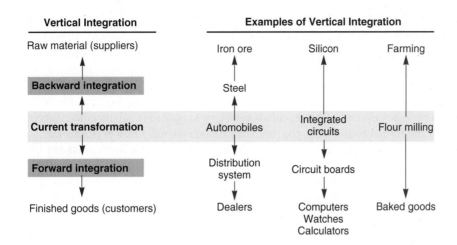

FIGURE 11.2
Vertical Integration Can Be
Forward or Backward

Because purchased items represent such a large part of the costs of sales, it is obvious why so many organizations find interest in vertical integration. Vertical integration appears to work best when the organization has large market share and the management talent to operate an acquired vendor successfully.

The relentless march of specialization continues, meaning that a model of "doing everything" or "vertical integration" is increasingly difficult. Backward integration may be particularly dangerous for firms in industries undergoing technological change if management cannot keep abreast of those changes or invest the financial resources necessary for the next wave of technology. The alternative, particularly in high-tech industries, is to establish close-relationship suppliers. This allows partners to focus on their specific contribution. Research and development costs are too high and technology changes are too rapid for one company to sustain leadership in every component. Most organizations are better served concentrating on their specialty and leveraging the partners' contributions. Exceptions do exist. Where capital, management talent, and technology are available and the components are also highly integrated, vertical integration may make sense. On the other hand, it made no sense for Jaguar to make commodity components for its autos as it did until recently.

JOINT VENTURES

Because vertical integration is so dangerous, firms may opt for some form of formal collaboration. As we noted in Chapter 5, firms may engage in collaboration to enhance their new product prowess or technological skills. But firms also engage in collaboration to secure supply or reduce costs. One version of a joint venture is the current Daimler–BMW effort to develop and produce standard automobile components. Given the global consolidation of the auto industry, these two rivals in the luxury segment of the automobile market are at a disadvantage in volume. Their relatively low volume means fewer units over which to spread fixed costs, hence the interest in consolidating to cut development and production costs. As in all other such collaborations, the trick is to cooperate without diluting the brand or conceding a competitive advantage.

KEIRETSU NETWORKS

Many large Japanese manufacturers have found another strategy; it is part collaboration, part purchasing from few suppliers, and part vertical integration. These manufacturers are often financial supporters of suppliers through ownership or loans. The supplier becomes part of a company coalition known as a **keiretsu**. Members of the keiretsu are assured long-term relationships and are therefore expected to collaborate as partners, providing technical expertise and stable quality production to the manufacturer. Members of the keiretsu can also have suppliers further down the chain, making second- and even third-tier suppliers part of the coalition.

Keiretsu

A Japanese term that describes suppliers who become part of a company coalition.

VIRTUAL COMPANIES

The limitations to vertical integration are severe. Our technological society continually demands more specialization, which complicates vertical integration. Moreover, a firm that has a department or division of its own for everything may be too bureaucratic to be world class. So rather than letting vertical integration lock an organization into businesses that it may not understand or be able to manage, another approach is to find good flexible suppliers. **Virtual companies** rely on a variety of supplier relationships to provide services on demand. Virtual companies have fluid, moving organizational boundaries that allow them to create a unique enterprise to meet changing market demands. Suppliers may provide a variety of services that include doing the payroll, hiring personnel, designing products, providing consulting services, manufacturing components, conducting tests, or distributing products. The relationships may be short- or long-term and may include true partners, collaborators, or simply able suppliers and subcontractors. Whatever the formal relationship, the result can be exceptionally lean performance. The advantages of virtual companies include specialized management expertise, low capital investment, flexibility, and speed. The result is efficiency.

The apparel business provides a *traditional* example of virtual organizations. The designers of clothes seldom manufacture their designs; rather, they license the manufacture. The manufacturer may then rent space, lease sewing machines, and contract for labour. The result is an organization that has low overhead, remains flexible, and can respond rapidly to the market.

A *contemporary* example is exemplified by Vizio, Inc., a North American producer of LCD TVs that has only 85 employees but huge sales. Vizio uses modules to assemble its own brand of TVs. Because the key components of TVs are now readily available and sold almost as commodities, innovative firms such as Vizio can specify the components, hire a contract manufacturer, and market the TVs with very little start-up cost. In a virtual company, the supply chain is the company. Managing it is dynamic and demanding.

Managing the Supply Chain

As managers move towards integration of the supply chain, substantial efficiencies are possible. The cycle of materials—as they flow from suppliers, to production, to warehousing, to distribution, to the customer—takes place among separate and often very independent organizations. Therefore, there are significant management issues that may result in serious inefficiencies. Success begins with mutual agreement on goals, followed by mutual trust, and continues with compatible organizational cultures.

MUTUAL AGREEMENT ON GOALS

An integrated supply chain requires more than just agreement on the contractual terms of a buy/sell relationship. Partners in the chain must appreciate that the only entity that puts money into a supply chain is the end customer. Therefore, establishing a mutual understanding of the mission, strategy, and goals of participating organizations is essential. The integrated supply chain is about adding economic value and maximizing the total content of the product.

TRUST

Trust is critical to an effective and efficient supply chain. Members of the chain must enter into a relationship that shares information. Visibility throughout the supply chain—what Darden Restaurants calls a *transparent supply chain*—is a requirement. Supplier relationships are more likely to be successful if risk and cost savings are shared—and activities such as end customer research, sales analysis, forecasting, and production planning are joint activities. Such relationships are built on mutual trust.

COMPATIBLE ORGANIZATIONAL CULTURES

A positive relationship between the purchasing and supplying organizations that comes with compatible organizational cultures can be a real advantage when making a supply chain hum. A champion within one of the two firms promotes both formal and informal contacts, and those contacts contribute to the alignment of the organizational cultures, further strengthening the relationship.

The operations manager is dealing with a supply chain that is made up of independent specialists, each trying to satisfy its own customers at a profit. This leads to actions that may not optimize the entire chain. On the other hand, the supply chain is replete with opportunities to reduce waste and enhance value. We now look at some of the significant issues and opportunities.

ISSUES IN AN INTEGRATED SUPPLY CHAIN

LO3 Explain issues and opportunities in the supply chain

Three issues complicate development of an efficient, integrated supply chain: local optimization, incentives, and large lots.

LOCAL OPTIMIZATION Members of the chain are inclined to focus on maximizing local profit or minimizing immediate cost based on their limited knowledge. Slight upturns in demand are overcompensated for because no one wants to be caught short. Similarly, slight downturns are overcompensated for because no one wants to be caught holding excess inventory. So fluctuations are magnified. For instance, a pasta distributor does not want to run out of pasta for its retail customers; the natural response to an extra-large order from the retailer is to compensate with an even larger order to the manufacturer on the assumption that retail sales are picking up. Neither the distributor nor the manufacturer knows that the retailer had a major one-time promotion that moved a lot of pasta. This is exactly the issue that complicated the implementation of efficient distribution at the Italian pasta maker Barilla.

INCENTIVES (SALES INCENTIVES, QUANTITY DISCOUNTS, QUOTAS, AND PROMOTIONS) Incentives push merchandise into the chain for sales that have not occurred. This generates fluctuations that are ultimately expensive to all members of the chain.

LARGE LOTS There is often a bias towards large lots because large lots tend to reduce unit costs. A logistics manager wants to ship large lots, preferably in full trucks, and a production manager wants long production runs. Both actions drive down unit shipping and production costs but fail to reflect actual sales and increased holding costs.

These three common occurrences—local optimization, incentives, and large lots—contribute to distortions of information about what is really occurring in the supply chain. A well-running supply system needs to be based on accurate information about how many products are truly being pulled through the chain. The inaccurate information is unintentional, but it results in distortions and fluctuations in the supply chain and causes what is known as the bullwhip effect.

The **bullwhip effect** occurs as orders are relayed from retailers, to distributors, to wholesalers, to manufacturers, with fluctuations increasing at each step in the sequence. The "bullwhip" fluctuations in the supply chain increase the costs associated with inventory, transportation, shipping, and receiving, while decreasing customer service and profitability. Procter & Gamble found that although the use of Pampers diapers was steady and the retail store orders had little fluctuation, as orders moved through the supply chain, fluctuations increased. By the time orders were initiated for raw material, the variability was substantial. Similar behaviour has been observed and documented at many companies, including Cisco Canada, Campbell Soup, Hewlett-Packard, and Applied Materials.

Bullwhip effect
The increasing fluctuation in orders that often occurs as orders move through the supply chain.

The bullwhip effect can occur when orders decrease as well as when they increase. A number of opportunities exist for reducing the bullwhip effect and improving opportunities in the supply chain. These are discussed in the following section.

OPPORTUNITIES IN AN INTEGRATED SUPPLY CHAIN

Opportunities for effective management in the supply chain include the following 11 items.

ACCURATE "PULL" DATA Accurate **pull data** are generated by sharing (1) point-of-sales (POS) information so that each member of the chain can schedule effectively and (2) computer-assisted ordering (CAO). This implies using POS systems that collect sales data and then adjusting that data for market factors, inventory on hand, and outstanding orders. Then a net order is sent directly to the supplier who is responsible for maintaining the finished goods inventory.

Pull data
Accurate sales data that initiate transactions to "pull" product through the supply chain.

LOT-SIZE REDUCTION Lot sizes are reduced through aggressive management. This may include (1) developing economical shipments of less than truckload lots; (2) providing discounts based on total annual volume rather than size of individual shipments; and (3) reducing the cost of ordering through techniques such as standing orders and various forms of electronic purchasing.

SINGLE-STAGE CONTROL OF REPLENISHMENT **Single-stage control of replenishment** means designating a member in the chain as responsible for monitoring and managing inventory in the supply chain based on the "pull" from the end user. This approach removes distorted information and multiple forecasts that create the bullwhip effect. Control may be in the hands of:

Single-stage control of replenishment
Fixing responsibility for monitoring and managing inventory for the retailer.

In this section, we discuss traditional techniques of electronic ordering and funds transfer and then move on to online catalogues, auctions, RFQs, and real-time inventory tracking.

ELECTRONIC ORDERING AND FUNDS TRANSFER

Electronic data interchange (EDI)

A standardized data-transmittal format for computerized communications between organizations.

Advanced shipping notice (ASN)

A shipping notice delivered directly from vendor to purchaser.

Electronic ordering and bank transfers are traditional approaches to speeding transactions and reducing paperwork. Transactions between firms often use **electronic data interchange (EDI)**, which is a standardized data-transmittal format for computerized communications between organizations. EDI provides data transfer for virtually any business application, including purchasing. Under EDI, data for a purchase order—such as order date, due date, quantity, part number, purchase order number, address, and so forth—are fitted into the standard EDI format. EDI also provides for the use of **advanced shipping notice (ASN)**, which notifies the purchaser that the vendor is ready to ship. Although some firms are still moving to EDI and ASN, the internet's ease of use and lower cost is proving more popular.

ONLINE CATALOGUES

Purchase of standard items is often accomplished via online catalogues. Such catalogues provide current information about products in electronic form. Online catalogues support cost comparisons and incorporate voice and video clips, making the process efficient for both buyers and sellers. Online catalogues are available in three versions:

1. Typical of *catalogues provided by vendors* are those of IKEA Canada and Grand & Toy. Well known for its clear and comprehensive catalogue, IKEA is a retailer of furniture and housewares, while Grand & Toy provides the same service for office supplies.
2. *Catalogues provided by intermediaries* are internet sites where business buyers and sellers can meet. These intermediaries typically create industry-specific catalogues with content from many suppliers.
3. One of the first online *exchanges provided by buyers* was Avendra (**www.avendra.com**). Avendra was created by Marriott and Hyatt (and subsequently joined by other large hotel firms) to economically purchase the huge range of goods needed by the 2800 hotels now in the exchange.

Such exchanges—and there are many—move companies from a multitude of individual phone calls, faxes, and emails to a centralized online system, and drive billions of dollars of waste out of the supply chain.

AUCTIONS

Online auction sites can be maintained by sellers, buyers, or intermediaries. Operations managers find online auctions a fertile area for disposing of excess raw material and discontinued or excess inventory. Online auctions lower entry barriers, encouraging sellers to join and simultaneously increase the potential number of buyers.

The key for auction firms is to find and build a huge base of potential bidders, improve client buying procedures, and qualify new suppliers.

RFQs

When purchasing requirements are nonstandard, time spent preparing requests for quotes (RFQs) and the related bid package can be substantial. Consequently, eprocurement has now moved these often expensive parts of the purchasing process online, allowing purchasing agents to inexpensively attach electronic copies of the necessary drawings to RFQs.

REAL-TIME INVENTORY TRACKING

FedEx's pioneering efforts at tracking packages from pickup to delivery have shown the way for operations managers to do the same for their shipments and inventory. Because tracking cars and trucks has been a chronic and embarrassingly inexact science, Ford has hired UPS to track millions of vehicles as they move from factory to dealers. Using barcodes and the internet, Ford dealers are now able to log onto a website and find out exactly where the ordered vehicles are in the distribution system. As operations managers move to an era of mass customization, with customers ordering exactly the cars they want, customers will expect to know where their cars are and exactly when they can be picked up. Eprocurement, supported by barcodes and RFID, can provide economical inventory tracking on the shop floor, in warehouses, and in logistics.

Vendor Selection

For those goods and services a firm buys, vendors (also known as suppliers) must be selected. Vendor selection considers numerous factors, such as strategic fit, vendor competence, delivery, and quality performance. Because a firm may have some competence in all areas and may have exceptional competence in only a few, selection can be challenging. Procurement policies also need to be established. Those might address issues such as percent of business done with any one supplier or with minority businesses. We now examine vendor selection as a three-stage process: (1) vendor evaluation, (2) vendor development, and (3) negotiations.

LO4 Describe the steps in supplier selection

VENDOR EVALUATION

The first stage of vendor selection, *vendor evaluation*, involves finding potential vendors and determining the likelihood of their becoming good suppliers. This phase requires the development of evaluation criteria such as criteria shown in Example 2. However, both the criteria and the weights selected vary depending on the supply chain strategy being implemented. (Refer to Table 11.1.)

Madhu Ranadive, president of Davisville Toys in Stratford, Ontario, is interested in evaluating suppliers who will work with her to make nontoxic, environmentally friendly paints and dyes for her line of children's toys. This is a critical strategic element of her supply chain, and she desires a firm that will contribute to her product.

EXAMPLE 2

Weighted Approach to Vendor Evaluation

APPROACH ▶ Madhu begins her analysis of one potential supplier, Faber Paint and Dye, by using the weighted approach to vendor evaluation.

SOLUTION ▶ Madhu first reviews the supplier-differentiation attributes in Table 11.1 and develops the following list of selection criteria. She then assigns the weights shown to help her perform an objective review of potential vendors. Her staff assigns the scores shown and computes the total weighted score.

Criteria	Weights	Scores (1–5) (5 highest)	Weight × Score
Engineering/research/innovation skills	0.20	5	1.0
Production process capability (flexibility/technical assistance)	0.15	4	0.6
Distribution/delivery capability	0.05	4	0.2
Quality systems and performance	0.10	2	0.2
Facilities/location	0.05	2	0.1
Financial and managerial strength (stability and cost structure)	0.15	4	0.6
Information systems capability (eprocurement, ERP)	0.10	2	0.2
Integrity (environmental compliance/ethics)	0.20	5	1.0
	1.00		3.9 Total

Faber Paint and Dye receives an overall score of 3.9.

INSIGHT ▶ Madhu now has a basis for comparison with other potential vendors, selecting the one with the highest overall rating.

LEARNING EXERCISE ▶ If Madhu believes that the weight for "engineering/research/innovation skills" should be increased to 0.25 and the weight for "financial and managerial strength" reduced to 0.10, what is the new score? [Answer: Faber Paint and Dye now goes to 3.95.]

RELATED PROBLEMS ▶ 11.2, 11.3, 11.4

The selection of competent suppliers is critical. If good suppliers are not selected, then all other supply chain efforts are wasted. As firms move towards using fewer longer-term suppliers, the issues of financial strength, quality, management, research, technical ability, and potential for a close long-term relationship play an increasingly important role. These attributes should be noted in the evaluation process.

SUPPLIER CERTIFICATION International quality certifications such as ISO 9000 and ISO 14000 are designed to provide an external verification that a firm follows sound quality management and environmental management standards. Buying firms can use such certifications to pre-qualify potential suppliers. Despite the existence of the ISO standards, firms often create their own supplier certification programs. Buyers audit potential suppliers and award a certified status to those that meet the specified qualification. A certification process often involves three steps: (1) qualification, (2) education, and (3) the certification performance process. Once certified, the supplier may be awarded special treatment and priority, allowing the buying firm to reduce or eliminate incoming inspection of materials. Such an arrangement may facilitate JIT production for the buying firm. Most large companies use some sort of supplier certification program.

VENDOR DEVELOPMENT

The second stage of vendor selection is *vendor development*. Assuming that a firm wants to proceed with a particular vendor, how does it integrate this supplier into its system? The buyer makes sure the vendor has an appreciation of quality requirements, product specifications, schedules and delivery, the purchaser's payment system, and procurement policies. *Vendor development* may include everything from training, to engineering and production help, to procedures for information transfer.

NEGOTIATIONS

Negotiation strategies
Approaches taken by supply chain personnel to develop contractual relationships with suppliers.

Regardless of the supply chain strategy adopted, negotiations regarding the critical elements of the contractual relationship must take place. These negotiations often focus on quality, delivery, payment, and cost. We will look at three classic types of **negotiation strategies**: the cost-based price model, the market-based price model, and competitive bidding.

COST-BASED PRICE MODEL The cost-based price model requires that the supplier open its books to the purchaser. The contract price is then based on time and materials or on a fixed cost with an escalation clause to accommodate changes in the vendor's labour and materials cost.

MARKET-BASED PRICE MODEL In the market-based price model, price is based on a published, auction, or index price. Many commodities (agriculture products, paper, metal, etc.) are priced this way. For instance, a market detail report is available for paperboard prices in Canada from Bharat Book Bureau at **www.bharatbook.com**. Nonferrous metal prices and prices of other metals can be found at **www.statcan.gc.ca**.

COMPETITIVE BIDDING When suppliers are not willing to discuss costs or where near-perfect markets do not exist, competitive bidding is often appropriate. Infrequent work (such as construction, tooling, and dies) is usually purchased based on a bid. Bidding may take place via mail, fax, or an internet auction. Competitive bidding is the typical policy in many firms for the majority of their purchases. Bidding policies usually require that the purchasing agent have several potential suppliers of the product (or its equivalent) and quotations from each. The major disadvantage of this method, as mentioned earlier, is that the development of long-term relations between buyer and seller is hindered. Competitive bidding may effectively determine initial cost. However, it may also make difficult the communication and performance that are vital for engineering changes, quality, and delivery.

Yet a fourth approach is *to combine two or more* of the preceding negotiation techniques. The supplier and purchaser may agree on review of certain cost data, accept some form of market data for raw material costs, or agree that the supplier will "remain competitive". In any case, a good supplier relationship is one in which both partners have established a degree of mutual trust and a belief in each other's competence, honesty, and fair dealing.

CONTRACTING

Supply chain partners often develop contracts to spell out terms of the relationship. Contracts are designed to share risks, share benefits, and create incentive structures to encourage supply chain members to adopt policies that are optimal for the entire chain. The idea is to make the total pie (of supply chain profits) bigger and then divide the bigger pie among all participants. The goal is collaboration. Some common features of contracts include *quantity discounts* (lower prices for larger orders), *buybacks* (common in the magazine and book business where there is a buyback of unsold units), and *revenue sharing* (where both partners share the risk of uncertainty by sharing revenue).

CENTRALIZED PURCHASING

Companies with multiple facilities (e.g., multiple manufacturing plants or multiple retail outlets) must determine which items to purchase centrally and which to allow local sites to purchase for themselves. Unmonitored decentralized purchasing can create havoc. For example, different plants for Nestle USA's brands used to pay 29 different prices for its vanilla ingredient *to the same supplier*! Important cost, efficiency, and "single-voice" benefits often accrue from a centralized purchasing function. Typical benefits include:

- Leverage purchase volume for better pricing
- Develop specialized staff expertise
- Develop stronger supplier relationships
- Maintain professional control over the purchasing process
- Devote more resources to the supplier selection and negotiation process
- Reduce the duplication of tasks
- Promote standardization

However, local managers enjoy having their own purchasing control, and decentralized purchasing can offer certain inventory control, transportation cost, or lead-time benefits. Often firms use a hybrid approach—using centralized purchasing for some items and/or sites while allowing local purchasing for others.

E-PROCUREMENT

E-procurement speeds purchasing, reduces costs, and integrates the supply chain. It reduces the traditional barrage of paperwork and, at the same time, provides purchasing personnel with an extensive database of supplier, delivery, and quality data.

E-procurement
Purchasing facilitated through the internet.

ONLINE CATALOGUES AND EXCHANGES Purchase of standard items is often accomplished via online catalogues. Such catalogues support cost comparisons and incorporate voice and video clips, making the process efficient for both buyers and sellers.

Online exchanges are typically industry-specific internet sites that bring buyers and sellers together. Marriott and Hyatt created one of the first, Avendra (**www.avendra.com**), which facilitates economic purchasing of the huge range of goods needed by the 5000 hospitality industry customers now in the exchange. Online catalogues and exchanges can help move companies from a multitude of individual phone calls, faxes, and emails to a centralized system and drive billions of dollars of waste out of the supply chain.

ONLINE AUCTIONS In addition to catalogues some suppliers and buyers have established online auction sites. Operations managers find online auctions a fertile area for disposing of excess raw material and discontinued or excess inventory. Online auctions lower entry barriers, encourage sellers to join, and simultaneously increase the potential number of buyers. The key for intermediaries is to find and build a huge base of potential bidders, improve client buying procedures, and qualify new suppliers.

In a traditional auction, a seller offers a product or service and generates competition between bidders—bidding the price up. In contrast, buyers often utilize online *reverse auctions* (or *Dutch auctions*). In reverse auctions, a buyer initiates the process by submitting a description of the desired product or service. Potential suppliers then submit bids, which may include price and other delivery information. Thus, price competition occurs on the selling side of the transaction—bidding the price down. Note that, as with traditional supplier selection decisions, price is important but may not be the only factor in winning the bid.

LO5 Explain major issues in logistics management

Logistics management
An approach that seeks efficiency of operations through the integration of all material acquisition, movement, and storage activities.

Logistics Management

Procurement activities may be combined with various shipping, warehousing, and inventory activities to form a logistics system. The purpose of **logistics management** is to obtain efficiency of operations through the integration of all material acquisition, movement, and storage activities. When transportation and inventory costs are substantial on both the input and output sides of the production process, an emphasis on logistics may be appropriate. When logistics issues are significant or expensive, many firms opt for outsourcing the logistics function. Logistics specialists can often bring expertise not available in-house. For instance, logistics companies often have tracking technology that reduces transportation losses and supports delivery schedules that adhere to precise delivery windows. The potential for competitive advantage is found via both reduced costs and improved customer service.

Firms recognize that the distribution of goods to and from their facilities can represent as much as 25% of the cost of products. In addition, the total distribution cost in Canada is over 10% of the gross national product (GNP). Because of this high cost, firms constantly evaluate their means of distribution. Five major means of distribution are trucking, railroads, airfreight, waterways, and pipelines.

DISTRIBUTION SYSTEMS

TRUCKING The vast majority of manufactured goods moves by truck. The flexibility of shipping by truck is only one of its many advantages. Companies that have adopted JIT programs in recent years have put increased pressure on truckers to pick up and deliver on time, with no damage, with paperwork in order, and at low cost. Trucking firms are using computers to monitor weather, find the most effective route, reduce fuel cost, and analyze the most efficient way to unload. In spite of these advances, the motor carrier industry averages a capacity utilization of only 50%. That underutilized space costs the Canadian economy over $3 billion per year. To improve logistics efficiency, the industry is establishing websites such as Schneider National's connection (**www.schneider.com**), which lets shippers and truckers find each other to use some of this idle capacity. Shippers may pick from thousands of approved North American carriers that have registered with Schneider.

RAILROADS Canadian rail is the third-largest rail system in the world and it handles the fourth-largest volume of goods on the planet. Containerization has made intermodal shipping of truck trailers on railroad flat cars, often piggybacked as double-deckers, a popular means of distribution. Every year, Canadian rail moves over 70 million people and 70% of all surface goods. With the growth of JIT, however, rail transport has been the biggest loser because small-batch manufacture requires frequent, smaller shipments that are likely to move via truck or air.

AIRFREIGHT Airfreight represents less than 5% of tonnage shipped in Canada. However, the recent proliferation of airfreight carriers, such as Purolator, FedEx, UPS, and DHL, makes it a fast-growing mode of shipping. Clearly, for national and international movement of lightweight items—such as medical and emergency supplies, flowers, fruits, and electronic components—airfreight offers speed and reliability.

WATERWAYS Waterways are one of the nation's oldest means of freight transportation, dating back to construction of the Welland Canal in 1829. Included in Canadian waterways are the nation's rivers, canals, the Great Lakes, coastlines, and oceans connecting to other countries. The usual cargo on waterways is bulky, low-value cargo such as iron ore, grains, cement, coal, chemicals, limestone, and petroleum products. Internationally, millions of containers are shipped at very low cost via huge oceangoing ships each year. Water transportation is important when shipping cost is more important than speed.

PIPELINES Pipelines are an important form of transporting crude oil, natural gas, and other petroleum and chemical products. In 2010, the petroleum industry paid $10.3 billion to the province of Alberta, which accounted for 26% of that province's annual revenue. Much of the petroleum that was pumped through pipelines ran through Alberta.

MULTIMODAL Multimodal shipping combines shipping methods and is a common means of getting a product to its final destination, particularly for international shipments. The use of

As this photo of the port of Vancouver suggests, with millions of containers entering Canada annually, tracking location, content, and condition of trucks and containers is a challenge. But new technology may improve both security and JIT shipments.

standardized containers facilitates easy transport from truck to rail to ship and back again, without having to unload products from the containers until the very end.

While freight rates are often based on very complicated pricing systems, in general, clients pay for speed. Faster methods such as airfreight tend to be much more expensive, while slower methods, such as waterways, provide a much cheaper shipping rate per unit. The size of shipments follows a similar pattern. The faster methods tend to involve smaller shipment sizes, while the slower methods involve very large shipment sizes.

WAREHOUSING

Warehouses come in all shapes and sizes, from tiny rooms in the back of a store to enormous facilities that could fit multiple football fields. Warehouses may be extremely expensive to operate, but the alternatives (e.g., either no storage at all or storage at local operating facilities, along with the related logistics issues) may be much more costly. The fundamental purpose of a warehouse

Seven farms within a two-hour drive of Kenya's Nairobi Airport supply 300 tonnes of fresh beans, bok choy, okra, and other produce that is packaged at the airport and shipped overnight to Europe. The time between harvest and arrival in Europe is two days. When a good supply chain and good logistics work together, the results can be startling—and fresh food.

OM in Action   DHL's Role in the Supply Chain

It's the dead of night at DHL International's air express hub in Brussels, yet the massive building is alive with busy forklifts and sorting workers. The boxes going on and off the DHL plane range from Dell computers and Cisco routers to Caterpillar mufflers and Komatsu hydraulic pumps. Sun Microsystems computers from California are earmarked for Finland; DVDs from Teac's plant in Malaysia are destined for Bulgaria.

The door-to-door movement of time-sensitive packages is key to the global supply chain. JIT, short product life cycles, mass customization, and reduced inventories depend on logistics firms such as DHL, FedEx, and UPS. These powerhouses are in continuous motion.

With a decentralized network covering 225 countries and territories (more than are in the United Nations), DHL is a true multinational. The Brussels headquarters has only 450 of the company's 124 000 employees but includes 26 nationalities.

DHL has assembled an extensive global network of express logistics centres for strategic goods. In its Brussels logistics centre, for instance, DHL upgrades, repairs, and configures Fujitsu computers, InFocus projectors, and Johnson & Johnson medical equipment. It stores and provides parts for EMC and Hewlett-Packard and replaces Nokia and Philips phones. "If something breaks down on a Thursday at 4 o'clock, the relevant warehouse knows at 4:05, and the part is on a DHL plane at 7 or 8 that evening," says Robert Kuijpers, DHL International's CEO.

Sources: Journal of Commerce (August 15, 2005): 1; *Hoover's Company Records* (May 1, 2009): 40126; and *Forbes* (October 18, 1999): 120–124.

---

is to store goods. However, some warehouses also provide other crucial functions. For example, a warehouse can serve as a consolidation point, gathering shipments from multiple sources to send outbound in one cheaper, fully loaded truck. Alternatively, a warehouse can provide a break-bulk function by accepting a cheaper full truckload inbound shipment and then dividing it for distribution to individual sites. Further, similar to a major airport hub, a warehouse can serve simply as a cross-docking facility—accepting shipments from a variety of sources and recombining them for distribution to a variety of destinations, often without actually storing any goods during the transition. Finally, a warehouse can serve as a point of postponement in the process, providing final customer-specific value-added processing to the product before final shipment.

THIRD-PARTY LOGISTICS

Supply chain managers may find that outsourcing logistics is advantageous in driving down inventory investment and costs while improving delivery reliability and speed. Specialized logistics firms support this goal by coordinating the supplier's inventory system with the service capabilities of the delivery firm. FedEx, for example, has a successful history of using the internet for online tracking. At **www.FedEx.com**, a customer can compute shipping costs, print labels, adjust invoices, and track package status all on the same website. FedEx, UPS, and DHL play a core role in other firms' logistics processes. In some cases, they even run the server for retailer websites. In other cases, such as for Dell Computer, FedEx operates warehouses that pick, pack, test, and assemble products, then it handles delivery and customs clearance when necessary. The *OM in Action* box "DHL's Role in the Supply Chain" provides another example of how outsourcing logistics can reduce costs while shrinking inventory and delivery times.

COST OF SHIPPING ALTERNATIVES

The longer a product is in transit, the longer the firm has its money invested. But faster shipping is usually more expensive than slow shipping. A simple way to obtain some insight into this trade-off is to evaluate holding cost against shipping options. We do this in Example 3.

EXAMPLE 3

Determining Daily Cost of Holding

A shipment of new connectors for semiconductors needs to go from Vancouver to Singapore for assembly. The value of the connectors is $1750 and holding cost is 40% per year. One airfreight carrier can ship the connectors one day faster than its competitor, at an extra cost of $20.00. Which carrier should be selected?

APPROACH ▶ First we determine the daily holding cost and then compare the daily holding cost with the cost of faster shipment.

SOLUTION ▶

$$\text{Daily cost of holding the product} = (\text{Annual holding cost} \times \text{Product value})/365$$

$$= (0.40 \times \$1750)/365$$

$$= \$1.92$$

Since the cost of saving one day is $20.00, which is much more than the daily holding cost of $1.92, we decide on the less costly of the carriers and take the extra day to make the shipment. This saves $18.08 (= $20.00 − $1.92).

INSIGHT ▶ The solution becomes radically different if the one-day delay in getting the connectors to Singapore delays delivery (making a customer angry) or delays payment of a $150 000 final product. (Even one day's interest on $150 000 or an angry customer makes a savings of $18.08 insignificant.)

LEARNING EXERCISE ▶ If the holding cost is 100% per year, what is the decision? [Answer: Even with a holding cost of $4.79 per day, the less costly carrier is selected.]

RELATED PROBLEMS ▶ 11.8, 11.9, 11.10

Example 3 looks only at holding cost versus shipping cost. For the operations or logistics manager there are many other considerations, including coordinating shipments to maintain a schedule, getting a new product to market, and keeping a customer happy. Estimates of these other costs can be added to the estimate of daily holding cost. Determining the impact and cost of these many other considerations makes the evaluation of shipping alternatives interesting.

SECURITY AND JIT

There is probably no society more open than that of Canada and the United States. This includes the borders and ports—but they are swamped. Over 7 million containers enter these ports each year, along with thousands of planes, cars, and trucks each day. Even under the best of conditions, some 5% of the container movements are misrouted, stolen, damaged, or excessively delayed.

Since the September 11, 2001, terrorist attacks, supply chains have become more complex. Technological innovations in the supply chain are improving security and JIT, making logistics more reliable. Technology is now capable of knowing truck and container location, content, and condition.

Speed and accuracy in the supply chain are supported by barcode tracking of shipments. At each step of a journey, from initial pickup to final destination, barcodes are read and stored. Within seconds, this tracking information is available online to customers worldwide.

New devices can detect whether someone has broken into a sealed container and can communicate that information to the shipper or receiver via satellite or radio. Motion detectors can also be installed inside containers. Other sensors can record interior data including temperature, shock, radioactivity, and whether a container is moving. Tracking lost containers, identifying delays, or just reminding individuals in the supply chain that a shipment is on its way will help expedite shipments. Improvements in security may aid JIT, and improvements in JIT may aid security—both of which can improve supply chain logistics.

STUDENT TIP

If you can't measure it, you can't control it.

LO6 Compute the percentage of assets committed to inventory and inventory turnover

Measuring Supply Chain Performance

Like all other managers, supply chain managers require standards (or *metrics*, as they are often called) to evaluate performance. Evaluation of the supply chain is particularly critical for these managers because they spend most of the organization's money. In addition, they make scheduling and quantity decisions that determine the assets committed to inventory. Only with effective metrics can managers determine: (1) how well the *supply chain is performing* and (2) *the assets committed to inventory*. We will now discuss these two metrics.

SUPPLY CHAIN PERFORMANCE

The benchmark metrics shown in Table 11.5 focus on procurement and vendor performance issues. World-class benchmarks are the result of well-managed supply chains that drive down costs, lead times, late deliveries, and shortages while improving quality.

ASSETS COMMITTED TO INVENTORY

Three specific measures can be helpful here. The first is the amount of money invested in inventory, usually expressed as a percentage of assets, as shown in Equation (11-1) and Example 4:

$$\text{Percentage invested in inventory} = (\text{Total inventory investment/Total assets}) \times 100 \quad \textbf{(11-1)}$$

EXAMPLE 4

Tracking Home Depot's Inventory Investment

Home Depot's management wishes to track its investment in inventory as one of its performance measures. Home Depot had $11.4 billion invested in inventory and total assets of $44.4 billion in 2006.

APPROACH ▶ Determine the investment in inventory and total assets and then use Equation (11-1).

SOLUTION ▶ Percent invested in inventory = (11.4/44.4) × 100 = 25.7%

INSIGHT ▶ Over one-fourth of Home Depot's assets are committed to inventory.

LEARNING EXERCISE ▶ If Home Depot can drive its investment down to 20% of assets, how much money will it free up for other uses? [Answer: 11.4 − (44.4 × 0.2) = $2.52 billion.]

RELATED PROBLEMS ▶ 11.11b, 11.12b

Specific comparisons with competitors may assist evaluation. Total assets committed to inventory in manufacturing approach 15%, in wholesale 34%, and retail 27%—with wide variations, depending on the specific business model, the business cycle, and management (see Table 11.6).

Table 11.5
Metrics for Supply Chain Performance

	Typical Firms	Benchmark Firms
Lead time (weeks)	15	8
Time spent placing an order	42 minutes	15 minutes
Percent of late deliveries	33%	2%
Percent of rejected material	1.5%	0.0001%
Number of shortages per year	400	4

Source: Adapted from a McKinsey & Company report.

Table 11.6

Inventory as Percentage of Total Assets (with examples of exceptional performance)

Manufacturer (Toyota 5%)	15%
Wholesale (Coca-Cola 2.9%)	34%
Restaurants (McDonald's 0.05%)	2.9%
Retail (Home Depot 25.7%)	27%

Table 11.7

Examples of Annual Inventory Turnover

Food, Beverage, Retail	
Molson Coors	8
Coca-Cola	14
Home Depot	5
McDonald's	112
Manufacturing	
Dell Computer	90
Magna International	11
Toyota (overall)	13
Nissan (assembly)	150

The second common measure of supply chain performance is *inventory turnover* (see Table 11.7). Its reciprocal, *weeks of supply*, is the third. **Inventory turnover** is computed on an annual basis, using Equation (11-2):

Inventory turnover
Cost of goods sold divided by average inventory.

$$\text{Inventory turnover} = \text{Cost of goods sold/Inventory investment} \qquad \textbf{(11-2)}$$

Cost of goods sold is the cost to produce the goods or services sold for a given period. Inventory investment is the average inventory value for the same period. This may be the average of several periods of inventory or beginning and ending inventory added together and divided by two. Often, average inventory investment is based on nothing more than the inventory investment at the end of the period—typically at year-end.[3]

In Example 5, we look at inventory turnover applied to PepsiCo.

PepsiCo, Inc., manufacturer and distributor of drinks, Frito-Lay, and Quaker Foods, provides the following in its 2005 annual report (shown here in $ billions). Determine PepsiCo's turnover.

Net revenue		$32.5
Cost of goods sold		$14.2
Inventory:		
Raw material inventory	$0.74	
Work-in-process inventory	$0.11	
Finished goods inventory	$0.84	
Total inventory investment		$1.69

EXAMPLE 5

Inventory Turnover at PepsiCo, Inc.

APPROACH ▶ Use the inventory turnover computation in Equation (11-2) to measure inventory performance. Cost of goods sold is $14.2 billion. Total inventory is the sum of raw material at $0.74 billion, work-in-process at $0.11 billion, and finished goods at $0.84 billion, for total inventory investment of $1.69 billion.

SOLUTION ▶ Inventory turnover = Cost of goods sold/Inventory investment

$$= 14.2/1.69$$

$$= 8.4$$

INSIGHT ▶ We now have a standard, popular measure by which to evaluate performance.

LEARNING EXERCISE ▶ If Coca-Cola's cost of goods sold is $10.8 billion and inventory investment is $0.76 billion, what is its inventory turnover? [Answer: 14.2.]

RELATED PROBLEMS ▶ 11.11a, 11.12c, 11.13

---

[3] Inventory quantities often fluctuate wildly, and various types of inventory exist (e.g., raw material, work-in-process, finished goods, and maintenance, repair, and operating supplies [MRO]). Therefore, care must be taken when using inventory values; they may reflect more than just supply chain performance.

Weeks of supply, as shown in Example 6, may have more meaning in the wholesale and retail portions of the service sector than in manufacturing. It is computed below as the reciprocal of inventory turnover:

$$\text{Weeks of supply} = \text{Inventory investment}/(\text{Annual cost of goods sold}/52 \text{ weeks}) \quad \textbf{(11-3)}$$

EXAMPLE 6

Determining Weeks of Supply at PepsiCo, Inc.

Using the PepsiCo data in Example 5, management wants to know the weeks of supply.

APPROACH ▶ We know that inventory investment is $1.69 billion and that weekly sales equal annual cost of goods sold ($14.2 billion) divided by 52 = $14.2/52 = $.273 billion.

SOLUTION ▶ Using Equation (11-3), we compute weeks of supply as:

$$\text{Weeks of supply} = (\text{Inventory investment}/\text{Average weekly cost of goods sold})$$

$$= 1.69/0.273 = 6.19 \text{ weeks}$$

INSIGHT ▶ We now have a standard measurement by which to evaluate a company's continuing performance or by which to compare companies.

LEARNING EXERCISE ▶ If Coca-Cola's average inventory investment is $0.76 billion and its average weekly cost of goods sold is $0.207 billion, what is the firm's weeks of supply? [Answer: 3.67 weeks.]

RELATED PROBLEMS ▶ 11.12a, 11.14

Supply chain management is critical in driving down inventory investment. The rapid movement of goods is key. Walmart, for example, has set the pace in the retailing sector with its world-renowned supply chain management. By doing so, it has established a competitive advantage. With its own truck fleet, distribution centres, and a state-of-the-art communication system, Walmart (with the help of its suppliers) replenishes store shelves an average of twice per week. Competitors resupply every other week. Economical and speedy resupply means rapid response to both product changes and customer preferences, as well as lower inventory investment. Similarly, while many manufacturers struggle to move inventory turnover up to 10 times per year, Dell Computer has inventory turns exceeding 90 and supply measured in *days*—not weeks. Supply chain management provides a competitive advantage when firms effectively respond to the demands of global markets and global sources.

THE SCOR MODEL

Supply Chain Operations Reference (SCOR) model

A set of processes, metrics, and best practices developed by the Supply Chain Council.

In addition to the metrics presented above, the Supply Chain Council (SCC) has developed 200 process elements, 550 metrics, and 500 best practices. The SCC (**www.supply-chain.org**, **www.supplychaincanada.org**) is a 900-member not-for-profit association for the improvement of supply chain effectiveness. The council has developed the five-part **Supply Chain Operations Reference (SCOR) model**. The five parts are *plan*, *source*, *make*, *deliver*, and *return*, as shown in Figure 11.3.

The council believes the model provides a structure for its processes, metrics, and best practices to be (1) implemented for competitive advantage; (2) defined and communicated precisely; (3) measured, managed, and controlled; and (4) fine-tuned as necessary to a specific application.

FIGURE 11.3

The Supply Chain Operations Reference (SCOR) Model

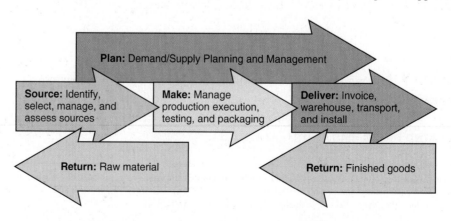

CHAPTER | SUMMARY

Competition is no longer between companies but between supply chains. For many firms, the supply chain determines a substantial portion of product cost and quality, as well as opportunities for responsiveness and differentiation. Six supply chain strategies have been identified: (1) many suppliers, (2) few suppliers, (3) vertical integration, (4) joint ventures, (5) keiretsu networks, and (6) virtual companies. Skillful supply chain management provides a great strategic opportunity for competitive advantage.

ETHICAL | DILEMMA

For generations, the policy of Sears Roebuck and Company, the granddaddy of retailers, was not to purchase more than 50% of any of its suppliers' output. The rationale of this policy was that it allowed Sears to move to other suppliers, as the market dictated, without destroying the supplier's ability to stay in business. In contrast, Walmart purchases more and more of a supplier's output. Eventually, Walmart can be expected to sit down with that supplier and explain why the supplier no longer needs a sales force and that the supplier should eliminate the sales force, passing the cost savings on to Walmart.

Sears has closed its Canadian operations and is losing market share in the United States. It has been acquired by Kmart and is eliminating jobs; Walmart is gaining market share and hiring. What are the ethical issues involved, and which firm has a more ethical position?

Spencer Tirey/AP Images

Discussion Questions

1. Define *supply chain management*.
2. What are the objectives of supply chain management?
3. What is the objective of logistics management?
4. How do we distinguish between the types of risk in the supply chain?
5. What is vertical integration? Give examples of backward and forward integration.
6. What are three basic approaches to negotiations?
7. How does a traditional adversarial relationship with suppliers change when a firm makes a decision to move to a few suppliers?
8. What is the difference between postponement and channel assembly?
9. What is CPFR?
10. What is the value of online auctions in ecommerce?
11. Explain how FedEx uses the internet to meet requirements for quick and accurate delivery.
12. How does Walmart use drop shipping?
13. What are blanket orders? How do they differ from invoiceless purchasing?
14. What can purchasing do to implement just-in-time deliveries?
15. What is eprocurement?
16. How does Darden Restaurants, described in the *Global Company Profile*, find competitive advantage in its supply chain?
17. What is SCOR, and what purpose does it serve?

Solved Problems Virtual Office Hours help is available at MyLab Operations Management.

▼ SOLVED PROBLEM 11.1

Jack's Pottery Outlet has total end-of-year assets of $5 million. The first-of-the-year inventory was $375 000, with a year-end inventory of $325 000. The annual cost of goods sold was $7 million.

The owner, Eric Jack, wants to evaluate his supply chain performance by measuring his percentage of assets in inventory, his inventory turnover, and his weeks of supply. We use Equations (11-1), (11-2), and (11-3) to provide these measures.

▼ SOLUTION

First, determine *average inventory*:

$$(\$375\,000 + \$325\,000)/2 = \$350\,000$$

Second, use Equation (11-1) to determine percent invested in inventory:

$$\text{Percent invested in inventory} = (\text{Total inventory investment}/\text{Total assets}) \times 100$$

$$= (350\,000/5\,000\,000) \times 100$$

$$= 7\%$$

Third, determine inventory turnover, using Equation (11-2):

$$\text{Inventory turnover} = \text{Cost of goods sold/Inventory investment}$$

$$= 7\,000\,000/350\,000$$

$$= 20$$

Finally, to determine weeks of inventory, use Equation (11-3), adjusted to weeks:

$$\text{Weeks of inventory} = \text{Inventory investment/Weekly cost of goods sold}$$

$$= 350\,000/(7\,000\,000/52)$$

$$= 350\,000/134\,615$$

$$= 2.6$$

We conclude that Jack's Pottery Outlet has 7% of its assets invested in inventory, that the inventory turnover is 20, and that weeks of supply are 2.6.

Problems

•• **11.1** Choose a local establishment that is a member of a relatively large chain. From interviews with workers and information from the internet, identify the elements of the supply chain. Determine whether the supply chain represents a low-cost, rapid response, or differentiation strategy (refer to Chapter 2). Are the supply chain characteristics significantly different from one product to another?

•• **11.2** As purchasing agent for Laurentian Enterprises in Quebec City, you ask your buyer to provide you with a ranking of "excellent," "good," "fair," or "poor" for a variety of characteristics for two potential vendors, Donna, Inc., and Kay Corp. You suggest that "Products" total be weighted 40% and the other three categories' totals be weighted 20% each. The buyer has returned the ranking shown below.

VENDOR RATING

Company	Excellent (4)	Good (3)	Fair (2)	Poor (1)
Financial Strength			K	D
Manufacturing Range			KD	
Research Facilities	K		D	
Geographical Locations		K	D	
Management		K	D	
Labour Relations			K	D
Trade Relations			KD	

Service	Excellent (4)	Good (3)	Fair (2)	Poor (1)
Deliveries on Time		KD		
Handling of Problems		KD		
Technical Assistance			K	D

Products	Excellent (4)	Good (3)	Fair (2)	Poor (1)
Quality	KD			
Price			KD	
Packaging			KD	

Sales	Excellent (4)	Good (3)	Fair (2)	Poor (1)
Product Knowledge			D	K
Sales Calls			K	D
Sales Service			K	D

Donna, Inc. = D
KAY CORP. = K

Which of the two vendors would you select?

•• **11.3** Using the data in Problem 11.2, assume that both Donna, Inc., and Kay Corp. are able to move all their "poor" ratings to "fair". How would you then rank the two firms?

•• **11.4** Develop a vendor-rating form that represents your comparison of the education offered by universities in which you considered (or are considering) enrolling. Fill in the necessary data, and identify the "best" choice. Are you attending that "best" choice? If not, why not?

•• **11.5** Using sources from the internet, identify some of the problems faced by a company of your choosing as it moves towards, or operates as, a virtual organization. Does its operating as a virtual organization simply exacerbate old problems, or does it create new ones?

• **11.6** Using Table 11.4, determine the sales necessary to equal a dollar of savings on purchases for a company that:
a) Has a net profit of 4% and spends 40% of its revenue on purchases.
b) Has a net profit of 6% and spends 80% of its revenue on purchases.

• **11.7** Using Table 11.4, determine the sales necessary to equal a dollar of savings on purchases for a company that:
a) Has a net profit of 6% and spends 60% of its revenue on purchases.
b) Has a net profit of 8% and spends 80% of its revenue on purchases.

•• **11.8** Your options for shipping $100\,000 of machine parts from Hamilton to Kuala Lumpur, Malaysia, are (1) use a ship that will take 30 days at a cost of $3800, or (2) truck the parts to Vancouver and then ship at a total cost of $4800. The second option will take only 20 days. You are paid via a letter of credit the day the parts arrive. Your holding cost is estimated at 30% of the value per year.
a) Which option is more economical?
b) What customer issues are not included in the data presented?

•• **11.9** If you have a third option for the data in Problem 11.8, and it costs only $4000 and also takes 20 days, what is your most economical plan?

•• **11.10** Monczka-Trent Shipping is the logistics vendor for Handfield Manufacturing Co. in New Brunswick. Handfield has daily shipments of a power-steering pump from its New Brunswick plant to an auto assembly line in Ontario. The value of the standard shipment is $250 000. Monczka-Trent has two options: (1) its standard two-day shipment, or (2) a subcontractor who will team drive overnight with an effective delivery of one day. The extra driver costs $175. Handfield's holding cost is 35% annually for this kind of inventory.
a) Which option is more economical?
b) What production issues are not included in the data presented?

•• **11.11** Baker Mfg Inc. (see Table 11.8) wishes to compare its inventory turnover to those of industry leaders, who have turnover of about 13 times per year and 8% of their assets invested in inventory.
a) What is Baker's inventory turnover?
b) What is Baker's percentage of assets committed to inventory?
c) How does Baker's performance compare to the industry leaders?

Table 11.8
For Problems 11.11 and 11.12

Arrow Distributing Corp.

Net revenue	$16 500
Cost of sales	$13 500
Inventory	$ 1 000
Total assets	$ 8 600

Baker Mfg. Inc.

Net revenue	$27 500
Cost of sales	$21 500
Inventory	$ 1 250
Total assets	$16 600

•• **11.12** Arrow Distributing Corp. (see Table 11.8) likes to track inventory by using weeks of supply as well as by inventory turnover.
a) What is its weeks of supply?
b) What percentage of Arrow's assets is committed to inventory?
c) What is Arrow's inventory turnover?
d) Is Arrow's supply chain performance, as measured by these inventory metrics, better than that of Baker in Problem 11.11?

• **11.13** The grocery industry has an annual inventory turnover of about 14 times. Organic Grocers, Inc., had a cost of goods sold last year of $10.5 million; its average inventory was $1.0 million. What was Organic Grocers's inventory turnover, and how does that performance compare with that of the industry?

•• **11.14** Mattress Wholesalers, Inc., is constantly trying to reduce inventory in its supply chain. Last year, cost of goods sold was $7.5 million and inventory was $1.5 million. This year, costs of goods sold is $8.6 million and inventory investment is $1.6 million.
a) What were the weeks of supply last year?
b) What are the weeks of supply this year?
c) Is Mattress Wholesalers making progress in its inventory-reduction effort?

•••• **11.15** Kamal Fatehl, production manager of Kennesaw Manufacturing, finds his profit at $15 000 (as shown in the statement below)—inadequate for expanding his business. The bank is insisting on an improved profit picture prior to approval of a loan for some new equipment. Kamal would like to improve the profit line to $25 000 so he can obtain the bank's approval for the loan.

		% of Sales
Sales	$250 000	100%
Cost of supply chain purchases	175 000	70%
Other production costs	30 000	12%
Fixed costs	30 000	12%
Profit	15 000	6%

a) What percentage improvement is needed in a *supply chain strategy* for profit to improve to $25 000? What is the cost of material with a $25 000 profit?
b) What percentage improvement is needed in a *sales strategy* for profit to improve to $25 000? What must sales be for profit to improve to $25 000? (*Hint:* See Example 1.)

••• **11.16** Hau Lee Furniture, Inc., described in Example 1 of this chapter, finds its current profit of $10 000 inadequate. The bank is insisting on an improved profit picture prior to approval of a loan for some new equipment. Hau would like to improve the profit line to $25 000 so he can obtain the bank's approval for the loan.
a) What percentage improvement is needed in the *supply chain strategy* for profit to improve to $25 000? What is the cost of material with a $25 000 profit?
b) What percentage improvement is needed in the *sales strategy* for profit to improve to $25 000? What must sales be for profit to improve to $25 000?

CASE STUDIES

Dell's Value Chain

Dell Computer, with close supplier relationships, encourages suppliers to focus on their individual technological capabilities to sustain leadership in their components. Research and development costs are too high and technological changes are too rapid for any one company to sustain leadership in every component. Suppliers are also pressed to drive down lead times, lot sizes, and inventories. Dell, in turn, keeps its research customer-focused and leverages that research to help itself and suppliers. Dell also constructs special web pages for suppliers, allowing them to view orders for components they produce as well as current levels of inventory at Dell. This allows suppliers to plan based on actual end customer demand; as a result, it reduces the bullwhip effect. The intent is to work with suppliers to keep the supply chain moving rapidly, the products current, and the customer order queue short. Then, with supplier collaboration, Dell can offer the latest options, can build to order, and can achieve rapid throughput. The payoff is a competitive advantage, growing market share, and low capital investment.

On the distribution side, Dell uses direct sales, primarily via the internet, to increase revenues by offering a virtually

The 2011 Tōhoku earthquake and tsunami devastated eastern sections of Japan. The economic impact was felt around the globe, as manufacturers had been relying heavily—in some cases, exclusively—on suppliers located in the affected zones. In the month immediately following the earthquake, the Japanese-built vehicle outputs for both Toyota and Honda were down 63%. Plants in other countries ceased or reduced operations due to part shortages. Manufacturers in several industries worldwide took six months or longer before they saw their supply chains working normally again. While disasters such as this one occur relatively infrequently, supply chain managers should consider their probabilities and repercussions when determining the makeup of the supply base.

mTaira/Shutterstock

An interesting implication of Equation (S11-1) is that as the probability of a super-event (S) increases, the advantage of utilizing multiple suppliers diminishes (all would be knocked out anyway). On the other hand, large values of the unique event (U) increase the likelihood of needing more suppliers. These two phenomena taken together suggest that when multiple suppliers

---

EXAMPLE S1

How Many Suppliers Are Best for Managing Risk?

Xiaotian Geng, president of Shanghai Manufacturing Corp., wants to create a portfolio of suppliers for the motors used in her company's products that will represent a reasonable balance between costs and risks. While she knows that the single-supplier approach has many potential benefits with respect to quality management and just-in-time production, she also worries about the risk of fires, natural disasters, or other catastrophes at supplier plants disrupting her firm's performance. Based on historical data and climate and geological forecasts, Xiaotian estimates the probability of a "super-event" that would negatively impact all suppliers simultaneously to be 0.5% (i.e., probability = 0.005) during the supply cycle. She further estimates the "unique event" risk for any of the potential suppliers to be 4% (probability = 0.04). Assuming that the marginal cost of managing an additional supplier is $10 000, and the financial loss incurred if a disaster caused all suppliers to be down simultaneously is $10 000 000, how many suppliers should Xiaotian use? Assume that up to three nearly identical suppliers are available.

APPROACH ▶ Use of a decision tree seems appropriate, as Shanghai Manufacturing Corp. has the basic ingredients: a choice of decisions, probabilities, and payoffs (costs).

SOLUTION ▶ We draw a decision tree (Figure S11.1) with a branch for each of the three decisions (one, two, or three suppliers), assign the respective probabilities [using Equation (S11-1)] and payoffs for each branch, and then compute the respective expected monetary values (EMVs). The EMVs have been identified at each step of the decision tree.

Using Equation (S11-1), the probability of a total disruption equals:

One supplier: $0.005 + (1 - 0.005)0.04 = 0.005 + 0.0398 = 0.044800$, or 4.4800%

Two suppliers: $0.005 + (1 - 0.005)0.04^2 = 0.005 + 0.001592 = 0.006592$, or 0.6592%

Three suppliers: $0.005 + (1 - 0.005)0.04^3 = 0.005 + 0.000064 = 0.005064$, or 0.5064%

INSIGHT ▶ Even with significant supplier management costs and unlikely probabilities of disaster, a large enough financial loss incurred during a total supplier shutdown will suggest that multiple suppliers may be needed.

LEARNING EXERCISE ▶ Suppose that the probability of a super-event increases to 50%. How many suppliers are needed now? [Answer: 2.] Using the 50% probability of a super-event, suppose

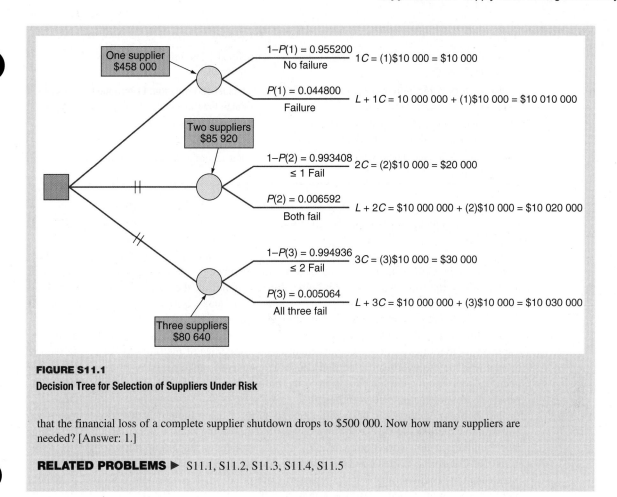

FIGURE S11.1
Decision Tree for Selection of Suppliers Under Risk

that the financial loss of a complete supplier shutdown drops to $500 000. Now how many suppliers are needed? [Answer: 1.]

RELATED PROBLEMS ▶ S11.1, S11.2, S11.3, S11.4, S11.5

are used, managers may consider using ones that are geographically dispersed to lessen the probability of all failing simultaneously.

Managing the Bullwhip Effect

Figure S11.2 provides an example of the **bullwhip effect**, which describes the tendency for larger order size fluctuations as orders are relayed to the supply chain from retailers. "Bullwhip" fluctuations create unstable production schedules, resulting in expensive capacity change adjustments such as overtime, subcontracting, extra inventory, backorders, hiring and laying off of

Bullwhip effect
The increasing fluctuation in orders that often occurs as orders move through the supply chain.

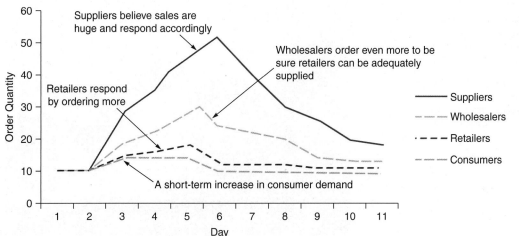

FIGURE S11.2
The Bullwhip Effect
The bullwhip effect causes members of the supply chain to overreact to changes in demand at the retail level. Minor demand changes at the consumer level may result in large ones at the supplier level.

Table S11.1
The Bullwhip Effect

Cause	Remedy
Demand forecast errors (cumulative uncertainty in the supply chain)	Share demand information throughout the supply chain.
Order batching (large, infrequent orders leading suppliers to order even larger amounts)	Channel coordination: Determine lot sizes as though the full supply chain was one company.
Price fluctuations (buying in advance of demand to take advantage of low prices, discounts, or sales)	Price stabilization (everyday low prices).
Shortage gaming (hoarding supplies for fear of a supply shortage)	Allocate orders based on past demand.

workers, equipment additions, underutilization, longer lead times, or obsolescence of overproduced items.

Procter & Gamble found that although the use of Pampers diapers was steady and the retail-store orders had little fluctuation, as orders moved through the supply chain, fluctuations increased. By the time orders were initiated for raw material, the variability was substantial. Similar behaviour has been observed and documented by many companies, including Campbell Soup, Hewlett-Packard, Barilla SpA, and Applied Materials.

The bullwhip effect can occur when orders decrease as well as when they increase. Table S11.1 identifies some of the major causes and remedies of the bullwhip effect. Often the human tendency to overreact to stimuli causes managers to make decisions that exacerbate the phenomenon. The overarching solution to the bullwhip effect is simply for supply chain members to share information and work together.

Supplier coordination can help with demand shifts. During the recent worldwide recession, but prior to experiencing the economic recovery and increasing sales, Caterpillar started ordering more supplies. It also worked proactively with its suppliers to prepare them for a sharp increase in output. Caterpillar visited key suppliers individually. In some cases it helped suppliers obtain bank financing at favourable rates. As part of Caterpillar's risk assessment activities, suppliers had to submit written plans describing their ability to ramp production back up once the economy improved. Careful, coordinated planning can help alleviate shortages and delays that might otherwise occur as the bullwhip snaps back upward.

A BULLWHIP EFFECT MEASURE

LO2 Explain and measure the bullwhip effect

A straightforward way to analyze the extent of the bullwhip effect at any link in the supply chain is to calculate the *bullwhip measure*:

$$\text{Bullwhip} = \frac{\text{Variance of orders}}{\text{Variance of demand}} = \frac{\sigma^2_{\text{orders}}}{\sigma^2_{\text{demand}}} \qquad \text{(S11-2)}$$

The U.S. Cash for Clunkers program produced an unintended bullwhip effect in the automobile industry. In an effort to stimulate the economy and improve fuel efficiency, the United States offered attractive rebates for trading old cars in exchange for new, more fuel-efficient vehicles. The $3 billion, eight-week program proved to be very popular with consumers. Fearing a shortage and assuming that they would not receive 100% of their orders, some dealers inflated orders for new cars to try to receive a larger pool of allocated vehicles. In one month, Cash for Clunkers increased demand by 50% for automakers, many of whom had already cut capacity significantly. Almost overnight, manufacturers and parts suppliers had to transform from a shift reduction mode to an overtime mode.

Paul Brennan/Shutterstock

Variance *amplification* (i.e., the bullwhip effect) is present if the bullwhip measure is greater than 1. This means the size of a company's orders fluctuates more than the size of its incoming demand. If the measure equals 1, then no amplification is present. A value less than 1 would imply a *smoothing* or *dampening* scenario as orders move up the supply chain towards suppliers. Example S2 illustrates how to use Equation (S11-2) to analyze the extent of the bullwhip effect at each stage in the supply chain.

Chieh Lee Metals, Inc., orders sheet metal and transforms it into 50 formed tabletops that are sold to furniture manufacturers. The table below shows the weekly variance of demand and orders for each major company in this supply chain for tables. Each firm has one supplier and one customer, so the order variance for one firm will equal the demand variance for its supplier. Analyze the relative contributions to the bullwhip effect in this supply chain.

EXAMPLE S2

Calculating the Bullwhip Effect

Firm	Variance of Demand	Variance of Orders	Bullwhip Measure
Furniture Mart, Inc.	100	110	110/100 = 1.10
Furniture Distributors, Inc.	110	180	180/110 = 1.64
Furniture Makers of America	180	300	300/180 = 1.67
Chieh Lee Metals, Inc.	300	750	750/300 = 2.50
Metal Suppliers Ltd.	750	2000	2000/750 = 2.67

APPROACH ▶ Use Equation (S11-2) to calculate the bullwhip measure for each firm in the chain.

SOLUTION ▶ The last column of the table displays the bullwhip measure for each firm.

INSIGHT ▶ This supply chain exhibits a classic bullwhip effect. Despite what might be a very stable demand pattern at the retail level, order sizes to suppliers vary significantly. Chieh Lee should attempt to identify the causes for her own firm's order amplification, and she should attempt to work with her supply chain partners to try to reduce amplification at every level of the chain.

LEARNING EXERCISE ▶ Suppose that Chieh Lee is able to reduce her bullwhip measure from 2.50 to 1.20. If the measure for all other firms remained the same, what would be the new reduced variance of orders from Metal Suppliers? [Answer: 961.]

RELATED PROBLEMS ▶ S11.6, S11.7, S11.8, S11.9

Supplier Selection Analysis

Selecting suppliers from among a multitude of candidates can be a daunting task. Choosing suppliers simply based on the lowest bid has become a somewhat rare approach. Various, sometimes competing, factors often play a role in the decision. Buyers may consider such supplier characteristics as product quality, delivery speed, delivery reliability, customer service, and financial performance.

The *factor-weighting* technique, presented here, simultaneously considers multiple supplier criteria. Each factor must be assigned an importance *weight,* and then each potential supplier is *scored* on each factor. The weights typically sum to 100%. Factors are scored using the same scale (e.g., 1–10). Sometimes a key is provided for supplier raters that converts qualitative ratings into numerical scores (e.g., "Very good" = 8). Example S3 illustrates the weighted criteria in comparing two competing suppliers.

STUDENT TIP

The factor-weighting model adds objectivity to decision making.

LO3 Describe the factor-weighting approach to supplier evaluation

---

Erick Davis, president of Creative Toys in Palo Alto, California, is interested in evaluating suppliers who will work with him to make nontoxic, environmentally friendly paints and dyes for his line of children's toys. This is a critical strategic element of his supply chain, and he desires a firm that will contribute to his product.

APPROACH ▶ Erick has narrowed his choices to two suppliers: Faber Paint and Smith Dye. He will use the factor-weighting approach to supplier evaluation to compare the two.

EXAMPLE S3

Factor-Weighting Approach to Supplier Evaluation

SOLUTION ▶ Erick develops the following list of selection criteria. He then assigns the weights shown to help him perform an objective review of potential suppliers. His staff assigns the scores and computes the total weighted score.

Criterion	Weight	Faber Paint Score (1–5) (5 highest)	Faber Paint Weight × Score	Smith Dye Score (1–5) (5 highest)	Smith Dye Weight × Score
Engineering/innovation skills	0.20	5	1.0	5	1.0
Production process capability	0.15	4	0.6	5	0.75
Distribution capability	0.05	4	0.2	3	0.15
Quality performance	0.10	2	0.2	3	0.3
Facilities/location	0.05	2	0.1	3	0.15
Financial strength	0.15	4	0.6	5	0.75
Information systems	0.10	2	0.2	5	0.5
Integrity	0.20	5	1.0	3	0.6
Total	1.00		3.9		4.2

Smith Dye received the higher score of 4.2, and based on this analysis, would be the preferred vendor.

INSIGHT ▶ The use of a factor-weighting approach can help firms systematically identify the features that are important to them and evaluate potential suppliers in an objective manner. A certain degree of subjectivity remains in the process, however, with regard to the criteria chosen, the weights applied to those criteria, and the supplier scores that are applied to each criterion.

LEARNING EXERCISE ▶ If Erick believes that integrity should be twice as important while production process capability and financial strength should both only be 1/3 as important, how does the analysis change? [Answer: Faber Paint's score becomes 4.1, while Smith Dye's score becomes 3.8, so Faber Paint is now the preferred vendor.]

RELATED PROBLEMS ▶ S11.10, S11.11, S11.12

Transportation Mode Analysis

LO4 Evaluate cost-of-shipping alternatives

The longer a product is in transit, the longer the firm has its money invested. But faster shipping is usually more expensive than slow shipping. A simple way to obtain some insight into this trade-off is to evaluate holding cost against shipping options. We do this in Example S4.

EXAMPLE S4

Determining Daily Cost of Holding

A shipment of new connectors for semiconductors needs to go from San Jose to Singapore for assembly. The value of the connectors is $1750, and holding cost is 40% per year. One airfreight carrier can ship the connectors one day faster than its competitor, at an extra cost of $20.00. Which carrier should be selected?

APPROACH ▶ First we determine the daily holding cost and then compare the daily holding cost with the cost of faster shipment.

SOLUTION ▶ Daily cost of holding the product = (Annual holding cost × Product value)/365
$$= (0.40 \times \$1750)/365$$
$$= \$1.92$$

Since the cost of saving one day is $20.00, which is much more than the daily holding cost of $1.92, we decide on the less costly of the carriers and take the extra day to make the shipment. This saves $18.08 (= $20.00–$1.92).

INSIGHT ▶ The solution becomes radically different if the one-day delay in getting the connectors to Singapore delays delivery (making a customer angry) or delays payment of a $150 000 final product. (Even one day's interest on $150 000 or an angry customer makes a savings of $18.08 insignificant.)

LEARNING EXERCISE ▶ If the holding cost is 100% per year, what is the decision? [Answer: Even with a holding cost of $4.79 per day, the less costly carrier is selected.]

RELATED PROBLEMS ▶ S11.13, S11.14, S11.15, S11.16

Example S4 looks only at holding cost versus shipping cost. For the operations or logistics manager there are many other considerations, including ensuring on-time delivery, coordinating shipments to maintain a schedule, getting a new product to market, and keeping a customer happy. Estimates of these other costs can be added to the estimate of the daily holding cost. Determining the impact and cost of these considerations makes the evaluation of shipping alternatives a challenging OM task.

Warehouse Storage

Storage represents a significant step for many items as they travel through their respective supply chains. The United States alone has more than 13 000 buildings dedicated to warehouse and storage. Some exceed the size of several connected football fields. In fact, more than 35% have over 100 000 square feet of floor space.

Care should be taken when determining which items to store in various locations in a warehouse. In large warehouses in particular, hundreds or thousands of trips are made each day along very long aisles. Proper placement of items can improve efficiency by shaving significant travel time for workers. In Example S5, we observe a simple way to determine storage locations in a warehouse.

LO5 *Allocate* items to storage locations in a warehouse

Erika Marsillac manages a warehouse for a local chain of specialty hardware stores. As seen in Figure S11.3, the single-aisle rectangular warehouse has a dock for pickup and delivery, along with 16 equal-sized storage blocks for inventory items.

EXAMPLE S5

Determining Storage Locations In A Warehouse

FIGURE S11.3

Storage Locations in the Warehouse

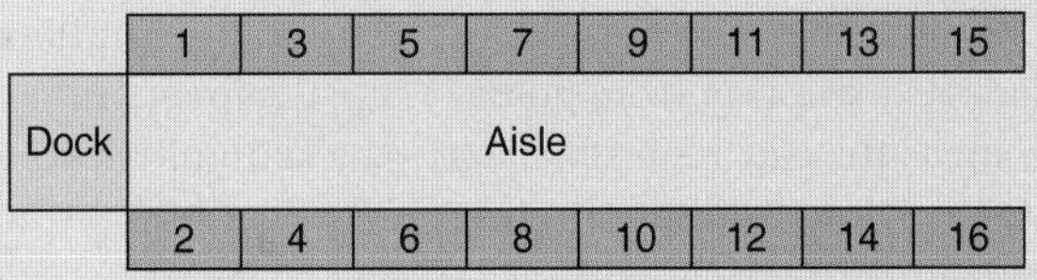

Dock	1	3	5	7	9	11	13	15
	Aisle							
	2	4	6	8	10	12	14	16

The following table shows: (1) the category of each item stored in the warehouse, (2) the estimated number of times per month (trips) that workers need to either store or retrieve those items, and (3) the area (number of specialized blocks) required to store the items. Erika wishes to assign items to the storage blocks to minimize average distance traveled.

Item	Monthly trips to Storage	Blocks of Storage Space Needed
Lumber	600	5
Paint	260	2
Tools	150	3
Small hardware	400	2
Chemical bags	90	3
Light bulbs	220	1

APPROACH ▶ For each item, calculate the ratio of the number of trips to blocks of storage area needed. Rank the items according to this ratio, and place the *highest*-ranked items closest to the dock.

SOLUTION ▶ The following table calculates the ratio for each item and ranks the items from highest to lowest. Based on the ranking, items are assigned to the remaining blocks that are as close to the dock as possible. (Where applicable, given a choice between two equidistant blocks, items should be placed next to items of the same type rather than across the aisle from them.)

Item	Trips/Blocks	Ranking	Assigned Blocks
Lumber	600/5 = 120	4	6, 7, 8, 9, 10
Paint	260/2 = 130	3	3, 5
Tools	150/3 = 50	5	11, 12, 13
Small hardware	400/2 = 200	2	2, 4
Chemical bags	90/3 = 30	6	14, 15, 16
Light bulbs	220/1 = 220	1	1

INSIGHT ▶ This procedure allocates items with the highest "bang-for-the-buck" first. The "bang" (value) here is the number of trips. Because we want to minimize travel, we would like to place items with high-frequency visits near the front. The storage space represents the "buck" (cost). We want items that take up a lot of space moved towards the back because if they were placed near the front, we would have to travel past their multiple blocks every time we needed to store or retrieve an item from a different category. This bang versus buck trade-off is neatly accommodated by using the trips/blocks ratio (column 2 of the solution table). In this example, even though lumber has the highest number of trips, the lumber takes up so much storage space that it is placed further back, towards the middle of the warehouse.

LEARNING EXERCISE ▶ Order frequency for paint is expected to increase to 410 trips per month. How will that change the storage plan? [Answer: Paint and small hardware will switch storage locations.]

RELATED PROBLEMS ▶ S11.18, S11.19, S11.20

SUPPLEMENT SUMMARY

A myriad of tools have been developed to help supply chain managers make well-informed decisions. We have provided a small sampling in this supplement. A decision tree can help determine the best number of suppliers to protect against supply disruption from potential disasters. The bullwhip measure can identify each supply chain member's contribution to exacerbating ordering fluctuations. The factor-weighting approach can be used to help select suppliers based on multiple criteria. Inventory holding costs can be computed for various shipping alternatives to better compare their overall cost impact. Finally, items can be ranked according to the ratio of trips/blocks of storage to determine their best placement in a warehouse.

Discussion Questions

1. What is the difference between "unique event" risk and "super-event" risk?
2. If the probability of a "super-event" increases, does the "unique event" risk increase or decrease in importance? Why?
3. If the probability of a "super-event" decreases, what happens to the likelihood of needing multiple suppliers?
4. Describe some ramifications of the bullwhip effect.
5. Describe causes of the bullwhip effect and their associated remedies.
6. Describe how the bullwhip measure can be used to analyze supply chains.
7. Describe some potentially useful categories to include in a factor-weighting analysis for supplier selection.
8. Describe some potential pitfalls in relying solely on the results of a factor-weighting analysis for supplier selection.
9. Describe some disadvantages of using a slow shipping method.
10. Besides warehouse layout decisions, what are some other applications where ranking items according to "bang/buck" might make sense?

Solved Problems Virtual Office Hours help is available at MyLab Operations Management.

▼ SOLVED PROBLEM S11.1

Jon Jackson Manufacturing is searching for suppliers for its new line of equipment. Jon has narrowed his choices to two sets of suppliers. Believing in diversification of risk, Jon would select two suppliers under each choice. However, he is still concerned about the risk of both suppliers failing at the same time. The "San Francisco option" uses both suppliers in San Francisco. Both are stable, reliable, and profitable firms, so Jon calculates the "unique event" risk for either of them to be 0.5%. However, since San Francisco is in an earthquake zone, he estimates the probability of an event that would knock out both suppliers to be 2%. The "North American option" uses one supplier in Canada and another in Mexico. These are upstart firms; Jon calculates the "unique event" risk for either of them to be 10%. But he estimates the "super-event" probability that would knock out both of these suppliers to be only 0.1%. Purchasing costs would be $500 000 per year using the San Francisco option and $510 000 per year using the North American option. A total disruption would create an annualized loss of $800 000. Which option seems best?

▼ SOLUTION

Using Equation (S11-1), the probability of a total disruption equals:

San Francisco option: $0.02 + (1 - 0.02)0.005^2 = 0.02 + 0.0000245 = 0.0200245$, or 2.00245%

North American option: $0.001 + (1 - 0.001)0.1^2 = 0.001 + 0.0099 = 0.01099$, or 1.099%

Total annual expected costs = Annual purchasing costs + Expected annualized disruption costs

San Francisco option: $500\,000 + $800\,000(0.0200245) = $500\,000 + $16\,020 = $516\,020$

North American option: $510\,000 + $800\,000(0.01099) = $510\,000 + $8\,792 = $518\,792$

In this case, the San Francisco option appears to be slightly cheaper. (Solutions may vary depending upon method of rounding.)

▼ SOLVED PROBLEM S11.2

Over the past 10 weeks, demand for gears at Michael's Metals has been 140, 230, 100, 175, 165, 220, 200, and 178. Michael has placed weekly orders of 140, 250, 90, 190, 140, 240, 190, and 168 units.

The sample variance of a data set can be found by using the VAR.S function in Excel or by plugging each value (x) of the data set into the formula: Variance $= \dfrac{\Sigma(x - \bar{x})^2}{(n - 1)}$, where $\bar{x}$ is the mean of the data set and n is the number of values in the set. Using Equation (S11-2), calculate the bullwhip measure for Michael's Metals over the 10-week period.

▼ SOLUTION

Mean demand $= (140 + 230 + 100 + 175 + 165 + 220 + 200 + 178)/8 = 1408/8 = 176$

Variance of demand

$$= \frac{(140 - 176)^2 + (230 - 176)^2 + (100 - 176)^2 + (175 - 176)^2 + (165 - 176)^2 + (220 - 176)^2 + (200 - 176)^2 + (178 - 176)^2}{(8 - 1)}$$

$$= \frac{36^2 + 54^2 + 76^2 + 1^2 + 11^2 + 44^2 + 24^2 + 2^2}{7} = \frac{1296 + 2916 + 5776 + 1 + 121 + 1936 + 576 + 4}{7}$$

$$= \frac{12\,626}{7} = 1804$$

Mean orders $= (140 + 250 + 90 + 190 + 140 + 240 + 190 + 168)/8 = 1408/8 = 176$

Variance of orders

$$= \frac{(140 - 176)^2 + (250 - 176)^2 + (90 - 176)^2 + (190 - 176)^2 + (140 - 176)^2 + (240 - 176)^2 + (190 - 176)^2 + (168 - 176)^2}{(8 - 1)}$$

$$= \frac{36^2 + 74^2 + 86^2 + 14^2 + 36^2 + 64^2 + 14^2 + 8^2}{7} = \frac{1296 + 5476 + 7396 + 196 + 1296 + 4096 + 196 + 64}{7}$$

$$= \frac{20\,016}{7} = 2859$$

From Equation (S11-2), the bullwhip measure $= 2859/1804 \approx 158$.
Since $1.58 > 1$, Michael's Metals is contributing to the bullwhip effect in its supply chain. (Solutions may vary depending upon method of rounding.)

▼ SOLVED PROBLEM S11.3

Victor Pimentel, purchasing manager of Office Supply Center of Mexico, is searching for a new supplier for its paper. The most important supplier criteria for Victor include paper quality, delivery reliability, customer service, and financial condition, and he believes that paper quality is twice as important as each of the other three criteria. Victor has narrowed the choice to two suppliers, and his staff has rated each supplier on each criterion (using a scale of 1 to 100, with 100 being highest), as shown in the following table:

	Paper Quality	Delivery Reliability	Customer Service	Financial Condition
Monterrey Paper	85	70	65	80
Papel Grande	80	90	95	75

Use the factor-weighting approach to determine the best supplier choice.

▼ SOLUTION

To determine the appropriate weights for each category, create a simple algebraic relationship:

Let $x =$ weight for criteria 2, 3, and 4.

Then $2x + x + x + x = 100\%$ or, $5x = 1$, or $x = 0.2 = 20\%$

Thus, paper quality has a weight of $2(20\%) = 40\%$, and the other three criteria each have a weight of 20%.

The following table presents the factor-weighting analysis:

		Monterrey Paper		Papel Grande	
Criterion	**Weight**	**Score (1–100) (100 highest)**	**Weight × Score**	**Score (1–100) (100 highest)**	**Weight × Score**
Paper quality	0.40	85	34	80	32
Delivery reliability	0.20	70	14	90	18
Customer service	0.20	65	13	95	19
Financial condition	0.20	80	16	75	15
	Total 1.00		77		84

Since 84 > 77, Papel Grande should be the chosen supplier according to the factor-weighting method.

▼ SOLVED PROBLEM S11.4

A French car company ships 120 000 cars annually to the United Kingdom. The current method of shipment uses ferries to cross the English Channel and averages 10 days. The firm is considering shipping by rail through the Chunnel (the tunnel that goes through the English Channel) instead. That transport method would average approximately two days. Shipping through the Chunnel costs $80 more per vehicle. The firm has a holding cost of 25% per year. The average value of each car shipped is $20 000. Which transportation method should be selected?

▼ SOLUTION

Daily cost of holding the product $= (0.25 \times \$20\,000)/365$
$= \$13.70$

Total holding cost savings by using the Chunnel $= (10 - 2) \times \$13.70 = \$110$ (rounded)

Since the $110 savings exceeds the $80 higher shipping cost, the Chunnel option appears best.

This switch would save the firm $(120\,000)(\$110 - \$80) = \$3,600\,000$ per year.

Problems*

· S11.1 How would you go about attempting to come up with the probability of a "super-event" or the probability of a "unique event"? What factors would you consider?

·· S11.2 Phillip Witt, president of Witt Input Devices, wishes to create a portfolio of local suppliers for his new line of keyboards. As the suppliers all reside in a location prone to hurricanes, tornadoes, flooding, and earthquakes, Phillip believes that the probability in any year of a "super-event" that might shut down all suppliers at the same time for at least two weeks is 3%. Such a total shutdown would cost the company approximately $400 000. He estimates the "unique event" risk for any of the suppliers to be 5%. Assuming that the marginal cost of managing an additional supplier is $15 000 per year, how many suppliers should Witt Input Devices use? Assume that up to three nearly identical local suppliers are available.

·· S11.3 Still concerned about the risk in Problem S11.2, suppose that Phillip is willing to use one local supplier and up to two more located in other territories within the country. This would reduce the probability of a "super-event" to 0.5%, but due to increased distance the annual costs for managing each of the distant suppliers would be $25 000 (still $15 000 for the local supplier). Assuming that the local supplier would be the first one chosen, how many suppliers should Witt Input Devices use now?

·· S11.4 Johnson Chemicals is considering two options for its supplier portfolio. Option 1 uses two local suppliers. Each has a "unique event" risk of 5%, and the probability of a "super-event"

that would disable both at the same time is estimated to be 1.5%. Option 2 uses two suppliers located in different countries. Each has a "unique event" risk of 13%, and the probability of a "super-event" that would disable both at the same time is estimated to be 0.2%.
a) What is the probability that both suppliers will be disrupted using option 1?
b) What is the probability that both suppliers will be disrupted using option 2?
c) Which option would provide the lowest risk of a total shutdown?

·· S11.5 Bloom's Jeans is searching for new suppliers, and Debbie Bloom, the owner, has narrowed her choices to two sets. Debbie is very concerned about supply disruptions, so she has chosen to use three suppliers no matter what. For option 1, the suppliers are well established and located in the same country. Debbie calculates the "unique event" risk for each of them to be 4%. She estimates the probability of a nationwide event that would knock out all three suppliers to be 2.5%. For option 2, the suppliers are newer but located in three different countries. Debbie calculates the "unique event" risk for each of them to be 20%. She estimates the "super-event" probability that would knock out all three of these suppliers to be 0.4%. Purchasing and transportation costs would be $1 000 000 per year using option 1 and $1 010 000 per year using option 2. A total disruption would create an annualized loss of $500 000.
a) What is the probability that all three suppliers will be disrupted using option 1?
b) What is the probability that all three suppliers will be disrupted using option 2?
c) What is the total annual purchasing and transportation cost plus expected annualized disruption cost for option 1?

---

* *Note:* **PX** means the problem may be solved with POM for Windows and/or Excel OM.

d) What is the total annual purchasing and transportation cost plus expected annualized disruption cost for option 2?

e) Which option seems best?

•• **S11.6** Consider the supply chain illustrated below:

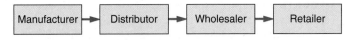

Last year, the retailer's weekly variance of demand was 200 units. The variances of orders were 500, 600, 750, and 1350 units for the retailer, wholesaler, distributor, and manufacturer, respectively. (Note that the variance of orders equals the variance of demand for that firm's supplier.)

a) Calculate the bullwhip measure for the retailer.

b) Calculate the bullwhip measure for the wholesaler.

c) Calculate the bullwhip measure for the distributor.

d) Calculate the bullwhip measure for the manufacturer.

e) Which firm appears to be contributing the most to the bullwhip effect in this supply chain?

•• **S11.7** Over the past five weeks, demand for wine at Winston's Winery has been 1000, 2300, 3200, 1750, and 1200 bottles. Winston has placed weekly orders for glass bottles of 1100, 2500, 4000, 1000, and 900 units. (Recall that the sample variance of a data set can be found by using the VAR.S function in Excel or by plugging each x value of the data set into the formula:

$$\text{Variance} = \frac{\sum(x - \bar{x})^2}{(n - 1)}, \text{ where } \bar{x} \text{ is the mean of the data set and } n$$

is the number of values in the set.)

a) What is the variance of demand for Winston's Winery?

b) What is the variance of orders from Winston's Winery for glass bottles?

c) What is the bullwhip measure for glass bottles for Winston's Winery?

d) Is Winston's Winery providing an amplifying or smoothing effect?

•• **S11.8** Over the past 12 months, Super Toy Mart has experienced a demand variance of 10 000 units and has produced an order variance of 12 000 units.

a) What is the bullwhip measure for Super Toy Mart?

b) If Super Toy Mart had made a perfect forecast of demand over the past 12 months and had decided to order 1/12 of that annual demand each month, what would its bullwhip measure have been?

•••**S11.9** Consider a three-firm supply chain consisting of a retailer, manufacturer, and supplier. The retailer's demand over an eight-week period was 100 units each of the first two weeks, 200 units each of the second two weeks, 300 units each of the third two weeks, and 400 units each of the fourth two weeks. The following table presents the orders placed by each firm in the supply chain. Notice, as is often the case in supply chains due to economies of scale, that total units are the same in each case, but firms further up the supply chain (away from the retailer) place larger, less frequent, orders.

Week	Retailer	Manufacturer	Supplier
1	100	200	600
2	100		
3	200	400	
4	200		
5	300	600	1400
6	300		
7	400	800	
8	400		

Recall that the sample variance of a data set can be found by using the VAR.S function in Excel or by plugging each x value of the data set into the formula: $\text{Variance} = \frac{\sum(x - \bar{x})^2}{(n - 1)}$, where $\bar{x}$ is the mean of the data set and n is the number of values in the set.

a) What is the bullwhip measure for the retailer?

b) What is the bullwhip measure for the manufacturer?

c) What is the bullwhip measure for the supplier?

d) What conclusions can you draw regarding the impact that economies of scale may have on the bullwhip effect?

•• **S11.10** As purchasing agent for Woolsey Enterprises, you ask your buyer to provide you with a ranking of "excellent," "good," "fair," or "poor" for a variety of characteristics for two potential vendors. You suggest that the "Products" total be weighted 40% and the other three categories totals be weighted 20% each. The buyer has returned the rankings shown in Table S11.2.

Which of the two vendors would you select? **Px**

Table S11.2
Vendor Rating for Problem S11.10

VENDOR RATING

Company	Excellent (4)	Good (3)	Fair (2)	Poor (1)
Financial Strength			K	D
Manufacturing Range			KD	
Research Facilities	K		D	
Geographical Locations		K	D	
Management		K	D	
Labour Relations			K	D
Trade Relations			KD	

Service	Excellent (4)	Good (3)	Fair (2)	Poor (1)
Deliveries on Time		KD		
Handling of Problems		KD		
Technical Assistance		K	D	

Products	Excellent (4)	Good (3)	Fair (2)	Poor (1)
Quality	KD			
Price			KD	
Packaging			KD	

Sales	Excellent (4)	Good (3)	Fair (2)	Poor (1)
Product Knowledge			D	K
Sales Calls			K	D
Sales Service		K	D	

Donna, Inc. = D
KAY CORP. = K

•• **S11.11** Using the data in Problem S11.10, assume that both Donna, Inc., and Kay Corp. are able to move all their "poor" ratings to "fair". How would you then rank the two firms? **Px**

•• **S11.12** Develop a vendor rating form that represents your comparison of the education offered by universities in which you considered (or are considering) enrolling. Fill in the necessary data, and identify the "best" choice. Are you attending that "best" choice? If not, why not?

•• **S11.13** Your options for shipping $100 000 of machine parts from Baltimore to Kuala Lumpur, Malaysia, are (1) use a ship that will take 30 days at a cost of $3800 or (2) truck the parts to Los Angeles and then ship at a total cost of $4800. The second option will take only 20 days. You are paid via a letter of credit the day the parts arrive. Your holding cost is estimated at 30% of the value per year.
a) Which option is more economical?
b) What customer issues are not included in the data presented?

•• **S11.14** If you have a third option for the data in Problem S11.13 and it costs only $4000 and also takes 20 days, what is your most economical plan?

•• **S11.15** Monczka-Trent Shipping is the logistics vendor for Handfield Manufacturing Co. in Ohio. Handfield has daily shipments of a power-steering pump from its Ohio plant to an auto assembly line in Alabama. The value of the standard shipment is $250 000. Monczka-Trent has two options: (1) its standard two-day shipment or (2) a subcontractor who will team drive overnight with an effective delivery of one day. The extra driver costs $175. Handfield's holding cost is 35% annually for this kind of inventory.
a) Which option is more economical?
b) What production issues are not included in the data presented?

•••**S11.16** Recently, Abercrombie & Fitch (A&F) began shifting a large portion of its Asian deliveries to the United States from air freight to slower but cheaper ocean freight. Shipping costs have been cut dramatically, but shipment times have gone from days to weeks. In addition to having less control over inventory and being less responsive to fashion changes, the holding costs have risen for the goods in transport. Meanwhile, Central America might offer an inexpensive manufacturing alternative that could reduce shipping time through the Panama Canal to, say, six days, compared to, say, 27 days from Asia. Suppose that A&F uses an annual holding rate of 30%. Suppose further that the product costs $20 to produce in Asia. Assuming that the transportation cost via ocean liner would be approximately the same whether coming from Asia or Central America, what would the maximum production cost in Central America need to be in order for that to be a competitive source compared to the Asian producer?

•••**S11.17** The items listed in the following table are stored in a warehouse.

Item	Weekly Trips	Area Needed (Blocks)
A	300	60
B	219	3
C	72	1
D	90	10
E	24	3

a) Which item should be stored at the very front (closest to the dock)?
b) Which item should be stored at the very back (furthest from the dock)?

•••**S11.18** Amy Zeng, owner of Zeng's Restaurant Distributions, supplies nonperishable goods to restaurants around the metro area. She stores all the goods in a warehouse. The goods are divided into five categories according to the following table. The table indicates the number of trips per month to store or retrieve items in each category, as well as the number of storage blocks taken up by each.

Item Category	Monthly Trips	Area Needed (Blocks)
Paper Products	50	2
Dishes, Glasses, and Silverware	16	4
Cleaning Agents	6	2
Cooking Oils and Seasonings	30	2
Pots and Pans	12	6

The following picture of the warehouse provides an identification number for each of the 16 storage blocks. For each item category, indicate into which blocks it should be stored.

•••**S11.19** The items listed in the following table are stored in a warehouse.

Item	Weekly Trips	Area Needed (Blocks)
A	2	1
B	160	8
C	16	1
D	40	4
E	24	2
F	15	1
G	4	1

Using the following figure, indicate the best storage location for each item to minimize average distance traveled.

SUPPLEMENT 11 | RAPID REVIEW

MyLab Operations Management

Main Heading	Review Material	
TECHNIQUES FOR EVALUATING SUPPLY CHAINS (p. 453)	Many supply chain metrics exist that can be used to evaluate performance within a company and for its supply chain partners.	
	The 2011 Tōhoku earthquake and tsunami devastated eastern sections of Japan. The economic impact was felt around the globe, as manufacturers had been relying heavily, in some cases exclusively, on suppliers located in the affected zones. Manufacturers in several industries worldwide took six months or longer before they saw their supply chains working normally again.	
EVALUATING DISASTER RISK IN THE SUPPLY CHAIN (pp. 453 – 455)	Disasters that disrupt supply chains can take on many forms, including tornadoes, fires, hurricanes, typhoons, tsunamis, earthquakes, and terrorism.	Problems: S11.1–S11.5
	Firms often use multiple suppliers for important components to mitigate the risks of total supply disruption. *The probability of all n suppliers being disrupted simultaneously:*	Virtual Office Hours for Solved Problem: S11.1

$$P(n) = S + (1 - S)U^n \qquad (S11\text{-}1)$$

where: S = probability of a "super-event" disrupting all suppliers simultaneously
  U = probability of a "unique event" disrupting only one supplier
  L = financial loss incurred in a supply chain if all suppliers were disrupted
  C = marginal cost of managing a supplier

All suppliers will be disrupted simultaneously if either the super-event occurs or the super-event does not occur but a unique event occurs for all of the suppliers.

As the probability of a super-event (S) increases, the advantage of utilizing multiple suppliers diminishes (all would be knocked out anyway). On the other hand, large values of the unique event (U) increase the likelihood of needing more suppliers.

These two phenomena taken together suggest that when multiple suppliers are used, managers may consider using ones that are geographically dispersed to lessen the probability of all failing simultaneously.

A decision tree can be used to help operations managers make this important decision regarding number of suppliers.

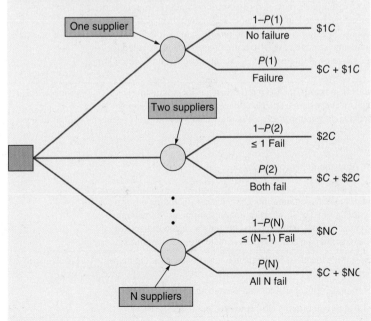

Main Heading	Review Material	

MANAGING THE BULLWHIP EFFECT (pp. 455 – 458)	*Demand forecast updating, order batching, price fluctuations,* and *shortage gaming* can all produce inaccurate information, resulting in distortions and fluctuations in the supply chain and causing the *bullwhip effect*.
	
	• **Bullwhip effect**—The increasing fluctuation in orders that often occurs as orders move through the supply chain.
	
	"Bullwhip" fluctuations create unstable production schedules, resulting in expensive capacity change adjustments such as overtime, subcontracting, extra inventory, backorders, hiring and laying off of workers, equipment additions, equipment underutilization, longer lead times, or obsolescence of overproduced items. The bullwhip effect can occur when orders decrease as well as when they increase. Often the human tendency to overreact to stimuli causes managers to make decisions that exacerbate the phenomenon. The overarching solution to the bullwhip effect is simply for supply chain members to share information and work together.
	
	Specific remedies for the four primary causes include:
	    Demand forecast errors—Share demand information throughout the chain
	    Order batching—Think of the supply chain as one firm when choosing order sizes
	    Price fluctuations—Institute everyday low prices
	    Shortage gaming—Allocate orders based on past demand
	
	A straightforward way to measure the extent of the bullwhip effect at any link in the supply chain is to calculate the *bullwhip measure*:
	
	$$\text{Bullwhip} = \frac{\text{Variance of orders}}{\text{Variance of demand}} = \frac{\sigma^2_{\text{orders}}}{\sigma^2_{\text{demand}}} \quad \text{(S11-2)}$$
	
	Variance *amplification* (i.e., the bullwhip effect) is present if the bullwhip measure is greater than 1. The means the size of a company's orders fluctuates more than the size of its incoming demand. If the measure equals 1, then no amplification is present. A value less than 1 would imply a *smoothing* or *dampening* scenario as orders move up the supply chain from the retailer towards suppliers.
		Problems: S11.6–S11.9
		
		Virtual Office Hours for Solved Problem: S11.2

SUPPLIER SELECTION ANALYSIS (pp. 458 – 459)	Choosing suppliers simply based on the lowest bid has become a somewhat rare approach. Various, sometimes competing, factors often play a role in the decision. Buyers may consider such supplier characteristics as product quality, delivery speed, delivery reliability, customer service, and financial performance. The *factor-weighting* technique simultaneously considers multiple supplier criteria. Each factor must be assigned an importance *weight*, and then each potential supplier is *scored* on each factor. The weights typically sum to 100%. Factors are scored using the same scale (e.g., 1–10). Sometimes a key is provided for supplier raters that converts qualitative ratings into numerical scores (e.g., "Very good" = 8).	Problems: S11.10-S11.11 Virtual Office Hours for Solved Problem: S11.3
TRANSPORTATION MODE ANALYSIS (pp. 459 – 460)	The longer a product is in transit, the longer the firm has its money invested. But faster shipping is usually more expensive than slow shipping. A simple way to obtain some insight into this trade-off is to evaluate holding cost against shipping options. Daily cost of holding the product: (Annual holding cost × Product value)/365 There are many other considerations beyond holding versus shipping costs when choosing the appropriate transportation mode and carrier, including ensuring on-time delivery (whether fast or slow), coordinating shipments to maintain a schedule, getting a new product to market, and keeping a customer happy. Estimates of these other costs can be added to the estimate of the daily holding cost.	Problems: S11.13-S11.16 Virtual Office Hours for Solved Problem: S11.4
WAREHOUSE STORAGE (pp. 458 – 459)	When determining storage locations for items in a warehouse, rank the items according to the ratio: (Number of trips/Blocks of storage needed) Place the items with the *highest* ratios closest to the dock.	Problems: S11.17–S11.19

Self-Test

■ **Before taking the self-test,** refer to the learning objectives listed at the beginning of the supplement.

LO1 Which of the following combinations would result in needing to utilize the largest number of suppliers?
a) a high value of S and high value of U
b) a high value of S and low value of U
c) a low value of S and high value of U
d) a low value of S and low value of U

LO2 Typically, the bullwhip effect is most pronounced at which level of the supply chain?
a) consumers   b) suppliers
c) wholesalers   d) retailers

LO3 Which of the following is not a characteristic of the factor-weighting approach to supplier evaluation?
a) It applies quantitative scores to qualitative criteria.
b) The weights typically sum to 100%.
c) Multiple criteria can be considered simultaneously.

d) Subjective judgment is often involved.
e) It applies qualitative assessments to quantitative criteria.

LO4 A more expensive shipper tends to provide:
a) faster shipments and lower holding costs.
b) faster shipments and higher holding costs.
c) slower shipments and lower holding costs.
d) slower shipments and higher holding costs.

LO5 Which of the following items is most likely to be stored at the back of a warehouse, farthest away from the shipping dock?
a) low number of trips and low number of storage blocks.
b) low number of trips and high number of storage blocks.
c) high number of trips and low number of storage blocks.
d) high number of trips and high number of storage blocks.

Answers: LO1. c; LO2. b; LO3. e; LO4. a. LO5. b.

MyLab Operations Management

Most of these questions can be found in MyLab Operations Management. Visit MyLab Operations Management to access cases, videos, downloadable software, and much more. MyLab Operations Management Management also features a personalized Study Plan that helps you identify which chapter concepts you've mastered and guides you towards study tools for additional practice.

Inventory Models

We now examine a variety of inventory models and the costs associated with them.

INDEPENDENT VERSUS DEPENDENT DEMAND

VIDEO 12.2
Inventory Control at Wheeled Coach Ambulance

Inventory control models assume that demand for an item is either independent of or dependent on the demand for other items. For example, the demand for refrigerators is *independent* of the demand for toaster ovens. However, the demand for toaster oven components is *dependent* on the requirements of toaster ovens.

This chapter focuses on managing inventory where demand is *independent*. Chapter 14 presents *dependent* demand management.

HOLDING, ORDERING, AND SETUP COSTS

Holding cost

The cost to keep or carry inventory in stock.

Holding cost is the cost associated with holding or "carrying" inventory over time. Therefore, holding cost also includes obsolescence and costs related to storage, such as insurance, extra staffing, and interest payments. Table 12.1 shows the kinds of costs that need to be evaluated to determine holding cost. Many firms fail to include all the inventory holding costs. Consequently, inventory holding costs are often understated.

Ordering cost

The cost of the ordering process.

Setup cost

The cost to prepare a machine or process for production.

Ordering cost includes costs of supplies, forms, order processing, purchasing, clerical support, and so forth. When orders are being manufactured, ordering costs also exist, but they are a part of what is called setup costs. **Setup cost** is the cost to prepare a machine or process for manufacturing an order. This includes time and labour to clean and change tools or holders. Operations managers can lower ordering costs by reducing setup costs and by using such efficient procedures as electronic ordering and payment.

Setup time

The time required to prepare a machine or process for production.

In manufacturing environments, setup cost is highly correlated with **setup time**. Setups usually require a substantial amount of work even before a setup is actually performed at the work centre. With proper planning, much of the preparation required by a setup can be done prior to shutting down the machine or process. Setup times can thus be reduced substantially. Machines and processes that traditionally have taken hours to set up are now being set up in less than a minute by the more imaginative world-class manufacturers. As we shall see later in this chapter, reducing setup times is an excellent way to reduce inventory investment and to improve productivity.

Inventory Models for Independent Demand

In this section, we introduce three inventory models that address two important questions: *when to order* and *how much to order*. These *independent* demand models are:

1. Basic economic order quantity (EOQ) model
2. Production order quantity model
3. Quantity discount model

Table 12.1
Determining Inventory Holding Costs

Category	Cost (and Range) as a Percentage of Inventory Value
Housing costs (building rent or depreciation, operating cost, taxes, insurance)	6% (3–10%)
Material handling costs (equipment lease or depreciation, power, operating cost)	3% (1–3.5%)
Labour cost (receiving, warehousing, security)	3% (3–5%)
Investment costs (borrowing costs, taxes, and insurance on inventory)	11% (6–24%)
Pilferage, scrap, and obsolescence (much higher in industries undergoing rapid change such as those making tablets and smartphones)	3% (2–5%)
Overall carrying cost	26%

STUDENT TIP

An overall inventory carrying cost of less than 15% is very unlikely, but this cost can exceed 40%, especially in high-tech and fashion industries.

Note: All numbers are approximate, as they vary substantially depending on the nature of the business, location, and current interest rates.

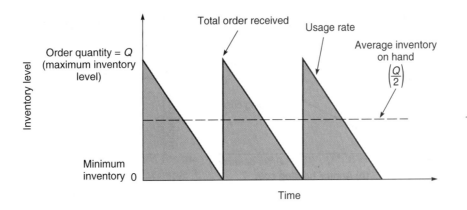

FIGURE 12.3

Inventory Usage Over Time

THE BASIC ECONOMIC ORDER QUANTITY (EOQ) MODEL

The **economic order quantity (EOQ) model** is one of the most commonly used inventory control techniques. This technique is relatively easy to use but is based on several assumptions:

1. Demand for an item is known, reasonably constant, and independent of decisions for other items.
2. Lead time—that is, the time between placement and receipt of the order—is known and consistent.
3. Receipt of inventory is instantaneous and complete. In other words, the inventory from an order arrives in one batch at one time.
4. Quantity discounts are not possible.
5. The only variable costs are the cost of setting up or placing an order (setup or ordering cost) and the cost of holding or storing inventory over time (holding or carrying cost). These costs were discussed in the previous section.
6. Stockouts (shortages) can be completely avoided if orders are placed at the right time.

Economic order quantity (EOQ) model

An inventory control technique that minimizes the total of ordering and holding costs.

LO3 Explain and use the EOQ model for independent inventory demand

With these assumptions, the graph of inventory usage over time has a sawtooth shape, as in Figure 12.3. In Figure 12.3, Q represents the amount that is ordered. If this amount is 500 dresses, all 500 dresses arrive at one time (when an order is received). Thus, the inventory level jumps from 0 to 500 dresses. In general, an inventory level increases from 0 to Q units when an order arrives.

Because demand is constant over time, inventory drops at a uniform rate over time. (Refer to the sloped lines in Figure 12.3.) Each time the inventory level reaches 0, the new order is placed and received, and the inventory level again jumps to Q units (represented by the vertical lines). This process continues indefinitely over time.

MINIMIZING COSTS

The objective of most inventory models is to minimize total costs. With the assumptions just given, significant costs are setup (or ordering) cost and holding (or carrying) cost. All other costs, such as the cost of the inventory itself, are constant. Thus, if we minimize the sum of setup and holding costs, we will also be minimizing total costs. To help you visualize this, in Figure 12.4, we graph total costs as a function of the order quantity, Q. The optimal order size, Q^*, will be the quantity that minimizes the total costs. As the quantity ordered increases, the total number of orders placed per year will decrease. Thus, as the quantity ordered increases, the annual setup or ordering cost will decrease (see Figure 12.4[a]). But as the order quantity increases, the holding cost will increase due to the larger average inventories that are maintained (see Figure 12.4[b]).

As we can see in Figure 12.4(c), a reduction in either holding or setup cost will reduce the total cost curve. A reduction in the setup cost curve also reduces the optimal order quantity (lot size). In addition, smaller lot sizes have a positive impact on quality and production flexibility. At Toshiba, the $77-billion Japanese conglomerate, workers can make as few as 10 laptop computers before changing models. This lot-size flexibility has allowed Toshiba to move towards a "build-to-order" mass customization system, an important ability in an industry that has product life cycles measured in months, not years.

SOLUTION ▶ From the equation we get:

$$ROP = (10 \text{ units} \times 6 \text{ days}) + 2.055(10 \text{ units})(3)$$

$$= 60 + 61.65 = 121.65$$

The reorder point is about 122 cameras.

INSIGHT ▶ Note how the very high service level of 98% drives the ROP up.

LEARNING EXERCISE ▶ If a 90% service level is applied, what does the ROP drop to? [Answer: ROP = 60 + (1.28)(10)(3) = 60 + 38.4 = 98.4, since the Z-value is only 1.28.]

RELATED PROBLEM ▶ 12.33

BOTH DEMAND AND LEAD TIME ARE VARIABLE When both the demand and lead time are variable, the formula for reorder point becomes more complex:[4]

$$ROP = (\text{Average daily demand} \times \text{Average lead time}) + Z\sigma_{dLT} \qquad \textbf{(12-17)}$$

where $\quad \sigma_d = $ Standard deviation of demand per day

$\sigma_{LT} = $ Standard deviation of lead time in days

and $\sigma_{dLT} = \sqrt{(\text{Average lead time} \times \sigma_d^2) + (\text{Average daily demand})^2 \sigma_{LT}^2}$

EXAMPLE 14

ROP for Variable Demand and Variable Lead Time

The Circuit Town store's most popular item is a six-pack of 9-volt batteries. About 150 packs are sold per day, following a normal distribution with a standard deviation of 16 packs. Batteries are ordered from an out-of-town distributor; lead time is normally distributed with an average of five days and a standard deviation of one day. To maintain a 95% service level, what ROP is appropriate?

APPROACH ▶ Determine a quantity at which to reorder by applying Equation (12-17) to the following data:

Average daily demand = 150 packs
Standard deviation of demand = σ_d = 16 packs
Average lead time = 5 days
Standard deviation of lead time = σ_{LT} = 1 day
Service level = 95%, so Z = 1.65 (from Appendix I)

SOLUTION ▶ From the equation we compute:

$$ROP = (150 \text{ packs} \times 5 \text{ days}) + 1.65 \, \sigma_{dLT}$$

$$\text{where} \quad \sigma_{dLT} = \sqrt{(5 \text{ days} \times 16^2) + (150^2 \times 1^2)}$$

$$= \sqrt{(5 \times 256) + (22\,500 \times 1)}$$

$$= \sqrt{1280 + 22\,500} = \sqrt{23\,780} \cong 154$$

$$\text{So, ROP} = (150 \times 5) + 1.65(154) \cong 750 + 254 = 1004 \text{ packs}$$

INSIGHT ▶ When both demand and lead time are variable, the formula looks quite complex. But it is just the result of squaring the standard deviations in Equations (12-15) and (12-16) to get their variances, then summing them, and finally taking the square root.

LEARNING EXERCISE ▶ For an 80% service level, what is the ROP? [Answer: Z = 0.84 and ROP = 879 packs.]

RELATED PROBLEM ▶ 12.34

---

[4] Refer to S. Narasimhan, D. W. McLeavey, and P. Billington, *Production Planning and Inventory Control*, 2nd ed. (Upper Saddle River, NJ: Prentice Hall), 1995, Chapter 6, for details. Note that Equation (12-17) can also be expressed as ROP = (Average daily demand × Average lead time) + $Z\sqrt{(\text{Average lead time} \times \sigma_d^2) + \bar{d}^2 \sigma_{LT}^2}$.

Single-Period Model

A **single-period inventory model** describes a situation in which *one* order is placed for a product. At the end of the sales period, any remaining product has little or no value. This is a typical problem for Christmas trees, seasonal goods, bakery goods, newspapers, and magazines. (Indeed, this inventory issue is often called the "newsstand problem".) In other words, even though items at a newsstand are ordered weekly or daily, they cannot be held over and used as inventory in the next sales period. So, our decision is how much to order at the beginning of the period.

Because the exact demand for such seasonal products is never known, we consider a probability distribution related to demand. If the normal distribution is assumed, and we stocked and sold an average (mean) of 100 Christmas trees each season, then there is a 50% chance we would stock out and a 50% chance we would have trees left over. To determine the optimal stocking policy for trees before the season begins, we also need to know the standard deviation and consider these two marginal costs:

> **Single-period inventory model**
> A system for ordering items that have little or no value at the end of a sales period.

C_s = Cost of shortage (we underestimated) = Sales price/unit − Cost/unit

C_o = Cost of overage (we overestimated) = Cost/unit − Salvage value/unit (if there is any)

The service level, that is, the probability of *not* stocking out, is set at:

$$\text{Service level} = \frac{C_s}{C_s + C_o} \qquad \text{(12-18)}$$

Therefore, we should consider increasing our order quantity until the service level is less than or equal to the ratio of $[C_s/(C_s + C_o)]$.

This model, illustrated in Example 15, is used in many service industries, from hotels to airlines to bakeries to clothing retailers.

Chris Ellis's newsstand, inside the Museum subway station in Toronto, usually sells 120 copies of *The Globe and Mail* each day. Chris believes the sale of the *Globe* is normally distributed, with a standard deviation of 15 papers. He pays 70 cents for each paper, which sells for $1.25. The *Globe* gives him a 30-cent credit for each unsold paper. He wants to determine how many papers he should order each day and the stockout risk for that quantity.

EXAMPLE 15

Single-Period Inventory Decision

APPROACH ▶ Chris's data are as follows:

$$C_s = \text{cost of shortage} = \$1.25 - \$0.70 = \$0.55$$

$$C_o = \text{cost of overage} = \$0.70 - \$0.30 \text{ (salvage value)} = \$0.40$$

Chris will apply Equation (12-18) and the normal table, using $\mu = 120$ and $\sigma = 15$.

SOLUTION ▶

a) Service level $= \dfrac{C_s}{C_s + C_o} = \dfrac{0.55}{0.55 + 0.40} = \dfrac{0.55}{0.95} = 0.578$

b) Chris needs to find the Z-score for his normal distribution that yields a probability of 0.578.

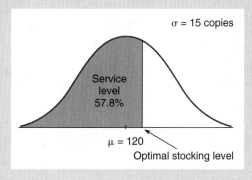

So, 57.8% of the area under the normal curve must be to the left of the optimal stocking level.

c) Using the normal table[5] (Appendix I), for an area of 0.578, the Z-value $\cong$ 0.20.

Then, the optimal stocking level = 120 copies + (0.20)(σ)

$$= 120 + (0.20)(15) = 120 + 3 = 123 \text{ papers}$$

The stockout risk if Chris orders 123 copies of the *Globe* each day is 1 – service level = 1 – 0.578 = 0.422 = 42.2%.

INSIGHT ▶ If the service level is ever under 0.50, Chris should order fewer than 120 copies per day.

LEARNING EXERCISE ▶ How does Chris's decision change if the *Globe* changes its policy and offers *no credit* for unsold papers, a policy many publishers are adopting?

[Answer: Service level = 0.44, Z = –0.15. Therefore, stock 120 + (–0.15)(15) = 117.75 or 118 papers.]

RELATED PROBLEMS ▶ 12.36, 12.37, 12.38

Fixed-Period (*P*) Systems

The inventory models that we have considered so far are in the **fixed-quantity (*Q*) system** category. That is, the same fixed amount is added to inventory every time an order for an item is placed. We saw that orders are event triggered. When inventory decreases to the reorder point (ROP), a new order for *Q* units is placed.

To use the fixed-quantity model, inventory must be continuously monitored.[6] This requires a **perpetual inventory system**. Every time an item is added to or withdrawn from inventory, records must be updated to determine whether the ROP has been reached.

In a **fixed-period (*P*) system** (also called a periodic review system), on the other hand, inventory is ordered at the end of a given period. Then, and only then, is on-hand inventory counted. Only the amount necessary to bring total inventory up to a prespecified target level (*T*) is ordered. Figure 12.9 illustrates this concept.

Fixed-period systems have several of the same assumptions as the basic EOQ fixed-quantity system:

- The only relevant costs are the ordering and holding costs.
- Lead times are known and constant.
- Items are independent of one another.

The downward-sloped lines in Figure 12.9 again represent on-hand inventory levels. But now, when the time between orders (*P*) passes, we place an order to raise inventory up to the target quantity (*T*). The amount ordered during the first period may be Q_1, the second period Q_2, and so on. The Q_i value is the difference between current on-hand inventory and the target inventory level.

FIGURE 12.9

Inventory Level in a Fixed-Period (*P*) System

Various amounts (Q_1, Q_2, Q_3, etc.) are ordered at regular time intervals (*P*) based on the quantity necessary to bring inventory up to the target quantity (*T*).

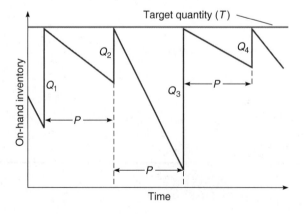

---

[5] Alternatively, Microsoft Excel's NORMSINV (probability) function can be applied.
[6] Some in OM call these continuous review systems.

The advantage of the fixed-period system is that there is no physical count of inventory items after an item is withdrawn—this occurs only when the time for the next review comes up. This procedure is also convenient administratively.

A fixed-period system is appropriate when vendors make routine (i.e., at fixed-time interval) visits to customers to take fresh orders or when purchasers want to combine orders to save ordering and transportation costs (therefore, they will have the same review period for similar inventory items). For example, a vending machine company may come to refill its machines every Tuesday.

The disadvantage of the *P* system is that because there is no tally of inventory during the review period, there is the possibility of a stockout during this time. This scenario is possible if a large order draws the inventory level down to zero right after an order is placed. Therefore, a higher level of safety stock (as compared to a fixed-quantity system) needs to be maintained to provide protection against stockout during both the time between reviews and the lead time.

CHAPTER SUMMARY

Inventory represents a major investment for many firms. This investment is often larger than it should be because firms find it easier to have "just-in-case" inventory rather than "just-in-time" inventory. Inventories are of four types:

1. Raw material and purchased components.
2. Work-in-process.
3. Maintenance, repair, and operating (MRO).
4. Finished goods.

In this chapter, we discussed independent inventory, ABC analysis, record accuracy, cycle counting, and inventory models used to control independent demands. The EOQ model, production order quantity model, and quantity discount model can all be solved using Excel, Excel OM, or POM for Windows software.

ETHICAL DILEMMA

The Selkirk & District General Hospital in Selkirk, Manitoba, faces a problem common to large, urban hospitals as well as to small, remote ones like itself. That problem is deciding how much of each type of whole blood to keep in stock. Because blood is expensive and has a limited shelf life (up to five weeks under 1–6°C refrigeration), Selkirk naturally wants to keep its stock as low as possible. Unfortunately, past disasters such as a major flood and a train wreck demonstrated that lives would be lost when not enough blood was available to handle massive needs. The hospital administrator wants to set an 85% service level based on demand over the past decade. Discuss the implications of this decision. What is the hospital's responsibility with regard to stocking lifesaving medicines with short shelf lives? How would you set the inventory level for a commodity such as blood?

Discussion Questions

1. Describe the four types of inventory.
2. With the advent of low-cost computing, do you see alternatives to the popular ABC classifications?
3. What is the purpose of the ABC classification system?
4. Identify and explain the types of costs that are involved in an inventory system.
5. Explain the major assumptions of the basic EOQ model.
6. What is the relationship of the economic order quantity to demand? To the holding cost? To the setup cost?
7. Explain why it is not necessary to include product cost (price or price times quantity) in the EOQ model, but the quantity discount model requires this information.
8. What are the advantages of cycle counting?
9. What impact does a decrease in setup time have on EOQ?
10. When quantity discounts are offered, why is it not necessary to check discount points that are below the EOQ or points above the EOQ that are not discount points?

11. What is meant by *service level*?
12. Explain the following: All things being equal, the production inventory quantity will be larger than the economic order quantity.
13. Describe the difference between a fixed-quantity (*Q*) and a fixed-period (*P*) inventory system.
14. Explain what is meant by the expression *robust model*. Specifically, what would you tell a manager who exclaimed, "Uh-oh, we're in trouble! The calculated EOQ is wrong; actual demand is 10% greater than estimated."
15. What is *safety stock*? What does safety stock provide safety against?
16. When demand is not constant, the reorder point is a function of what four parameters?
17. How are inventory levels monitored in retail stores?
18. State a major advantage, and a major disadvantage, of a fixed-period (*P*) system.

Using Software to Solve Inventory Problems

This section presents three ways to solve inventory problems with computer software. First, you can create your own Excel spreadsheets. Second, you can use the Excel OM software that comes with this text and is found on our website. Third, POM for Windows, also on our website at **MyLab Operations Management**, can solve all problems marked with a **P**.

PROGRAM 12.1

Using Excel for a Production Model, With Data From Example 8

Source: Microsoft product screen shot(s) reprinted with permission from Microsoft Corporations.

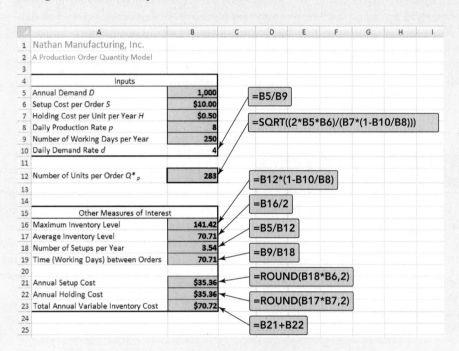

PROGRAM 12.2 Using Excel OM for an ABC Analysis, With Data From Example 1

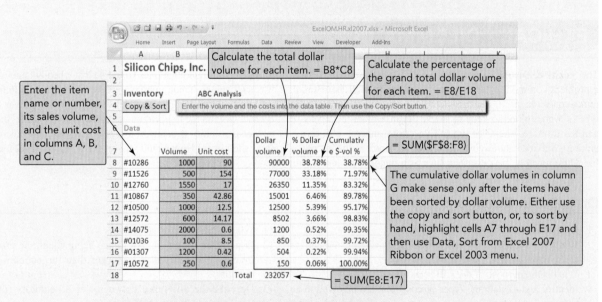

Source: Microsoft product screen shot(s) reprinted with permission from Microsoft Corporation.

Creating Your Own Excel Spreadsheets

Program 12.1 illustrates how you can make an Excel model to solve Example 8. This is a production order quantity model. A listing of the formulas needed to create the spreadsheet is shown.

✗ USING EXCEL OM

Excel OM allows us to easily model inventory problems ranging from ABC analysis, to the basic EOQ model, to the production model, to quantity discount situations.

Program 12.2 shows the input data, selected formulas, and results for an ABC analysis, using data from Example 1. After the data are entered, we use the *Data* and *Sort* Excel commands to rank the items from largest to smallest dollar volumes.

P USING POM FOR WINDOWS

The POM for Windows Inventory module can also solve the entire EOQ family of problems. Please refer to Appendix IV for further details.

Solved Problems Virtual Office Hours help is available at MyLab Operations Management.

▼ SOLVED PROBLEM 12.1

David Alexander has compiled the following table of six items in inventory at Angelo Products, along with the unit cost and the annual demand in units:

Identification Code	Unit Cost ($)	Annual Demand (units)
XX1	5.84	1200
B66	5.40	1110
3CPO	1.12	896
33CP	74.54	1104
R2D2	2.00	1110
RMS	2.08	961

Use ABC analysis to determine which item(s) should be carefully controlled using a quantitative inventory technique and which item(s) should not be closely controlled.

▼ SOLUTION

The item that needs strict control is 33CP, so it is an A item. Items that do not need to be strictly controlled are 3CPO, R2D2, and RMS; these are C items. The B items will be XX1 and B66.

Code	Annual dollar volume = Unit Cost × Demand
XX1	$ 7 008.00
B66	$ 5 994.00
3CPO	$ 1 003.52
33CP	$82 292.16
R2D2	$ 2 220.00
RMS	$ 1 998.88

Total cost = $100 516.56

▼ SOLVED PROBLEM 12.2

The Warren W. Fisher Computer Corporation purchases 8000 transistors each year as components in minicomputers. The unit cost of each transistor is $10, and the cost of carrying one transistor in inventory for a year is $3. Ordering cost is $30 per order.

What are (a) the optimal order quantity, (b) the expected number of orders placed each year, and (c) the expected time between orders? Assume that Fisher operates on a 200-day working year.

▼ SOLUTION

a) $Q^* = \sqrt{\dfrac{2DS}{H}} = \sqrt{\dfrac{2(8000)(30)}{3}} = 400$ units

b) $N = \dfrac{D}{Q^*} = \dfrac{8000}{400} = 20$ orders

c) Time between orders $= T = \dfrac{\text{Number of working days}}{N} = \dfrac{200}{20}$

With 20 orders placed each year, an order for 400 transistors is placed every 10 working days.

▼ SOLVED PROBLEM 12.3

Annual demand for notebook binders at Meyer's Stationery Shop is 10 000 units. Brad Meyer operates his business 300 days per year and finds that deliveries from his supplier generally take five working days. Calculate the reorder point for the notebook binders.

▼ SOLUTION

$$L = 5 \text{ days}$$

$$d = \frac{10\,000}{300} = 33.3 \text{ units per day}$$

$$\text{ROP} = d \times L = (33.3 \text{ units per day})(5 \text{ days})$$
$$= 166.7 \text{ units}$$

Thus, Brad should reorder when his stock reaches 167 units.

▼ SOLVED PROBLEM 12.4

Leonard Presby, Inc., has an annual demand rate of 1000 units but can produce at an average production rate of 2000 units. Setup cost is $10; carrying cost is $1. What is the optimal number of units to be produced each time?

▼ SOLUTION

$$Q_p^* = \sqrt{\dfrac{2DS}{H\left(1 - \dfrac{\text{Annual demand rate}}{\text{Annual production rate}}\right)}} = \sqrt{\dfrac{2(1000)(10)}{1[1 - (1000/2000)]}}$$

$$= \sqrt{\dfrac{20\,000}{1/2}} = \sqrt{40\,000} = 200 \text{ units}$$

▼ SOLVED PROBLEM 12.5

Whole Nature Foods sells a gluten-free product for which the annual demand is 5000 boxes. At the moment, it is paying $6.40 for each box; carrying cost is 25% of the unit cost; ordering costs are $25. A new supplier has offered to sell the same item for $6.00 if Whole Nature Foods buys at least 3000 boxes per order. Should the firm stick with the old supplier, or take advantage of the new quantity discount?

▼ SOLUTION

Under the present price of $6.40 per box:
Economic order quantity, using Equation (12-10):

$$Q^* = \sqrt{\dfrac{2DS}{IP}}$$

$$Q^* = \sqrt{\dfrac{2(5000)(25)}{(0.25)(6.40)}}$$

$$= 395.3, \text{ or } 395 \text{ boxes}$$

where D = period demand
  S = ordering cost
  P = price per box
  I = holding cost as percent
  H = holding cost = IP

Total cost = Order cost + Holding cost + Purchase cost

$$= \dfrac{DS}{Q} + \dfrac{Q}{2}H + PD$$

$$= \dfrac{(5000)(25)}{395} + \dfrac{(395)(0.25)(6.40)}{2} + (6.40)(5000)$$

$$= 316 + 316 + 32\,000$$

$$= \$32\,632$$

Note: Order and carrying costs are rounded.
Under the quantity discount price of $6.00 per box:

We compute Q^* = 408.25, which is below the required order level of 3000 boxes. So Q^* is adjusted to 3000.

Total cost = Ordering cost + Holding cost + Purchase cost

$$= \dfrac{DS}{Q} + \dfrac{Q}{2}H + PD$$

$$= \dfrac{(5000)(25)}{3000} + \dfrac{(3000)(0.25)(6.00)}{2} + (6.00)(5000)$$

$$= 42 + 2250 + 30\,000$$

$$= \$32\,292$$

Therefore, the new supplier with which Whole Nature Foods would incur a total cost of $32 292 is preferable, but not by a large amount. If buying 3000 boxes at a time raises problems of storage or freshness, the company may very well wish to stay with the current supplier.

▼ SOLVED PROBLEM 12.6

Children's art sets are ordered once each year by Ashok Kumar, Inc., and the reorder point without safety stock (dL) is 100 art sets. Inventory carrying cost is $10 per set per year, and the cost of a stockout is $50 per set per year. Given the following demand probabilities during the lead time, how much safety stock should be carried?

Demand During Lead Time	Probability
0	0.1
50	0.2
ROP →100	0.4
150	0.2
200	0.1
	1.0

▼ **SOLUTION**

		Incremental Costs	
Safety Stock	Carrying Cost	Stockout Cost	Total Cost
0	0	$50 \times (50 \times 0.2 + 100 \times 0.1) = 1000$	$1000
50	$50 \times 10 = 500$	$50 \times (0.1 \times 50) = 250$	750
100	$100 \times 10 = 1000$	0	1000

The safety stock that minimizes total incremental cost is 50 sets. The reorder point then becomes $100 + 50$ sets, or 150 sets.

▼ **SOLVED PROBLEM 12.7**

What safety stock should Ron Satterfield Corporation maintain if mean sales are 80 during the reorder period, the standard deviation is 7, and Ron can tolerate stockouts 10% of the time?

▼ **SOLUTION**

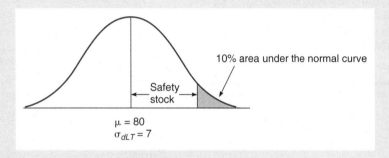

From Appendix I, Z at an area of 0.9 (or $1 - 0.10$) = 1.28, and Equation (12-14):

$$\text{Safety stock} = Z\sigma_{dLT}$$

$$= 1.28(7) = 8.96 \text{ units, or } 9 \text{ units}$$

▼ **SOLVED PROBLEM 12.8**

The daily demand for 52-inch plasma TVs at Sarah's Discount Emporium is normally distributed, with an average of five and a standard deviation of two units. The lead time for receiving a shipment of new TVs is 10 days and is fairly constant. Determine the reorder point and safety stock for a 95% service level.

▼ **SOLUTION**

The ROP for this variable demand and constant lead time model uses Equation (12-15):

$$\text{ROP} = (\text{Average daily demand} \times \text{Lead time in days}) + Z\sigma_{dLT}$$

where $\sigma_{dLT} = \sigma_d \sqrt{\text{Lead time}}$

So, with $Z = 1.65$,

$$\text{ROP} = (5 \times 10) + 1.65(2)\sqrt{10}$$

$$= 50 + 10.4 = 60.4 \cong 60 \text{ TVs}$$

The safety stock is 10.4, or about 10 TVs.

▼ **SOLVED PROBLEM 12.9**

The demand at Charlottetown's Queen Elizabeth Hospital for a specialized surgery pack is 60 per week, virtually every week. The lead time from McKesson, its main supplier, is normally distributed, with a mean of six weeks for this product and a standard deviation of two weeks. A 90% weekly service level is desired. Find the ROP.

▼ SOLUTION

Here, the demand is constant and lead time is variable, with data given in weeks, not days. We apply Equation (12-16):

$$\text{ROP} = (\text{Weekly demand} \times \text{Average lead time in weeks}) + Z\,(\text{Weekly demand})\,\sigma_{LT}$$

where σ_{LT} = standard deviation of lead time in weeks = 2

So, with $Z = 1.28$, for a 90% service level:

$$\text{ROP} = (60 \times 6) + 1.28(60)(2)$$

$$= 360 + 153.6 = 513.6 \cong 514 \text{ surgery packs}$$

Problems*

•• 12.1 L. Houts Plastics is a large manufacturer of injection-moulded plastics in Ontario. An investigation of the company's manufacturing facility in Mississauga yields the information presented in the table below. How would the plant classify these items according to an ABC classification system? **PX**

L. Houts Plastics Mississauga Inventory Levels

Item Code #	Average Inventory (units)	Value ($/unit)
1289	400	3.75
2347	300	4.00
2349	120	2.50
2363	75	1.50
2394	60	1.75
2395	30	2.00
6782	20	1.15
7844	12	2.05
8210	8	1.80
8310	7	2.00
9111	6	3.00

•• 12.2 Boreki Enterprises has the following 10 items in inventory. Theodore Boreki asks you, a recent OM graduate, to divide these items into ABC classifications.

Item	Annual Demand	Cost/Unit
A2	3000	$ 50
B8	4000	12
C7	1500	45
D1	6000	10
E9	1000	20
F3	500	500
G2	300	1500
H2	600	20
I5	1750	10
J8	2500	5

a) Develop an ABC classification system for the 10 items.
b) How can Boreki use this information?
c) Boreki reviews the classification and then places item A2 into the A category. Why might he do so? **PX**

•• 12.3 Jean-Marie Bourjolly's restaurant has the following inventory items that it orders on a weekly basis:

Inventory Item	$ Value/Case	# Ordered/Week
Rib eye steak	135	3
Lobster tail	245	3
Pasta	23	12
Salt	3	2
Napkins	12	2
Tomato sauce	23	11
French fries	43	32
Pepper	3	3
Garlic powder	11	3
Trash can liners	12	3
Tablecloths	32	5
Fish fillets	143	10
Prime rib roasts	166	6
Oil	28	2
Lettuce (case)	35	24
Chickens	75	14
Order pads	12	2
Eggs (case)	22	7
Bacon	56	5
Sugar	4	2

a) Which is the most expensive item, using annual dollar volume?
b) Which are C items?
c) What is the annual dollar volume for all 20 items? **PX**

• 12.4 Howard Electronics, a small manufacturer of electronic research equipment, has approximately 7000 items in its inventory and has hired Joan Blasco-Paul to manage its inventory. Joan has determined that 10% of the items in inventory are A items, 35% are B items, and 55% are C items. She would like to set up a system in which all A items are counted monthly (every 20 working days), all B items are counted quarterly (every 60 working days), and all C items are counted semiannually (every 120 working days). How many items need to be counted each day?

---

* *Note:* **PX** means the problem may be solved with POM for Windows and/or Excel OM.

• **12.5** William Beville's computer training school, in Richmond, stocks workbooks with the following characteristics:

$$\text{Demand } D = 19\ 500 \text{ units/year}$$
$$\text{Ordering cost } S = \$25/\text{order}$$
$$\text{Holding cost } H = \$4/\text{unit/year}$$

a) Calculate the EOQ for the workbooks.
b) What are the annual holding costs for the workbooks?
c) What are the annual ordering costs? **Px**

•• **12.6** If $D = 8000$ per month, $S = \$45$ per order, and $H = \$2$ per unit per month,
a) What is the economic order quantity?
b) How does your answer change if the holding cost doubles?
c) What if the holding cost drops to half? **Px**

•• **12.7** Henry Crouch's law office has traditionally ordered ink refills 60 units at a time. The firm estimates that carrying cost is 40% of the $10 unit cost and that annual demand is about 240 units per year. The assumptions of the basic EOQ model are thought to apply.
a) For what value of ordering cost would its action be optimal?
b) If the true ordering cost turns out to be much greater than your answer to part (a), what is the impact on the firm's ordering policy?

• **12.8** Madeline Thimmes's Dream Store sells waterbeds and assorted supplies. Her best-selling bed has an annual demand of 400 units. Ordering cost is $40; holding cost is $5 per unit per year.
a) To minimize the total cost, how many units should be ordered each time an order is placed?
b) If the holding cost per unit was $6 instead of $5, what would be the optimal order quantity? **Px**

• **12.9** Bell Canada stocks a certain switch connector at its central warehouse for supplying field service offices. The yearly demand for these connectors is 15 000 units. Bell estimates its annual holding cost for this item to be $25 per unit. The cost to place and process an order from the supplier is $75. The company operates 300 days per year, and the lead time to receive an order from the supplier is two working days.
a) Find the economic order quantity.
b) Find the annual holding costs.
c) Find the annual ordering costs.
d) What is the reorder point? **Px**

• **12.10** Lead time for one of your fastest-moving products is 21 days. Demand during this period averages 100 units per day.
a) What would be an appropriate reorder point?
b) How does your answer change if demand during lead time doubles?
c) How does your answer change if demand during lead time drops to half?

• **12.11** Annual demand for the notebook binders at Duncan's Stationery Shop is 10 000 units. Dana Duncan operates her business 300 days per year and finds that deliveries from her supplier generally take five working days.
a) Calculate the reorder point for the notebook binders that she stocks.
b) Why is this number important to Duncan?

•• **12.12** Thomas Kratzer is the purchasing manager for the headquarters of a large insurance company chain with a central inventory operation. Thomas's fastest-moving inventory item has a demand of 6000 units per year. The cost of each unit is $100, and the inventory carrying cost is $10 per unit per year. The average ordering cost is $30 per order. It takes about five days for an order

to arrive, and the demand for one week is 120 units. (This is a corporate operation, and there are 250 working days per year.)
a) What is the EOQ?
b) What is the average inventory if the EOQ is used?
c) What is the optimal number of orders per year?
d) What is the optimal number of days between any two orders?
e) What is the annual cost of ordering and holding inventory?
f) What is the total annual inventory cost, including cost of the 6000 units? **Px**

•• **12.13** Joe Henry's machine shop uses 2500 brackets during the course of a year. These brackets are purchased from a supplier 90 kilometres away. The following information is known about the brackets:

Annual demand:	2500
Holding cost per bracket per year:	$1.50
Order cost per order:	$18.75
Lead time:	2 days
Working days per year:	250

a) Given the above information, what would be the economic order quantity (EOQ)?
b) Given the EOQ, what would be the average inventory? What would be the annual inventory holding cost?
c) Given the EOQ, how many orders would be made each year? What would be the annual order cost?
d) Given the EOQ, what is the total annual cost of managing the inventory?
e) What is the time between orders?
f) What is the reorder point (ROP)? **Px**

•• **12.14** Myriah Fitzgibbon, of L.A. Plumbing, uses 1200 of a certain spare part that costs $25 for each order, with an annual holding cost of $24.
a) Calculate the total cost for order sizes of 25, 40, 50, 60, and 100.
b) Identify the economic order quantity and consider the implications for making an error in calculating economic order quantity. **Px**

••• **12.15** M. Cotteleer Electronics supplies microcomputer circuitry to a company that incorporates microprocessors into refrigerators and other home appliances. One of the components has an annual demand of 250 units, and this is constant throughout the year. Carrying cost is estimated to be $1 per unit per year, and the ordering cost is $20 per order.
a) To minimize cost, how many units should be ordered each time an order is placed?
b) How many orders per year are needed with the optimal policy?
c) What is the average inventory if costs are minimized?
d) Suppose that the ordering cost is not $20, and Cotteleer has been ordering 150 units each time an order is placed. For this order policy (of $Q = 150$) to be optimal, determine what the ordering cost would have to be. **Px**

•• **12.16** Race One Motors is an Indonesian car manufacturer. At its largest manufacturing facility, in Jakarta, the company produces subcomponents at a rate of 300 per day, and it uses these subcomponents at a rate of 12 500 per year (of 250 working days). Holding costs are $2 per item per year, and ordering costs are $30 per order.
a) What is the economic production quantity?
b) How many production runs per year will be made?
c) What will be the maximum inventory level?
d) What percentage of time will the facility be producing components?
e) What is the annual cost of ordering and holding inventory?

•• **12.17** Drolet Manufacturing Company, in Saint-Hubert, Quebec, makes flashing lights for toys. The company operates its production facility 300 days per year. It has orders for about 12 000 flashing lights per year and has the capability of producing 100 per day. Setting up the light production costs $50. The cost of each light is $1. The holding cost is $0.10 per light per year.
a) What is the optimal size of the production run?
b) What is the average holding cost per year?
c) What is the average setup cost per year?
d) What is the total cost per year, including the cost of the lights? **Px**

•• **12.18** Arthur Meiners is the production manager of Wheel-Rite, a small producer of metal parts. Wheel-Rite supplies Cal-Tex, a larger assembly company, with 10 000 wheel bearings each year. This order has been stable for some time. Setup cost for Wheel-Rite is $40, and holding cost is $0.60 per wheel bearing per year. Wheel-Rite can produce 500 wheel bearings per day. Cal-Tex is a just-in-time manufacturer and requires that 50 bearings be shipped to it each business day.
a) What is the optimum production quantity?
b) What is the maximum number of wheel bearings that will be in inventory at Wheel-Rite?
e) How many production runs of wheel bearings will Wheel-Rite have in a year?
d) What is the total setup plus holding cost for Wheel-Rite? **Px**

•• **12.19** Cesar Rego Computers, a British Columbia chain of computer hardware and software retail outlets, supplies both educational and commercial customers with memory and storage devices. It currently faces the following ordering decision relating to purchases of high-density disks:

$$D = 36\ 000\ \text{disks}$$
$$S = \$25$$
$$H = \$0.45$$
$$\text{Purchase price} = \$0.85$$
$$\text{Discount price} = \$0.82$$

Quantity needed to qualify for the discount = 6000 disks

Should the discount be taken? **Px**

•• **12.20** Bell Computers purchases integrated chips at $350 per chip. The holding cost is $35 per unit per year, the ordering cost is $120 per order, and sales are steady, at 400 per month. The company's supplier, Rich Blue Chip Manufacturing, Inc., decides to offer price concessions in order to attract larger orders. The price structure is shown below.

Rich Blue Chip's Price Structure

Quantity Purchased	Price/Unit
1–99 units	$350
100–199 units	$325
200 or more units	$300

a) What is the optimal order quantity and the minimum cost for Bell Computers to order, purchase, and hold these integrated chips?
b) Bell Computers wishes to use a 10% holding cost rather than the fixed $35 holding cost in part (a). What is the optimal order quantity, and what is the optimal cost? **Px**

•• **12.21** Wang Distributors has an annual demand for an airport metal detector of 1400 units. The cost of a typical detector to Wang is $400. Carrying cost is estimated to be 20% of the unit cost, and the ordering cost is $25 per order. If Ping Wang, the owner, orders in quantities of 300 or more, he can get a 5% discount on the cost of the detectors. Should Wang take the quantity discount? **Px**

•• **12.22** The catering manager of LaVista Hotel, Lisa Ferguson, is disturbed by the amount of silverware she is losing every week. Last Friday night, when her crew tried to set up for a banquet for 500 people, they did not have enough knives. She decides she needs to order some more silverware but wants to take advantage of any quantity discounts her vendor will offer.

For a small order (2000 or fewer pieces), her vendor quotes a price of $1.80/piece.

If she orders 2001–5000 pieces, the price drops to $1.60/piece.

For 5001–10 000 pieces, the price is $1.40/piece, and 10 001 and above reduces the price to $1.25.

Lisa's order costs are $200 per order, her annual holding costs are 5%, and the annual demand is 45 000 pieces. For the best option:
a) What is the optimal order quantity?
b) What is the annual holding cost?
c) What is the annual ordering (setup) cost?
d) What are the annual costs of the silverware itself with an optimal order quantity?
e) What is the total annual cost, including ordering, holding, and purchasing the silverware? **Px**

•• **12.23** Rocky Mountain Tire Centre sells 20 000 go-kart tires per year. The ordering cost for each order is $40, and the holding cost is 20% of the purchase price of the tires per year. The purchase price is $20 per tire if fewer than 500 tires are ordered, $18 per tire if 500 or more—but fewer than 1000—tires are ordered, and $17 per tire if 1000 or more tires are ordered.
a) How many tires should Rocky Mountain order each time it places an order?
b) What is the total cost of this policy? **Px**

•• **12.24** M.P. VanOyen Manufacturing has gone out on bid for a regulator component. Expected demand is 700 units per month. The item can be purchased from either Allen Manufacturing or Baker Manufacturing. Their price lists are shown in the table. Ordering cost is $50, and annual holding cost per unit is $5.

Allen Mfg.		Baker Mfg.	
Quantity	Unit Price	Quantity	Unit Price
1–499	$16.00	1–399	$16.10
500–999	15.50	400–799	15.60
1000+	15.00	800+	15.10

a) What is the economic order quantity?
b) Which supplier should be used? Why?
c) What is the optimal order quantity and total annual cost of ordering, purchasing, and holding the component? **Px**

••• **12.25** Chris Sandvig Irrigation, Inc., has summarized the price list from four potential suppliers of an underground control valve. See the table below. Annual usage is 2400 valves; order cost is $10 per order; and annual inventory holding costs are $3.33 per unit.

Which vendor should be selected and what order quantity is best if Sandvig Irrigation wants to minimize total cost? **Px**

Vendor A		Vendor B	
Quantity	**Price**	**Quantity**	**Price**
1–49	$35.00	1–74	$34.75
50–74	34.75	75–149	34.00
75–149	33.55	150–299	32.80
150–299	32.35	300–499	31.60
300–499	31.15	500+	30.50
500+	30.75		

Vendor C		Vendor D	
Quantity	**Price**	**Quantity**	**Price**
1–99	$34.50	1–199	$34.25
100–199	33.75	200–399	33.00
200–399	32.50	400+	31.00
400+	31.10		

••• **12.26** Emery Pharmaceutical uses an unstable chemical compound that must be kept in an environment where both temperature and humidity can be controlled. Emery uses 800 pounds per month of the chemical, estimates the holding cost to be 50% of the purchase price (because of spoilage), and estimates order costs to be $50 per order. The cost schedules of two suppliers are as follows:

Vendor 1		Vendor 2	
Quantity	**Price/lb**	**Quantity**	**Price/lb**
1–499	$17.00	1–399	$17.10
500–999	16.75	400–799	16.85
1000+	16.50	800–1199	16.60
		1200+	16.25

a) What is the economic order quantity for each supplier?
b) What quantity should be ordered, and which supplier should be used?
c) What is the total cost for the most economic order size?
d) What factor(s) should be considered besides total cost? **Px**

•• **12.27** Barbara Flynn is in charge of maintaining hospital supplies at General Hospital. During the past year, the mean lead time demand for bandage BX-5 was 60 (and was normally distributed). Furthermore, the standard deviation for BX-5 was seven. Ms. Flynn would like to maintain a 90% service level.
a) What safety stock level do you recommend for BX-5?
b) What is the appropriate reorder point? **Px**

•• **12.28** Based on available information, lead time demand for PC jump drives averages 50 units (normally distributed), with a standard deviation of five drives. Management wants a 97% service level.
a) What value of Z should be applied?
b) How many drives should be carried as safety stock?
c) What is the appropriate reorder point? **Px**

••• **12.29** Authentic Thai rattan chairs are delivered to Gary Schwartz's chain of retail stores, called The Kathmandu Shop, once a year. The reorder point, without safety stock, is 200 chairs. Carrying cost is $30 per unit per year, and the cost of a stockout is $70 per chair per year. Given the following demand probabilities during the lead time, how much safety stock should be carried?

Demand During Lead Time	Probability
0	0.2
100	0.2
200	0.2
300	0.2
400	0.2

•• **12.30** Tobacco is shipped from Tillsonburg, Ontario, to a cigarette manufacturer in Cambodia once a year. The reorder point, without safety stock, is 200 kilograms. The carrying cost is $15 per kilogram per year, and the cost of a stockout is $70 per kilogram per year. Given the following demand probabilities during the lead time, how much safety stock should be carried?

Demand During Lead Time (kg)	Probability
0	0.1
100	0.1
200	0.2
300	0.4
400	0.2

••• **12.31** Mr. Beautiful, an organization that sells weight training sets, has an ordering cost of $40 for the BB-1 set. (BB-1 stands for Body Beautiful Number 1.) The carrying cost for BB-1 is $5 per set per year. To meet demand, Mr. Beautiful orders large quantities of BB-1 seven times a year. The stockout cost for BB-1 is estimated to be $50 per set. Over the past several years, Mr. Beautiful has observed the following demand during the lead time for BB-1:

Demand During Lead Time	Probability
40	0.1
50	0.2
60	0.2
70	0.2
80	0.2
90	0.1
	1.0

The reorder point for BB-1 is 60 sets. What level of safety stock should be maintained for BB-1? **Px**

•• **12.32** Ottawa's Fairmont Château Laurier hotel distributes a mean of 1000 bath towels per day to guests at the pool and in their rooms. This demand is normally distributed with a standard deviation of 100 towels per day, based on occupancy. The laundry firm that has the linen contract requires a two-day lead time. The hotel expects a 98% service level to satisfy high guest expectations.
a) What is the ROP?
b) What is the safety stock? **Px**

•• **12.33** First Printing has contracts with legal firms in Regina to copy their court documents. Daily demand is almost constant at 12 500 pages of documents. The lead time for paper delivery is normally distributed with a mean of four days and a standard deviation of one day. A 97% service level is expected. Compute First's ROP. **Px**

••• **12.34** Halifax Cigar stocks Cuban cigars that have variable lead times because of the difficulty in importing the product: Lead time is normally distributed with an average of six weeks and a standard deviation of two weeks. Demand is also a variable and normally distributed with a mean of 200 cigars per week and a standard deviation of 25 cigars.

a) For a 90% service level, what is the ROP?
b) What is the ROP for a 95% service level?
c) Explain what these two service levels mean. Which is preferable? **Px**

• • • 12.35 Kim Clark has asked you to help him determine the best ordering policy for a new product. The demand for the new product has been forecasted to be about 1000 units annually. To help you get a handle on the carrying and ordering costs, Kim has given you the list of last year's costs. He thought that these costs might be appropriate for the new product.

Cost Factor	Cost ($)	Cost Factor	Cost ($)
Taxes for the warehouse	2 000	Warehouse supplies	280
Receiving and incoming inspection	1 500	Research and development	2 750
New product development	2 500	Purchasing salaries & wages	30 000
Acct. dept. costs to pay invoices	500	Warehouse salaries & wages	12 800
Inventory insurance	600	Pilferage of inventory	800
Product advertising	800	Purchase order supplies	500
Spoilage	750	Inventory obsolescence	300
Sending purchasing orders	800	Purchasing dept. overhead	1 000

He also told you that these data were compiled for 10 000 inventory items that were carried or held during the year. You have also determined that 200 orders were placed last year. Your job as a new operations management graduate is to help Kim determine the economic order quantity for the new product.

• • 12.36 Cynthia Knott's seafood restaurant buys fresh Nova Scotia lobster for $5 per pound and sells them for $9 per pound. Any lobsters not sold that day are sold to her cousin's nearby grocery store for $2 per pound. Cynthia believes that demand follows the normal distribution, with a mean of 100 pounds and a standard deviation of 15 pounds. How many pounds should she order each day?

• • 12.37 Henrique Correa's bakery prepares all its cakes between 4:00 a.m. and 6:00 a.m. so they will be fresh when customers arrive. Day-old cakes are virtually always sold, but at a 50% discount off the regular $10 price. The cost of baking a cake is $6, and demand is estimated to be normally distributed, with a mean of 25 and a standard deviation of four. What is the optimal stocking level?

• • • 12.38 The monthly Toronto Maple Leafs fan magazines are printed one week prior to the start of sales for each monthly issue during the season. Attendance averages 90 000 screaming and loyal Leafs fans during the life of each issue. Two-thirds of these fans usually buy the program, following a normal distribution, for $4 each. Unsold programs are sent to a recycling centre that pays only 10 cents per program. The standard deviation is 5000 programs, and the cost to print each program is $1.

a) What is the cost of underestimating demand for each program?
b) What is the overage cost per program?
c) How many programs should be ordered per game?
d) What is the stockout risk for this order size?

• • • • 12.39 Emarpy Appliance is a company that produces all kinds of major appliances. Bud Banis, the president of Emarpy, is concerned about the production policy for the company's best-selling refrigerator. The annual demand for this has been about 8000 units each year, and this demand has been constant throughout the year. The production capacity is 200 units per day. Each time production starts, it costs the company $120 to move materials into place, reset the assembly line, and clean the equipment. The holding cost of a refrigerator is $50 per year. The current production plan calls for 400 refrigerators to be produced in each production run. Assume there are 250 working days per year.

a) What is the daily demand of this product?
b) If the company were to continue to produce 400 units each time production starts, how many days would production continue?
c) Under the current policy, how many production runs per year would be required? What would the annual setup cost be?
d) If the current policy continued, how many refrigerators would be in inventory when production stops? What would the average inventory level be?
e) If the company produced 400 refrigerators at a time, what would the total annual setup cost and holding cost be?
f) If Bud Banis wants to minimize the total annual inventory cost, how many refrigerators should be produced in each production run? How much would this save the company in inventory costs compared to the current policy of producing 400 in each production run? **Px**

• • • • 12.40 A gourmet coffee shop in downtown Vancouver is open 200 days a year and sells an average of 75 pounds of Kona coffee beans a day. (Demand can be assumed to be distributed normally with a standard deviation of 15 pounds per day.) After ordering (fixed cost = $16 per order), beans are always shipped from Hawaii within exactly four days. Per-pound annual holding costs for the beans are $3.

a) What is the economic order quantity (EOQ) for Kona coffee beans?
b) What are the total annual holding costs of stock for Kona coffee beans?
c) What are the total annual ordering costs for Kona coffee beans?
d) Assume that management has specified that no more than a 1% risk of stockout is acceptable. What should the reorder point (ROP) be?
e) What is the safety stock needed to attain a 1% risk of stockout during lead time?
f) What is the annual holding cost of maintaining the level of safety stock needed to support a 1% risk?
g) If management specified that a 2% risk of stockout during lead time would be acceptable, would the safety stock holding costs decrease or increase?

CASE | STUDIES

Zhou Bicycle Company

Zhou Bicycle Company (ZBC), located in Vancouver, is a wholesale distributor of bicycles and bicycle parts. Formed in 1981 by Yong-Pin Zhou, the firm's primary retail outlets are located within a 650-kilometre radius of the distribution centre. These retail outlets receive the order from ZBC within two days after notifying the distribution centre, provided that the stock is available. However, if an order is not fulfilled by the company, no backorder is placed; the retailers arrange to get their shipment from other distributors, and ZBC loses that amount of business.

The company distributes a wide variety of bicycles. The most popular model, and the major source of revenue to the company, is the AirWing. ZBC receives all the models from a single manufacturer in China, and shipment takes as long as four weeks from the time an order is placed. With the cost of communication, paperwork, and customs clearance included, ZBC estimates that each time an order is placed, it incurs a cost of $65. The purchase price paid by ZBC, per bicycle, is roughly 60% of the suggested retail price for all the styles available, and the inventory carrying cost is 1% per month (12% per year) of the purchase price paid by ZBC. The retail price (paid by the customers) for the AirWing is $170 per bicycle.

Demands for AirWing Model

Month	2017	2018	Forecast for 2019
January	6	7	8
February	12	14	15
March	24	27	31
April	46	53	59
May	75	86	97
June	47	54	60
July	30	34	39
August	18	21	24
September	13	15	16
October	12	13	15
November	22	25	28
December	38	42	47
Total	343	391	439

ZBC is interested in making an inventory plan for 2019. The firm wants to maintain a 95% service level with its customers to minimize the losses on the lost orders. The data collected for the past two years are summarized in the preceding table. A forecast for AirWing model sales in 2019 has been developed and will be used to make an inventory plan for ZBC.

Discussion Questions

1. Develop an inventory plan to help ZBC.
2. Discuss ROPs and total costs.
3. How can you address demand that is not at the level of the planning horizon?

Source: Professor Kala Chand Seal, Loyola Marymount University.

Managing Inventory at Frito-Lay

Frito-Lay has flourished since its origin—the 1931 purchase of a small San Antonio firm for $100 that included a recipe, 19 retail accounts, and a hand-operated potato ricer. The multibillion-dollar company, headquartered in Dallas, now has 41 products—15 with sales of over $100 million per year and 7 at over $1 billion in sales. Production takes place in 36 product-focused plants in the United States and Canada, with 48 000 employees.

Inventory is a major investment and an expensive asset in most firms. Holding costs often exceed 25% of product value, but in Frito-Lay's prepared food industry, holding costs can be much higher because the raw materials are perishable. In the food industry, inventory spoils. So, poor inventory management is not only expensive but can also yield an unsatisfactory product that, in the extreme, can also ruin market acceptance.

Major ingredients at Frito-Lay are corn meal, corn, potatoes, oil, and seasoning. Using potato chips to illustrate rapid inventory flow: potatoes are moved via truck from farm, to regional plants for processing, to warehouse, to the retail store. This happens in a matter of hours—not days or weeks. This keeps freshness high and holding costs low.

Frequent deliveries of main ingredients at the Florida plant, for example, take several forms:

- Potatoes are delivered in 10 truckloads per day, with 150 000 pounds consumed in one shift: the entire potato storage area will only hold 7.5 hours' worth of potatoes.
- Oil inventory arrives by rail car, which lasts only 4.5 days.
- Corn meal arrives from various farms in the Midwest, and inventory typically averages 4 days' production.
- Seasoning inventory averages 7 days.
- Packaging inventory averages 8 to 10 days.

Frito-Lay's product-focused facility is expensive. It represents a major capital investment that must achieve high utilization to be efficient. The capital cost must be spread over a substantial volume to drive down total cost of the snack foods produced. This demand for high utilization requires reliable equipment and tight schedules. Reliable machinery requires an inventory of critical components: This is known as MRO, or maintenance, repair, and operating supplies. MRO inventory of motors, switches, gears, bearings, and other critical specialized components can be costly but is necessary.

Frito-Lay's non-MRO inventory moves rapidly. Raw material quickly becomes work-in-process, moving through the system and out the door as a bag of chips in about 1.5 shifts. Packaged finished products move from production to the distribution chain in less than 1.4 days.

Discussion Questions*

1. How does the mix of Frito-Lay's inventory differ from those at a machine or cabinet shop (a process-focused facility)?
2. What are the major inventory items at Frito-Lay, and how rapidly do they move through the process?
3. What are the four types of inventory? Give an example of each at Frito-Lay.
4. How would you rank the dollar investment in each of the four types (from the most investment to the least investment)?

5. Why does inventory flow so quickly through a Frito-Lay plant?
6. Why does the company keep so many plants open?
7. Why doesn't Frito-Lay make all its 41 products at each of its plants?

* You may wish to view the video that accompanies this case before answering these questions.

Sources: Professors Jay Heizer, Texas Lutheran University; Barry Render, Rollins College; and Bev Amer, Northern Arizona University.

Video Case | **Inventory Control at Wheeled Coach Ambulance**

Controlling inventory is one of Wheeled Coach's toughest problems. Operating according to a strategy of mass customization and responsiveness, management knows that success is dependent on tight inventory control. Anything else results in an inability to deliver promptly, chaos on the assembly line, and a huge inventory investment. Wheeled Coach finds that almost 50% of the $40 000 to $100 000 cost of every ambulance it manufactures is purchased materials. A large proportion of that 50% is in chassis (purchased from Ford), aluminum (from Reynolds Metal), and plywood used for flooring and cabinetry construction (from local suppliers). Wheeled Coach tracks these class A inventory items quite carefully, maintaining tight security/control and ordering carefully so as to maximize quantity discounts while minimizing on-hand stock. Because of long lead times and scheduling needs at Reynolds, aluminum must actually be ordered as much as eight months in advance.

In a crowded ambulance industry in which it is the only giant, its 45 competitors don't have the purchasing power to draw the same discounts as Wheeled Coach. But this competitive cost advantage cannot be taken lightly, according to the president, Bob Collins. "Cycle counting in our stockrooms is critical. No part can leave the locked stockrooms without appearing on a bill of materials."

Accurate bills of materials (BOM) are a requirement if products are going to be built on time. Additionally, because of the custom nature of each vehicle, most orders are won only after a bidding process. Accurate BOMs are critical to cost estimation and the resulting bid. For these reasons, Collins was emphatic that Wheeled Coach maintain outstanding inventory control. The *Global Company Profile* featuring Wheeled Coach (which opens Chapter 14) provides further details about the ambulance inventory control and production process.

Discussion Questions*

1. Explain how Wheeled Coach implements ABC analysis.
2. If you were to take over as inventory control manager at Wheeled Coach, what additional policies and techniques would you initiate to ensure accurate inventory records?
3. How would you go about implementing these suggestions?

* You may wish to view the video that accompanies this case before answering these questions.

▶**Additional Case Studies:** Visit **MyLab Operations Management** for these case studies:

Fast Creek Lightning (F): The town must decide how many hockey day programs to order, and from whom.

CHAPTER 12 | RAPID REVIEW

MyLab Operations Management

Main Heading	Review Material	
THE IMPORTANCE OF INVENTORY (pp. 470–472)	Inventory is one of the most expensive assets of many companies. *The objective of inventory management is to strike a balance between inventory investment and customer service.* The two basic inventory issues are how much to order and when to order. • **Raw material inventory**—Materials that are usually purchased but have yet to enter the manufacturing process. • **Work-in-process (WIP) inventory**—Products or components that are no longer raw materials but have yet to become finished products. • **MRO**—Maintenance, repair, and operating materials. • **Finished goods inventory**—An end item ready to be sold, but still an asset on the company's books.	**VIDEO 12.1** Managing Inventory at Frito-Lay

Main Heading	**Review Material**	
MANAGING INVENTORY (pp. 472–477)	• **ABC analysis**—A method for dividing on-hand inventory into three classifications based on annual dollar volume. • **Cycle counting**—A continuing reconciliation of inventory with inventory records. • **Shrinkage**—Retail inventory that is unaccounted for between receipt and sale. • **Pilferage**—A small amount of theft.	Problems: 12.1–12.4 Virtual Office Hours for Solved Problem: 12.1
INVENTORY MODELS (p. 478)	• **Holding cost**—The cost to keep or carry inventory in stock. • **Ordering cost**—The cost of the ordering process. • **Setup cost**—The cost to prepare a machine or process for production. • **Setup time**—The time required to prepare a machine or process for production.	**VIDEO 12.2** Inventory Control at Wheeled Coach Ambulance
INVENTORY MODELS FOR INDEPENDENT DEMAND (pp. 478–489)	• **Economic order quantity (EOQ) model**—An inventory control technique that minimizes the total of ordering and holding costs: $$Q^* = \sqrt{\frac{2DS}{H}} \qquad (12\text{-}1)$$ $$\text{Expected number of orders} = N = \frac{\text{Demand}}{\text{Order quantity}} = \frac{D}{Q^*} \qquad (12\text{-}2)$$ $$\text{Expected time between orders} = T = \frac{\text{Number of working days per year}}{N} \qquad (12\text{-}3)$$ $$\text{Total annual cost} = \text{Setup (order) cost} + \text{Holding cost} \qquad (12\text{-}4)$$ $$TC = \frac{D}{Q}S + \frac{Q}{2}H \qquad (12\text{-}5)$$ • **Robust**—Giving satisfactory answers even with substantial variation in the parameters. • **Lead time**—In purchasing systems, the time between placing an order and receiving it; in production systems, the wait, move, queue, setup, and run times for each component produced. • **Reorder point (ROP)**—The inventory level (point) at which action is taken to replenish the stocked item. *ROP for known demand:* $$\text{ROP} = (\text{Demand per day}) \times (\text{Lead time for a new order in days}) = d \times L \qquad (12\text{-}6)$$ • **Safety stock**—Extra stock to allow for uneven demand; a buffer. • **Production order quantity model**—An economic order quantity technique applied to production orders: $$Q_p^* = \sqrt{\frac{2DS}{H[1 - (d/p)]}} \qquad (12\text{-}7)$$ $$Q_p^* = \sqrt{\frac{2DS}{H\left(1 - \dfrac{\text{Annual demand rate}}{\text{Annual production rate}}\right)}} \qquad (12\text{-}8)$$ • **Quantity discount**—A reduced price for items purchased in large quantities. $$TC = \frac{D}{Q}S + \frac{Q}{2}H + PD \qquad (12\text{-}9)$$ $$Q^* = \sqrt{\frac{2DS}{IP}} \qquad (12\text{-}10)$$	Problems: 12.5–12.25, 12.35, 12.37, 12.39 Virtual Office Hours for Solved Problems: 12.2–12.5 **ACTIVE MODELS 12.1, 12.2**

Main Heading	Review Material	
PROBABILISTIC MODELS AND SAFETY STOCK (pp. 490–494)	• **Probabilistic model**—A statistical model applicable when product demand or any other variable is not known but can be specified by means of a probability distribution.	Problems: 12.27–12.34, 12.40 Virtual Office Hours for Solved Problems: 12.6–12.8
	• **Service level**—The complement of the probability of a stockout.	
	ROP for unknown demand:	
	$$ROP = d \times L + ss \qquad \textbf{(12-11)}$$	
	Annual stockout costs = The sum of the units short for each demand level $\times$ The probability of that demand level $\times$ The stockout cost/unit $\times$ The number of orders per year	
	$$\textbf{(12-12)}$$	
	ROP for unknown demand and given service level:	
	$$ROP = \text{Expected demand during lead time} + Z\sigma_{dLT} \quad \textbf{(12-13)}$$	
	$$\text{Safety stock} = Z\sigma_{dLT} \qquad \textbf{(12-14)}$$	
	ROP for variable demand and constant lead time:	
	$$ROP = (\textit{Average} \text{ daily demand} \times \text{Lead time in days}) + Z\sigma_{dLT} \quad \textbf{(12-15)}$$	
	ROP for constant demand and variable lead time:	
	$$ROP = (\text{Daily demand} \times \textit{Average} \text{ lead time in days})$$	
	$$+ Z(\text{Daily demand}) \times \sigma_{LT} \qquad \textbf{(12-16)}$$	
	ROP for variable demand and variable lead time:	
	$$ROP = (\text{Average daily demand} \times \text{Average lead time}) + Z\sigma_{dLT} \quad \textbf{(12-17)}$$	
	In each case, $\sigma_{dLT} = \sqrt{(\text{Average lead time} \times \sigma_d^2) + \bar{d}^2\sigma_{LT}^2}$ but under constant demand: $\sigma_d^2 = 0$ and while under constant lead time: $\sigma_{LT}^2 = 0$	
SINGLE-PERIOD MODEL (pp. 495–496)	• **Single-period inventory model**—A system for ordering items that have little or no value at the end of a sales period.	Problems: 12.36–12.38
	$$\text{Service Level} = \frac{C_s}{C_s + C_o} \qquad \textbf{(12-18)}$$	
FIXED-PERIOD (*P*) SYSTEMS (pp. 496–497)	• **Fixed-quantity (*Q*) system**—An ordering system with the same order amount each time.	
	• **Perpetual inventory system**—A system that keeps track of each withdrawal or addition to inventory continuously, so records are always current.	
	• **Fixed-period (*P*) system**—A system in which inventory orders are made at regular time intervals.	

Self-Test

■ **Before taking the self-test,** refer to the learning objectives listed at the beginning of the chapter.

LO1 ABC analysis divides on-hand inventory into three classes, based on:
 a) unit price.
 b) the number of units on hand.
 c) annual demand.
 d) annual dollar values.

LO2 Cycle counting:
 a) provides a measure of inventory turnover.
 b) assumes that all inventory records must be verified with the same frequency.
 c) is a process by which inventory records are periodically verified.
 d) all of the above.

LO3 The two most important inventory-based questions answered by the typical inventory model are:
 a) when to place an order and the cost of the order.
 b) when to place an order and how much of an item to order.
 c) how much of an item to order and the cost of the order.
 d) how much of an item to order and with whom the order should be placed.

LO4 Extra units in inventory to help reduce stockouts are called:
 a) reorder point.
 b) safety stock.
 c) just-in-time inventory.
 d) all of the above.

LO5 The difference(s) between the basic EOQ model and the production order quantity model is(are) that:
- **a)** the production order quantity model does not require the assumption of known, constant demand.
- **b)** the EOQ model does not require the assumption of negligible lead time.
- **c)** the production order quantity model does not require the assumption of instantaneous delivery.
- **d)** all of the above.

LO6 The EOQ model with quantity discounts attempts to determine:
- **a)** the lowest amount of inventory necessary to satisfy a certain service level.

- **b)** the lowest purchase price.
- **c)** whether to use a fixed-quantity or fixed-period order policy.
- **d)** how many units should be ordered.
- **a)** the shortest lead time.

LO7 The appropriate level of safety stock is typically determined by:
- **a)** minimizing an expected stockout cost.
- **b)** choosing the level of safety stock that assures a given service level.
- **c)** carrying sufficient safety stock so as to eliminate all stockouts.
- **d)** annual demand.

Answers: LO1. d; LO2. c; LO3. b; LO4. b; LO5. c; LO6. d; LO7. b.

MyLab Operations Management

Most of these questions can be found in MyLab Operations Management. Visit MyLab Operations Management to access cases, videos, downloadable software, and much more. MyLab Operations Management Management also features a personalized Study Plan that helps you identify which chapter concepts you've mastered and guides you towards study tools for additional practice.

David Goldman/AP Images

13

Aggregate Planning and Sales and Operations Planning

Global > Company Profile Frito-Lay

Aggregate Planning Provides a Competitive Advantage at Frito-Lay

Like other organizations throughout the world, Frito-Lay relies on effective aggregate planning to match fluctuating multibillion-dollar demand to capacity in its 36 North American plants. Planning for the intermediate term (three to 18 months) is the heart of aggregate planning. Effective aggregate planning combined with tight scheduling, effective maintenance, and efficient employee and facility scheduling are the keys to high plant utilization. High utilization is a critical factor in facilities such as Frito-Lay, where capital investment is substantial.

Frito-Lay has more than three dozen brands of snacks and chips, 15 of which sell more than U.S. $100 million annually and seven of which sell over U.S. $1 billion. Its brands include such well-known names as Fritos, Lay's, Doritos, Sun Chips, Cheetos, Tostitos, Flat Earth, and Ruffles. Unique processes using specially designed equipment are required to produce each of these products. Because these specialized processes generate high fixed cost, they must operate at very high volume. But such product-focused facilities benefit by having low variable costs. High utilization and performance above the break-even point require a good match between demand and capacity. Idle equipment is disastrous.

At Frito-Lay's headquarters near Dallas, planners create a total demand profile. They use historical product sales, forecasts of new products, product innovations, product promotions, and dynamic local demand data from account managers to forecast demand. Planners then match the total demand profile to existing capacity, capacity expansion plans, and cost. This becomes the aggregate plan. The aggregate plan is communicated to each of the firm's 17 regions and to the 36 plants. Every quarter, headquarters and each plant modify the respective plans to incorporate changing market conditions and plant performance.

Each plant uses its quarterly plan to develop a four-week plan, which in turn assigns specific products to specific product lines for production runs. Finally, each week raw materials and labour are assigned to each

The last step in Frito-Lay's process involves packing the chips, such as Doritos, for shipment to customers. The entire process from cooking to shipping happens in a matter of hours.

process. Effective aggregate planning is a major factor in high utilization and low cost. As the company's 60% market share indicates, excellent aggregate planning yields a competitive advantage at Frito-Lay.

The Planning Process

STUDENT | TIP

Idle capacity is expensive, and inadequate capacity loses customers.

In Chapter 4, we saw that demand forecasting can address long-, medium-, and short-range decisions. Figure 13.1 illustrates how managers translate these forecasts into long-, intermediate-, and short-range plans. Long-range forecasts, the responsibility of top management, provide data for a firm's multiyear plans. These long-range plans require policies and strategies related to issues such as capacity and capital investment (Supplement 7), facility location (Chapter 8), new products (Chapter 5) and processes (Chapter 7), and supply chain development (Chapter 11).

Intermediate plans are designed to be consistent with top management's long-range plans and strategy, and work within the resource constraints determined by earlier strategic decisions. The challenge is to have these plans match production to the ever-changing demands of the market. Intermediate plans are the job of the operations manager, working with other functional areas of the firm. In this chapter we deal with intermediate plans, typically measured in months.

Short-range plans are usually for less than three months. These plans are also the responsibility of operations personnel. Operations managers work with supervisors to translate the intermediate plan into short-term plans consisting of weekly, daily, and hourly schedules. Short-term planning techniques are discussed in Chapter 15.

Intermediate planning is initiated by a process known as sales and operations planning (S&OP).

SALES AND OPERATIONS PLANNING

Good intermediate planning requires the coordination of demand forecasts with functional areas of a firm and its supply chain. And because each functional part of a firm and the supply chain has its own limitations and constraints, the coordination can be difficult. This coordinated planning effort has evolved into a process known as **sales and operations planning (S&OP)**. As Figure 13.2 shows, S&OP receives input from a variety of sources both internal and external to the firm. Because of the diverse inputs, S&OP is typically done by cross-functional teams that align the competing constraints.

One of the tasks of S&OP is to determine which plans are feasible in the coming months and which are not. Any limitations, both within the firm and in the supply chain, must be reflected in an intermediate plan that brings day-to-day sales and operational realities together. When the

LO1 Define *aggregate planning* and *sales and operations planning*

Sales and operations planning (S&OP)

A process of balancing resources and forecasted demand, aligning an organization's competing demands from supply chain to final customer, while linking strategic planning with operations over all planning horizons.

FIGURE 13.1

Planning Tasks and Responsibilities

Long-range plans (over 1 year)
Capacity decisions (Supplement 7) are critical to long-range plans.

Issues:
Research and development
New product plans
Capital investments
Facility location/capacity

Intermediate-range plans (3 to 18 months)
The aggregate planning techniques of this chapter help managers build intermediate-range plans.

Issues:
Sales and operations planning
Production planning and budgeting
Setting employment, inventory,
  subcontracting levels
Analyzing operating plans

Short-range plans (up to 3 months)
The scheduling techniques (Chapter 15) help managers prepare short-range plans.

Issues:
Job assignments
Ordering
Job scheduling
Dispatching
Overtime
Part-time help

Top executives

Operations managers with sales and operations planning team

Operations managers, supervisors, foremen

Responsibility   Planning tasks and time horizons

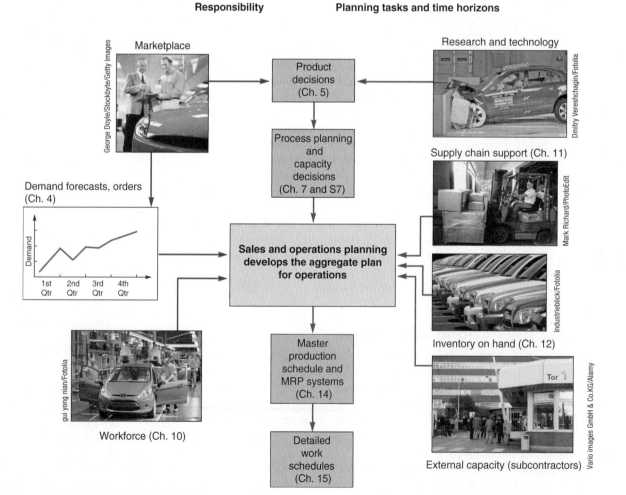

Marketplace

Research and technology

Product decisions (Ch. 5)

Process planning and capacity decisions (Ch. 7 and S7)

Demand forecasts, orders (Ch. 4)

Demand

1st Qtr 2nd Qtr 3rd Qtr 4th Qtr

Sales and operations planning develops the aggregate plan for operations

Supply chain support (Ch. 11)

Inventory on hand (Ch. 12)

External capacity (subcontractors)

Master production schedule and MRP systems (Ch. 14)

Detailed work schedules (Ch. 15)

Workforce (Ch. 10)

FIGURE 13.2   Relationships of an Aggregate Plan

resources appear to be substantially at odds with market expectations, S&OP provides advance warning to top management. If the plan cannot be implemented in the short run, the planning exercise is useless. And if the plan cannot be supported in the long run, strategic changes need to be made. To keep aggregate plans current and to support its intermediate planning role, S&OP uses rolling forecasts that are frequently updated—often weekly or monthly.

The output of S&OP is called an **aggregate plan**. The aggregate plan is concerned with determining the quantity and timing of production for the intermediate future, often from 3 to 18 months ahead. Aggregate plans use information regarding families or product lines rather than individual products. These plans are concerned with the total, or aggregate, of the individual product lines.

Rubbermaid, OfficeMax, and Rackspace have developed formal systems for S&OP, each with its own planning focus. Rubbermaid may use S&OP with a focus on production decisions; OfficeMax may focus S&OP on supply chain and inventory decisions; while Rackspace, a data storage firm, tends to have its S&OP focus on its critical and expensive investments in capacity. In all cases, though, the decisions must be tied to strategic planning and integrated with all areas of the firm over all planning horizons. Specifically, S&OP is aimed at (1) the coordination and integration of the internal and external resources necessary for a successful aggregate plan and (2) communication of the plan to those charged with its execution. An added advantage of an aggregate plan is that it can be an effective tool to engage members of the supply chain in achieving the firm's goals.

Besides being representative, timely, and comprehensive, an effective S&OP process needs these four additional features to generate a useful aggregate plan:

1. A logical unit for measuring sales and output, such as pounds of Doritos at Frito-Lay, air-conditioning units at GE, or terabytes of storage at Rackspace
2. A forecast of demand for a reasonable intermediate planning period in aggregate terms
3. A method to determine the relevant costs
4. A model that combines forecasts and costs so scheduling decisions can be made for the planning period

In this chapter, we describe several techniques that managers use when developing an aggregate plan for both manufacturing and service sector firms. For manufacturers, an aggregate schedule ties a firm's strategic goals to production plans. For service organizations, an aggregate schedule ties strategic goals to workforce schedules.

Aggregate plan

A plan that includes forecast levels for families of products of finished goods, inventory, shortages, and changes in the workforce.

The Nature of Aggregate Planning

As the term *aggregate* implies, an aggregate plan means combining appropriate resources into general, or overall, terms. Given demand forecast, facility capacity, inventory levels, workforce size, and related inputs, the planner has to select the rate of output for a facility over the next three to 18 months. The plan can be for firms such as Frito-Lay and Whirlpool, hospitals, colleges, or Pearson, the company that published this textbook.

Let's look at Snapper, which produces many different models of lawn mowers. It makes walk-behind mowers, rear-engine riding mowers, garden tractors, and many more, for a total of 145 models. For each month in the upcoming three quarters, the aggregate plan for Snapper might have the following output (in units of production) for Snapper's "family" of mowers:

Quarter 1			Quarter 2			Quarter 3		
Jan.	Feb.	March	April	May	June	July	Aug.	Sept.
150 000	120 000	110 000	100 000	130 000	150 000	180 000	150 000	140 000

Note that the plan looks at production *in the aggregate* (the family of mowers), not as a product-by-product breakdown. Likewise, an aggregate plan for BMW tells the auto manufacturer how many cars to make but not how many should be two-door versus four-door or red versus green. It tells Nucor Steel how many tons of steel to produce but does not differentiate grades of steel. (We extend the discussion of planning at Snapper in the *OM in Action* box "Building the Plan at Snapper".)

Every bright red Snapper lawn mower sold anywhere in the world comes from one North American factory. Years ago, the Snapper line had about 40 models of mowers, leaf blowers, and snow blowers. Today, reflecting the demands of mass customization, the product line is much more complex. Snapper designs, manufactures, and sells 145 models. This means that aggregate planning and the related short-term scheduling have become more complex, too.

In the past, Snapper met demand by carrying a huge inventory for 52 regional distributors and thousands of independent dealerships. It manufactured and shipped tens of thousands of lawn mowers, worth tens of millions of dollars, without quite knowing when they would be sold—a very expensive approach to meeting demand. Some changes were necessary. The new plan's goal is for each distribution centre to receive only the minimum inventory necessary to meet demand. Today, operations managers at Snapper evaluate production capacity and

use frequent data from the field as inputs to sophisticated software to forecast sales. The new system tracks customer demand and aggregates forecasts for every model in every region of the country. It even adjusts for holidays and weather. And the number of distribution centres has been cut from 52 to four.

Once evaluation of the aggregate plan against capacity determines the plan to be feasible, Snapper's planners break the plan down into production needs for each model. Production by model is accomplished by building rolling monthly and weekly plans. These plans track the pace at which various units are selling. Then, the final step requires juggling work assignments to various work centres for each shift, such as 265 lawn mowers in an eight-hour shift. That's a new Snapper every 109 seconds.

Sources: Fair Disclosure Wire (January 17, 2008); *The Wall Street Journal* (July 14, 2006): B1, B6; *Fast Company* (January/February 2006): 67–71; and **www.snapper.com**.

Operations personnel build an aggregate plan using the total expected demand for all of the family products, such as 145 models at Snapper (an example is shown on the right). Only when the forecasts are assembled in the aggregate plan does the company decide how to meet the total requirement with the available resources. These resource constraints include facility capacity, workforce size, supply chain limitations, inventory issues, and financial resources.

Disaggregation

The process of breaking an aggregate plan into greater detail.

Master production schedule

A timetable that specifies what is to be made and when.

Karen Sherlock/MCT/Newscom

Aggregate planning is part of a larger production planning system. Therefore, understanding the interfaces between the plan and several internal and external factors is useful. Figure 13.2 shows that the operations manager not only receives input from the marketing department's demand forecast but must also deal with financial data, personnel, capacity, and availability of raw materials. In a manufacturing environment, the process of breaking the aggregate plan down into greater detail is called **disaggregation**. Disaggregation results in a **master production schedule**, which provides input to material requirements planning (MRP) systems. The master production schedule addresses the purchasing or production of parts or components needed to make final products (see Chapter 14). Detailed work schedules for people and priority scheduling for products result as the final step of the production planning system (and are discussed in Chapter 15).

STUDENT TIP

Managers can meet aggregate plans by adjusting either capacity or demand.

LO2 Identify optional strategies for developing an aggregate plan

Aggregate Planning Strategies

When generating an aggregate plan, the operations manager must answer several questions:

1. Should inventories be used to absorb changes in demand during the planning period?
2. Should changes be accommodated by varying the size of the workforce?
3. Should part-timers be used, or should overtime and idle time absorb fluctuations?
4. Should subcontractors be used on fluctuating orders so a stable workforce can be maintained?
5. Should prices or other factors be changed to influence demand?

All of these are legitimate planning strategies. They involve the manipulation of inventory, production rates, labour levels, capacity, and other controllable variables. We will now examine eight options in more detail. The first five are called *capacity options* because they do not try to change demand but attempt to absorb demand fluctuations. The last three are *demand options* through which firms try to smooth out changes in the demand pattern over the planning period.

CAPACITY OPTIONS

A firm can choose from the following basic capacity (production) options:

1. *Changing inventory levels:* Managers can increase inventory during periods of low demand to meet high demand in future periods. If this strategy is selected, costs associated with storage, insurance, handling, obsolescence, pilferage, and capital invested will increase. On the other hand, with low inventory on hand and increasing demand, shortages can occur, resulting in longer lead times and poor customer service.

2. *Varying workforce size by hiring or layoffs:* One way to meet demand is to hire or lay off production workers to match production rates. However, new employees need to be trained, and productivity drops temporarily as they are absorbed into the workforce. Layoffs or terminations lower the morale of all workers, of course, and also lead to lower productivity.

3. *Varying production rates through overtime or idle time:* Keeping a constant workforce while varying working hours may be possible. Yet when demand is on a large upswing, there is a limit on how much overtime is realistic. Overtime pay increases costs and too much overtime can result in worker fatigue and a drop in productivity. Overtime also implies added overhead costs to keep a facility open. On the other hand, when there is a period of decreased demand, the company must somehow absorb workers' idle time—often a difficult and expensive process.

4. *Subcontracting:* A firm can acquire temporary capacity by subcontracting work during peak demand periods. Subcontracting has several pitfalls, however: it may be costly; it risks opening the door to a competitor; and developing the perfect subcontract supplier can be a challenge.

5. *Using part-time workers:* Especially in the service sector, part-time workers can fill labour needs. This practice is common in restaurants, retail stores, and supermarkets.

DEMAND OPTIONS

The basic demand options are:

1. *Influencing demand:* When demand is low, a company can try to increase demand through advertising, promotion, personal selling, and price cuts. Airlines and hotels have long offered weekend discounts and off-season rates; some electricity providers charge less in off-peak times; some colleges and universities give discounts to senior citizens; and air conditioners are least expensive in winter. However, even special advertising, promotions, selling, and pricing are not always able to balance demand with production capacity.

John Deere and Company, the "granddaddy" of farm equipment manufacturers, uses sales incentives to smooth demand. During the fall and winter off-seasons, sales are boosted with price cuts and other incentives. About 70% of Deere's big machines are ordered in advance of seasonal use—about double the industry rate. Incentives hurt margins, but Deere keeps its market share and controls costs by producing more steadily all year long. Similarly, in service businesses like Chapters Indigo Books & Music, some customers are offered free shipping on orders placed before the Christmas rush.

Stefan Kiefer/imageBROKER/Alamy Stock Photo

Table 13.1
Aggregate Planning Options: Advantages and Disadvantages

Option	Advantages	Disadvantages	Comments
Changing inventory levels	Changes in human resources are gradual or none; no abrupt production changes.	Inventory holding costs may increase. Shortages may result in lost sales.	Applies mainly to production, not service, operations.
Varying workforce size by hiring or layoffs	Avoids the costs of other alternatives.	Hiring, layoff, and training costs may be significant.	Used where size of labour pool is large.
Varying production rates through overtime or idle time	Matches seasonal fluctuations without hiring/training costs.	Overtime premiums; tired workers; may not meet demand.	Allows flexibility within the aggregate plan.
Subcontracting	Permits flexibility and smoothing of the firm's output.	Loss of quality control; reduced profits; loss of future business.	Applies mainly in production settings.
Using part-time workers	Is less costly and more flexible than full-time workers.	High turnover/training costs; quality suffers; scheduling difficult.	Good for unskilled jobs in areas with large temporary labour pools.
Influencing demand	Tries to use excess capacity. Discounts draw new customers.	Uncertainty in demand. Hard to match demand to supply exactly.	Creates marketing ideas. Overbooking used in some businesses.
Backordering during high-demand periods	May avoid overtime. Keeps capacity constant.	Customer must be willing to wait, but goodwill is lost.	Many companies backorder.
Counter-seasonal product and service mixing	Fully utilizes resources; allows stable workforce.	May require skills or equipment outside firm's areas of expertise.	Risky finding products or services with opposite demand patterns.

2. *Backordering during high-demand periods:* Backorders are orders for goods or services that a firm accepts but is unable (either on purpose or by chance) to fill at the moment. If customers are willing to wait without loss of their goodwill or order, backordering is a possible strategy. Many firms backorder, but the approach often results in lost sales.

3. *Counter-seasonal product and service mixing:* A widely used active smoothing technique among manufacturers is to develop a product mix of counter-seasonal items. Examples include companies that make both furnaces and air conditioners or lawn mowers and snowblowers. However, companies that follow this approach may find themselves involved in products or services beyond their area of expertise or beyond their target market.

These five capacity options and three demand options, along with their advantages and disadvantages, are summarized in Table 13.1.

MIXING OPTIONS TO DEVELOP A PLAN

Although each of the five capacity options and three demand options discussed above may produce an effective aggregate schedule, some combination of capacity options and demand options may be better.

Many manufacturers assume that the use of the demand options has been fully explored by the marketing department and those reasonable options incorporated into the demand forecast. The operations manager then builds the aggregate plan based on that forecast. However, using the five capacity options, the operations manager still has a multitude of possible plans. These plans can embody, at one extreme, a *chase strategy* and, at the other, a *level-scheduling strategy*. They may, of course, fall somewhere in between.

Chase strategy

A planning strategy that sets production equal to forecasted demand.

CHASE STRATEGY A **chase strategy** typically attempts to achieve output rates for each period that match the demand forecast for that period. This strategy can be accomplished in a variety of ways. For example, the operations manager can vary workforce levels by hiring or laying off or can vary production by means of overtime, idle time, part-time employees, or subcontracting. Many service organizations favour the chase strategy because the changing inventory levels option is difficult or impossible to adopt. Industries that have moved towards a chase strategy include education, hospitality, and construction.

LEVEL STRATEGY A level strategy (or **level scheduling**) is an aggregate plan in which production is uniform from period to period. Firms such as Toyota and Nissan attempt to keep production at uniform levels and may (1) let the finished goods inventory vary to buffer the difference between demand and production, or (2) find alternative work for employees. Their philosophy is that a stable workforce leads to a better-quality product, less turnover and absenteeism, and more employee commitment to corporate goals. Other hidden savings include employees who are more experienced, easier scheduling and supervision, and fewer dramatic start-ups and shutdowns. Level scheduling works well when demand is reasonably stable.

For most firms, neither a chase strategy nor a level strategy is likely to prove ideal, so a combination of the eight options (called a **mixed strategy**) must be investigated to achieve minimum cost. However, because there are a huge number of possible mixed strategies, managers find that aggregate planning can be a challenging task. Finding the one "optimal" plan is not always possible, but, as we will see in the next section, a number of techniques have been developed to aid the aggregate planning process.

> **Level scheduling**
> Maintaining a constant output rate, production rate, or workforce level over the planning horizon.

> **Mixed strategy**
> A planning strategy that uses two or more controllable variables to set a feasible production plan.

Methods for Aggregate Planning

In this section, we introduce several techniques that operations managers use to develop aggregate plans. They range from the widely used graphical method to a series of more formal mathematical approaches, including the transportation method of linear programming.

> Managers must commit to employment levels, material purchases, and inventory levels; aggregate plans help managers do that.

GRAPHICAL METHODS

Graphical techniques are popular because they are easy to understand and use. These plans work with a few variables at a time to allow planners to compare projected demand with existing capacity. They are trial-and-error approaches that do not guarantee an optimal production plan, but they require only limited computations and can be performed by clerical staff. Following are the five steps in the graphical method:

> **LO3** Prepare a graphical aggregate plan

> **Graphical techniques**
> Aggregate planning techniques that work with a few variables at a time to allow planners to compare projected demand with existing capacity.

1. Determine the demand in each period.
2. Determine capacity for regular time, overtime, and subcontracting each period.
3. Find labour costs, hiring and layoff costs, and inventory holding costs.
4. Consider company policy that may apply to the workers or to stock levels.
5. Develop alternative plans and examine their total costs.

These steps are illustrated in Examples 1 through 4.

A Juárez, Mexico, manufacturer of roofing supplies has developed monthly forecasts for a family of products. Data for the six-month period January to June are presented in Table 13.2. The firm would like to begin development of an aggregate plan.

 EXAMPLE 1

Graphical Approach to Aggregate Planning for a Roofing Supplier

Month	Expected Demand	Production Days	Demand per Day (computed)
Jan.	900	22	41
Feb.	700	18	39
Mar.	800	21	38
Apr.	1200	21	57
May	1500	22	68
June	1100	20	55
	6200	124	

Table 13.2
Monthly Forecasts

APPROACH ▶ Plot daily and average demand to illustrate the nature of the aggregate planning problem.

SOLUTION ▶ First, compute demand per day by dividing the expected monthly demand by the number of production days (working days) each month and drawing a graph of those forecasted demands

FIGURE 13.3
Graph of Forecast and
Average Forecast Demand

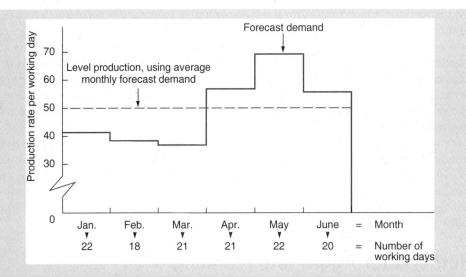

(Figure 13.3). Second, draw a dotted line across the chart that represents the production rate required to meet average demand over the six-month period. The chart is computed as follows:

$$\text{Average requirement} = \frac{\text{Total expected demand}}{\text{Number of production days}} = \frac{6200}{124} = 50 \text{ complete units per day}$$

INSIGHT ▶ Changes in the production rate become obvious when the data are graphed. Note that in the first three months, expected demand is lower than average, while expected demand in April, May, and June is above average.

LEARNING EXERCISE ▶ If demand for June increases to 1200 (from 1100), what is the impact on Figure 13.3? [Answer: The daily rate for June will go up to 60, and average production will increase to 50.8 (= 6300/124).]

RELATED PROBLEMS ▶ 13.1

The graph in Figure 13.3 illustrates how the forecast differs from the average demand. Some strategies for meeting the forecast were listed earlier. For example, the firm might staff in order to yield a production rate that meets *average* demand (as indicated by the dashed line). Or it might produce a steady rate of, say, 30 units and then subcontract excess demand to other roofing suppliers. Other plans might combine overtime work with subcontracting to absorb demand. Examples 2 to 4 illustrate three possible strategies.

**Plan 1 for the Roofing
Supplier—A Constant
Workforce**

Table 13.3
Cost Information

One possible strategy (call it plan 1) for the manufacturer described in Example 1 is to maintain a constant workforce throughout the six-month period. A second (plan 2) is to maintain a constant workforce at a level necessary to meet the lowest demand month (March) and to meet all demand above this level by subcontracting. Both plan 1 and plan 2 have level production and are, therefore, called *level strategies*. Plan 3 is to hire and lay off workers as needed to produce exact monthly requirements—*a chase strategy*. Table 13.3 provides cost information necessary for analyzing these three alternatives:

Inventory carrying cost	$5 per unit per month
Subcontracting cost per unit	$20 per unit
Average pay rate	$10 per hour ($80 per day)
Overtime pay rate	$17 per hour (above 8 hours per day)
Labour-hours to produce a unit	1.6 hours per unit
Cost of increasing daily production rate (hiring and training)	$300 per unit
Cost of decreasing daily production rate (layoffs)	$600 per unit

ANALYSIS OF PLAN 1 APPROACH ▶ Here we assume that 50 units are produced per day and that we have a constant workforce, no overtime or idle time, no safety stock, and no subcontractors. The firm accumulates inventory during the slack period of demand, January through March, and depletes it during the higher-demand warm season, April through June. We assume beginning inventory = 0 and planned ending inventory = 0.

SOLUTION ▶ We construct the table below and accumulate the costs:

Month	Production Days	Production at 50 Units per Day	Demand Forecast	Monthly Inventory Change	Ending Inventory
Jan.	22	1100	900	+200	200
Feb.	18	900	700	+200	400
Mar.	21	1050	800	+250	650
Apr.	21	1050	1200	−150	500
May	22	1100	1500	−400	100
June	20	1000	1100	−100	0
					1850

Total units of inventory carried over from one month to the next month = 1850 units

Workforce required to produce 50 units per day = 10 workers

Because each unit requires 1.6 labour-hours to produce, each worker can make 5 units in an 8-hour day. Therefore, to produce 50 units, 10 workers are needed.

Finally, the costs of plan 1 are computed as follows:

Cost		Calculations
Inventory carrying	$ 9 250	(= 1850 units carried × $5 per unit)
Regular-time labour	99 200	(= 10 workers × $80 per day × 124 days)
Other costs (overtime, hiring, layoffs, subcontracting)	0	
Total cost	$108 450	

INSIGHT ▶ Note the significant cost of carrying the inventory.

LEARNING EXERCISE ▶ If demand for June decreases to 1000 (from 1100), what is the change in cost (all other things being equal)? [Answer: Total inventory carried will increase to 1950 at $5, for an inventory cost of $9750 and total cost of $108 950.]

RELATED PROBLEMS ▶ 13.2, 13.3, 13.4, 13.5, 13.6, 13.7, 13.8, 13.9, 13.10, 13.11, 13.12, 13.19

EXCEL OM Data File **Ch13Ex2.xlsx** can be found at **MyLab Operations Management**.

ACTIVE MODEL 13.1 This example is further illustrated in Active Model 13.1 at **MyLab Operations Management**.

The graph for Example 2 was shown in Figure 13.3. Some planners prefer a *cumulative* graph to display visually how the forecast deviates from the average requirements. Such a graph is provided in Figure 13.4. Note that both the level production line and the forecast line produce the same total production.

EXAMPLE 3

Plan 2 for the Roofing Supplier—Use of Subcontractors Within a Constant Workforce

ANALYSIS OF PLAN 2 APPROACH ▶ Although a constant workforce is also maintained in plan 2, it is set low enough to meet demand only in March, the lowest demand-per-day month. To produce 38 units per day (800/21) in-house, 7.6 workers are needed. (You can think of this as seven full-time workers and one part-timer.) *All* other demand is met by subcontracting. Subcontracting is thus required in every other month. No inventory holding costs are incurred in plan 2.

SOLUTION ▶ Because 6200 units are required during the aggregate plan period, we must compute how many can be made by the firm and how many must be subcontracted:

In-house production = 38 units per day × 124 production days

= 4712 units

Subcontract units = 6200 − 4712 = 1488 units

The costs of plan 2 are computed as follows:

Cost		Calculations
Regular-time labour	$ 75 392	(= 7.6 workers × $80 per day × 124 days)
Subcontracting	29 760	(= 1488 units × 20 per unit)
Total cost	$105 152	

INSIGHT ▶ Note the lower cost of regular labour but the added subcontracting cost.

LEARNING EXERCISE ▶ If demand for June increases to 1200 (from 1100), what is the change in cost (all other things being equal)? [Answer: Subcontracting requirements increase to 1588 at $20 per unit, for a subcontracting cost of $31 760 and a total cost of $107 152.]

RELATED PROBLEMS ▶ 13.2, 13.3, 13.4, 13.5, 13.6, 13.7, 13.8, 13.9, 13.10, 13.11, 13.12, 13.19

FIGURE 13.4
Cumulative Graph for Plan 1

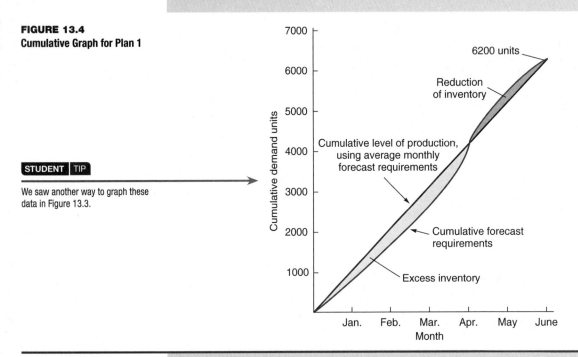

STUDENT TIP

We saw another way to graph these data in Figure 13.3.

EXAMPLE 4

Plan 3 for the Roofing Supplier—Hiring and Layoffs

ANALYSIS OF PLAN 3 APPROACH ▶ The final strategy, plan 3, involves varying the work-force size by hiring and layoffs as necessary. The production rate will equal the demand, and there is no change in production from the previous month, December.

SOLUTION ▶ Table 13.4 shows the calculations and the total cost of plan 3. Recall that it costs $600 per unit produced to reduce production from the previous month's daily level and $300 per unit change to increase the daily rate of production through hirings.

Table 13.4
Cost Computations for Plan 3

Month	Forecast (units)	Daily Production Rate	Basic Production Cost (demand × 1.6 hr per unit × $10 per hr)	Extra Cost of Increasing Production (hiring cost)	Extra Cost of Decreasing Production (layoff cost)	Total Cost
Jan.	900	41	$14 400	—	—	$ 14 400
Feb.	700	39	11 200	—	$1200 (= 2 × $600)	12 400
Mar.	800	38	12 800	—	$600 (= 1 × $600)	13 400
Apr.	1200	57	19 200	$5700 (= 19 × $300)	—	24 900
May	1500	68	24 000	$3300 (= 11 × $300)	—	27 300
June	1100	55	17 600	—	$7800 (= 13 × $600)	25 400
			$99 200	$9000	$9600	$117 800

Thus, the total cost, including production, hiring, and layoff, for plan 3 is $117 800.

The final step in the graphical method is to compare the costs of each proposed plan and to select the approach with the least total cost. A summary analysis is provided in Table 13.5. We see that because plan 2 has the lowest cost, it is the best of the three options.

Table 13.5
Comparison of the Three Plans

Cost	Plan 1 (constant workforce of 10 workers)	Plan 2 (workforce of 7.6 workers plus subcontract)	Plan 3 (hiring and layoffs to meet demand)
Inventory carrying	$ 9 250	$ 0	$ 0
Regular labour	99 200	75 392	99 200
Overtime labour	0	0	0
Hiring	0	0	9 000
Layoffs	0	0	9 600
Subcontracting	0	29 760	0
Total cost	$108 450	$105 152	$117 800

Of course, many other feasible strategies can be considered in a problem like this, including combinations that use some overtime. Although graphing is a popular management tool, its help is in evaluating strategies, not generating them. To generate strategies, a systematic approach that considers all costs and produces an effective solution is needed.

MATHEMATICAL APPROACHES

This section briefly describes some of the mathematical approaches to aggregate planning.

THE TRANSPORTATION METHOD OF LINEAR PROGRAMMING When an aggregate planning problem is viewed as one of allocating operating capacity to meet forecasted demand, it can be formulated in a linear programming format. The **transportation method of linear programming** is not a trial-and-error approach like graphing but rather produces an optimal plan for minimizing costs. It is also flexible in that it can specify regular and overtime production in each time period, the number of units to be subcontracted, extra shifts, and the inventory carryover from period to period.

Transportation method of linear programming
A way of solving for the optimal solution to an aggregate planning problem.

In Example 5, the supply consists of on-hand inventory and units produced by regular time, overtime, and subcontracting. Costs per unit, in the upper right corner of each cell of the matrix in Table 13.7, relate to units produced in a given period or units carried in inventory from an earlier period.

Farnsworth Tire Company would like to develop an aggregate plan via the transportation method. Data that relate to production, demand, capacity, and cost at its New Brunswick plant are shown in Table 13.6.

APPROACH ▶ Solve the aggregate planning problem by minimizing the costs of matching production in various periods to future demands.

SOLUTION ▶ Table 13.7 illustrates the structure of the transportation table and an initial feasible solution.

EXAMPLE **5**

Aggregate Planning With the Transportation Method

Table 13.6
Farnsworth's Production, Demand, Capacity, and Cost Data

	Sales Period		
	Mar.	Apr.	May
Demand	800	1000	750
Capacity:			
Regular	700	700	700
Overtime	50	50	50
Subcontracting	150	150	130
Beginning inventory	100 tires		

Costs	
Regular time	$40 per tire
Overtime	$50 per tire
Subcontract	$70 per tire
Carrying cost	$ 2 per tire per month

Table 13.7
Farnsworth's Transportation Table[a]

SUPPLY FROM		Period 1 (Mar.)	Period 2 (Apr.)	Period 3 (May)	Unused Capacity (dummy)	TOTAL CAPACITY AVAILABLE (supply)
		DEMAND FOR				
Beginning inventory		0 / **100**	2	4	0	100
Period 1	Regular time	40 / **700**	42	44	0	700
	Overtime	50	52 / **50**	54	0	50
	Subcontract	70	72 / **150**	74	0	150
Period 2	Regular time	×	40 / **700**	42	0	700
	Overtime	×	50 / **50**	52	0	50
	Subcontract	×	70 / **50**	72	0 / **100**	150
Period 3	Regular time	×	×	40 / **700**	0	700
	Overtime	×	×	50 / **50**	0	50
	Subcontract	×	×	70	0 / **130**	130
TOTAL DEMAND		800	1000	750	230	2780

[a]Cells with an X indicate that backorders are not used at Farnsworth. When using Excel OM or POM for Windows to solve, you must insert a *very* high cost (e.g., 9999) in each cell that is not used for production.

LO4 Solve an aggregate plan via the transportation method of linear programming

When setting up and analyzing this table, you should note the following:

1. Carrying costs are $2/tire per month. Tires produced in one period and held for one month will have a $2 higher cost. Because holding cost is linear, two months' holdover costs $4. So, when you move across a row from left to right, regular time, overtime, and subcontracting costs are lowest when output is used the same period it is produced. If goods are made in one period and carried over to the next, holding costs are incurred. Beginning inventory, however, is generally given a unit cost of 0 if it is used to satisfy demand in Period 1.
2. Transportation problems require that supply equals demand; so, a dummy column called "unused capacity" has been added. Costs of not using capacity are zero.

3. Because backordering is not a viable alternative for this particular company, no production is possible in those cells that represent production in a period to satisfy demand in a past period (i.e., those periods with an "X"). If backordering is allowed, costs of expediting, loss of goodwill, and loss of sales revenues are summed to estimate backorder cost.

4. Quantities in red in each column of Table 13.7 designate the levels of inventory needed to meet demand requirements (shown in the bottom row of the table). Demand of 800 tires in March is met by using 100 tires from beginning inventory and 700 tires from regular time.

5. In general, to complete the table, allocate as much production as you can to a cell with the smallest cost without exceeding the unused capacity in that row or demand in that column. If there is still some demand left in that row, allocate as much as you can to the next-lowest-cost cell. You then repeat this process for periods 2 and 3 (and beyond, if necessary). When you are finished, the sum of all your entries in a row must equal the total row capacity, and the sum of all entries in a column must equal the demand for that period. (This step can be accomplished by the transportation method or by using POM for Windows or Excel OM software.)

Try to confirm that the cost of this initial solution is $105 900. The initial solution is not optimal, however. See if you can find the production schedule that yields the least cost (which turns out to be $105 700) using software or by hand.

INSIGHT ▶ The transportation method is flexible when costs are linear but does not work when costs are nonlinear.

LEARNING EXERCISE ▶ What is the impact on this problem if there is no beginning inventory? [Answer: Total capacity (units) available is reduced by 100 units and the need to subcontract increases by 100 units.]

RELATED PROBLEMS ▶ 13.13, 13.14, 13.15, 13.16, 13.17, 13.18

EXCEL **OM** Data File **Ch13Ex5.xlsx** can be found at **MyLab Operations Management.**

The transportation method of linear programming described in the above example was originally formulated by E. H. Bowman in 1956. Although it works well in analyzing the effects of holding inventories, using overtime, and subcontracting, it does not work when nonlinear or negative factors are introduced. Thus, when other factors such as hiring and layoffs are introduced, the more general method of linear programming must be used.

MANAGEMENT COEFFICIENTS MODEL Bowman's **management coefficients model**[1] builds a formal decision model around a manager's experience and performance. The assumption is that the manager's past performance is pretty good; therefore, it can be used as a basis for future decisions. The technique uses a regression analysis of past production decisions made by managers. The regression line provides the relationship between variables (such as demand and labour) for future decisions. According to Bowman, managers' deficiencies are mostly inconsistencies in decision making.

> **Management coefficients model**
> A formal planning model built around a manager's experience and performance.

OTHER MODELS Two additional aggregate planning models are the linear decision rule and simulation. The *linear decision rule (LDR)* attempts to specify an optimum production rate and workforce level over a specific period. It minimizes the total costs of payroll, hiring, layoffs, overtime, and inventory through a series of quadratic cost curves.[2]

A computer model called *scheduling by simulation* uses a search procedure to look for the minimum-cost combination of values for workforce size and production rate.

COMPARISON OF AGGREGATE PLANNING METHODS

Although these mathematical models have been found by researchers to work well under certain conditions, and linear programming has found some acceptance in industry, the fact is that most sophisticated planning models are not widely used. Why? Perhaps it reflects the average manager's attitude about what he or she views as overly complex models. Like all of us, planners

---

[1] E. H. Bowman, "Consistency and Optimality in Managerial Decision Making," *Management Science* 9, no. 2 (January 1963): 310–321.

[2] Because LDR was developed by Charles C. Holt, Franco Modigliani, John F. Muth, and Herbert Simon, it is popularly known as the HMMS rule. For details, see Martin K. Starr, *Production and Operations Management* (Cincinnati, OH: Atomic Dog Publishing), 2004: 490–493.

Table 13.8
Summary of Four Major Aggregate Planning Methods

Technique	Solution Approaches	Important Aspects
Graphical methods	Trial and error	Simple to understand and easy to use. Many solutions; one chosen may not be optimal.
Transportation method of linear programming	Optimization	LP software available; permits sensitivity analysis and new constraints; linear functions may not be realistic.
Management coefficients model	Heuristic	Simple, easy to implement; tries to mimic manager's decision process; uses regression.
Simulation	Change parameters	Complex; model may be difficult to build and for managers to understand.

like to understand how and why the models on which they are basing important decisions work. Additionally, operations managers need to make decisions quickly based on the changing dynamics of the competitive environment—and building good models is time-consuming. This may explain why the simpler graphical approach is more generally accepted.

Table 13.8 highlights some of the main features of graphing, transportation, management coefficients, and simulation planning models.

A number of commercial S&OP software packages that incorporate the techniques of this chapter are available to ease the mechanics of aggregate planning. These include Arkieva's S&OP *Workbench* for process industries, Demand Solutions's *S&OP Software,* and Steelwedge's S&OP Suite.

Aggregate Planning in Services

Some service organizations conduct aggregate planning in exactly the same way as we did in Examples 1 through 5 in this chapter, but with demand management taking a more active role. Because most services pursue *combinations* of the eight capacity and demand options discussed earlier, they usually formulate mixed aggregate planning strategies. In industries such as banking, trucking, and fast food, aggregate planning may be easier than in manufacturing.

Controlling the cost of labour in service firms is critical. Successful techniques include:

1. Accurate scheduling of labour-hours to assure quick response to customer demand.
2. An on-call labour resource that can be added or deleted to meet unexpected demand.
3. Flexibility of individual worker skills that permits reallocation of available labour.
4. Flexibility in rate of output or hours of work to meet changing demand.

These options may seem demanding, but they are not unusual in service industries, in which labour is the primary aggregate planning vehicle. For instance:

- Excess capacity is used to provide study and planning time by real estate and auto salespersons.
- Police and fire departments have provisions for calling in off-duty personnel for major emergencies. Where the emergency is extended, police or fire personnel may work longer hours and extra shifts.
- When business is unexpectedly light, restaurants and retail stores send personnel home early.
- Supermarket stock clerks work cash registers when checkout lines become too lengthy.
- Experienced servers increase their pace and efficiency of service as crowds of customers arrive.

Approaches to aggregate planning differ by the type of service provided. Here we discuss five service scenarios.

RESTAURANTS

In a business with a highly variable demand, such as a restaurant, aggregate scheduling is directed towards (1) smoothing the production rate and (2) finding the optimal size of the workforce. The general approach usually requires building very modest levels of inventory during slack periods and depleting inventory during peak periods but using labour to accommodate most of the changes in demand. Because this situation is very similar to those found in manufacturing, traditional aggregate planning methods may be applied to services as well. One difference that should be noted is that even modest amounts of inventory may be perishable. In addition, the relevant units of time may be much

Solved Problems Virtual Office Hours help is available at MyLab Operations Management.

▼ SOLVED PROBLEM 13.1

The roofing manufacturer described in Examples 1 to 4 of this chapter wishes to consider yet a fourth planning strategy (plan 4). This one maintains a constant workforce of eight people and uses overtime whenever necessary to meet demand. Use the information found in Table 13.3. Again, assume beginning and ending inventories are equal to zero.

▼ SOLUTION

Employ eight workers and use overtime when necessary. Note that carrying costs will be encountered in this plan.

Month	Production Days	Production at 40 Units per Day	Beginning-of-Month Inventory	Forecast Demand This Month	Overtime Production Needed	Ending Inventory
Jan.	22	880	—	900	20 units	0 units
Feb.	18	720	0	700	0 units	20 units
Mar.	21	840	20	800	0 units	60 units
Apr.	21	840	60	1200	300 units	0 units
May	22	880	0	1500	620 units	0 units
June	20	800	0	1100	300 units	0 units
					1240 units	80 units

Carrying cost totals = 80 units × $5/unit/month = $400

Regular pay:

$$8 \text{ workers} \times \$80/\text{day} \times 124 \text{ days} = \$79\,360$$

Overtime pay:

To produce 1240 units at overtime rate requires 1240 × 1.6 hours/unit = 1984 hours.

$$\text{Overtime cost} = \$17/\text{hour} \times 1984 \text{ hours} = \$33\,728$$

Plan 4		
Costs (workforce of 8 plus overtime)		
Carrying cost	$ 400	(80 units carried × $5/unit)
Regular labour	79 360	(8 workers × $80/day × 124 days)
Overtime	33 728	(1984 hours × $17/hour)
Hiring or firing	0	
Subcontracting	0	
Total costs	$113 488	

Plan 2 is still preferable at $105 152.

▼ SOLVED PROBLEM 13.2

A Saskatoon area plant has developed the following supply, demand, cost, and inventory data. The firm has a constant workforce and meets all its demand. Allocate production capacity to satisfy demand at a minimum cost. What is the cost of this plan?

Supply Capacity Available (units)

Period	Regular Time	Overtime	Subcontract
1	300	50	200
2	400	50	200
3	450	50	200

Demand Forecast

Period	Demand (units)
1	450
2	550
3	750

Other Data

Initial inventory	50 units
Regular-time cost per unit	$50
Overtime cost per unit	$65
Subcontract cost per unit	$80
Carrying cost per unit per period	$ 1
Backorder cost per unit per period	$ 4

▼ SOLUTION

SUPPLY FROM		DEMAND FOR			Unused Capacity (dummy)	TOTAL CAPACITY AVAILABLE (supply)
		Period 1	Period 2	Period 3		
Beginning inventory		[0] 50	[1]	[2]	[0]	50
Period 1	Regular time	[50] 300	[51]	[52]	[0]	300
	Overtime	[65] 50	[66]	[67]	[0]	50
	Subcontract	[80] 50	[81]	[82]	[0] 150	200
Period 2	Regular time	[54]	[50] 400	[51]	[0]	400
	Overtime	[69]	[65] 50	[66]	[0]	50
	Subcontract	[84]	[80] 100	[81] 50	[0] 50	200
Period 3	Regular time	[58]	[54]	[50] 450	[0]	450
	Overtime	[73]	[69]	[65] 50	[0]	50
	Subcontract	[88]	[84]	[80] 200	[0]	200
TOTAL DEMAND		450	550	750	200	1950

Cost of plan:

Period 1: 50($0) + 300($50) + 50($65) + 50($80) = $22 250

Period 2:   400($50) + 50($65) + 100($80) = $31 250

Period 3: 50($81) + 450($50) + 50($65) + 200($80) = $45 800*
                                     Total cost $99 300

*Includes 50 units of subcontract and carrying cost coming from period 2.

Problems*

· **13.1** Prepare a graph of the monthly forecasts and average forecasted demand for Industrial Air Corp., a manufacturer of a variety of large air conditioners for commercial applications.

Month	Production Days	Demand Forecast
January	22	1000
February	18	1100
March	22	1200
April	21	1300
May	22	1350
June	21	1350
July	21	1300
August	22	1200
September	21	1100
October	22	1100
November	20	1050
December	20	900

*Note: **Px** means the problem may be solved with POM for Windows and/or Excel OM.

·· **13.2** Refer to Examples 1 to 4 and Solved Problem 13.1.

a) Develop another plan for the Mexican roofing manufacturer. For this plan, plan 5, the firm wants to maintain a constant workforce of six, using subcontracting to meet remaining demand. Is this plan preferable?

b) The same roofing manufacturer has yet a sixth plan. A constant workforce of seven is selected, with the remainder of demand filled by subcontracting.

c) Is this better than plans 1–5? **Px**

··· **13.3** The president of Hill Enterprises, Terri Hill, projects the firm's aggregate demand requirements over the next eight months as follows:

Jan.	1400	May	2200
Feb.	1600	June	2200
Mar.	1800	July	1800
Apr.	1800	Aug.	1400

Her operations manager is considering a new plan, which begins in January with 200 units on hand. Stockout cost of lost sales is $100 per unit. Inventory holding cost is $20 per unit per month. Ignore any idle-time costs. The plan is called Plan A.

Plan A: Vary the workforce level to execute a "chase" strategy by producing the quantity demanded in the *prior* month. The December demand and rate of production are both 1600 units per month. The cost of hiring additional workers is $5000 per 100 units. The cost of laying off workers is $7500 per 100 units. Evaluate this plan. **Px**

•• **13.4** Using the information in Problem 13.3, develop plan B. Produce at a constant rate of 1400 units per month, which will meet minimum demands. Then use subcontracting, with additional units at a premium price of $75 per unit. Evaluate this plan by computing the costs for January through August. **Px**

•• **13.5** Hill is now considering Plan C. Beginning inventory, stockout costs, and holding costs are provided in Problem 13.3.
a) Plan C: Keep a stable workforce by maintaining a constant production rate equal to the average requirements and allow varying inventory levels.
b) Plot the demand with a graph that also shows average requirements. Conduct your analysis for January through August. **Px**

••• **13.6** Hill's operations manager (see Problems 13.3 through 13.5) is also considering two mixed strategies for January–August:
a) Plan D: Keep the current workforce stable at producing 1600 units per month. Permit a maximum of 20% overtime at an additional cost of $50 per unit. A warehouse now constrains the maximum allowable inventory on hand to 400 units or fewer.
b) Plan E: Keep the current workforce, which is producing 1600 units per month, and subcontract to meet the rest of the demand.
c) Evaluate plans D and E and make a recommendation. **Px**

••• **13.7** Michael Carrigg, Inc., is a disk manufacturer in need of an aggregate plan for July through December. The company has gathered the following data:

Costs	
Holding cost	$8/disk/month
Subcontracting	$80/disk
Regular-time labour	$12/hour
Overtime labour	$18/hour for hours above 8 hours/worker/day
Hiring cost	$40/worker
Layoff cost	$80/worker

Demand*	
July	400
Aug.	500
Sept.	550
Oct.	700
Nov.	800
Dec.	700

*No costs are incurred for unmet demand.

Other Data	
Current workforce (June)	8 people
Labour-hours/disk	4 hours
Workdays/month	20 days
Beginning inventory	150 disks**
Ending inventory	0 disks

**Note that there is no holding cost for June.

What will each of the two following strategies cost?
a) Vary the workforce so that production meets demand. Carrigg had eight workers on board in June.
b) Vary overtime only and use a constant workforce of eight. **Px**

•• **13.8** You manage a consulting firm down the street from Michael Carrigg, Inc., and to get your foot in the door, you have told Mr. Carrigg (see Problem 13.7) that you can do a better job at aggregate planning than his current staff. He said, "Fine. You do that, and you have a one-year contract." You now have to make good on your boast using the data in Problem 13.7. You decide to hire five workers in August and five more in October.

••• **13.9** Mary Rhodes, operations manager at Burnaby Furniture, has received the following estimates of demand requirements:

July	Aug.	Sept.	Oct.	Nov.	Dec.
1000	1200	1400	1800	1800	1600

a) Assuming stockout costs for lost sales of $100 per unit, inventory carrying costs of $25 per unit per month, and zero beginning and ending inventory, evaluate these two plans on an *incremental* cost basis:
  • Plan A: Produce at a steady rate (equal to minimum requirements) of 1000 units per month and subcontract additional units at a $60 per unit premium cost.
  • Plan B: Vary the workforce, which performs at a current production level of 1300 units per month. The cost of hiring additional workers is $3000 per 100 units produced. The cost of layoffs is $6000 per 100 units cut back. **Px**
b) Which plan is best and why?

••• **13.10** Mary Rhodes (see Problem 13.9) is considering two more mixed strategies. Using the data in Problem 13.9, compare plans C and D with plans A and B and make a recommendation.
  • Plan C: Keep the current workforce steady at a level producing 1300 units per month. Subcontract the remainder to meet demand. Assume that 300 units remaining from June are available in July.
  • Plan D: Keep the current workforce at a level capable of producing 1300 units per month. Permit a maximum of 20% overtime at a premium of $40 per unit. Assume that warehouse limitations permit no more than a 180-unit carryover from month to month. This plan means that any time inventories reach 180, the plant is kept idle. Idle time per unit is $60. Any additional needs are subcontracted at a cost of $60 per incremental unit.

••• **13.11** Liz Perry Health and Beauty Products has developed a new shampoo, and you need to develop its aggregate schedule. The cost accounting department has supplied you the cost relevant to the aggregate plan, and the marketing department has provided a four-quarter forecast. All are shown as follows:

Quarter	Forecast
1	1400
2	1200
3	1500
4	1300

Costs	
Previous quarter's output	1500 units
Beginning inventory	0 units
Stockout cost for backorders	$50 per unit
Inventory holding cost	$10 per unit for every unit held at the end of the quarter
Hiring workers	$40 per unit
Layoff of workers	$80 per unit
Unit cost	$30 per unit
Overtime	$15 extra per unit
Subcontracting	Not available

Your job is to develop an aggregate plan for the next four quarters.
a) First, try a chase plan by hiring and layoffs (to meet the forecast) as necessary.
b) Then try a plan that holds employment steady.
c) Which is the more economical plan for Liz Perry Health and Beauty Products? **Px**

••• 13.12 New Brunswick's Soda Pop, Inc., has a new fruit drink for which it has high hopes. Steve Allen, the production planner, has assembled the following cost data and demand forecast:

Quarter	Forecast
1	1800
2	1100
3	1600
4	900

Costs/Other Data	
Previous quarter's output = 1300 cases
Beginning inventory = 0 cases
Stockout cost = $150 per case
Inventory holding cost = $40 per case at end of quarter
Hiring employees = $40 per case
Terminating employees = $80 per case
Subcontracting cost = $60 per case
Unit cost on regular time = $30 per case
Overtime cost = $15 extra per case
Capacity on regular time = 1800 cases per quarter

Steve's job is to develop an aggregate plan. The three initial options he wants to evaluate are:

- Plan A: a chase strategy that hires and fires personnel as necessary to meet the forecast.
- Plan B: a level strategy.
- Plan C: a level strategy that produces 1200 cases per quarter and meets the forecasted demand with inventory and subcontracting.

a) Which strategy is the lowest-cost plan?
b) If you are Steve's boss, the VP for operations, which plan do you implement and why? **Px**

•• 13.13 Josie Gall's firm has developed the following supply, demand, cost, and inventory data. Allocate production capacity to meet demand at a minimum cost using the transportation method. What is the cost? Assume that the initial inventory has no holding cost in the first period and backorders are not permitted.

Period	Regular Time	Overtime	Subcontract	Demand Forecast
1	30	10	5	40
2	35	12	5	50
3	30	10	5	40

Initial inventory	20 units
Regular-time cost per unit	$100
Overtime cost per unit	$150
Subcontract cost per unit	$200
Carrying cost per unit per month	$ 4

Px

•• 13.14 Haifa Instruments, an Israeli producer of portable kidney dialysis units and other medical products, develops a four-month aggregate plan. Demand and capacity (in units) are forecast as follows:

Capacity Source	Month 1	Month 2	Month 3	Month 4
Labour				
Regular time	235	255	290	300
Overtime	20	24	26	24
Subcontract	12	15	15	17
Demand	255	294	321	301

The cost of producing each dialysis unit is $985 on regular time, $1310 on overtime, and $1500 on a subcontract. Inventory carrying cost is $100 per unit per month. There is to be no beginning or ending inventory in stock and backorders are not permitted. Set up a production plan that minimizes cost using the transportation method. **Px**

•• 13.15 The production planning period for flat-screen monitors at Winnipeg's Iqaluk Electronics, Inc., is four months. Cost data are as follows:

Regular-time cost per monitor	$ 70
Overtime cost per monitor	$110
Subcontract cost per monitor	$120
Carrying cost per monitor per month	$ 4

For each of the next four months, capacity and demand for flat-screen monitors are as follows:

	Period			
	Month 1	Month 2	Month 3[a]	Month 4
Demand	2000	2500	1500	2100
Capacity				
Regular time	1500	1600	750	1600
Overtime	400	400	200	400
Subcontract	600	600	600	600

[a]Factory closes for two weeks of vacation.

Iqaluk Electronics expects to enter the planning period with 500 monitors in stock. Backordering is not permitted (meaning, for example, that monitors produced in the second month cannot be used in the first month to cover the first month's demand). Develop a production plan that minimizes costs using the transportation method. **Px**

••• **13.16** A large Saskatchewan feed mill, B. Swart Processing, prepares its six-month aggregate plan by forecasting demand for 50-pound bags of cattle feed as follows: January, 1000 bags; February, 1200; March, 1250; April, 1450; May, 1400; and June, 1400. The feed mill plans to begin the new year with no inventory left over from the previous year, and backorders are not permitted. It projects that capacity (during regular hours) for producing bags of feed will remain constant at 800 until the end of April, and then increase to 1100 bags per month when a planned expansion is completed on May 1. Overtime capacity is set at 300 bags per month until the expansion, at which time it will increase to 400 bags per month. A friendly competitor in Alberta is also available as a backup source to meet demand—but can provide only 500 bags total during the six-month period. Develop a six-month production plan for the feed mill using the transportation method.

Cost data are as follows:

Regular-time cost per bag (until April 30)	$12.00
Regular-time cost per bag (after May 1)	$11.00
Overtime cost per bag (during entire period)	$16.00
Cost of outside purchase per bag	$18.50
Carrying cost per bag per month	$ 1.00

Px

•• **13.17** Lon Min has developed a specialized airtight vacuum bag to extend the freshness of seafood shipped to restaurants. He has put together the following demand cost data:

Quarter	Forecast (units)	Regular time	Overtime	Subcontract
1	500	400	80	100
2	750	400	80	100
3	900	800	160	100
4	450	400	80	100

Initial inventory = 250 units	
Regular-time cost = $1.00/unit	
Overtime cost = $1.50/unit	
Subcontracting cost = $2.00/unit	
Carrying cost = $0.20/unit/quarter	
Backorder cost = $0.50/unit/quarter	

Min decides that the initial inventory of 250 units will incur the 20¢/unit cost from each prior quarter (unlike the situation in most companies, where a zero unit cost is assigned).
a) Find the optimal plan using the transportation method.
b) What is the cost of the plan?
c) Does any regular time capacity go unused? If so, how much, and in which periods?
d) What is the extent of backordering in units and dollars? **Px**

••• **13.18** José Martinez of Brampton has developed a polished stainless steel tortilla machine that is a "showpiece" for display in Mexican restaurants. He needs to develop a five-month aggregate plan. His forecast of capacity and demand follows:

	Month				
	1	2	3	4	5
Demand	150	160	130	200	210
Capacity					
Regular	150	150	150	150	150
Overtime	20	20	10	10	10

Subcontracting: 100 units available over the 5-month period	
Beginning inventory: 0 units	
Ending inventory required: 20 units	

Costs	
Regular-time cost per unit	$100
Overtime cost per unit	$125
Subcontract cost per unit	$135
Inventory holding cost per unit per month	$ 3

Assume that backorders are not permitted. Using the transportation method, what is the total cost of the optimal plan? **Px**

•••• **13.19** Chris Fisher, owner of an Ontario firm that manufactures display cabinets, develops an eight-month aggregate plan. Demand and capacity (in units) are forecast as follows:

Capacity Source (units)	Jan.	Feb.	Mar.	Apr.	May	June	July	Aug.
Regular time	235	255	290	300	300	290	300	290
Overtime	20	24	26	24	30	28	30	30
Subcontract	12	16	15	17	17	19	19	20
Demand	255	294	321	301	330	320	345	340

The cost of producing each unit is $1000 on regular time, $1300 on overtime, and $1800 on a subcontract. Inventory carrying cost is $200 per unit per month. There is no beginning or ending inventory in stock, and no backorders are permitted from period to period.
a) Set up a production plan that minimizes cost by producing exactly what the demand is each month. Let the workforce vary by using regular time first, then overtime, and then subcontracting. This plan allows no backorders or inventory. What is this plan's cost?
b) Through better planning, regular-time production can be set at exactly the same amount, 275 units, per month. Does this alter the solution?
c) If overtime costs rise from $1300 to $1400, will your answer to part (a) change? What if overtime costs then fall to $1200? **Px**

•• 13.20 Forrester and Cohen is a small accounting firm, managed by Joseph Cohen since the retirement in December of his partner, Brenda Forrester. Cohen and his three CPAs can together bill 640 hours per month. When Cohen or another accountant bills more than 160 hours per month, he or she gets an additional "overtime" pay of $62.50 for each of the extra hours: This is above and beyond the $5000 salary each draws during the month. (Cohen draws the same base pay as his employees.) Cohen strongly discourages any CPA from working (billing) more than 240 hours in any given month. The demand for billable hours for the firm over the next six months is estimated below:

Month	Estimate of Billable Hours
Jan.	600
Feb.	500
Mar.	1000
Apr.	1200
May	650
June	590

Cohen has an agreement with Forrester, his former partner, to help out during the busy tax season, if needed, for an hourly fee of $125. Cohen will not even consider laying off one of his colleagues in the case of a slow economy. He could, however, hire another CPA at the same salary, as business dictates.

a) Develop an aggregate plan for the six-month period.
b) Compute the cost of Cohen's plan of using overtime and Forrester.
c) Should the firm remain as is, with a total of four CPAs?

•• 13.21 Refer to the CPA firm in Problem 13.20. In planning for next year, Cohen estimates that billable hours will increase by 10% in each of the six months. He therefore proceeds to hire a fifth CPA. The same regular time, overtime, and outside consultant (i.e., Forrester) costs still apply.

a) Develop the new aggregate plan and compute its costs.
b) Comment on the staffing level with five accountants. Was it a good decision to hire the additional accountant?

•• 13.22 WestJet's daily flight from Edmonton to Toronto uses a Boeing 737, with all-coach seating for 120 people. In the past, the airline has priced every seat at $140 for the one-way flight. An average of 80 passengers are on each flight. The variable cost of a filled seat is $25. Katie Morgan, the new operations manager, has decided to try a yield-revenue approach, with seats priced at $80 for early bookings and at $190 for bookings within one week of the flight. She estimates that the airline will sell 65 seats at the lower price and 35 at the higher price. Variable cost will not change. Which approach is preferable to Ms. Morgan?

CASE STUDIES

Fast Creek Lightning (G)*

With the rising demands of a successful hockey program, the chief of police in Fast Creek, Greg Frazier, wants to develop a two-year plan that involves a request for additional resources.

The Fast Creek police department currently has 26 sworn officers. The size of the force has not changed over the past 15 years, but the following changes have prompted the chief to seek more resources:

• The size of local recreational programs, especially hockey, has increased.
• Traffic and parking problems have increased.
• More portable, expensive computers and equipment with high theft potential are dispersed around the various public buildings.
• Alcohol and drug problems have increased.
• The size of the surrounding community has doubled.
• The police need to spend more time on education and prevention programs.

The hockey arena is located in Fast Creek, a small town in south-central Saskatchewan. A large university and also a college are situated nearby. During the summer months, the student population in Fast Creek and the surrounding towns is around 5000. The number swells to 20 000 during fall and spring semesters. Thus demand for police and other services is significantly lower during the summer months. Demand for police services also varies by:

• Time of day (peak time is between 10:00 p.m. and 2:00 a.m.).
• Day of the week (weekends are the busiest).
• Weekend of the year (on hockey weekends, thousands of extra people come to town).
• Special events.

Hockey home games are especially difficult to staff. All 26 officers are called in to work double shifts. More than 40 law enforcement officers from surrounding locations are paid to come in on their own time, and a dozen RCMP officers lend a hand free of charge (when available), provided they have a view of the game. Twenty-five students and local residents are paid to work traffic and parking. During the last year, overtime payments to police officers totalled over $120 000.

Other relevant data include the following:

• The average starting salary for a police officer is $28 000.
• Work-study and part-time students and local residents who help with traffic and parking are paid $9.00 an hour.
• Overtime is paid to police officers who work over 40 hours a week at a rate of $18.00 an hour. Extra officers who are hired part-time from outside agencies also earn $18.00 an hour.
• There seems to be an unlimited supply of officers who will work when needed for special events.
• With days off, vacations, and average sick leave considered, it takes five persons to cover one 24-hour, seven-day-a-week position.

The schedule of officers during fall and spring semesters is:

	Weekdays	Weekend
First shift (7:00 a.m. to 3:00 p.m.)	5	4
Second shift (3:00 p.m. to 11:00 p.m.)	5	6
Third shift (11:00 p.m. and 7:00 a.m.)	6	8

Staffing for hockey home games and special events is in addition to the preceding schedule. Summer staffing is, on average, half that shown.

Chief Frazier thinks that his present staff is stretched to the limit. Fatigued officers are potential problems for the police force and the community. In addition, neither time nor personnel has been set aside for crime prevention, safety, or health programs. Interactions between police officers and members of the community are often negative in nature. In light of these problems, the chief would like to request funding for four additional officers, two assigned to new programs and two to alleviate the overload on his current staff. He would also like to begin limiting overtime to 10 hours per week for each officer.

Discussion Questions

1. Which variations in demand for police services should be considered in an aggregate plan for resources? Which variations can be accomplished with short-term scheduling adjustments?
2. Evaluate the current staffing plan. What does it cost? Are 26 officers sufficient to handle the normal workload?

3. What would be the additional cost of the chief's proposal? How would you suggest that he justify his request?
4. How much does it currently cost the community to provide police services for hockey games? What would be the pros and cons of completely subcontracting this work to outside security agencies?
5. Propose other alternatives.*

---

* This integrated study runs throughout the text. Other issues facing Fast Creek's hockey expansion include (a) managing the arena project (Chapter 3), (b) forecasting game attendance (Chapter 4), (c) quality of facilities (Chapter 6), (d) break-even analysis for food services (Supplement 7 MyLab Operations Management), (e) location of the new arena (Chapter 8 MyLab Operations Management), and (f) inventory planning of hockey programs (Chapter 12 MyLab Operations Management). Recurring cases are also available in a separate file for instructors using the PCL.

Andrew-Carter, Inc.

Andrew-Carter, Inc. (A-C), is a major Canadian producer and distributor of outdoor lighting fixtures. Its products are distributed throughout North and South America and have been in high demand for several years. The company operates three plants to manufacture fixtures and distribute them to five distribution centres (warehouses).

During the present global slowdown, A-C has seen a major drop in demand for its products, largely because the housing market has declined. Based on the forecast of interest rates, the head of operations feels that demand for housing and thus for A-C's products will remain depressed for the foreseeable future. A-C is considering closing one of its plants, as it is now operating with a forecast excess capacity of 34 000 units per week. The forecast weekly demands for the coming year are as follows:

Warehouse 1	9000 units
Warehouse 2	13 000
Warehouse 3	11 000
Warehouse 4	15 000
Warehouse 5	8000

Plant capacities, in units per week, are as follows:

Plant 1, regular time	27 000 units
Plant 1, on overtime	7000
Plant 2, regular time	20 000
Plant 2, on overtime	5000
Plant 3, regular time	25 000
Plant 3, on overtime	6000

If A-C shuts down any plants, its weekly costs will change, because fixed costs will be lower for a nonoperating plant. Table 1

shows production costs at each plant, both variable at regular time and overtime, and fixed when operating and shut down. Table 2 shows distribution costs from each plant to each distribution centre.

Table 1
Andrew-Carter, Inc., Variable Costs and Fixed Production Costs per Week

		Fixed Cost per Week	
Plant	Variable Cost (per unit)	Operating	Not Operating
1, regular time	$2.80	$14 000	$6000
1, overtime	3.52		
2, regular time	2.78	12 000	5000
2, overtime	3.48		
3, regular time	2.72	15 000	7500
3, overtime	3.42		

Table 2
Andrew-Carter, Inc., Distribution Costs per Unit

	To Distribution Centres				
From Plants	W1	W2	W3	W4	W5
1	$0.50	$0.44	$0.49	$0.46	$0.56
2	0.40	0.52	0.50	0.56	0.57
3	0.56	0.53	0.51	0.54	0.35

Discussion Questions

1. Evaluate the various configurations of operating and closed plants that will meet weekly demand. Determine which configuration minimizes total costs.
2. Discuss the implications of closing a plant.

Source: Reprinted by permission of Professor Michael Ballot, University of the Pacific, Stockton, CA.

▶ **Additional Case Study:** Visit **MyLab Operations Management** for this case study:
Cornwell Glass: Involves setting a production schedule for an auto glass producer.

Using Revenue Management to Set Orlando Magic Ticket Prices

Revenue management was once the exclusive domain of the airline industry. But it has since spread its wings into the hotel business, auto rentals, and now even professional sports, with the San Francisco Giants, Boston Celtics, and Orlando Magic as leaders in introducing dynamic pricing into their ticketing systems. Dynamic pricing means looking at unsold tickets for every single game, every day, to see if the current ticket price for a particular seat needs to be lowered (because of slow demand) or raised (because of higher-than-expected demand).

Pricing can be impacted by something as simple as bad weather or by whether the team coming to play in the arena is on a winning streak or has just traded for a new superstar player. For example, a few years ago, a basketball star was traded in midseason to the Denver Nuggets; this resulted in an immediate runup in unsold ticket prices for the teams the Nuggets were facing on the road. Had the Nuggets been visiting the Orlando Magic two weeks after the trade and the Magic not raised prices, they would have been "leaving money on the table" (as shown in Figure 13.5).

As the Magic became more proficient in revenue management, they evolved from (1) setting the price for each seat at the start of the season and never changing it; to (2) setting the prices for each seat at season onset, based on the popularity of the opponent, the day of the week, and the time of season, but keeping the prices frozen once the season began (see Table 13.10); to (3) pricing tickets based on projected demand, but adjusting them frequently to match market demand as the season progressed.

To track market demand, the Magic use listed prices on Stub Hub and other online ticket exchange services. The key is to sell out all 18 500 seats every home game, keeping the pressure on Anthony Perez, the director of business strategy, and Chris Dorso, the Magic's vice-president of sales.

Perez and Dorso use every tool available to collect information on demand, including counting unique page views at the Ticketmaster website. If, for example, there are 5000 page views for the Miami Heat game near Thanksgiving, it indicates enough demand that prices of unsold seats can be notched up. If there are only 150 Ticketmaster views for the Utah Jazz game three days later, there may not be sufficient information to make any changes yet.

Table 13.10
An Example of Variable Pricing for a $68 Terrace V seat in Zone 103

Opponent Popularity Rating	Number of Games in this Category	Price
Tier I	3	$187
Tier II	3	$170
Tier III	4	$ 85
Tier IV	6	$ 75
Tier V	14	$ 60
Tier VI	9	$ 44
Tier VII	6	$ 40
Average		$ 68

With a database of 650 000, the Magic can use email blasts to react quickly right up to game day. The team may discount seat prices, offer other perks, or just point out that prime seats are still available for a game against an exciting opponent.

Discussion Questions*

1. After researching revenue (yield) management in airlines, describe how the Magic system differs from that of American or other air carriers.
2. The Magic used its original pricing systems of several years ago and set the price for a Terrace V, Zone 103 seat at $68 per game. There were 230 such seats *not* purchased as part of season ticket packages and thus available to the public. If the team switched to the seven-price dynamic system (illustrated in Table 13.10), how would the profit-contribution for the 45-game season change? (Note that the 45-game season includes four preseason games.)
3. What are some concerns the team needs to consider when using dynamic pricing with frequent changes in price?

*You may wish to view the video that accompanies this case before addressing these questions.

CHAPTER 13 | RAPID REVIEW

MyLab Operations Management

Main Heading	Review Material
THE PLANNING PROCESS (pp. 513–515)	• **Sales and operations planning (S&OP)**—A process of balancing resources and forecasted demand, aligning an organization's competing demands from supply chain to final customer, while linking strategic planning with operations over all planning horizons. • **Aggregate plan**—A plan that includes forecast levels for families of products of finished goods, inventory, shortages, and changes in the workforce. Usually, *the objective of aggregate planning is to meet forecasted demand while minimizing cost over the planning period.* Four things are needed for aggregate planning: 1. A logical overall unit for measuring sales and output. 2. A forecast of demand for a reasonable intermediate planning period in these aggregate terms.

MyLab Operations Management

Main Heading	Review Material
	3. A method for determining the relevant costs.
	4. A model that combines forecasts and costs so that scheduling decisions can be made for the planning period.
THE NATURE OF AGGREGATE PLANNING (pp. 515–516)	An aggregate plan looks at production *in the aggregate* (a family of products), not as a product-by-product breakdown. • **Disaggregation**—The process of breaking an aggregate plan into greater detail. • **Master production schedule**—A timetable that specifies what is to be made and when.
AGGREGATE PLANNING STRATEGIES (pp. 516–519)	The basic aggregate planning capacity (production) options are: 1. Changing inventory levels. 2. Varying workforce size by hiring or layoffs. 3. Varying production rates through overtime or idle time. 4. Subcontracting. 5. Using part-time workers. The basic aggregate planning demand options are: 1. Influencing demand. 2. Backordering during high-demand periods. 3. Counter-seasonal product and service mixing. • **Chase strategy**—A planning strategy that sets production equal to forecasted demand. Many service organizations favour the chase strategy because the inventory option is difficult or impossible to adopt. • **Level scheduling**—Maintaining a constant output rate, production rate, or workforce level over the planning horizon. Level scheduling works well when demand is reasonably stable. • **Mixed strategy**—A planning strategy that uses two or more controllable variables to set a feasible production plan.
METHODS FOR AGGREGATE PLANNING (pp. 519–526)	• **Graphical techniques**—Aggregate planning techniques that work with a few variables at a time to allow planners to compare projected demand with existing capacity. Graphical techniques are trial-and-error approaches that do not guarantee an optimal production plan, but they require only limited computations. Five steps of the graphical method are: 1. Determine the demand in each period. 2. Determine capacity for regular time, overtime, and subcontracting each period. 3. Find labour costs, hiring and layoff costs, and inventory holding costs. 4. Consider company policy that may apply to the workers or to stock levels. 5. Develop alternative plans and examine their total costs. A *cumulative* graph displays visually how the forecast deviates from the average requirements. • **Transportation method of linear programming**—A way of solving for the optimal solution to an aggregate planning problem. The transportation method of linear programming is flexible in that it can specify regular and overtime production in each time period, the number of units to be subcontracted, extra shifts, and the inventory carryover from period to period. Transportation problems require that supply equals demand, so when it does not, a dummy column called "unused capacity" may be added. Costs of not using capacity are zero. Demand requirements are shown in the bottom row of a transportation table. Total capacity available (supply) is shown in the far right column. In general, to complete a transportation table, allocate as much production as you can to a cell with the smallest cost, without exceeding the unused capacity in that row or demand in that column. If there is still some demand left in that row, allocate as much as you can to the next-lowest-cost cell. You then repeat this process for periods 2 and 3 (and beyond, if necessary). When you are finished, the sum of all your entries in a row must equal total row capacity, and the sum of all entries in a column must equal the demand for that period.	Problems: 13.2–13.19 Virtual Office Hours for Solved Problems: 13.1 **ACTIVE MODEL 13.1**

Main Heading	Review Material	MyLab Operations Management
	The transportation method was originally formulated by E. H. Bowman in 1956. It does not work when nonlinear or negative factors are introduced. • **Management coefficients model**—A formal planning model built around a manager's experience and performance.	
AGGREGATE PLANNING IN SERVICES (pp. 526–528)	Successful techniques for controlling the cost of labour in service firms include: 1. Accurate scheduling of labour-hours to ensure quick response to customer demand. 2. An on-call labour resource that can be added or deleted to meet unexpected demand. 3. Flexibility of individual worker skills that permits reallocation of available labour. 4. Flexibility in rate of output or hours of work to meet changing demand.	Related problems: 13.20, 13.21
YIELD MANAGEMENT (pp. 528–531)	• **Yield (or revenue) management**—Capacity decisions that determine the allocation of resources to maximize profit or yield. Organizations that have perishable inventory, such as airlines, hotels, car rental agencies, and cruise lines, have the following shared characteristics that make yield management of interest: 1. Service or product can be sold in advance of consumption. 2. Demand fluctuates. 3. The resource (capacity) is relatively fixed. 4. Demand can be segmented. 5. Variable costs are low, and fixed costs are high. To make yield management work, the company needs to manage three issues: 1. Multiple pricing structures. 2. Forecasts of the use and duration of the use. 3. Changes in demand.	Related problem: 13.22

Self-Test

■ **Before taking the self-test,** refer to the learning objectives listed at the beginning of the chapter.

LO1 Aggregate planning is concerned with determining the quantity and timing of production in the:
a) short term.
b) intermediate term.
c) long term.
d) all of the above.

LO2 Aggregate planning deals with a number of constraints. These typically are:
a) job assignments, job ordering, dispatching, and overtime help.
b) part-time help, weekly scheduling, and SKU production scheduling.
c) subcontracting, employment levels, inventory levels, and capacity.
d) capital investment, expansion or contracting capacity, and R&D.
e) facility location, production budgeting, overtime, and R&D.

LO3 Which of the following is not one of the graphical method steps?
a) Determine the demand in each period.
b) Determine capacity for regular time, overtime, and subcontracting each period.
c) Find labour costs, hiring and layoff costs, and inventory holding costs.

d) Construct the transportation table.
e) Consider company policy that may apply to the workers or stock levels.
f) Develop alternative plans and examine their total costs.

LO4 When might a dummy column be added to a transportation table?
a) When supply does not equal demand
b) When overtime is greater than regular time
c) When subcontracting is greater than regular time
d) When subcontracting is greater than regular time plus overtime
e) When production needs to spill over into a new period

LO5 Yield management requires management to deal with:
a) multiple pricing structures.
b) changes in demand.
c) forecasts of use.
d) forecasts of duration of use.
e) all of the above.

Answers: LO1. b; LO2. c; LO3. d; LO4. a; LO5. e.

MyLab Operations Management

Most of these questions can be found in MyLab Operations Management. Visit MyLab Operations Management to access cases, videos, downloadable software, and much more. MyLab Operations Management Management also features a personalized Study Plan that helps you identify which chapter concepts you've mastered and guides you towards study tools for additional practice.

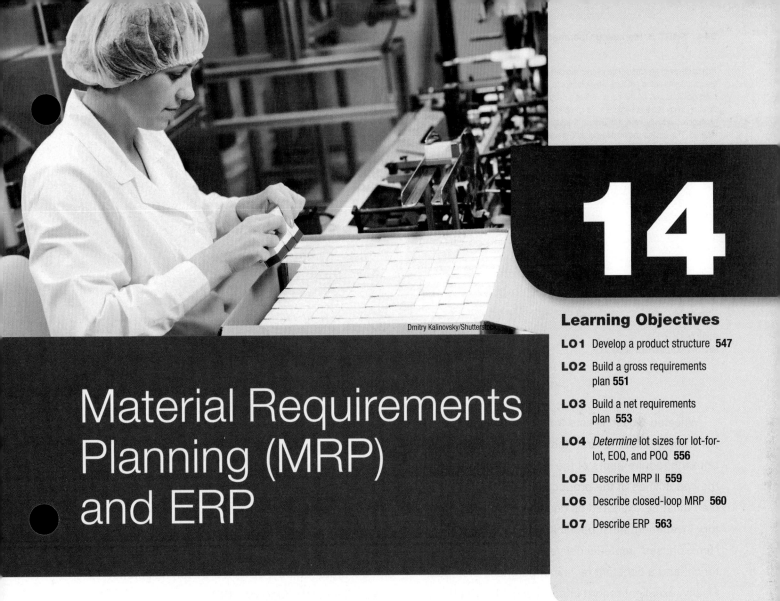

Dmitry Kalinovsky/Shutterstock

14

Material Requirements Planning (MRP) and ERP

MRP Provides a Competitive Advantage for Wheeled Coach

Wheeled Coach, headquartered in Winter Park, Florida, is the largest manufacturer of ambulances in the world. The U.S. $200 million firm is an international competitor that sells more than 25% of its vehicles to markets outside the United States. Twelve major ambulance designs are produced on assembly lines (i.e., a repetitive process) at the Florida plant, using 18 000 different inventory items, of which 6000 are manufactured and 12 000 purchased. Most of the product line is custom designed and assembled to meet the specific and often unique requirements demanded by the ambulance's application and customer preferences.

This variety of products and the nature of the process demand good material requirements planning. Effective use of an MRP system requires accurate bills of material and inventory records. The Wheeled Coach system provides daily updates and has reduced inventory by more than 30% in just two years.

< Global
Company
Profile
Wheeled
Coach

543

This cutaway of an ambulance interior indicates the complexity of the product, which for some rural locations may be the equivalent of a hospital emergency room in miniature. To complicate production, virtually every ambulance is custom ordered. This customization necessitates precise orders, excellent bills of materials, exceptional inventory control from supplier to assembly, and an MRP system that works.

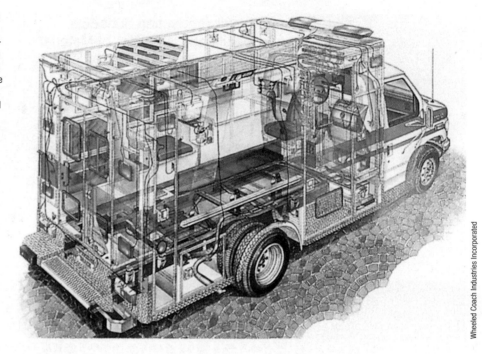

Wheeled Coach Industries Incorporated

VIDEO 14.1
MRP at Wheeled Coach Ambulance

Wheeled Coach insists that four key tasks be performed properly. First, the material plan must meet both the requirements of the master schedule and the capabilities of the production facility. Second, the plan must be executed as designed. Third, inventory investment must be minimized through effective "time-phased" material deliveries, consignment inventories, and a constant review of purchase methods. Finally, excellent record integrity must be maintained.

Record accuracy is recognized as a fundamental ingredient of Wheeled Coach's successful MRP program. Its cycle counters are charged with material audits that not only correct errors but also investigate and correct problems.

Wheeled Coach Industries uses MRP as the catalyst for low inventory, high quality, tight schedules, and accurate records. Wheeled Coach has found competitive advantage via MRP.

STUDENT TIP

"Dependent demand" means the demand for one item is related to the demand for another item.

Dependent Demand

Wheeled Coach and many other firms have found important benefits in MRP. These benefits include (1) better response to customer orders as the result of improved adherence to schedules, (2) faster response to market changes, (3) improved utilization of facilities and labour, and (4) reduced inventory levels. Better response to customer orders and to the market wins orders and market share. Better utilization of facilities and labour yields higher productivity and return on investment. Less inventory frees up capital and floor space for other uses. These benefits are the result of a strategic decision to use a *dependent* inventory scheduling system. Demand for every component of an ambulance is dependent.

Demand for items is dependent when the relationship between the items can be determined. Therefore, once management receives an order or makes a forecast for the final product, quantities for all components can be computed. All components are dependent items. The Boeing Aircraft operations manager who schedules production of one plane per week, for example, knows the requirements down to the last rivet. For any product, all components of that product are dependent demand items. *More generally, for any product for which a schedule can be established, dependent techniques should be used.*

When the requirements of MRP are met, dependent models are preferable to the EOQ models described in Chapter 12.[1] Dependent models are better not only for manufacturers and distributors

---

[1] The inventory models (EOQ) discussed in Chapter 12 assume that the demand for one item is independent of the demand for another item. For example, EOQ assumes the demand for refrigerator parts is *independent* of the demand for refrigerators and that demand for parts is constant.

but also for a wide variety of firms from restaurants to hospitals. The dependent technique used in a production environment is called **material requirements planning (MRP)**.

Because MRP provides such a clean structure for dependent demand, it has evolved as the basis for enterprise resource planning (ERP). ERP is an information system for identifying and planning the enterprise-wide resources needed to take, make, ship, and account for customer orders. We will discuss ERP in the latter part of this chapter.

Material requirements planning (MRP)

A dependent demand technique that uses a bill of material, inventory, expected receipts, and a master production schedule to determine material requirements.

Dependent Inventory Model Requirements

Effective use of dependent inventory models requires that the operations manager know the following:

1. Master production schedule (what is to be made and when).
2. Specifications or bill of material (materials and parts required to make the product).
3. Inventory availability (what is in stock).
4. Purchase orders outstanding (what is on order, also called expected receipts).
5. Lead times (how long it takes to get various components).

We now discuss each of these requirements in the context of material requirements planning.

MASTER PRODUCTION SCHEDULE

A **master production schedule (MPS)** specifies what is to be made (i.e., the number of finished products or items) and when. The schedule must be in accordance with a production plan. The production plan sets the overall level of output in broad terms (e.g., product families, standard hours, or dollar volume). The plan also includes a variety of inputs, including financial plans, customer demand, engineering capabilities, labour availability, inventory fluctuations, supplier performance, and other considerations. Each of these inputs contributes in its own way to the production plan, as shown in Figure 14.1.

As the planning process moves from the production plan to execution, each of the lower-level plans must be feasible. When one is not, feedback to the next higher level is used to make the necessary adjustment. One of the major strengths of MRP is its ability to determine precisely the feasibility of a schedule within aggregate capacity constraints. This planning process can yield excellent results. The production plan sets the upper and lower bounds on the master production schedule. The result of this production planning process is the master production schedule.

The master production schedule tells us what is required to satisfy demand and meet the production plan. This schedule establishes what items to make and when: It *disaggregates* the

Master production schedule (MPS)

A timetable that specifies what is to be made and when.

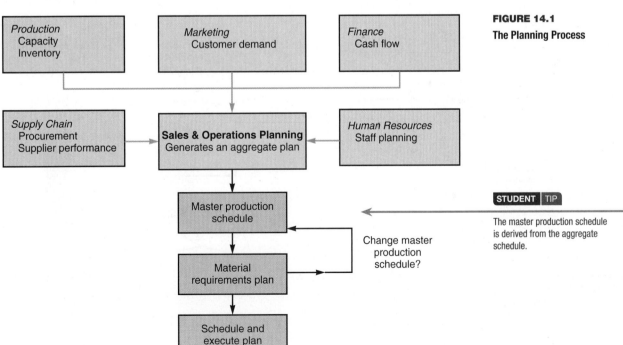

FIGURE 14.1

The Planning Process

STUDENT TIP

The master production schedule is derived from the aggregate schedule.

FIGURE 14.2

The Aggregate Production Plan Is the Basis for Development of the Detailed Master Production Schedule

Months		January				February			
Aggregate Production Plan (Shows the total quantity of amplifiers.)		1500				1200			
Weeks		1	2	3	4	5	6	7	8
Master Production Schedule (Shows the specific type and quantity of amplifier to be produced.)									
240-watt amplifier	100		100		100		100		
150-watt amplifier		500		500		450		450	
75-watt amplifier			300				100		

aggregate production plan. While the *aggregate production plan* (as discussed in Chapter 13) is established in gross terms such as families of products or tons of steel, the *master production schedule* is established in terms of specific products. Figure 14.2 shows the master production schedules for three stereo models that flow from the aggregate production plan for a family of stereo amplifiers.

Managers must adhere to the schedule for a reasonable length of time (usually a major portion of the production cycle—the time it takes to produce a product). Many organizations establish a master production schedule and establish a policy of not changing ("fixing") the near-term portion of the plan. This near-term portion of the plan is then referred to as the "fixed," "firm," or "frozen" schedule. Wheeled Coach, the subject of the *Global Company Profile* for this chapter, fixes the last 14 days of its schedule. Only changes further out, beyond the fixed schedule, are permitted. The master production schedule is a "rolling" production schedule. For example, a fixed seven-week plan has an additional week added to it as each week is completed, so a seven-week fixed schedule is maintained. Note that the master production schedule is a statement of *what is to be produced*, not a forecast of demand. The master schedule can be expressed in any of the following terms:

1. A *customer order in a job shop* (make-to-order) company.
2. *Modules in a repetitive* (assemble-to-order or forecast) company.
3. An *end item in a continuous* (stock-to-forecast) company.

This relationship of the master production schedule to the processes is shown in Figure 14.3.

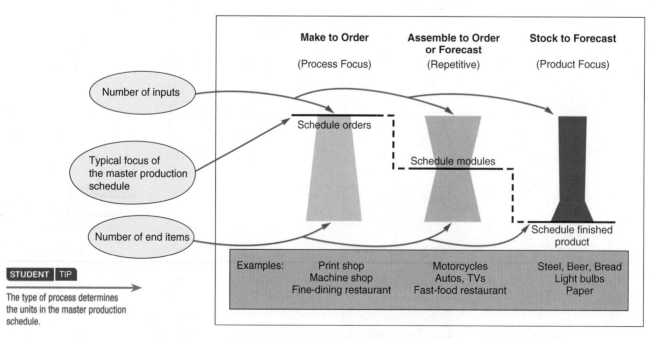

FIGURE 14.3 **Typical Focus of the Master Production Schedule in Three Process Strategies**

Table 14.1

Master Production Schedule for Crabmeat Quiche and Spinach Quiche at Nancy's Specialty Foods

Gross Requirements for Crabmeat Quiche										
Day	6	7	8	9	10	11	12	13	14	and so on
Amount	50		100	47	60		110	75		

Gross Requirements for Spinach Quiche										
Day	7	8	9	10	11	12	13	14	15	16	and so on
Amount	100	200	150			60	75		100		

A master production schedule for two of Nancy's Specialty Foods' products, crabmeat quiche and spinach quiche, might look like Table 14.1.

BILLS OF MATERIAL

Defining what goes into a product may seem simple, but it can be difficult in practice. As we noted in Chapter 5, to aid this process, manufactured items are defined via a bill of material. A **bill of material (BOM)** is a list of quantities of components, ingredients, and materials required to make a product. Individual drawings describe not only physical dimensions but also any special processing as well as the raw material from which each part is made. Nancy's Specialty Foods has a recipe for quiche, specifying ingredients and quantities, just as Wheeled Coach has a full set of drawings for an ambulance. Both are bills of material (although we call one a recipe, and they do vary somewhat in scope). For an example of this concept see the Video Case, "When 18 500 Orlando Magic Fans Come to Dinner".

Because there is often a rush to get a new product to market, however, drawings and bills of material may be incomplete or even nonexistent. Moreover, complete drawings and BOMs (as well as other forms of specifications) often contain errors in dimensions, quantities, or countless other areas. When errors are identified, engineering change notices (ECNs) are created, further complicating the process. An *engineering change notice* is a change or correction to an engineering drawing or bill of material.

One way a bill of material defines a product is by providing a product structure. Example 1 shows how to develop the product structure and "explode" it to reveal the requirements for each component. A bill of material for item A in Example 1 consists of items B and C. Items above any level are called *parents*; items below any level are called *components* or *children*. By convention, the top level in a BOM is the 0 level.

Bill of material (BOM)

A listing of the components, their description, and the quantity of each required to make one unit of a product.

VIDEO 14.2

When 18 500 Orlando Magic Fans Come to Dinner

Speaker Kits, Inc., packages high-fidelity components for mail order. Components for the top-of-the-line speaker kit, "Awesome" (A), include two standard 30-cm speaker kits (Bs) and three speaker kits with amp-boosters (Cs).

Each B consists of two speakers (Ds) and two shipping boxes each with an installation kit (E). Each of the three 300-watt speaker kits (Cs) has two speaker boosters (Fs) and two installation kits (Es). Each speaker booster (F) includes two speakers (Ds) and one amp-booster (G). The total for each Awesome is four standard 30-cm speakers and twelve 30-cm speakers with the amp-booster. (Most purchasers require hearing aids within three years, and at least one court case is pending because of structural damage to a men's dormitory.) As we can see, the demand for B, C, D, E, F, and G is completely dependent on the master production schedule for A—the Awesome speaker kits.

APPROACH ▶ Given the above information, we construct a product structure and "explode" the requirements.

SOLUTION ▶ This structure has four levels: 0, 1, 2, and 3. There are four parents: A, B, C, and F. Each parent item has at least one level below it. Items B, C, D, E, F, and G are components because each item has at least one level above it. In this structure, B, C, and F are both parents and components. The number in parentheses indicates how many units of that particular item are needed to make the item immediately above it. Thus, $B_{(2)}$ means that it takes two units of B for every unit of A, and $F_{(2)}$ means that it takes two units of F for every unit of C.

EXAMPLE **1**

Developing a Product Structure and Gross Requirements

LO1 Develop a product structure

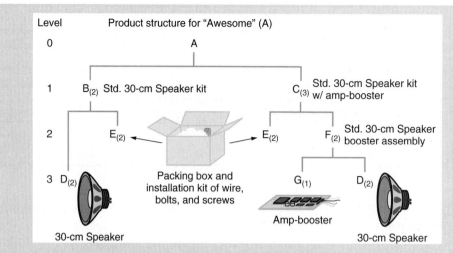

Once we have developed the product structure, we can determine the number of units of each item required to satisfy demand for a new order of 50 Awesome speaker kits. We "explode" the requirements as shown:

Part B:	$2 \times$ number of As $=$	$(2)(50) =$	100
Part C:	$3 \times$ number of As $=$	$(3)(50) =$	150
Part D:	$2 \times$ number of Bs 1 $+ 2 \times$ number of Fs $=$	$(2)(100) + (2)(300) =$	800
Part E:	$2 \times$ number of Bs $+ 2 \times$ number of Cs $=$	$(2)(100) + (2)(150) =$	500
Part F:	$2 \times$ number of Cs $=$	$(2)(150) =$	300
Part G:	$1 \times$ number of Fs $=$	$(1)(300) =$	300

INSIGHT ▶ We now have a visual picture of the Awesome speaker kit requirements and knowledge of the quantities required. Thus, for 50 units of A, we will need 100 units of B, 150 units of C, 800 units of D, 500 units of E, 300 units of F, and 300 units of G.

LEARNING EXERCISE ▶ If there are 100 Fs in stock, how many Ds do you need? [Answer: 600.]

RELATED PROBLEMS ▶ 14.1, 14.3a, 14.13a, 14.25a

Bills of material not only specify requirements but also are useful for costing, and they can serve as a list of items to be issued to production or assembly personnel. When bills of material are used in this way, they are usually called *pick lists*.

MODULAR BILLS Bills of material may be organized around product modules (see Chapter 5). *Modules* are not final products to be sold but are components that can be produced and assembled into units. They are often major components of the final product or product options. Bills of material for modules are called **modular bills**. Bills of material are sometimes organized as modules (rather than as part of a final product) because production scheduling and production are often facilitated by organizing around relatively few modules rather than a multitude of final assemblies. For instance, a firm may make 138 000 different final products but may have only 40 modules that are mixed and matched to produce those 138 000 final products. The firm builds an aggregate production plan and prepares its master production schedule for the 40 modules, not the 138 000 configurations of the final product. This approach allows the MPS to be prepared for a reasonable number of items (the narrow portion of the middle graphic in Figure 14.3) and to postpone assembly. The 40 modules can then be configured for specific orders at final assembly.

PLANNING BILLS AND PHANTOM BILLS Two other special kinds of bills of material are planning bills and phantom bills. **Planning bills** (sometimes called "pseudo" bills or super bills) are created in order to assign an artificial parent to the bill of material. Such bills are used (1) when we want to group subassemblies so the number of items to be scheduled is reduced and (2) when we want to issue "kits" to the production department. For instance, it may not be efficient to issue inexpensive items such as washers and cotter pins with each of numerous subassemblies, so we call this a *kit* and generate a planning bill. The planning bill specifies the *kit* to be issued. Consequently, a planning bill may also be known as kitted material, or a kit. **Phantom bills of material** are bills of material for components, usually subassemblies, that exist only temporarily. These components go directly into another assembly and are never inventoried. Therefore,

Modular bills

Bills of material organized by major subassemblies or by product options.

Planning bills

A material grouping created in order to assign an artificial parent to a bill of material; also called "pseudo" bills, kitted material, or kits.

Phantom bills of material

Bills of material for components, usually assemblies, that exist only temporarily; they are never inventoried.

components of phantom bills of material are coded to receive special treatment; lead times are zero, and they are handled as an integral part of their parent item. An example is a transmission shaft with gears and bearings assembly that is placed directly into a transmission.

LOW-LEVEL CODING Low-level coding of an item in a BOM is necessary when identical items exist at various levels in the BOM. **Low-level coding** means that the item is coded at the lowest level at which it occurs. For example, item D in Example 1 is coded at the lowest level at which it is used. Item D could be coded as part of B and occur at level 2. However, because D is also part of F, and F is level 2, item D becomes a level 3 item. Low-level coding is a convention to allow easy computing of the requirements of an item. When the BOM has thousands of items or when requirements are frequently recomputed, the ease and speed of computation become a major concern.

Low-level coding

A number that identifies items at the lowest level at which they occur.

ACCURATE INVENTORY RECORDS

As we saw in Chapter 12, knowledge of what is in stock is the result of good inventory management. Good inventory management is an absolute necessity for an MRP system to work. If the firm does not exceed 99% record accuracy, then material requirements planning will not work.[2]

PURCHASE ORDERS OUTSTANDING

Knowledge of outstanding orders exists as a by-product of well managed purchasing and inventory-control departments. When purchase orders are executed, records of those orders and their scheduled delivery dates must be available to production personnel. Only with good purchasing data can managers prepare meaningful production plans and effectively execute an MRP system.

Lead time

In purchasing systems, the time between recognition of the need for an order and receiving it; in production systems, it is the order, wait, move, queue, setup, and run times for each component.

LEAD TIMES FOR COMPONENTS

Once managers determine when products are needed, they determine when to acquire them. The time required to acquire (i.e., purchase, produce, or assemble) an item is known as **lead time**. Lead time for a manufactured item consists of *move*, *setup*, and *assembly* or *run times* for each component. For a purchased item, the lead time includes the time between recognition of need for an order and when it is available for production.

When the bill of material for Awesome speaker kits (As), in Example 1, is turned on its side and modified by adding lead times for each component (see Table 14.2), we then have a *time-phased product structure*. Time in this structure is shown on the horizontal axis of Figure 14.4 with item A due for completion in week 8. Each component is then offset to accommodate lead times.

Table 14.2

Lead Times for Awesome Speaker Kits (As)

Component	Lead Time
A	1 week
B	2 weeks
C	1 week
D	1 week
E	2 weeks
F	3 weeks
G	2 weeks

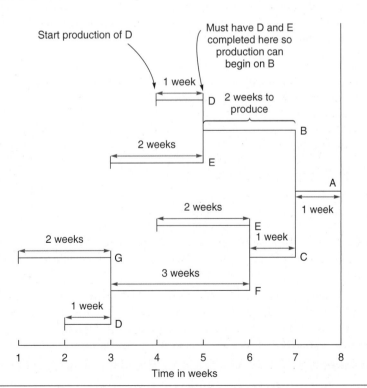

FIGURE 14.4

Time-Phased Product Structure

---

[2] Record accuracy of 99% may sound good, but note that even when each component has an availability of 99% and a product has only seven components, the likelihood of a product being completed is only 0.932 (because $0.99^7 = 0.932$).

FIGURE 14.5
Structure of the MRP System

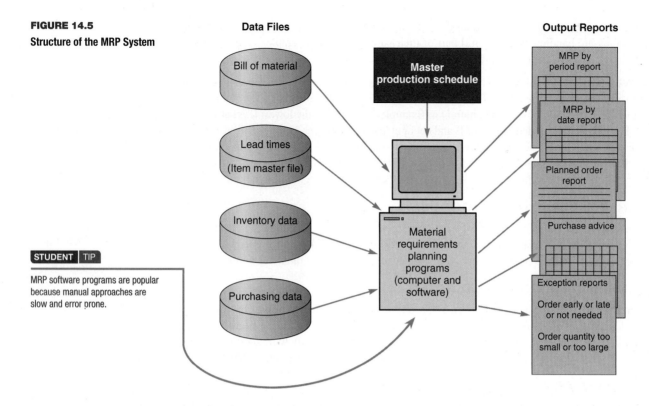

MRP Structure

Although most MRP systems are computerized, the MRP procedure is straightforward, and we can illustrate a small one by hand. A master production schedule, a bill of material, inventory and purchase records, and lead times for each item are the ingredients of a material requirements planning system (see Figure 14.5).

Once these ingredients are available and accurate, the next step is to construct a gross material requirements plan. The **gross material requirements plan** is a schedule, as shown in Example 2. It combines a master production schedule (that requires one unit of A in week 8) and the time-phased schedule (Figure 14.4). It shows when an item must be ordered from suppliers if there is no inventory on hand or when the production of an item must be started to satisfy demand for the finished product by a particular date.

Gross material requirements plan

A schedule that shows the total demand for an item (prior to subtraction of on-hand inventory and scheduled receipts) and (1) when it must be ordered from suppliers, or (2) when production must be started to meet its demand by a particular date.

EXAMPLE 2

Building a Gross Requirements Plan

Each Awesome speaker kit (item A of Example 1) requires all the items in the product structure for A. Lead times are shown in Table 14.2.

APPROACH ▶ Using the information in Example 1 and Table 14.2, we construct the gross material requirements plan with a production schedule that will satisfy the demand of 50 units of A by week 8.

SOLUTION ▶ We prepare a schedule as shown in Table 14.3.

You can interpret the gross material requirements shown in Table 14.3 as follows: If you want 50 units of A at week 8, you must start assembling A in week 7. Thus, in week 7, you will need 100 units of B and 150 units of C. These two items take two weeks and one week, respectively, to produce. Production of B, therefore, should start in week 5, and production of C should start in week 6 (lead time subtracted from the required date for these items). Working backward, we can perform the same computations for all of the other items. Because D and E are used in two different places in Awesome speaker kits, there are two entries in each data record.

INSIGHT ▶ The gross material requirements plan shows when production of each item should begin and end in order to have 50 units of A at week 8. Management now has an initial plan.

LEARNING EXERCISE ▶ If the lead time for G decreases from two weeks to one week, what is the new order release date for G? [Answer: 300 in week 2.]

RELATED PROBLEMS ▶ 14.2, 14.4, 14.6, 14.8b, 14.9, 14.10a, 14.11a, 14.13b, 14.25b

EXCEL OM Data File **Ch14Ex2.xlsx** can be found at **MyLab Operations Management.**

	Week								
	1	2	3	4	5	6	7	8	Lead Time
A. Required date								50	
Order release date							50		1 week
B. Required date							100		
Order release date					100				2 weeks
C. Required date							150		
Order release date						150			1 week
E. Required date					200	300			
Order release date			200	300					2 weeks
F. Required date						300			
Order release date			300						3 weeks
D. Required date			600		200				
Order release date		600		200					1 week
G. Required date			300						
Order release date	300								2 weeks

Table 14.3

Gross Material Requirements Plan for 50 Awesome Speaker Kits (As)

LO2 Build a gross requirements plan

So far, we have considered *gross material requirements*, which assumes that there is no inventory on hand. When there is inventory on hand, we prepare a **net material requirements plan**. When considering on-hand inventory, we must realize that many items in inventory contain subassemblies or parts. If the gross requirement for Awesome speaker kits (As) is 100 and there are 20 of those speakers on hand, the net requirement for Awesome speaker kits (As) is 80 (i.e., 100 – 20). However, each Awesome speaker kit on hand contains 2 Bs. As a result, the requirement for Bs drops by 40 Bs (20 A kits on hand × 2 Bs per A). Therefore, if inventory is on hand for a parent item, the requirements for the parent item and all its components decrease because each Awesome kit contains the components for lower-level items. Example 3 shows how to create a net requirements plan.

Net material requirements plan
The result of adjusting gross requirements for inventory on hand and scheduled receipts.

Speaker Kits, Inc., developed a product structure from a bill of material in Example 1. Example 2 developed a gross requirements plan. Given the following on-hand inventory, Speaker Kits, Inc., now wants to construct a net requirements plan.

Item	On Hand	Item	On Hand
A	10	E	10
B	15	F	5
C	20	G	0
D	10		

EXAMPLE 3

Determining Net Requirements

APPROACH ▶ A net material requirements plan includes gross requirements, on-hand inventory, net requirements, planned order receipt, and planned order release for each item. We begin with A and work backward through the components.

SOLUTION ▶ Shown in the chart is the net material requirements plan for product A.

Constructing a net requirements plan is similar to constructing a gross requirements plan. Starting with item A, we work backward to determine net requirements for all items. To do these computations, we refer to the product structure, on-hand inventory, and lead times. The gross requirement for A is 50 units in week 8. Ten items are on hand; therefore, the net requirements and the scheduled **planned order receipt** are both 40 items in week 8. Because of the one-week lead time, the **planned order release** is 40 items in week 7 (see the arrow connecting the order receipt and order release). Referring to week 7 and the product structure in Example 1, we can see that 80 (= 2 × 40) items of B and 120 (= 3 × 40) items of C are required in week 7 to have a total for 50 items of A in week 8. The letter superscripted A to the right of the gross figure for items B and C was generated as a result of the demand for the parent, A. Performing the same type of analysis for B and C yields

Planned order receipt
The quantity planned to be received at a future date.

Planned order release
The scheduled date for an order to be released.

Net Material Requirements Plan for Product A *(the superscript is the source of the demand)*

Lot Size	Lead Time (weeks)	On Hand	Safety Stock	Allocated	Low-Level Code	Item Identification		Proj OH	1	2	3	4	5	6	7	8
Lot-for-Lot	1	10	—	—	0	A	Gross Requirements									50
							Scheduled Receipts									
							Projected On Hand	10	10	10	10	10	10	10	10	10
							Net Requirements									40
							Planned Order Receipts									40
							Planned Order Releases								40	
Lot-for-Lot	2	15	—	—	1	B	Gross Requirements								80[A]	
							Scheduled Receipts									
							Projected On Hand	15	15	15	15	15	15	15	15	
							Net Requirements								65	
							Planned Order Receipts								65	
							Planned Order Releases						65			
Lot-for-Lot	1	20	—	—	1	C	Gross Requirements								120[A]	
							Scheduled Receipts									
							Projected On Hand	20	20	20	20	20	20	20	20	
							Net Requirements								100	
							Planned Order Receipts								100	
							Planned Order Releases							100		
Lot-for-Lot	2	10	—	—	2	E	Gross Requirements						130[B]	200[C]		
							Scheduled Receipts									
							Projected On Hand	10	10	10	10	10	10			
							Net Requirements						120	200		
							Planned Order Receipts						120	200		
							Planned Order Releases				120	200				
Lot-for-Lot	3	5	—	—	2	F	Gross Requirements							200[C]		
							Scheduled Receipts									
							Projected On Hand	5	5	5	5	5	5	5		
							Net Requirements							195		
							Planned Order Receipts							195		
							Planned Order Releases				195					
Lot-for-Lot	1	10	—	—	3	D	Gross Requirements				390[F]		130[B]			
							Scheduled Receipts									
							Projected On Hand	10	10	10	10					
							Net Requirements				380		130			
							Planned Order Receipts				380		130			
							Planned Order Releases			380		130				
Lot-for-Lot	2	0	—	—	3	G	Gross Requirements				195[F]					
							Scheduled Receipts									
							Projected On Hand				0					
							Net Requirements				195					
							Planned Order Receipts				195					
							Planned Order Releases		195							

the net requirements for D, E, F, and G. Note the on-hand inventory in row E in week 6 is zero. It is zero because the on-hand inventory (10 units) was used to make B in week 5. By the same token, the inventory for D was used to make F in week 3.

INSIGHT ▶ Once a net requirement plan is completed, management knows the quantities needed, an ordering schedule, and a production schedule for each component.

LEARNING EXERCISE ▶ If the on-hand inventory quantity of component F is 95 rather than 5, how many units of G will need to be ordered in week 1? [Answer: 105 units.]

RELATED PROBLEMS ▶ 14.5, 14.7, 14.8c, 14.10b, 14.11b, 14.12, 14.13c, 14.14b, 14.15a,b,c, 14.16a, 14.25c, 14.27

ACTIVE MODEL 14.1 This example is further illustrated in Active Model 14.1 at **MyLab Operations Management.**

EXCEL OM Data File **Ch14Ex3.xlsx** can be found at **MyLab Operations Management.**

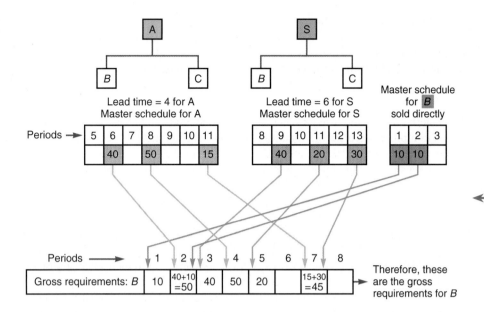

FIGURE 14.6

Several Schedules Contributing to a Gross Requirements Schedule for B

One B is in each A, and one B is in each S; in addition, 10 Bs sold directly are scheduled in week 1, and 10 more that are sold directly are scheduled in week 2.

STUDENT TIP

MRP gross requirements can combine multiple products, spare parts, and items sold directly.

Examples 2 and 3 considered only product A, the Awesome speaker kit, and its completion only in week 8. Fifty units of A were required in week 8. Normally, however, there is a demand for many products over time. For each product, management must prepare a master production schedule (as we saw earlier in Table 14.1). Scheduled production of each product is added to the master schedule and, ultimately, to the net material requirements plan. Figure 14.6 shows how several product schedules, including requirements for components sold directly, can contribute to one gross material requirements plan.

Most inventory systems also note the number of units in inventory that have been assigned to specific future production but not yet used or issued from the stockroom. Such items are often referred to as *allocated* items. Allocated items increase requirements and may then be included in an MRP planning sheet, as shown in Figure 14.7.

The allocated quantity has the effect of increasing the requirements (or, alternatively, reducing the quantity on hand). The logic, then, of a net requirements MRP is:

$$\underbrace{[(\text{Gross requirements}) + (\text{Allocations})]}_{\text{Total requirements}} - \underbrace{[(\text{On hand}) + (\text{Scheduled receipts})]}_{\text{Available inventory}} = \begin{array}{c}\text{Net} \\ \text{requirements}\end{array}$$

LO3 Build a net requirements plan

SAFETY STOCK The continuing task of operations managers is to remove variability. This is the case in MRP systems as in other operations systems. Realistically, however, managers need to realize that bills of material and inventory records, like purchase and production quantities, as well as lead times, may not be perfect. This means that some consideration of safety stock may be prudent. Because of the significant domino effect of any change in requirements, safety stock should be minimized, with a goal of ultimate elimination. When safety stock is deemed absolutely necessary, the usual policy is to build it into the projected on-hand inventory of the MRP logic. Distortion can be minimized when safety stock is held at the finished goods level and at the purchased component or raw material level.

Lot Size	Lead Time	On Hand	Safety Stock	Allocated	Low-Level Code	Item ID		Period							
								1	2	3	4	5	6	7	8
Lot FoR Lot	1	0	0	10	0	Z	Gross Requirements								80 90
							Scheduled Receipts								0
							Projected On Hand	0	0	0	0	0	0	0	0	0
							Net Requirements								90
							Planned Order Receipts								90
							Planned Order Releases							90	

FIGURE 14.7 Sample MRP Planning Sheet for Item Z

MRP Management

The material requirements plan is not static. And since MRP systems increasingly are integrated with just-in-time (JIT) techniques, we now discuss these two issues.

MRP DYNAMICS

Bills of material and material requirements plans are altered as changes in design, schedules, and production processes occur. In addition, changes occur in material requirements whenever the master production schedule is modified. Regardless of the cause of any changes, the MRP model can be manipulated to reflect them. In this manner, an up-to-date requirements schedule is possible.

The inputs to MRP (the master schedule, BOM, lead times, purchasing, and inventory) frequently change. Conveniently, a central strength of MRP systems is timely and accurate replanning. This occurs in one of two ways: by recomputing (also known as *regenerating*) the requirement and schedule periodically, often weekly, or via a *net change* calculation. Net change in an MRP system means the MRP system creates new requirements in response to transactions. However, many firms find they do not want to respond to minor scheduling or quantity changes even if they are aware of them. These frequent changes generate what is called **system nervousness** and can create havoc in purchasing and production departments if implemented. Consequently, OM personnel reduce such nervousness by evaluating the need and impact of changes prior to disseminating requests to other departments. Two tools are particularly helpful when trying to reduce MRP system nervousness.

The first is time fences. **Time fences** allow a segment of the master schedule to be designated as "not to be rescheduled". This segment of the master schedule is therefore not changed during the periodic regeneration of schedules. The second tool is pegging. **Pegging** means tracing upward in the BOM from the component to the parent item. By pegging upward, the production planner can determine the cause for the requirement and make a judgment about the necessity for a change in the schedule.

With MRP, the operations manager *can* react to the dynamics of the real world. How frequently the manager wishes to impose those changes on the firm requires professional judgment. Moreover, if the nervousness is caused by legitimate changes, then the proper response may be to investigate the production environment—not adjust via MRP.

System nervousness

Frequent changes in an MRP system.

Time fences

A means for allowing a segment of the master schedule to be designated as "not to be rescheduled".

Pegging

In material requirements planning systems, tracing upward in the bill of material from the component to the parent item.

MRP AND JIT

MRP does not do detailed scheduling—it plans. MRP will tell you that a job needs to be completed on a certain week or day but does not tell you that Job X needs to run on Machine A at 10:30 a.m. and be completed by 11:30 a.m. so that Job X can then run on Machine B. MRP is also a planning technique with *fixed* lead times. Fixed lead times can be a limitation. For instance, the lead time to produce 50 units may vary substantially from the lead time to produce five units. These limitations complicate the marriage of MRP and just-in-time (JIT). What is needed is a way to make MRP more responsive to moving material rapidly in small batches. An MRP system combined with JIT can provide the best of both worlds. MRP provides the plan and an accurate picture of requirements; then JIT rapidly moves material in small batches, reducing work-in-process inventory. Let's look at four approaches for integrating MRP and JIT: finite capacity scheduling, small buckets, balanced flow, and supermarkets.

FINITE CAPACITY SCHEDULING (FCS) Most MRP software loads work into infinite size "buckets". The **buckets** are time units, usually one week. Traditionally, when work is to be done in a given week, MRP puts the work there without regard to capacity. Consequently, MRP is considered an *infinite* scheduling technique. Frequently, as you might suspect, this is not realistic. Finite capacity scheduling (FCS), which we discuss in Chapter 15, considers department and machine capacity, which is *finite*, hence the name. FCS provides the precise scheduling needed for rapid material movement. We are now witnessing a convergence of FCS and MRP. Sophisticated FCS systems modify the output from MRP systems to provide a finite schedule.

Buckets

Time units in a material requirements planning system.

SMALL BUCKET APPROACH MRP is an excellent tool for resource and scheduling management in process-focused facilities, that is, in job shops. Such facilities include machine shops, hospitals, and restaurants, where lead times are relatively stable and poor balance between work centres is expected. Schedules are often driven by work orders, and lot sizes are the exploded bill-of-material size. In these enterprises, MRP can be integrated with JIT through the following steps.

STEP 1: Reduce MRP buckets from weekly to daily to perhaps hourly. Buckets are time units in an MRP system. Although the examples in this chapter have used weekly *time buckets*, many firms now use daily or even fraction-of-a-day time buckets. Some systems use a **bucketless system** in which all time-phased data have dates attached rather than defined time periods or buckets.

STEP 2: The planned receipts that are part of a firm's planned orders in an MRP system are communicated to the work areas for production purposes and used to sequence production.

STEP 3: Inventory is moved through the plant on a JIT basis.

STEP 4: As products are completed, they are moved into inventory (typically finished goods inventory) in the normal way. Receipt of these products into inventory reduces the quantities required for subsequent planned orders in the MRP system.

STEP 5: A system known as **back flush** is used to reduce inventory balances. Back flushing uses the bill of material to deduct component quantities from inventory as each unit is completed.

Bucketless system
Time-phased data are referenced using dated records rather than defined time periods, or buckets.

Back flush
A system to reduce inventory balances by deducting everything in the bill of material on completion of the unit.

The focus in these facilities becomes one of maintaining schedules. Nissan achieves success with this approach by computer communication links to suppliers. These schedules are confirmed, updated, or changed every 15 to 20 minutes. Suppliers provide deliveries 4 to 16 times per day. Master schedule performance is 99% on time, as measured every hour. On-time delivery from suppliers is 99.9% and for manufactured piece parts, 99.5%.

BALANCED FLOW APPROACH MRP supports the planning and scheduling necessary for repetitive operations, such as the assembly lines at Magna International, Harley-Davidson, Whirlpool, and a thousand other places. In these environments, the planning portion of MRP is combined with JIT execution. The JIT portion uses kanbans, visual signals, and reliable suppliers to pull the material through the facility. In these systems, execution is achieved by maintaining a carefully balanced flow of material to assembly areas with small lot sizes.

SUPERMARKET Another technique that joins MRP and JIT is the use of a *supermarket*. In many firms, subassemblies, their components, and hardware items are common to a variety of products. In such cases, releasing orders for these common items with traditional lead-time offset, as is done in an MRP system, is not necessary. The subassemblies, components, and hardware items can be maintained in a common area, sometimes called a **supermarket**, adjacent to the production areas where they are used. For instance, Ducati, Italy's high-performance motorcycle manufacturer, pulls "kits" with the materials needed for one engine or vehicle from the supermarket and delivers them to the assembly line on a JIT basis. Items in the supermarket are replenished by a JIT/kanban system.

Supermarket
An inventory area that holds common items that are replenished by a kanban system.

Lot-Sizing Techniques

An MRP system is an excellent way to determine production schedules and net requirements. However, whenever we have a net requirement, a decision must be made about *how much* to order. This decision is called a **lot-sizing decision**. There are a variety of ways to determine lot sizes in an MRP system; commercial MRP software usually includes the choice of several lot-sizing techniques. We now review a few of them.

Lot-sizing decision
The process of, or techniques used in, determining lot size.

LOT-FOR-LOT

In Example 3, we used a lot-sizing technique known as **lot-for-lot**, which produced exactly what was required. This decision is consistent with the objective of an MRP system, which is to meet the requirements of *dependent* demand. Thus, an MRP system should produce units only as needed, with no safety stock and no anticipation of further orders. When frequent orders are economical and just-in-time inventory techniques implemented, lot-for-lot can be very efficient. However, when setup costs are significant or management has been unable to implement JIT, lot-for-lot can be expensive. Example 4 uses the lot-for-lot criteria and determines cost for 10 weeks of demand.

Lot-for-lot
A lot-sizing technique that generates exactly what is required to meet the plan.

Speaker Kits, Inc., wants to compute its ordering and carrying cost of inventory on lot-for-lot criteria.

APPROACH ▶ With lot-for-lot, we order material only as it is needed. Once we have the cost of ordering (setting up), the cost of holding each unit for a given time period, and the production schedule, we can assign orders to our net requirements plan.

SOLUTION ▶ Speaker Kits has determined that, for the 30-cm speaker unit, setup cost is $100 and holding cost is $1 per period. The production schedule, as reflected in net requirements for assemblies, is as follows:

MRP Lot Sizing: Lot-for-Lot Technique*

		1	2	3	4	5	6	7	8	9	10
Gross requirements		35	30	40	0	10	40	30	0	30	55
Scheduled receipts											
Projected on hand	35	35	0	0	0	0	0	0	0	0	0
Net requirements		0	30	40	0	10	40	30	0	30	55
Planned order receipts			30	40		10	40	30		30	55
Planned order releases		30	40		10	40	30		30	55	

*Holding costs = $1/unit/week; setup cost = $100; gross requirements average per week = 27; lead time = 1 week.

The lot-sizing solution using the lot-for-lot technique is shown in the table. The holding cost is zero as there is never any inventory. (Inventory in the first period is used immediately and therefore has no holding cost.) But seven separate setups (one associated with each order) yield a total cost of $700. (Holding cost = 0 × 1 = 0; ordering cost = 7 × 10 = 700.)

INSIGHT ▶ When supply is reliable and frequent orders are inexpensive, but holding cost or obsolescence is high, lot-for-lot ordering can be very efficient.

LEARNING EXERCISE ▶ What is the impact on total cost if holding cost is $2 per period rather than $1? [Answer: Total holding cost remains zero, as no units are held from one period to the next with lot-for-lot.]

RELATED PROBLEMS ▶ 14.17, 14.20, 14.21, 14.22

ECONOMIC ORDER QUANTITY (EOQ)

We now extend our discussion of EOQ in Chapter 12, to use it as a lot-sizing technique for MRP systems. As we indicated there, EOQ is useful when we have relatively constant demand. However, demand may change every period in MRP systems. Therefore, EOQ lot sizing often

This Toyota line in Cambridge, Ontario, has little inventory because Toyota schedules to a razor's edge. At Toyota, MRP helps reduce inventory to world-class standards. World-class automobile assembly requires that purchased parts have a turnover of slightly more than once a day and that overall turnover approaches 150 times per year.

does not perform well in MRP. Operations managers should take advantage of demand information when it is known, rather than assuming a constant demand. EOQ is used to do lot sizing in Example 5 for comparison purposes.

With a setup cost of $100 and a holding cost per week of $1, Speaker Kits, Inc., wants to examine its cost for **component B**, with lot sizes based on an EOQ criteria.

APPROACH ▶ Using the same cost and production schedule as in Example 4, we determine net requirements and EOQ lot sizes.

SOLUTION ▶ Ten-week usage equals a gross requirement of 270 units; therefore, weekly usage equals 27, and 52 weeks (annual usage) equals 1404 units. From Chapter 12, the EOQ model is:

$$Q^* = \sqrt{\frac{2DS}{H}}$$

where
$$D = \text{annual usage} = 1404$$
$$S = \text{setup cost} = \$100$$
$$H = \text{holding (carrying) cost, on an annual basis per unit}$$
$$= \$1 \times 52 \text{ weeks} = \$52$$
$$Q^* = 73.5 \text{ (or 73) units}$$

Therefore, place an order of 73 units, as necessary, to avoid a stockout.

MRP Lot Sizing: EOQ Technique*											
Week		**1**	**2**	**3**	**4**	**5**	**6**	**7**	**8**	**9**	**10**
Gross requirements		35	30	40	0	10	40	30	0	30	55
Scheduled receipts											
Projected on hand	35	35	0	43	3	3	66	26	69	69	39
Net requirements		0	30	0	0	7	0	4	0	0	16
Planned order receipts			73			73		73			73
Planned order releases		73			73		73			73	

*Holding costs = $1/unit/week; setup cost = $100; gross requirements average per week = 27; lead time = 1 week.

For the 10-week planning period:

Holding cost = 375 units × $1 = $375 (includes 57 remaining at the end of week 10)

Ordering cost = 4 × $100 = $400

Total = $375 + $400 = $775

INSIGHT ▶ EOQ can be a reasonable lot-sizing technique when demand is relatively constant. However, notice that actual holding cost will vary substantially depending on the rate of actual usage. If any stockouts had occurred, these costs too would need to be added to our actual EOQ cost of $775.

LEARNING EXERCISE ▶ What is the impact on total cost if holding cost is $2 per period rather than $1? [Answer: The EOQ quantity becomes 52, the theoretical annual total cost becomes $5404, and the 10-week cost is $1039 ($5404 × (10/52).]

RELATED PROBLEMS ▶ 14.23, 14.25, 14.26b, 14.27c (14.28a is available in **MyLab Operations Management.**)

EXAMPLE 5
Lot Sizing With EOQ

PERIODIC ORDER QUANTITY

Periodic order quantity (POQ) is a lot-sizing technique that orders the quantity needed during a predetermined time between orders, such as every three weeks. We define the *POQ interval* as the EOQ divided by the average demand per period (e.g., one week).[3] The POQ is the order quantity that covers the specific demand for that interval. *Each order quantity is recalculated at the time of the order release*, never leaving extra inventory. An application of POQ is shown in Example 6.

Periodic order quantity (POQ)
An inventory ordering technique that issues orders on a predetermined time interval, with the order quantity covering the total of the interval's requirements.

---

[3] Using EOQ is a convenient approach for determining the time between orders, but other rules can be used.

EXAMPLE 6

LOT SIZING WITH POQ

With a setup cost of $100 and a holding cost per week of $1, Speaker Kits, Inc., wants to examine its cost for **component B**, with lot sizes based on POQ.

APPROACH ▶ Using the same cost and production schedule as in Example 4, we determine net requirements and POQ lot sizes.

SOLUTION ▶ Ten-week usage equals a gross requirement of 270 units; therefore, average weekly usage equals 27, and from Example 4, we know the EOQ is 73 units.

We set the *POQ interval* equal to the EOQ divided by the average weekly usage.

Therefore:

$$\text{POQ interval} = \text{EOQ/Average weekly usage} = 73/27 = 2.7, \text{ or 3 weeks.}$$

The *POQ order size* will vary by the quantities required in the respective weeks, as shown in the following table, with first planned order release in week 1.

Note: Orders are postponed if no demand exists, which is why week 7's order is postponed until week 8.

MRP Lot Sizing: POQ Technique*

WEEK		1	2	3	4	5	6	7	8	9	10
Gross requirements		35	30	40	0	10	40	30	0	30	55
Scheduled receipts											
Projected on hand	35	35	0	40	0	0	70	30	0	0	55
Net requirements		0	30	0	0	10	0	0	0	55	0
Planned order receipts			70			80			0		85	0
Planned order releases		70			80				85		

*Holding costs = $1/unit/week; setup cost = $100; gross requirements average per week = 27; lead time = 1 week.

$$\text{Setups} = 3 \times \$100 = \$300$$
$$\text{Holding cost} = (40 + 70 + 30 + 55) \text{ units} \times \$1 \text{ each} = \$195$$
The POQ solution yields a computed 10@week cost of $300 + $195 = $495

INSIGHT ▶ Because POQ tends to produce a balance between holding and ordering costs with no excess inventory, POQ typically performs much better than EOQ. Notice that even with frequent recalculations, actual holding cost can vary substantially, depending on the demand fluctuations. We are assuming no stockouts. In this and similar examples, we are also assuming no safety stock; such costs would need to be added to our actual cost.

LEARNING EXERCISE ▶ What is the impact on total cost if holding cost is $2 per period rather than $1? [Answer: EOQ = 52; POQ interval = 52/27 = 1.93 ≈ 2 weeks; holding cost = $270; setups = $400. The POQ total cost becomes $670.]

RELATED PROBLEMS ▶ 14.24, 14.25, 14.26c, 14.27b (14.28c is available in MyLab Operations Management)

Other lot-sizing techniques, known as *dynamic lot-sizing*, are similar to periodic order quantity as they attempt to balance the lot size against the setup cost. These are *part period balancing* (also called *least total cost*), *least unit cost*, and *least period cost* (also called *Silver-Meal*). Another technique, *Wagner-Whitin*, takes a different approach by using dynamic programming to optimize ordering over a finite time horizon.

LOT-SIZING SUMMARY

In the three speaker kits lot-sizing examples, we found the following costs:

	COSTS		
	SETUP	HOLDING	TOTAL
Lot-for-lot	$700	$0	$700
Economic order quantity (EOQ)	$400	$375	$775
Periodic order quantity (POQ)	$300	$195	$495

These examples should not, however, lead operations personnel to hasty conclusions about the preferred lot-sizing technique. In theory, new lot sizes should be computed whenever there is a schedule or lot-size change anywhere in the MRP hierarchy. In practice, such changes cause the instability and system nervousness referred to earlier in this chapter. Consequently, such frequent changes are not made. This means that all lot sizes are wrong because the production system cannot and should not respond to frequent changes. Note that there are no "shortage" (out of stock) charges in any of these lot-sizing techniques. This limitation places added demands on accurate forecasts and "time fences".

In general, the lot-for-lot approach should be used whenever low-cost setup can be achieved. Lot-for-lot is the goal. Lots can be modified as necessary for scrap allowances, process constraints (e.g., a heat-treating process may require a lot of a given size), or raw material purchase lots (e.g., a truckload of chemicals may be available in only one lot size). However, caution should be exercised prior to any modification of lot size because the modification can cause substantial distortion of actual requirements at lower levels in the MRP hierarchy. When setup costs are significant and demand is reasonably smooth, POQ or even EOQ should provide satisfactory results. Too much concern with lot sizing yields false accuracy because of MRP dynamics. A correct lot size can be determined only after the fact, based on what actually happened in terms of requirements.

Extensions of MRP

In this section, we review three extensions of MRP.

MATERIAL REQUIREMENTS PLANNING II (MRP II)

Material requirements planning II (MRP II) is an extremely powerful technique. Once a firm has MRP in place, requirements data can be enriched by resources other than just components. When MRP is used this way, *resource* is usually substituted for *requirements,* and MRP becomes MRP II. It then stands for material *resource* planning.

So far in our discussion of MRP, we have scheduled products and their components. However, products require many resources, such as energy and money, beyond the product's tangible components. In addition to these resource inputs, *outputs* can be generated as well. Outputs can include such things as scrap, packaging waste, effluent, and carbon emissions. As OM becomes increasingly sensitive to environmental and sustainability issues, identifying and managing by-products becomes increasingly important. MRP II provides a vehicle for doing so. Table 14.4 provides an example of labour-hours, machine-hours, kilograms of scrap, and cash, in the format of a gross

Material requirements planning II (MRP II)

A system that allows, with MRP in place, inventory data to be augmented by other resource variables; in this case, MRP becomes *material resource planning.*

LO5 Describe MRP II

	Lead Time	WEEKS			
		5	6	7	8
Computer	1				100
Labour-hours: 0.2 each					20
Machine-hours: 0.2 each					20
Scrap: 28 grams fibreglass each					2.8 kg
Payables: $0					$0
PC board (1 each)	2			100	
Labour-hours: 0.15 each				15	
Machine-hours: 0.1 each				10	
Scrap: 14 grams copper each				1.42 kg	
Payables: raw material at $5 each				$500	
Processors (5 each)	4	500			
Labour-hours: 0.2 each		100			
Machine-hours: 0.2 each		100			
Scrap: 0.3 grams of acid waste each		0.14 kg			
Payables: processors at $10 each		$5000			

Table 14.4

Material Resource Planning (MRP II)

By utilizing the logic of MRP, resources such as labour, machine-hours, scrap, and cost can be accurately determined and scheduled. Weekly demand for labour, machine-hours, scrap, and payables for 100 computers are shown.

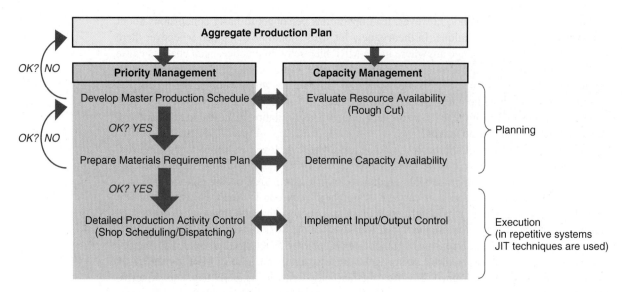

FIGURE 14.8 Closed-Loop Material Requirements Planning

requirements plan. With MRP II, management can identify both the inputs and outputs as well as the relevant schedule. MRP II provides another tool in OM's battle for sustainable operations.

MRP II systems are seldom stand-alone programs. Most are tied into other computer software that provide data to the MRP system or receive data from the MRP system. Purchasing, production scheduling, capacity planning, inventory, and warehouse management are a few examples of this data integration.

LO6 Describe closed-loop MRP

CLOSED-LOOP MRP

Closed-loop MRP system

A system that provides feedback to the capacity plan, master production schedule, and production plan so planning can be kept valid at all times.

Closed-loop material requirements planning implies an MRP system that provides feedback to scheduling from the inventory control system. Specifically, a **closed-loop MRP system** provides information to the capacity plan, master production schedule, and ultimately to the production plan (as shown in Figure 14.8). Virtually all commercial MRP systems are closed-loop.

CAPACITY PLANNING

Load report

A report for showing the resource requirements in a work centre for all work currently assigned there as well as all planned and expected orders.

In keeping with the definition of closed-loop MRP, feedback about workload is obtained from each work centre. A **load report** shows the resource requirements in a work centre for all work currently assigned to the work centre, all work planned, and expected orders. Figure 14.9(a) shows that the initial load in the milling centre exceeds capacity on days 2, 3, and 5. Closed-loop MRP systems allow production planners to move the work between time periods to smooth the load or at least bring it within capacity. (This is the "capacity planning" part of Figure 14.8.) The closed-loop MRP system can then reschedule all items in the net requirements plan (see Figure 14.9[b]).

FIGURE 14.9

(a) Initial Resource Requirements Profile for a Work Centre (b) Smoothed Resource Requirements Profile for a Work Centre

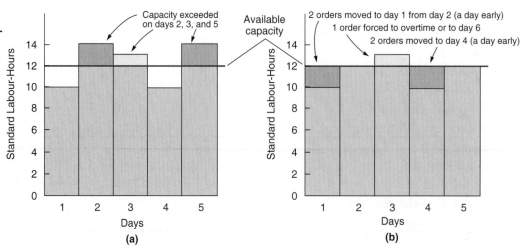

Tactics for smoothing the load and minimizing the impact of changed lead time include the following:

1. *Overlapping*, which reduces the lead time, sends pieces to the second operation before the entire lot is completed on the first operation.
2. *Operations splitting* sends the lot to two different machines for the same operation. This involves an additional setup but results in shorter throughput times, because only part of the lot is processed on each machine.
3. *Order* or *lot splitting* involves breaking up the order and running part of it earlier (or later) in the schedule.

Example 7 shows a brief detailed capacity scheduling example using order splitting to improve utilization.

Kevin Watson, the production planner at Wiz Products, needs to develop a capacity plan for a work centre. He has the production orders shown below for the next five days. There are 12 hours available in the work cell each day. The parts being produced require one hour each.

EXAMPLE 7
Order Splitting

Day	1	2	3	4	5
Orders	10	14	13	10	14

APPROACH ▶ Compute the time available in the work centre and the time necessary to complete the production requirements.

SOLUTION ▶

Day	Units Ordered	Capacity Required (hours)	Capacity Available (hours)	Utilization Over/(Under) (hours)	Production Planner's Action	New Production Schedule
1	10	10	12	(2)		12
2	14	14	12	2	Split order: move 2 units to day 1	12
3	13	13	12	1	Split order: move 1 unit to day 6 or request overtime	13
4	10	10	12	(2)		12
5	14 / 61	14	12	2	Split order: move 2 units to day 4	12

INSIGHT ▶ By moving orders, the production planner is able to utilize capacity more effectively and still meet the order requirements, with only one order produced on overtime in day 3.

LEARNING EXERCISE ▶ If the units ordered for day 5 increase to 16, what are the production planner's options? [Answer: In addition to moving two units to day 4, move two units of production to day 6, or request overtime.]

RELATED PROBLEMS ▶ 14.23, 14.24

When the workload consistently exceeds work-centre capacity, the tactics just discussed are not adequate. This may mean adding capacity. Options include adding capacity via personnel, machinery, overtime, or subcontracting.

MRP in Services

The demand for many services or service items is classified as dependent demand when it is directly related to or derived from the demand for other services. Such services often require product-structure trees, bills of material and labour, and scheduling. MRP can make a major contribution to operational performance in such services. Examples from restaurants, hospitals, and hotels follow.

FIGURE 14.10

Product Structure Tree, Bill of Material, and Bill of Labour for Veal Picante

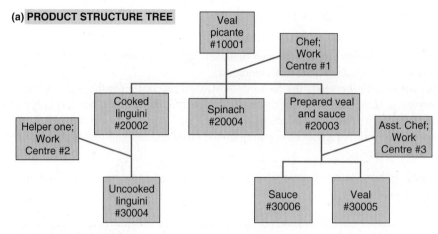

(a) PRODUCT STRUCTURE TREE

(b) BILL OF MATERIALS

Part Number	Description	Quantity	Unit of Measure	Unit Cost
10001	Veal picante	1	Serving	—
20002	Cooked linguini	1	Serving	—
20003	Prepared veal and sauce	1	Serving	—
20004	Spinach	0.1	Bag	0.94
30004	Uncooked linguini	0.25	Kilogram	—
30005	Veal	1	Serving	2.15
30006	Sauce	1	Serving	0.80

(c) BILL OF LABOUR FOR VEAL PICANTE

Work Centre	Operation	Labour Type	Labour-Hours Setup Time	Labour-Hours Run Time
1	Assemble dish	Chef	.0069	.0041
2	Cook linguini	Helper one	.0005	.0022
3	Cook veal and sauce	Assistant chef	.0125	.0500

RESTAURANTS

In restaurants, ingredients and side dishes (bread, vegetables, and condiments) are typically meal components. These components are dependent on the demand for meals. The meal is an end item in the master schedule. Figure 14.10 shows (a) a product-structure tree and (b) a bill of material for veal picante, a top-selling entrée in a Montreal restaurant. Note that the various components of veal picante (i.e., veal, sauce, spinach, and linguini) are prepared by different kitchen personnel (see part [a] of Figure 14.10). These preparations also require different amounts of time to complete. Figure 14.10(c) shows a bill of labour for the veal dish. It lists the operations to be performed, the order of operations, and the labour requirements for each operation (types of labour and labour-hours).

HOSPITALS

MRP is also applied in hospitals, especially when dealing with surgeries that require known equipment, materials, and supplies. Toronto's Hospital for Sick Children and many hospital suppliers, for example, use the technique to improve the scheduling and management of expensive surgical inventory.

HOTELS

Marriott develops a bill of material (BOM) and a bill of labour when it renovates each of its hotel rooms. Marriott managers explode the BOM to compute requirements for materials, furniture, and decorations. MRP then provides net requirements and a schedule for use by purchasing and contractors.

DISTRIBUTION RESOURCE PLANNING (DRP)

When dependent techniques are used in the supply chain, they are called distribution resource planning (DRP). **Distribution resource planning (DRP)** is a time-phased stock-replenishment plan for all levels of the supply chain.

DRP procedures and logic are analogous to MRP. With DRP, expected demand becomes gross requirements. Net requirements are determined by allocating available inventory to gross requirements. The DRP procedure starts with the forecast at the retail level (or the most distant point of the distribution network being supplied). All other levels are computed. As is the case with MRP, inventory is then reviewed with an aim to satisfying demand. In order that stock will arrive when it is needed, net requirements are offset by the necessary lead time. A planned order release quantity becomes the gross requirement at the next level down the distribution chain.

DRP *pulls* inventory through the system. Pulls are initiated when the retail level orders more stock. Allocations are made to the retail level from available inventory and production after being adjusted to obtain shipping economies. Effective use of DRP requires an integrated information system to rapidly convey planned order releases from one level to the next. The goal of the DRP system is small and frequent replenishment within the bounds of economical ordering and shipping.[4]

Distribution resource planning (DRP)

A time-phased stock-replenishment plan for all levels of a distribution network.

Enterprise Resource Planning (ERP)

ERP tries to integrate all of a firm's information.

Advances in MRP II systems that tie customers and suppliers to MRP II have led to the development of enterprise resource planning (ERP) systems. **Enterprise resource planning (ERP)** is software that allows companies to (1) automate and integrate many of their business processes, (2) share a common database and business practices throughout the enterprise, and (3) produce information in real time. A schematic showing some of these relationships for a manufacturing firm appears in Figure 14.11.

The objective of an ERP system is to coordinate a firm's whole business, from supplier evaluation to customer invoicing. This objective is seldom achieved, but ERP systems are evolving as umbrella systems that tie together a variety of specialized systems. This is accomplished by using a centralized database to assist the flow of information among business functions. Exactly what is tied together, and how, varies on a case-by-case basis. In addition to the traditional components of MRP, ERP systems usually provide financial and human resource (HR) management information. ERP systems also include:

Enterprise resource planning (ERP)

An information system for identifying and planning the enterprise-wide resources needed to take, make, ship, and account for customer orders.

LO7 Describe ERP

- *Supply chain management (SCM)* software to support sophisticated vendor communication, ecommerce, and those activities necessary for efficient warehousing and logistics. The idea is to tie operations (MRP) to procurement, to materials management, and to suppliers, providing the tools necessary for effective management of all four areas.
- *Customer relationship management (CRM)* software for the incoming side of the business. CRM is designed to aid analysis of sales, target the most profitable customers, and manage the sales force.
- *Sustainability* software to tie together sustainable workforce issues and provide transparency for supply chain sustainability issues, as well as monitor health and safety activities, energy use and efficiency, emissions (carbon footprint, greenhouse gases), and environmental compliance.

In addition to data integration, ERP software promises reduced transaction costs and fast, accurate information. A strategic emphasis on just-in-time systems and supply chain integration drives the desire for enterprise-wide software. The *OM in Action* box "Managing Benetton With ERP Software" provides an example of how ERP software helps integrate company operations.

In an ERP system, data are entered only once into a common, complete, and consistent database shared by all applications. For example, when a Nike salesperson enters an order into his ERP system for 20 000 pairs of sneakers for Foot Locker, the data are instantly available on the manufacturing floor. Production crews start filling the order if it is not in stock, accounting prints Foot Locker's invoice, and shipping notifies the Foot Locker of the future delivery date. The salesperson, or even the customer, can check the progress of the order at any point. This is

---

[4] For an expanded discussion of time-phased stock-replenishment plans, see Chapter 11 of this text.

FIGURE 14.11

MRP and ERP Information Flows, Showing Customer Relationship Management (CRM), Supply Chain Management (SCM), and Finance/Accounting

Other functions such as human resources and sustainability are often also included in ERP systems.

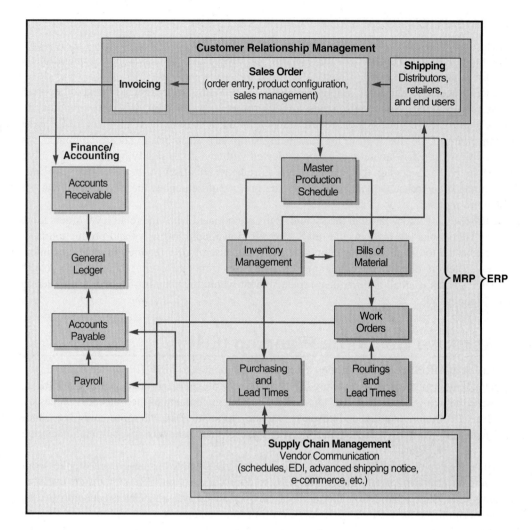

| OM in Action | Managing Benetton with ERP Software |

Thanks to ERP, the Italian sportswear company Benetton can probably claim to have the world's fastest factory and the most efficient distribution in the garment industry. Located in Ponzano, Italy, Benetton makes and ships 50 million pieces of clothing each year. That is 30 000 boxes every day—boxes that must be filled with exactly the items ordered going to the correct store of the 5000 Benetton outlets in 60 countries. This highly automated distribution centre uses only 19 people. Without ERP, hundreds of people would be needed.

Here is how ERP software works:

1. *Ordering:* A salesperson in the Ottawa store finds that she is running out of a best-selling blue sweater. Using a laptop PC, her local Benetton sales agent taps into the ERP sales module.

2. *Availability:* ERP's inventory software simultaneously forwards the order to the mainframe in Italy and finds that half the order can be filled immediately from the Italian warehouse. The rest will be manufactured and shipped in four weeks.

3. *Production:* Because the blue sweater was originally created by computer-aided design (CAD), ERP manufacturing software passes the specifications to a knitting machine. The knitting machine makes the sweaters.

4. *Warehousing:* The blue sweaters are boxed with a radio frequency ID (RFID) tag addressed to the Ottawa store and placed in one of the 300 000 slots in the Italian warehouse. A robot flies by, reading RFID tags, picks out any and all boxes ready for the Ottawa store, and loads them for shipment.

5. *Order tracking:* The Ottawa salesperson logs onto the ERP system through the internet and sees that the sweater (and other items) are completed and being shipped.

6. *Planning:* Based on data from ERP's forecasting and financial modules, Benetton's chief buyer decides that blue sweaters are in high demand and quite profitable. She decides to add three new hues.

Sources: The Wall Street Journal (April 10, 2007): B1; *Frontline Solutions* (April 2003): 54; and *MIT Sloan Management Review* (Fall 2001): 46–53.

FIGURE 14.12 SAP's Modules for ERP

	End-User Service Delivery					Shared Service Delivery	SAP NetWeaver®
Analytics	Financial Analytics		Operations Analytics		Workforce Analytics		
Financials	Financial Supply Chain Management	Treasury	Financial Accounting	Management Accounting	Corporate Governance		
Human Capital Management	Talent Management		Workforce Process Management		Workforce Deployment		
Procurement and Logistics Execution	Procurement		Inventory and Warehouse Management	Inbound and Outbound Logistics	Transportation Management		
Product Development and Manufacturing	Production Planning		Manufacturing Execution	Product Development	Life-Cycle Data Management		
Sales and Service	Sales Order Management		Aftermarket Sales and Service		Professional-Service Delivery		
Corporate Services	Real Estate Management	Enterprise Asset Management	Project and Portfolio Management	Travel Management	Environment, Health, and Safety Compliance Mgmt.	Quality Management	Global Trade Services

Source: Pearson Education.

all accomplished using the same data and common applications. To reach this consistency, however, the data fields must be defined identically across the entire enterprise. In Nike's case, this means integrating operations at production sites from Vietnam to China to Mexico, at business units across the globe, in many currencies, and with reports in a variety of languages.

Each ERP vendor produces unique products. The major vendors—SAP AG (a German firm), SSAGlobal, American Software, PeopleSoft/Oracle, and CMS Software (all based in the United States)—sell software or modules designed for specific industries (a set of SAP's modules is shown in Figure 14.12). However, companies must determine if their way of doing business will fit the standard ERP module. If they determine that the product will not fit the standard ERP product, they can change the way they do business to accommodate the software. But such a change can have an adverse impact on their business process, reducing a competitive advantage. Alternatively, ERP software can be customized to meet their specific process requirements. Although the vendors build the software to keep the customization process simple, many companies spend up to five times the cost of the software to customize it. In addition to the expense, the major downside of customization is that when ERP vendors provide an upgrade or enhancement to the software, the customized part of the code must be rewritten to fit into the new version. ERP programs cost from a minimum of $300 000 for a small company to hundreds of millions of dollars for global giants like Ford and Coca-Cola. It is easy to see, then, that ERP systems are expensive, full of hidden issues, and time-consuming to install.

ERP IN THE SERVICE SECTOR

ERP vendors have developed a series of service modules for such markets as healthcare, government, retail stores, and financial services. Springer-Miller Systems, for example, has created an ERP package for the hotel market with software that handles all front- and back-office functions. This system integrates tasks such as maintaining guest histories, booking room and dinner reservations, scheduling golf tee times, and managing multiple properties in a chain. PeopleSoft/Oracle combines ERP with supply chain management to coordinate airline meal preparation. In the grocery industry, these supply chain systems are known as *efficient consumer response* systems. As is the case in manufacturing, **efficient consumer response (ECR)** systems tie sales to buying, to inventory, to logistics, and to production.

Efficient consumer response (ECR)

Supply chain management systems in the grocery industry that tie sales to buying, to inventory, to logistics, and to production.

CHAPTER SUMMARY

Material requirements planning (MRP) schedules production and inventory when demand is dependent. For MRP to work, management must have a master schedule, precise requirements for all components, accurate inventory and purchasing records, and accurate lead times.

When properly implemented, MRP can contribute in a major way to reduction in inventory while improving customer service levels. MRP techniques allow the operations manager to schedule and replenish stock on a "need-to-order" basis rather than simply a "time-to-order" basis. Many firms using MRP systems find that lot-for-lot can be the low-cost lot-sizing option.

The continuing development of MRP systems has led to its use with lean manufacturing techniques. In addition, MRP can integrate production data with a variety of other activities, including the supply chain and sales. As a result, we now have integrated database-oriented enterprise resource planning (ERP) systems. These expensive and difficult-to-install ERP systems, when successful, support strategies of differentiation, response, and cost leadership.

ETHICAL DILEMMA

For many months, your prospective ERP customer has been analyzing the hundreds of assumptions built into the $900 000 ERP software you are selling. So far, you have knocked yourself out to try to make this sale. If the sale goes through, you will reach your yearly quota and get a nice bonus. On the other hand, loss of this sale may mean you start looking for other employment.

The accounting, human resource, supply chain, and marketing teams put together by the client have reviewed the specifications and finally recommended purchase of the software. However, as you looked over their shoulders and helped them through the evaluation process, you began to realize that their purchasing procedures—with much of the purchasing being done at hundreds of regional stores—were not a good fit for the software. At the very least, the customizing will add $250 000 to the implementation and training cost. The team is not aware of the issue, and you know that the necessary $250 000 is not in the budget.

What do you do?

Discussion Questions

1. What is the difference between a *gross* requirements plan and a *net* requirements plan?
2. Once a material requirements plan (MRP) has been established, what other managerial applications might be found for the technique?
3. What are the similarities between MRP and DRP?
4. How does MRP II differ from MRP?
5. Which is the best lot-sizing policy for manufacturing organizations?
6. What impact does ignoring carrying cost in the allocation of stock in a DRP system have on lot sizes?
7. MRP is more than an inventory system; what additional capabilities does MRP possess?
8. What are the options for the production planner who has:
   (a) scheduled more than capacity in a work centre next week?
   (b) a consistent lack of capacity in that work centre?
9. Master schedules are expressed in three different ways depending on whether the process is continuous, a job shop, or repetitive. What are these three ways?
10. What functions of the firm affect an MRP system? How?
11. What is the rationale for (a) a phantom bill of material, (b) a planning bill of material, and (c) a pseudo bill of material?
12. Identify five specific requirements of an effective MRP system.
13. What are the typical benefits of ERP?
14. What are the distinctions between MRP, DRP, and ERP?
15. As an approach to inventory management, how does MRP differ from the approach taken in Chapter 12, dealing with economic order quantities (EOQ)?
16. What are the disadvantages of ERP?
17. Use the web or other sources to:
    a) Find stories that highlight the advantages of an ERP system.
    b) Find stories that highlight the difficulties of purchasing, installing, or failure of an ERP system.
18. Use the web or other sources to identify what an ERP vendor (SAP, PeopleSoft/Oracle, American Software, etc.) includes in these software modules:
    a) Customer relationship management.
    b) Supply chain management.
    c) Product life cycle management.
19. The very structure of MRP systems suggests fixed lead times. However, many firms have moved towards JIT and kanban techniques. What are the techniques, issues, and impact of adding JIT inventory and purchasing techniques to an organization that has MRP?

Using Software to Solve MRP Problems

There are many commercial MRP software packages, for companies of all sizes. MRP software for small and medium-size companies includes User Solutions, Inc., a demo of which is available at **www.usersolutions.com**, and MAX, from Exact Software North America, Inc. Software for larger systems is available from SAP, CMS, BEA, Oracle, i2 Technologies, and many others. The Excel OM software that accompanies this text includes an MRP module, as does POM for Windows. The use of both is explained in the following sections.

✗ USING EXCEL OM

Using Excel OM's MRP module requires the careful entry of several pieces of data. The initial MRP screen is where we enter (1) the total number of occurrences of items in the BOM (including the top item), (2) what we want the BOM items to be called (i.e., Item no., Part), (3) total number of periods to be scheduled, and (4) what we want the periods called (i.e., days, weeks).

Excel OM's second MRP screen provides the data entry for an indented bill of material. Here we enter (1) the name of each item in the BOM, (2) the quantity of that item in the assembly, and (3) the correct indent (i.e., parent/child relationship) for each item. The indentations are critical as they provide the logic for the BOM explosion. The indentations should follow the logic of the product structure tree with indents for each assembly item in that assembly.

PROGRAM 14.1

Using Excel OM's MRP Module to Solve Examples 1, 2, and 3

Source: Microsoft product screen shot(s) reprinted with permission from Microsoft Corporation.

The data in columns A, B, C, D (down to row 15) are entered on the second screen and automatically transferred here.

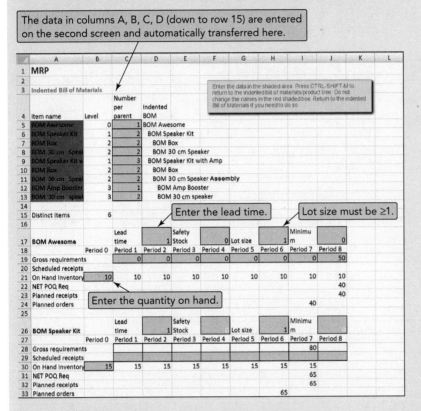

Excel OM's third MRP screen repeats the indented BOM and provides the standard MRP tableau for entries. This is shown in Program 14.1 using the data from Examples 1, 2, and 3.

ℙ USING POM FOR WINDOWS

The POM for Windows MRP module can also solve Examples 1 to 3. Up to 18 periods can be analyzed. Here are the inputs required:

1. *Item names:* The item names are entered in the left column. The same item name will appear in more than one row if the item is used by two parent items. Each item must follow its parents.
2. *Item level:* The level in the indented BOM must be given here. The item *cannot* be placed at a level more than one below the item immediately above.
3. *Lead time:* The lead time for an item is entered here. The default is one week.
4. *Number per parent:* The number of units of this subassembly needed for its parent is entered here. The default is 1.
5. *On hand:* List current inventory on hand once, even if the subassembly is listed twice.
6. *Lot size:* The lot size can be specified here. A 0 or 1 will perform lot-for-lot ordering. If another number is placed here, then all orders for that item will be in integer multiples of that number.
7. *Demands:* The demands are entered in the end item row in the period in which the items are demanded.
8. *Scheduled receipts:* If units are scheduled to be received in the future, they should be listed in the appropriate time period (column) and item (row). (An entry here in level 1 is a demand; all other levels are receipts.)

Further details regarding POM for Windows are seen in Appendix IV.

Solved Problems Virtual Office Hours help is available at MyLab Operations Management.

▼ SOLVED PROBLEM 14.1

Determine the low-level coding and the quantity of each component necessary to produce 10 units of an assembly we will call Alpha. The product structure and quantities of each component needed for each assembly are noted in parentheses.

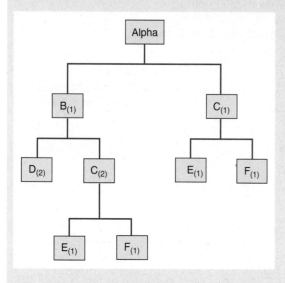

▼ SOLUTION

Redraw the product structure with low-level coding. Then multiply down the structure until the requirements of each branch are determined. Then add across the structure until the total for each is determined.

Es required for left branch:

$$(1_{alpha} \times 1_B \times 2_C \times 1_E) = 2 \text{ Es}$$

and Es required for right branch:

$$(1_{alpha} \times 1_C \times 1_E) = \frac{1E}{3Es \text{ required in total}}$$

Then "explode" the requirement by multiplying each by 10, as shown in the table:

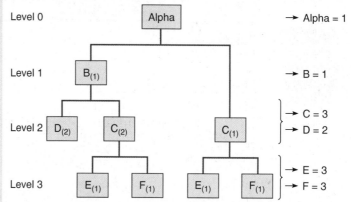

Level	Item	Quantity per Unit	Total Requirements for 10 Alpha
0	Alpha	1	10
1	B	1	10
2	C	3	30
2	D	2	20
3	E	3	30
3	F	3	30

SOLVED PROBLEM 14.2

Using the product structure for Alpha in Solved Problem 14.1, and the following lead times, quantity on hand, and master production schedule, prepare a net MRP table for Alphas.

Item	Lead Time	Quantity on Hand
Alpha	1	10
B	2	20
C	3	0
D	1	100
E	1	10
F	1	50

Master Production Schedule for Alpha

Period	6	7	8	9	10	11	12	13
Gross requirements			50			50		100

▼ SOLUTION

Net Material Requirements Planning Sheet for Alpha

Item	Lot Size	Lead Time (# of Periods)	On Hand	Safety Stock	Allocated	Low-Level Code
Alpha (A)	Lot-for-Lot	1	10	—	—	0
B	Lot-for-Lot	2	20	—	—	1
C	Lot-for-Lot	3	0	—	—	2
D	Lot-for-Lot	1	100	—	—	2
E	Lot-for-Lot	1	10	—	—	3
F	Lot-for-Lot	1	50	—	—	3

Item ID: Alpha (A)

	1	2	3	4	5	6	7	8	9	10	11	12	13
Gross Requirements								50			50		100
Scheduled Receipts													
Projected On Hand = 10													
Net Requirements								40			50		100
Planned Order Receipts								40			50		100
Planned Order Releases							40			50		100	

Item ID: B

	1	2	3	4	5	6	7	8	9	10	11	12	13
Gross Requirements							40(A)			50(A)		100(A)	
Scheduled Receipts													
Projected On Hand = 20													
Net Requirements							20			50		100	
Planned Order Receipts							20			50		100	
Planned Order Releases					20			50		100			

Item ID: C

	1	2	3	4	5	6	7	8	9	10	11	12	13
Gross Requirements					40(B)		40(A)	100(B)		200(B) + 50(A)		100(A)	
Scheduled Receipts													
Projected On Hand = 0													
Net Requirements					40		40	100		250		100	
Planned Order Receipts					40		40	100		250		100	
Planned Order Releases		40		40	100		250		100				

Item ID: D

	1	2	3	4	5	6	7	8	9	10	11	12	13
Gross Requirements					40(B)			100(B)		200(B)			
Scheduled Receipts													
Projected On Hand = 100					60								
Net Requirements					0			40		200			
Planned Order Receipts								40		200			
Planned Order Releases							40		200				

Item ID: E

	1	2	3	4	5	6	7	8	9	10	11	12	13
Gross Requirements		40(C)		40(C)	100(C)		250(C)		100(C)				
Scheduled Receipts													
Projected On Hand = 10													
Net Requirements		30		40	100		250		100				
Planned Order Receipts		30		40	100		250		100				
Planned Order Releases	30		40	100		250		100					

Item ID: F

	1	2	3	4	5	6	7	8	9	10	11	12	13
Gross Requirements		40(C)		40(C)	100(C)		250(C)		100(C)				
Scheduled Receipts													
Projected On Hand = 50		10											
Net Requirements				30	100		250		100				
Planned Order Receipts				30	100		250		100				
Planned Order Releases			30	100		250		100					

Period (week, day)

Net Material Requirements Planning Sheet for Alpha
The letter in parentheses (A) is the source of the demand.

SOLVED PROBLEM 14.3

Hip Replacements, Inc., has a master production schedule for its newest model, as shown below, a setup cost of $50, a holding cost per week of $2, beginning inventory of 0, and lead time of 1 week. What are the costs of using lot-for-lot for this 10-week period?

▼ SOLUTION

Holding cost = $0 (as there is never any end-of-period inventory)

Ordering costs = 4 orders × $50 = $200

Total cost for lot-for-lot = $0 + $200 = $200

WEEK		1	2	3	4	5	6	7	8	9	10
Gross requirements		0	0	50	0	0	35	15	0	100	0
Scheduled receipts											
Projected on hand	0	0	0	0	0	0	0	0	0	0	0
Net requirements		0	0	50	0	0	35	15	0	100	
Planned order receipts				50			35	15		100	
Planned order releases			50				35	15		100	

SOLVED PROBLEM 14.4

Hip Replacements, Inc., has a master production schedule for its newest model, as shown in Problem 14.3, a setup cost of $50, a holding cost per week of $2, beginning inventory of 0, and lead time of 1 week. What are the costs of using (a) EOQ and (b) POQ for this 10-week period?

▼ SOLUTION

a) For the **EOQ** lot size, first determine the EOQ.

Annual usage = 200 units for 10 weeks; weekly usage = 200/10 weeks = 20 per week. Therefore, 20 units × 52 weeks (annual demand) = 1 040 units. From Chapter 12 , the EOQ model is:

$$Q^* = \sqrt{\frac{2DS}{H}}$$

where D = annual demand = 1,040

   S = Setup cost = $50

   H = holding (carrying) cost, on an annual basis per unit = $2 × 52 = $104

   Q^* = 31.62 ≈ 32 units (order the EOQ or in multiples of the EOQ)

WEEK		1	2	3	4	5	6	7	8	9	10
Gross requirements		0	0	50	0	0	35	15	0	100	0
Scheduled receipts											
Projected on hand	0	0	0	0	14	14	14	11	28	28	24	24
Net requirements		0	0	50	0	0	21	0	0	72	0
Planned order receipts				64			32	32		96	
Planned order releases			64			32	32		96		

Holding cost = 157 units × $2 = $314 (note the 24 units available in period 11, for which there is an inventory charge as they are in on-hand inventory at the end of period 10)

Ordering costs = 4 orders × $50 = $200

Total cost for EOQ lot sizing = $314 + $200 = $514

b) For the POQ lot size we use the EOQ computed above to find the time period between orders:

Period interval = EOQ/average weekly usage = 32/20 = 1.6 ≈ 2 periods

POQ order size = Demand required in the two periods, postponing orders in periods with no demand.

WEEK	1	2	3	4	5	6	7	8	9	10
Gross requirements		0	0	50	0	0	35	15	0	100	0
Scheduled receipts											
Projected on hand	0	0	0	0	0	0	0	15	0	0	
Net requirements		0	0	50	0	0	50	0	0	100	0
Planned order receipts				50			50			100	
Planned order releases			50			50			100		

Holding cost = 15 units × $2 = $30

Ordering costs = 3 orders × $50 = $150

Total cost for POQ lot sizing = $30 + $150 = $180

Problems*

· 14.1 You have developed the following simple product structure of items needed for your gift bag for a rush party for prospective pledges in your organization. You forecast 200 attendees. Assume that there is no inventory on hand of any of the items. Explode the bill of material. (Subscripts indicate the number of units required.)

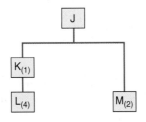

*Note: **PX** means the problem may be solved with POM for Windows and/or Excel OM. Many of the exercises in this chapter (14.1 through 14.16 and 14.23 through 14.27) can be done on *Resource Manager for Excel*, a commercial system made available by User Solutions, Inc. Access to a trial version of the software and a set of notes for the user is available at www.usersolutions.com.

·· 14.2 You are expected to have the gift bags in Problem 14.1 ready at 5:00 p.m. However, you need to personalize the items (monogrammed pens, note pads, literature from the printer, etc.). The lead time is one hour to assemble 200 Js once the other items are prepared. The other items will take a while as well. Given the volunteers you have, the other time estimates are item K (two hours), item L (one hour), and item M (four hours). Develop a time-phased assembly plan to prepare the gift bags.

·· 14.3 The demand for subassembly S is 100 units in week 7. Each unit of S requires 1 unit of T and 2 units of U. Each unit of T requires 1 unit of V, 2 units of W, and 1 unit of X. Finally, each unit of U requires 2 units of Y and 3 units of Z. One firm manufactures all items. It takes 2 weeks to make S, 1 week to make T, 2 weeks to make U, 2 weeks to make V, 3 weeks to make W, 1 week to make X, 2 weeks to make Y, and 1 week to make Z.

a) Construct a product structure. Identify all levels, parents, and components.

b) Prepare a time-phased product structure.

·· 14.4 Using the information in Problem 14.3, construct a gross material requirements plan. **PX**

·· 14.5 Using the information in Problem 14.3, construct a net material requirements plan using the following on-hand inventory.

Item	On-Hand Inventory	Item Inventory	On Hand
S	20	W	30
T	20	X	25
U	40	Y	240
V	30	Z	40 **PX**

·· 14.6 Refer again to Problems 14.3 and 14.4. In addition to 100 units of S, there is also a demand for 20 units of U, which is a component of S. The 20 units of U are needed for maintenance purposes. These units are needed in week 6. Modify the *gross material requirements plan* to reflect this change. **PX**

·· 14.7 Refer again to Problems 14.3 and 14.5. In addition to 100 units of S, there is also a demand for 20 units of U, which is a component of S. The 20 units of U are needed for maintenance purposes. These units are needed in week 6. Modify the *net material requirements plan* to reflect this change. **PX**

·· 14.8 As the production planner for Gerry Cook Products, Inc., you have been given a bill of material for a bracket that is made up of a base, two springs, and four clamps. The base is assembled from one clamp and two housings. Each clamp has one handle and one casting. Each housing has two bearings and one shaft. There is no inventory on hand.

a) Design a product structure noting the quantities for each item and show the low-level coding.

b) Determine the gross quantities needed of each item if you are to assemble 50 brackets.

c) Compute the net quantities needed if there are 25 of the base and 100 of the clamp in stock. **PX**

·· 14.9 Your boss at Gerry Cook Products, Inc., has just provided you with the schedule and lead times for the bracket in

MRP Form for Homework Problems in this chapter

For several problems in this chapter, a copy of this form may be helpful.

Lot Size	Lead Time (# of periods)	On Hand	Safety Stock	Allo-cated	Low-Level Code	Item ID		Period (week, day)							
								1	2	3	4	5	6	7	8
							Gross Requirements								
							Scheduled Receipts								
							Projected On Hand								
							Net Requirements								
							Planned Order Receipts								
							Planned Order Releases								
							Gross Requirements								
							Scheduled Receipts								
							Projected On Hand								
							Net Requirements								
							Planned Order Receipts								
							Planned Order Releases								
							Gross Requirements								
							Scheduled Receipts								
							Projected On Hand								
							Net Requirements								
							Planned Order Receipts								
							Planned Order Releases								
							Gross Requirements								
							Scheduled Receipts								
							Projected On Hand								
							Net Requirements								
							Planned Order Receipts								
							Planned Order Releases								
							Gross Requirements								
							Scheduled Receipts								
							Projected On Hand								
							Net Requirements								
							Planned Order Receipts								
							Planned Order Releases								

Problem 14.8. The unit is to be prepared in week 10. The lead times for the components are bracket (1 week), base (1 week), spring (1 week), clamp (1 week), housing (2 weeks), handle (1 week), casting (3 weeks), bearing (1 week), and shaft (1 week).

a) Prepare the time-phased product structure for the bracket.

b) In what week do you need to start the castings? **Px**

•• **14.10**

a) Given the product structure and master production schedule (Figure 14.14), develop a gross requirements plan for all items.

b) Given the preceding product structure, master production schedule, and inventory status (Figure 14.14), develop a net materials requirements (planned order release) for all items. **Px**

FIGURE 14.14 Information for Problem 14.10

Master Production Schedule for X1

PERIOD	7	8	9	10	11	12
Gross requirements		50		20		100

ITEM	LEAD TIME	ON HAND		ITEM	LEAD TIME	ON HAND
X1	1	50		C	1	0
B1	2	20		D	1	0
B2	2	20		E	3	10
A1	1	5				

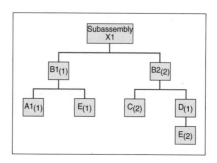

• • 14.11 Given the following product structure, master production schedule, and inventory status (Figure 14.15) and assuming the requirement for each BOM item is 1: (a) develop a gross requirements plan for Item C; (b) develop a net requirements plan for Item C. **Px**

• • 14.12 Based on the data in Figure 14.15, complete a net material requirements schedule for:
a) All items (10 schedules in all), assuming the requirement for each BOM item is 1.
b) All 10 items, assuming the requirement for all items is 1, except B, C, and F, which require *2 each* **Px**

• • 14.13 Electro Fans has just received an order for one thousand 50-cm fans due at the end of week 7. Each fan consists of a housing assembly, two grills, a fan assembly, and an electrical unit. The housing assembly consists of a frame, two supports, and a handle. The fan assembly consists of a hub and five blades. The electrical unit consists of a motor, a switch, and a knob. The accompanying table gives lead times, on-hand inventory, and scheduled receipts.
a) Construct a product structure.
b) Construct a time-phased product structure.
c) Prepare a net material requirements plan. **Px**

Data Table for Problem 14.13

Component	Lead Time	On-Hand Inventory	Lot Size*	Scheduled Receipt
50-cm Fan	1	100	—	
Housing	1	100	—	
Frame	2	—	—	
Supports (2)	1	50	100	
Handle	1	400	500	
Grills (2)	2	200	500	
Fan Assembly	3	150	—	
Hub	1	—	—	
Blades (5)	2	—	100	
Electrical Unit	1	—	—	
Motor	1	—	—	
Switch	1	20	12	
Knob	1	—	25	200 knobs in week 2

Lot-for-lot unless otherwise noted

• • 14.14 A part structure, lead time (weeks), and on-hand quantities for product A are shown in Figure 14.16. From the information shown, generate:
a) An indented bill of material for product A (see Figure 5.9 in Chapter 5 as an example of a BOM).
b) Net requirements for each part to produce 10 As in week 8 using lot-for-lot. **Px**

• • 14.15 You are product planner for product A (in Problem 14.14 and Figure 14.16). The field service manager, Al Trostel, has just called and told you that the requirements for B and F should each be increased by 10 units for his repair requirements in the field.
a) Prepare a list showing the quantity of each part required to produce the requirements for the service manager *and* the production request of 10 Bs and Fs.

b) Prepare a net requirement plan by date for the new requirements (for both production and field service), assuming that the field service manager wants his 10 units of B and F in week 6 and the 10 production units of A in week 8. **Px**

• • 14.16 You have just been notified that the lead time for component G of product A (Problem 14.15 and Figure 14.16) has been increased to four weeks.
a) Which items have changed and why?
b) What are the implications for the production plan?
c) As production planner, what can you do? **Px**

Data Table for Problems 14.17 through 14.19*

Period	1	2	3	4	5	6	7	8	9	10	11	12
Gross requirements	30		40		30	70	20		10	80		50

*Holding cost = $2.50/unit/week; setup cost = $150; lead time = 1 week; beginning inventory = 40.

• • 14.17 Develop a lot-for-lot solution and calculate total relevant costs for the data in the table for Problems 14.17 through 14.19. **Px**

• • 14.18 Develop an EOQ solution and calculate total relevant costs for the data in the table for Problems 14.17 through 14.19. Stockout costs equal $10 per unit. **Px**

• • 14.19 Develop a POQ solution and calculate total relevant costs for the data in the table for Problems 14.17 through 14.19. **Px**

• • 14.20 Using the gross requirements schedule in Examples 4, 5, and 6, prepare an alternative ordering system that always orders 100 units the week prior to a shortage (a fixed order quantity of 100) with the same costs as in the example (setup at $100 each, holding at $1 per unit per period). What is the cost of this ordering system? **Px**

• • 14.21 Using the gross requirements schedule in Examples 4, 5, and 6, prepare an alternative ordering system that orders every three weeks for three weeks ahead (a periodic order quantity). Use the same costs as in the example (setup at $100 each, holding at $1 per unit per period). What is the cost of this ordering system? **Px**

• • 14.22 Using the gross requirements schedule in Examples 4, 5, and 6, prepare an alternative ordering system of your own design that uses the same cost as in the example (setup at $100 each, holding at $1 per unit per period). Can you do better than the costs shown in the text? What is the cost of your ordering system? **Px**

• • 14.23 Katharine Hepburn, Inc., has received the following orders:

Period	1	2	3	4	5	6	7	8	9	10
Order size	0	40	30	40	10	70	40	10	30	60

The entire fabrication for these units is scheduled on one machine. There are 2250 usable minutes in a week, and each unit will take 65 minutes to complete. Develop a capacity plan, using lot splitting, for the 10-week time period.

• • 14.24 David Jurman, Ltd., has received the following orders:

Period	1	2	3	4	5	6	7	8	9	10
Order size	60	30	10	40	70	10	40	30	40	0

The entire fabrication for these units is scheduled on one machine. There are 2250 usable minutes in a week, and each unit will take

FIGURE 14.15

Information for Problems 14.11 and 14.12

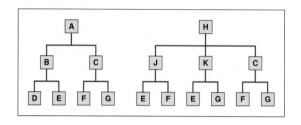

Period	8	9	10	11	12
Gross requirements: A	100		50		150
Gross requirements: H		100		50	

Item	On Hand	Lead Time	Item	On Hand	Lead Time
A	0	1	F	75	2
B	100	2	G	75	1
C	50	2	H	0	1
D	50	1	J	100	2
E	75	2	K	100	2

FIGURE 14.16

Information for Problems 14.14, 14.15, and 14.16

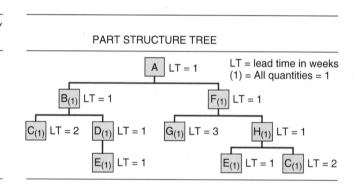

PART	INVENTORY ON HAND
A	0
B	2
C	10
D	5
E	4
F	5
G	1
H	10

PART STRUCTURE TREE

LT = lead time in weeks
(1) = All quantities = 1

65 minutes to complete. Develop a capacity plan, using lot splitting, for the 10-week time period.

•• **14.25** Heather Adams, production manager for a Newfoundland exercise equipment manufacturer, needs to schedule an order for 50 UltimaSteppers, which are to be shipped in week 8. Subscripts indicate quantity required for each parent. Assume lot-for-lot ordering. Below is information about the steppers:

Item	Lead Time	On-Hand Inventory	Components
Stepper	2	20	$A_{(1)}, B_{(3)}, C_{(2)}$
A	1	10	$D_{(1)}, F_{(2)}$
B	2	30	$E_{(1)}, F_{(3)}$
C	3	10	$D_{(2)}, E_{(3)}$
D	1	15	
E	2	5	
F	2	20	

a) Develop a product structure for Heather.
b) Develop a time-phased structure.
c) Develop a net material requirements plan for F. **Px**

•• **14.26** You are scheduling production of your popular rustic coffee table. The table requires a top, four legs, $\frac{1}{8}$ litre of stain, $\frac{1}{16}$ litre of glue, two short braces between the legs and two long braces between the legs, and a brass cap that goes on the bottom of each leg. You have 100 litres of glue in inventory, but none of the other components. All items except the brass caps, stain, and glue are ordered on a lot-for-lot basis. The caps are purchased in quantities of 1000, stain and glue by the litre. Lead time is one day for each item. Schedule the order releases necessary to produce 640 coffee tables on days 5 and 6, and 128 on days 7 and 8. **Px**

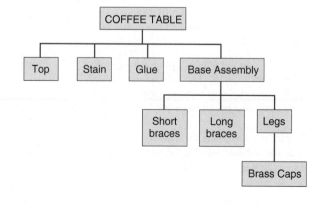

•• **14.27** Using the data for the coffee table in Problem 14.26, build a labour schedule when the labour standard for each top is two labour-hours; each leg including brass cap installation requires $\frac{1}{4}$ hour, as does each pair of braces. Base assembly requires one labour-hour, and final assembly requires two labour-hours. What is the total number of labour-hours required each day, and how many employees are needed each day at eight hours per day?

•• **14.28** M. de Koster, of Rene Enterprises, has the master production plan shown below:

Period (weeks)	1	2	3	4	5	6	7	8	9
Gross requirements		15		20		10			25

Lead time = 1 period; setup cost = $200; holding cost = $10 per week; stockout cost = $10 per week. Your job is to develop an ordering plan and costs for:

a) Lot-for-lot.   b) EOQ.
c) POQ.   d) Which plan has the lowest cost?

•• **14.29** Grace Greenberg, production planner for Science and Technology Labs, in New Jersey, has the master production plan shown below:

Period (weeks)	1	2	3	4	5	6	7	8	9	10	11	12
Gross requirements	35		40		10			25	10			45

Lead time = 1 period; setup costs = $200; holding cost = $10 per week; stockout cost = $10 per week. Develop an ordering plan and costs for Grace, using these techniques:

a) Lot-for-lot.   b) EOQ.
c) POQ.   d) Which plan has the lowest cost?

CASE STUDIES

Hill's Automotive, Inc.

Hill's Automotive, Inc., is an aftermarket producer and distributor of automotive replacement parts. Art Hill has slowly expanded the business, which began as a supplier of hard-to-get auto air-conditioning units for classic cars and hot rods. The firm has limited manufacturing capability, but a state-of-the-art MRP system and extensive inventory and assembly facilities. Components are purchased, assembled, and repackaged. Among its products are private-label air-conditioning, carburetors, and ignition kits. The downturn in the economy, particularly the company's discretionary segment, has put downward pressure on volume and margins. Profits have fallen considerably. In addition, customer service levels have declined, with late deliveries now exceeding 25% of orders. And to make matters worse, customer returns have been rising at a rate of 3% per month.

Wally Hopp, vice-president of sales, claims that most of the problem lies with the assembly department. He says that although the firm has accurate bills of materials, indicating what goes into each product, it is not producing the proper mix of the product. He also believes the firm has poor quality control and low productivity, and as a result, its costs are too high.

Melanie Thompson, treasurer, believes that problems are due to investing in the wrong inventories. She thinks that marketing has too many options and products. Melanie also thinks that purchasing department buyers have been hedging their inventories and requirements with excess purchasing commitments.

The assembly manager, Kalinga Jagoda, says, "The symptom is that we have a lot of parts in inventory, but no place to assemble them in the production schedule. When we have the right part, it is not very good, but we use it anyway to meet the schedule."

Marshall Fisher, manager of purchasing, has taken the stance that purchasing has not let Hill's Automotive down. He has stuck by his old suppliers, used historical data to determine requirements, maintained what he views as excellent prices from suppliers, and evaluated new sources of supply with a view towards lowering cost. Where possible, Marshall reacted to the increased pressure for profitability by emphasizing low cost and early delivery.

Discussion Questions

1. Prepare a plan for Art Hill that gets the firm back on a course towards improved profitability. Be sure to identify the symptoms, the problems, and the specific changes you would implement.
2. Explain how MRP plays a role in this plan.

Video Case | When 18 500 Orlando Magic Fans Come to Dinner

With vast experience at venues such as the American Airlines Arena (in Miami), the Kentucky Derby, and Super Bowls, Chef John Nicely now also plans huge culinary events at Orlando's Amway Center, home of the Orlando Magic basketball team. With his unique talent and exceptional operations skills, Nicely serves tens of thousands of cheering fans at some of the world's largest events. And when more than 18 500 basketball fans show up for a game, expecting great food and great basketball, he puts his creative as well as operations talent to work.

Chef John must be prepared. This means determining not only a total demand for all 18 500 fans, but also translating that demand into specific menu items and beverages. He prepares a forecast from current ticket sales, history of similar events at other venues, and his own records, which reflect the demand with this particular opponent, night of week, time of year, and even time of day. He then breaks the demand for specific menu items and quantities into items to be available at each of the 22 concession stands, 7 restaurants, and 68 suites. He must also be prepared to accommodate individual requests from players on both teams.

Chef John frequently changes the menu to keep it interesting for the fans who attend many of the 41 regular season home games each season. Even the culinary preference of the opponent's fans who may be attending influences the menu. Additionally, when entertainment other than the Magic is using the Amway Center, the demographic mix is likely to be different, requiring additional tweaking of the menu. The size of the wait staff and the kitchen staff change to reflect the size of the crowd; Chef John may be supervising as many as 90 people working in the kitchen. Similarly, the concessions stands, 40% of which have their own grills and fryers, present another challenge, as they are managed by volunteers from nonprofit organizations. The use of these volunteers adds the need for special training and extra enforcement of strict quality standards.

Once deciding on the overall demand and the menu, Chef John must prepare the production specifications (a bill of material) for each item. For the evening game with the Celtics, Chef John is preparing his unique Cheeto Crusted Mac & Cheese dish. The ingredients, quantity, costs, and labour requirements are shown below:

Production Specifications

	Cheeto Crusted Mac & Cheese (6 Portions)				
Ingredients	**Quantity**	**Measure**	**Unit Cost**	**Total Cost**	**Labour-Hours**
Elbow macaroni (large, uncooked)	20.00	oz.	$0.09	$1.80	
Cheese—cheddar shredded	10.00	oz.	0.16	1.60	
Mac and cheese base (see recipe)	44.00	oz.	0.80	35.20	
Milk	4.00	oz.	0.03	0.12	
Cheetos, crushed	6.00	oz.	0.27	1.62	
Sliced green onion—garnish	0.50	oz.	0.18	0.09	
Whole Cheetos—garnish	2.00	oz.	0.27	0.54	
Total labour-hours					0.2 hours

The yield on this dish is six portions, and labour cost is $15 per hour, with fringes. The entire quantity required for the evening is prepared prior to the game and kept in warming ovens until needed. Demand for each basketball game is divided into five periods: prior to the game, first quarter, second quarter, half-time, and second half. At the Magic vs. Celtics game next week, the demand (number of portions) in each period is 60, 36, 48, 60, and 12 for the Cheeto Crusted Mac & Cheese dish, respectively.

Discussion Questions*

1. Prepare a bill of material explosion and total cost for the 216 portions of Cheeto Crusted Mac & Cheese.
2. Assuming that there is no beginning inventory of the Cheeto Crusted Mac & Cheese and cooking time for the entire 216 portions is 0.6 hours, when must preparation begin?

---

* You may wish to view the video that accompanies this case before answering the questions.

MRP at Wheeled Coach Ambulance

Wheeled Coach Ambulance, the world's largest manufacturer of ambulances, builds thousands of different and constantly changing configurations of its products. The custom nature of its business means lots of options and special designs—and a potential scheduling and inventory nightmare. Wheeled Coach addressed such problems, and succeeded in solving a lot of them, with an MRP system (described in the *Global Company Profile* that opens this chapter). As with most MRP installations, however, solving one set of problems uncovers a new set.

One of the new issues that had to be addressed by plant manager Lynn Whalen was newly discovered excess inventory. Managers discovered a substantial amount of inventory that was not called for in any finished products. Excess inventory was evident because of the new level of inventory accuracy required by the MRP system. The other reason was a new series of inventory reports generated by the IBM MAPICS MRP system purchased by Wheeled Coach. One of those reports indicates where items are used and is known as the "Where Used" report. Interestingly, many inventory items were not called out on bills of material (BOMs) for any current products. In some cases, the reason some parts were in the stockroom remained a mystery.

The discovery of this excess inventory led to renewed efforts to ensure that the BOMs were accurate. With substantial work, BOM accuracy increased and the number of engineering change notices (ECNs) decreased. Similarly, purchase-order accuracy, with regard to both part numbers and quantities ordered, was improved. Additionally, receiving department and stockroom accuracy went up, all helping to maintain schedule, costs, and ultimately, shipping dates and quality.

Eventually, Lynn Whalen concluded that the residual amounts of excess inventory were the result, at least in part, of rapid changes in ambulance design and technology. Another source was customer changes made after specifications had been determined and materials ordered. This latter excess occurs because, even though Wheeled Coach's own throughput time is only 17 days, many of the items that it purchases require much longer lead times.

Discussion Questions*

1. Why is accurate inventory such an important issue at Wheeled Coach?
2. Why does Wheeled Coach have excess inventory, and what kind of a plan would you suggest for dealing with it?

3. Be specific in your suggestions for reducing inventory and how to implement them.

* You may wish to view the video that accompanies this case before answering the questions.

▶**Additional Case Study:** Visit **MyLab Operations Management** for this case study:

Ikon's Attempt at ERP: The giant office technology firm faces hurdles with ERP implementation.

CHAPTER 14 | RAPID REVIEW

MyLab Operations Management

Main Heading	Review Material	
DEPENDENT DEMAND (pp. 544–545)	Demand for items is *dependent* when the relationship between the items can be determined. For any product, all components of that product are dependent demand items. • **Material requirements planning (MRP)**—A dependent demand technique that uses a bill of material, inventory, expected receipts, and a master production schedule to determine material requirements.	**VIDEO 14.1** MRP at Wheeled Coach Ambulance
DEPENDENT INVENTORY MODEL REQUIREMENTS (pp. 545–549)	Dependent inventory models require that the operations manager know the: (1) master production schedule; (2) specifications or bill of material; (3) inventory availability; (4) purchase orders outstanding; and (5) lead times. • **Master production schedule (MPS)**—A timetable that specifies what is to be made and when. The MPS is a statement of *what is to be produced*, not a forecast of demand. • **Bill of material (BOM)**—A listing of the components, their description, and the quantity of each required to make one unit of a product. Items above any level in a BOM are called *parents*; items below any level are called *components*, or *children*. The top level in a BOM is the 0 level. • **Modular bills**—Bills of material organized by major subassemblies or by product options. • **Planning bills**— A material grouping created in order to assign an artificial parent to a bill of material; also called "pseudo" bills, kitted material, or kits. • **Phantom bills of material**—Bills of material for components, usually subassemblies, that exist only temporarily; they are never inventoried. • **Low-level coding**—A number that identifies items at the lowest level at which they occur. • **Lead time**—In purchasing systems, the time between recognition of the need for an order and receiving it; in production systems, it is the order, wait, move, queue, setup, and run times for each component. When a bill of material is turned on its side and modified by adding lead times for each component, it is called a *time-phased product structure*.	Problems: 14.1, 14.3 Virtual Office Hours for Solved Problem: 14.1 **VIDEO 14.2** When 18 500 Orlando Magic Fans Come to Dinner

Main Heading	Review Material	
MRP STRUCTURE (pp. 550–553)	• **Gross material requirements plan**—A schedule that shows the total demand for an item (prior to subtraction of on-hand inventory and scheduled receipts) and (1) when it must be ordered from suppliers, or (2) when production must be started to meet its demand by a particular date. • **Net material requirements plan**—The result of adjusting gross requirements for inventory on hand and scheduled receipts. • **Planned order receipt**—The quantity planned to be received at a future date. • **Planned order release**—The scheduled date for an order to be released. Net requirements = (Gross requirements + Allocations) – (On hand + Scheduled receipts)	Problems: 14.2, 14.4–14.8 Virtual Office Hours for Solved Problem: 14.2 **ACTIVE MODEL 14.1**
MRP MANAGEMENT (pp. 554–555)	• **System nervousness**—Frequent changes in an MRP system. • **Time fences**—A means for allowing a segment of the master schedule to be designated as "not to be rescheduled". • **Pegging**—In material requirements planning systems, tracing upward in the bill of material from the component to the parent item. Four approaches for integrating MRP and JIT are (1) finite capacity scheduling, (2) small buckets, (3) balanced flow, and (4) supermarkets. • **Buckets**—Time units in a material requirements planning system. Finite capacity scheduling (FCS) considers department and machine capacity. FCS provides the precise scheduling needed for rapid material movement. • **Bucketless system**—Time-phased data are referenced using dated records rather than defined time periods, or buckets. • **Back flush**—A system to reduce inventory balances by deducting everything in the bill of material on completion of the unit. • **Supermarket**—An inventory area that holds common items that are replenished by a kanban system.	
LOT-SIZING TECHNIQUES (pp. 555–559)	• **Lot-sizing decision**—The process of, or techniques used in, determining lot size. • **Lot-for-lot**—A lot-sizing technique that generates exactly what is required to meet the plan. • **Periodic order quantity (POQ)**—A lot-sizing technique that issues orders on a predetermined time interval with an order quantity equal to all of the interval's requirements. • **Economic part period (EPP)**—A period of time when the ratio of setup cost to holding cost is equal. • **Wagner-Whitin procedure**—A technique for lot-size computation that assumes a finite time horizon beyond which there are no additional net requirements to arrive at an ordering strategy. In general, the lot-for-lot approach should be used whenever low-cost deliveries can be achieved.	Problems: 14.17–14.22
EXTENSIONS OF MRP (pp. 559–561)	• **Material requirements planning II (MRP II)**—A system that allows, with MRP in place, inventory data to be augmented by other resource variables; in this case, MRP becomes *material resource planning*. • **Closed-loop MRP system**—A system that provides feedback to the capacity plan, master production schedule, and production plan so planning can be kept valid at all times. • **Load report**—A report for showing the resource requirements in a work centre for all work currently assigned there as well as all planned and expected orders. Tactics for smoothing the load and minimizing the impact of changed lead time include *overlapping*, *operations splitting*, and *order* or *lot splitting*.	
MRP IN SERVICES (pp. 561–563)	• **Distribution resource planning (DRP)**—A time-phased stock-replenishment plan for all levels of a distribution network.	

MyLab Operations Management

Main Heading	Review Material
ENTERPRISE RESOURCE PLANNING (ERP) (pp. 563–565)	• **Enterprise resource planning (ERP)**—An information system for identifying and planning the enterprise-wide resources needed to take, make, ship, and account for customer orders. In an ERP system, data are entered only once into a common, complete, and consistent database shared by all applications. • **Efficient consumer response (ECR)**—Supply chain management systems in the grocery industry that tie sales to buying, to inventory, to logistics, and to production.

Self-Test

■ **Before taking the self-test,** refer to the learning objectives listed at the beginning of the chapter.

LO1 In a product structure diagram:
  a) parents are found only at the top level of the diagram.
  b) parents are found at every level in the diagram.
  c) children are found at every level of the diagram except the top level.
  d) all items in the diagrams are both parents and children.
  e) all of the above.

LO2 The difference between a gross material requirements plan (gross MRP) and a net material requirements plan (net MRP) is:
  a) the gross MRP may not be computerized, but the net MRP must be computerized.
  b) the gross MRP includes consideration of the inventory on hand, whereas the net MRP doesn't include the inventory consideration.
  c) the net MRP includes consideration of the inventory on hand, whereas the gross MRP doesn't include the inventory consideration.
  d) the gross MRP doesn't take taxes into account, whereas the net MRP includes the tax considerations.
  e) the net MRP is only an estimate, whereas the gross MRP is used for actual production scheduling.

LO3 Net requirements =
  a) Gross requirements + Allocations – On-hand inventory + Scheduled receipts.
  b) Gross requirements – Allocations – On-hand inventory – Scheduled receipts.
  c) Gross requirements – Allocations – On-hand inventory + Scheduled receipts.
  d) Gross requirements + Allocations – On-hand inventory – Scheduled receipts.

LO4 A lot-sizing procedure that orders on a predetermined time interval with the order quantity equal to the total of the interval's requirement is:
  a) periodic order quantity.
  b) part period balancing.
  c) economic order quantity.
  d) all of the above.

LO5 MRP II stands for:
  a) material resource planning.
  b) management requirements planning.
  c) management resource planning.
  d) material revenue planning.
  e) material risk planning.

LO6 A(n) ___ MRP system provides information to the capacity plan, to the master production schedule, and ultimately to the production plan.
  a) dynamic
  b) closed-loop
  c) continuous
  d) retrospective
  e) introspective

LO7 Which system extends MRP II to tie in customers and suppliers?
  a) MRP III
  b) JIT
  c) IRP
  d) ERP
  e) Enhanced MRP II

Answers: LO1. c; LO2. c; LO3. d; LO4. a; LO5. a; LO6. b; LO7. d.

MyLab Operations Management

Most of these questions can be found in MyLab Operations Management. Visit MyLab Operations Management to access cases, videos, downloadable software, and much more. MyLab Operations Management Management also features a personalized Study Plan that helps you identify which chapter concepts you've mastered and guides you towards study tools for additional practice.

DEPARTURES

TIME	TO	FLIGHT NO.	GATE	REMARKS
15:35	AMSTERDAM	TK3946	A1	CANCELLED
15:40	WASHINGTON	LN3211	C3	CANCELLED
15:45	BERLIN	GT4638	A2	CANCELLED
:45	MIAMI	RV3323	B4	CANCELLED
:50	STOCKHOLM	FD2753	A6	CANCELLED
:55	MADRID	LV2317	A5	CANCELLED
:05	SEATTLE	BD9032	B1	CANCELLED
:15	RIO DE JANEIRO	FB5610	C4	CANCELLED
:20	MILAN	NB7792	A4	CANCELLED
:25	TORONTO	GC5433	C1	CANCELLED
16:35	DENVER	LY4488	B2	CANCELLED
16:40	PARIS	KF3280	B4	CANCELLED
16:50	CHICAGO	TK7252	A4	CANCELLED
16:55	SYDNEY	LX3100	A2	CANCELLED

nmcandre/Fotolia

15

Learning Objectives

Short-Term Scheduling

Scheduling Airplanes When Weather Is the Enemy

Operations managers at airlines learn to expect the unexpected. Events that require rapid rescheduling are a regular part of life. Throughout the ordeals of tornadoes, ice storms, and snowstorms, airlines across the globe struggle to cope with delays, cancellations, and furious passengers. The inevitable changes to the schedule often create a ripple effect that impacts passengers at dozens of airports in the network. Roughly one out of 10 of Air Canada's flights are disrupted in a typical year. Half are because of weather; the cost is millions of dollars in lost revenue, overtime pay, and food and lodging vouchers.

Now Air Canada is taking the sting out of the scheduling nightmares that come from weather-related problems with its central, multimillion-dollar, high-tech nerve centre at Toronto's Pearson Airport. From computers to tele-communications systems to de-icers, Air Canada's operations control centre more quickly notifies customers of schedule changes, reroutes flights, and gets jets into the air. The operations control centre's job is to keep flights flowing as smoothly as possible in spite of the disruptions.

Global > Company Profile Air Canada

With earlier access to information, the centre's staff pores over streams of data transmitted by computers and adjusts to changes quickly. Using mathematical scheduling models described in this chapter, Air Canada decides on schedule and route changes. This means coordinating incoming and outgoing aircraft, ensuring that the right crews are on hand, rescheduling connections to coordinate arrival times, and making sure information gets to passengers as soon as possible.

4:00 a.m.
FORECAST:
Rain with a chance of light snow for Toronto.

ACTION:
Discuss status of planes and possible need for cancellations.

10:00 a.m.
FORECAST:
Freezing rain after 5:00 p.m.

ACTION:
Ready de-icing trucks; develop plans to cancel 50% to 80% of flights after 6:00 p.m.

1:30 p.m.
FORECAST:
Rain changing to snow.

ACTION:
Cancel half the flights from 6:00 p.m. to 10:00 a.m. notify passengers and reroute planes.

5:00 p.m.
FORECAST:
Less snow than expected.

ACTION:
Continue calling passengers and arrange alternate flights.

10:00 p.m.
FORECAST:
Snow tapering off.

ACTION:
Find hotels for 1600 passengers stranded by the storm.

Here is what Air Canada officials had to do one December day when a storm bore down on Toronto.

Mimadeo/Alamy Stock Photo

In addition to weather-related scheduling issues, Air Canada must occasionally respond to labour disruptions affecting passengers' travel plans. On Friday the 13 (April 2012), several Air Canada pilots staged a "sick-out" causing numerous cancellations and a need for rescheduling.

The Importance of Short-Term Scheduling

STUDENT TIP

Good scheduling means lower costs and faster and more dependable delivery.

Air Canada doesn't schedule just its huge fleet of aircraft every day. It also schedules over 1000 pilots and flight attendants to accommodate passengers who wish to reach their destinations. This schedule, based on huge computer programs, plays a major role in satisfying customers. Air Canada finds competitive advantage with its flexibility for last-minute adjustments to demand and weather disruptions.

Manufacturing firms also make schedules that match production to customer demand. Magna International schedules machines, tools, and people to make automotive parts. Magna's mainframe computer downloads schedules for parts production into a flexible machining system (FMS) in which a manager makes the final scheduling decision. The FMS allows parts of many

LO1 Explain the relationship between short-term scheduling, capacity planning, aggregate planning, and a master schedule

sizes or shapes to be made, in any order. This scheduling versatility results in parts produced on a just-in-time basis, with low setup times, little work-in-process, and high machine utilization. Efficient scheduling is how companies like Magna International meet due dates promised to customers and face time-based competition.

The strategic importance of scheduling is clear:

- Effective scheduling means faster movement of goods and services through a facility. This means greater use of assets and, hence, greater capacity per dollar invested, which, in turn, *lowers cost*.
- Added capacity, faster throughput, and the related flexibility mean better customer service through *faster delivery*.
- Good scheduling also contributes to realistic commitments and hence *dependable delivery*.

Scheduling Issues

STUDENT TIP

Scheduling decisions range from years, for capacity planning, to minutes/hours/days, called short-term scheduling. This chapter focuses on the latter.

Scheduling deals with the timing of operations. The types of scheduling decisions made in five organizations—a hospital, a college, a manufacturer, a restaurant, and an airline—are shown in Table 15.1. As you can see from Figure 15.1, a sequence of decisions affects scheduling. Schedule decisions begin with *capacity* planning, which involves *total facility and equipment resources available* (discussed in Chapter 7 and Supplement 7). Capacity plans are usually annual or quarterly as new equipment and facilities are purchased or discarded. Aggregate planning (Chapter 13) makes decisions regarding the use of facilities, inventory, people, and outside contractors. Aggregate plans are typically monthly, and *resources are allocated in terms of an aggregate measure such as total units, tons, or shop hours*. However, the master schedule breaks down the aggregate plan and develops a *schedule for specific products or product lines for each week*. Short-term schedules then translate capacity decisions, aggregate (intermediate) planning, and master schedules into job sequences and *specific assignments of personnel, materials, and machinery*. In this chapter, we describe the narrow issue of scheduling goods and services in the *short run* (i.e., matching daily or hourly requirements to specific personnel and equipment).

The objective of scheduling is to allocate and prioritize demand (generated by either forecasts or customer orders) to available facilities. Three significant factors in achieving this allocation and prioritizing are (1) the type of scheduling, forward or backward, (2) finite and infinite loading, and (3) the criteria for priorities. We discuss these three topics next. See the video case at the end of this chapter, "From the Eagles to the Magic: Converting the Amway Center".

VIDEO 15.1
From the Eagles to the Magic: Converting the Amway Center.

Table 15.1
Scheduling Decisions

Organization	Managers Schedule the Following:
The Hospital for Sick Children	Operating room use Patient admissions Nursing, security, maintenance staff Outpatient treatments
University of Manitoba	Classrooms and audiovisual equipment Student and instructor schedules Graduate and undergraduate courses
Magna International factory	Production of goods Purchases of materials Workers
Hard Rock Cafe	Chef, waiters, bartenders Delivery of fresh foods Entertainers Opening of dining areas
Air Canada	Maintenance of aircraft Departure timetables Flight crews, catering, gate, and ticketing personnel

VIDEO 15.2
Scheduling at Hard Rock

Capacity Planning
(Long term; years)
Changes in facilities
Changes in equipment

Capacity Plan for New Facilities
Adjust capacity to the demand suggested by strategic plan

Aggregate Planning
(Intermediate term; quarterly or monthly)
Facility utilization
Personnel changes
Subcontracting

Aggregate Production Plan for All Bikes
(Determine personnel or subcontracting necessary to
match aggregate demand to existing facilities/capacity)

Month	1	2
Bike Production	800	850

Master Schedule
(Intermediate term; weekly)
Material requirements planning
Disaggregate the aggregate plan

Master Production Schedule for Bike Models
(Determine weekly capacity schedule)

	Month 1				Month 2			
Week	1	2	3	4	5	6	7	8
Model 22		200		200		200		200
Model 24	100		100		150		100	
Model 26	100		100		100		100	

Short-Term Scheduling
(Short term; days, hours, minutes)
Work centre loading
Job sequencing/dispatching

Work Assigned to Specific Personnel and Work Centres
Make finite capacity schedule by matching specific
tasks to specific people and machines

Assemble
Model 22 in
work centre 6

FIGURE 15.1 **The Relationship Between Capacity Planning, Aggregate Planning, Master Schedule, and Short-Term Scheduling for a Bike Company**

FORWARD AND BACKWARD SCHEDULING

Scheduling involves assigning due dates to specific jobs, but many jobs compete simultaneously for the same resources. To help address the difficulties inherent in scheduling, we can categorize scheduling techniques as (1) forward scheduling and (2) backward scheduling.

Forward scheduling starts the schedule as soon as the job requirements are known. It is used in a variety of organizations such as hospitals, clinics, fine-dining restaurants, and machine tool manufacturers. In these facilities, jobs are performed to customer order, and delivery is often requested as soon as possible. Forward scheduling is usually designed to produce a schedule that can be accomplished even if it means not meeting the due date. In many instances, forward scheduling causes a buildup of work-in-process inventory.

Backward scheduling begins with the due date, scheduling the *final* operation first. Steps in the job are then scheduled, one at a time, in reverse order. By subtracting the lead time for each item, the start time is obtained. However, the resources necessary to accomplish the schedule may not exist. Backward scheduling is used in many manufacturing environments, as well as service environments such as catering a banquet or scheduling surgery. In practice, a combination of forward and backward scheduling is often used to find a reasonable trade-off between what can be achieved and customer due dates.

Machine breakdowns, absenteeism, quality problems, shortages, and other factors further complicate scheduling. (See the *OM in Action* box "Scheduling Workers Who Fall Asleep Is a Killer—Literally".) Consequently, assignment of a date does not ensure that the work will be

Forward scheduling
Scheduling that begins the schedule as soon as the requirements are known.

Backward scheduling
Scheduling that begins with the due date and schedules the final operation first and the other job steps in reverse order.

Computerized scheduling software helps managers monitor production.

Dan Lee/Alamy Stock Photo

performed according to the schedule. Many specialized techniques have been developed to aid in preparing reliable schedules.

FINITE AND INFINITE LOADING

Loading is the process of assigning jobs to work stations or processes. Scheduling techniques that load (or assign) work only up to the capacity of the process are called *finite loading*. The advantage of finite loading is that, in theory, all of the work assigned can be accomplished. However, because only work that can be accomplished is loaded into workstations—when in fact there may be more work than capacity—the due dates may be pushed out to an unacceptable future time.

OM in Action Scheduling Workers Who Fall Asleep Is a Killer—Literally

The accidents at the nuclear plants at Three Mile Island, Pennsylvania, and Chernobyl, Russia, and the disaster at Bhopal, India, all had one thing in common: they occurred between midnight and 4:00 a.m. These facilities had other problems, but the need for sleep simply results in unreliable workplace performance. In some cases, unable to cope with a constantly changing work schedule, workers just plain fall asleep.

The same is true for pilots. Their inconsistent schedules and long flights often force them to snooze in the cockpit to get enough sleep. (Air Canada's flight from Toronto to Mumbai, India, for example, takes about 17 hours.) The Bombardier regional jet flying from Honolulu to Hilo, Hawaii, encountered a serious problem in 2008 as it flew over Maui: both pilots were so fast asleep that they failed to respond to frantic calls from air-traffic controllers for 18 minutes. (The plane, with 40 passengers, overshot its destination as it flew 26 miles over the Pacific.) One FedEx pilot even complained of falling asleep while taxiing to take off.

Millions of people work in industries that maintain round-the-clock schedules. Employees from graveyard shifts report tales of seeing sleeping assembly-line workers fall off their stools, batches of defective parts slide past dozing inspectors, and exhausted forklift operators crash into walls. Virtually all shift workers are sleep deprived. And Transport Canada indicates that drowsiness may be a factor in as many as 20% of all fatal collisions.

Scheduling is a major problem in firms with 24/7 shifts, but some managers are taking steps to deal with schedule-related sleep problems among workers. Large Canadian companies such as Bombardier, Imperial Oil, and Magna, for instance, all give workers several days off between shift changes.

Operations managers can make shift work less dangerous with shifts that do not exceed 12 hours, that encourage eight hours of sleep each day, and that have extended time off between shift changes. As more is learned about the economic toll of non-daytime schedules and changing schedules, companies are learning to improve scheduling.

Sources: The Wall Street Journal (September 12, 2008): A1, A14 and (October 25, 2009): A:1; and *Air Safety and Health* (January 2004): 14.

Techniques that load work without regard for the capacity of the process are *infinite loading*. All the work that needs to be accomplished in a given time period is assigned. The capacity of the process is not considered. Most material requirements planning (MRP) systems (discussed in Chapter 14) are infinite loading systems. The advantage of infinite loading is an initial schedule that meets due dates. Of course, when the workload exceeds capacity, either the capacity or the schedule must be adjusted.

SCHEDULING CRITERIA

The correct scheduling technique depends on the volume of orders, the nature of operations, and the overall complexity of jobs, as well as the importance placed on each of four criteria. These four criteria are:

1. *Minimize completion time:* This criterion is evaluated by determining the average completion time per job.
2. *Maximize utilization:* This is evaluated by determining the percentage of the time the facility is utilized.
3. *Minimize work-in-process (WIP) inventory:* This is evaluated by determining the average number of jobs in the system. The relationship between the number of jobs in the system and WIP inventory will be high. Therefore, the fewer the number of jobs that are in the system, the lower the inventory.
4. *Minimize customer waiting time:* This is evaluated by determining the average number of late days.

These four criteria are used in this chapter, as they are in industry, to evaluate scheduling performance. In addition, good scheduling approaches should be simple, clear, easily understood, easy to carry out, flexible, and realistic.

Table 15.2 provides an overview of different processes and approaches to scheduling.

We now examine scheduling in process-focused facilities, in repetitive facilities, and in the service sector.

Table 15.2
Different Processes Suggest Different Approaches to Scheduling

Process-focused facilities (job shops)

- Focus is on generating a forward-looking schedule.
- MRP generates due dates that are refined with finite capacity scheduling techniques.
- *Examples:* foundries, machine shops, cabinet shops, print shops, many restaurants, and the fashion industry.

Work cells (focused facilities that process families of similar components)

- Focus is on generating a forward-looking schedule.
- MRP generates due dates, and subsequent detail scheduling/dispatching is done at the work cell with kanbans and priority rules.
- *Examples:* work cells at ambulance manufacturer Wheeled Coach, aircraft engine rebuilder Standard Aero, greeting-card maker Hallmark.

Repetitive facilities (assembly lines)

- Focus is on generating a forward-looking schedule that is achieved by balancing the line with traditional assembly-line techniques.
- Pull techniques, such as JIT and kanban, signal component scheduling to support the assembly line.
- Challenging scheduling problems typically occur only when the process is new or when products or models change.
- *Examples:* assembly lines for a wide variety of products from autos to home appliances and computers.

Product-focused facilities (continuous)

- Focus is on generating a forward-looking schedule that can meet a reasonably stable demand with the existing fixed capacity.
- Capacity in such facilities is usually limited by long-term capital investment.
- Capacity is usually known, as is the setup and run time for the limited range of products.
- *Examples:* facilities with very high volume production and limited-variety products such as paper on huge machines at International Paper, beer in a brewery at Labatt Brewing Company, or rolled steel in a Dofasco plant.

Scheduling Process-Focused Facilities

Process-focused facilities (also known as *intermittent* or *job-shop facilities*),[1] as we see in Table 15.2, are high-variety, low-volume systems commonly found in manufacturing and service organizations. These are production systems in which products are made to order. Items made under this system usually differ considerably in terms of materials used, order of processing, processing requirements, time of processing, and setup requirements. Because of these differences, scheduling can be complex. To run a facility in a balanced and efficient manner, the manager needs a production planning and control system. This system should:

- Schedule incoming orders without violating capacity constraints of individual work centres.
- Check the availability of tools and materials before releasing an order to a department.
- Establish due dates for each job and check progress against need dates and order lead times.
- Check work in progress as jobs move through the shop.
- Provide feedback on plant and production activities.
- Provide work efficiency statistics and monitor operator times for payroll and labour distribution analyses.

Whether the scheduling system is manual or automated, it must be accurate and relevant. This means it requires a production database with both planning and control files. Three types of planning files are:

1. An *item master file*, which contains information about each component the firm produces or purchases.
2. A *routing file*, which indicates each component's flow through the shop.
3. A *work-centre master file*, which contains information about the work centre, such as capacity and efficiency.

Control files track the actual progress made against the plan for each work order.

Loading Jobs

Loading

The assigning of jobs to work or processing centres.

Loading means the assignment of jobs to work or processing centres. Operations managers assign jobs to work centres so that costs, idle time, and completion times are kept to a minimum. Loading work centres takes two forms.[2] One is oriented to capacity; the second is related to assigning specific jobs to work centres.

First, we examine loading from the perspective of capacity via a technique known as *input–output* control. Then, we present two approaches used for loading: *Gantt charts* and the *assignment method* of linear programming.

INPUT–OUTPUT CONTROL

Many firms have difficulty scheduling (i.e., achieving effective throughput) because they overload the production processes. This often occurs because they do not know actual performance in the work centres. Effective scheduling depends on matching the schedule to performance. Lack of knowledge about capacity and performance causes reduced throughput.

Input–output control

A system that allows operations personnel to manage facility work flows by tracking work added to a work centre and its work completed.

Input–output control is a technique that allows operations personnel to manage facility work flows. If the work is arriving faster than it is being processed, the facility is overloaded, and a backlog develops. Overloading causes crowding in the facility, leading to inefficiencies and quality problems. If the work is arriving at a slower rate than jobs are being performed, the facility is underloaded, and the work centre may run out of work. Underloading the facility results in idle capacity and wasted resources. Example 1 shows the use of input–output controls.

---

[1] Much of the literature on scheduling is about manufacturing; therefore, the traditional term *job-shop scheduling* is often used.

[2] Note that this discussion can apply to facilities that might be called a "shop" in a manufacturing firm, a "unit" in a hospital, or a "department" in an office or a large kitchen.

DNC Machining, Inc., manufactures driveway security fences and gates. It wants to develop an input–output control report for the aluminum machining work centre for five weeks (weeks 6/6 through 7/4). The planned input is 280 standard hours per week. The actual input is close to this figure, varying between 250 and 285. Output is scheduled at 320 standard hours, which is the assumed capacity. A backlog exists in the work centre.

APPROACH ▶ DNC uses schedule information to create Figure 15.2, which monitors the workload–capacity relationship at the work centre.

SOLUTION ▶ The deviations between scheduled input and actual output are shown in Figure 15.2. Actual output (270 hours) is substantially less than planned. Therefore, neither the input plan nor the output plan is being achieved.

INSIGHT ▶ The backlog of work in this work centre has actually increased by five hours by week 6/27. This increases work-in-process inventory, complicating the scheduling task and indicating the need for manager action.

EXAMPLE 1

Input–Output Control

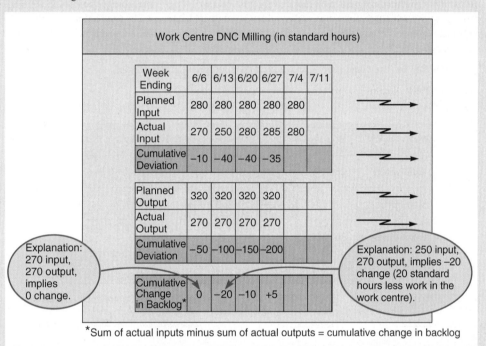

FIGURE 15.2

Input–Output Control

Work Centre DNC Milling (in standard hours)						
Week Ending	6/6	6/13	6/20	6/27	7/4	7/11
Planned Input	280	280	280	280	280	
Actual Input	270	250	280	285	280	
Cumulative Deviation	–10	–40	–40	–35		
Planned Output	320	320	320	320		
Actual Output	270	270	270	270		
Cumulative Deviation	–50	–100	–150	–200		
Cumulative Change in Backlog*	0	–20	–10	+5		

Explanation: 270 input, 270 output, implies 0 change.

Explanation: 250 input, 270 output, implies –20 change (20 standard hours less work in the work centre).

*Sum of actual inputs minus sum of actual outputs = cumulative change in backlog

LEARNING EXERCISE ▶ If actual output for the week of 6/27 was 275 (instead of 270), what changes? [Answer: Output cumulative deviation now is –195, and cumulative change in backlog is 0.]

RELATED PROBLEM ▶ 15.21

Input–output control can be maintained by a system of **ConWIP cards**, which control the amount of work in a work centre. ConWIP is an acronym for *constant work-in-process*. The ConWIP card travels with a job (or batch) through the work centre. When the job is finished, the card is released and returned to the initial workstation, authorizing the entry of a new batch into the work centre. The ConWIP card effectively limits the amount of work in the work centre, controls lead time, and monitors the backlog.

The options available to operations personnel to manage facility work flow include the following:

1. Correcting performances.
2. Increasing capacity.
3. Increasing or reducing input to the work centre by (a) routing work to or from other work centres, (b) increasing or decreasing subcontracting, (c) producing less (or producing more).

Producing less is not a popular solution, but the advantages can be substantial. First, customer-service levels may improve because units may be produced on time. Second, efficiency may actually improve because there is less work-in-process cluttering the work centre and adding to overhead costs. Third, quality may improve because less work-in-process hides fewer problems.

ConWIP cards

Cards that control the amount of work in a work centre, aiding input–output control.

GANTT CHARTS

Gantt charts

Planning charts used to schedule resources and allocate time.

Gantt charts are visual aids that are useful in loading and scheduling. The name is derived from Henry Gantt, who developed them in the late 1800s. The charts show the use of resources, such as work centres and labour.

LO2 Draw Gantt loading and scheduling charts

When used in *loading*, Gantt charts show the loading and idle times of several departments, machines, or facilities. They display the relative workloads in the system so that the manager knows what adjustments are appropriate. For example, when one work centre becomes overloaded, employees from a low-load centre can be transferred temporarily to increase the workforce. Or if waiting jobs can be processed at different work centres, some jobs at high-load centres can be transferred to low-load centres. Versatile equipment may also be transferred among centres. Example 2 illustrates a simple Gantt load chart.

EXAMPLE 2

Gantt Load Chart

A Hamilton washing machine manufacturer accepts special orders for machines to be used in such unique facilities as submarines, hospitals, and large industrial laundries. The production of each machine requires varying tasks and durations. The company wants to build a load chart for the week of March 8.

APPROACH ▶ The Gantt chart is selected as the appropriate graphical tool.

SOLUTION ▶ Figure 15.3 shows the completed Gantt chart.

FIGURE 15.3

Gantt Load Chart for the Week of March 8

Work Centre \ Day	Monday	Tuesday	Wednesday	Thursday	Friday
Metalworks	Job 349	✕		◀— Job 350 —▶	
Mechanical		◀— Job 349 —▶		Job 408	
Electronics	Job 408			Job 349	
Painting	◀— Job 295 —▶		Job 408	✕	Job 349

☐ Processing ☐ Unscheduled ✕ Centre not available (e.g., maintenance time, repairs, shortages)

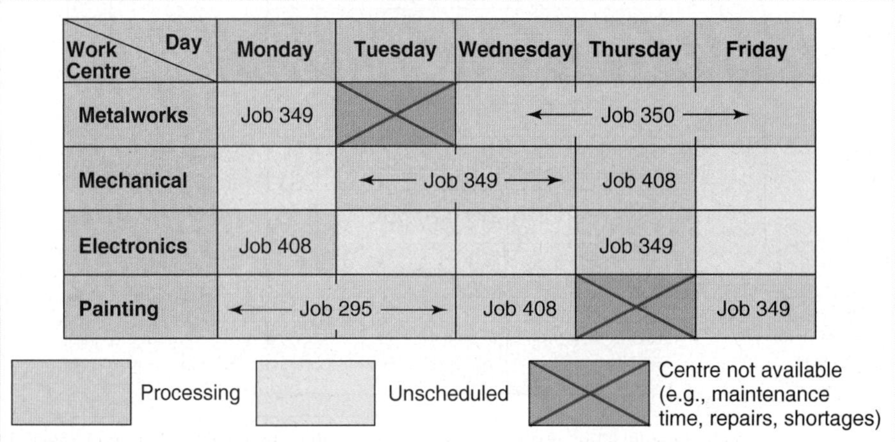

INSIGHT ▶ The four work centres process several jobs during the week. This particular chart indicates that the metalworks and painting centres are completely loaded for the entire week. The mechanical and electronic centres have some idle time scattered during the week. We also note that the metalworks centre is unavailable on Tuesday, and the painting centre is unavailable on Thursday, perhaps for preventive maintenance.

LEARNING EXERCISE ▶ What impact results from the electronics work centre closing on Tuesday for preventive maintenance? [Answer: None.]

RELATED PROBLEM ▶ 15.1b

The Gantt *load chart* has a major limitation: It does not account for production variability such as unexpected breakdowns or human errors that require reworking a job. Consequently, the chart must also be updated regularly to account for new jobs and revised time estimates.

A Gantt *schedule chart* is used to monitor jobs in progress (and is also used for project scheduling). It indicates which jobs are on schedule and which are ahead of or behind schedule. In practice, many versions of the chart are found. The schedule chart in Example 3 places jobs in progress on the vertical axis and time on the horizontal axis.

Assignment method

A special class of linear programming models that involves assigning tasks or jobs to resources.

ASSIGNMENT METHOD

The **assignment method** involves assigning tasks or jobs to resources. Examples include assigning jobs to machines, contracts to bidders, people to projects, and salespeople to territories. The objective is most often to minimize total costs or time required to perform the tasks at hand. One important characteristic of assignment problems is that only one job (or worker) is assigned to one machine (or project).

Each assignment problem uses a table. The numbers in the table will be the costs or times associated with each particular assignment. For example, if First Printing has three available typesetters (A, B, and C) and three new jobs to be completed, its table might appear as follows. The dollar entries represent the firm's estimate of what it will cost for each job to be completed by each typesetter.

	Typesetter		
Job	**A**	**B**	**C**
R-34	$11	$14	$ 6
S-66	$ 8	$10	$11
T-50	$ 9	$12	$ 7

LO3 Apply the assignment method for loading jobs

First Printing in Burnaby wants to use a Gantt chart to show the scheduling of three orders: jobs A, B, and C.

APPROACH ▶ In Figure 15.4, each pair of brackets on the time axis denotes the estimated starting and finishing of a job enclosed within it. The solid bars reflect the actual status or progress of the job. We are just finishing day 5.

SOLUTION ▶

EXAMPLE 3

Gantt Scheduling Chart

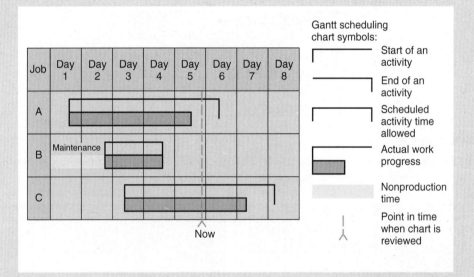

FIGURE 15.4

Gantt Scheduling Chart for Jobs A, B, and C at a Printing Firm

INSIGHT ▶ Figure 15.4 illustrates that job A is about a half day behind schedule at the end of day 5. Job B was completed after equipment maintenance. We also see that job C is ahead of schedule.

LEARNING EXERCISE ▶ Redraw the Gantt chart to show that job A is a half day *ahead* of schedule. [Answer: The orange bar now extends all the way to the end of the activity.]

RELATED PROBLEMS ▶ 15.1a, 15.2

The assignment method involves adding and subtracting appropriate numbers in the table to find the lowest *opportunity cost*[3] for each assignment. There are four steps to follow:

1. Subtract the smallest number in each row from every number in that row and then, from the resulting matrix, subtract the smallest number in each column from every number in that column. This step has the effect of reducing the numbers in the table until a series of zeros, meaning *zero opportunity costs*, appear. Even though the numbers change, this reduced problem is equivalent to the original one, and the same solution will be optimal.

---

[3] Opportunity costs are those profits forgone or not obtained.

2. Draw the minimum number of vertical and horizontal straight lines necessary to cover all zeros in the table. If the number of lines equals either the number of rows or the number of columns in the table, then we can make an optimal assignment (see step 4). If the number of lines is less than the number of rows or columns, we proceed to step 3.

3. Subtract the smallest number not covered by a line from every other uncovered number. Add the same number to any number(s) lying at the intersection of any two lines. Do not change the value of the numbers that are covered by only one line. Return to step 2 and continue until an optimal assignment is possible.

4. Optimal assignments will always be at zero locations in the table. One systematic way of making a valid assignment is first to select a row or column that contains only one zero square. We can make an assignment to that square and then draw lines through its row and column. From the uncovered rows and columns, we choose another row or column in which there is only one zero square. We make that assignment and continue the procedure until we have assigned each person or machine to one task.

Example 4 shows how to use the assignment method.

EXAMPLE 4

Assignment Method

First Printing wants to find the minimum total cost assignment of three jobs to three typesetters.

APPROACH ▶ The cost table shown earlier in this section is repeated here, and steps 1 through 4 are applied.

TYPESETTER / JOB	A	B	C
R-34	$11	$14	$ 6
S-66	$ 8	$10	$11
T-50	$ 9	$12	$ 7

SOLUTION ▶

STEP 1A: Using the previous table, subtract the smallest number in each row from every number in the row. The result is shown in the table on the left.

TYPESETTER / JOB	A	B	C
R-34	5	8	0
S-66	0	2	3
T-50	2	5	0

TYPESETTER / JOB	A	B	C
R-34	5	6	0
S-66	0	0	3
T-50	2	3	0

STEP 1B: Using the above left table, subtract the smallest number in each column from every number in the column. The result is shown in the table on the right.

STEP 2: Draw the minimum number of vertical and horizontal straight lines needed to cover all zeros. Because two lines suffice, the solution is not optimal.

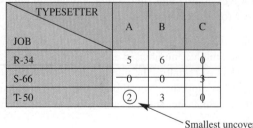

TYPESETTER / JOB	A	B	C
R-34	5	6	0
S-66	0	0	3
T-50	②	3	0

Smallest uncovered number

STEP 3: Subtract the smallest uncovered number (2 in this table) from every other uncovered number and add it to numbers at the intersection of two lines.

TYPESETTER / JOB	A	B	C
R-34	3	4	0
S-66	0	0	5
T-50	0	1	0

Return to step 2. Cover the zeros with straight lines again.

TYPESETTER / JOB	A	B	C
R-34	3	4	0
S-66	0	0	
T-50	0	1	0

Because three lines are necessary, an optimal assignment can be made (see step 4). Assign R-34 to person C, S-66 to person B, and T-50 to person A. Referring to the original cost table, we see that:

$$\text{Minimum cost} = \$6 + \$10 + \$9 = 25$$

INSIGHT ▶ If we had assigned S-66 to typesetter A, we could not assign T-50 to a zero location.

LEARNING EXERCISE ▶ If it costs $10 for typesetter C to complete Job R-34 (instead of $6), how does the solution change? [Answer: R-34 to A, S-66 to B, T-50 to C: cost = $28.]

RELATED PROBLEMS ▶ 15.3, 15.4, 15.5, 15.6, 15.7, 15.8, 15.9

EXCEL OM Data File **Ch15Ex4.xlsx** can be found at **MyLab Operations Management**

The problem of scheduling Major League Baseball umpiring crews from one series of games to the next is complicated by many restrictions on travel, ranging from coast-to-coast time changes, airline flight schedules, and night games running late. The league strives to achieve these two conflicting objectives: (1) balance crew assignments relatively evenly among all teams over the course of a season and (2) minimize travel costs. Using the assignment problem formulation, the time it takes the league to generate a schedule has been significantly decreased, and the quality of the schedule has improved.

Nicholas D. Cacchione/Shutterstock

Some assignment problems entail *maximizing* profit, effectiveness, or payoff of an assignment of people to tasks or of jobs to machines. An equivalent minimization problem can be obtained by converting every number in the table to an *opportunity loss*. To convert a maximizing problem to an equivalent minimization problem, we create a minimizing table by subtracting every number in the original payoff table from the largest single number in that table. We then proceed to step 1 of the four-step assignment method. Minimizing the opportunity loss produces the same assignment solution as the original maximization problem.

STUDENT **TIP**

Once jobs are loaded, managers must decide the sequence in which they are to be completed.

LO4 Name and describe each of the priority sequencing rules

Sequencing

Determining the order in which jobs should be done at each work centre.

Priority rules

Rules used to determine the sequence of jobs in process-oriented facilities.

First come, first served (FCFS)

Jobs are completed in the order they arrived.

Shortest processing time (SPT)

Jobs with the shortest processing times are assigned first.

Earliest due date (EDD)

Earliest due date jobs are performed first.

Longest processing time (LPT)

Jobs with the longest processing time are completed first.

Sequencing Jobs

Scheduling provides a basis for assigning jobs to work centres. *Loading* is a capacity-control technique that highlights overloads and underloads. **Sequencing** (also referred to as *dispatching*) specifies the order in which jobs should be done at each centre. For example, suppose that 10 patients are assigned to a medical clinic for treatment. In what order should they be treated? Should the first patient to be served be the one who arrived first or the one who needs emergency treatment? Sequencing methods provide such guidelines. These methods are referred to as priority rules for sequencing or dispatching jobs to work centres.

PRIORITY RULES FOR DISPATCHING JOBS

Priority rules provide guidelines for the sequence in which jobs should be worked. The rules are especially applicable for process-focused facilities such as clinics, print shops, and manufacturing job shops. We will examine a few of the most popular priority rules. Priority rules try to minimize completion time, number of jobs in the system, and job lateness while maximizing facility utilization.

The most popular priority rules are:

- **First come, first served (FCFS).** The first job to arrive at a work centre is processed first.
- **Shortest processing time (SPT).** The shortest jobs are handled first and completed.
- **Earliest due date (EDD).** The job with the earliest due date is selected first.
- **Longest processing time (LPT).** The longer, bigger jobs are often very important and are selected first.

Example 5 compares these rules.

EXAMPLE **5**

Priority Rules for Dispatching

Five architectural rendering jobs are waiting to be assigned at Avanti Sethi Architects. Their work (processing) times and due dates are given in the following table. The firm wants to determine the sequence of processing according to (1) FCFS, (2) SPT, (3) EDD, and (4) LPT rules. Jobs were assigned a letter in the order they arrived.

JOB	JOB WORK (PROCESSING)TIME (DAYS)	JOB DUE DATE (DAYS)
A	6	8
B	2	6
C	8	18
D	3	15
E	9	23

APPROACH ▶ Each of the four priority rules is examined in turn. Four measures of effectiveness can be computed for each rule and then compared to see which rule is best for the company.

SOLUTION ▶

1. The FCFS sequence shown in the next table is simply A–B–C–D–E. The "flow time" in the system for this sequence measures the time each job spends waiting plus time being processed. Job B, for example, waits six days while job A is being processed, then takes two more days of operation time itself; so, it will be completed in eight days—which is two days later than its due date.

JOB SEQUENCE	JOB WORK (PROCESSING) TIME	FLOW TIME	JOB DUE DATE	JOB LATENESS
A	6	6	8	0
B	2	8	6	2
C	8	16	18	0
D	3	19	15	4
E	9	28	23	5
	28	77		11

The first-come, first-served rule results in the following measures of effectiveness:

a. Average completion time $= \dfrac{\text{Sum of total flow time}}{\text{Number of jobs}}$

$= \dfrac{77 \text{ days}}{5} = 15.4 \text{ days}$

b. Utilization metric $= \dfrac{\text{Total job work (processing) time}}{\text{Sum of total flow time}}$

$= \dfrac{28}{77} = 36.4\%$

c. Average number of jobs in the system $= \dfrac{\text{Sum of total flow time}}{\text{Total job work (processing) time}}$

$= \dfrac{77 \text{ days}}{28 \text{ days}} = 2.75 \text{ jobs}$

d. Average job lateness $= \dfrac{\text{Total late days}}{\text{Number of jobs}} = \dfrac{11}{5} = 2.2 \text{ days}$

2. The SPT rule shown in the next table results in the sequence B–D–A–C–E. Orders are sequenced according to processing time, with the highest priority given to the shortest job.

JOB SEQUENCE	JOB WORK (PROCESSING) TIME	FLOW TIME	JOB DUE DATE	JOB LATENESS
B	2	2	6	0
D	3	5	15	0
A	6	11	8	3
C	8	19	18	1
E	9	28	23	5
	28	65		9

Measurements of effectiveness for SPT are:

a. Average completion time $= \dfrac{65}{5} = 13 \text{ days}$

b. Utilization metric $= \dfrac{28}{65} = 43.1\%$

c. Average number of jobs in the system $= \dfrac{65}{28} = 2.32 \text{ jobs}$

d. Average job lateness $= \dfrac{9}{5} = 1.8 \text{ days}$

3. The EDD rule shown in the next table gives the sequence B–A–D–C–E. Note that jobs are ordered by earliest due date first.

JOB SEQUENCE	JOB WORK (PROCESSING) TIME	FLOW TIME	JOB DUE DATE	JOB LATENESS
B	2	2	6	0
A	6	8	8	0
D	3	11	15	0
C	8	19	18	1
E	9	28	23	5
	28	68		6

Measurements of effectiveness for EDD are:

a. Average completion time $= \dfrac{68}{5} = 13.6 \text{ days}$

b. Utilization metric $= \dfrac{28}{68} = 41.2\%$

c. Average number of jobs in the system $= \dfrac{68}{28} = 2.43 \text{ jobs}$

d. Average job lateness $= \dfrac{6}{5} = 1.2 \text{ days}$

4. The LPT rule shown in the next table results in the order E–C–A–D–B.

JOB SEQUENCE	JOB WORK (PROCESSING) TIME	FLOW TIME	JOB DUE DATE	JOB LATENESS
E	9	9	23	0
C	8	17	18	0
A	6	23	8	15
D	3	26	15	11
B	2	28	6	22
	28	103		48

Measures of effectiveness for LPT are:

a. Average completion time $= \dfrac{103}{5} = 20.6$ days

b. Utilization metric $= \dfrac{28}{103} = 27.2\%$

c. Average number of jobs in the system $= \dfrac{103}{28} = 3.68$ jobs

d. Average job lateness $= \dfrac{48}{5} = 9.6$ days

The results of these four rules are summarized in the following table:

RULE	AVERAGE COMPLETION TIME (DAYS)	UTILIZATION METRIC (%)	AVERAGE NUMBER OF JOBS IN SYSTEM	AVERAGE LATENESS (DAYS)
FCFS	15.4	36.4	2.75	2.2
SPT	13.0	43.1	2.32	1.8
EDD	13.6	41.2	2.43	1.2
LPT	20.6	27.2	3.68	9.6

INSIGHT ▶ LPT is the least effective measurement for sequencing for the Avanti Sethi firm. SPT is superior in three measures, and EDD is superior in the fourth (average lateness).

LEARNING EXERCISE ▶ If job A takes seven days (instead of six), how do the four measures of effectiveness change under the FCFS rule? [Answer: 16.4 days, 35.4%, 2.83 jobs, 2.8 days late.]

RELATED PROBLEMS ▶ 15.10, 15.12a–d, 15.13, 15.14

EXCEL OM Data File **Ch15Ex5.xlsx** can be found at **MyLab Operations Management.**

ACTIVE MODEL 15.1 This example is further illustrated in Active Model 15.1 at **MyLab Operations Management.**

Your doctor may use a first-come, first-served priority rule satisfactorily. However, such a rule may be less than optimal for this emergency room. What priority rule might be best, and why? What priority rule is often used on TV hospital dramas?

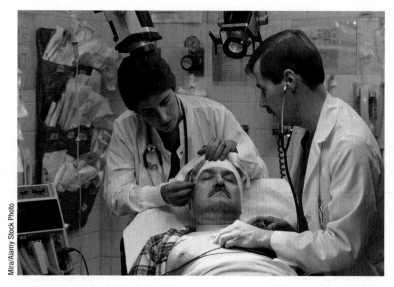

Mira/Alamy Stock Photo

The results in Example 5 are typically true in the real world also. No single sequencing rule always excels on all criteria. Experience indicates the following:

1. *Shortest processing time* is generally the best technique for minimizing job flow and minimizing the average number of jobs in the system. Its chief disadvantage is that long-duration jobs may be continuously pushed back in priority in favour of short-duration jobs. Customers may view this dimly, and a periodic adjustment for longer jobs must be made.

2. *First come, first served* does not score well on most criteria (but neither does it score particularly poorly). It has the advantage, however, of appearing fair to customers, which is important in service systems.

3. *Earliest due date* minimizes maximum tardiness, which may be necessary for jobs that have a very heavy penalty after a certain date. In general, EDD works well when lateness is an issue.

CRITICAL RATIO

Another type of sequencing rule is the critical ratio. The **critical ratio (CR)** is an index number computed by dividing the time remaining until the due date by the work time remaining. As opposed to the priority rules, critical ratio is dynamic and easily updated. It tends to perform better than FCFS, SPT, EDD, or LPT on the average job-lateness criterion.

Critical ratio (CR)
A sequencing rule that is an index number computed by dividing the time remaining until the due date by the work time remaining.

The critical ratio gives priority to jobs that must be done to keep shipping on schedule. A job with a low critical ratio (less than 1.0) is one that is falling behind schedule. If CR is exactly 1.0, the job is on schedule. A CR greater than 1.0 means the job is ahead of schedule and has some slack.

The formula for critical ratio is:

$$CR = \frac{\text{Time remaining}}{\text{Workdays remaining}} = \frac{\text{Due date} - \text{Today's data}}{\text{Work (lead) time remaining}}$$

Example 6 shows how to use the critical ratio.

EXAMPLE 6

Critical Ratio

Today is day 25 on Zyco Medical Testing Laboratories' production schedule. Three jobs are on order, as indicated here:

Job	Due Date	Workdays Remaining
A	30	4
B	28	5
C	27	2

APPROACH ▶ Zyco wants to compute the critical ratios, using the formula for CR.

SOLUTION ▶

Job	Critical Ratio	Priority Order
A	(30 − 25)/4 = 1.25	3
B	(28 − 25)/5 = 0.60	1
C	(27 − 25)/2 = 1.00	2

INSIGHT ▶ Job B has a critical ratio of less than 1, meaning it will be late unless expedited. Thus, it has the highest priority. Job C is on time and job A has some slack. Once job B has been completed, we would recompute the critical ratios for jobs A and C to determine whether their priorities have changed.

LEARNING EXERCISE ▶ Today is day 24 (a day earlier) on Zyco's schedule. Recompute the critical ratios and determine the priorities. [Answer: 1.5, 0.8, 1.5; B is still number 1, but now jobs A and C are tied for second.]

RELATED PROBLEMS ▶ 15.11, 15.12e, 15.16

In most production scheduling systems, the critical-ratio rule can help do the following:

1. Determine the status of a specific job.
2. Establish relative priority among jobs on a common basis.
3. Relate both make-to-stock and make-to-order jobs on a common basis.
4. Adjust priorities (and revise schedules) automatically for changes in both demand and job progress.
5. Dynamically track job progress.

LO5 Use Johnson's rule

SEQUENCING *N* JOBS ON TWO MACHINES: JOHNSON'S RULE

The next step in complexity is the case in which *N* jobs (where *N* is 2 or more) must go through two different machines or work centres in the same order. This is called the *N*/2 problem.

Johnson's rule

An approach that minimizes processing time for sequencing a group of jobs through two work centres while minimizing total idle time in the work centres.

Johnson's rule can be used to minimize the processing time for sequencing a group of jobs through two work centres. It also minimizes total idle time on the machines. *Johnson's rule* involves four steps:

1. All jobs are to be listed, and the time that each requires on a machine is to be shown.
2. Select the job with the shortest activity time. If the shortest time lies with the first machine, the job is scheduled first. If the shortest time lies with the second machine, schedule the job last. Ties in activity times can be broken arbitrarily.
3. Once a job is scheduled, eliminate it.
4. Apply steps 2 and 3 to the remaining jobs, working towards the centre of the sequence.

Example 7 shows how to apply Johnson's rule.

Johnson's Rule

Five specialty jobs at an Edmonton tool and die shop must be processed through two work centres (drill press and lathe). The time for processing each job follows:

Work (processing) Time for Jobs (hours)

Job	Work Centre 1 (drill press)	Work Centre 2 (lathe)
A	5	2
B	3	6
C	8	4
D	10	7
E	7	12

The owner, Niranjan Pati, wants to set the sequence to minimize his total processing time for the five jobs.

APPROACH ▶ Pati applies the four steps of Johnson's rule.

SOLUTION ▶

1. The job with the shortest processing time is A, in work centre 2 (with a time of 2 hours). Because it is at the second centre, schedule A last. Eliminate it from consideration.

				A

2. Job B has the next shortest time (3 hours). Because that time is at the first work centre, we schedule it first and eliminate it from consideration.

B				A

3. The next shortest time is job C (4 hours) on the second machine. Therefore, it is placed as late as possible.

B			C	A

4. There is a tie (at 7 hours) for the shortest remaining job. We can place E, which was on the first work centre, first. Then D is placed in the last sequencing position.

B	E	D	C	A

The sequential times are:

Work centre 1	3	7	10	8	5
Work centre 2	6	12	7	4	2

The time-phased flow of this job sequence is best illustrated graphically:

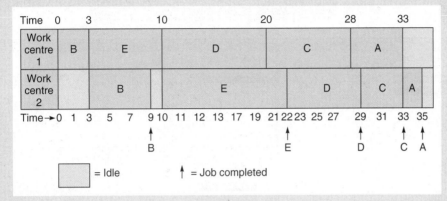

Thus, the five jobs are completed in 35 hours.

INSIGHT ▶ The second work centre will wait 3 hours for its first job, and it will also wait 1 hour after completing job B.

LEARNING EXERCISE ▶ If job C takes 8 hours in work centre 2 (instead of 4 hours), what sequence is best? [Answer: B–E–C–D–A.]

RELATED PROBLEMS ▶ 15.15, 15.17, 15.18

EXCEL OM Data File **Ch15Ex7.xlsx** can be found at **MyLab Operations Management.**

LIMITATIONS OF RULE-BASED DISPATCHING SYSTEMS

The scheduling techniques just discussed are rule-based techniques, but rule-based systems have a number of limitations. Among these are the following:

1. Scheduling is dynamic; therefore, rules need to be revised to adjust to changes in orders, process, equipment, product mix, and so forth.
2. Rules do not look upstream or downstream; idle resources and bottleneck resources in other departments may not be recognized.
3. Rules do not look beyond due dates. For instance, two orders may have the same due date. One order involves restocking a distributor and the other is a custom order that will shut down the customer's factory if not completed. Both may have the same due date, but clearly the custom order is more important.

Despite these limitations, schedulers often use sequencing rules such as SPT, EDD, or critical ratio. They apply these methods at each work centre and then modify the sequence to address a multitude of real-world variables. They may do this manually or with finite capacity scheduling software.

Finite Capacity Scheduling (FCS)

Short-term scheduling is also called finite capacity scheduling.[4] **Finite capacity scheduling (FCS)** overcomes the disadvantages of systems based exclusively on rules by providing the scheduler with interactive computing and graphic output. In dynamic scheduling environments such as job shops (with high variety, low volume, and shared resources), we expect changes—but changes disrupt schedules. Therefore, operations managers are moving towards FCS systems

Finite capacity scheduling (FCS)
Computerized short-term scheduling that overcomes the disadvantage of rule-based systems by providing the user with graphical interactive computing.

---

[4] Finite capacity scheduling (FCS) systems go by a number of names, including *finite scheduling and advance planning systems (APS)*. The name *manufacturing execution systems (MES)* may also be used, but MES tends to suggest an emphasis on the reporting system from shop operations back to the scheduling activity.

This Lekin® finite capacity scheduling software presents a schedule of the five jobs and the two work centres shown in Example 7 in Gantt chart form. The software is capable of using a variety of priority rules, several shop types, up to 50 jobs, 20 work centres, and 100 machines to generate a schedule. The Lekin software is available for free at **http://community.stern.nyu.edu/om/software/lekin/download.html** and can solve many of the problems at the end of this chapter. Reprinted with permission from "Lekin flexible Job Shop scheduling System, Stern School of Business New York University."

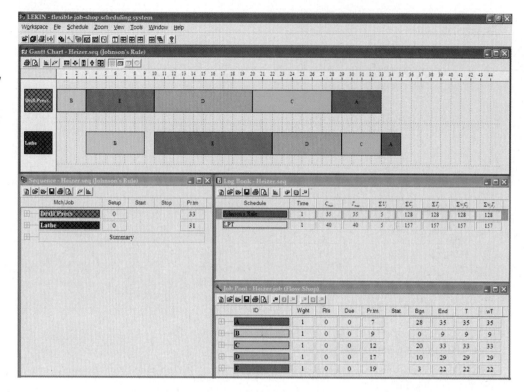

LO6 Define *finite capacity scheduling*

that allow virtually instantaneous change by the operator. Improvements in communication on the shop floor are also enhancing the accuracy and speed of information necessary for effective control in job shops. Computer-controlled machines can monitor events and collect information in near-real time. This means the scheduler can make schedule changes based on up-to-the-minute information. These schedules are often displayed in Gantt chart form. In addition to including priority rule options, many of the current FCS systems also combine an "expert system" or simulation techniques and allow the scheduler to assign costs to various options. The scheduler has the flexibility to handle any situation, including order, labour, or machine changes.

The initial data for finite scheduling systems is often the output from an MRP system. The output from MRP systems is traditionally in weekly "buckets" that have no capacity constraint. These systems just tell the planner when the material is needed, ignoring the capacity issue. Because *infinite*-size buckets are unrealistic and inadequate for detail scheduling, MRP data require refinement. MRP output is combined with routing files, due dates, capacity of work centres, tooling, and other resource availability to provide the data needed for effective FCS. These are the same data needed in any manual system, but FCS software formalizes them, speeds analysis, and makes changes easier. The combining of MRP and FCS data, priority rules, models to assist analysis, and Gantt chart output is shown in Figure 15.5.

FIGURE 15.5

Finite Capacity Scheduling Systems Combine MRP and Shop-Floor Production Data to Generate a Gantt Chart that Can Be Manipulated by the User on a Computer Screen

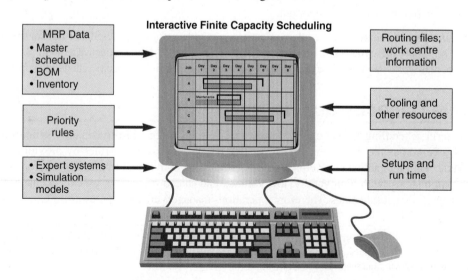

Finite capacity scheduling allows delivery requirements to be based on today's conditions and today's orders, not according to some predefined rule. The scheduler determines what constitutes a "good" schedule. FCS software packages such as Lekin, ProPlanner, Preactor, Asprova, Schedlyzer, and Jobplan are currently used at over 60% of North American plants.

Scheduling Repetitive Facilities

The scheduling goals defined at the beginning of this chapter are also appropriate for repetitive production. You may recall from Chapter 7 that repetitive producers make standard products from modules. The usual approach is to develop a forward-looking schedule on a balanced assembly line. (Refer to Table 15.2.)

Repetitive producers want to satisfy customer demands, lower inventory investment, and reduce the batch (or lot) size, with existing equipment and processes. A technique to move towards these goals is to use a level-material-use schedule. **Level material use** means frequent, high-quality, small lot sizes that contribute to just-in-time production. This is exactly what world-class producers such as Harley-Davidson, John Deere, and Johnson Controls do. The advantages of level material use are:

Level material use
The use of frequent, high-quality, small lot sizes that contribute to just-in-time production.

1. Lower inventory levels, which releases capital for other uses.
2. Faster product throughput (i.e., shorter lead times).
3. Improved component quality and hence improved product quality.
4. Reduced floor-space requirements.
5. Improved communication among employees because they are closer together (which can result in improved teamwork and *esprit de corps*).
6. Smoother production process because large lots have not "hidden" the problems.

Suppose a repetitive producer runs large monthly batches: With a level-material-use schedule, management would move towards shortening this monthly cycle to a weekly, daily, or even hourly cycle.

One way to develop a level-material-use schedule is to first determine the minimum lot size that will keep the production process moving. This is illustrated in Chapter 16, "Lean Operations".

Scheduling Services

Scheduling service systems differs from scheduling manufacturing systems in several ways:

- In manufacturing, the scheduling emphasis is on machines and materials; in services, it is on staffing levels.
- Inventories can help smooth demand for manufacturers, but many service systems do not maintain inventories.
- Services are labour intensive, and the demand for this labour can be highly variable.
- Legal considerations—such as wage and hour laws and union contracts that limit hours worked per shift, week, or month—constrain scheduling decisions.
- Because services usually schedule people rather than material, behavioural, social, seniority, and status issues complicate scheduling.

The following examples note the complexity of scheduling services.

HOSPITALS

A hospital is an example of a service facility that may use a scheduling system every bit as complex as one found in a job shop. Hospitals seldom use a machine shop priority system such as first-come, first-served (FCFS) for treating emergency patients. However, they do schedule products (such as surgeries) just like a factory, and capacities must meet wide variations in demand.

BANKS

Cross-training of the workforce in a bank allows loan officers and other managers to provide short-term help for tellers if there is a surge in demand. Banks also employ part-time personnel to provide a variable capacity.

Starbucks's Controversial Scheduling Software

Starbucks recently announced revisions to the way the company schedules its 130 000 baristas, saying it wanted to improve "stability and consistency" in work hours from week to week. The company intends to curb the much-loathed practice of "clopening," or workers closing the store late at night and returning just a few hours later to reopen. All work hours must be posted at least one week in advance, a policy that has been only loosely followed in the past. Baristas with more than an hour's commute will be given the option to transfer to more convenient locations, and scheduling software will be revised to allow more input from managers.

The revisions came in response to a newspaper article about a single mother struggling to keep up with erratic hours set by automated software. A growing push to curb scheduling practices, enabled by sophisticated software, has caused havoc in employees' lives: giving only a few days' notice of working hours; sending workers home early when sales are slow; and shifting hours significantly from week to week. Those practices have been common at Starbucks. And many other chains use even more severe methods, such as requiring workers to have "open availability," or be able to work anytime they are needed, or to stay "on call," meaning they only find out that morning if they are needed.

Starbucks prides itself on progressive labour practices, such as offering health benefits, free online degrees at Arizona State University, and stock. But baristas

Education & Exploration 2/Alamy Stock Photo

across North America say that their actual working conditions vary wildly, and that the company often fails to live up to its professed ideals, by refusing to offer any guaranteed hours to part-time workers and keeping many workers' pay at minimum wage. Scheduling has been an issue for years. Said a former company executive: "Labour is the biggest controllable cost for front-line operators, who are under incredible pressure to hit financial targets."

Sources: New York Times (September 24, 2015 and August 15, 2014) and *BloombergBusinessweek* (August 15, 2014).

RETAIL STORES

Scheduling optimization systems—such as Workbrain, Cybershift, and Kronos—are used at retailers including Walmart, Payless Shoes, Target, and The Source. These systems track individual store sales, transactions, units sold, and customer traffic in 15-minute increments to create work schedules. Walmart's 2.2 million and Target's 350 000 employees used to take thousands of managers' hours to schedule; now staffing is drawn up nationwide in a few hours, and customer checkout experience has improved dramatically. See the *OM in Action* box for a discussion on "Starbucks's Controversial Scheduling Software".

AIRLINES

Airlines face two constraints when scheduling flight crews: (1) a complex set of regulatory work-time limitations and (2) union contracts that guarantee crew pay for some number of hours each day or each trip. Airline planners must build crew schedules that meet or exceed crews' pay guarantees. Planners must also make efficient use of their other expensive resource: aircraft. These schedules are typically built using linear programming models. The *OM in Action* box "Scheduling Aircraft Turnaround" details how very short-term schedules (20 minutes) can help an airline become more efficient.

24/7 OPERATIONS

Emergency hotlines, police/fire departments, telephone operations, and mail-order businesses (such as Lee Valley) schedule employees 24 hours a day, 7 days a week. To allow management flexibility in staffing, part-time workers can sometimes be employed. This provides both benefits (in using odd shift lengths or matching anticipated workloads) and difficulties (from the large number of possible alternatives in terms of days off, lunch hour times, rest

OM in Action Scheduling Aircraft Turnaround

Airlines that face increasingly difficult financial futures have recently discovered the importance of efficient scheduling of ground turnaround activities for flights. For some low-cost, point-to-point carriers like WestJet, scheduling turnarounds in 20 minutes has been standard policy for years. Yet for others, like Air Canada, the approach is new. This figure illustrates how Air Canada deals with speedier schedules. Now its planes average more trips per day, meaning the carrier can sell thousands more seats each day. And with this improved scheduling, its punctuality improved dramatically.

Air Canada has cut the turnaround time on commercial flights from the current 45 minutes to 20 minutes in most cases. Here is a list of procedures that must be completed before the flight can depart:

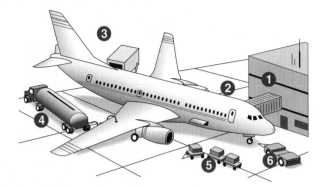

1 Ticket agent takes flight plan to pilot, who loads information into aircraft computer. About 130 passengers disembark from the plane.

2 Workers clean trash cans, seat pockets, lavatories, etc.

3 Catering personnel board plane and replenish supply of drinks and ice.

4 A fuel truck loads up to 20 000 litres of fuel into aircraft's wings.

5 Baggage crews unload up to 4000 pounds of luggage and 2000 pounds of freight. "Runners" rush the luggage to baggage claim area in terminal.

6 Ramp agents, who help park aircraft upon arrival, "push" plane back away from gate.

periods, starting times). Most companies use computerized scheduling systems to cope with these complexities.

SCHEDULING SERVICE EMPLOYEES WITH CYCLICAL SCHEDULING

A number of techniques and algorithms exist for scheduling service sector employees such as police officers, nurses, restaurant staff, tellers, and retail sales clerks. Managers, trying to set a timely and efficient schedule that keeps personnel happy, can spend substantial time each month developing employee schedules. Such schedules often consider a fairly long planning period (say, six weeks). One approach that is workable yet simple is *cyclical scheduling*.

CYCLICAL SCHEDULING

Cyclical scheduling with inconsistent staffing needs is often the case in services such as restaurants and police work. Here, the objective focuses on developing a schedule with the minimum number of workers. In these cases, each employee is assigned to a shift and has time off. Let's look at Example 8.

LO7 Use the cyclical scheduling technique

Hospital administrator Doris Laughlin wants to staff the oncology ward using a standard five-day workweek with two consecutive days off but also wants to minimize the staff. However, as in most hospitals, she faces an inconsistent demand. Weekends have low usage. Doctors tend to work early in the week, and patients peak on Wednesday then taper off.

APPROACH ▶ Doris must first establish staffing requirements. Then the following five-step process is applied.

EXAMPLE 8

Cyclical Scheduling

SOLUTION ▶

1. Determine the necessary daily staffing requirements. Doris has done this:

Day	Monday	Tuesday	Wednesday	Thursday	Friday	Saturday	Sunday
Staff required	5	5	6	5	4	3	3

2. Identify the two consecutive days that have the *lowest total requirement* and circle these. Assign these two days off to the first employee. In this case, the first employee has Saturday and Sunday off because 3 plus 3 is the *lowest sum* of any two days. In the case of a tie, choose the days with the lowest adjacent requirement, or by first assigning Saturday and Sunday as an "off" day. If there are more than one, make an arbitrary decision.

3. We now have an employee working each of the uncircled days; therefore, make a new row for the next employee by subtracting 1 from the first row (because one day has been worked)—except for the circled days (which represent the days not worked) and any day that has a zero. That is, do not subtract from a circled day or a day that has a value of zero.

4. In the new row, identify the two consecutive days that have the lowest total requirement and circle them. Assign the next employee to the remaining days.

5. Repeat the process (steps 3 and 4) until all staffing requirements are met.

	MONDAY	TUESDAY	WEDNESDAY	THURSDAY	FRIDAY	SATURDAY	SUNDAY
Employee 1	5	5	6	5	4	③	③
Employee 2	4	4	5	4	3	③	③
Employee 3	3	3	4	3	②	③	3
Employee 4	2	2	3	②	②	3	2
Employee 5	①	①	2	2	2	2	1
Employee 6	1	1	1	1	1	①	⓪
Employee 7						1	
Capacity (measured in number of employees)	5	5	6	5	4	3	3
Excess capacity	0	0	0	0	0	1	0

Doris needs six full-time employees to meet the staffing needs and one employee to work Saturday. Notice that capacity (number of employees) equals requirements, provided an employee works overtime on Saturday, or a part-time employee is hired for Saturday.

INSIGHT ▶ Doris has implemented an efficient scheduling system that accommodates two consecutive days off for every employee.

LEARNING EXERCISE ▶ If Doris meets the staffing requirement for Saturday with a full-time employee, how does she schedule that employee? [Answer: That employee can have any two days off, except Saturday, and capacity will exceed requirements by one person each day the employee works (except Saturday).]

RELATED PROBLEMS ▶ 15.19, 15.20

Using the approach in Example 8, the hospital saved an average of 10 to 15 hours a month and found these added advantages: (1) No computer was needed, (2) the nurses were happy with the schedule, (3) the cycles could be changed seasonally to accommodate avid skiers, and (4) recruiting was easier because of predictability and flexibility. This approach yields an optimum, although there may be multiple optimal solutions.

Other cyclical scheduling techniques have been developed to aid service scheduling. Some approaches use linear programming: This is how the Hard Rock Cafe schedules its services (see the Video Case Study at the end of this chapter). There is a natural bias in scheduling to use tools that are understood and yield solutions that are accepted.

CHAPTER | SUMMARY

Scheduling involves the timing of operations to achieve the efficient movement of units through a system. This chapter addressed the issues of short-term scheduling in process-focused, repetitive, and service environments. We saw that process-focused facilities are production systems in which products are made to order and that scheduling tasks in them can become complex. Several aspects and approaches to scheduling, loading, and sequencing of jobs were introduced.

These ranged from Gantt charts and the assignment method of scheduling to a series of priority rules, the critical-ratio rule, Johnson's rule for sequencing, and finite capacity scheduling.

Service systems generally differ from manufacturing systems. This leads to the use of first-come, first-served rules and appointment and reservation systems, as well as linear programming approaches for matching capacity to demand in service environments.

ETHICAL | DILEMMA

Scheduling people to work second and third shifts (evening and "graveyard") is a problem in almost every 24-hour company. The *OM in Action* box "Scheduling Workers Who Fall Asleep Is a Killer—Literally" describes potentially dangerous issues on the night shift at FedEx and at a nuclear power plant. Perhaps even more significantly, ergonomic data indicate the body does not respond well to significant shifts in its natural circadian rhythm of sleep. There are also significant long-run health issues with frequent changes in work and sleep cycles.

Consider yourself the manager of a nonunion steel mill that must operate 24-hour days, and where the physical demands are

such that 8-hour days are preferable to 10- or 12-hour days. Your empowered employees have decided that they want to work weekly rotating shifts. That is, they want a repeating work cycle of 1 week, 7:00 a.m. to 3:00 p.m., followed by a second week from 3:00 p.m. to 11:00 p.m., and the third week from 11:00 p.m. to 7:00 a.m. You are sure this is not a good idea in terms of both productivity and the long-term health of the employees. If you do not accept their decision, you undermine the work empowerment program, generate a morale issue, and, perhaps more significantly, generate more votes for a union. What is the ethical position, and what do you do?

Discussion Questions

1. What is the overall objective of scheduling?
2. List the four criteria for determining the effectiveness of a *scheduling* decision. How do these criteria relate to the four criteria for *sequencing* decisions?
3. Describe what is meant by "loading" work centres. What are the two ways work centres can be loaded? What are two techniques used in loading?
4. Name five priority sequencing rules. Explain how each works to assign jobs.
5. What are the advantages and disadvantages of the shortest processing time (SPT) rule?
6. What is a due date?
7. Explain the terms *flow time* and *lateness*.
8. Which shop-floor scheduling rule would you prefer to apply if you were the leader of the only team of experts charged with defusing several time bombs scattered throughout your building? You can see the bombs; they are of different types. You can tell how long each one will take to defuse. Discuss.
9. When is Johnson's rule best applied in job-shop scheduling?
10. State the four effectiveness measures for dispatching rules.
11. What are the steps of the assignment method of linear programming?
12. What are the advantages to finite capacity scheduling?
13. What is input–output control?

Using Software for Short-Term Scheduling

In addition to the commercial software we noted in this chapter, short-term scheduling problems can be solved with the Excel OM software at **MyLab Operations Management**. POM for Windows also includes a scheduling module. The use of each of these programs is explained next.

✗ USING EXCEL OM

Excel OM has two modules that help solve short-term scheduling problems: Assignment and Job Shop Scheduling. The Assignment module is illustrated in Programs 15.1 and 15.2. The input screen, using the Example 4 data, appears first, as Program 15.1. Once the data are all entered, we choose the **Tools** command, followed by the **Solver** command. Excel's Solver uses linear programming to optimize assignment problems. The constraints are also shown in Program 15.1. We then select the **Solve** command and the solution appears in Program 15.2.

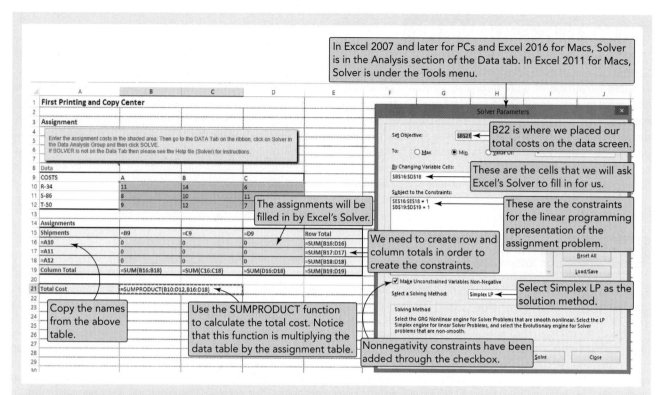

In Excel 2007 and later for PCs and Excel 2016 for Macs, Solver is in the Analysis section of the Data tab. In Excel 2011 for Macs, Solver is under the Tools menu.

B22 is where we placed our total costs on the data screen.

These are the cells that we will ask Excel's Solver to fill in for us.

These are the constraints for the linear programming representation of the assignment problem.

We need to create row and column totals in order to create the constraints.

The assignments will be filled in by Excel's Solver.

Copy the names from the above table.

Use the SUMPRODUCT function to calculate the total cost. Notice that this function is multiplying the data table by the assignment table.

Select Simplex LP as the solution method.

Nonnegativity constraints have been added through the checkbox.

PROGRAM 15.1 **Excel OM's Assignment Module Using Example 4's Data**
After entering the problem data in the yellow area, select Data, then Solver.

Source: Microsoft product screen shot(s) reprinted with permission from Microsoft Corporation.

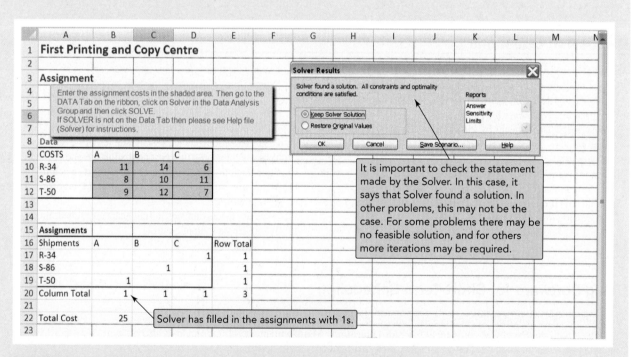

It is important to check the statement made by the Solver. In this case, it says that Solver found a solution. In other problems, this may not be the case. For some problems there may be no feasible solution, and for others more iterations may be required.

Solver has filled in the assignments with 1s.

PROGRAM 15.2 **Excel OM Output Screen for Assignment Problem Described in Program 15.1**

Source: Microsoft product screen shot(s) reprinted with permission from Microsoft Corporation.

Excel OM's Job Shop Scheduling module is illustrated in Program 15.3. Program 15.3 uses Example 5's data. Because jobs are listed in the sequence in which they arrived (see column A), the results are for the FCFS rule. Program 15.3 also shows some of the formulas (columns F, G, H, I, J) used in the calculations.

To solve with the SPT rule, we need four intermediate steps: (1) Select (i.e., highlight) the data in columns A, B, C for all jobs; (2) invoke the **Data** command; (3) invoke the **Sort** command; and (4) sort by **Time** (column C) in *ascending* order. To solve for EDD, step 4 changes to sort by **Due Date** (column D) in *ascending* order. Finally, for an LPT solution, step 4 becomes sort by **Due Date** (column D) in *descending* order.

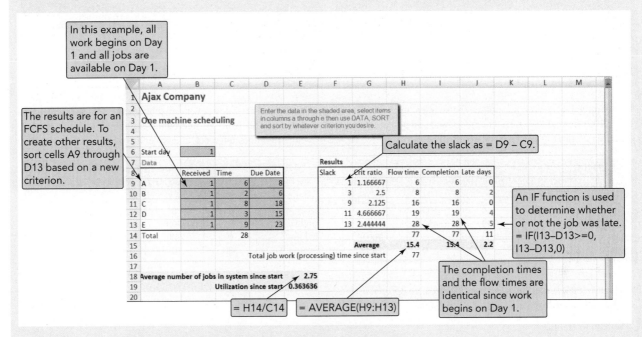

PROGRAM 15.3   **Excel OM's Job Shop Scheduling Module Applied to Example 5's Data**

Source: Microsoft product screen shot(s) reprinted with permission from Microsoft Corporation.

P USING POM FOR WINDOWS

POM for Windows can handle both categories of scheduling problems we see in this chapter. Its Assignment module is used to solve the traditional one-to-one assignment problem of people to tasks, machines to jobs, and so on. Its Job Shop Scheduling module can solve a one- or two-machine job-shop problem. Available priority rules include SPT, FCFS, EDD, and LPT. Each can be examined in turn once the data are all entered. Refer to Appendix IV for specifics regarding POM for Windows.

Solved Problems Virtual Office Hours help is available at MyLab Operations Management.

▼ SOLVED PROBLEM 15.1

King Finance Corporation, headquartered in Montreal, wants to assign three recently hired college graduates, Julie Jones, Al Smith, and Pat Wilson, to regional offices. However, the firm also has an opening in Montreal and would send one of the three there if it were more economical than a move to Halifax, Winnipeg, or Kingston. It will cost $1000 to relocate Jones to Montreal, $800 to relocate Smith there, and $1500 to move Wilson. What is the optimal assignment of personnel to offices?

OFFICE HIREE	HALIFAX	KINGSTON	WINNIPEG
Jones	$800	$1100	$1200
Smith	$500	$1600	$1300
Wilson	$500	$1000	$2300

▼ SOLUTION

a) The cost table has a fourth column to represent Montreal. To "balance" the problem, we add a "dummy" row (person) with a zero relocation cost to each city.

OFFICE HIREE	HALIFAX	KINGSTON	WINNIPEG	MONTREAL
Jones	$800	$1100	$1200	$1000
Smith	$500	$1600	$1300	$ 800
Wilson	$500	$1000	$2300	$1500
Dumm y	0	0	0	0

b) Subtract the smallest number in each row and cover all zeros (column subtraction of each column's zero will give the same numbers and therefore is not necessary):

OFFICE / HIREE	HALIFAX	KINGSTON	WINNIPEG	MONTREAL
Jones	0̶	300	400	200
Smith	0̶	1100	800	300
Wilson	0̶	500	1800	1000
Dummy	0̶	0̶	0̶	0̶

c) Only two lines cover, so subtract the smallest uncovered number (200) from all uncovered numbers, and add it to each square where two lines intersect. Then cover all zeros:

OFFICE / HIREE	HALIFAX	KINGSTON	WINNIPEG	MONTREAL
Jones	0̶	100	200	0̶
Smith	0̶	900	600	100
Wilson	0̶	300	1600	800
Dummy	2̶0̶0̶	0̶	0̶	0̶

d) Only three lines cover, so subtract the smallest uncovered number (100) from all uncovered numbers, and add it to each square where two lines intersect. Then cover all zeros:

OFFICE / HIREE	HALIFAX	KINGSTON	WINNIPEG	MONTREAL
Jones	1̶0̶0̶	0̶	1̶0̶0̶	0̶
Smith	0̶	7̶0̶0̶	4̶0̶0̶	0̶
Wilson	0̶	1̶0̶0̶	1̶4̶0̶0̶	7̶0̶0̶
Dummy	4̶0̶0̶	0̶	0̶	1̶0̶0̶

e) Still only three lines cover, so subtract the smallest uncovered number (100) from all uncovered numbers, add it to squares where two lines intersect, and cover all zeros:

OFFICE / HIREE	HALIFAX	KINGSTON	WINNIPEG	MONTREAL
Jones	0̶	0̶	1̶0̶0̶	0̶
Smith	0̶	800	500	100
Wilson	0̶	200	1500	800
Dummy	3̶0̶0̶	0̶	0̶	1̶0̶0̶

f) Because it takes four lines to cover all zeros, an optimal assignment can be made at zero squares. We assign:

Wilson to Halifax
Jones to Kingston
Dummy (no one) to Winnipeg
Smith to Montreal

$$Cost = \$500 + \$1100 + \$0 + \$800$$

$$= \$2400$$

A defence contractor in Dartmouth has six jobs awaiting processing. Processing time and due dates are given in the table. Assume that jobs arrive in the order shown. Set the processing sequence according to FCFS and evaluate.

JOB	JOB PROCESSING TIME (DAYS)	JOB DUE DATE (DAYS)
A	6	22
B	12	14
C	14	30
D	2	18
E	10	25
F	4	34

FCFS has the sequence A–B–C–D–E–F.

JOB SEQUENCE	JOB PROCESSING TIME	FLOW TIME	DUE DATE	JOB LATENESS
A	6	6	22	0
B	12	18	14	4
C	14	32	30	2
D	2	34	18	16
E	10	44	25	19
F	4	48	34	14
	48	182		55

1. Average completion time = 182/6 = 30.33 days
2. Average number of jobs in system = 182/48 = 3.79 jobs
3. Average job lateness = 55/6 = 9.16 days
4. Utilization = 48/182 = 26.4%

▼ SOLVED PROBLEM 15.3

The Dartmouth firm in Solved Problem 15.2 also wants to consider job sequencing by the SPT priority rule. Apply SPT to the same data and provide a recommendation.

> **▼ SOLUTION**
> SPT has the sequence D–F–A–E–B–C.

JOB SEQUENCE	JOB PROCESSING TIME	FLOW TIME	DUE DATE	JOB LATENESS
D	2	2	18	0
F	4	6	34	0
A	6	12	22	0
E	10	22	25	0
B	12	34	14	20
C	14	48	30	18
	48	124		38

1. Average completion time = 124/6 = 20.67 days
2. Average number of jobs in system = 124/48 = 2.58 jobs
3. Average job lateness = 38/6 = 6.33 days
4. Utilization = 48/124 = 38.7%

SPT is superior to FCFS in this case on all four measures. If we were to also analyze EDD, we would, however, find its average job lateness to be lowest at 5.5 days. SPT is a good recommendation. SPT's major disadvantage is that it makes long jobs wait, sometimes for a long time.

▼ SOLVED PROBLEM 15.4

Use Johnson's rule to find the optimum sequence for processing the jobs shown through two work centres. Times at each centre are in hours.

JOB	WORK CENTRE 1	WORK CENTRE 2
A	6	12
B	3	7
C	18	9
D	15	14
E	16	8
F	10	15

> **▼ SOLUTION**

B	A	F	D	C	E

The sequential times are:

Work centre 1	3	6	10	15	18	16
Work centre 2	7	12	15	14	9	8

▼ SOLVED PROBLEM 15.5

Illustrate the throughput time and idle time at the two work centres in Solved Problem 15.4 by constructing a time-phased chart.

> **▼ SOLUTION**

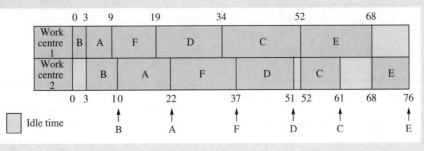

Problems*

•• 15.1 Ron Satterfield's excavation company uses both Gantt scheduling charts and Gantt load charts.

a) Today, which is the end of day 7, Ron is reviewing the Gantt chart depicting these schedules:
- Job #151 was scheduled to begin on day 3 and to take 6 days. As of now, it is 1 day ahead of schedule.
- Job #177 was scheduled to begin on day 1 and take 4 days. It is currently on time.
- Job #179 was scheduled to start on day 7 and take 2 days. It actually got started on day 6 and is progressing according to plan.
- Job #211 was scheduled to begin on day 5, but missing equipment delayed it until day 6. It is progressing as expected and should take 3 days.
- Job #215 was scheduled to begin on day 4 and take 5 days. It got started on time but has since fallen behind 2 days.

Draw the Gantt scheduling chart for the activities above.

b) Ron now wants to use a Gantt load chart to see how much work is scheduled in each of his three work teams: Able, Baker, and Charlie. Five jobs constitute the current work load for these three work teams: Job #250, requiring 48 hours and #275 requiring 32 hours for Work Team Able; Jobs #210, and #280 requiring 16 and 24 hours, respectively, for Team Baker; and Job #225, requiring 40 hours, for Team Charlie.

Prepare the Gantt load chart for these activities.

•• 15.2 First Printing and Copy Centre has four more jobs to be scheduled, in addition to those shown in Example 3 in the chapter. Production scheduling personnel are reviewing the Gantt chart at the end of day 4.
- Job D was scheduled to begin early on day 2 and to end on the middle of day 9. As of now (the review point after day 4), it is 2 days ahead of schedule.
- Job E should begin on day 1 and end on day 3. It was on time.
- Job F was to begin on day 3, but maintenance forced a delay of 1½ days. The job should now take 5 full days. It is now on schedule.
- Job G is a day behind schedule. It started at the beginning of day 2 and should require 6 days to complete.

Develop a Gantt schedule chart for First Printing and Copy Centre.

• 15.3 The Orange Top Cab Company has a taxi waiting at each of four cabstands in Vancouver. Four customers have called and requested service. The distances, in kilometres, from the waiting taxis to the customers are given in the following table. Find the optimal assignment of taxis to customers so as to minimize total driving distances to the customers.

Cab Site	Customer			
	A	**B**	**C**	**D**
Stand 1	7	3	4	8
Stand 2	5	4	6	5
Stand 3	6	7	9	6
Stand 4	8	6	7	4

• 15.4 Molly Riggs's medical testing company wishes to assign a set of jobs to a set of machines. The following table provides the production data of each machine when performing the specific job:

Job	Machine			
	A	**B**	**C**	**D**
1	7	9	8	10
2	10	9	7	6
3	11	5	9	6
4	9	11	5	8

a) Determine the assignment of jobs to machines that will *maximize* total production.

b) What is the total production of your assignments? **PX**

• 15.5 The Johnny Ho Manufacturing Company in Calgary is putting out four new electronic components. Each of Ho's four plants has the capacity to add one more product to its current line of electronic parts. The unit-manufacturing costs for producing the different parts at the four plants are shown in the accompanying table. How should Ho assign the new products to the plants to minimize manufacturing costs?

Electronic Component	Plant			
	1	**2**	**3**	**4**
C53	$0.10	$0.12	$0.13	$0.11
C81	0.05	0.06	0.04	0.08
D5	0.32	0.40	0.31	0.30
D44	0.17	0.14	0.19	0.15

• 15.6 Claire Consultants has been entrusted with the task of evaluating a business plan that has been divided into four sections—marketing, finance, operations, and human resources. Chris, Steve, Juana, and Rebecca form the evaluation team. Each of them has expertise in a certain field and tends to finish that section faster. The estimated times taken by each team member for each section have been outlined in the table below. Further information states that each of these individuals is paid $60/hour.

a) Assign each member to a different section such that Claire Consultants's overall cost is minimized.

b) What is the total cost of these assignments?

Times Taken by Team Members for Different Sections (minutes)

	Marketing	Finance	Operations	HR
Chris	80	120	125	140
Steve	20	115	145	160
Juana	40	100	85	45
Rebecca	65	35	25	75

•• 15.7 The Winnipeg Police Department has five detective squads available for assignment to five open crime cases. The chief of detectives, Paul Kuzdrall, wishes to assign the squads so that the total time to conclude the cases is minimized. The average number of days, based on past performance, for each squad to complete each case is as follows:

	Case				
Squad	A	B	C	D	E
1	14	7	3	7	27
2	20	7	12	6	30
3	10	3	4	5	21
4	8	12	7	12	21
5	13	25	24	26	8

Each squad is composed of different types of specialists, and whereas one squad may be very effective in certain types of cases, it may be almost useless in others.
a) Solve the problem by using the assignment method.
b) Assign the squads to the above cases, but with the constraint that squad 5 cannot work on case E because of a conflict. **Px**

• **15.8** Tigers Sports Club has to select four separate co-ed doubles teams to participate in an inter-club table tennis tournament. The pre-selection results in the selection of a group of four men—Raul, Jack, Gray, and Ajay—and four women—Barbara, Dona, Stella, and Jackie. Now, the task ahead lies in pairing these men and women in the best fashion. The table below shows a matrix that has been designed for this purpose, indicating how each of the men complements the game of each of the women. A higher score indicates a higher degree of compatibility in the games of the two individuals concerned. Find the best pairs.

Game Compatibility Matrix

	Barbara	Dona	Stella	Jackie
Raul	30	20	10	40
Jack	70	10	60	70
Gray	40	20	50	40
Ajay	60	70	30	90

••• **15.9** James Gross, chairman of the College of Oshkosh's business department, needs to assign professors to courses next semester. As a criterion for judging who should teach each course, Professor Gross reviews the past two years' teaching evaluations (which were filled out by students). Since each of the four professors taught each of the four courses at one time or another during the two-year period, Gross is able to record a course rating for each instructor. These ratings are shown in the following table.
a) Find the assignment of professors to courses to maximize the overall teaching rating.
b) Assign the professors to the courses with the exception that Professor Fisher cannot teach Statistics. **Px**

	Course			
Professor	Statistics	Management	Finance	Economics
W. W. Fisher	90	65	95	40
D. Golhar	70	60	80	75
Z. Hug	85	40	80	60
N. K. Rustagi	55	80	65	55

•• **15.10** The following jobs are waiting to be processed at the same machine centre. Jobs are logged as they arrive:

Job	Due Date	Duration (days)
A	313	8
B	312	16
C	325	40
D	314	5
E	314	3

In what sequence would the jobs be ranked according to the following decision rules: (a) FCFS, (b) EDD, (c) SPT, and (d) LPT? All dates are specified as manufacturing planning calendar days. Assume that all jobs arrive on day 275. Which decision is best and why? **Px**

• **15.11** The following five overhaul jobs are waiting to be processed at Avianic's Engine Repair Inc. These jobs were logged as they arrived. All dates are specified as planning calendar days. Assume that all jobs arrived on day 180; today is day 200.

Job	Due Date	Remaining Time (days)
103	214	10
205	223	7
309	217	11
412	219	5
517	217	15

Using the critical-ratio scheduling rule, in what sequence would the jobs be processed? **Px**

•• **15.12** A Northern British Columbia lumberyard has four jobs on order, as shown in the following table. Today is day 205 on the yard's schedule.

Job	Due Date	Remaining Time (days)
A	212	6
B	209	3
C	208	3
D	210	8

In what sequence would the jobs be ranked according to the following decision rules:
a) FCFS
b) SPT
c) LPT
d) EDD
e) Critical ratio

Which is best and why? Which has the minimum lateness? **Px**

•• **15.13** The following jobs are waiting to be processed at Rick Carlson's machine centre. Carlson's machine centre has a relatively long backlog and sets fresh schedules every two weeks, which do not disturb earlier schedules. Below are the jobs received during the previous two weeks. They are ready to be scheduled today, which is day 241 (day 241 is a work day). Job names refer to names of clients and contract numbers.

Job	Date Job Received	Production Days Needed	Date Job Due
BR-02	228	15	300
CX-01	225	25	270
DE-06	230	35	320
RG-05	235	40	360
SY-11	231	30	310

a) Complete the table below. (Show your supporting calculations.)
b) Which dispatching rule has the best score for flow time?
c) Which dispatching rule has the best score for utilization metric?
d) Which dispatching rule has the best score for lateness?
e) Which dispatching rule would you select? Support your decision.

Dispatching Rule	Job Sequence	Flow Time	Utilization Metric	Average Number of Jobs	Average Lateness
EDD					
SPT					
LPT					
FCFS					

•• **15.14** The following jobs are waiting to be processed at Julie Morel's machine centre:

Job	Date Order Received	Production Days Needed	Date Order Due
A	110	20	180
B	120	30	200
C	122	10	175
D	125	16	230
E	130	18	210

In what sequence would the jobs be ranked according to the following rules: (a) FCFS, (b) EDD, (c) SPT, and (d) LPT? All dates are according to shop calendar days. Today on the planning calendar is day 130, and none of the jobs has been started or scheduled. Which rule is best? **Px**

•• **15.15** Sunny Park Tailors has been asked to make three different types of wedding suits for separate customers. The table below highlights the time taken in hours for (1) cutting and sewing and (2) delivery of each of the suits. Which schedule finishes sooner: First-come, first-served (123) or a schedule using Johnson's rule?

Times Taken for Different Activities (hours)

Suit	Cut and Sew	Deliver
1	4	2
2	7	7
3	6	5

•• **15.16** The following jobs are waiting to be processed at Jeremy LaMontagne's machine centre. Today is day 250.

Job	Date Job Received	Production Days Needed	Date Job Due
1	215	30	260
2	220	20	290
3	225	40	300
4	240	50	320
5	250	20	340

Using the critical-ratio scheduling rule, in what sequence would the jobs be processed? **Px**

••••**15.17** The following set of seven jobs is to be processed through two work centres at George Heinrich's printing company. The sequence is first printing, then binding. Processing time at each of the work centres is shown in the following table:

Job	Printing (hours)	Binding (hours)
T	15	3
U	7	9
V	4	10
W	7	6
X	10	9
Y	4	5
Z	7	8

a) What is the optimal sequence for these jobs to be scheduled?
b) Chart these jobs through the two work centres.
c) What is the total length of time of this optimal solution?
d) What is the idle time in the binding shop, given the optimal solution?
e) How much would the binding machine's idle time be cut by splitting job Z in half? **Px**

••• **15.18** Six jobs are to be processed through a two-step operation. The first operation involves sanding, and the second involves painting. Processing times are as follows:

Job	Operation 1 (hours)	Operation 2 (hours)
A	10	5
B	7	4
C	5	7
D	3	8
E	2	6
F	4	3

Determine a sequence that will minimize the total completion time for these jobs. Illustrate graphically. **Px**

•• **15.19** Jesse's Barber Shop at the Regina Airport is open seven days a week but has fluctuating demand. Jesse is interested in treating his barbers as well as he can with steady work and preferably five days of work with two consecutive days off. His analysis of his staffing needs resulted in the following plan. Schedule Jesse's staff with the minimum number of barbers.

	Day						
	Mon.	Tue.	Wed.	Thu.	Fri.	Sat.	Sun.
Barbers needed	6	5	5	5	6	4	3

•• **15.20** Given the following demand for wait staff at S. Ghosh Bar and Grill, determine the minimum wait staff needed with a policy of two consecutive days off.

			Day				
	Mon.	**Tue.**	**Wed.**	**Thu.**	**Fri.**	**Sat.**	**Sun.**
Wait staff needed	3	4	4	5	6	7	4

•• **15.21** Lifang Wu owns an automated machine shop that makes precision auto parts. He has just compiled an input–output report for the grinding work centre. Complete this report and analyze the results.

Input–Output Report

Period	1	2	3	4	Total
Planned input	80	80	100	100	
Actual input	85	85	85	85	
Deviation					
Planned output	90	90	90	90	
Actual output	85	85	80	80	
Deviation					
Initial backlog: 30					

CASE STUDIES

Old Muskoka Wood Store

In 2015, George Wright started the Old Muskoka Wood Store to manufacture Old Muskoka tables. Each table is carefully constructed by hand using the highest-quality oak. Old Muskoka tables can support more than 250 kilograms, and since the start of the Old Muskoka Wood Store, not one table has been returned because of faulty workmanship or structural problems. In addition to being rugged, each table is beautifully finished using a urethane varnish that George developed over 20 years of working with wood-finishing materials.

The manufacturing process consists of four steps: preparation, assembly, finishing, and packaging. Each step is performed by one person. In addition to overseeing the entire operation, George does all of the finishing. Tom Surowski performs the preparation step, which involves cutting and forming the basic components of the tables. Leon Davis is in charge of the assembly, and Cathy Stark performs the packaging.

Although each person is responsible for only one step in the manufacturing process, everyone can perform any one of the steps. It is George's policy that occasionally everyone should complete several tables on his or her own without any assistance. A small competition is used to see who can complete an entire table in the least amount of time. George maintains average total and intermediate completion times. The data are shown in Figure 15.6.

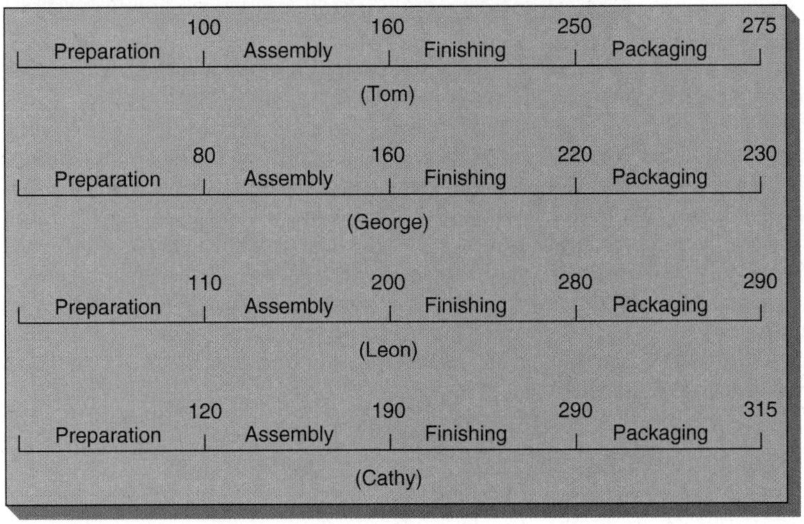

FIGURE 15.6
Manufacturing Time in Minutes

It takes Cathy longer than the other employees to construct an Old Muskoka table. In addition to being slower than the other employees, Cathy is also unhappy about her current responsibility of packaging, which leaves her idle most of the day. Her first preference is finishing, and her second preference is preparation.

In addition to quality, George is concerned with costs and efficiency. When one of the employees misses a day, it causes major scheduling problems. In some cases, George assigns another employee overtime to complete the necessary work. At other times, George simply waits until the employee returns to work to complete his or her step in the manufacturing process. Both solutions cause problems. Overtime is expensive, and waiting causes delays and sometimes stops the entire manufacturing process.

To overcome some of these problems, Randy Lane was hired. Randy's major duties are to perform miscellaneous jobs and to help out if one of the employees is absent. George has given Randy training in all phases of the manufacturing process, and he is pleased with the speed at which Randy has been able to learn

FIGURE 15.7

Randy's Completion Times in Minutes

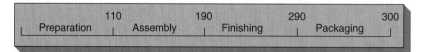

	110	190	290	300
Preparation	Assembly	Finishing	Packaging	

how to completely assemble Old Muskoka tables. Randy's average total and intermediate completion times are given in Figure 15.7.

Discussion Questions

1. What is the fastest way to manufacture Old Muskoka tables using the original crew? How many could be made per day?
2. Would production rates and quantities change significantly if George would allow Randy to perform one of the four functions and make one of the original crew the backup person?
3. What is the fastest time to manufacture a table with the original crew if Cathy is moved to either preparation or finishing?
4. Whoever performs the packaging function is severely underutilized. Can you find a better way of utilizing the four- or five-person crew than either giving each a single job or allowing each to manufacture an entire table? How many tables could be manufactured per day with this scheme?

Video Case | **From the Eagles to the Magic: Converting the Amway Center**

The massive 875 000-square-foot Amway Center in Orlando, Florida, is a state-of-the-art sports entertainment centre. While it is the home of the Orlando Magic basketball team, it is a flexible venue designed to accommodate a vast array of entertainment. The facility is used for everything from a concert by the Eagles or Britney Spears, to ice hockey, to arena football, to conventions, as well as 41 regular season home games played by its major tenant, the National Basketball Association's Orlando Magic.

The building is a LEED-certified (Leadership in Energy and Environmental Design), sustainable, environmentally friendly design, with unmatched technology. Dispersed throughout the building are over 1000 digital monitors, the latest in broadcasting technology, and the tallest high-definition video board in an NBA venue. To fully utilize this nearly $500 million complex, conversions from one event to the next must be done rapidly—often in a matter of hours. Letting the facility sit idle because of delays in conversion is not an option.

Well-executed conversions help maximize facility revenue and at the same time minimize expenses. Fast and efficient conversions are critical. Like any other process, a conversion can be analyzed and separated into its component activities, each requiring its own human and capital resources. The operations manager must determine when to do the conversion, how to train and schedule the crew, which tools and capital equipment are necessary, and the specific steps necessary to break down the current event and set up for the next. In addition to trying to maintain a stable crew (typically provided by local staffing companies) and to maintain control during the frenzied pace of a conversion, managers divide

Fernando Medina

the workforce into cross-trained crews, with each crew operating in its own uniquely coloured shirt.

At the Amway Center, Charlie Leone makes it happen. Charlie is the operations manager, and as such, he knows that any conversion is loaded with complications and risks. Concerts add a special risk because each concert has its own idiosyncrasies—and the breakdown for the Eagles concert will be unique. Charlie and his crews must anticipate and eliminate any potential problems. Charlie's immediate issue is making a schedule for converting the Eagles' concert venue to an NBA basketball venue. The activities and the time for various tasks have been determined and are shown in Table 15.3.

Table 15.3

Concert-to-Basketball Conversion Tasks

Available crew size = 16, including two fork truck drivers

Time Allowed	Tasks	Crew and Time Required
3 to 4 hr	**11:20 p.m.** Performance crew begins teardown of concert stage & equipment	Concert's Responsibility
45 min	**11:20 p.m. Clear Floor Crew**	
	Get chair carts from storage	10 for 15 min
	Clear all chairs on floor, loading carts starting at south end, working north	16 for 30 min
	Move chair carts to north storage and stack as they become full	(includes 1 fork truck operator)

(Continued)

Table 15.3 *(Continued)*

Time Allowed	Tasks	Crew and Time Required
15 min	**11:50 p.m.** *(Or as soon as area under rigging is cleared)*	6 for 15 min
	Set up retractable basketball seating on north end	
	Take down railing above concert stage	
	Place railings on cart and move to storage	
2.5 hr	**12:05 p.m. Basketball Floor Crew**	8
	Position 15 basketball floor carts on floor	
	Mark out arena floor for proper placement of basketball floor	
	Position basketball floor by section	
	Assemble/join flooring/lay carpets over concrete	
	Position basketball nets in place	
	Set up scorer tables	
	Install risers for all courtside seating	
	Install 8-ft tables on east side of court	
2.5 hr	**Seating Unit Crew** *Starts same time as Basketball Floor Crew*	8
	Set up retractable basketball seating on north end	(includes 2 fork truck operators)
	Set up retractable basketball seating on south end	
	(Can only be done after concert stage and equipment is out of way)	
	Install stairs to Superstar Seating	
2 hr	**Board Crew** *Starts after Seating Unit Crew finishes*	4
	Install dasher board on south end	
	Move stairs to storage	
2 hr	**Chair Crew** *Starts after Seating Unit Crew finishes*	12
	Get chair carts from storage	
	Position chair carts on floor	
	Position chairs behind goals, courtside, and scorer tables	
	Clean, sweep, and place carts in order	
45 min	**End-of-Shift Activities** *Starts after Chair Crew finishes*	12
	Perform checklist items	
	Ensure that steps and stairways and railings are in place and tight	
	Check all seats are in upright position and locked in place	
	Report any damaged seats or armrests in need of repair	
	Verify exact number of chairs behind goals, courtside, and scorer tables	
15 min	**Check Out** *Starts after End-of-Shift Activities*	16
	Check for next conversion date and time and inform crew	
	Report any injuries	
	Punch out all employees before leaving	
	8:00 a.m. Floor ready for Magic practice	

Discussion Questions*

1. Make a Gantt chart to help Charlie organize his crew to perform the concert-to-basketball conversion. *Note*: Do not include the teardown of the concert stage and equipment, as that is the responsibility of the concert crew.

2. What time will the floor be ready?

3. Does Charlie have any extra personnel or a shortage of personnel? If so how many?

---

*You may wish to view the video that accompanies this case before answering the questions.

Scheduling at Hard Rock Cafe

Whether it's scheduling nurses at the Hospital for Sick Children, pilots at Air Canada, classrooms at UCLA, or servers at a Hard Rock Cafe, it's clear that good scheduling is important. Proper schedules use an organization's assets (1) more effectively, by serving customers promptly, and (2) more efficiently, by lowering costs.

Hard Rock Cafe at Universal Studios, Orlando, is the world's largest restaurant, with 1100 seats on two main levels. With typical turnover of employees in the restaurant industry at 80% to 100% per year, Hard Rock general manager Ken Hoffman takes scheduling very seriously. Hoffman wants his 160 servers to be effective, but he also wants to treat them fairly. He has done so with scheduling software and flexibility that has increased productivity while contributing to turnover that is half the industry average. His goal is to find the fine balance that gives employees financially productive daily work shifts while setting the schedule tight enough so as to not overstaff between lunch and dinner.

The weekly schedule begins with a sales forecast. "First, we examine last year's sales at the cafe for the same day of the week," says Hoffman. "Then we adjust our forecast for this year based on a variety of closely watched factors. For example, we call the Orlando Convention Bureau every week to see what major groups will be in town. Then we send two researchers out to check on the occupancy of nearby hotels. We watch closely to see what concerts are scheduled at Hard Rock Live—the 3000-seat concert stage next door. From the forecast, we calculate how many people we need to have on duty each day for the kitchen, the bar, as hosts, and for table service."

Once Hard Rock determines the number of staff needed, servers submit request forms, which are fed into the software's linear programming mathematical model. Individuals are given priority rankings from 1 to 9, based on their seniority and how important they are to fill each day's schedule. Schedules are then posted by day and by workstation. Trades are handled between employees, who understand the value of each specific shift and station.

Hard Rock employees like the system, as does the general manager, since sales per labour-hour are rising and turnover is dropping.

Discussion Questions*

1. Name and justify several factors that Hoffman could use in forecasting weekly sales.
2. What can be done to lower turnover in large restaurants?
3. Why is seniority important in scheduling servers?
4. How does the schedule affect productivity?

---

*You may wish to view the video that accompanies this case before answering these questions.

CHAPTER 15 | RAPID REVIEW

MyLab Operations Management

Main Heading	Review Material	
THE IMPORTANCE OF SHORT-TERM SCHEDULING (pp. 581–582)	The strategic importance of scheduling is clear: • Effective scheduling means *faster movement* of goods and services through a facility. This means greater use of assets and hence greater capacity per dollar invested, which, in turn, *lowers cost*. • Added capacity, faster throughput, and the related flexibility mean better customer service through *faster delivery*. • Good scheduling contributes to realistic commitments, hence *dependable delivery*.	
SCHEDULING ISSUES (pp. 582–586)	The objective of scheduling is to allocate and prioritize demand (generated by either forecasts or customer orders) to available facilities. • **Forward scheduling**—Scheduling that begins the schedule as soon as the requirements are known. • **Backward scheduling**—Scheduling that begins with the due date and schedules the final operation first and the other job steps in reverse order. The four scheduling criteria are (1) minimize completion time, (2) maximize utilization, (3) minimize work-in-process (WIP) inventory, and (4) minimize customer waiting time.	**VIDEO 15.1** From the Eagles to the Magic: Converting the Amway Center **VIDEO 15.2** Scheduling at Hard Rock
SCHEDULING PROCESS-FOCUSED FACILITIES (pp. 586)	A process-focused facility is a high-variety, low-volume system commonly found in manufacturing and services. It is also called an intermittent, or job shop, facility. Control files track the actual progress made against the plan for each work order.	

MyLab Operations Management

Main Heading	Review Material	
LOADING JOBS (pp. 586–591)	• **Loading**—The assigning of jobs to work or processing centres. • **Input–output control**—A system that allows operations personnel to manage facility work flows by tracking work added to a work centre and its work completed. • **ConWIP cards**—Cards that control the amount of work in a work centre, aiding input–output control. ConWIP is an acronym for *constant work-in-process*. A ConWIP card travels with a job (or batch) through the work centre. When the job is finished, the card is released and returned to the initial workstation, authorizing the entry of a new batch into the work centre. • **Gantt charts**—Planning charts used to schedule resources and allocate time. The Gantt *load chart* shows the loading and idle times of several departments, machines, or facilities. It displays the relative workloads in the system so that the manager knows what adjustments are appropriate. The Gantt *schedule chart* is used to monitor jobs in progress (and is also used for project scheduling). It indicates which jobs are on schedule and which are ahead of or behind schedule. • **Assignment method**—A special class of linear programming models that involves assigning tasks or jobs to resources. In assignment problems, only one job (or worker) is assigned to one machine (or project). The assignment method involves adding and subtracting appropriate numbers in the table to find the lowest *opportunity cost* for each assignment.	Problems: 15.1–15.9, 15.21
SEQUENCING JOBS (pp. 592–597)	• **Sequencing**—Determining the order in which jobs should be done at each work centre. • **Priority rules**—Rules used to determine the sequence of jobs in process-oriented facilities. • **First-come, first-served (FCFS)**—Jobs are completed in the order they arrived. • **Shortest processing time (SPT)**—Jobs with the shortest processing times are assigned first. • **Earliest due date**—Earliest due date jobs are performed first. • **Longest processing time (LPT)**—Jobs with the longest processing time are completed first: $$\text{Average completion time} = \frac{\text{Sum of total flow time}}{\text{Number of jobs}}$$ $$\text{Utilization metric} = \frac{\text{Total job work (processing) time}}{\text{Sum of total flow time}}$$ $$\text{Average number of jobs in the system} = \frac{\text{Sum of total flow time}}{\text{Total job work (processing) time}}$$ $$\text{Average job lateness} = \frac{\text{Total late days}}{\text{Number of jobs}}$$ SPT is the best technique for minimizing job flow and average number of jobs in the system. FCFS performs about average on most criteria, and it appears fair to customers. EDD minimizes maximum tardiness. • **Critical ratio (CR)**—A sequencing rule that is an index number computed by dividing the time remaining until the due date by the work time remaining: $$CR = \frac{\text{Time remaining}}{\text{Workdays remaining}} = \frac{\text{Due date} - \text{Today's date}}{\text{Work (lead) time remaining}}$$ As opposed to the priority rules, the critical ratio is dynamic and easily updated. It tends to perform better than FCFS, SPT, EDD, or LPT on the average job-lateness criterion.	Problems: 15.10–15.18 Virtual Office Hours for Solved Problems: 15.4–15.5 **ACTIVE MODEL 15.1**

Main Heading	Review Material
	• **Johnson's rule**—An approach that minimizes processing time for sequencing a group of jobs through two work centres while minimizing total idle time in the work centres. Rule-based scheduling systems have the following limitations: (1) Scheduling is dynamic, (2) rules do not look upstream or downstream, and (3) rules do not look beyond due dates.
FINITE CAPACITY SCHEDULING (FCS) (pp. 597–599)	• **Finite capacity scheduling (FCS)**—Computerized short-term scheduling that overcomes the disadvantage of rule-based systems by providing the user with graphical interactive computing.
SCHEDULING REPETITIVE FACILITIES (pp. 599)	• **Level material use**—The use of frequent, high-quality, small lot sizes that contribute to just-in-time production. Advantages of level material use are (1) lower inventory levels, (2) faster product throughput, (3) improved component and product quality, (4) reduced floor-space requirements, (5) improved communication among employees, and (6) a smoother production process.
SCHEDULING SERVICES (pp. 599–602)	Cyclical scheduling with inconsistent staffing needs is often the case in services. The objective focuses on developing a schedule with the minimum number of workers. In these cases, each employee is assigned to a shift and has time off.

Problems: 15.19–15.20

Self-Test

■ Before taking the self-test, refer to the learning objectives listed at the beginning of the chapter.

LO1 Which of the following decisions covers the longest time period?
a) Short-term scheduling
b) Capacity planning
c) Aggregate planning
d) A master schedule

LO2 A visual aid used in loading and scheduling jobs is a:
a) Gantt chart.   b) planning file.
c) bottleneck.   d) load-schedule matrix.
e) level material chart.

LO3 The assignment method involves adding and subtracting appropriate numbers in the table to find the lowest _____ for each assignment.
a) profit
b) number of steps
c) number of allocations
d) range per row
e) opportunity cost

LO4 The most popular priority rules include:
a) FCFS.   b) EDD.
c) SPT.   d) all of the above.

LO5 The job that should be scheduled last when using Johnson's rule is the job with the:
a) largest total processing time on both machines.
b) smallest total processing time on both machines.
c) longest activity time if it lies with the first machine.
d) longest activity time if it lies with the second machine.
e) shortest activity time if it lies with the second machine.

LO6 What is computerized short-term scheduling that overcomes the disadvantage of rule-based systems by providing the user with graphical interactive computing?
a) LPT   b) FCS
c) CSS   d) FCFS
e) GIC

LO7 Cyclical scheduling is used to schedule:
a) jobs.   b) machines.
c) shipments.   d) employees.

Answers: LO1. b; LO2. a; LO3. e; LO4. d; LO5. e; LO6. b; LO7. d.

MyLab Operations Management

Most of these questions can be found in MyLab Operations Management. Visit MyLab Operations Management to access cases, videos, downloadable software, and much more. MyLab Operations Management Management also features a personalized Study Plan that helps you identify which chapter concepts you've mastered and guides you towards study tools for additional practice.

Lean Operations

Achieving Competitive Advantage with Lean Operations at Toyota Motor Corporation

Toyota Motor Corporation, with annual sales of over 9 million cars and trucks, is one of the largest vehicle manufacturers in the world. Two Lean techniques—just-in-time (JIT) and the Toyota Production System (TPS)—have been instrumental in its growth. Toyota, with a wide range of vehicles, competes head-to-head with successful long-established companies in Europe and North America. Taiichi Ohno, a former vice-president of Toyota, created the basic framework for the world's most discussed systems for improving productivity: JIT and TPS. These two concepts provide much of the foundation for Lean operations:

- Central to JIT is a philosophy of continued problem solving. In practice, JIT means making only what is needed, when it is needed. JIT provides an excellent vehicle for finding and eliminating problems—because problems are easy to find in a system that has no slack. When excess inventory is eliminated, quality, layout, scheduling, and supplier issues become immediately evident—as does excess production.

< Global Company Profile Toyota Motor Corporation

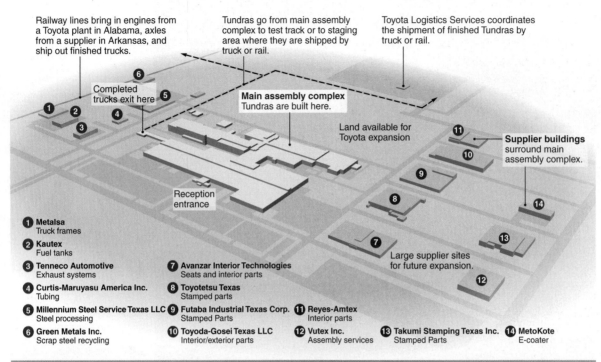

14 Suppliers outside the main plant

Outside: Toyota has a 2000-acre site with 14 of the 21 onsite suppliers, adjacent rail lines, and nearby interstate highway. The site provides expansion space for both Toyota and for its suppliers — and provides an environment for just-in-time.

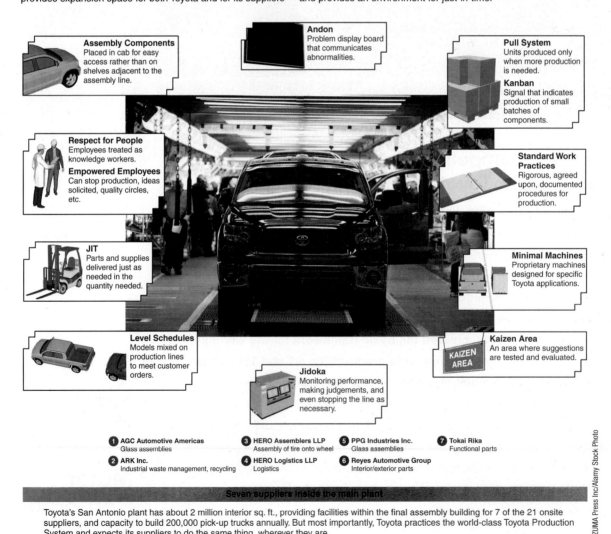

Seven suppliers inside the main plant

Toyota's San Antonio plant has about 2 million interior sq. ft., providing facilities within the final assembly building for 7 of the 21 onsite suppliers, and capacity to build 200,000 pick-up trucks annually. But most importantly, Toyota practices the world-class Toyota Production System and expects its suppliers to do the same thing, wherever they are.

ZUMA Press Inc/Alamy Stock Photo

- Central to TPS is employee learning and a continuing effort to create and produce products under ideal conditions. Ideal conditions exist only when facilities, machines, and people are brought together, adding value without waste. Waste undermines productivity by diverting resources to excess inventory, unnecessary processing, and poor quality. Fundamental to TPS are respect for people, extensive training, cross-training, and standard work practices of empowered employees focusing on driving out waste.

Toyota's latest implementation of TPS and JIT is present at its new San Antonio plant, the largest Toyota land site for an automobile assembly plant in North America. Interestingly, despite its annual production capability of 200 000 Tundra pick-up trucks, a throughput time of 20.5 hours, and the output of a truck every 63 seconds, the building itself is one of the smallest in the industry. Modern automobiles have 30 000 parts, but at Toyota, independent suppliers combine many of these parts into subassemblies. Twenty-one of these suppliers are onsite at the San Antonio facility and transfer components to the assembly line on a JIT basis.

Operations such as these taking place in the new San Antonio plant are why Toyota continues to perform near the top in quality and maintain the lowest labour-hour assembly time in the industry. JIT, TPS, and Lean operations work—and they provide a competitive advantage at Toyota Motor Corporation.

Lean Operations

As shown in the *Global Company Profile*, the Toyota Production System (TPS) contributes to a world-class operation at Toyota Motor Corporation. In this chapter, we discuss Lean operations as approaches to continuing improvement that drive out waste and lead to world-class organizations.

LO1 Define *Lean operations*

Just-in-time (JIT) is an approach of continuous and forced problem solving via a focus on throughput and reduced inventory. The **Toyota Production System (TPS)**, with its emphasis on continuous improvement, respect for people, and standard work practices, is particularly suited for assembly lines. **Lean operations** supply the customer with exactly what the customer wants when the customer wants it, without waste, through continuous improvement. Lean operations are driven by workflow initiated by the "pull" of the customer's order. When implemented as a comprehensive manufacturing strategy, JIT, TPS, and Lean systems sustain competitive advantage and result in increased overall returns to stakeholders.

Just-in-time (JIT)
Continuous and forced problem solving via a focus on throughput and reduced inventory.

Toyota Production System (TPS)
Focus on continuous improvement, respect for people, and standard work practices.

If there is any distinction between JIT, TPS, and Lean operations, it is that:

- JIT emphasizes forced problem solving.
- TPS emphasizes employee learning and empowerment in an assembly-line environment.
- Lean operations emphasize understanding the customer.

Lean operations
Eliminate waste through a focus on exactly what the customer wants.

However, in practice, there is little difference, and the terms are often used interchangeably. Leading organizations use the approaches and techniques that make sense for them. In this chapter, we use the term *Lean operations* to encompass all of the related approaches and techniques.

Regardless of the label put on operations improvement, good production systems require that managers address three issues that are pervasive and fundamental to operations management: eliminate waste, remove variability, and improve throughput. We first introduce these three issues and then discuss the major attributes of JIT, TPS, and Lean operations. Finally, we look at Lean operations applied to services. See the video case at the end of this chapter, "Lean Operations at Alaska Airlines".

VIDEO 16.1
Lean Operations at Alaska Airlines

ELIMINATE WASTE

LO2 Define the *seven wastes* and the *5Ss*

Lean producers set their sights on perfection; no bad parts, no inventory, only value-added activities, and no waste. Any activity that does not add value in the eyes of the customer is a waste. The customer defines product value. If the customer does not want to pay for it, it is a waste.

Taiichi Ohno, noted for his work on the Toyota Production System, identified seven categories of waste. These categories have become popular in Lean organizations and cover many of the ways organizations waste or lose money. Ohno's **seven wastes** are:

- *Overproduction:* Producing more than the customer orders or producing early (before it is demanded) is waste. Inventory of any kind is usually a waste.
- *Queues:* Idle time, storage, and waiting are wastes (they add no value).
- *Transportation:* Moving material between plants or between work centres and handling more than once is waste.
- *Inventory:* Unnecessary raw material, work-in-process (WIP), finished goods, and excess operating supplies add no value and are wastes.
- *Motion:* Movement of equipment or people that adds no value is waste.
- *Overprocessing:* Work performed on the product that adds no value is waste.
- *Defective product:* Returns, warranty claims, rework, and scrap are a waste.

A broader perspective—one that goes beyond immediate production—suggests that other resources, such as energy, water, and air, are often wasted but should not be. Efficient, sustainable production minimizes inputs and maximizes outputs, wasting nothing.

For over a century, managers have pursued "housekeeping" for a neat, orderly, and efficient workplace and as a means of reducing waste. Operations managers have embellished housekeeping to include a checklist—now known as the 5Ss.[1] The Japanese developed the initial 5Ss. Not only do the 5Ss provide a good checklist for Lean operations, but they also provide an easy vehicle with which to assist the culture change that is often necessary to bring about Lean operations. The **5Ss** follow:

- *Sort/segregate:* Keep what is needed and remove everything else from the work area; when in doubt, throw it out. Identify non-value-added items and remove them. Getting rid of these items makes space available and usually improves work flow.
- *Simplify/straighten:* Arrange and use methods analysis tools (see Chapter 7 and Chapter 10) to improve work flow and reduce wasted motion. Consider long-run and short-run ergonomic issues. Label and display for easy use only what is needed in the immediate work area. For examples of visual displays see Chapter 10, Figure 10.8.
- *Shine/sweep:* Clean daily; eliminate all forms of dirt, contamination, and clutter from the work area.
- *Standardize:* Remove variations from the process by developing standard operating procedures and checklists; good standards make the abnormal obvious. Standardize equipment and tooling so that cross-training time and cost are reduced. Train and retrain the work team so that when deviations occur, they are readily apparent to all.
- *Sustain/self-discipline:* Review periodically to recognize efforts and to motivate to sustain progress. Use visuals wherever possible to communicate and sustain progress.

North American managers often add two additional Ss that contribute to establishing and maintaining a Lean workplace:

- *Safety:* Build good safety practices into the preceding five activities.
- *Support/maintenance:* Reduce variability, unplanned downtime, and costs. Integrate daily shine tasks with preventive maintenance.

The Ss provide a vehicle for continuous improvement with which all employees can identify. Operations managers need think only of the examples set by a well-run hospital emergency room or the spit-and-polish of a fire department for a benchmark. Offices and retail stores, as well as manufacturers, have successfully used the 5Ss in their respective efforts to eliminate waste and move to Lean operations. A place for everything and everything in its place does make a difference in a well-run office. And retail stores successfully use the Ss to reduce misplaced merchandise and improve customer service. An orderly workplace reduces waste so that assets are released for other, more productive purposes.

---

[1] The term *5S* comes from the Japanese words *seiri* (*sort* and clear out), *seiton* (*straighten* and configure), *seiso* (*scrub* and clean up), *seiketsu* (maintain *sanitation* and cleanliness of self and workplace), and *shitsuke* (*self-discipline and standardization* of these practices).

REMOVE VARIABILITY

Managers seek to remove variability caused by both internal and external factors. **Variability** is any deviation from the optimum process that delivers perfect product on time, every time. *Variability* is a polite word for *problems*. The less variability in a system, the less waste in the system. Most variability is caused by tolerating waste or by poor management. Among the many sources of variability are:

- Poor production processes that allow employees and suppliers to produce improper quantities or late or nonconforming units.
- Inadequate maintenance of facilities and processes
- Unknown and changing customer demands.
- Incomplete or inaccurate drawings, specifications, and bills of material.

Both JIT and inventory reduction are effective tools for identifying causes of variability. The precise timing of JIT makes variability evident, just as reducing inventory exposes variability. The removal of variability allows managers to move good materials on schedule, add value at each step of the process, drive down costs, and win orders.

Variability
Any deviation from the optimum process that delivers perfect product on time, every time.

IMPROVE THROUGHPUT

Throughput is a measure (in units or time) of what it takes to move an order from receipt to delivery. Each minute that products remain on the books, costs accumulate and competitive advantage is lost. The time that an order is in the shop is called **manufacturing cycle time**. This is the time between the arrival of raw materials and the shipping of finished product. For example, phone-system manufacturer Nortel now has materials pulled directly from qualified suppliers to the assembly line. This effort has reduced a segment of Nortel's manufacturing cycle time from three weeks to just four hours, decreased the incoming inspection staff from 47 to 24, and reduced problems on the shop floor caused by defective materials by 97%. Driving down manufacturing cycle time can make a major improvement in throughput.

A technique for increasing throughput is a pull system. A **pull system** *pulls* a unit to where it is needed just as it is needed. Pull systems are a standard tool of Lean. Pull systems use signals to request production and delivery from supplying stations to stations that have production capacity available. The pull concept is used both within the immediate production process and with suppliers. By *pulling* material through the system in very small lots—just as it is needed—waste and inventory are removed. As inventory is removed, clutter is reduced, problems become evident, and continuous improvement is emphasized. Removing the cushion of inventory also reduces both investment in inventory and manufacturing cycle time. A push system dumps orders on the next downstream workstation, regardless of timeliness and resource availability. Push systems are the antithesis of Lean. Pulling material through a production process as it is needed rather than in a "push" mode typically lowers cost and improves schedule performance, enhancing customer satisfaction.

Throughput
The time required to move orders through the production process, from receipt to delivery.

Manufacturing cycle time
The time between the arrival of raw materials and the shipping of finished products.

Pull system
A concept that results in material being produced only when requested and moved to where it is needed just as it is needed.

Lean and Just-in-Time

With its forced problem solving via a focus on rapid throughput and reduced inventory, JIT provides a powerful strategy for improving operations. With JIT, materials arrive *where* they are needed only *when* they are needed. When good units do not arrive just as needed, a "problem" has been identified. By driving out waste and delay in this manner, JIT reduces costs associated with excess inventory, cuts variability and waste, and improves throughput. JIT is a key ingredient of Lean operations and is particularly helpful in supporting strategies of rapid response and low cost. Every moment material is held, an activity that adds value should be occurring. Consequently, as Figure 16.1 suggests, JIT often yields a competitive advantage.

Effective JIT requires a meaningful buyer–supplier partnership.

STUDENT TIP
JIT places added demands on performance, but that is why it pays off.

LO3 Identify the concerns of suppliers when moving to supplier partnerships

SUPPLIER PARTNERSHIPS

Supplier partnerships exist when a supplier and a purchaser work together with open communication and a goal of removing waste and driving down costs. Close relationships and trust are critical to the success of Lean Figure 16.2 shows the characteristics of supplier partnerships. Some specific goals are:

Supplier partnerships
Partnership of suppliers and purchasers that removes waste and drives down costs for mutual benefits.

Many services have adopted Lean techniques as a normal part of their business. Restaurants like Olive Garden expect and receive JIT deliveries. Both buyer and supplier expect fresh, high-quality produce delivered without fail just when it is needed. The system doesn't work any other way.

Corto_Maltese_83/Fotolia

- *Removal of unnecessary activities*, such as receiving, incoming inspection, and paperwork related to bidding, invoicing, and payment.
- *Removal of in-plant inventory* by delivery in small lots directly to the using department as needed.

FIGURE 16.1

Lean Contributes to Competitive Advantage

JIT TECHNIQUES:

Suppliers:	Few vendors; Supportive supplier relationships; Quality deliveries on time, directly to work areas.
Layout:	Work-cells; Group technology; Flexible machinery; Organized workplace; Reduced space for inventory.
Inventory:	Small lot sizes; Low setup time; Specialized parts bins
Scheduling:	Zero deviation from schedules; Level schedules; Suppliers informed of schedules; Kanban techniques
Preventive maintenance:	Schedules; Daily routine; Operator involvement
Quality production:	Statistical process control; Quality suppliers; Quality within the firm
Employee empowerment:	Empowered and cross-trained employees; Training support; Few job classifications to ensure flexibility of employees
Commitment:	Support of management, employees, and suppliers

WHICH RESULTS IN:

Rapid throughput frees assets

Quality improvement reduces waste

Cost reduction adds pricing flexibility

Variability reduction

Rework reduction

WHICH WINS ORDERS BY:

Faster response to the customer at lower cost and higher quality—

A Competitive Advantage

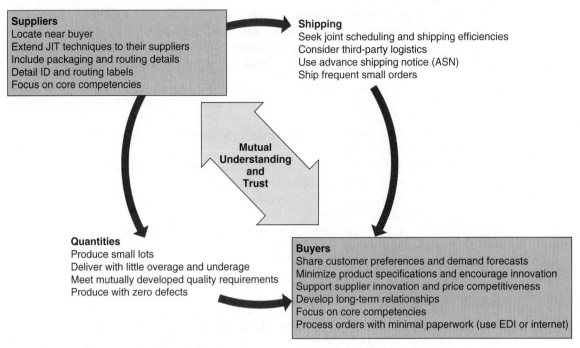

Suppliers
Locate near buyer
Extend JIT techniques to their suppliers
Include packaging and routing details
Detail ID and routing labels
Focus on core competencies

Shipping
Seek joint scheduling and shipping efficiencies
Consider third-party logistics
Use advance shipping notice (ASN)
Ship frequent small orders

Mutual Understanding and Trust

Quantities
Produce small lots
Deliver with little overage and underage
Meet mutually developed quality requirements
Produce with zero defects

Buyers
Share customer preferences and demand forecasts
Minimize product specifications and encourage innovation
Support supplier innovation and price competitiveness
Develop long-term relationships
Focus on core competencies
Process orders with minimal paperwork (use EDI or internet)

FIGURE 16.2 Characteristics of Supplier Partnerships

- *Removal of in-transit inventory* by encouraging suppliers to locate nearby and provide frequent small shipments. The shorter the flow of material in the resource pipeline, the less inventory. Inventory can also be reduced through a technique known as *consignment*. **Consignment inventory** (see the *OM in Action* box "Lean Production at Cessna Aircraft"), a variation of vendor-managed inventory (Chapter 11), means the supplier maintains the title to the inventory until it is used. For instance, an assembly plant may find a hardware supplier that is willing to locate its warehouse where the user currently has its stockroom. In this manner, when hardware is needed, it is no farther away than the stockroom. Schedule and production information must be shared with the consignment supplier, or inventory holding costs will just be transferred from the buyer to the supplier, with no net cost reduction. Another option is to have the supplier ship to other, perhaps smaller, purchasers from the "stockroom".
- *Obtaining improved quality and reliability* through long-term commitments, communication, and co-operation.

Consignment inventory
An arrangement in which the supplier maintains title to the inventory until it is used.

OM in Action   Lean Production at Cessna Aircraft Company

When Cessna Aircraft opened its new plant in Independence, Kansas, it saw the opportunity to switch from craftwork to a Lean manufacturing system. The initial idea was to focus on three Lean concepts: (1) vendor-managed inventory, (2) cross-training of employees, and (3) using technology and manufacturing cells to move away from batch processing.

After several years, with these goals accomplished, Cessna began working on the next phase of Lean. This phase focuses on *Team Build* and *Area Team Development*.

Team Build at Cessna empowers employees to expand their skills, sequence their own work, and then sign off on it. This reduces wait time, inventory, part shortages, rework, and scrap, all contributing to improved productivity.

Area Team Development (ATD) provides experts when a factory employee cannot complete his or her standard

work in the time planned. Team members trained in the ATD process are called Skill Coaches. Skill Coaches provide support throughout each area to improve response time to problems. Andon boards and performance metrics are used for evaluating daily performance.

Cessna Aircraft Company

These commitments to Lean manufacturing are a major contributor to Cessna being the world's largest manufacturer of single-engine aircraft.

Sources: Interviews with Cessna executives, 2013.

Leading organizations view suppliers as extensions of their own organizations and expect suppliers to be fully committed to improvement. Such relationships require a high degree of respect by both supplier and purchaser. Supplier concerns can be significant and must be addressed. These concerns include:

1. *Diversification:* Suppliers may not want to tie themselves to long-term contracts with one customer. The suppliers' perception is that they reduce their risk if they have a variety of customers.
2. *Scheduling:* Many suppliers have little faith in the purchaser's ability to produce orders to a smooth, coordinated schedule.
3. *Lead time:* Engineering or specification changes can play havoc with JIT because of inadequate lead time for suppliers to implement the necessary changes.
4. *Quality:* Suppliers' capital budgets, processes, or technology may limit ability to respond to changes in product and quality.
5. *Lot sizes:* Suppliers may see frequent delivery in small lots as a way to transfer buyers' holding costs to suppliers.

Lean Layout

Lean layouts reduce another kind of waste—movement. The movement of material on a factory floor (or paper in an office) does not add value. Consequently, managers want flexible layouts that reduce the movement of both people and material. Lean layouts place material directly in the location where needed. For instance, an assembly line should be designed with delivery points next to the line so material need not be delivered first to a receiving department and then moved again. Toyota has gone one step further and places hardware and components in the chassis of each vehicle moving down the assembly line. This is not only convenient, but it allows Toyota to save space and opens areas adjacent to the assembly line previously occupied by shelves. When a layout reduces distance, firms often save labour and space and may have the added bonus of eliminating potential areas for accumulation of unwanted inventory. Table 16.1 provides a list of Lean layout tactics.

Table 16.1
Lean Layout Tactics

Build work cells for families of products

Include a large number of operations in a small area

Minimize distance

Design little space for inventory

Improve employee communication

Use poka-yoke devices

Build flexible or movable equipment

Cross-train workers to add flexibility

DISTANCE REDUCTION

Reducing distance is a major contribution of work cells, work centres, and focused factories (see Chapter 9). The days of long production lines and huge economic lots, with goods passing through monumental, single-operation machines, are gone. Now firms use work cells, often arranged in a U shape, containing several machines performing different operations. These work cells are often based on group technology codes (as discussed in Chapter 5). Group technology codes help identify components with similar characteristics so we can group them into families. Once families are identified, work cells are built for them. The result can be thought of as a small product-oriented facility where the "product" is actually a group of similar products—a family of products. The cells produce one good unit at a time, and ideally they produce the units *only* after a customer orders them.

INCREASED FLEXIBILITY

Modern work cells are designed so they can be easily rearranged to adapt to changes in volume, product improvements, or even new designs. Almost nothing in these new departments is bolted down. This same concept of layout flexibility applies to office environments. Not only is most office furniture and equipment movable, but so are office walls, computer connections, and telecommunications. Equipment is modular. Layout flexibility aids the changes that result from product *and* process improvements that are inevitable with a philosophy of continuous improvement.

IMPACT ON EMPLOYEES

Lean layouts allow cross-trained employees to bring flexibility and efficiency to the work cell. Employees working together can tell each other about problems and opportunities for improvement. When layouts provide for sequential operations, feedback can be immediate. Defects are waste. When workers produce units one at a time, they test each product or component at each subsequent production stage. Machines in work cells with self-testing poka-yoke functions detect defects and stop automatically when they occur. Before Lean, defective products were replaced from inventory. Because surplus inventory is not kept in Lean facilities, there are no such buffers. Getting it right the first time is critical.

REDUCED SPACE AND INVENTORY

Because Lean layouts reduce travel distance, they also reduce inventory by removing space for inventory. When there is little space, inventory must be moved in very small lots or even single units. Units are always moving because there is no storage. For example, Canada's Bombardier developed and engineered an innovative solution for transport—a returnable packaging system that consists of metal racks in which textile bags are suspended. By removing a cover fitted with Velcro strips, an operator can access the parts from both the front and back of the rack. This kit allows the company to work according to Lean principles since the flow of outgoing and incoming kits can be adjusted to the pace of the assembly line, thus keeping inventory as low as possible. In addition, the design allows for more parts to be transported per cubic metre and with fewer truck movements. This has created an attractive return on investment.

Lean Inventory

Inventories in production and distribution systems often exist "just in case" something goes wrong. That is, they are used just in case some variation from the production plan occurs. The "extra" inventory is then used to cover variations or problems. Effective inventory tactics require "just in time," not "just in case". **Lean inventory** is the minimum inventory necessary to keep a perfect system running. With Lean inventory, the exact amount of goods arrives at the moment it is needed, not a minute before or a minute after. Some useful Lean inventory tactics are shown in Table 16.2 and discussed in more detail in the following sections.

REDUCE INVENTORY AND VARIABILITY

Operations managers move towards Lean by first removing inventory. The idea is to eliminate variability in the production system hidden by inventory. Reducing inventory uncovers the "rocks" in Figure 16.3(a) that represent the variability and problems currently being tolerated. With reduced inventory, management chips away at the exposed problems. After the lake is lowered, managers make additional cuts in inventory and continue to chip away at the next level of exposed problems (see Figure 16.3[b, c]). Ultimately, there will be little inventory and few problems (variability).

Firms with technology-sensitive products estimate that the rapid changes in technology costs 0.5% to 2% of its inventory's value *each week*. Shigeo Shingo, co-developer of the Toyota JIT system, says, "Inventory is evil." He is not far from the truth. If inventory itself is not evil, it hides evil at great cost.

Accountants book inventory as an asset, but operations managers know it is a cost.

Lean inventory
The minimum inventory necessary to keep a perfect system running.

"Inventory is evil."—S. Shingo

Table 16.2
Lean Inventory Tactics

Use a pull system to move inventory

Reduce lot size

Develop just-in-time delivery systems with suppliers

Deliver directly to the point of use

Perform to schedule

Reduce setup time

Use group technology

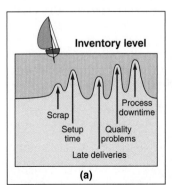

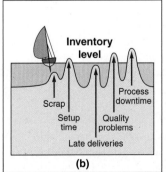

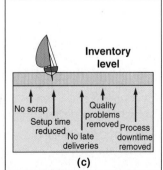

FIGURE 16.3 High levels of inventory hide problems (a), but as we reduce inventory, problems are exposed (b), and finally after reducing inventory and removing problems, we have lower inventory, lower costs, and smooth sailing (c).

FIGURE 16.4

Frequent Orders Reduce Average Inventory

A lower order size increases the number of orders and total ordering cost but reduces average inventory and total holding cost.

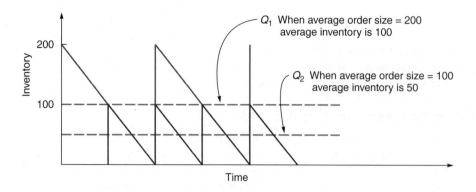

Q_1 When average order size = 200 average inventory is 100

Q_2 When average order size = 100 average inventory is 50

REDUCE LOT SIZES

Lean has also come to mean elimination of waste by reducing investment in inventory. The key is producing good product in small lot sizes. Reducing the size of batches can be a major help in reducing inventory and inventory costs. As we saw in Chapter 12, when inventory usage is constant, the average inventory level is the sum of the maximum inventory plus the minimum inventory divided by 2. Figure 16.4 shows that lowering the order size increases the number of orders but drops inventory levels.

Ideally, in a Lean environment, order size is one and single units are being pulled from one adjacent process to another. More realistically, analysis of the process, transportation time, and containers used for transport are considered when determining lot size. Such analysis typically results in a small lot size but a lot size larger than one. Once a lot size has been determined, the EOQ production order quantity model can be modified to determine the desired setup time. We saw in Chapter 12 that the production order quantity model takes the form:

$$Q^* = \sqrt{\frac{2DS}{H[1 - (d/p)]}} \tag{16-1}$$

where D = Annual demand d = Daily demand
         S = Setup cost p = Daily production
         H = Holding cost

Example 1 shows how to determine the desired setup time.

EXAMPLE **1**

Determining Optimal Setup Time

LO4 Determine optimal setup time

Crate Furniture, Inc., a firm that produces rustic furniture, desires to move towards a reduced lot size. Crate's production analyst, Aleda Roth, determined that a two-hour production cycle would be acceptable between two departments. Further, she concluded that a setup time that would accommodate the two-hour cycle time should be achieved.

APPROACH ▶ Roth developed the following data and procedure to determine optimum setup time analytically:

D = Annual demand = 400 000 units
d = Daily demand = 400 000 per 250 days = 1600 units per day
p = Daily production rate = 4000 units per day
Q = EOQ desired = 400 (which is the two-hour demand; that is, 1600 per day
   per four two-hour periods)
H = Holding cost = $20 per unit per year
S = Setup cost (to be determined)

SOLUTION ▶ Roth determines that the cost, on an hourly basis, of setting up equipment is $30. Further, she computes that the setup cost per setup should be:

$$Q = \sqrt{\frac{2DS}{H(1 - d/p)}}$$

$$Q^2 = \frac{2DS}{H(1 - d/p)} \qquad (16\text{-}2)$$

$$S = \frac{(Q^2)(H)(1 - d/p)}{2D}$$

$$= \frac{(400)^2(20)(1 - 1600/4000)}{2(400\,000)}$$

$$= \frac{(3\,200\,000)(0.6)}{800\,000} = \$2.40$$

$$\text{Setup time} = \$2.40/(\text{hourly labour rate})$$

$$= \$2.40/(\$30 \text{ per hour})$$

$$= 0.08 \text{ hour, or } 4.8 \text{ minutes}$$

INSIGHT ▶ Now, rather than produce components in large lots, Crate Furniture can produce in a two-hour cycle with the advantage of an inventory turnover of four *per day*.

LEARNING EXERCISE ▶ If labour cost goes to $40 per hour, what should be the setup time? [Answer: 0.06 hour, or 3.6 minutes.]

RELATED PROBLEMS ▶ 16.8, 16.9, 16.10

Only two changes need to be made for small-lot material flow to work. First, material handling and work flow need to be improved. With short production cycles, there can be very little wait time. Improving material handling is usually easy and straightforward. The second change is more challenging, and that is a radical reduction in setup times. We discuss setup reduction next.

REDUCE SETUP COSTS

STUDENT **TIP**

Reduced lot sizes must be accompanied by reduced setup times.

Both inventory and the cost of holding it go down as the inventory-reorder quantity and the maximum inventory level drop. However, because inventory requires incurring an ordering or setup cost that must be applied to the units produced, managers tend to purchase (or produce) large orders. With large orders, each unit purchased or ordered absorbs only a small part of the setup cost. Consequently, the way to drive down lot sizes *and* reduce average inventory is to reduce setup cost, which in turn lowers the optimum order size.

The effect of reduced setup costs on total cost and lot size is shown in Figure 16.5. Moreover, smaller lot sizes hide fewer problems. In many environments, setup cost is highly correlated with setup time. In a manufacturing facility, setups usually require a substantial amount of preparation. Much of the preparation required by a setup can be done prior to shutting down the machine or process. Setup times can be reduced substantially, as shown in Figure 16.6. For instance, in Kodak's Guadalajara, Mexico, plant, a team reduced the setup time to change a bearing from 12 hours to 6 minutes! This is the kind of progress that is typical of world-class manufacturers.

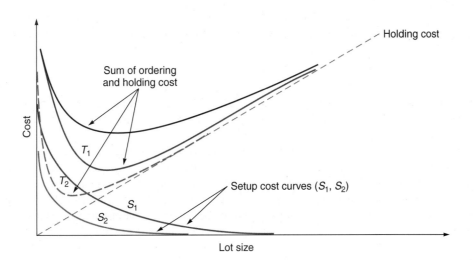

FIGURE 16.5

Lower Setup Costs Will Lower Total Cost

More frequent orders require reducing setup costs; otherwise, inventory costs will rise. As the setup costs are lowered (from S_1 to S_2), total inventory costs also fall (from T_1 to T_2).

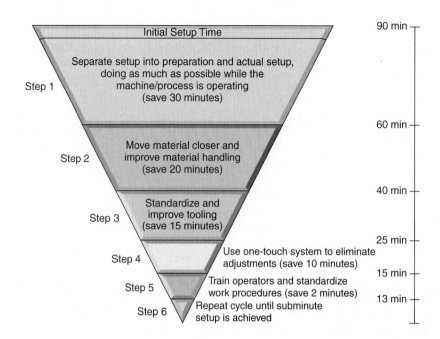

Just as setup costs can be reduced at a machine in a factory, setup time can also be reduced during the process of getting the order ready. It does little good to drive down factory setup time from hours to minutes if orders are going to take two weeks to process or "set up" in the office. This is exactly what happens in organizations that forget that Lean concepts have applications in offices as well as in the factory. Reducing setup time (and cost) is an excellent way to reduce inventory investment, improve productivity, and speed throughput.

Lean Scheduling

Effective schedules, communicated both within the organization and to outside suppliers, support Lean. Better scheduling also improves the ability to meet customer orders, drives down inventory by allowing smaller lot sizes, and reduces work-in-process. For instance, Ford Motor Company now ties some suppliers to its final assembly schedule. Ford communicates its schedules to bumper manufacturer Polycon Industries from the Ford Oakville production control system. The scheduling system describes the style and colour of the bumper needed for each vehicle moving down the final assembly line. The scheduling system transmits the information to portable terminals carried by Polycon warehouse personnel who load the bumpers onto conveyors leading to the loading dock. The bumpers are then trucked 80 kilometres to the Ford plant. Total time is four hours. However, as we saw in our opening *Global Company Profile*, Toyota has moved its seat supplier inside the new Tundra plant; this has driven down delivery time even further.

Table 16.3 suggests several items that can contribute to achieving these goals, but two techniques (in addition to communicating schedules) are paramount. They are *level schedules* and *kanban*.

LEVEL SCHEDULES

Level schedules process frequent small batches rather than a few large batches. Because this technique schedules many small lots that are always changing, it has on occasion been called "jelly bean" scheduling. Figure 16.7 contrasts a traditional large-lot approach using large batches with a Lean level schedule using many small batches. The operations manager's task is to make and move small lots so the level schedule is economical. This requires success with the issues discussed in this chapter that allow small lots. As lots get smaller, the constraints may change and become increasingly challenging. At some point, processing a unit or two may not be feasible. The constraint may be the way units are sold and shipped (four to a carton), or an expensive paint changeover (on an automobile assembly line), or the proper number of units in a sterilizer (for a food-canning line).

Table 16.3

Lean Scheduling Tactics

Communicate schedules to suppliers

Make level schedules

Freeze part of the schedule

Perform to schedule

Seek one-piece-make and one-piece-move

Eliminate waste

Produce in small lots

Use kanbans

Make each operation produce a perfect part

Level schedules

Scheduling products so that each day's production meets the demand for that day.

Lean Level Material-Use Approach

AA BBB C AA BBB C AA BBB C AA BBB C AA BBB C AA BBB C AA BBB C AA BBB C

Large-Lot Approach

AAAAAA BBBBBBBBB CCC AAAAAA BBBBBBBBB CCC AAAAAA BBBBBBBBB CCC

Time

FIGURE 16.7

Scheduling Small Lots of Parts A, B, and C Increases Flexibility to Meet Customer Demand and Reduces Inventory

The Lean approach to scheduling produces just as many of each model per time period as the large-lot approach, provided that setup times are lowered.

The scheduler may find that *freezing* the portion of the schedule closest to due dates allows the production system to function and the schedule to be met. Freezing means not allowing changes to be part of the schedule. Operations managers expect the schedule to be achieved with no deviations from the schedule.

KANBAN

One way to achieve small lot sizes is to move inventory through the shop only as needed rather than *pushing* it on to the next workstation whether or not the personnel there are ready for it. As noted earlier, when inventory is moved only as needed, it is referred to as a *pull* system, and the ideal lot size is one. The Japanese call this system *kanban*. Kanbans allow arrivals at a work centre to match (or nearly match) the processing time.

Kanban is a Japanese word for *card*. In their effort to reduce inventory, the Japanese use systems that "pull" inventory through work centres. They often use a "card" to signal the need for another container of material—hence the name *kanban*. *The card is the authorization for the next container of material to be produced.* Typically, a kanban signal exists for each container of items to be obtained. An order for the container is then initiated by each kanban and "pulled" from the producing department or supplier. A sequence of kanbans "pulls" the material through the plant.

The system has been modified in many facilities so that even though it is called a *kanban*, the card itself does not exist. In some cases, an empty position on the floor is sufficient indication that the next container is needed. In other cases, some sort of signal, such as a flag or rag (see Figure 16.8), alerts that it is time for the next container.

When there is visual contact between producer and user, the process works like this:

1. The user removes a standard-size container of parts from a small storage area, as shown in Figure 16.8.
2. The signal at the storage area is seen by the producing department as authorization to replenish the using department or storage area. Because there is an optimum lot size, the producing department may make several containers at a time.

LO5 Define *kanban*

Kanban

The Japanese word for *card*, which has come to mean "signal"; a kanban system moves parts through production via a "pull" from a signal.

A kanban need not be as formal as signal lights or empty carts. The cook in a fast-food restaurant knows that when six cars are in line, eight meat patties and six orders of French fries should be cooking.

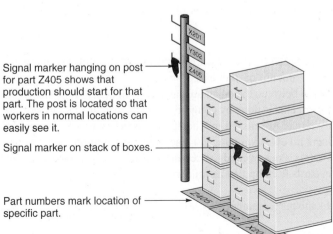

Signal marker hanging on post for part Z405 shows that production should start for that part. The post is located so that workers in normal locations can easily see it.

Signal marker on stack of boxes.

Part numbers mark location of specific part.

FIGURE 16.8

Diagram of Storage Area with Warning-Signal Marker

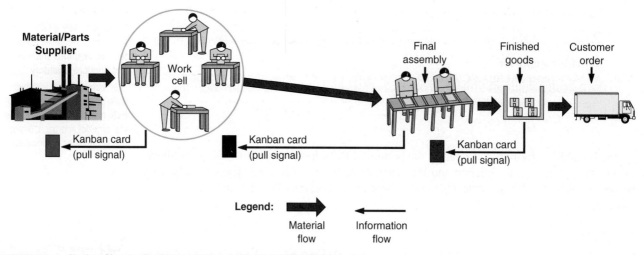

FIGURE 16.9 Kanban Signals "Pull" Material Through the Production Process

As a customer "pulls" an order from finished goods, a signal (kanban card) is sent to the final assembly area. Final assembly produces and resupplies finished goods. When final assembly needs components, it sends a signal to *its* supplier, a work cell. The work cell, in turn, sends a signal to the material/parts supplier.

Figure 16.9 shows how a kanban works, pulling units as needed from production. This system is similar to the resupply that occurs in your neighbourhood supermarket: The customer buys; the stock clerk observes the shelf or receives notice from the end-of-day sales list and restocks. When the limited supply, if any, in the store's storage is depleted, a "pull" signal is sent to the warehouse, distributor, or manufacturer for resupply, usually that night. The complicating factor in a manufacturing firm is the time needed for actual manufacturing (production) to take place.

Several additional points regarding kanbans may be helpful:

- When the producer and user are not in visual contact, a card can be used; otherwise, a light or flag or empty spot on the floor may be adequate.
- Because a pull station may require several resupply components, several kanban pull techniques can be used for different products at the same pull station.
- Usually, each card controls a specific quantity of parts, although multiple card systems are used if the producing work cell produces several components or if the lot size is different from the move size.
- In an MRP system (see Chapter 14), the schedule can be thought of as a "build" authorization and the kanban as a type of "pull" system that initiates the actual production.
- The kanban cards provide a direct control (limit) on the amount of work-in-process between cells.
- If there is an immediate storage area, a two-card system may be used—one card circulates between user and storage area, and the other circulates between the storage area and the producing area.

DETERMINING THE NUMBER OF KANBAN CARDS OR CONTAINERS The number of kanban cards, or containers, sets the amount of authorized inventory. To determine the number of containers moving back and forth between the using area and the producing areas, management first sets the size of each container. This is done by computing the lot size, using a model such as the production order quantity model (discussed in Chapter 12 and shown in Equation [16-1]). Setting the number of containers involves knowing (1) lead time needed to produce a container of parts and (2) the amount of safety stock needed to account for variability or uncertainty in the system. The number of kanban cards is computed as follows:

$$\text{Number of kanbans (containers)} = \frac{\text{Demand during lead time } + \text{ Safety stock}}{\text{Size of container}} \qquad \textbf{(16-3)}$$

Example 2 illustrates how to calculate the number of kanbans needed.

EXAMPLE 2

Determining the Number of Kanban Containers

Hobbs Bakery produces short runs of cakes that are shipped to grocery stores. The owner, Ken Hobbs, wants to try to reduce inventory by changing to a kanban system. He has developed the following data and asked you to finish the project.

$$\text{Daily demand} = 500 \text{ cakes}$$

$$\text{Production lead time} = \text{Wait time} + \text{Material handling time} + \text{Processing time} = 2 \text{ days}$$

$$\text{Safety stock} = \tfrac{1}{2} \text{ day}$$

$$\text{Container size (determined on a production order size EOQ basis)} = 250 \text{ cakes}$$

APPROACH ▶ Having determined that the EOQ size is 250, we then determine the number of kanbans (containers) needed.

SOLUTION ▶ Demand during lead time = Lead time × Daily demand = 2 days × 500 cakes = 1000

$$\text{safety stock} = 250$$

Number of kanbans (containers) needed =

$$\frac{\text{Demand during lead time} + \text{Safety stock}}{\text{Container size}} = \frac{1000 + 250}{250} = 5$$

INSIGHT ▶ Once the reorder point is hit, five containers should be released.

LEARNING EXERCISE ▶ If lead time drops to 1 day, how many containers are needed? [Answer: 3.]

RELATED PROBLEMS ▶ 16.1, 16.2, 16.3, 16.4, 16.5, 16.6

LO6 Compute the required number of kanbans

ADVANTAGES OF KANBAN Containers are typically very small, usually a matter of a few hours' worth of production. Such a system requires tight schedules. Small quantities must be produced several times a day. The process must run smoothly with little variability in quality of lead time because any shortage has an almost immediate impact on the entire system. Kanban places added emphasis on meeting schedules, reducing the time and cost required by setups, and economical material handling.

Whether it is called kanban or something else, the advantages of small inventory and *pulling* material through the plant only when needed are significant. For instance, small batches allow only a very limited amount of faulty or delayed material. Problems are immediately evident. Numerous aspects of inventory are bad; only one aspect—availability—is good. Among the bad aspects are poor quality, obsolescence, damage, occupied space, committed assets, increased insurance, increased material handling, and increased accidents. Kanban systems put downward pressure on all these negative aspects of inventory.

In-plant kanban systems often use standardized, reusable containers that protect the specific quantities to be moved. Such containers are also desirable in the supply chain. Standardized containers reduce weight and disposal costs, generate less wasted space in trailers, and require less labour to pack, unpack, and prepare items.

Lean Quality

The relationship between Lean and quality is a strong one. They are related in three ways. First, Lean cuts the cost of obtaining good quality. This saving occurs because scrap, rework, inventory investment, and damage costs are buried in inventory. Lean forces down inventory; therefore, fewer bad units are produced and fewer units must be reworked. In short, whereas inventory *hides* bad quality, Lean immediately *exposes* it.

Second, Lean improves quality. As Lean shrinks queues and lead time, it keeps evidence of errors fresh and limits the number of potential sources of error. In effect, Lean creates an early warning system for quality problems so that fewer bad units are produced and feedback is immediate. This advantage can accrue both within the firm and with goods received from outside vendors.

Third and finally, better quality means fewer buffers are needed and, therefore, a better, easier-to-employ Lean system can exist. Often the purpose of keeping inventory is to protect against unreliable quality. If consistent quality exists, Lean allows firms to reduce all costs associated with inventory. Table 16.4 suggests some requirements for quality in a Lean environment.

STUDENT TIP

Good quality costs less.

Table 16.4
Lean Quality Tactics

Use statistical process control

Empower employees

Build fail-safe methods (poka-yoke, checklists, etc.)

Expose poor quality with small lots

Provide immediate feedback

Toyota Motor Corporation

This auto plant, like most Lean facilities, empowers employees so they can stop the entire production line by pulling the overhead cord if any quality problems are spotted.

LO7 Identify six attributes of Lean organizations

Kaizen
A focus on continuous improvement.

Toyota Production System

Toyota Motor's Eiji Toyoda and Taiichi Ohno are given credit for the Toyota Production System (TPS) (see the *Global Company Profile* that opens this chapter). Three core components of TPS are continuous improvement, respect for people, and standard work practice.

CONTINUOUS IMPROVEMENT

Continuous improvement under TPS means building an organizational culture and instilling in its people a value system stressing that processes can be improved—indeed, that improvement is an integral part of every employee's job. This process is formalized in TPS by **kaizen**, the Japanese word for change for the good, or what is more generally known as *continuous improvement*. In application, it means making a multitude of small or incremental changes as one seeks elusive perfection. (See the *OM in Action* box "Toyota's New Challenge".) Instilling the mantra

---

OM in Action   Toyota's New Challenge

With the generally high value of the yen, making a profit on cars built in Japan but sold in foreign markets is a challenge. As a result, Honda and Nissan are moving plants overseas, closer to customers. But Toyota, despite marginal profit on cars produced for export, is maintaining its current Japanese capacity. Toyota, which led the way with Lean and the TPS, is doubling down on its manufacturing prowess and continuous improvement. For an organization that traditionally does things slowly and step-by-step, the changes are radical. With its first new plant in Japan in 18 years, Toyota believes it can once again set new production benchmarks. It is drastically reforming its production processes in a number of ways:

- The assembly line has cars sitting side-by-side, rather than bumper-to-bumper, shrinking the length of the line by 35% and requiring fewer steps by workers.
- Instead of having car chassis dangling from overhead conveyors, they are perched on raised platforms, reducing heating and cooling costs by 40%.

Conventional

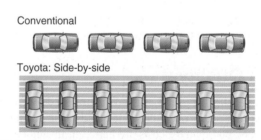

Toyota: Side-by-side

- Retooling permits faster changeovers, allowing for shorter product runs of components, supporting level scheduling.
- The assembly line uses quiet friction rollers with fewer moving parts, requiring less maintenance than conventional lines and reducing worker fatigue.

These TPS innovations, efficient production with small lot sizes, rapid changeover, level scheduling, half the workers, and half the square footage, are being duplicated in Toyota's new plant in Blue Springs, Mississippi.

Sources: Forbes (July 29, 2012); *Automotive News* (February, 2011); and *The Wall Street Journal* (November 29, 2011).

of continuous improvement begins at recruiting and continues through extensive and continuing training. One of the reasons continuous improvement works at Toyota, we should note, is because of another core value at Toyota, Toyota's respect for people.

RESPECT FOR PEOPLE

At Toyota, people are recruited, trained, and treated as knowledge workers. Aided by aggressive cross-training and few job classifications, Lean engages the mental as well as physical capacities of employees in the challenging task of improving operations. Employees are empowered to make improvements and to stop machines and processes when quality problems exist. Indeed, empowered employees are a necessary part of Lean. This means that those tasks that have traditionally been assigned to staff are moved to employees. Toyota recognizes that employees know more about their jobs than anyone else. Lean respects employees by giving them the opportunity to enrich both their jobs and their lives.

PROCESSES AND STANDARD WORK PRACTICE

Standard work practice at Toyota includes these underlying principles:

- Work is completely specified as to content, sequence, timing, and outcome.
- Internal and external customer–supplier connections are direct, specifying personnel, methods, timing, and quantity.
- Material and service flows are to be simple and direct. Goods and services are directed to a specific person or machine.
- Improvements in the system must be made in accordance with the "scientific method," at the lowest possible level in the organization.[2]

Lean requires that activities, connections, and flows include built-in tests to automatically signal problems. Any gap between what is expected and what occurs becomes immediately evident. The education and training of Toyota's employees and the responsiveness of the system to problems make the seemingly rigid system flexible and adaptable to changing circumstances. The result is ongoing improvements in reliability, flexibility, safety, and efficiency.

Lean Organizations

STUDENT TIP

Lean drives out non–value-added activities.

Lean production can be thought of as the end result of a well-run OM function. While TPS tends to have an *internal* focus, Lean production begins *externally* with a focus on the customer. Understanding what the customer wants and ensuring customer input and feedback are starting points for Lean production. Lean operations mean identifying customer value by analyzing all the activities required to produce the product and then optimizing the entire process from the customer's perspective.

BUILDING A LEAN ORGANIZATION

The transition to Lean production is difficult. Building an organizational culture where learning, empowerment, and continuous improvement are the norm is a challenge. However, organizations that focus on JIT, quality, and employee empowerment are often Lean producers. Such firms drive out activities that do not add value in the eyes of the customer: They include leaders like United Parcel Service, Harley-Davidson, and, of course, Toyota. Even traditionally idiosyncratic organizations such as hospitals (see the *OM in Action* box "Lean Delivers the Medicine") find improved productivity with Lean operations. Lean organizations adopt a philosophy of minimizing waste by striving for perfection through continuous learning, creativity, and teamwork. They tend to share the following attributes:

- *Use Lean techniques* to eliminate virtually all inventory.
- *Build systems that help employees* produce a perfect part every time.
- *Reduce space requirements* by minimizing travel distance.

---

[2] Adapted from Steven J. Spear, "Learning to Lead at Toyota," *Harvard Business Review* 82, no. 5 (May 2004): 78–86; and Steven J. Spear and H. Kent Bowen, "Decoding the DNA of the Toyota Production System," *Harvard Business Review* 77, no. 5 (September–October 1999): 97–106.

OM in Action Lean Delivers the Medicine

Using kaizen techniques straight out of Lean, a team of employees at San Francisco General Hospital target and then analyze a particular area within the hospital for improvement. Hospitals today are focusing on through-put and quality in the belief that excelling on these measures will drive down costs and push up patient satisfaction. Doctors and nurses now work together in teams that immerse themselves in a weeklong kaizen event. These events generate plans that make specific improvements in flow, quality, costs, or the patients' experience.

One recent kaizen event focused on the number of minutes it takes from the moment a patient is wheeled into the operating room to when the first incision is made. A team spent a week coming up with ways to whittle 10 minutes off this "prep" time. Every minute saved reduces labour cost and opens up critical facilities. Another kaizen event targeted the Urgent Care Center, dropping the average wait from 5 hours down to 2.5, primarily by adding an on-site X-ray machine instead of requiring patients to walk 15 minutes to the main radiology department. Similarly, wait times in the Surgical Clinic dropped from 2.5 hours to 70 minutes. The operating room now uses a *5S* protocol and has implemented *Standard Work* for the preoperation process.

As hospitals focus on improving medical quality and patient satisfaction, they are exposed to some Japanese terms associated with Lean, many of which do not have a direct English translation: **Gemba**, the place where work is actually performed; **Hansei**, a period of critical

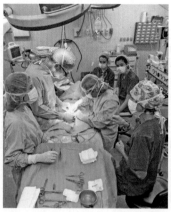

Frank Boston/Fotolia

self-reflection; **Heijunka**, a level production schedule that provides balance and smooths day-to-day variation; **Jidoka**, using both human intelligence and technology to stop a process at the first sign of a potential problem; **Kaizen**, continuous improvement; and **Muda**, anything that consumes resources, but provides no value.

Lean systems are increasingly being adopted by hospitals as they try to reduce costs while improving quality and increasing patient satisfaction—and as San Francisco General has demonstrated, Lean techniques are working.

Sources: San Francisco Chronicle (Oct. 14, 2013) and San Francisco General Hospital & Trauma Center Annual Report, 2012–2013.

- *Develop partnerships with suppliers*, helping them to understand the needs of the ultimate customer.
- *Educate suppliers* to accept responsibility for satisfying end customer needs.
- *Eliminate all but value-added activities.* Material handling, inspection, inventory, and rework are the likely targets because these do not add value to the product.
- *Develop employees* by constantly improving job design, training, employee commitment, teamwork, and empowerment.
- *Make jobs challenging*, pushing responsibility to the lowest level possible.
- *Build worker flexibility* through cross-training and reducing job classifications.

Success requires the full commitment and involvement of managers, employees, and suppliers. The rewards that Lean producers reap are spectacular. Lean producers often become benchmark performers.

LEAN SUSTAINABILITY

Lean and sustainability are two sides of the same coin. Both seek to maximize resource and economic efficiency. However, if Lean focuses on only the immediate process and system, then managers may miss the sustainability issues beyond the firm. As we discussed in Supplement 5, sustainability requires examining the systems in which the firm and its stakeholders operate. When this is done, both Lean and sustainability achieve higher levels of performance.

Lean drives out waste because waste adds nothing for the customer. Sustainability drives out waste because waste is both expensive and has an adverse effect on the environment. Driving out waste is the common ground of Lean sustainability.

Lean Operations in Services

STUDENT TIP

Lean began in factories but is now also used in services throughout the world.

The features of Lean operations apply to services just as they do in other sectors. Here are some examples applied to suppliers, layout, inventory, and scheduling in the service sector.

VIDEO 16.2
Lean at Arnold Palmer Hospital

SUPPLIERS

As we have noted, virtually every restaurant deals with its suppliers on a JIT basis. Those that do not are usually unsuccessful. The waste is too evident—food spoils, and customers complain or get sick.

LO8 Explain how Lean applies to services

LAYOUTS

Lean layouts are required in restaurant kitchens, where cold food must be served cold and hot food hot. McDonald's, for example, has reconfigured its kitchen layout at great expense to drive seconds out of the production process, thereby speeding delivery to customers. With the new process, McDonald's can produce made-to-order hamburgers in 45 seconds. Layouts also make a difference in airline baggage claim, where customers expect their bags just in time.

INVENTORY

Stockbrokers drive inventory down to nearly zero every day. Most sell and buy orders occur on an immediate basis because an unexecuted sell or buy order is not acceptable to the client. A broker may be in serious trouble if left holding an unexecuted trade. Similarly, McDonald's reduces inventory waste by maintaining a finished goods inventory of only 10 minutes; after that, it is thrown away. Hospitals, such as Arnold Palmer (described in this chapter's Video Case Study), manage Lean inventory and low safety stocks for many items. Even critical supplies such as pharmaceuticals may be held to low levels by developing community networks as backup systems. In this manner, if one pharmacy runs out of a needed drug, another member of the network can supply it until the next day's shipment arrives.

SCHEDULING

At airline ticket counters, the focus of the system is on adjusting to customer demand. But rather than being accommodated by inventory availability, demand is satisfied by personnel. Through elaborate scheduling, ticket counter personnel show up just in time to cover peaks in customer demand. In other words, rather than "things" inventoried, personnel are scheduled. At a salon, the focus is only slightly different: The *customer* and the staff are scheduled to assure prompt service. At McDonald's and Walmart, scheduling of personnel is down to 15-minute increments, based on precise forecasting of demand. Additionally, at McDonald's, production is done in small lots to ensure that fresh, hot hamburgers are delivered just in time. In short, both personnel and production are scheduled to meet specific demand. Notice that in all three of these Lean organizations—the airline ticket counter, the salon, and McDonald's—scheduling is a key ingredient. Excellent forecasts drive those schedules. Those forecasts may be very elaborate, with seasonal, daily, and even hourly components in the case of the airline ticket counter (holiday sales, flight time, etc.), seasonal and weekly components at the salon (holidays and Fridays create special problems), and down to a few minutes (to respond to the daily meal cycle) at McDonald's.

To deliver goods and services to customers under continuously changing demand, suppliers need to be reliable, inventories Lean, cycle times short, and schedules nimble. A Lean focus engages and empowers employees to create and deliver the customer's perception of value, eliminating whatever does not contribute to this goal. Lean operations are currently being developed with great success in many firms, regardless of their products. Lean techniques are widely used in both goods-producing and service-producing firms; they just look different.

CHAPTER SUMMARY

Lean operation is a philosophy of continuous improvement. Lean operations focus on customer desires, respect for people and standard work practices, and driving out waste by reducing inventory. But all three reduce waste in the production process. And because waste is found in anything that does not add value, organizations that implement these techniques are adding value more efficiently than other firms. The expectation of these systems is that empowered employees work with committed management to build systems that respond to customers with ever-lower cost and higher quality.

ETHICAL │ DILEMMA

In this Lean operations world, in an effort to lower handling costs, speed delivery, and reduce inventory, retailers are forcing their suppliers to do more and more in the way of preparing their merchandise for their cross-docking warehouses, shipment to specific stores, and shelf presentation. Your company, a small manufacturer of aquarium decorations, is in a tough position. First, Mega-Mart wanted you to develop barcode technology, then special packaging, then small individual shipments bar coded for each store (this way, when the merchandise hits the warehouse, it is cross-docked immediately to the correct truck and store and is ready for shelf placement). And now Mega-Mart wants you to develop RFID—immediately. Mega-Mart has made it clear that suppliers that cannot keep up with the technology will be dropped.

Earlier, when you didn't have the expertise for bar codes, you had to borrow money and hire an outside firm to do the development, purchase the technology, and train your shipping clerk. Then, meeting the special packaging requirement drove you into a loss for several months, resulting in a loss for last year. Now it appears that the RFID request is impossible. Your business, under the best of conditions, is marginally profitable, and the bank may not be willing to bail you out again. Over the years, Mega-Mart has slowly become your major customer, and without them you are probably out of business. What are the ethical issues, and what do you do?

Discussion Questions

1. What is JIT?
2. What is a Lean producer?
3. What is TPS?
4. What is level scheduling?
5. JIT attempts to remove delays, which do not add value. How then does JIT cope with weather and its impact on crop harvest and transportation times?
6. What are three ways in which Lean and quality are related?
7. How does TPS contribute to competitive advantage?
8. What are the characteristics of supplier partnerships with respect to suppliers?

9. Discuss how the Japanese word for *card* has application in the study of JIT.
10. Standardized, reusable containers have obvious benefits for shipping. What is the purpose of these devices within the plant?
11. Does Lean production work in the service sector? Provide an illustration.
12. Which Lean techniques work in both the manufacturing *and* service sectors?

Solved Problems Virtual Office Hours help is available at MyLab Operations Management.

▼ SOLVED PROBLEM 16.1

Krupp Refrigeration, Inc., is trying to reduce inventory and wants you to install a kanban system for compressors on one of its assembly lines. Determine the size of the kanban and the number of kanbans (containers) needed.

Setup cost = $10

Annual holding cost per compressor = $100

Daily production = 200 compressors

Annual usage = 25 000 (50 weeks × 5 days each
　　　　　　　　　　× daily usage of 100 compressors)

Lead time = 3 days

Safety stock = $\frac{1}{2}$ day's production of compressors

Daily usage = 100

▼ SOLUTION

First, we must determine kanban container size. To do this, we determine the production order quantity (see discussion in Chapter 12 or Equation [16-1]), which determines the kanban size:

$$Q_p^* = \sqrt{\frac{2DS}{H\left(1 - \frac{d}{p}\right)}} = \sqrt{\frac{2(25\,000)(10)}{H\left(1 - \frac{d}{p}\right)}} = \sqrt{\frac{500\,000}{100\left(1 - \frac{100}{200}\right)}} = \sqrt{\frac{500\,000}{50}}$$

$= \sqrt{10\,000} = 100$ compressors. So the production order size and the size of the kanban container $= 100.$

Then we determine the number of kanbans:

$$\text{Demand during lead time} = 300 \,(= 3 \text{ days} \times \text{daily usage of } 100)$$

$$\text{Safety stock} = 100 \,(= \tfrac{1}{2} \times \text{daily production of } 200)$$

$$\text{Number of kanbans} = \frac{\text{Demand during lead time} + \text{Safety stock}}{\text{Size of container}}$$

$$= \frac{300 + 100}{100} = \frac{400}{100} = 4 \text{ containers}$$

Problems*

• **16.1** Leblanc Electronics Inc. in Chicoutimi produces short runs of custom airwave scanners for the defence industry. You have been asked by the owner, Larry Leblanc, to reduce inventory by introducing a kanban system. After several hours of analysis, you develop the following data for scanner connectors used in one work cell. How many kanbans do you need for this connector?

Daily demand	1000 connectors
Lead time	2 days
Safety stock	$\frac{1}{2}$ day
Kanban size	500 connectors

• **16.2** Chip Gillikin's company wants to establish kanbans to feed a newly established work cell. The following data have been provided. How many kanbans are needed?

Daily demand	250 units
Production lead time	$\frac{1}{2}$ day
Safety stock	$\frac{1}{4}$ day
Kanban size	50 units

•• **16.3** Chris Millikan Manufacturing Inc. is moving to kanbans to support its telephone switching-board assembly lines. Determine the size of the kanban for subassemblies and the number of kanbans needed.

Setup cost = $30
Annual holding
        cost = $120 per subassembly
Daily production = 20 subassemblies
    Annual usage = 2500 (50 weeks × 5 days each
                  × daily usage of 10 subassemblies)
      Lead time = 16 days
    Safety stock = 4 days' production of subassemblies. **Px**

•• **16.4** Maggie Moylan Motorcycle Corp. uses kanbans to support its transmission assembly line. Determine the size of the kanban for the mainshaft assembly and the number of kanbans needed.

Setup cost = $20
Annual holding cost
of mainshaft assembly = $250 per unit
    Daily production = 300 mainshafts
      Annual usage = 20 000 (= 50 weeks × 5 days each
                × daily usage of 80 mainshafts)
      Lead time = 3 days
    Safety stock = $\frac{1}{2}$ days' production of mainshafts. **Px**

• **16.5** Discount-Mart, a major East Coast retailer, wants to determine the economic order quantity (see Chapter 12 for EOQ formulas) for its halogen lamps. It currently buys all halogen lamps from Specialty Lighting Manufacturers, in Antigonish. Annual demand is 2000 lamps, ordering cost per order is $30, and annual carrying cost per lamp is $12.

a) What is the EOQ?
b) What are the total annual costs of holding and ordering (managing) this inventory?
c) How many orders should Discount-Mart place with Specialty Lighting per year? **Px**

••• **16.6** Discount-Mart (see Problem 16.5), as part of its new JIT program, has signed a long-term contract with Specialty Lighting and will place orders electronically for its halogen lamps. Ordering costs will drop to $0.50 per order, but Discount-Mart also reassessed its carrying costs and raised them to $20 per lamp.
a) What is the new economic order quantity?
b) How many orders will now be placed?
c) What is the total annual cost of managing the inventory with this policy? **Px**

•• **16.7** How do your answers to Problems 16.5 and 16.6 provide insight into a JIT purchasing strategy?

••• **16.8** Bill Penny has a repetitive manufacturing plant producing trailer hitches in Sudbury, Ontario. The plant has an average inventory turnover of only 12 times per year. He has therefore determined that he will reduce his component lot sizes. He has developed the following data for one component, the safety chain clip:

Annual demand = 31 200 units
Daily demand = 120 units
Daily production (in 8 hours) = 960 units
Desired lot size (1 hour of production) = 120 units
Holding cost per unit per year = $12
Setup labour cost per hour = $20

How many minutes of setup time should he have his plant manager aim for regarding this component?

••• **16.9** Given the following information about a product, at Phyllis Simon's firm, what is the appropriate setup time?

Annual demand = 39 000 units
Daily demand = 150 units
Daily production = 1000 units
Desired lot size = 150 units
Holding cost per unit per year = $10
Setup labour cost per hour = $40

••• **16.10** Rick Wing has a repetitive manufacturing plant producing automobile steering wheels. Use the following data to prepare for a reduced lot size. The firm uses a work year of 305 days.

Annual demand for steering wheels	30 500
Daily demand	100
Daily production (8 hours)	800
Desired lot size (2 hours of production)	200
Holding cost per unit per year	$10

a) What is the setup cost, based on the desired lot size?
b) What is the setup time, based on $40 per hour setup labour?

Note: **Px** means the problem may be solved with POM for Windows and/or Excel OM.

CASE STUDIES

Lean Operations at Alaska Airlines

Alaska Airlines operates in a land of rugged beauty, crystal clear lakes, spectacular glaciers, majestic mountains, and bright blue skies. But equally awesome is its operating performance. Alaska Airlines consistently provides the industry's number one overall ranking and best on-time performance. A key ingredient of this excellent performance is Alaska Airlines's Lean initiative.

With an aggressive implementation of Lean, Ben Minicucci, Executive VP for Operations, is finding ever-increasing levels of performance. He pushes this initiative throughout the company with: (1) a focus on continuous improvement, (2) metrics that measure performance against targets, and (3) making performance relevant to Alaska Airlines's empowered employees.

With leadership training that includes a strong focus on participative management, Minicucci has created a seven-person Lean Department. The department provides extensive training in Lean via one-week courses, participative workshops, and two-week classes that train employees to become a Six Sigma Green Belt. Some employees even pursue the next step, Black Belt certification.

A huge part of any airline's operations is fuel cost, but capital utilization and much of the remaining cost is dependent upon ground equipment and crews that handle aircraft turnaround and maintenance, in-flight services, and customer service.

As John Ladner, Director of Seattle Airport Operations, has observed, "Lean eliminates waste, exposes nonstandard work, and is forcing a focus on variations in documented best practices and work time."

Lean is now part of the Alaska Airlines corporate culture, with some 60 ongoing projects. Kaizen events (called "Accelerated Improvement Workshops" at Alaska Airlines), Gemba Walks (called "waste walks" by Alaska Airlines), and 5S are now a part of everyday conversation at Alaska Airlines. Lean projects have included:

- Applying 5S to identify aircraft ground equipment and its location on the tarmac.
- Improving preparation for and synchronization of the arrival and departure sequences; time to open the front door after arrival has been reduced from 4.5 to 1 min.
- Redefining the disconnect procedure for tow bars used to "push back" aircraft at departure time; planes now depart 2–3 minutes faster.
- Revising the deicing process, meaning less time for the plane to be on the tarmac.

Alaska Airlines

- Improving pilot staffing, making Alaska's pilot productivity the highest in the industry. Every 1% improvement in productivity leads to a $5 million savings on a recurring basis. Alaska Airlines has achieved a 7% productivity improvement over the last five years.

Another current Lean project is passenger unloading and loading. Lean instructor Allison Fletcher calls this "the most unique project I have worked on". One exciting aspect of deplaning is Alaska's solar-powered "switchback" staircase for unloading passengers through the rear door (see photo). Alaska is saving two minutes, or nearly 17%, off previous unloading time with this new process. Alaska Airlines's Lean culture has made it a leader in the industry.

Discussion Questions*

1. What are the key ingredients of Lean, as identified at Alaska Airlines?
2. As an initial phase of a kaizen event, discuss the many ways passengers can be loaded and unloaded from airplanes.
3. Document the research that is being done on the aircraft passenger-loading problem.

---

*You may wish to view the video that accompanies this case before addressing these questions.

Saskatchewan Mutual Insurance Company

Saskatchewan Mutual Insurance Company (SMIC) has a major insurance office facility located in Regina. The Regina office is responsible for processing all of SMIC's insurance claims for all of Canada. The company's sales have experienced rapid growth during the last year, and as expected, record levels in claims followed.

Over 2500 forms for claims a day are now flowing into the office for processing. Unfortunately, fewer than 2500 forms a day are flowing out. The total time to process a claim, from the time it arrives to the time a cheque is mailed, has increased from 10 days to 10 weeks. As a result, some customers are threatening legal action.

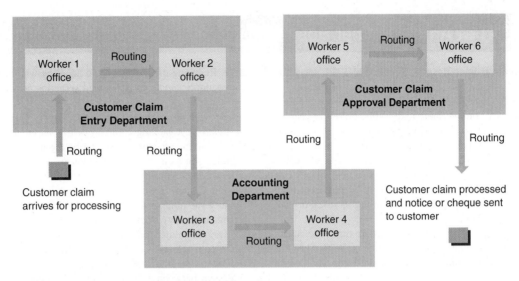

FIGURE 16.10 Claims Processing Department Layout

Sally Cook, the manager of Claims Processing, is particularly distressed, as she knows that a claim seldom requires more than three hours of actual work. Under the current administrative procedures, human resources limitations, and facility constraints, there appear to be no easy fixes for the problem. But clearly, something must be done, as the workload has overwhelmed the existing system.

SMIC management wants aggressive, but economical, action taken to fix the problem. Cook has decided to try a Lean approach to claim processing. With support from her bosses, and as a temporary fix, Cook has brought in part-time personnel from SMIC sales divisions across the country to help. They are to work down the claims backlog while a new Lean system is installed.

Meanwhile, claims processing managers and employees are to be trained in Lean principles. With Lean principles firmly in mind, managers will redesign jobs to move responsibilities for quality control activities to each employee, holding them responsible for quality work and any necessary corrections. Cook will also initiate worker-training programs that explain the entire claim processing flow, as well as provide comprehensive training on each step in the process. Data-entry skills will also be taught to both employees and managers in an effort to fix responsibility for data accuracy on the processor rather than on data entry clerks. Additionally, cross-training will be emphasized to enable workers within departments to process a variety of customer claim applications in their entirety.

Cook and her supervisors are also re-examining the insurance and claim forms currently in use. They want to see if standardization of forms will cut processing time, reduce data-entry time, and cut work-in-process.

They hope the changes will also save training time. Making changes in work methods and worker skills leads logically to a need for change in the layout of the Claims Processing Department. This potential change represents a major move from the departmental layout of the past, and will be a costly step. To help ensure the successful implementation of this phase of the changeover, Cook established a team made up of supervisors, employees, and an outside

office layout consultant. She also had the team visit the Toyota assembly plant in Cambridge, Ontario, to observe its use of work cells to aid Lean.

The team concluded that a change in the office facilities was necessary to successfully implement and integrate Lean concepts at SMIC. The team believes it should revise the layout of the operation and work methods to bring them in line with "group technology cell" layouts. An example of the current departmental layout and claim processing flow pattern is presented in Figure 16.10. As can be seen in this figure, customer claims arrive for processing at the facility and flow through a series of offices and departments to eventually complete the claim process. Although the arrangement of the offices and workers in Figure 16.10 is typical, the entire facility actually operates 20 additional flows, each consisting of the same three departments. However, not all of the 20 flows are configured in exactly the same way. The number of employees, for example, varies depending on the claim form requirements (larger claims have to be approved by more people). So while all forms must pass through the same three departments (Customer Claim Entry, Accounting, and Customer Claim Approval), the number of workers for each claim may vary from two to four. For this reason, the SMIC facility currently maintains a staff of over 180 office workers just to process and route claims. All of these people work for Cook.

Discussion Questions

1. Identify the attributes you would expect the Claims Processing Department at SMIC to have once the new Lean system is in place.
2. What will the restructured cell layout for claim processing in Figure 16.10 look like? Draw it.
3. What assumptions are you making about personnel and equipment in the new group technology cell layout?
4. How will the new Lean-oriented system benefit the SMIC operation? Explain.

Source: Schniederjans, Marc J. *Topics in Just-in-Time Management*, 1st Edition © 1993, pp. 283–285. Reprinted by permission of Pearson Education, Inc. New York, NY.

JIT at Arnold Palmer Hospital

Orlando's Arnold Palmer Hospital, founded in 1989, specializes in treatment of women and children and is renowned for its high quality rankings (top 10% of 2000 benchmarked hospitals), its labour and delivery volume (more than 14 000 births per year, and growing), and its neonatal intensive care unit (one of the highest survival rates in the nation). But quality medical practices and high patient satisfaction require costly inventory—some U.S. $30 million per year and thousands of stock keeping units (SKUs). With pressure on medical care to manage and reduce costs, Arnold Palmer Hospital has turned towards controlling its inventory with just-in-time (JIT) techniques.

Within the hospital, for example, drugs are now distributed at nursing workstations via dispensing machines (almost like vending machines) that electronically track patient usage and post the related charge to each patient. The dispensing stations are refilled each night, based on patient demand and prescriptions written by doctors.

To address JIT issues externally, Arnold Palmer Hospital turned towards a major distribution partner, McKesson General Medical, which, as a first-tier supplier, provides the hospital with about one-quarter of all its medical/surgical inventory. McKesson supplies sponges, basins, towels, mayo stand covers, syringes, and hundreds of other medical/surgical items. To ensure coordinated daily delivery of inventory purchased from McKesson, an account executive has been assigned to the hospital on a full-time basis, as well as two other individuals who address customer service and product issues. The result has been a drop in central supply average daily inventory from $400 000 to $114 000 since JIT.

JIT success has also been achieved in the area of *custom surgical packs*. Custom surgical packs are the sterile coverings, disposable plastic trays, gauze, and the like, specialized to each type of surgical procedure. Arnold Palmer Hospital uses 10 different custom packs for various surgical procedures. "Over 50 000 packs are used each year, for a total cost of about US $1.5 million," says George DeLong, head of supply chain management.

The packs are not only delivered in a JIT manner but also packed that way as well. That is, they are packed in the reverse order they are used so each item comes out of the pack in the sequence it is needed. The packs are bulky and expensive, and must remain sterile. Reducing the inventory and handling while maintaining an assured sterile supply for scheduled surgeries presents a challenge to hospitals.

Here is how the supply chain works: Custom packs are *assembled* by a packing company with *components supplied* primarily from manufacturers selected by the hospital, and *delivered* by McKesson from its local warehouse. Arnold Palmer Hospital works with its own surgical staff (through the Medical Economics Outcome Committee) to identify and standardize the custom packs to reduce the number of custom pack SKUs. With this integrated system, pack safety stock inventory has been cut to one day.

The procedure to drive the custom surgical pack JIT system begins with a "pull" from the doctors' daily surgical schedule. Then, Arnold Palmer Hospital initiates an electronic order to McKesson between 1:00 and 2:00 p.m. daily. At 4:00 p.m. the next day, McKesson delivers the packs. Hospital personnel arrive at 7:00 p.m. and stock the shelves for scheduled surgeries. McKesson then reorders from the packing company, which in turn "pulls" necessary inventory for the quantity of packs needed from the manufacturers.

Arnold Palmer Hospital's JIT system reduces inventory investment, expensive traditional ordering, and bulky storage, and supports quality with a sterile delivery.

Discussion Questions*

1. What do you recommend be done when an error is found in a pack as it is opened for an operation?
2. How might the procedure for custom surgical packs described here be improved?
3. When discussing JIT in services, the text notes that suppliers, layout, inventory, and scheduling are all used. Provide an example of each of these at Arnold Palmer Hospital.
4. When a doctor proposes a new surgical procedure, how do you recommend the SKU for a new custom pack be entered into the hospital's supply chain system?

---

*You may wish to view the video that accompanies this case before answering these questions.

CHAPTER 16 | RAPID REVIEW

Main Heading	Review Material	MyLab Operations Management
LEAN OPERATIONS (pp. 619–621)	• **Just-in-time (JIT)**—Continuous and forced problem solving via a focus on throughput and reduced inventory. • **Toyota Production System (TPS)**—Focus on continuous improvement, respect for people, and standard work practices. • **Lean operations**—Eliminate waste through a focus on exactly what the customer wants. *When implemented as a comprehensive manufacturing strategy, JIT, TPS, and Lean systems sustain competitive advantage and result in increased overall returns.*	**VIDEO 16.1** Lean Operations at Alaska Airlines

Main Heading   **Review Material**

- **Seven wastes**—Overproduction; queues; transportation; inventory; motion; overprocessing; defective product.
- **5Ss**—A Lean production checklist: *sort; simplify; shine; standardize; sustain.*

North American managers often add two additional Ss to the five original ones: *safety* and *support/maintenance.*

- **Variability**—Any deviation from the optimum process that delivers perfect product on time, every time.

Both JIT and inventory reduction are effective tools for identifying causes of variability.

- **Throughput**—The time required to move orders through the production process, from receipt to delivery.
- **Manufacturing cycle time**—The time between the arrival of raw materials and the shipping of finished products.
- **Pull system**—A concept that results in material being produced only when requested and moved to where it is needed just as it is needed.

Pull systems use signals to request production and delivery from supplying stations to stations that have production capacity available.

Main Heading	Review Material	MyLab
LEAN AND JUST-IN-TIME (pp. 621–624)	• **Supplier partnership**—Partnership of suppliers and purchasers that removes waste and drives down costs for mutual benefits. Some specific goals of supplier partnerships are removal of unnecessary activities, removal of in-plant inventory, removal of in-transit inventory, and obtaining improved quality and reliability. • **Consignment inventory**—An arrangement in which the supplier maintains title to the inventory until it is used. Concerns of suppliers in supplier partnerships include (1) diversification, (2) scheduling, (3) lead time, (4) quality, and (5) lot sizes.	
LEAN LAYOUT (pp. 624–625)	Lean layout tactics include building work cells for families of products, including a large number of operations in a small area, minimizing distance, designing little space for inventory, improving employee communication, using poka-yoke devices, building flexible or movable equipment, and cross-training workers to add flexibility.	
LEAN INVENTORY (pp. 625–628)	• **Lean inventory**—The minimum inventory necessary to keep a perfect system running. The idea behind Lean is to eliminate inventory that hides variability in the production system. Lean inventory tactics include using a pull system to move inventory, reducing lot size, developing just-in-time delivery systems with suppliers, delivering directly to the point of use, performing to schedule, reducing setup time, and using group technology.	Problems: 16.8–16.10

$$Q^* = \sqrt{\frac{2DS}{H[1 - (d/p)]}} \qquad (16\text{-}1)$$

Using Equation (16-1), for a given desired lot size, Q, we can solve for the *optimal* setup cost, S:

$$S = \frac{(Q^2)(H)(1 - d/p)}{2D} \qquad (16\text{-}2)$$

Main Heading	Review Material	MyLab
LEAN SCHEDULING (pp. 628–631)	Lean scheduling tactics include: communicate schedules to suppliers, make level schedules, freeze part of the schedule, perform to schedule, seek one-piece-make and one-piece-move, eliminate waste, produce in small lots, use kanbans, and make each operation produce a perfect part. • **Level schedules**—Scheduling products so that each day's production meets the demand for that day. • **Kanban**—The Japanese word for *card*, which has come to mean "signal"; a kanban system moves parts through production via a "pull" from a signal:	Problems: 16.1–16.6 Virtual Office Hours for Solved Problem: 16.1

$$\text{Number of Kanbans (containers)} = \frac{\text{Demand during lead time + Safety stock}}{\text{Size of container}}$$

$$(16\text{-}3)$$

Main Heading	Review Material
LEAN QUALITY (pp. 631–632)	Whereas inventory *hides* bad quality, Lean immediately *exposes* it. Lean quality tactics include using statistical process control, empowering employees, building fail-safe methods (poka-yoke, checklists, etc.), exposing poor quality with small lot JIT, and providing immediate feedback.
TOYOTA PRODUCTION SYSTEM (pp. 632–633)	• **Kaizen**—A focus on continuous improvement. At Toyota, people are recruited, trained, and treated as knowledge workers. They are empowered. TPS employs aggressive cross-training and few job classifications.
LEAN ORGANIZATIONS (pp. 633–634)	Lean organizations tend to share the following attributes: *use Lean techniques* to eliminate virtually all inventory; *build systems that help employees* produce a perfect part every time; *reduce space requirements* by minimizing travel distance; *develop partnerships with suppliers*, helping them to understand the needs of the ultimate customer; *educate suppliers* to accept responsibility for satisfying end customer needs; *eliminate all but value-added activities*; *develop employees* by constantly improving job design, training, employee commitment, teamwork, and empowerment; *make jobs challenging*, pushing responsibility to the lowest level possible; and *build worker flexibility* through cross-training and reducing job classifications.
LEAN OPERATIONS IN SERVICES (p. 635)	The features of Lean operations apply to services just as they do in other sectors. Forecasts in services may be very elaborate, with seasonal, daily, hourly, or even shorter components. **VIDEO 16.2** JIT at Arnold Palmer Hospital

Self-Test

■ **Before taking the self-test,** refer to the learning objectives listed at the beginning of the chapter.

LO1 Match Lean operations, JIT, and TPS with the concepts shown below:
   a) Continuous improvement and a focus on exactly what the customer wants, and when.
   b) Supply the customer with exactly what the customer wants when the customer wants it, without waste, through continuous improvement.
   c) Emphasis on continuous improvement, respect for people, and standard work practices.

LO2 Define the seven wastes and the 5Ss. The seven wastes are _____, _____, _____, _____, _____. _____, and _____, and the 5Ss are _____, _____, _____, _____, and _____.

LO3 Concerns of suppliers when moving to supplier partnerships include:
   a) small lots sometimes seeming economically prohibitive.
   b) realistic quality demands.
   c) changes without adequate lead time.
   d) erratic schedules.
   e) all of the above.

LO4 What is the formula for optimal setup time?
   a) $\sqrt{2DQ/[H(1 - d/p)]}$
   b) $\sqrt{Q^2H(1 - d/p)/(2D)}$
   c) $QH(1 - d/p)/(2D)$
   d) $Q^2H(1 - d/p)/(2D)$
   e) $H(1 - d/p)$

LO5 Kanban is the Japanese word for:
   a) car.
   b) pull.
   c) card.
   d) continuous improvement.
   e) level schedule.

LO6 The required number of kanbans equals:
   a) 1.
   b) Demand during lead time / Q
   c) Size of container.
   d) Demand during lead time.
   e) Demand during lead time + Safety stock / Size of container

LO7 The six attributes of Lean organizations are: _____, _____, _____, _____, _____, and _____.

LO8 Lean applies to services:
   a) only in rare instances.
   b) except in terms of the supply chain.
   c) except in terms of employee issues.
   d) except in terms of both supply chain issues and employee issues.
   e) just as it applies to manufacturing.

Answers: LO1. Lean = a, JIT = b, TPS = c; LO2. overproduction, queues, transportation, inventory, motion, overprocessing, defective product; sort, simplify, shine, standardize, sustain; LO3. e; LO4. d; LO5. c; LO6. e; LO7. respect and develop people, empower employees, develop worker flexibility, build excellent processes, develop collaborative partnerships with suppliers, eliminate waste; LO8. e.

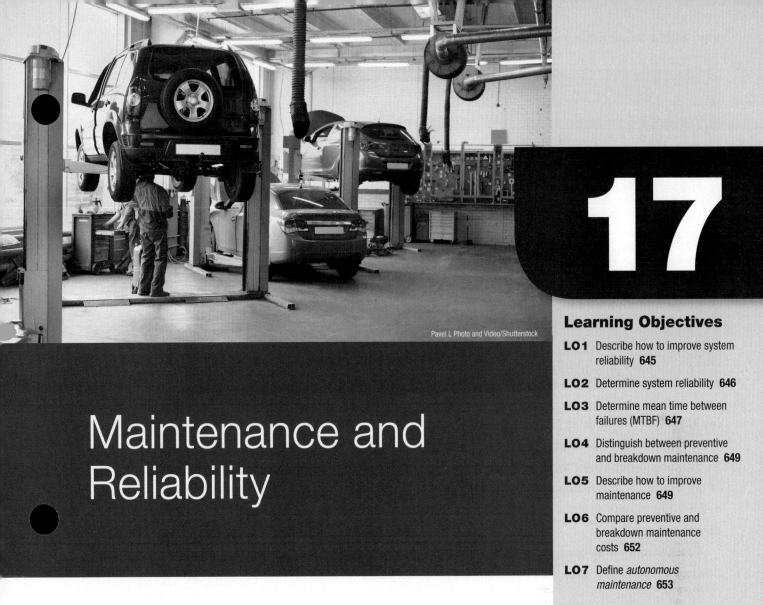

17

Maintenance and Reliability

Learning Objectives

LO1 Describe how to improve system reliability **645**

LO2 Determine system reliability **646**

LO3 Determine mean time between failures (MTBF) **647**

LO4 Distinguish between preventive and breakdown maintenance **649**

LO5 Describe how to improve maintenance **649**

LO6 Compare preventive and breakdown maintenance costs **652**

LO7 Define *autonomous maintenance* **653**

Scheduled Maintenance Is Vital at the Pickering Nuclear Station

Ontario Power Generation (OPG) operates the Pickering Nuclear Generating Station in Ontario, which supplies approximately 13% of the province's electricity supply. An interruption in the delivery of this significant amount of electricity would cause havoc for residents and businesses, thus it is imperative that the facility be well maintained and kept up to date. This is not only to prevent a disruption in supply, but also for safety reasons. The Canadian Nuclear Safety Commission (CNSC) requires that Pickering's vacuum buildings be inspected at least every 10 years. To achieve this, all of the nuclear units linked to the vacuum building must be shut down. Springtime is selected to undertake this event as the demand for electricity is lower at that time of year compared to winter or summer.

This shutdown requires coordination on the part of many groups, including the Independent Electricity System Operator. Additional support is provided by 1900 extra staff members who are brought in to work with the existing 2730 employees. In total, the process involves the performance of 40 000 tasks related to the facility's inspection and maintenance. The process is the

< Global Company Profile Ontario Power Generation

The Pickering Nuclear Generating Station in Pickering, Ontario.

ZUMA Press, Inc./Alamy Stock Photo

result of months of detailed planning and rehearsing. The crews practise their roles in advance, particularly on the complicated tasks, and they do so in mock-ups of the work area. This reduces the learning curve and helps to identify any potential challenges in the methods and protocols.

The shutdowns and associated maintenance protocols typically last about six to eight weeks and are rotated between the various units within the Pickering Nuclear Station. This ensures that the supply of electricity is not cut off completely. Although there are significant costs associated with this procedure, they pale in comparison to the impact of an interruption in the supply of electricity or the detrimental effect of a nuclear accident. This maintenance contributes to Ontario Power Generation's excellent record of reliability.

The Strategic Importance of Maintenance and Reliability

VIDEO 17.1
Maintenance Drives Profits at Frito-Lay

Managers at Ontario Power Generation (OPG), the subject of the *Global Company Profile*, fight for reliability to avoid the undesirable results of equipment failure. At the Pickering Nuclear Generating Station, a generator failure is very expensive for both the company and its customers. Power outages are instantaneous, with potentially devastating consequences. Similarly, managers at Frito-Lay, Walt Disney Company, and United Parcel Service (UPS) are intolerant of failures or breakdowns. Maintenance is critical at Frito-Lay to achieve high plant utilization and excellent sanitation. At Disney, sparkling-clean facilities and safe rides are necessary to retain its standing as one of the most popular vacation destinations in the world. Likewise, UPS's famed maintenance strategy keeps its delivery vehicles operating and looking as good as new for 20 years or more.

These companies, like most others, know that poor maintenance can be disruptive, inconvenient, wasteful, and expensive in dollars and even in lives. As Figure 17.1 illustrates, the interdependency of operator, machine, and mechanic is a hallmark of successful maintenance and reliability. Good maintenance and reliability management enhances a firm's performance and protects its investment.

The objective of maintenance and reliability is to maintain the capability of the system. Good maintenance removes variability. Systems must be designed and maintained to reach expected performance and quality standards. **Maintenance** includes all activities involved in keeping a system's equipment in working order. **Reliability** is the probability that a machine part or product will function properly for a specified time under stated conditions.

In this chapter, we examine four important tactics for improving the reliability and maintenance not only of products and equipment but also of the systems that produce them. The four tactics are organized around reliability and maintenance.

Maintenance

The activities involved in keeping a system's equipment in working order.

Reliability

The probability that a machine part or product will function properly for a specified time under stated conditions.

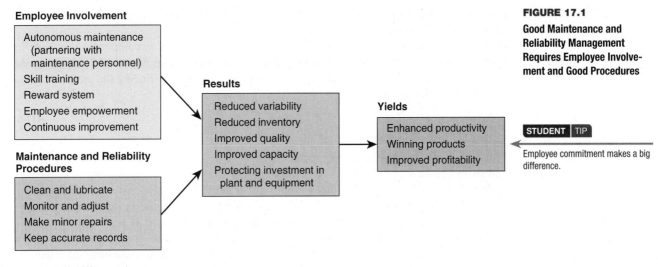

Employee Involvement

- Autonomous maintenance (partnering with maintenance personnel)
- Skill training
- Reward system
- Employee empowerment
- Continuous improvement

Maintenance and Reliability Procedures

- Clean and lubricate
- Monitor and adjust
- Make minor repairs
- Keep accurate records

Results

- Reduced variability
- Reduced inventory
- Improved quality
- Improved capacity
- Protecting investment in plant and equipment

Yields

- Enhanced productivity
- Winning products
- Improved profitability

FIGURE 17.1

Good Maintenance and Reliability Management Requires Employee Involvement and Good Procedures

> STUDENT | TIP
>
> Employee commitment makes a big difference.

The reliability tactics are:

1. Improving individual components
2. Providing redundancy

The maintenance tactics are:

1. Implementing or improving preventive maintenance
2. Increasing repair capabilities or speed

Variability corrupts processes and creates waste. The operations manager must drive out variability: Designing for reliability and managing for maintenance are crucial ingredients for doing so.

Reliability

> STUDENT | TIP
>
> Designing for reliability is an excellent place to start reducing variability.

Systems are composed of a series of individual interrelated components, each performing a specific job. If any *one* component fails to perform, for whatever reason, the overall system (e.g., an airplane or machine) can fail. First, we discuss improving individual components, and then we discuss providing redundancy.

IMPROVING INDIVIDUAL COMPONENTS

Because failures do occur in the real world, understanding their occurrence is an important reliability concept. We now examine the impact of failure in a series. Figure 17.2 shows that as the number of components in a *series* increases, the reliability of the whole system declines very quickly. A system of $n = 50$ interacting parts, each of which has a 99.5% reliability, has an overall

> **LO1** Describe how to improve system reliability

FIGURE 17.2

Overall System Reliability as a Function of Number of *n* Components (Each with the Same Reliability) and Component Reliability with Components in a Series

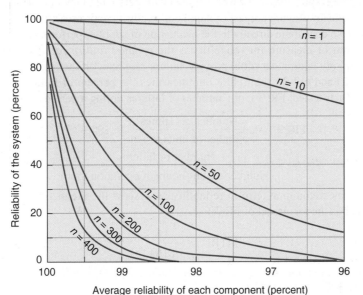

reliability of 78%. If the system or machine has 100 interacting parts, each with an individual reliability of 99.5%, the overall reliability will be only about 60%!

To measure reliability in a system in which each individual part or component may have its own unique rate of reliability, we cannot use the reliability curve in Figure 17.2. However, the method of computing system reliability (R_s) is simple. It consists of finding the product of individual reliabilities as follows:

$$R_s = R_1 \times R_2 \times R_3 \times \ldots \times R_n \tag{17-1}$$

where R_1 = reliability of component 1
R_2 = reliability of component 2

and so on.

Equation (17-1) assumes that the reliability of an individual component does not depend on the reliability of other components (i.e., each component is independent). Additionally, in this equation as in most reliability discussions, reliabilities are presented as *probabilities*. Thus, a 0.90 reliability means that the unit will perform as intended 90% of the time. It also means that it will fail $1 - 0.90 = 0.10 = 10\%$ of the time. We can use this method to evaluate the reliability of a service or a product, such as the one we examine in Example 1.

EXAMPLE **1**

Reliability in a Series

LO2 Determine system reliability

The Bank of Montreal's loan-processing centre processes loan applications through three clerks set up in series, with reliabilities of 0.90, 0.80, and 0.99. It wants to find the system reliability.

APPROACH ▶ Apply Equation (17-1) to solve for

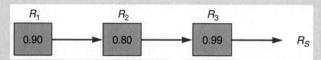

SOLUTION ▶ The reliability of the loan process is:

$$R_s = R_1 \times R_2 \times R_3 = (0.90)(0.80)(0.99) = 0.713, \text{ or } 71.3\%$$

INSIGHT ▶ Because each clerk in the series is less than perfect, the error probabilities are cumulative and the resulting reliability for this series is 0.713, which is less than any one clerk.

LEARNING EXERCISE ▶ If the lowest-performing clerk (0.80) is replaced by a clerk performing at 0.95 reliability, what is the new expected reliability? [Answer: 0.846.]

RELATED PROBLEMS ▶ 17.1, 17.2, 17.5, 17.11

EXCEL OM Data File **Ch17Ex1.xlsx** can be found at **MyLab Operations Management.**

ACTIVE MODEL 17.1 This example is further illustrated in Active Model 17.1 at **MyLab Operations Management.**

Component reliability is often a design or specification issue for which engineering design personnel may be responsible. However, supply chain personnel may be able to improve components of systems by staying abreast of suppliers' products and research efforts. Supply chain personnel can also contribute directly to the evaluation of supplier performance.

The basic unit of measure for reliability is the *product failure rate* (FR). Firms producing high-technology equipment often provide failure-rate data on their products. As shown in Equations (17-2) and (17-3), the failure rate measures the percent of failures among the total number of products tested, FR(%), or a number of failures during a period of time, FR(N):

$$FR(\%) = \frac{\text{Number of failures}}{\text{Number of units tested}} \times 100\% \tag{17-2}$$

$$FR(N) = \frac{\text{Number of failures}}{\text{Number of unit-hours of operation time}} \tag{17-3}$$

Mean time between failures (MTBF)

The expected time between a repair and the next failure of a component, machine, process, or product.

Perhaps the most common term in reliability analysis is the **mean time between failures (MTBF)**, which is the reciprocal of FR(N):

$$MTBF = \frac{1}{FR(N)} \tag{17-4}$$

In Example 2, we compute the percentage of failure FR(%), number of failures FR(N), and mean time between failures (MTBF).

Twenty air-conditioning systems designed for use by astronauts in NASA's space shuttles were operated for 1000 hours at NASA's Huntsville, Alabama, test facility. Two of the systems failed during the test—one after 200 hours and the other after 600 hours.

APPROACH ▶ To determine the percent of failures [FR(%)], the number of failures per unit of time [FR(N)], and the mean time between failures (MTBF), we use Equations (17-2), (17-3), and (17-4), respectively.

SOLUTION ▶ Percentage of failures:

$$FR(\%) = \frac{\text{Number of failures}}{\text{Number of units tested}} = \frac{2}{20}(100\%) = 10\%$$

Number of failures per operating hour:

$$FR(N) = \frac{\text{Number of failures}}{\text{Operating time}}$$

where

Total time $= (1000 \text{ hr})(20 \text{ units})$
$= 20\,000$ unit-hours
Nonoperating time $= 800$ hr for 1st failure $+ 400$ hr for 2nd failure
$= 1200$ unit-hours
Operating time $=$ Total time $-$ Nonoperating time

$$FR(N) = \frac{2}{20\,000 - 1200} = \frac{2}{18\,800}$$
$$= 0.000106 \text{ failure/unit-hour}$$

Because $\text{MTBF} = \dfrac{1}{FR(N)}$

$$\text{MTBF} = \frac{1}{0.000106} = 9434 \text{ hr}$$

If the typical space shuttle trip lasts six days, NASA may be interested in the failure rate per trip:

$$\text{Failure rate} = (\text{Failures/unit-hr})(24 \text{ hr/day})(6 \text{ days/trip})$$
$$= (0.000106)(24)(6)$$
$$= 0.0153 \text{ failure/trip}$$

INSIGHT ▶ Mean time between failures (MTBF) is the standard means of stating reliability.

LEARNING EXERCISE ▶ If nonoperating time drops to 800, what is the new MTBF? [Answer: 9606 hr.]

RELATED PROBLEMS ▶ 17.6, 17.7

EXAMPLE 2

Determining Mean Time Between Failures

LO3 Determine mean time between failures (MTBF)

If the failure rate recorded in Example 2 is too high, NASA will have to either increase the reliability of individual components, and thus of the system, or install several backup air-conditioning units on each space shuttle. Backup units provide redundancy.

PROVIDING REDUNDANCY

To increase the reliability of systems, **redundancy** is added. The technique here is to "back up" components with additional components. This is known as putting units in parallel and is a standard operations management tactic. Redundancy is provided to ensure that if one component fails, the system has recourse to another. One way to express this is as (Probability that first component works) + [(Probability that backup works) × (Probability that first component fails)]. For instance, say that reliability of a component is 0.80 and we back it up with another component with reliability of 0.80. The resulting reliability is the probability of the first component working plus the probability of the backup (or parallel) component working multiplied by the probability of needing the backup component (1 − 0.8 = 0.2). Therefore:

Redundancy
The use of components in parallel to raise reliability.

$$\begin{pmatrix}\text{Probability} \\ \text{of first} \\ \text{component} \\ \text{working}\end{pmatrix} + \left[\begin{pmatrix}\text{Probability} \\ \text{of second} \\ \text{component} \\ \text{working}\end{pmatrix} \times \begin{pmatrix}\text{Probability} \\ \text{of needing} \\ \text{second} \\ \text{component}\end{pmatrix}\right] =$$
$$\quad (0.8) \quad\quad + \quad\quad [(0.8) \quad\times\quad (1-0.8)] \quad\quad = 0.8 + 0.16 = 0.96$$

Example 3 shows how redundancy can improve the reliability of the loan process presented in Example 1.

The Bank of Montreal is disturbed that its loan-application process has a reliability of only 0.713 (see Example 1) and would like to improve this situation.

APPROACH ▶ The bank decides to provide redundancy for the two least reliable clerks.

SOLUTION ▶ This procedure results in the following system:

$$
\begin{array}{ccc}
R_1 & R_2 & R_3 \\
0.90 & 0.80 & \\
\downarrow & \downarrow & \\
\boxed{0.90} \to \boxed{0.80} \to 0.99
\end{array}
$$

$$= [0.9 + 0.9(1 - 0.9)] \times [0.8 + 0.8(1 - 0.8)] \times 0.99$$

$$= [0.9 + (0.9)(0.1)] \times [0.8 + (0.8)(0.2)] \times 0.99$$

$$= 0.99 \times 0.96 \times 0.99$$

$$= 0.94$$

INSIGHT ▶ By providing redundancy for two clerks, the Bank of Montreal has increased reliability of the loan process from 0.713 to 0.94.

LEARNING EXERCISE ▶ What happens when the bank replaces both R_2 clerks with one new clerk who has a reliability of 0.90? [Answer: $R_s = 0.88$.]

RELATED PROBLEMS ▶ 17.8, 17.9, 17.10, 17.12, 17.13, 17.14, 17.16, 17.18

EXCEL OM Data File **Ch17Ex3.xlsx** can be found at **MyLab Operations Management.**

ACTIVE MODEL 17.2 This example is further illustrated in **Active Model 17.2** at **MyLab Operations Management.**

PARALLEL REDUNDANCY Another way to enhance reliability is to provide parallel paths. In a parallel system, the paths are assumed to be independent; therefore, success on any one path allows the system to perform. In Example 4, we determine the reliability of a process with three parallel paths.

A new iPad design that is more reliable because of its parallel circuits is shown below. What is its reliability?

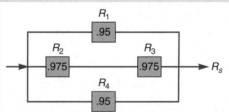

APPROACH ▶ Identify the reliability of each path, then compute the likelihood of needing additional paths (likelihood of failure), and finally subtract the product of those failures from 1.

SOLUTION ▶

Reliability for the middle path $= R_2 \times R_3 = .975 \times .975 = .9506$

Then determine the probability of *failure* for all three paths $= (1 - 0.95) \times (1 - .9506)$
$$\times (1 - 0.95)$$
$$= (.05) \times (.0494) \times (.05) = .00012$$

Therefore the reliability of the new design is 1 minus the probability of failures, or

$$= 1 - .00012 = .99988$$

INSIGHT ▶ Even in a system where no component has reliability over .975, the parallel design increases reliability to over .999. Parallel paths can add substantially to reliability.

LEARNING EXERCISE ▶ If reliability of *all* all components is only .90, what is the new reliability? [Answer: .9981.]

RELATED PROBLEMS ▶ 17.6, 17.8, 17.11

ACTIVE MODEL 17.3 This example is further illustrated in **Active Model 17.3** in **MyLab Operations Management.**

Managers often use a combination of backup components or parallel paths to improve reliability.

Maintenance

STUDENT **TIP**

There are two types of maintenance: preventive maintenance and breakdown maintenance. **Preventive maintenance** involves performing routine inspections and servicing and keeping facilities in good repair. These activities are intended to build a system that will find potential failures and make changes or repairs that will prevent failure. Preventive maintenance is much more than just keeping machinery and equipment running. It also involves designing technical and human systems that will keep the production process working within tolerance; it allows the system to perform. The emphasis of preventive maintenance is on understanding the process and keeping it working without interruption. **Breakdown maintenance** occurs when equipment fails and must be repaired on an emergency or priority basis.

Even the most reliable systems require maintenance.

Preventive maintenance
A plan that involves routine inspections, servicing, and keeping facilities in good repair to prevent failure.

Breakdown maintenance
Remedial maintenance that occurs when equipment fails and must be repaired on an emergency or priority basis.

IMPLEMENTING PREVENTIVE MAINTENANCE

Preventive maintenance implies that we can determine when a system needs service or will need repair. Therefore, to perform preventive maintenance, we must know when a system requires service or when it is likely to fail. Failures occur at different rates during the life of a product. A high initial failure rate, known as **infant mortality**, may exist for many products.[1] This is why many electronic firms "burn in" their products prior to shipment: That is to say, they execute a variety of tests (such as a full wash cycle at Whirlpool) to detect "startup" problems prior to shipment. Firms may also provide 90-day warranties. We should note that many infant mortality failures are not product failures *per se*, but rather failure due to improper use. This fact points out the importance in many industries of operations management's building an after-sales service system that includes installing and training.

Once the product, machine, or process "settles in," a study can be made of the MTBF (mean time between failures) distribution. Such distributions often follow a normal curve. When these distributions exhibit small standard deviations, then we know we have a candidate for preventive maintenance, even if the maintenance is expensive.

Once our firm has a candidate for preventive maintenance, we want to determine *when* preventive maintenance is economical. Typically, the more expensive the maintenance, the narrower must be the MTBF distribution (i.e., the distribution should have a small standard deviation). In addition, if the process is no more expensive to repair when it breaks down than the cost of preventive maintenance, perhaps we should let the process break down and then do the repair. However, the consequence of the breakdown must be fully considered. Even some relatively minor breakdowns have catastrophic consequences. (See the *OM in Action* box "Preventive Maintenance Saves Lives".) At the other extreme, preventive maintenance costs may be so incidental that preventive maintenance is appropriate even if the MTBF distribution is rather flat (i.e., it has a large standard deviation). In any event, consistent with job enrichment practices, machine operators must be held responsible for preventive maintenance of their own equipment and tools.

With good reporting techniques, firms can maintain records of individual processes, machines, or equipment. Such records can provide a profile of both the kinds of maintenance required and the timing of maintenance needed. Maintaining equipment history is an important part of a preventive maintenance system, as is a record of the time and cost to make the repair. Such records can also provide information about the family of equipment and suppliers.

LO4 Distinguish between preventive and breakdown maintenance

Infant mortality
The failure rate early in the life of a product or process.

LO5 Describe how to improve maintenance

---

[1] Infant mortality failures often follow a negative exponential distribution.

OM in Action   Preventive Maintenance Saves Lives

Flight 5481's trip was short. It lasted 70 seconds. The flight left the Charlotte Airport, bound for Greenville/Spartanburg, but seconds after lift-off, the nose of the aircraft pitched upward, the plane rolled, and, moments later, slammed into the corner of a maintenance facility at the airport. The Beech 1900D commuter plane carried 21 people to their death. The following are selected comments from the final moments of the flight:

8:47:02—Co-pilot Jonathan Gibbs: "Wuh."
8:47:03—Capt. Katie Leslie: "Help me. . . . You got it?"
8:47:05—Gibbs: "Oh (expletive). Push down."
8:47:12—Leslie: "Push the nose down."
8:47:14—Leslie: "Oh my God."
8:47:16—Leslie (calling to controllers): "We have an emergency for Air Midwest fifty-four eighty-one."
8:47:18—Faint voice from passenger area: "Daddy."
8:47:26—Leslie: "Oh my God, ahh."
8:47:26—Gibbs: "Uh, uh, God, ahh (expletive)."
8:47:28—End of recording.

The National Transportation Safety Board's focus in this situation is a preventive maintenance error made two days prior to the crash. The mechanic and a supervisor skipped at least 12 steps required in the maintenance of the tension of the pitch-control cables during the *Detail 6* check that includes the pitch of the control cable tension. Data show that the control column position changed during the maintenance and the plane lost about two-thirds down-elevator capability. Investigators believe that the aircraft would have been flyable with fully functioning controls had it been given proper preventive maintenance. Maintenance can improve quality, reduce costs, and win orders. It can also be a matter of life and death.

Sources: Aviation Week and Space Technology (May 26, 2003): 52; *USA Today* (May 21, 2003): 8A; and *The Wall Street Journal* (May 21, 2003): D3 and (May 20, 2003): D1, D3.

Reliability and maintenance are of such importance that most systems are now computerized. Figure 17.3 shows the major components of such a system with files to be maintained on the left and reports generated on the right.

Both Boeing and General Motors are pursuing competitive advantage via their reliability and maintenance information systems. Boeing can now monitor the health of an airplane in flight and relay relevant information in real time to the ground, providing a head start on reliability and maintenance issues. Similarly, General Motors, with its wireless satellite service, alerts car owners to 1600 possible diagnostic failures, such as a faulty airbag sensor or even the need for an oil change. For GM, the service provides immediate data that its engineers can use to jump

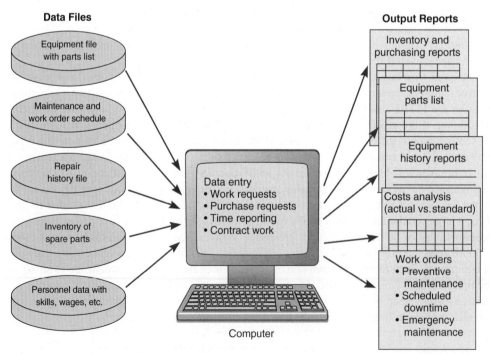

FIGURE 17.3   A Computerized Maintenance System

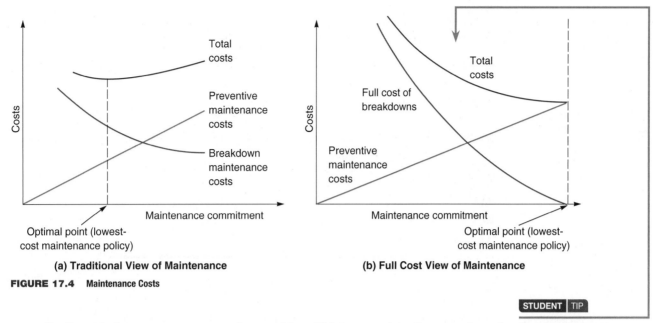

(a) Traditional View of Maintenance

(b) Full Cost View of Maintenance

FIGURE 17.4   **Maintenance Costs**

on quality issues before customers even notice a problem. This has saved the firm an estimated $100 million in warranty costs by catching problems early.

Figure 17.4(a) shows a traditional view of the relationship between preventive maintenance and breakdown maintenance. In this view, operations managers consider a *balance* between the two costs. Allocating more resources to preventive maintenance will reduce the number of breakdowns. At some point, however, the decrease in breakdown maintenance costs may be less than the increase in preventive maintenance costs. At this point, the total cost curve begins to rise. Beyond this optimal point, the firm will be better off waiting for breakdowns to occur and repairing them when they do.

Unfortunately, cost curves such as in Figure 17.4(a) seldom consider the *full costs of a breakdown*. Many costs are ignored because they are not *directly* related to the immediate breakdown. For instance, the cost of inventory maintained to compensate for downtime is not typically considered. Moreover, downtime can have a devastating effect on safety and morale. Employees may also begin to believe that performance to standard and maintaining equipment are not important. Finally, downtime adversely affects delivery schedules, destroying customer relations and future sales. When the full impact of breakdowns is considered, Figure 17.4(b) may be a better representation of maintenance costs. In Figure 17.4(b), total costs are at a minimum when the system does not break down.

Assuming that all potential costs associated with downtime have been identified, the operations staff can compute the optimal level of maintenance activity on a theoretical basis. Of course, such analysis also requires accurate historical data on maintenance costs, breakdown probabilities, and repair times. Example 5 shows how to compare preventive and breakdown maintenance costs to select the least expensive maintenance policy.

Farlen & Halikman is a CPA firm specializing in payroll preparation. The firm has been successful in automating much of its work, using high-speed printers for cheque processing and report preparation. The computerized approach, however, has problems. Over the past 20 months, the printers have broken down at the rate indicated in the following table:

EXAMPLE 5

Comparing Preventive and Breakdown Maintenance Costs

Number of Breakdowns	Number of Months that Breakdowns Occurred
0	2
1	8
2	6
3	4
	Total: 20

Each time the printers break down, Farlen & Halikman estimates that it loses an average of $300 in production time and service expenses. One alternative is to purchase a service contract for preventive maintenance. Even if Farlen & Halikman contracts for preventive maintenance, there will still be breakdowns, *averaging* one breakdown per month. The price for this service is $150 per month.

LO6 Compare preventive and breakdown maintenance costs

APPROACH ▶ To determine if the CPA firm should follow a "run until breakdown" policy or contract for preventive maintenance, we follow a four-step process:

STEP 1: Compute the *expected number* of breakdowns (based on past history) if the firm continues as is, without the service contract.
STEP 2: Compute the expected breakdown cost per month with no preventive maintenance contract.
STEP 3: Compute the cost of preventive maintenance.
STEP 4: Compare the two options and select the one that will cost less.

SOLUTION ▶

STEP 1:

Number of Breakdowns	Frequency	Number of Breakdowns	Frequency
0	2/20 = 0.1	2	6/20 = 0.3
1	8/20 = 0.4	3	4/20 = 0.2

$$\begin{pmatrix} \text{Expected number} \\ \text{of breakdowns} \end{pmatrix} = \Sigma \left[\begin{pmatrix} \text{Number of} \\ \text{breakdowns} \end{pmatrix} \times \begin{pmatrix} \text{Corresponding} \\ \text{frequency} \end{pmatrix} \right]$$
$$= (0)(0.1) + (1)(0.4) + (2)(0.3) + (3)(0.2)$$
$$= 0 + 0.4 + 0.6 + 0.6$$
$$= 1.6 \text{ breakdowns/month}$$

STEP 2:

$$\text{Expected breakdown cost} = \begin{pmatrix} \text{Expected number} \\ \text{of breakdowns} \end{pmatrix} \times \begin{pmatrix} \text{Cost per} \\ \text{breakdown} \end{pmatrix}$$
$$= (1.6)(\$300)$$
$$= \$480/\text{month}$$

STEP 3:

$$\begin{pmatrix} \text{Preventive} \\ \text{maintenance cost} \end{pmatrix} = \begin{pmatrix} \text{Cost of expected} \\ \text{breakdowns if service} \\ \text{contract signed} \end{pmatrix} + \begin{pmatrix} \text{Cost of} \\ \text{service contract} \end{pmatrix}$$
$$= (1 \text{ breakdown/month})(\$300) + \$150/\text{month}$$
$$= \$450/\text{month}$$

STEP 4: Because it is less expensive overall to hire a maintenance service firm ($450) than not to do so ($480), Farlen & Halikman should hire the service firm.

INSIGHT ▶ Determining the expected number of breakdowns for each option is crucial to making a good decision. This typically requires good maintenance records.

LEARNING EXERCISE ▶ What is the best decision if the preventive maintenance contract cost increases to $195 per month? [Answer: At $495 (= $300 + $195) per month, "run until breakdown" becomes less expensive (assuming that all costs are included in the $300 per breakdown cost).]

RELATED PROBLEMS ▶ 17.3, 17.4, 17.17

Using variations of the technique shown in Example 5, operations managers can examine maintenance policies.

INCREASING REPAIR CAPABILITIES

Because reliability and preventive maintenance are seldom perfect, most firms opt for some level of repair capability. Enlarging or improving repair facilities can get the system back in operation faster. A good maintenance facility should have these six features:

1. Well-trained personnel
2. Adequate resources

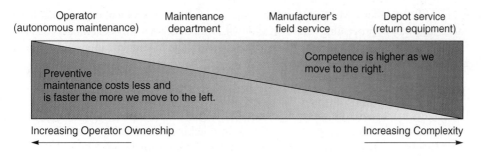

FIGURE 17.5

The Operations Manager Determines How Maintenance Will Be Performed

3. Ability to establish a repair plan and priorities[2]
4. Ability and authority to do material planning
5. Ability to identify the cause of breakdowns
6. Ability to design ways to extend MTBF

However, not all repairs can be done in the firm's facility. Managers must therefore decide where repairs are to be performed. Figure 17.5 provides a continuum of options and how they rate in terms of speed, cost, and competence. Moving to the right in Figure 17.5 may improve the competence of the repair work, but at the same time it increases costs and replacement time.

AUTONOMOUS MAINTENANCE

Preventive maintenance policies and techniques must include an emphasis on employees accepting responsibility for the "observe, check, adjust, clean, and notify" type of equipment maintenance. Such policies are consistent with the advantages of employee empowerment. This approach is known as **autonomous maintenance**. Employees can predict failures, prevent breakdowns, and prolong equipment life. With autonomous maintenance, the manager is making a step towards both employee empowerment and maintaining system performance.

> **LO7** Define *autonomous maintenance*
>
> **Autonomous maintenance**
> Operators partner with maintenance personnel to observe, check, adjust, clean, and notify.

Total Productive Maintenance

Many firms have moved to bring total quality management concepts to the practice of preventive maintenance with an approach known as **total productive maintenance (TPM)**. It involves the concept of reducing variability through autonomous maintenance and excellent maintenance practices. Total productive maintenance includes:

- Designing machines that are reliable, easy to operate, and easy to maintain.
- Emphasizing total cost of ownership when purchasing machines, so that service and maintenance are included in the cost.
- Developing preventive maintenance plans that utilize the best practices of operators, maintenance departments, and depot service.
- Training for autonomous maintenance so operators maintain their own machines and partner with maintenance personnel.

High utilization of facilities, tight scheduling, low inventory, and consistent quality demand reliability. Total productive maintenance is the key to reducing variability and improving reliability.

> **STUDENT** TIP
>
> Maintenance improves productivity.
>
> **Total productive maintenance (TPM)**
> Combines total quality management with a strategic view of maintenance from process and equipment design to preventive maintenance.

Techniques for Enhancing Maintenance

Three techniques have proven beneficial to effective maintenance: simulation, expert systems, and automated sensors.

> **STUDENT** TIP
>
> Both OM techniques and the physical sciences can improve maintenance.

SIMULATION

Because of the complexity of some maintenance decisions, computer simulation is a good tool for evaluating the impact of various policies. For instance, operations personnel can decide whether to add more staff by determining the trade-offs between machine reliability and the

---

[2] You may recall from our discussion of network planning in Chapter 3 that DuPont developed the critical path method (CPM) to improve the scheduling of maintenance projects.

costs of additional labour. Management can also simulate the replacement of parts that have not yet failed as a way of preventing future breakdowns. Simulation via physical models can also be useful. For example, a physical model can vibrate an airplane to simulate thousands of hours of flight time to evaluate maintenance needs.

EXPERT SYSTEMS

OM managers use expert systems (i.e., computer programs that mimic human logic) to assist staff in isolating and repairing various faults in machinery and equipment. For instance, General Electric's DELTA system asks a series of detailed questions that aid the user in identifying a problem. DuPont uses expert systems to monitor equipment and to train repair personnel.

AUTOMATED SENSORS

Sensors warn when production machinery is about to fail or is becoming damaged by heat, vibration, or fluid leaks. The goal of such procedures is not only to avoid failures but also to perform preventive maintenance before machines are damaged.

CHAPTER | SUMMARY

Operations managers focus on design improvements and backup components to improve reliability. Reliability improvements also can be made through the use of preventive maintenance and excellent repair facilities.

Firms give employees "ownership" of their equipment. When workers repair or do preventive maintenance on their own machines, breakdowns are less common. Well-trained and empowered employees ensure reliable systems through preventive maintenance. In turn, reliable, well-maintained equipment not only provides higher utilization but also improves quality and performance to schedule. Top firms build and maintain systems that drive out variability so that customers can rely on products and services to be produced to specifications and on time.

ETHICAL | DILEMMA

We place our trust in authorities for many things, and when this trust is breached, we demand answers. Such was the case in Walkerton, Ontario, in May 2000. Starting May 15 of that year, many residents of the town of about 5000 began to simultaneously experience gastrointestinal problems and symptoms of *E. coli* infection. Following this, the Walkerton Public Utilities Commission insisted the water supply was safe despite possessing laboratory tests that had found it to be contaminated. Later that month, an increase in the number of patients with similar symptoms caused the region's medical officer of health to issue a "boil water" advisory warning residents not to drink the water without boiling it first.

An inquiry into the matter concluded that the operators did not have any formal training for the duties they were hired to do. They engaged in a number of improper operating practices, including failing to apply sufficient doses of chlorine, failing to monitor chlorine residuals daily, making false entries in the daily operating records, and misstating the locations at which water samples were taken. The operators were fully aware that these practices were unacceptable and contravened the Ministry of the Environment guidelines and directives.

At least seven people died from drinking the water contaminated with *E. coli*. These residents might have been saved if the Walkerton Public Utilities Commission had admitted sooner that the water was contaminated. In addition, about 2500 people became ill. An experimental drug in Phase III clinical trials, Synsorb Pk, was used to treat 19 children on compassionate grounds under Health Canada's Special Access Program.

In spite of the fact that Ministry of the Environment guidelines and directives existed before this tragedy, not to mention that the staff at Walkerton Public Utilities Commission failed to adhere to these guidelines, how much responsibility do you feel the provincial government had in this case? Also, comment on the decision to distribute the experimental drug to the 19 affected children.

Discussion Questions

1. What is the objective of maintenance and reliability?
2. How does one identify a candidate for preventive maintenance?
3. Explain the notion of *infant mortality* in the context of product reliability.
4. Why is simulation often an appropriate technique for maintenance problems?
5. What is the trade-off between operator-performed maintenance versus supplier-performed maintenance?
6. How can a manager evaluate the effectiveness of the maintenance function?
7. How does machine design contribute to either increasing or alleviating the maintenance problem?

8. What roles can computerized maintenance management systems play in the maintenance function?

9. During an argument as to the merits of preventive maintenance at Windsor Printers, the company owner asked, "Why fix it before it breaks?" How would you, as the director of maintenance, respond?

10. Will preventive maintenance eliminate *all* breakdowns?

Using Software to Solve Reliability Problems

PxExcel OM and POM for Windows may be used to solve reliability problems. The reliability module allows us to enter (1) number of systems (components) in the series (1 through 10); (2) number of backup, or parallel, components (1 through 12); and (3) component reliability for both series and parallel data.

Solved Problems Virtual Office Hours help is available at MyLab Operations Management.

▼ SOLVED PROBLEM 17.1

The semiconductor used in the Sullivan Wrist Calculator has five circuits, each of which has its own reliability rate. Component 1 has a reliability of 0.90; component 2, 0.95; component 3, 0.98; component 4, 0.90; and component 5, 0.99. What is the reliability of one semiconductor?

▼ SOLUTION

Semiconductor reliability $= R_1 \times R_2 \times R_3 \times R_4 \times R_5$
$= (0.90)(0.95)(0.98)(0.90)(0.99)$
$= 0.7466$

▼ SOLVED PROBLEM 17.2

A recent engineering change at Sullivan Wrist Calculator places a backup component in each of the two least reliable transistor circuits. The new circuits will look like the following:

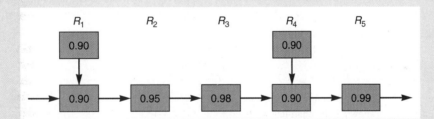

What is the reliability of the new system?

▼ SOLUTION

$$\text{Reliability} = [0.9 + (1 - 0.9)(0.9)] \times 0.95 \times 0.98 \times [0.9 + (1 - 0.9)(0.9)] \times 0.99$$
$$= [0.9 + 0.09] \times 0.95 \times 0.98 \times [0.9 + 0.09] \times 0.99$$
$$= 0.99 \times 0.95 \times 0.98 \times 0.99 \times 0.99$$
$$= 0.903$$

Problems*

• **17.1** The Beta II computer's electronic processing unit contains 50 components in series. The average reliability of each component is 99.0%. Using Figure 17.2, determine the overall reliability of the processing unit.

• **17.2** A testing process at Boeing Aircraft has 400 components in series. The average reliability of each component is 99.5%. Use Figure 17.2 to find the overall reliability of the whole testing process.

• **17.3** What are the *expected* number of yearly breakdowns for the power generator at Niagara Falls that has exhibited the following data over the past 20 years? **Px**

Number of breakdowns	0	1	2	3	4	5	6
Number of years in which breakdown occurred	2	2	5	4	5	2	0

*Note: **Px** means the problem may be solved with POM for Windows and/or Excel OM.

• **17.4** Each breakdown of a graphic plotter table at Airbus Industries costs $50. Find the expected daily breakdown cost, given the following data: ℙ𝕏

Number of breakdowns	0	1	2	3	4
Daily breakdown probability	0.1	0.2	0.4	0.2	0.1

•• **17.5** A new aircraft control system is being designed that must be 98% reliable. This system consists of three components in series. If all three of the components are to have the same level of reliability, what level of reliability is required? ℙ𝕏

•• **17.6** Robert Klassan Manufacturing, a medical equipment manufacturer, subjected 100 heart pacemakers to 5000 hours of testing. Halfway through the testing, five pacemakers failed. What was the failure rate in terms of the following:
a) Percentage of failures?
b) Number of failures per unit-hour?
c) Number of failures per unit-year?
d) If 1100 people receive pacemaker implants, how many units can we expect to fail during the following year?

•• **17.7** A manufacturer of touch screens for tablets wants a MTBF of at least 50 000 hours. Recent test results for 10 units were one failure at 10 000 hrs, another at 25 000 hrs, and two more at 45 000 hrs. The remaining units were still running at 60 000 hours. Determine the following:
a) Percentage of failures
b) Number of failures per unit-hour
c) MTBF at this point in the testing

•• **17.8** What is the reliability of the following production process? $R_1 = 0.95$, $R_2 = 0.90$, $R_3 = 0.98$.

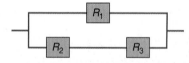

•• **17.9** What is the reliability that bank loans will be processed accurately if each of the five clerks shown in the chart has the reliability shown?

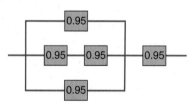

•• **17.10** Merrill Kim Sharp has a system composed of three components in parallel. The components have the following reliabilities:

$$R_1 = 0.90, R_2 = 0.95, R_3 = 0.85$$

What is the reliability of the system? (*Hint:* See Example 3.) ℙ𝕏

• **17.11** A medical control system has three components in series with individual reliabilities (R_1, R_2, R_3) as shown:

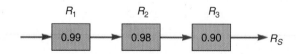

What is the reliability of the system? ℙ𝕏

•• **17.12** a) What is the reliability of the system shown?

b) How much did reliability improve if the medical control system shown in Problem 17.11 changed to the redundant parallel system shown here? ℙ𝕏

••• **17.13** Assume that for cardiac bypass surgery, 85% of patients survive the surgery, 95% survive the recovery period after surgery, 80% are able to make the lifestyle changes needed to extend their survival to one year or more, and only 10% of those who do not make the lifestyle changes survive more than a year. What is the likelihood that a given patient will survive more than a year? ℙ𝕏

•• **17.14** Elizabeth Irwin's design team has proposed the following system with component reliabilities as indicated:

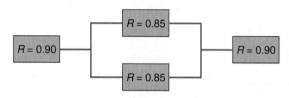

What is the reliability of the system? ℙ𝕏

•• **17.15** The maintenance department at Mechanical Dynamics has presented you with the failure curve shown. What does it suggest?

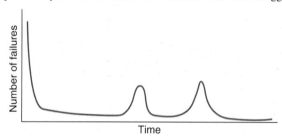

•• **17.16** Rick Wing, salesperson for Wave Soldering Systems Inc. (WSSI), has provided you with a proposal for improving the temperature control on your present machine. The machine uses a hot-air knife to cleanly remove excess solder from printed circuit boards; this is a great concept, but the hot-air temperature control lacks reliability. According to Wing, engineers at WSSI have improved the reliability of the critical temperature controls. The new system still has the four sensitive integrated circuits controlling the temperature, but the new machine has a backup for each. The four integrated circuits have reliabilities of 0.90, 0.92, 0.94, and 0.96. The four backup circuits all have a reliability of 0.90.
a) What is the reliability of the new temperature controller?
b) If you pay a premium, Wing says he can improve all four of the backup units to 0.93. What is the reliability of this option? ℙ𝕏

••• **17.17** The fire department has a number of failures with its oxygen masks and is evaluating the possibility of outsourcing preventive maintenance to the manufacturer. Because of the risk associated with a failure, the cost of each failure is estimated at $2000.

The current maintenance policy (with station employees performing maintenance) has yielded the following history:

Number of breakdowns	0	1	2	3	4	5
Number of years in which breakdowns occurred	4	3	1	5	5	0

This manufacturer will guarantee repairs on any and all failures as part of a service contract. The cost of this service is $5000 per year.
a) What is the expected number of breakdowns per year with station employees performing maintenance?
b) What is the cost of the current maintenance policy?
c) What is the more economical policy?

••• **17.18** As VP of operations at Brian Normoyle Engineering, you must decide which product design, A or B, has the higher reliability. B is designed with backup units for components R_3 and R_4. What is the reliability of each design?

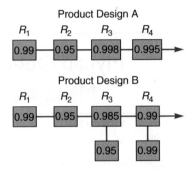

Product Design A

R_1 R_2 R_3 R_4
0.99 — 0.95 — 0.998 — 0.995 →

Product Design B

R_1 R_2 R_3 R_4
0.99 — 0.95 — 0.985 — 0.99 →
            0.95   0.99

•••• **17.19** A typical retail transaction consists of several smaller steps, which can be considered components subject to failure. A list of such components might include:

Component	Description	Definition of Failure
1	Find product in proper size, colour, etc.	Can't find product
2	Enter cashier line	No lines open; lines too long; line experiencing difficulty
3	Scan product UPC for name, price, etc.	Won't scan; item not on file; scans incorrect name or price
4	Calculate purchase total	Wrong weight; wrong extension; wrong data entry; wrong tax
5	Make payment	Customer lacks cash; cheque not acceptable; credit card refused
6	Make change	Makes change incorrectly
7	Bag merchandise	Damages merchandise while bagging; bag splits
8	Conclude transaction and exit	No receipt; unfriendly, rude, or aloof clerk

Let the eight probabilities of success be 0.92, 0.94, 0.99, 0.99, 0.98, 0.97, 0.95, and 0.96. What is the reliability of the system, that is, the probability that there will be a satisfied customer? If you were the store manager, what do you think should be an acceptable value for this probability? Which components would be good candidates for backup, which for redesign?

Video Case

Maintenance Drives Profits at Frito-Lay

Frito-Lay, the multibillion-dollar subsidiary of food and beverage giant PepsiCo, maintains 36 plants in the United States and Canada. These facilities produce dozen of snacks, including the well-known Lay's, Fritos, Cheetos, Doritos, Ruffles, and Tostitos brands, each of which sells over $1 billion per year.

Frito-Lay plants produce in the high-volume, low-variety process model common to commercial baked goods, steel, glass, and beer industries. In this environment, preventive maintenance of equipment takes a major role by avoiding costly downtime. Tom Rao, vice-president of Florida operations, estimates that each 1% of downtime has a negative annual profit impact of $200 000. He is proud of the percent unscheduled downtime his plant is able to reach—well below the 2% that is considered the "world-class" benchmark. This excellent performance is possible because the maintenance department takes an active role in setting the parameters for preventive maintenance. This is done with weekly input to the production schedule.

Maintenance policy impacts energy use as well. The Florida plant's technical manager, Jim Wentzel, states, "By reducing production interruptions, we create an opportunity to bring energy and utility use under control. Equipment maintenance and a solid production schedule are keys to utility efficiency. With every production interruption, there is substantial waste."

As a part of its total productive maintenance (TPM) program,[*] Frito-Lay empowers employees with what it calls the "Run Right" system. Run Right teaches employees to "identify and do". This means each shift is responsible for identifying problems and making the necessary corrections, when possible. This is accomplished through (1) a "power walk" at the beginning of the shift to ensure that equipment and process settings are performing to standard, (2) mid-shift and post-shift reviews of standards and performance, and (3) posting of any issues on a large whiteboard in the shift office. Items remain on the whiteboard until corrected, which is seldom more than a shift or two.

With good manpower scheduling and tight labour control to hold down variable costs, making time for training is challenging. But supervisors, including the plant manager, are available to fill in on the production line when that is necessary to free an employee for training.

---

[*]Preventive maintenance, autonomous maintenance, and total productive maintenance are part of a Frito-Lay program known as total productive manufacturing.

LO4 The process that is intended to find potential failures and make changes or repairs is known as:
a) breakdown maintenance.
b) failure maintenance.
c) preventive maintenance.
d) all of the above.

LO5 The two main tactics for improving maintenance are _____ and _____.

LO6 The appropriate maintenance policy is developed by balancing preventive maintenance costs with breakdown maintenance costs. The problem is that:
a) preventive maintenance costs are very difficult to identify.
b) full breakdown costs are seldom considered.

c) preventive maintenance should be performed, regardless of the cost.
d) breakdown maintenance must be performed, regardless of the cost.

LO7 _____ maintenance partners operators with maintenance personnel to observe, check, adjust, clean, and notify.
a) Partnering
b) Operator
c) Breakdown
d) Six Sigma
e) Autonomous

Answers: LO1. improving individual components, providing redundancy; LO2. d; LO3. b; LO4. c; LO5. implementing or improving preventive maintenance, increasing repair capabilities or speed; LO6. b; LO7. e.

MyLab Operations Management

Most of these questions can be found in MyLab Operations Management. Visit MyLab Operations Management to access cases, videos, downloadable software, and much more. MyLab Operations Management Management also features a personalized Study Plan that helps you identify which chapter concepts you've mastered and guides you towards study tools for additional practice.

Decision-Making Tools

Learning Objectives

LO1 Create a simple decision tree **663**

LO2 Build a decision table **663**

LO3 Explain when to use each of the three types of decision-making environments **664**

LO4 Calculate an expected monetary value (EMV) **665**

LO5 Compute the expected value of perfect information (EVPI) **666**

LO6 Evaluate the nodes in a decision tree **668**

LO7 Create a decision tree with sequential decisions **669**

The Decision Process in Operations

Operations managers are not gamblers, but they *are* decision makers. To achieve the goals of their organizations, managers must understand how decisions are made and know which decision-making tools to use. To a great extent, the success or failure of both people and companies depends on the quality of their decisions. Overcoming uncertainty is a manager's challenge.

What makes the difference between a good decision and a bad decision? A "good" decision—one that uses analytic decision making—is based on logic and considers all available data and possible alternatives. It also follows these six steps:

1. Clearly define the problem and the factors that influence it.
2. Develop specific and measurable objectives.
3. Develop a model—that is, a relationship between objectives and variables (which are measurable quantities).
4. Evaluate each alternative solution based on its merits and drawbacks.
5. Select the best alternative.
6. Implement the decision and set a timetable for completion.

So analytic decision making requires models, objectives, and quantifiable variables, often in the form of probabilities and payoffs. Such information is not always easy to obtain or derive from existing data. This challenge exists because of either a lack of data or an overabundance of data. However, because data are now easily generated and stored in digital form, we tend to have the latter—massive volumes of data. Data are collected automatically from production processes, as well as from websites, credit cards, point-of-sale records, and social media. Although this mass of data is a potential source of information, it requires sophistication in how it is stored, processed, and analyzed. **Big data** is the term used to describe this huge amount of data, which often cannot be efficiently processed by traditional data techniques.

Throughout this book, we have introduced a broad range of mathematical models and tools that help operations managers make better decisions. Effective operations depend on careful decision making. Fortunately, there are a whole variety of analytic tools to help make these decisions. This module introduces two of them—decision tables and decision trees. They are used in a wide number of OM situations, ranging from new product analysis (Chapter 5), to capacity planning (Supplement 7), location planning (Chapter 8), scheduling (Chapter 15), and maintenance planning (Chapter 17).

Big data

The huge amount of economic, production, and consumer data now being collected in digital form.

WOULD *YOU* GO ALL IN?

At the Legends of Poker tournament, veteran T. J. Cloutier opens with a $60 000 bet. (Antes and required bets of $39 000 are already on the table.) Former Go2net CTO Paul Phillips ponders going "all in"—betting virtually all his chips. Using decision theory, here's how he decided.

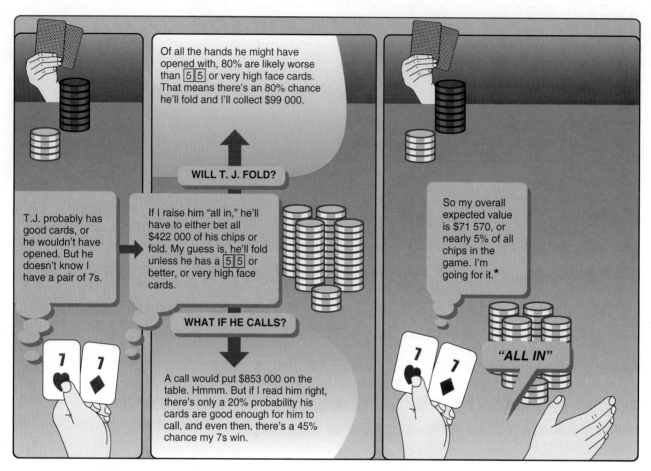

*To see the details of Phillips's decision, see Example A9.

Source: Based on *Business 2.0* (November 2003): 128–134.

Fundamentals of Decision Making

Regardless of the complexity of a decision or the sophistication of the technique used to analyze it, all decision makers are faced with alternatives and "states of nature". The following notation will be used in this module:

1. Terms:
   a. **Alternative**—A course of action or strategy that may be chosen by a decision maker (e.g., not carrying an umbrella tomorrow).
   b. **State of nature**—An occurrence or a situation over which the decision maker has little or no control (e.g., tomorrow's weather).
2. Symbols used in a decision tree:
   a. □—decision node from which one of several alternatives may be selected.
   b. ○—a state-of-nature node out of which one state of nature will occur.

Alternative

A course of action or strategy that may be chosen by a decision maker.

State of nature

An occurrence or a situation over which a decision maker has little or no control.

To present a manager's decision alternatives, we can develop *decision trees* using the above symbols. When constructing a decision tree, we must be sure that all alternatives and states of nature are in their correct and logical places and that we include *all* possible alternatives and states of nature. Example A1 illustrates an example of a decision tree.

Getz Products Company is investigating the possibility of producing and marketing backyard storage sheds. Undertaking this project would require the construction of either a large or a small manufacturing plant. The market for the product produced—storage sheds—could be either favourable or unfavourable. Getz, of course, has the option of not developing the new product line at all.

APPROACH ▶ Getz decides to build a decision tree.

SOLUTION ▶ Figure A.1 illustrates Getz's decision tree.

EXAMPLE A1

A Simple Decision Tree

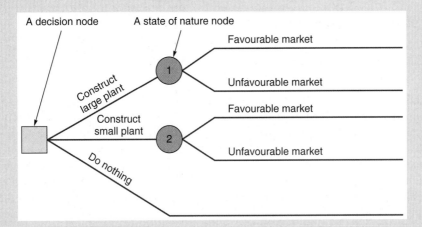

FIGURE A.1
Getz Products Decision Tree

LO1 Create a simple decision tree

INSIGHT ▶ We never want to overlook the option of "doing nothing" as that is usually a possible decision.

LEARNING EXERCISE ▶ Getz now considers constructing a medium-sized plant as a fourth option. Redraw the tree in Figure A.1 to accommodate this. [Answer: Your tree will have a new node and branches between "Construct large plant" and "Construct small plant".]

RELATED PROBLEMS ▶ A.2e, A.8b, A.14a, A.15a, A.17a, A.18

Decision Tables

We may also develop a decision or payoff table to help Getz Products define its alternatives. For any alternative and a particular state of nature, there is a *consequence* or *outcome*, which is usually expressed as a monetary value. This is called a *conditional value*. Note that all of the alternatives in Example A2 are listed down the left side of the table, that states of nature (outcomes) are listed across the top, and that conditional values (payoffs) are in the body of the **decision table**.

STUDENT TIP

Decision tables force logic into decision making.

Decision table
A tabular means of analyzing decision alternatives and states of nature.

Getz Products now wishes to organize the following information into a table. With a favourable market, a large facility will give Getz Products a net profit of $200 000. If the market is unfavourable, a $180 000 net loss will occur. A small plant will result in a net profit of $100 000 in a favourable market, but a net loss of $20 000 will be encountered if the market is unfavourable.

APPROACH ▶ These numbers become conditional values in the decision table. We list alternatives in the left column and states of nature across the top of the table.

SOLUTION ▶ The completed table is shown in Table A.1.

EXAMPLE A2

A Decision Table

LO2 Build a decision table

Table A.1
Decision Table With Conditional Values for Getz Products

	States of Nature	
Alternatives	**Favourable Market**	**Unfavourable Market**
Construct large plant	$200 000	−$180 000
Construct small plant	$100 000	−$ 20 000
Do nothing	$ 0	$ 0

INSIGHT ▶ The toughest part of decision tables is obtaining the data to analyze.

LEARNING EXERCISE ▶ In Examples A3 and A4, we see how to use decision tables to make decisions.

LO3 Explain when to use each of the three types of decision-making environments

Types of Decision-Making Environments

The types of decisions people make depend on how much knowledge or information they have about the situation. There are three decision-making environments:

- Decision making under uncertainty
- Decision making under risk
- Decision making under certainty

DECISION MAKING UNDER UNCERTAINTY

When there is complete *uncertainty* as to which state of nature in a decision environment may occur (i.e., when we cannot even assess probabilities for each possible outcome), we rely on three decision methods:

Maximax

A criterion that finds an alternative that maximizes the maximum outcome.

Maximin

A criterion that finds an alternative that maximizes the minimum outcome.

Equally likely

A criterion that assigns equal probability to each state of nature.

1. **Maximax**: This method finds an alternative that *maxi*mizes the *max*imum outcome for every alternative. First, we find the maximum outcome within every alternative, and then we pick the alternative with the maximum number. Because this decision criterion locates the alternative with the *highest* possible *gain*, it has been called an "optimistic" decision criterion.
2. **Maximin**: This method finds the alternative that *maxi*mizes the *min*imum outcome for every alternative. First, we find the minimum outcome within every alternative, and then we pick the alternative with the maximum number. Because this decision criterion locates the alternative that has the *least* possible *loss*, it has been called a "pessimistic" decision criterion.
3. **Equally likely**: This method finds the alternative with the highest average outcome. First, we calculate the average outcome for every alternative, which is the sum of all outcomes divided by the number of outcomes. We then pick the alternative with the maximum number. The equally likely approach assumes that each state of nature is equally likely to occur.

EXAMPLE A3

A Decision Table Analysis Under Uncertainty

Table A.2
Decision Table for Decision Making Under Uncertainty

Getz Products Company would like to apply each of these three approaches now.

APPROACH ▶ Given Getz's decision table of Example A2, the company determines the maximax, maximin, and equally likely decision criteria.

SOLUTION ▶ Table A.2 provides the solution.

	States of Nature				
Alternatives	**Favourable Market**	**Unfavourable market**	**Maximum in Row**	**Minimum in Row**	**Row Average**
Construct large plant	$ 200 000	–$180 000	$200 000	–$180 000	$10 000
Construct small plant	$ 10 000	–$200 000	$100 000	–$ 20 000	$40 000
Do nothing	$ 0	$ 0	$ 0	$ 0	$ 0
			Maximax	Maximin	Equally likely

1. The maximax choice is to construct a large plant. This is the *max*imum of the *max*imum number within each row, or alternative.
2. The maximin choice is to do nothing. This is the *max*imum of the *min*imum number within each row, or alternative.
3. The equally likely choice is to construct a small plant. This is the maximum of the average outcome of each alternative. This approach assumes that all outcomes for any alternative are *equally likely*.

INSIGHT ▶ There are optimistic decision makers ("maximax") and pessimistic ones ("maximin"). Maximax and maximin present best case–worst case planning scenarios.

LEARNING EXERCISE ▶ Getz re-estimates the outcome for constructing a large plant when the market is favourable and raises it to $250 000. What numbers change in Table A.2? Do the decisions change? [Answer: The maximax is now $250 000, and the row average is $35 000 for large plant. No decision changes.]

RELATED PROBLEMS ▶ A.1, A.2b–d, A.4, A.6

DECISION MAKING UNDER RISK

Decision making under risk, a more common occurrence, relies on probabilities. Several possible states of nature may occur, each with an assumed probability. The states of nature must be mutually exclusive and collectively exhaustive and their probabilities must sum to 1.[1] Given a decision table with conditional values and probability assessments for all states of nature, we can determine the **expected monetary value (EMV)** for each alternative. This figure represents the expected value or *mean* return for each alternative *if we could repeat this decision (or similar types of decisions) a large number of times.*

The EMV for an alternative is the sum of all possible payoffs from the alternative, each weighted by the probability of that payoff occurring:

$$
\begin{aligned}
\text{EMV(Alternative } i) = \ & (\text{Payoff of 1st state of nature}) \\
& \times (\text{Probability of 1st state of nature}) \\
+ \ & (\text{Payoff of 2nd state of nature}) \\
& \times (\text{Probability of 2nd state of nature}) \\
+ \ & \ldots + (\text{Payoff of last state of nature}) \\
& \times (\text{Probability of last state of nature})
\end{aligned}
$$

Example A4 illustrates how to compute the maximum EMV.

Expected monetary value (EMV)
The expected payout or value of a variable that has different possible states of nature, each with an associated probability.

LO4 Calculate an expected monetary value (EMV)

Getz would like to find the EMV for each alternative.

APPROACH ▶ Getz Products's operations manager believes that the probability of a favourable market is exactly the same as that of an unfavourable market; that is, each state of nature has a 0.50 chance of occurring. He can now determine the EMV for each alternative (see Table A.3):

EXAMPLE **A4**

Expected Monetary Value

Table A.3
Decision Table for Getz Products

	States of Nature	
Alternatives	**Favourable Market**	**Unfavourable Market**
Construct large plant (A_1)	$200 000	–$180 000
Construct small plant (A_2)	$100 000	–$ 20 000
Do nothing (A_3)	$ 0	$ 0
Probabilities	0.50	0.50

SOLUTION ▶
1. $\text{EMV}(A_1) = (0.5)(\$200\,000) + (0.5)(-\$180\,000) = \$10\,000$
2. $\text{EMV}(A_2) = (0.5)(\$100\,000) + (0.5)(-\$20\,000) = \$40\,000$
3. $\text{EMV}(A_3) = (0.5)(\$0) + (0.5)(\$0) = \$0$

INSIGHT ▶ The maximum EMV is seen in alternative A_2. Thus, according to the EMV decision criterion, Getz would build the small facility.

LEARNING EXERCISE ▶ What happens to the three EMVs if Getz increases the conditional value on the "large plant/favourable market" result to $250 000? [Answer: $\text{EMV}(A_1) = \$35\,000$. No change in decision.]

RELATED PROBLEMS ▶ A.2e, A.3a, A.5a, A.7a, A.8, A.9a, A.10, A.11, A.12, A.14a,b, A.16a, A.22

EXCEL OM Data File **ModAEx4.xlsx** can be found at **MyLab Operations Management**.

DECISION MAKING UNDER CERTAINTY

Now, suppose that the Getz operations manager has been approached by a marketing research firm that proposes to help him make the decision about whether to build the plant to produce storage sheds. The marketing researchers claim that their technical analysis will tell Getz with certainty whether the market is favourable for the proposed product. In other words, it will

---

[1] To review these other statistical terms, refer to Tutorial 1, "Statistical Review for Managers," at MyLab Operations Management.

change Getz's environment from one of decision making *under risk* to one of decision making *under certainty*. This information could prevent Getz from making a very expensive mistake. The marketing research firm would charge Getz $65 000 for the information. What would you recommend? Should the operations manager hire the firm to make the study? Even if the information from the study is perfectly accurate, is it worth $65 000? What might it be worth? Although some of these questions are difficult to answer, determining the value of such *perfect information* can be very useful. It places an upper limit on what you would be willing to spend on information, such as that being sold by a marketing consultant. This is the concept of the expected value of perfect information (EVPI), which we now introduce.

STUDENT **TIP**

EVPI places an upper limit on what you should pay for information.

EXPECTED VALUE OF PERFECT INFORMATION (EVPI)

If a manager were able to determine which state of nature would occur, then he or she would know which decision to make. Once a manager knows which decision to make, the payoff increases because the payoff is now a certainty, not a probability. Because the payoff will increase with knowledge of which state of nature will occur, this knowledge has value. Therefore, we now look at how to determine the value of this information. We call this difference between the payoff under perfect information and the payoff under risk the **expected value of perfect information (EVPI)**.

Expected value of perfect information (EVPI)

The difference between the payoff under perfect information and the payoff under risk.

Expected value with perfect information (EVwPI)

The expected (average) return if perfect information is available.

$$\text{EVPI} = \text{Expected value with perfect information} - \text{Maximum EMV}$$

To find the EVPI, we must first compute the **expected value with perfect information (EVwPI)**, which is the expected (average) return if we have perfect information before a decision has to be made. To calculate this value, we choose the best alternative for each state of nature and multiply its payoff times the probability of occurrence of that state of nature:

Expected value *with*
perfect information (EVwPI) = (Best outcome or consequence for 1st state of nature)
$\times$ (Probability of 1st state of nature)

+ (Best outcome for 2nd state of nature)
$\times$ (Probability of 2nd state of nature)

+ $\cdots$ + (Best outcome for last state of nature)
$\times$ (Probability of last state of nature)

LO5 Compute the expected value of perfect information (EVPI)

In Example A5, we use the data and decision table from Example A4 to examine the expected value of perfect information.

EXAMPLE **A5**

Expected Value of Perfect Information

The Getz operations manager would like to calculate the maximum that he would pay for information—that is, the expected value of perfect information, or EVPI.

APPROACH ▶ In referring to Table A.3 in Example 4, we find the approach follows a two-stage process. First, the expected value *with* perfect information (EVwPI) is computed. Then, using this information, EVPI is calculated.

SOLUTION ▶

1. The best outcome for the state of nature "favourable market" is "build a large facility" with a payoff of $200 000. The best outcome for the state of nature "unfavourable market" is "do nothing" with a payoff of $0. Expected value *with* perfect information = ($200 000)(0.50) + ($0)(0.50) = $100 000. Thus, if we had perfect information, we would expect (on the average) $100 000 if the decision could be repeated many times.

2. The maximum EMV is $40 000 for A_2, which is the expected outcome without perfect information. Thus:

$$\text{EVPI} = \text{EV}_W\text{PI} - \text{Maximum EMV}$$
$$= \$100\ 000 - \$40\ 000 = \$60\ 000$$

INSIGHT ▶ The *most* Getz should be willing to pay for perfect information is $60 000. This conclusion, of course, is again based on the assumption that the probability of each state of nature is 0.50.

LEARNING EXERCISE ▶ How does the EVPI change if the "large plant/favourable market" conditional value is $250 000? [Answer: EVPI = $85 000.]

RELATED PROBLEMS ▶ A.3b, A.5b, A.7, A.9, A.14, A.16

Decision Trees

Decisions that lend themselves to display in a decision table also lend themselves to display in a decision tree. We will therefore analyze some decisions using decision trees. Although the use of a decision table is convenient in problems having one set of decisions and one set of states of nature, many problems include *sequential* decisions and states of nature.

When there are two or more sequential decisions, and later decisions are based on the outcome of prior ones, the decision tree approach becomes appropriate. A **decision tree** is a graphic display of the decision process that indicates decision alternatives, states of nature and their respective probabilities, and payoffs for each combination of decision alternative and state of nature.

Expected monetary value (EMV) is the most commonly used criterion for decision tree analysis. One of the first steps in such analysis is to graph the decision tree and to specify the monetary consequences of all outcomes for a particular problem.

Analyzing problems with *decision trees* involves five steps:

1. Define the problem.
2. Structure or draw the decision tree.
3. Assign probabilities to the states of nature.
4. Estimate payoffs for each possible combination of decision alternatives and states of nature.
5. Solve the problem by computing the expected monetary value (EMV) for each state-of-nature node. This is done by working *backward*—that is, by starting at the right of the tree and working back to decision nodes on the left.

Decision tree

A graphical means of analyzing decision alternatives and states of nature.

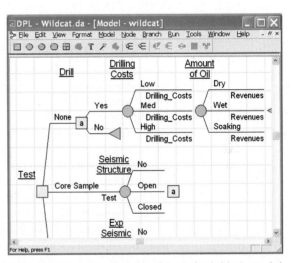

When Canadian-based Brownstone Energy Inc., an oil and gas exploration company, had to decide upon which of its sites to drill for oil, it turned to decision tree analysis. The 74 different factors—including geological, engineering, economic, and political factors—became much clearer. Decision tree software such as DPL (shown here), Tree Plan, and Supertree allows decision problems to be analyzed with less effort and greater depth than ever before.

Getz wants to develop a completed and solved decision tree.

APPROACH ▶ The payoffs are placed at the right-hand side of each of the tree's branches (see Figure A.2). The probabilities (first used by Getz in Example A4) are placed in parentheses next to each state of nature. The expected monetary value for each state-of-nature node is then calculated and placed by its respective node. The EMV of the first node is $10 000. This represents the branch from the decision node to "construct a large plant". The EMV for node 2, to "construct a small plant," is $40 000. The option of "doing nothing" has, of course, a payoff of $0.

SOLUTION ▶ The branch leaving the decision node leading to the state-of-nature node with the highest EMV will be chosen. In Getz's case, a small plant should be built.

INSIGHT ▶ This graphical approach is an excellent way for managers to understand all the options in making a major decision. Visual models are often preferred over tables.

Solving a Tree for EMV

FIGURE A.2

Completed and Solved Decision Tree for Getz Products

LO6 Evaluate the nodes in a decision tree

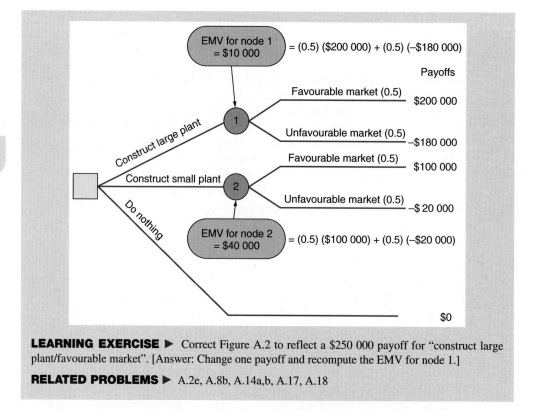

LEARNING EXERCISE ▶ Correct Figure A.2 to reflect a $250 000 payoff for "construct large plant/favourable market". [Answer: Change one payoff and recompute the EMV for node 1.]

RELATED PROBLEMS ▶ A.2e, A.8b, A.14a,b, A.17, A.18

A MORE COMPLEX DECISION TREE

When a *sequence* of decisions must be made, decision trees are much more powerful tools than are decision tables. Let's say that Getz Products has two decisions to make, with the second decision dependent on the outcome of the first. Before deciding about building a new plant, Getz has the option of conducting its own marketing research survey, at a cost of $10 000. The information from this survey could help it decide whether to build a large plant, to build a small plant, or not to build at all. Getz recognizes that although such a survey will not provide it with *perfect* information, it may be extremely helpful.

Getz's new decision tree is represented in Figure A.3 of Example A7. Take a careful look at this more complex tree. Note that *all possible outcomes and alternatives* are included in their logical sequence. This procedure is one of the strengths of using decision trees. The manager is forced to examine all possible outcomes, including unfavourable ones. He or she is also forced to make decisions in a logical, sequential manner.

EXAMPLE A7

A Decision Tree with Sequential Decisions

Getz Products wishes to develop the new tree for this sequential decision.

APPROACH ▶ Examining the tree in Figure A.3, we see that Getz's first decision point is whether to conduct the $10 000 market survey. If it chooses not to do the study (the lower part of the tree), it can either build a large plant, a small plant, or no plant. This is Getz's second decision point. If the decision is to build, the market will be either favourable (0.50 probability) or unfavourable (also 0.50 probability). The payoffs for each of the possible consequences are listed along the right-hand side. As a matter of fact, this lower portion of Getz's tree is *identical* to the simpler decision tree shown in Figure A.2.

SOLUTION ▶ The upper part of Figure A.3 reflects the decision to conduct the market survey. State-of-nature node number 1 has two branches coming out of it. Let us say there is a 45% chance that the survey results will indicate a favourable market for the storage sheds. We also note that the probability is 0.55 that the survey results will be negative.

The rest of the probabilities shown in parentheses in Figure A.3 are all *conditional* probabilities. For example, 0.78 is the probability of a favourable market for the sheds given a favourable result from the market survey. Of course, you would expect to find a high probability of a favourable market given that the research indicated that the market was good. Don't forget, though: There is a chance that Getz's $10 000 market survey did not result in perfect or even reliable information. Any market research study

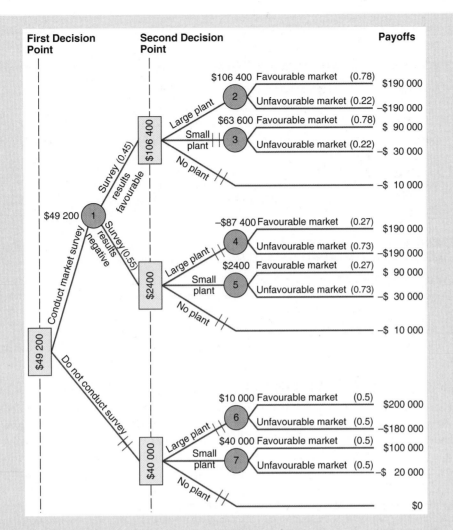

FIGURE A.3

Getz Products Decision Tree with Probabilities and EMVs Shown

STUDENT TIP

The short parallel lines mean "prune" that branch, as it is less favourable than another available option and may be dropped.

LO7 Create a decision tree with sequential decisions

is subject to error. In this case, there remains a 22% chance that the market for sheds will be unfavourable given positive survey results.

Likewise, we note that there is a 27% chance that the market for sheds will be favourable given negative survey results. The probability is much higher, 0.73, that the market will actually be unfavourable given a negative survey.

Finally, when we look to the payoff column in Figure A.3, we see that $10 000—the cost of the marketing study—has been subtracted from each of the top 10 tree branches. Thus, a large plant constructed in a favourable market would normally net a $200 000 profit. Yet, because the market study was conducted, this figure is reduced by $10 000. In the unfavourable case, the loss of $180 000 would increase to $190 000. Similarly, conducting the survey and building *no plant* now results in a −$10 000 payoff.

With all probabilities and payoffs specified, we can start calculating the expected monetary value of each branch. We begin at the end or right-hand side of the decision tree and work back towards the origin. When we finish, the best decision will be known.

1. Given favourable survey results:

$$\text{EMV(node 2)} = (0.78)(\$190\,000) + (0.22)(-\$190\,000) = \$106\,400$$
$$\text{EMV(node 3)} = (0.78)(\$90\,000) + (0.22)(-\$30\,000) = \$63\,600$$

The EMV of no plant in this case is −$10 000. Thus, if the survey results are favourable, a large plant should be built.

2. Given negative survey results:

$$\text{EMV(node 4)} = (0.27)(\$190\,000) + (0.73)(-\$190\,000) = -\$87\,400$$
$$\text{EMV(node 5)} = (0.27)(\$90\,000) + (0.73)(-\$30\,000) = \$2400$$

The EMV of no plant is again −$10 000 for this branch. Thus, given a negative survey result, Getz should build a small plant with an expected value of $2400.

3. Continuing on the upper part of the tree and moving backward, we compute the expected value of conducting the market survey:

$$\text{EMV(node 1)} = (0.45)(\$106\ 400) + (0.55)(\$2400) = \$49\ 200$$

4. If the market survey is *not* conducted:

$$\text{EMV(node 6)} = (0.50)(\$200\ 000) + (0.50)(-\$180\ 000) = \$10\ 000$$
$$\text{EMV(node 7)} = (0.50)(\$100\ 000) + (0.50)(-\$20\ 000) = \$40\ 000$$

The EMV of no plant is $0. Thus, building a small plant is the best choice, given the marketing research is not performed.

5. Because the expected monetary value of conducting the survey is $49 200—versus an EMV of $40 000 for not conducting the study—the best choice is to *seek marketing information*. If the survey results are favourable, Getz Products should build the large plant; if they are unfavourable, it should build the small plant.

INSIGHT ▶ You can reduce complexity in a large decision tree by viewing and solving a number of smaller trees—start at the end branches of a large one. Take one decision at a time.

LEARNING EXERCISE ▶ Getz estimates that if he conducts a market survey, there is really only a 35% chance the results will indicate a favourable market for the sheds. How does the tree change? [Answer: The EMV of conducting the survey = $38 800, so Getz should not do it now.]

RELATED PROBLEMS ▶ A.13, A.18, A.19, A.20, A.21, A.23

USING DECISION TREES IN ETHICAL DECISION MAKING

Decision trees can also be a useful tool to aid ethical corporate decision making. The decision tree illustrated in Example A8, developed by Harvard professor Constance Bagley, provides guidance as to how managers can both maximize shareholder value and behave ethically. The tree can be applied to any action a company contemplates, whether it is expanding operations in a developing country or reducing a workforce at home.

EXAMPLE A8

Ethical Decision Making

Smithson Corp. is opening a plant in Malaysia, a country with much less stringent environmental laws than the United States, its home nation. Smithson can save $18 million in building the manufacturing facility—and boost its profits—if it does not install pollution-control equipment that is mandated in the United States but not in Malaysia. But Smithson also calculates that pollutants emitted from the plant, if unscrubbed, could damage the local fishing industry. This could cause a loss of millions of dollars in income as well as create health problems for local inhabitants.

APPROACH ▶ Smithson decides to build a decision tree to model the problem.

SOLUTION ▶ Figure A.4 outlines the choices management can consider. For example, if in management's best judgment the harm to the Malaysian community by building the plant will be greater than the loss in company returns, the response to the question "Is it ethical?" will be no.

FIGURE A.4

Smithson's Decision Tree for Ethical Dilemma

Source: Modified from Constance E. Bagley, "The Ethical Leader's Decision Tree," *Harvard Business Review* January–February 2003): 18–19.

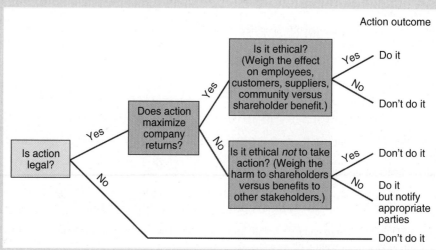

Now, say Smithson proposes building a somewhat different plant, one *with* pollution controls, despite a negative impact on company returns. That decision takes us to the branch "Is it ethical *not* to take action?" If the answer (for whatever reason) is no, the decision tree suggests proceeding with the plant but notifying the Smithson board of directors, shareholders, and others about its impact.

INSIGHT ▶ This tree allows managers to view the options graphically. This is a good way to start the process.

Ethical decisions can be quite complex: What happens, for example, if a company builds a polluting plant overseas, but this allows the company to sell a life-saving drug at a lower cost around the world? Does a decision tree deal with all possible ethical dilemmas? No—but it does provide managers with a framework for examining those choices.

THE POKER DECISION PROCESS

We opened this module with ex–dot-commer Paul Phillips's decision to go "all in" at the Legends of Poker tournament. Example A9 shows how he computed the expected value. Homework Problem A.24 gives you a chance to create a decision tree for this process.

EXAMPLE A9

Phillips's Poker Decision

Paul Phillips is deciding whether to bet all his chips ($422 000) against poker star T. J. Cloutier. Phillips holds a pair of sevens. Phillips reasons that T.J. will fold (with 80% probability) if he does not have a pair of fives or better, or very high cards like a jack, queen, king, or ace. But he also figures that a call would put $853 000 into the pot and surmises that even then, there is a 45% chance his pair of sevens will win.

APPROACH ▶ Phillips does an expected monetary analysis.

SOLUTION ▶ If T.J. folds:

The amount of money already in the pot

$$EMV = (0.80)(\$99\,000)$$
$$= \$79\,200$$

If T.J. calls:

The chance T.J. will call

$$EMV = 0.20[(0.45)(\$853\,000) - \text{Phillips's bet of } \$422\,000]$$
$$= 0.20[\$383\,850 - \$422\,000]$$
$$= 0.20[-\$38\,150] = -\$7630$$

Overall EMV = $79 200 – $7630 = $71 570

INSIGHT ▶ The overall EMV of $71 570 indicates that if this decision were to be made many times, the average payoff would be large. So Phillips decides to bet almost all of his chips. As it turns out, T.J. was holding a pair of jacks. Even though Phillips's decision in this instance did not work out, his analysis and procedure were the correct ones.

LEARNING EXERCISE ▶ What would happen if the amount of money already in the pot were only $39 000? [Answer: The overall EMV = $23 570.]

RELATED PROBLEM ▶ A.24

MODULE | SUMMARY

This module examines two of the most widely used decision techniques—decision tables and decision trees. These techniques are especially useful for making decisions under risk. Many decisions in research and development, plant and equipment, and even new buildings and structures can be analyzed with these decision models. Problems in inventory control, aggregate planning, maintenance, scheduling, and production control also lend themselves to decision table and decision tree applications.

Discussion Questions

1. Identify the six steps in the decision process.
2. Give an example of a good decision you made that resulted in a bad outcome. Also give an example of a bad decision you made that had a good outcome. Why was each decision good or bad?
3. What is the *equally likely* decision model?

4. Discuss the differences between decision making under certainty, under risk, and under uncertainty.
5. What is a decision tree?
6. Explain how decision trees might be used in several of the 10 OM decisions.
7. What is the expected value of perfect information?
8. What is the expected value *with* perfect information?

9. Identify the five steps in analyzing a problem using a decision tree.
10. Why are the maximax and maximin strategies considered to be optimistic and pessimistic, respectively?
11. The expected value criterion is considered to be the rational criterion on which to base a decision. Is this true? Is it rational to consider risk?
12. When are decision trees most useful?

Using Software for Decision Models

Analyzing decision tables is straightforward with Excel, Excel OM, and POM for Windows. When decision trees are involved, Excel OM or commercial packages such as DPL, Tree Plan, and Supertree provide flexibility, power, and ease. POM for Windows will also analyze trees but does not have graphic capabilities.

✗ USING EXCEL OM

Excel OM allows decision makers to evaluate decisions quickly and to perform sensitivity analysis on the results. Program A.1 uses the Getz data to illustrate input, output, and selected formulas needed to compute the EMV and EVPI values.

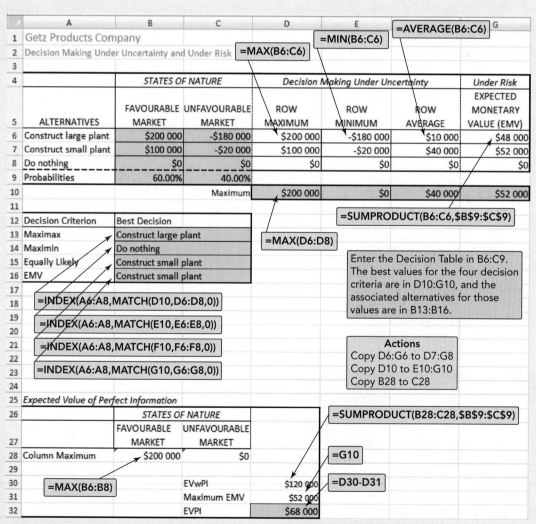

PROGRAM A.1 An Excel Spreadsheet for Analyzing Data in Examples A3 and A4 for Getz Products

Program A.2 uses Excel OM to create the decision tree for Getz Products shown earlier in Example A6. The tool to create the tree is seen in the window on the right.

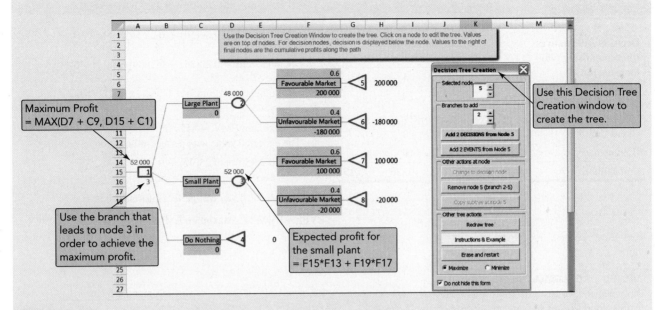

PROGRAM A.2
Getz Products' Decision Tree Using Excel OM

Source: Microsoft product screen shot(s) reprinted with permission from Microsoft Corporation.

ᵖ USING POM FOR WINDOWS

POM for Windows can be used to calculate all of the information described in the decision tables and decision trees in this module. For details on how to use this software, please refer to Appendix IV.

Solved Problems Virtual Office Hours help is available at MyLab Operations Management.

▼ SOLVED PROBLEM A.1

Stella Yan Hua is considering the possibility of opening a small dress shop on Fairbanks Avenue, a few blocks from the university. She has located a good mall that attracts students. Her options are to open a small shop, a medium-sized shop, or no shop at all. The market for a dress shop can be good, average, or bad. The probabilities for these three possibilities are 0.2 for a good market, 0.5 for an average market, and 0.3 for a bad market. The net profit or loss for the medium-sized or small shops for the various market conditions are given in the following table. Building no shop at all yields no loss and no gain. What do you recommend?

	States of Nature		
Alternatives	**Good Market ($)**	**Average Market ($)**	**Bad Market ($)**
Small shop	75 000	25 000	−40 000
Medium-sized shop	100 000	35 000	−60 000
No shop	0	0	0
Probabilities	0.20	0.50	0.30

▼ SOLUTION

The problem can be solved by computing the expected monetary value (EMV) for each alternative:

$$\text{EMV (Small shop)} = (0.2)(\$75\ 000) + (0.5)(\$25\ 000) + (0.3)(-\$40\ 000) = \$15\ 500$$
$$\text{EMV (Medium-sized shop)} = (0.2)(\$100\ 000) + (0.5)(\$35\ 000) + (0.3)(-\$60\ 000) = \$19\ 500$$
$$\text{EMV (No shop)} = (0.2)(\$0) + (0.5)(\$0) + (0.3)(\$0) = \$0$$

As you can see, the best decision is to build the medium-sized shop. The EMV for this alternative is $19 500.

▼ SOLVED PROBLEM A.2

T. S. Amer's Ski Shop in Whistler, B.C., has a 100-day season. T.S. has established the probabilities of various types of store traffic, based on historical records of skiing conditions, as indicated in the table. T.S. has four merchandising plans, each focusing on a popular name brand. Each plan yields a daily net profit as noted in the table. He also has a meteorologist friend who, for a small fee, will accurately tell tomorrow's weather so T.S. can implement one of his four merchandising plans.

a) What is the expected monetary value (EMV) under risk?
b) What is the expected value *with* perfect information (EVwPI)?
c) What is the expected value of perfect information (EVPI)?

Decision Alternatives (merchandising plan focusing on:)	*Traffic in Store Because of Ski Conditions (states of nature)*			
	1	**2**	**3**	**4**
Patagonia	$40	92	20	48
North Face	50	84	10	52
Cloud Veil	35	80	40	64
Columbia	45	72	10	60
Probabilities	0.20	0.25	0.30	0.25

▼ SOLUTION

a) The highest expected monetary value under risk is:

EMV (Patagonia) = 0.20(40) + 0.25(92) + 0.30(20) + 0.25(48) = $49

EMV (North Face) = 0.20(50) + 0.25(84) + 0.30(10) + 0.25(52) = $47

EMV (Cloud Veil) = 0.20(35) + 0.25(80) + 0.30(40) + 0.25(64) = $55

EMV (Columbia) = 0.20(45) + 0.25(72) + 0.30(10) + 0.25(60) = $45

So, the maximum EMV = $55

b) The expected value *with* perfect information is:

EVwPI = 0.20(50) + 0.25(92) + 0.30(40) + 0.25(64)
= 10 + 23 + 12 + 16 = $61

c) The expected value of perfect information is:

EVPI = EVwPI − Maximum EMV = 61 − 55 = $6

SOLVED PROBLEM A.3

Daily demand for cases of Tidy Bowl cleaner at Ravinder Nath's supermarket has always been 5, 6, or 7 cases. Develop a decision tree that illustrates her decision alternatives as to whether to stock 5, 6, or 7 cases.

▼ SOLUTION

The decision tree is shown in Figure A.5.

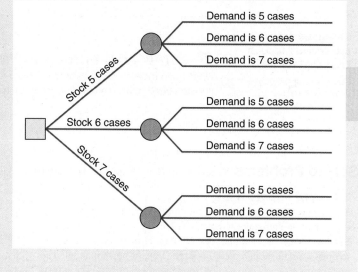

FIGURE A.5 **Demand at Ravinder Nath's Supermarket**

Problems*

•   A.1 Given the following conditional value table, determine the appropriate decision under uncertainty using:
a) Maximax
b) Maximin
c) Equally likely **Px**

Alternatives	*States of Nature*		
	Very Favourable Market	**Average Market**	**Unfavourable Market**
Build new plant	$350 000	$240 000	−$300 000
Subcontract	$180 000	$ 90 000	−$ 20 000
Overtime	$110 000	$ 60 000	−$ 10 000
Do nothing	$ 0	$ 0	$ 0

Note: **Px** means the problem may be solved with POM for Windows and/or Excel OM.

• •   A.2 Even though independent gasoline stations have been having a difficult time, Susan Helms has been thinking about starting her own independent gasoline station. Susan's problem is to decide how large her station should be. The annual returns will depend on both the size of her station and a number of marketing factors related to the oil industry and demand for gasoline. After a careful analysis, Susan developed the following table:

Size of First Station	Good Market ($)	Fair Market ($)	Poor Market ($)
Small	50 000	20 000	−10 000
Medium	80 000	30 000	−20 000
Large	100 000	30 000	−40 000
Very large	300 000	25 000	−160 000

For example, if Susan constructs a small station and the market is good, she will realize a profit of $50 000.

a) Develop a decision table for this decision, like the one illustrated in Table A.2 earlier.
b) What is the maximax decision?
c) What is the maximin decision?
d) What is the equally likely decision?
e) Develop a decision tree. Assume each outcome is equally likely, then find the highest EMV. **Px**

• **A.3** Clay Whybark, a soft drink vendor at Hard Rock Cafe's annual Rockfest, created a table of conditional values for the various alternatives (stocking decision) and states of nature (size of crowd):

	States of Nature (demand)		
Alternatives	**Big**	**Average**	**Small**
Large stock	$22 000	$12 000	–$2 000
Average stock	$14 000	$10 000	$6 000
Small stock	$ 9 000	$ 8 000	$4 000

The probabilities associated with the states of nature are 0.3 for a big demand, 0.5 for an average demand, and 0.2 for a small demand.
a) Determine the alternative that provides Clay Whybark the greatest expected monetary value (EMV).
b) Compute the expected value of perfect information (EVPI).

•• **A.4** Raymond Jacobs owns a health and fitness centre, the Muscle-Up, in Ashland. He is considering adding more floor space to meet increasing demand. He will either add no floor space (N), a moderate area of floor space (M), a large area of floor space (L), or an area of floor space that doubles the size of the facility (D). Demand will either stay fixed, increase slightly, or increase greatly. The following are the changes in Muscle-Up's annual profits under each combination of expansion level and demand change level:

	Expansion Level			
Demand Change	**N**	**M**	**L**	**D**
Fixed	$ 0	–$4 000	–$10 000	–$50 000
Slight increase	$2 000	$8 000	$ 6 000	$ 4 000
Major increase	$3 000	$9 000	$20 000	$40 000

Raymond is risk averse and wishes to use the maximin criterion.
a) What are his decision alternatives and what are the states of nature?
b) What should he do? **Px**

• **A.5** Howard Weiss Inc. is considering building a sensitive new airport scanning device. His managers believe that there is a probability of 0.4 that the ATR Co. will come out with a competitive product. If Weiss adds an assembly line for the product and ATR Co. does not follow with a competitive product, Weiss's expected profit is $40 000; if Weiss adds an assembly line and ATR follows suit, Weiss still expects $10 000 profit. If Weiss adds a new plant addition and ATR does not produce a competitive product, Weiss expects a profit of $600 000; if ATR does compete for this market, Weiss expects a loss of $100 000.
a) Determine the EMV of each decision
b) Compute the expected value of perfect information. **Px**

•• **A.6** Deborah Watson's factory is considering three approaches for meeting an expected increase in demand. These three approaches are increasing capacity, using overtime, and buying more equipment. Demand will increase either slightly (S), moderately (M), or greatly (G). The profits for each approach under each possible scenario are as follows:

	Demand Scenario		
Approach	**S**	**M**	**G**
Increasing capacity	$700 000	$700 000	$ 700 000
Using overtime	$500 000	$600 000	$1 000 000
Buying equipment	$600 000	$800 000	$ 800 000

Since the goal is to maximize, and Deborah is risk-neutral, she decides to use the *equally likely* decision criterion to make the decision as to which approach to use. According to this criterion, which approach should be used?

• **A.7** The following payoff table provides profits based on various possible decision alternatives and various levels of demand at Amber Gardner's software firm:

	Demand	
	Low	**High**
Alternative 1	$10 000	$30 000
Alternative 2	$ 5 000	$40 000
Alternative 3	–$ 2 000	$50 000

The probability of low demand is 0.4, whereas the probability of high demand is 0.6.
a) What is the highest possible expected monetary value?
b) What is the expected value *with* perfect information (EVwPI)?
c) Calculate the expected value of perfect information for this situation. **Px**

• **A.8** Leah Johnson, director of legal services of Brookline, wants to increase capacity to provide free legal advice but must decide whether to do so by hiring another full-time lawyer or by using part-time lawyers. The table below shows the expected *costs* of the two options for three possible demand levels:

	States of Nature		
Alternatives	**Low Demand**	**Medium Demand**	**High Demand**
Hire full-time	$300	$500	$ 700
Hire part-time	$ 0	$350	$1,000
Probabilities	0.2	0.5	0.3

a) Using expected value, what should Leah Johnson do?
b) Draw an appropriate decision tree showing payoffs and probabilities. **Px**

•• **A.9** Chung Manufacturing is considering the introduction of a family of new products. Long-term demand for the product group is somewhat predictable, so the manufacturer must be concerned with the risk of choosing a process that is inappropriate. Chen Chung is VP of operations. He can choose among batch manufacturing or custom manufacturing, or he can invest in group technology. Chen won't be able to forecast demand accurately until after he makes the process choice. Demand will be classified into four compartments: poor, fair, good, and excellent. The table indicates the payoffs (profits) associated with each process/demand combination, as well as the probabilities of each long-term demand level:

	Poor	Fair	Good	Excellent
Probability	0.1	0.4	0.3	0.2
Batch	-$ 200 000	$1 000 000	$1 200 000	$1 300 000
Custom	$ 100 000	$ 300 000	$ 700 000	$ 800 000
Technology	-$1 000 000	-$ 500 000	$ 500 000	$2 000 000

a) Based on expected value, what choice offers the greatest gain?
b) What would Chen Chung be willing to pay for a forecast that would accurately determine the level of demand in the future? **PX**

•• **A.10** Consider the following decision table, which Dinesh Dave has developed for Laurentian Enterprises:

		States of Nature		
Decision Alternatives	Probability:	0.40 Low	0.20 Medium	0.40 High
A		$40	$100	$60
B		$85	$ 60	$70
C		$60	$ 70	$70
D		$65	$ 75	$70
E		$70	$ 65	$80

Which decision alternative maximizes the expected value of the payoff? **PX**

•• **A.11** The University of Manitoba bookstore stocks textbooks in preparation for sales each semester. It normally relies on departmental forecasts and preregistration records to determine how many copies of a text are needed. Preregistration shows 90 operations management students enrolled, but bookstore manager Curtis Ketterman has second thoughts, based on his intuition and some historical evidence. Curtis believes that the distribution of sales may range from 70 to 90 units, according to the following probability model:

Demand	70	75	80	85	90
Probability	0.15	0.30	0.30	0.20	0.05

This textbook costs the bookstore $82 and sells for $112. Any unsold copies can be returned to the publisher, less a restocking fee and shipping, for a net refund of $36.
a) Construct the table of conditional profits.
b) How many copies should the bookstore stock to achieve highest expected value? **PX**

•• **A.12** Palmer Cheese Company is a small manufacturer of several different cheese products. One product is a cheese spread sold to retail outlets. Susan Palmer must decide how many cases of cheese spread to manufacture each month. The probability that demand will be 6 cases is 0.1, for 7 cases it is 0.3, for 8 cases it is 0.5, and for 9 cases it is 0.1. The cost of every case is $45, and the price Susan gets for each case is $95. Unfortunately, any cases not sold by the end of the month are of no value as a result of spoilage. How many cases should Susan manufacture each month? **PX**

••• **A.13** Ronald Lau, chief engineer at Dartmouth Electronics, has to decide whether to build a new state-of-the-art processing facility. If the new facility works, the company could realize a profit of

$200 000. If it fails, Dartmouth Electronics could lose $180 000. At this time, Lau estimates a 60% chance that the new process will fail.

The other option is to build a pilot plant and then decide whether to build a complete facility. The pilot plant would cost $10 000 to build. Lau estimates a 50–50 chance that the pilot plant will work. If the pilot plant works, there is a 90% probability that the complete plant, if it is built, will also work. If the pilot plant does not work, there is only a 20% chance that the complete project (if it is constructed) will work. Lau faces a dilemma. Should he build the plant? Should he build the pilot project and then make a decision? Help Lau by analyzing this problem. **PX**

•• **A.14** Karen Villagomez, president of Wright Industries, is considering whether to build a manufacturing plant in Edmonton. Her decision is summarized in the following table:

Alternatives	Favourable Market	Unfavourable Market
Build large plant	$400 000	-$300 000
Build small plant	$ 80 000	-$ 10 000
Don't build	$ 0	$ 0
Market probabilities	0.4	0.6

a) Construct a decision tree.
b) Determine the best strategy using expected monetary value (EMV).
c) What is the expected value of perfect information (EVPI)? **PX**

•• **A.15** Deborah Kellogg buys Breathalyzer test sets for the Montreal Police Department. The quality of the test sets from her two suppliers is indicated in the following table:

Percent Defective	Probability for Loomba Technology	Probability for Stewart-Douglas Enterprises
1	0.70	0.30
3	0.20	0.30
5	0.10	0.40

For example, the probability of getting a batch of tests that are 1% defective from Loomba Technology is 0.70. Because Kellogg orders 10 000 tests per order, this would mean that there is a 0.7 probability of getting 100 defective tests out of the 10 000 tests if Loomba Technology is used to fill the order. A defective Breathalyzer test set can be repaired for $0.50. Although the quality of the test sets of the second supplier, Stewart-Douglas Enterprises, is lower, it will sell an order of 10 000 test sets for $37 less than Loomba.
a) Develop a decision tree.
b) Which supplier should Kellogg use? **PX**

•• **A.16** Deborah Hollwager, a concessionaire for the Kitchener ballpark, has developed a table of conditional values for the various alternatives (stocking decision) and states of nature (size of crowd):

	States of Nature (size of crowd)		
Alternatives	Large	Average	Small
Large inventory	$20 000	$10 000	-$2 000
Average inventory	$15 000	$12 000	$6 000
Small inventory	$ 9 000	$ 6 000	$5 000

If the probabilities associated with the states of nature are 0.3 for a large crowd, 0.5 for an average crowd, and 0.2 for a small crowd, determine:

a) The alternative that provides the greatest expected monetary value (EMV).

b) The expected value of perfect information (EVPI). **PX**

• **A.17** Joseph Biggs owns his own snow cone business and lives 30 kilometres from a Prince Edward Island beach resort. The sale of snow cones is highly dependent on his location and on the weather. At the resort, his profit will be $120 per day in fair weather, $10 per day in bad weather. At home, his profit will be $70 in fair weather and $55 in bad weather. Assume that on any particular day, the weather service suggests a 40% chance of foul weather.

a) Construct Joseph's decision tree.

b) What decision is recommended by the expected value criterion? **PX**

•• **A.18** Kenneth Boyer is considering opening a bicycle shop in North Vancouver. Boyer enjoys biking, but this is to be a business endeavour from which he expects to make a living. He can open a small shop, a large shop, or no shop at all. Because there will be a five-year lease on the building that Boyer is thinking about using, he wants to make sure he makes the correct decision. Boyer is also thinking about hiring his old marketing professor to conduct a marketing research study to see if there is a market for his services. The results of such a study could be either favourable or unfavourable. Develop a decision tree for Boyer. **PX**

•• **A.19** F.J. Brewerton Retailers Inc. must decide whether to build a small or a large facility at a new location in south Winnipeg. Demand at the location will either be low or high, with probabilities 0.4 and 0.6, respectively. If Brewerton builds a small facility and demand proves to be high, Brewerton then has the option of expanding the facility. If a small facility is built and demand proves to be high, and then the retailer expands the facility, the payoff is $270 000. If a small facility is built and demand proves to be high, but Brewerton then decides not to expand the facility, the payoff is $223 000.

If a small facility is built and demand proves to be low, then there is no option to expand and the payoff is $200 000. If a large facility is built and demand proves to be low, Brewerton then has the option of stimulating demand through local advertising. If it does not exercise this option, then the payoff is $40 000. If it does exercise the advertising option, then the response to advertising will either be modest or sizable, with probabilities of 0.3 and 0.7, respectively. If the response is modest, the payoff is $20 000. If it is sizable, the payoff is $220 000. Finally, if a large facility is built and demand proves to be high, then no advertising is needed and the payoff is $800 000.

a) What should Brewerton do to maximize the expected payoff?

b) What is the value of this expected payoff?

••• **A.20** Dick Holliday is not sure what he should do. He can build either a large video rental section or a small one in his drugstore. He can also gather additional information or simply do nothing. If he gathers additional information, the results could suggest either a favourable or an unfavourable market, but it would cost him $3000 to gather the information. Holliday believes that there is a 50–50 chance that the information will be favourable. If the rental market is favourable, Holliday will earn $15 000 with a large section or $5000 with a small. With an unfavourable video rental market, however, Holliday could lose $20 000 with a large section or $10 000 with a small section. Without gathering additional information, Holliday estimates that the probability of a favourable rental market is 0.7. A favourable report from the study would increase the probability of a favourable rental market to 0.9. Furthermore, an unfavourable report from the additional information would decrease the probability of a favourable rental market to 0.4. Of course, Holliday could ignore these numbers and do nothing. What is your advice to Holliday?

•••• **A.21** Jeff Kaufmann's machine shop sells a variety of machines for job shops. A customer wants to purchase a model XPO2 drilling machine from Jeff's store. The model XPO2 sells for $180 000, but Jeff is out of XPO2s. The customer says he will wait for Jeff to get a model XPO2 in stock. Jeff knows that there is a wholesale market for XPO2s from which he can purchase an XPO2. Jeff can buy an XPO2 today for $150 000, or he can wait a day and buy an XPO2 (if one is available) tomorrow for $125 000. If at least one XPO2 is still available tomorrow, Jeff can wait until the day after tomorrow and buy an XPO2 (if one is still available) for $110 000.

There is a 0.40 probability that there will be no model XPO2s available tomorrow. If there are model XPO2s available tomorrow, there is a 0.70 probability that by the day after tomorrow, there will be no model XPO2s available in the wholesale market. Three days from now, it is certain that no model XPO2s will be available on the wholesale market. What is the maximum expected profit that Jeff can achieve? What should Jeff do?

•••• **A.22** The city of Segovia is contemplating building a second airport to relieve congestion at the main airport and is considering two potential sites, X and Y. Hard Rock Hotels would like to purchase land to build a hotel at the new airport. The value of land has been rising in anticipation and is expected to skyrocket once the city decides between sites X and Y. Consequently, Hard Rock would like to purchase land now. Hard Rock will sell the land if the city chooses not to locate the airport nearby. Hard Rock has four options: (1) buy land at X, (2) buy land at Y, (3) buy land at both X and Y, or (4) do nothing. Hard Rock has collected the following data (which are in millions of euros):

	Site X	Site Y
Current purchase price	27	15
Profits if airport and hotel built at this site	45	30
Sale price if airport not built at this site	9	6

Hard Rock determines there is a 45% chance the airport will be built at X (hence, a 55% chance it will be built at Y).

a) Set up the decision table.

b) What should Hard Rock decide to do to maximize total net profit? **PX**

•••• **A.23** Newfoundland and Labrador is busy designing new lottery scratch-off games. In the latest game, Bayside Boondoggle, the player is instructed to scratch off one spot: A, B, or C. A can reveal "Loser," "Win $1," or "Win $50". B can reveal "Loser" or "Take a Second Chance". C can reveal "Loser" or "Win $500". On the second chance, the player is instructed to scratch off D or E. D can reveal "Loser" or "Win $1". E can reveal "Loser" or "Win $10". The probabilities at A are 0.9, 0.09, and 0.01. The probabilities at B are 0.8 and 0.2. The probabilities at C are 0.999 and 0.001. The probabilities at D are 0.5 and 0.5. Finally, the probabilities at E are 0.95 and 0.05. Draw the decision tree that represents this scenario. Use proper symbols and label all branches clearly. Calculate the expected value of this game.

•••• **A.24** At the beginning of this module and in Example A9, we follow the poker decision made by Paul Phillips against veteran T. J. Cloutier. Create a decision tree that corresponds with the decision made by Phillips. **PX**

CASE | STUDY

Tom Tucker's Liver Transplant

Tom Tucker, a robust 50-year-old executive living in the northern suburbs of Toronto, has been diagnosed by a University of Toronto internist as having a decaying liver. Although he is otherwise healthy, Tucker's liver problem could prove fatal if left untreated.

Firm research data are not yet available to predict the likelihood of survival for a man of Tucker's age and condition without surgery. However, based on her own experience and recent medical journal articles, the internist tells him that if he elects to avoid surgical treatment of the liver problem, chances of survival will be approximately as follows: only a 60% chance of living one year, a 20% chance of surviving for two years, a 10% chance for five

years, and a 10% chance of living to age 58. She considers his probability of survival beyond age 58 without a liver transplant to be extremely low.

The transplant operation, however, is a serious surgical procedure. Five percent of patients die during the operation or its recovery stage, with an additional 45% dying during the first year. Twenty percent survive for five years, 13% survive for 10 years, and 8%, 5%, and 4% survive, respectively, for 15, 20, and 25 years.

Discussion Questions

1. Do you think that Tucker should select the transplant operation?
2. What other factors might be considered?

▶ **Additional Case Studies:** Visit **MyLab Operations Management** for these additional case studies:
Arctic, Inc.: A refrigeration company has several major options with regard to capacity and expansion.
Ski Right Corp.: Which of four manufacturers should be selected to manufacture ski helmets?

MODULE A | RAPID REVIEW

MyLab Operations
Management

Main Heading	Review Material
THE DECISION PROCESS IN OPERATIONS (pp. 661–662)	To achieve the goals of their organizations, managers must understand how decisions are made and know which decision-making tools to use. Overcoming uncertainty is a manager's mission.
	Decision tables and decision trees are used in a wide number of OM situations.
	• **Big data**—The huge amount of economic, production, and consumer data now being collected in digital form.
FUNDAMENTALS OF DECISION MAKING (pp. 662–663)	• **Alternative**—A course of action or strategy that may be chosen by a decision maker.
	• **State of nature**—An occurrence or a situation over which a decision maker has little or no control.
	Symbols used in a decision tree:
	1. □—A decision node from which one of several alternatives may be selected.
	2. ○—A state-of-nature node out of which one state of nature will occur.
	When constructing a decision tree, we must be sure that all alternatives and states of nature are in their correct and logical places and that we include *all* possible alternatives and states of nature, usually including the "do nothing" option.
DECISION TABLES (p. 663)	• **Decision table**—A tabular means of analyzing decision alternatives and states of nature.
	A decision table is sometimes called a *payoff table*. For any alternative and a particular state of nature, there is a *consequence*, or an *outcome*, which is usually expressed as a monetary value; this is called the *conditional value*.

Main Heading	Review Material	

TYPES OF DECISION-MAKING ENVIRONMENTS
(pp. 664–666)

There are three decision-making environments: (1) decision making under uncertainty, (2) decision making under risk, and (3) decision making under certainty.

When there is complete *uncertainty* about which state of nature in a decision environment may occur (i.e., when we cannot even assess probabilities for each possible outcome), we rely on three decision methods: (1) maximax, (2) maximin, and (3) equally likely.

- **Maximax**—A criterion that finds an alternative that maximizes the maximum outcome
- **Maximin**—A criterion that finds an alternative that maximizes the minimum outcome
- **Equally likely**—A criterion that assigns equal probability to each state of nature

Maximax is also called an "optimistic" decision criterion, while maximin is sometimes called a "pessimistic" decision criterion. Maximax and maximin present best case/worst case planning scenarios.

Decision making under risk relies on probabilities. The states of nature must be mutually exclusive and collectively exhaustive, and their probabilities must sum to 1.

- **Expected monetary value (EMV)**—The expected payout or value of a variable that has different possible states of nature, each with an associated probability.

The EMV represents the expected value or *mean* return for each alternative *if we could repeat this decision (or similar types of decisions) a large number of times*.

The EMV for an alternative is the sum of all possible payoffs from the alternative, each weighted by the probability of that payoff occurring:

EMV (Alternative *i*) = (Payoff of 1st state of nature)
$\times$ (Probability of 1st of state of nature)

+ (Payoff of 2nd state of nature)
$\times$ (Probability of 2nd state of nature)

+ . . . + (Payoff of last state of nature)
$\times$ (Probability of last state of nature)

- **Expected value of perfect information (EVPI)**—The difference between the payoff under perfect information and the payoff under risk.

EVPI represents an upper limit on what you would be willing to spend on state-of-nature information:

EVPI = Expected value with perfect information – Maximum EMV

- **Expected value with perfect information (EVwPI)**—The expected (average) return if perfect information is available.

Expected value *with*
perfect information (EVwPI) = (Best outcome or consequence for 1st state of nature)
$\times$ (Probability of 1st state of nature)

+ (Best outcome for 2nd state of nature)
$\times$ (Probability of 2nd state of nature)

+ . . . + (Best outcome for last state of nature)
$\times$ (Probability of last state of nature)

Problems: A.1–A.12, A.14, A.16s

Virtual Office Hours for Solved Problems: A.1, A.2

DECISION TREES
(pp. 667–671)

When there are two or more sequential decisions, and later decisions are based on the outcome of prior ones, the decision tree (as opposed to decision table) approach becomes appropriate.

- **Decision tree**—A graphical means of analyzing decision alternatives and states of nature.

Analyzing problems with *decision trees* involves five steps:

1. Define the problem.

2. Structure or draw the decision tree.

3. Assign probabilities to the states of nature.

Problems: A.2, A.8, A.14, A.17, A.18, A.19, A.20, A.21, A.23, A.24

Virtual Office Hours for Solved Problem: A.3

Main Heading   Review Material

4. Estimate payoffs for each possible combination of decision alternatives and states of nature.

5. Solve the problem by computing the expected monetary value (EMV) for each state-of-nature node. This is done by working *backward*—that is, by starting at the right of the tree and working back to decision nodes on the left:

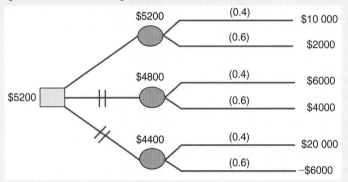

Decision trees force managers to examine all possible outcomes, including unfavourable ones. A manager is also forced to make decisions in a logical, sequential manner.

Short parallel lines on a decision tree mean "prune" that branch, as it is less favourable than another available option and may be dropped.

Self-Test

■ **Before taking the self-test,** refer to the learning objectives listed at the beginning of the module.

LO1 On a decision tree, at each state-of-nature node:
   a) the alternative with the greatest EMV is selected.
   b) an EMV is calculated.
   c) all probabilities are added together.
   d) the branch with the highest probability is selected.

LO2 In decision table terminology, a course of action or a strategy that may be chosen by a decision maker is called a(n):
   a) payoff.   b) alternative.
   c) state of nature.   d) all of the above.

LO3 If probabilities are available to the decision maker, then the decision-making environment is called:
   a) certainty.   b) uncertainty.
   c) risk.   d) none of the above.

LO4 What is the EMV for Alternative A_1 in the following decision table?

	State of nature	
Alternative	S_1	S_2
A_1	$15 000	$20 000
A_2	$10 000	$30 000
Probability	0.30	0.70

   a) $15 000   b) $17 000
   c) $17 500   d) $18 500
   e) $20 000

LO5 The most that a person should pay for perfect information is:
   a) the EVPI.
   b) the maximum EMV minus the minimum EMV.
   c) the minimum EMV.
   d) the maximum EMV.

LO6 On a decision tree, once the tree has been drawn and the payoffs and probabilities have been placed on the tree, the analysis (computing EMVs and selecting the best alternative):
   a) is done by working backward (starting on the right and moving to the left).
   b) is done by working forward (starting on the left and moving to the right).
   c) is done by starting at the top of the tree and moving down.
   d) is done by starting at the bottom of the tree and moving up.

LO7 A decision tree is preferable to a decision table when:
   a) a number of sequential decisions are to be made.
   b) probabilities are available.
   c) the maximax criterion is used.
   d) the objective is to maximize regret.

Answers: LO1. b; LO2. b; LO3. c; LO4. d; LO5. a; LO6. a; LO7. a.

MyLab Operations Management

Most of these questions can be found in MyLab Operations Management. Visit MyLab Operations Management to access cases, videos, downloadable software, and much more. MyLab Operations Management Management also features a personalized Study Plan that helps you identify which chapter concepts you've mastered and guides you towards study tools for additional practice.

Linear Programming

Learning Objectives

LO1 Formulate linear programming models, including an objective function and constraints **683**

LO2 Graphically solve an LP problem with the iso-profit line method **685**

LO3 *Graphically* solve an LP problem with the corner-point method **688**

LO4 Interpret sensitivity analysis and shadow prices **688**

LO5 Construct and solve a minimization problem **691**

LO6 Formulate production-mix, diet, and labour scheduling problems **692**

Why Use Linear Programming?

Many operations management decisions involve trying to make the most effective use of an organization's resources. Resources typically include machinery (such as planes, in the case of an airline), labour (such as pilots), money, time, and raw materials (such as jet fuel). These resources may be used to produce products (such as machines, furniture, food, or clothing) or services (such as airline schedules, advertising policies, or investment decisions). **Linear programming (LP)** is a widely used mathematical technique designed to help operations managers plan and make the decisions necessary to allocate resources.

A few examples of problems in which LP has been successfully applied in operations management are:

1. Scheduling school buses to *minimize* the total distance travelled when carrying students.
2. Allocating police patrol units to high crime areas to *minimize* response time to 911 calls.
3. Scheduling tellers at banks so that needs are met during each hour of the day while *minimizing* the total cost of labour.
4. Selecting the product mix in a factory to make best use of machine- and labour-hours available while *maximizing* the firm's profit.
5. Picking blends of raw materials in feed mills to produce finished feed combinations at *minimum* cost.
6. Determining the distribution system that will *minimize* total shipping cost from several warehouses to various market locations.
7. Developing a production schedule that will satisfy future demands for a firm's product and at the same time *minimize* total production and inventory costs.
8. Allocating space for a tenant mix in a new shopping mall so as to *maximize* revenues to the leasing company.

Linear programming (LP)

A mathematical technique designed to help operations managers plan and make decisions relative to the trade-offs necessary to allocate resources.

The storm front closed in quickly on Toronto's Pearson Airport, shutting it down without warning. The heavy snowstorm and poor visibility sent Air Canada passengers and ground crew scurrying. Because Air Canada uses linear programming (LP) to schedule flights, hotels, crews, and refuelling, LP has a direct impact on profitability. If Air Canada gets a major weather disruption at one of its hubs, a lot of flights may get cancelled, which means a lot of crews and airplanes in the wrong places. LP is the tool that helps airlines such as Air Canada unsnarl and cope with this weather mess.

Neil McAllister/Alamy Stock Photo

Requirements of a Linear Programming Problem

All LP problems have four requirements: an objective, constraints, alternatives, and linearity:

Objective function

A mathematical expression in linear programming that maximizes or minimizes some quantity (often profit or cost, but any goal may be used).

Constraints

Restrictions that limit the degree to which a manager can pursue an objective.

1. LP problems seek to *maximize* or *minimize* some quantity (usually profit or cost). We refer to this property as the **objective function** of an LP problem. The major objective of a typical firm is to maximize dollar profits in the long run. In the case of a trucking or airline distribution system, the objective might be to minimize shipping costs.
2. The presence of restrictions, or **constraints**, limits the degree to which we can pursue our objective. For example, deciding how many units of each product in a firm's product line to manufacture is restricted by available labour and machinery. We want, therefore, to maximize or minimize a quantity (the objective function) subject to limited resources (the constraints).
3. There must be *alternative courses of action* to choose from. For example, if a company produces three different products, management may use LP to decide how to allocate among them its limited production resources (of labour, machinery, and so on). If there were no alternatives to select from, we would not need LP.
4. The objective and constraints in linear programming problems must be expressed in terms of *linear equations* or inequalities. Linearity implies proportionality and additivity. If x_1 and x_2 are decision variables, there can be no products (e.g., $x_1 x_2$) or powers (e.g., x_1^3) in the objective or constraints. For example, the expression $5x_1 + 8x_2 \leq 250$ is linear; however, the expression $5x_1 + 8x_2 - 2x_1 x_2 \leq 300$ is not linear.

STUDENT TIP

Here we set up an LP example that we will follow for most of this module.

Formulating Linear Programming Problems

One of the most common linear programming applications is the *product-mix problem*. Two or more products are usually produced using limited resources. The company would like to determine how many units of each product it should produce to maximize overall profit given its limited resources. Let's look at an example.

GLICKMAN ELECTRONICS EXAMPLE

The Glickman Electronics Company produces two products: (1) the Glickman x-pod, a portable music player, and (2) the Glickman BlueBerry, an internet-connected colour telephone.

	Hours Required to Produce One Unit		
Department	x-pods (X_1)	BlueBerrys (X_2)	Available Hours this Week
Electronic	4	3	240
Assembly	2	1	100
Profit per unit	$7	$5	

Table B.1
Glickman Electronics Company Problem Data

The production processes for the products are similar in that both require a certain number of hours of electronic work and a certain number of labour-hours in the assembly department. Each x-pod takes 4 hours of electronic work and 2 hours in the assembly shop. Each BlueBerry requires 3 hours in electronics and 1 hour in assembly. During the current production period, 240 hours of electronic time are available, and 100 hours of assembly department time are available. Each x-pod sold yields a profit of $7; each BlueBerry produced may be sold for a $5 profit.

Glickman's problem is to determine the best possible combination of x-pods and BlueBerrys to manufacture to reach the maximum profit. This product-mix situation can be formulated as a linear programming problem.

We begin by summarizing the information needed to formulate and solve this problem (see Table B.1).

Further, let's introduce some simple notation for use in the objective function and constraints. Let:

$$X_1 = \text{number of x-pods to be produced}$$
$$X_2 = \text{number of BlueBerrys to be produced}$$

Now, we can create the LP *objective function* in terms of X_1 and X_2:

$$\text{Maximize profit} = \$7X_1 + \$5X_2$$

Our next step is to develop mathematical relationships to describe the two constraints in this problem. One general relationship is that the amount of a resource used is to be less than or equal to ($\leq$) the amount of resource *available*.

First constraint: Electronic time used is $\leq$ Electronic time available.

$$4X_1 + 3X_2 \leq 240 \text{ (hours of electronic time)}$$

Second constraint: Assembly time used is $\leq$ Assembly time available.

$$2X_1 + 1X_2 \leq 100 \text{ (hours of assembly time)}$$

Both these constraints represent production capacity restrictions and, of course, affect the total profit. For example, Glickman Electronics cannot produce 70 x-pods during the production period because if $X_1 = 70$ both constraints will be violated. It also cannot make $X_1 = 50$ x-pods and $X_2 = 10$ BlueBerrys. This constraint brings out another important aspect of linear programming; that is, certain interactions will exist between variables. The more units of one product that a firm produces, the fewer it can make of other products.

Graphical Solution to a Linear Programming Problem

The easiest way to solve a small LP problem such as that of the Glickman Electronics Company is the **graphical solution approach**. The graphical procedure can be used only when there are two **decision variables** (such as number of x-pods to produce, X_1, and number of BlueBerrys to produce, X_2). When there are more than two variables, it is *not* possible to plot the solution on a two-dimensional graph; we then must turn to more complex approaches described later in this module.

GRAPHICAL REPRESENTATION OF CONSTRAINTS

To find the optimal solution to a linear programming problem, we must first identify a set, or region, of feasible solutions. The first step in doing so is to plot the problem's constraints on a graph.

STUDENT TIP

This example is further illustrated in Active Model B.1 at MyLab Operations Management.

LO1 Formulate linear programming models, including an objective function and constraints

Graphical solution approach
A means of plotting a solution to a two-variable problem on a graph.

Decision variables
Choices available to a decision maker.

The variable X_1 (x-pods, in our example) is usually plotted as the horizontal axis of the graph, and the variable X_2 (BlueBerrys) is plotted as the vertical axis. The complete problem may be restated as:

$$\text{Maximize profit} = \$7X_1 + \$5X_2$$

Subject to the constraints:

$$4X_1 + 3X_2 \leq 240 \text{ (electronics constraint)}$$
$$2X_1 + 1X_2 \leq 100 \text{ (assembly constraint)}$$
$$X_1 \geq 0 \text{ (number of x-pods produced is greater than or equal to 0)}$$
$$X_2 \geq 0 \text{ (number of BlueBerrys produced is greater than or equal to 0)}$$

(These last two constraints are also called *nonnegativity constraints*.)

The first step in graphing the constraints of the problem is to convert the constraint *inequalities* into *equalities* (or equations).

$$\text{Constraint A: } 4X_1 + 3X_2 = 240$$
$$\text{Constraint B: } 2X_1 + 1X_2 = 100$$

The equation for constraint A is plotted in Figure B.1 and for constraint B in Figure B.2.

To plot the line in Figure B.1, all we need to do is find the points at which the line $4X_1 + 3X_2 = 240$ intersects the X_1 and X_2 axes. When $X_1 = 0$ (the location where the line touches the X_2 axis), it implies that $3X_2 = 240$ and that $X_2 = 80$. Likewise, when $X_2 = 0$, we see that $4X_1 = 240$ and that $X_1 = 60$. Thus, constraint A is bounded by the line running from $X_1 = 0, X_2 = 80$) to ($X_1 = 60, X_2 = 0$). The shaded area represents all points that satisfy the original *inequality*.

Constraint B is illustrated similarly in Figure B.2. When $X_1 = 0$ then $X_2 = 100$ and when $X_2 = 0$ then $X_1 = 50$. Constraint B, then, is bounded by the line between ($X_1 = 0, X_2 = 100$) and ($X_1 = 50, X_2 = 0$). The shaded area represents the original inequality.

Figure B.3 shows both constraints together. The shaded region is the part that satisfies both restrictions. The shaded region in Figure B.3 is called the *area of feasible solutions*, or simply the **feasible region**. This region must satisfy *all* conditions specified by the program's constraints and is thus the region where all constraints overlap. Any point in the region would be a *feasible solution* to the Glickman Electronics Company problem. Any point outside the shaded area would represent an *infeasible solution*. Hence, it would be feasible to manufacture 30 x-pods and 20 BlueBerrys ($X_1 = 30, X_2 = 20$), but it would violate the constraints to produce 70 x-pods and 40 BlueBerrys. This can be seen by plotting these points on the graph of Figure B.3.

Feasible region

The set of all feasible combinations of decision variables.

ISO-PROFIT LINE SOLUTION METHOD

Now that the feasible region has been graphed, we can proceed to find the *optimal* solution to the problem. The optimal solution is the point lying in the feasible region that produces the highest profit.

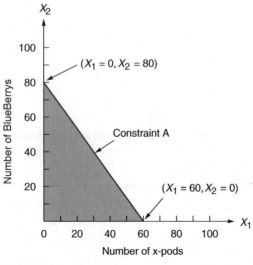

FIGURE B.1 **Constraint A**

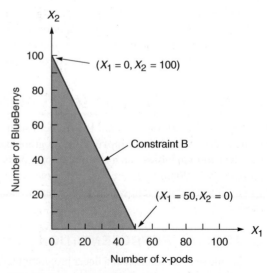

FIGURE B.2 **Constraint B**

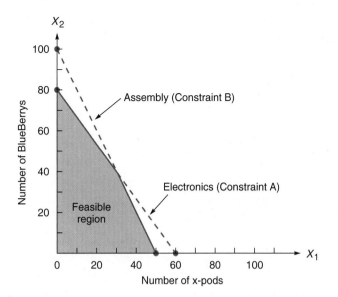

FIGURE B.3
Feasible Solution Region for the Glickman Electronics Company Problem

Once the feasible region has been established, several approaches can be taken in solving for the optimal solution. The speediest one to apply is called the **iso-profit line method**.[1]

We start by letting profits equal some arbitrary but small dollar amount. For the Glickman Electronics problem, we may choose a profit of $210. This is a profit level that can easily be obtained without violating either of the two constraints. The objective function can be written as $210 = 7X_1 + 5X_2$.

This expression is just the equation of a line; we call it an *iso-profit line*. It represents all combinations of (X_1, X_2) that will yield a total profit of $210. To plot the profit line, we proceed exactly as we did to plot a constraint line. First, let $X_1 = 0$ and solve for the point at which the line crosses the X_2 axis:

$$\$210 = \$7(0) + \$5X_2$$
$$X_2 = 42 \text{ BlueBerrys}$$

Then let $X_2 = 0$ and solve for X_1:

$$\$210 = \$7X_1 + \$5(0)$$
$$X_1 = 30 \text{ x-pods}$$

We can now connect these two points with a straight line. This profit line is illustrated in Figure B.4. All points on the line represent feasible solutions that produce a profit of $210.

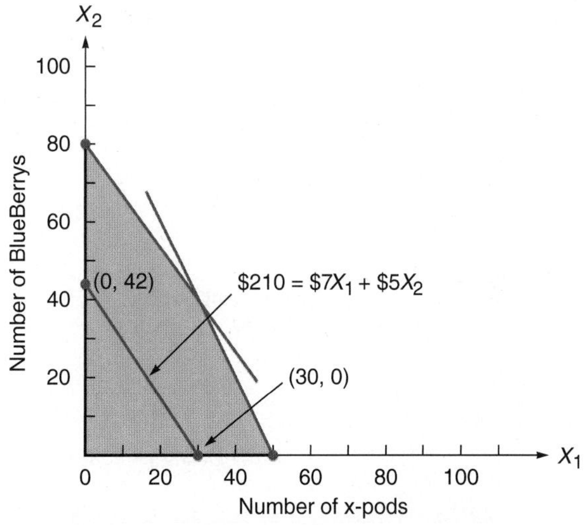

Iso-profit line method
An approach to solving a linear programming maximization problem graphically.

LO2 Graphically solve an LP problem with the iso-profit line method

FIGURE B.4
A Profit Line of $210 Plotted for the Glickman Electronics Company

[1] *Iso* means "equal" or "similar". Thus, an iso-profit line represents a line with all profits the same, in this case $210.

FIGURE B.5

Four Iso-Profit Lines Plotted for the Glickman Electronics Company

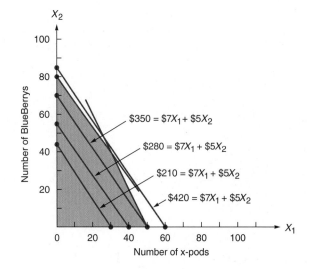

We see, however, that the iso-profit line for $210 does not produce the highest possible profit to the firm. In Figure B.5, we try graphing three more lines, each yielding a higher profit. The middle equation, $280 = $7X_1 + 5X_2$, was plotted in the same fashion as the lower line. When $X_1 = 0$:

$$\$280 = \$7(0) + \$5X_2$$
$$X_2 = 56 \text{ BlueBerrys}$$

When $X_2 = 0$:

$$\$280 = \$7X_1 + \$5(0)$$
$$X_1 = 40 \text{ x-pods}$$

Again, any combination of x-pods (X_1) and BlueBerrys (X_2) on this iso-profit line will produce a total profit of $280.

Note that the third line generates a profit of $350, even more of an improvement. The farther we move from the 0 origin, the higher our profit will be. Another important point to note is that these iso-profit lines are parallel. We now have two clues as to how to find the optimal solution to the original problem. We can draw a series of parallel profit lines (by carefully moving our ruler in a plane parallel to the first profit line). The highest profit line that still touches some point of the feasible region will pinpoint the optimal solution. Notice that the fourth line ($420) is too high to count because it does not touch the feasible region.

The highest possible iso-profit line is illustrated in Figure B.6. It touches the tip of the feasible region at the point where the two resource constraints intersect. To find its coordinates *accurately*,

FIGURE B.6

Optimal Solution for the Glickman Electronics Problem

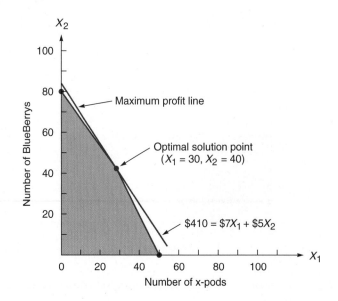

we will have to solve for the intersection of the two constraint lines. As you may recall from algebra, we can apply the method of *simultaneous equations* to the two constraint equations:

$$4X_1 + 3X_2 = 240 \quad (electronics\ time)$$

$$2X_1 + 1X_2 = 100 \quad (assembly\ time)$$

To solve these equations simultaneously, we multiply the second equation by -2:

$$-2(2X_1 + 1X_2 = 100) = -4X_1 - 2X_2 = -200$$

and then add it to the first equation:

$$
\begin{aligned}
+4X_1 + 3X_2 &= 240 \\
-4X_1 - 2X_2 &= -200 \\
\hline
+ 1X_2 &= 40
\end{aligned}
$$

or:

$$X_2 = 40$$

Doing this has enabled us to eliminate one variable, X_1, and to solve for X_2. We can now substitute 40 for X_2 in either of the original constraint equations and solve for X_1. Let us use the first equation. When $X_2 = 40$, then:

$$4X_1 + 3(40) = 240$$

$$4X_1 + 120 = 240$$

$$4X_1 = 120$$

$$X_1 = 30$$

Thus, the optimal solution has the coordinates ($X_1 = 30, X_2 = 40$). The profit at this point is $7(30) + \$5(40) = \$410$.

CORNER-POINT SOLUTION METHOD

A second approach to solving linear programming problems employs the **corner-point method**. This technique is simpler in concept than the iso-profit line approach, but it involves looking at the profit at every corner point of the feasible region.

The mathematical theory behind linear programming states that an optimal solution to any problem [i.e., the values of (X_1, X_2) that yield the maximum profit] will lie at a *corner point*, or *extreme point*, of the feasible region. Hence, it is necessary to find only the values of the variables at each corner; the maximum profit or optimal solution will lie at one (or more) of them.

Once again we can see (in Figure B.7) that the feasible region for the Glickman Electronics Company problem is a four-sided polygon with four corner—or extreme—points. These points

Corner-point method
A method for solving graphical linear programming problems.

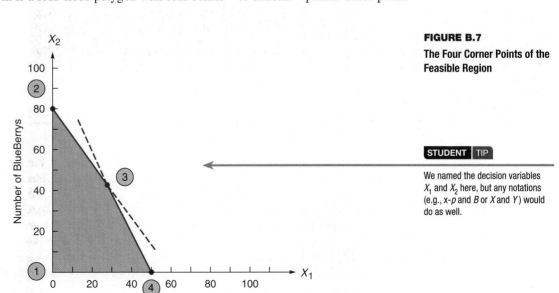

FIGURE B.7
The Four Corner Points of the Feasible Region

STUDENT TIP

We named the decision variables X_1 and X_2 here, but any notations (e.g., x-p and B or X and Y) would do as well.

are labelled ①, ②, ③, and ④ on the graph. To find the (X_1, X_2) values producing the maximum profit, we find out what the coordinates of each corner point are, then determine and compare their profit levels. (We showed how to find the coordinates for point ③ in the previous section describing the iso-profit line solution method.)

$$\text{Point ①: } (X_1 = 0, X_2 = 0) \quad \text{Profit } \$7(0) + \$5(0) \quad = \$0$$
$$\text{Point ②: } (X_1 = 0, X_2 = 80) \quad \text{Profit } \$7(0) + \$5(80) = \$400$$
$$\text{Point ③: } (X_1 = 30, X_2 = 40) \quad \text{Profit } \$7(30) + \$5(40) = \$410$$
$$\text{Point ④: } (X_1 = 50, X_2 = 0) \quad \text{Profit } \$7(50) + \$5(0) \quad = \$350$$

Because point ③ produces the highest profit of any corner point, the product mix of $X_1 = 30$ x-pods and $X_2 = 40$ BlueBerrys is the optimal solution to the Glickman Electronics problem. This solution will yield a profit of \$410 per production period; it is the same solution we obtained using the iso-profit line method.

LO3 *Graphically* solve an LP problem with the corner-point method

Sensitivity Analysis

STUDENT TIP

Here we look at the sensitivity of the final answers to changing inputs.

Parameter
A numerical value that is given in a model.

Sensitivity analysis
An analysis that projects how much a solution may change if there are changes in the variables or input data.

Operations managers are usually interested in more than the optimal solution to an LP problem. In addition to knowing the value of each decision variable (the X_i values) and the value of the objective function, they want to know how sensitive these answers are to input **parameter** changes. For example, what happens if the coefficients of the objective function are not exact, or if they change by 10% or 15%? What happens if right-hand-side values of the constraints change? Because solutions are based on the assumption that input parameters are constant, the subject of sensitivity analysis comes into play. **Sensitivity analysis**, or postoptimality analysis, is the study of how sensitive solutions are to parameter changes.

There are two approaches to determining just how sensitive an optimal solution is to changes. The first is simply a trial-and-error approach. This approach usually involves resolving the entire problem, preferably by computer, each time one input data item or parameter is changed. It can take a long time to test a series of possible changes in this way.

The approach we prefer is the analytic postoptimality method. After an LP problem has been solved, we determine a range of changes in problem parameters that will not affect the optimal solution or change the variables in the solution. This is done without resolving the whole problem. LP software, such as Excel's Solver or POM for Windows, has this capability. Let us examine several scenarios relating to the Glickman Electronics example.

Program B.1 is part of the Excel Solver computer-generated output available to help a decision maker know whether a solution is relatively insensitive to reasonable changes in one or more of the parameters of the problem. (The complete computer run for these data, including input and full output, is illustrated later in this module.)

LO4 Interpret sensitivity analysis and shadow prices

PROGRAM B.1
Sensitivity Analysis for Glickman Electronics, Using Excel's Solver

Source: Microsoft product screen shot(s) reprinted with permission from Microsoft Corporation.

Microsoft Excel 15.0 Sensitivity Report
Report Created: 9:22:18 AM

> The solution values for the variables appear. We should make 30 x-pods and 40 BlueBerrys.

Variable Cells

Cell	Name	Final Value	Reduced Cost	Objective Coefficient	Allowable Increase	Allowable Decrease
$B$5	Variable Values x-pods	30	0	7	3	0.333333333
$C$5	Variable Values BlueBerrys	40	0	5	0.25	1.5

Constraints

Cell	Name	Final Value	Shadow Price	Constraint R.H. Side	Allowable Increase	Allowable Decrease
$D$8	Electronic Time Available	240	1.5	240	60	40
$D$9	Assembly Time Available	100	0.5	100	20	20

> We will use 240 hours and 100 hours of Electronics and Assembly time, respectively.

> If we use 1 more Electronics hour, our profit will increase by \$1.50. This is true for up to 60 more hours. The profit will fall by \$1.50 for each Electronics hour less than 240 hours, down to as low as 200 hours.

SENSITIVITY REPORT

The Excel *Sensitivity Report* for the Glickman Electronics example in Program B.1 has two distinct components: (1) a table titled Variable Cells and (2) a table titled Constraints. These tables permit us to answer several what-if questions regarding the problem solution.

It is important to note that while using the information in the sensitivity report to answer what-if questions, we assume that we are considering a change to only a *single* input data value at a time. That is, the sensitivity information does not always apply to simultaneous changes in several input data values.

The *Variable Cells* table presents information regarding the impact of changes to the objective function coefficients (i.e., the unit profits of \$7 and \$5) on the optimal solution. The *Constraints* table presents information related to the impact of changes in constraint right-hand-side (RHS) values (i.e., the 240 hours and 100 hours) on the optimal solution. Although different LP software packages may format and present these tables differently, the programs all provide essentially the same information.

CHANGES IN THE RESOURCES OR RIGHT-HAND-SIDE VALUES

The right-hand-side values of the constraints often represent resources available to the firm. The resources could be labour-hours or machine time or perhaps money or production materials available. In the Glickman Electronics example, the two resources are hours available of electronics time and hours of assembly time. If additional hours were available, a higher total profit could be realized. How much should the company be willing to pay for additional hours? Is it profitable to have some additional electronics hours? Should we be willing to pay for more assembly time? Sensitivity analysis about these resources will help us answer these questions.

If the right-hand side of a constraint is changed, the feasible region will change (unless the constraint is redundant), and often the optimal solution will change. In the Glickman example, there were 100 hours of assembly time available each week and the maximum possible profit was \$410. If the available assembly hours are *increased* to 110 hours, the new optimal solution seen in Figure B.8(a) is (45, 20) and the profit is \$415. Thus, the extra 10 hours of time resulted in an increase in profit of \$5 or \$0.50 per hour. If the hours are *decreased* to 90 hours as shown in Figure B.8(b), the new optimal solution is (15, 60) and the profit is \$405. Thus, reducing the hours by 10 results in a decrease in profit of \$5 or \$0.50 per hour. This \$0.50 per hour change in profit that resulted from a change in the hours available is called the shadow price, or dual value. The **shadow price (or dual value)** for a constraint is the improvement in the objective function value that results from a one-unit increase in the right-hand side of the constraint.

> **Shadow price (or dual value)**
> The value of one additional unit of a scarce resource in LP.

VALIDITY RANGE FOR THE SHADOW PRICE? Given that Glickman Electronics's profit increases by \$0.50 for each additional hour of assembly time, does it mean that Glickman can do

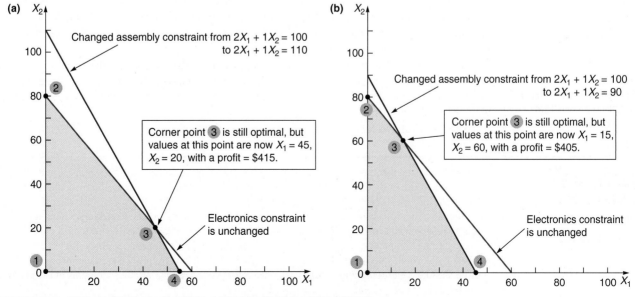

FIGURE B.8 Glickman Electronics Sensitivity Analysis on Right-Hand-Side (RHS) Resources

this indefinitely, essentially earning infinite profit? Clearly, this is illogical. How far can Glickman increase its assembly time availability and still earn an extra $0.50 profit per hour? That is, for what level of increase in the RHS value of the assembly time constraint is the shadow price of $0.50 valid?

The shadow price of $0.50 is valid as long as the available assembly time stays in a range within which all current corner points continue to exist. The information to compute the upper and lower limits of this range is given by the entries labelled Allowable Increase and Allowable Decrease in the *Sensitivity Report* in Program B.1. In Glickman's case, these values show that the shadow price of $0.50 for assembly time availability is valid for an increase of up to 20 hours from the current value and a decrease of up to 20 hours. That is, the available assembly time can range from a low of 80 (= 100 − 20) to a high of 120 (= 100 + 20) for the shadow price of $0.50 to be valid. Note that the allowable decrease implies that for each hour of assembly time that Glickman loses (up to 20 hours), its profit decreases by $0.50.

CHANGES IN THE OBJECTIVE FUNCTION COEFFICIENT

Let us now focus on the information provided in Program B.1 titled *Variable Cells*. Each row in the *Variable Cells* table contains information regarding a decision variable (i.e., x-pods or BlueBerrys) in the LP model.

ALLOWABLE RANGES FOR OBJECTIVE FUNCTION COEFFICIENTS As the unit profit contribution of either product changes, the slope of the iso-profit line we saw earlier in Figure B.5 changes. The size of the feasible region, however, remains the same. That is, the locations of the corner points do not change.

The limits to which the profit coefficient of x-pods or BlueBerrys can be changed without affecting the optimality of the current solution is revealed by the values in the *Allowable Increase* and *Allowable Decrease* columns of the *Sensitivity Report* in Program B.1. The allowable increase in the objective function coefficient for BlueBerrys is only $0.25. In contrast, the allowable decrease is $1.50. Hence, if the unit profit of BlueBerrys drops to $4 (i.e., a decrease of $1 from the current value of $5), it is still optimal to produce 30 x-pods and 40 BlueBerrys. The total profit will drop to $370 (from $410) because each BlueBerry now yields less profit (of $1 per unit). However, if the unit profit drops below $3.50 per BlueBerry (i.e., a decrease of more than $1.50 from the current $5 profit), the current solution is no longer optimal. The LP problem will then have to be resolved using Solver, or other software, to find the new optimal corner point.

Solving Minimization Problems

Many linear programming problems involve *minimizing* an objective such as cost instead of maximizing a profit function. A restaurant, for example, may wish to develop a work schedule to meet staffing needs while minimizing the total number of employees. Also, a manufacturer may seek to distribute its products from several factories to its many regional warehouses in such a way as to minimize total shipping costs.

Minimization problems can be solved graphically by first setting up the feasible solution region and then using either the corner-point method or an **iso-cost** line approach (which is analogous to the iso-profit approach in maximization problems) to find the values of X_1 and X_2 that yield the minimum cost.

Example B1 shows how to solve a minimization problem.

EXAMPLE **B1**

A Minimization Problem With Two Variables

Cohen Chemicals Inc. produces two types of photo-developing fluids. The first, a black-and-white picture chemical, costs Cohen $2500 per ton to produce. The second, a colour photo chemical, costs $3000 per ton.

Based on an analysis of current inventory levels and outstanding orders, Cohen's production manager has specified that at least 30 tons of the black-and-white chemical and at least 20 tons of the colour chemical must be produced during the next month. In addition, the manager notes that an existing inventory of a highly perishable raw material needed in both chemicals must be used within 30 days. To avoid wasting the expensive raw material, Cohen must produce a total of at least 60 tons of the photo chemicals in the next month.

APPROACH ▶ Formulate this information as a minimization LP problem.

Let:

X_1 = number of tons of black-and-white photo chemical produced

X_2 = number of tons of colour photo chemical produced

Objective: Minimize cost = $\$2500X_1 + \$3000X_2$

Subject to:

$X_1 \geq 30$ tons of black-and-white chemical

$X_2 \geq 20$ tons of colour chemical

$X_1 + X_2 \geq 60$ tons total

$X_1, X_2 \geq 0$ nonnegative requirements

SOLUTION ▶ To solve the Cohen Chemicals problem graphically, we construct the problem's feasible region, shown in Figure B.9.

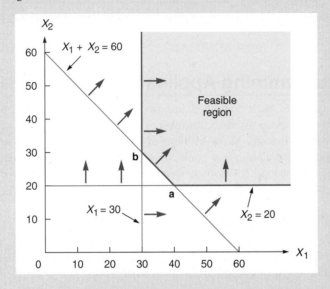

FIGURE B.9 Cohen Chemicals's Feasible Region

Minimization problems are often unbounded outward (i.e., on the right side and on the top), but this characteristic causes no problem in solving them. As long as they are bounded inward (on the left side and the bottom), we can establish corner points. The optimal solution will lie at one of the corners.

In this case, there are only two corner points, **a** and **b**, in Figure B.9. It is easy to determine that at point **a**, $X_1 = 40$ and $X_2 = 20$, and that at point **b**, $X_1 = 30$ and $X_2 = 30$. The optimal solution is found at the point yielding the lowest total cost.

Thus:

$$\text{Total cost a} = 2500X_1 + 3000X_2$$
$$= 2500(40) + 3000(20)$$
$$= \$160\ 000$$

$$\text{Total cost b} = 2500X_1 + 3000X_2$$
$$= 2500(30) + 3000(30)$$
$$= \$165\ 000$$

The lowest cost to Cohen Chemicals is at point **a**. Hence the operations manager should produce 40 tons of the black-and-white chemical and 20 tons of the colour chemical.

INSIGHT ▶ The area is either not bounded to the right or above in a minimization problem (as it is in a maximization problem).

LEARNING EXERCISE ▶ Cohen's second constraint is recomputed and should be $X_2 \geq 15$. Does anything change in the answer? [Answer: Now $14x + 6y = 42$ and $x - y \leq 3$ and total cost = $\$157\ 500$.]

RELATED PROBLEMS ▶ B.3, B.5, B.6, B.11, B.12, B.22, B.24

EXCEL OM Data File **ModBExB1.xlsx** can be found at **MyLab Operations Management.**

LO5 Construct and solve a minimization problem

OM in Action   The Canadian Airline Industry Saves Millions of Dollars With LP

It has been said that an airline seat is the most perishable commodity in the world. Each time an airliner takes off with an empty seat, a revenue opportunity is lost forever. For Air Canada, WestJet, Air Transat, Porter, and other Canadian airlines, which collectively fly hundreds of flights each day on hundreds of planes, the schedule is their very heartbeat. These schedules, all developed with massive LP models containing thousands of constraints and variables, assign aircraft to specific routes and assign pilots and flight attendants to each of these aircraft.

One flight leg for Air Canada might consist of a Boeing 737 assigned to fly at 8:05 a.m. from Montreal to Toronto to arrive at 9:10 a.m. The challenge for them, just as it is for their competitors, is to match planes such as the 737s to

flight legs similar to Montreal–Toronto and to fill seats with paying passengers. And when schedule disruptions occur due to snowstorms, mechanical problems, or crew unavailability, planes and people are often in the wrong place.

This is why the airlines rely upon LP models that include constraints such as aircraft unavailability, maintenance needs, crew-training requirements, arrival/departure needs, and so on. The airlines' objectives are to minimize a combination of operating costs and lost passenger revenue. The savings from LP have been in the millions of dollars per year at these airlines.

Source: **www.publications.gc.ca** and **www.statcan.gc.ca**.

STUDENT TIP

Now we look at three larger problems—ones that have more than two decision variables each and therefore are not graphed.

Linear Programming Applications

The foregoing examples each contained just two variables (X_1 and X_2). Most real-world problems contain many more variables, however. This is exemplified in the *OM in Action* box "The Canadian Airline Industry Saves Millions of Dollars With LP". Let's use the principles already developed to formulate a few more complex problems. The practice you will get by "paraphrasing" the following LP situations should help develop your skills for applying linear programming to other common operations situations.

LO6 Formulate production-mix, diet, and labour scheduling problems

PRODUCTION-MIX EXAMPLE

Example B2 involves another *production-mix* decision. Limited resources must be allocated among various products that a firm produces. The firm's overall objective is to manufacture the selected products in such quantities as to maximize total profits.

EXAMPLE B2

A Production-Mix Problem

Failsafe Electronics Corporation primarily manufactures four highly technical products, which it supplies to aerospace firms that hold NASA contracts. Each of the products must pass through the following departments before they are shipped: wiring, drilling, assembly, and inspection. The time requirements in each department (in hours) for each unit produced and its corresponding profit value are summarized in this table:

| Product | Department | | | | Unit Profit |
	Wiring	Drilling	Assembly	Inspection	
XJ201	0.5	3	2	0.5	$ 9
XM897	1.5	1	4	1.0	$12
TR29	1.5	2	1	0.5	$15
BR788	1.0	3	2	0.5	$11

The production time available in each department each month and the minimum monthly production requirement to fulfill contracts are as follows:

Department	Capacity (hours)	Product	Minimum Production Level
Wiring	1500	XJ201	150
Drilling	2350	XM897	100
Assembly	2600	TR29	200
Inspection	1200	BR788	400

APPROACH ▶ Formulate this production-mix situation as an LP problem. The production manager first specifies production levels for each product for the coming month. He lets:

$$X_1 = \text{number of units of XJ201 produced}$$
$$X_2 = \text{number of units of XM897 produced}$$
$$X_3 = \text{number of units of TR29 produced}$$
$$X_4 = \text{number of units of BR788 produced}$$

SOLUTION ▶ The LP formulation is:

Objective: Maximize profit $= 9X_1 + 12X_2 + 15X_3 + 11X_4$

subject to:

$$0.5X_1 + 1.5X_2 + 1.5X_3 + 1X_4 \leq 1500 \text{ hours of wiring available}$$
$$3X_1 + 1X_2 + 2X_3 + 3X_4 \leq 2350 \text{ hours of drilling available}$$
$$2X_1 + 4X_2 + 1X_3 + 2X_4 \leq 2600 \text{ hours of assembly available}$$
$$0.5X_1 + 1X_2 + 0.5X_3 + 0.5X_4 \leq 1200 \text{ hours of inspection}$$
$$X_1 \geq 150 \text{ units XJ201}$$
$$X_2 \geq 100 \text{ units of XM897}$$
$$X_3 \geq 200 \text{ units of TR29}$$
$$X_4 \geq 400 \text{ units of BR788}$$
$$X_1, X_2, X_3, X_4 \geq 0$$

INSIGHT ▶ There can be numerous constraints in an LP problem. The constraint right-hand sides may be in different units, but the objective function uses one common unit—dollars of profit, in this case. Because there are more than two decision variables, this problem is not solved graphically.

LEARNING EXERCISE ▶ Solve this LP problem as formulated. What is the solution? [Answer: $X_1 = 150, X_2 = 300, X_3 = 200, X_4 = 400$.]

RELATED PROBLEMS ▶ B.7, B.8, B.10, B.19, B.20, B.21, B.23, B.28, B.29

DIET PROBLEM EXAMPLE

Example B3 illustrates the *diet problem*, which was originally used by hospitals to determine the most economical diet for patients. Known in agricultural applications as the *feed-mix problem*, the diet problem involves specifying a food or feed ingredient combination that will satisfy stated nutritional requirements at a minimum cost level.

The Feed 'N Ship feedlot fattens cattle for local farmers and ships them to meat markets in Quebec City and Moncton. The owners of the feedlot seek to determine the amounts of cattle feed to import from the United States to satisfy minimum nutritional standards and, at the same time, minimize total feed costs.

Each grain stock contains different amounts of four nutritional ingredients: A, B, C, and D. Here are the ingredient contents of each grain, in *ounces per pound of grain*:

EXAMPLE B3

A Diet Problem

	Feed		
Ingredient	Stock X	Stock Y	Stock Z
A	3 oz	2 oz	4 oz
B	2 oz	3 oz	1 oz
C	1 oz	0 oz	2 oz
D	6 oz	8 oz	4 oz

The cost per pound of grains X, Y, and Z is $0.02, $0.04, and $0.025, respectively. The minimum requirement per cow per month is 64 ounces of ingredient A, 80 ounces of ingredient B, 16 ounces of ingredient C, and 128 ounces of ingredient D.

The feedlot faces one additional restriction—it can obtain only 500 pounds of stock Z per month from the feed supplier, regardless of its need. Because there are usually 100 cows at the Feed 'N Ship feedlot at any given time, this constraint limits the amount of stock Z for use in the feed of each cow to no more than 5 pounds, or 80 ounces, per month.

For details regarding the algebraic steps of the simplex algorithm, see Tutorial 3 at MyLab Operations Management or refer to a management science textbook.[2]

Integer and Binary Variables

All the examples we have seen in this module so far have produced integer solutions. But it is very common to see LP solutions where the decision variables are not whole numbers. Computer software provides a simple way to guarantee only integer solutions. In addition, computers allow us to create special decision variables called **binary variables** that can only take on the values of 0 or 1. Binary variables allow us to introduce "yes-or-no" decisions into our linear programs and to introduce special logical conditions.

Binary variables

Decision variables that can only take on the value of 0 or 1.

CREATING INTEGER AND BINARY VARIABLES

If we wish to ensure that decision variable values are integers rather than fractions, it is generally *not* good practice to simply round the solutions to the nearest integer values. The rounded solutions may not be optimal and, in fact, may not even be feasible. Fortunately, all LP software programs have simple ways to add constraints that enforce some or all of the decision variables to be either integer or binary. The main disadvantage of introducing such constraints is that larger programs may take longer to solve. The same LP that may take 3 seconds to solve on a computer could take several hours or more to solve if many of its variables are forced to be integer or binary. For relatively small programs, though, the difference may be unnoticeable.

Using Excel's Solver (see *Using Software to Solve LP Problems* later in this module), integer and binary constraints can be added by clicking <u>Add</u> from the main Solver dialogue box. Using the Add Constraint dialogue box (see Program B.2), highlight the decision variables themselves under Cell Reference:. Then select **int** or **bin** to ensure that those variables are integer or binary, respectively, in the optimal solution.

LINEAR PROGRAMMING APPLICATIONS WITH BINARY VARIABLES

In the written formulation of a linear program, binary variables are usually defined using the following form:

$$Y = \begin{cases} 1 & \text{if some condition holds} \\ 0 & \text{otherwise} \end{cases}$$

Sometimes we designate decision variables as binary if we are making a yes-or-no decision; for example, "Should we undertake this particular project?" "Should we buy that machine?" or "Should we locate a facility in Arkansas?" Other times, we create binary variables to introduce additional logic into our programs.

LIMITING THE NUMBER OF ALTERNATIVES SELECTED One common use of 0-1 variables involves limiting the number of projects or items that are selected from a group. Suppose a firm is required to select no more than two of three potential projects. This could be modelled with the following constraint:

$$Y_1 + Y_2 + Y_3 \leq 2$$

PROGRAM B.2
Excel's Solver Dialog Box to Add Integer or Binary Constraints on Variables

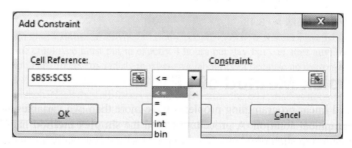

[2] See, for example, Barry Render, Ralph M. Stair, and Michael Hanna, *Quantitative Analysis for Management*, 11th ed. (Pearson Education, Inc., Upper Saddle River, NJ, 2013): Chapters 7–9; or Raju Balakrishnan, Barry Render, and Ralph M. Stair, *Managerial Decision Modeling with Spreadsheets*, 3rd ed. (Pearson Education, Inc., Upper Saddle River, NJ, 2012): Chapters 2–4.

If we wished to force the selection of *exactly* two of the three projects for funding, the following constraint should be used:

$$Y_1 + Y_2 + Y_3 = 2$$

This forces exactly two of the variables to have values of 1, whereas the other variable must have a value of 0.

DEPENDENT SELECTIONS At times the selection of one project depends in some way on the selection of another project. This situation can be modeled with the use of 0-1 variables. Suppose GE's new catalytic converter could be purchased ($Y_1 5 1$) only if the software was also purchased ($Y_2 51$). The following constraint would force this to occur:

$$Y_1 \leq Y_2$$

or, equivalently,

$$Y_1 - Y_2 \leq 0$$

Thus, if the software is not purchased, the value of Y_2 is 0, and the value of Y_1 must also be 0 because of this constraint. However, if the software is purchased ($Y_2 = 1$), then it is possible that the catalytic converter could also be purchased ($Y_1 = 1$), although this is not required.

If we wished for the catalytic converter and the software projects to either both be selected or both not be selected, we should use the following constraint:

$$Y_1 = Y_2$$

or, equivalently,

$$Y_1 - Y_2 = 0$$

Thus, if either of these variables is equal to 0, the other must also be 0. If either of these is equal to 1, the other must also be 1.

A FIXED-CHARGE INTEGER PROGRAMMING PROBLEM

Often businesses are faced with decisions involving a fixed charge that will affect the cost of future operations. Building a new factory or entering into a long-term lease on an existing facility would involve a fixed cost that might vary depending on the size of the facility and the location. Once a factory is built, the variable production costs will be affected by the labour cost in the particular city where it is located. Example B5 provides an illustration.

Sitka Manufacturing is planning to build at least one new plant, and three cities are being considered: Brampton, Ontario; Lethbridge, Alberta; and Montreal, Quebec. Once the plant or plants have been constructed, the company wishes to have sufficient capacity to produce at least 38 000 units each year. The costs associated with the possible locations are given in the following table.

A Fixed-Charge Problem Using Binary Variables

Site	Annual Fixed Cost	Variable Cost Per Unit	Annual Capacity
Brampton, ON	$340 000	$32	21 000
Lethbridge, AB	$270 000	$33	20 000
Montreal, QC	$290 000	$30	19 000

APPROACH ▶ In modeling this as an integer program, the objective function is to minimize the total of the fixed costs and the variable costs. The constraints are: (1) total production capacity is at least 38 000; (2) the number of units produced at the Brampton plant is 0 if the plant is not built, and it is no more than 21 000 if the plant is built; (3) the number of units produced at the Lethbridge plant is 0 if the plant is not built, and it is no more than 20 000 if the plant is built; and (4) the number of units produced at the Montreal plant is 0 if the plant is not built, and it is no more than 19 000 if the plant is built.

Then, we define the decision variables as

$$Y_1 = \begin{cases} 1 & \text{if factory is built in Brampton} \\ 0 & \text{otherwise} \end{cases}$$

$$Y_2 = \begin{cases} 1 & \text{if factory is built in Lethbridge} \\ 0 & \text{otherwise} \end{cases}$$

$$Y_3 = \begin{cases} 1 & \text{if factory is built in Montreal} \\ 0 & \text{otherwise} \end{cases}$$

X_1 = number of units produced at the Brampton plant
X_2 = number of units produced at the Lethbridge plant
X_3 = number of units produced at the Montreal plant

SOLUTION ▶ The integer programming problem formulation becomes

Objective: Minimize cost = $340\,000Y_1 + 270\,000Y_2 + 290\,000Y_3 + 32X_1 + 33X_2 + 30X_3$

subject to: $X_1 + X_2 + X_3 \geq 38\,000$

$X_1 \leq 21\,000Y_1$

$X_2 \leq 20\,000Y_2$

$X_3 \leq 19\,000Y_3$

$X_1, X_2, X_3 \geq 0$ and integer

$Y_1, Y_2, Y_3 = 0$ or 1

INSIGHT ▶ Examining the second constraint, the objective function will try to set the binary variable Y_1 equal to 0 because it wants to minimize cost. However, if $Y_1 = 0$, then the constraint will force X_1 to equal 0, in which case no units will be produced, and the plant will not be opened. Alternatively, if the rest of the program deems it worthwhile or necessary to produce some units of X_1, then Y_1 will have to equal 1 for the constraint to hold. And when $Y_1 = 1$, the firm will be charged the fixed cost of $340\,000$, and production will be limited to the capacity of 21 000 units. The same logic applies for constraints 3 and 4.

LEARNING EXERCISE ▶ Solve this integer program as formulated. What is the solution? [Answer: $Y_1 = 0$, $Y_2 = 1$, $Y_3 = 1$, $X_1 = 0$, $X_2 = 19\,000$, $X_3 = 19\,000$; Total Cost = $1\,757\,000$.]

RELATED PROBLEMS ▶ B.41, B.42

MODULE | SUMMARY

This module introduces a special kind of model, linear programming. LP has proven to be especially useful when trying to make the most effective use of an organization's resources.

The first step in dealing with LP models is problem formulation, which involves identifying and creating an objective function and constraints. The second step is to solve the problem. If there are only two decision variables, the problem can be solved graphically, using the corner-point method or the iso-profit/iso-cost line method. With either approach, we first identify the feasible region, then find the corner point yielding the greatest profit or least cost. LP is used in a wide variety of business applications, as the examples and homework problems in this module reveal.

Discussion Questions

1. List at least four applications of linear programming problems.
2. What is a *corner point*? Explain why solutions to linear programming problems focus on corner points.
3. Define the feasible region of a graphical LP problem. What is a feasible solution?
4. Each linear programming problem that has a feasible region has an infinite number of solutions. Explain.
5. Under what circumstances is the objective function more important than the constraints in a linear programming model?
6. Under what circumstances are the constraints more important than the objective function in a linear programming model?
7. Why is the diet problem, in practice, applicable for animals but not particularly for people?

8. How many feasible solutions are there in a linear program? Which ones do we need to examine to find the optimal solution?

9. Define shadow price (or dual value).

10. Explain how to use the iso-cost line in a graphical minimization problem.

11. Compare how the corner-point and iso-profit line methods work for solving graphical problems.

12. Where a constraint crosses the vertical or horizontal axis, the quantity is fairly obvious. How does one go about finding the quantity coordinates where two constraints cross, not at an axis?

13. Suppose a linear programming (maximization) problem has been solved and that the optimal value of the objective function is $300. Suppose an additional constraint is added to this problem. Explain how this might affect each of the following:
a) The feasible region.
b) The optimal value of the objective function.

Using Software to Solve LP Problems

All LP problems can be solved with the simplex method, using software such as Excel OM and POM for Windows or Excel. This approach produces valuable economic information such as the shadow price, or dual value, and provides complete sensitivity analysis on other inputs to the problems. Excel uses Solver, which requires that you enter your own constraints. Excel OM and POM for Windows require only that demand data, supply data, and shipping costs be entered. In the following section we illustrate how to create an Excel spreadsheet for LP problems.

✕ USING EXCEL SPREADSHEETS

Excel offers the ability to analyze linear programming problems using built-in problem-solving tools. Excel's tool is named Solver. Solver is limited to 200 changing cells (variables), each with 2 boundary constraints and up to 100 additional constraints. These capabilities make Solver suitable for the solution of complex, real-world problems.

We use Excel to set up the Glickman Electronics problem in Program B.3. The objective and constraints are repeated here:

Objective function: Maximize profit =

$$\$7(\text{No. of x-pods}) + \$5(\text{No. of BlueBerrys})$$

$$\text{Subject to: } 4(\text{x-pods}) + 3(\text{BlueBerrys}) \leq 240$$

$$2(\text{x-pods}) + 1(\text{BlueBerry}) \leq 100$$

PROGRAM B.3

Using Excel to Formulate the Glickman Electronics Problem

Source: Microsoft product screen shot(s) reprinted with permission from Microsoft Corporation.

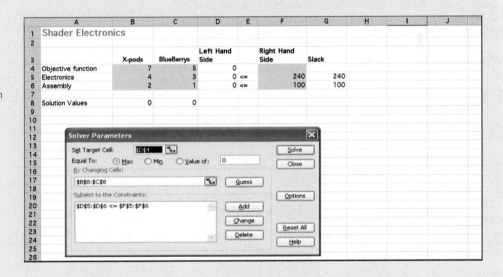

		Computations		
Value	**Cell**	**Excel Formula**	**Action**
Left Hand Side	D4	=SUMPRODUCT($B$8:$C$8,B4:C4)	Copy to D5:D6
Slack	G5	=F5–D5	Copy to G6 Select Tools, Solver Set Solver parameters as displayed Press Solve

The Excel screen in Program B.4 shows Solver's solution to the Glickman Electronics Company problem. Note that the optimal solution is now shown in the *changing cells* (cells B8 and C8, which served as the variables). The Reports selection performs more extensive analysis of the solution and its environment. Excel's sensitivity analysis capability was illustrated earlier in Program B.1.

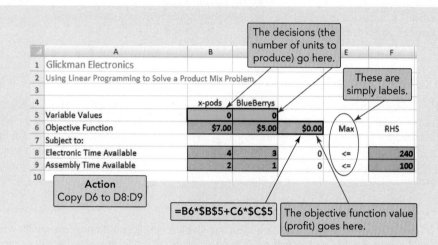

PROGRAM B.4

Using Excel to Formulate the Glickman Electronics Problem

Solved Problems Virtual Office Hours help is available at MyLab Operations Management.

▼ SOLVED PROBLEM B.1

Smith's, a Saint John, New Brunswick, clothing manufacturer that produces men's shirts and pajamas, has two primary resources available: sewing-machine time (in the sewing department) and cutting-machine time (in the cutting department). Over the next month, owner Barbara Smith can schedule up to 280 hours of work on sewing machines and up to 450 hours of work on cutting machines. Each shirt produced requires 1.00 hour of sewing time

and 1.50 hours of cutting time. Producing each pair of pajamas requires 0.75 hour of sewing time and 2 hours of cutting time.

To express the LP constraints for this problem mathematically, we let:

X_1 = number of shirts produced
X_2 = number of pajamas produced

▼ SOLUTION

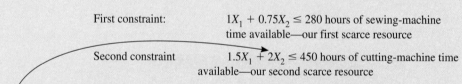

First constraint: $1X_1 + 0.75X_2 \leq 280$ hours of sewing-machine time available—our first scarce resource

Second constraint $1.5X_1 + 2X_2 \leq 450$ hours of cutting-machine time available—our second scarce resource

Note: This means that each pair of pajamas takes two hours of the cutting resource.

Smith's accounting department analyzes cost and sales figures and states that each shirt produced will yield a $4 contribution to profit and that each pair of pajamas will yield a $3 contribution to profit.

This information can be used to create the LP *objective function* for this problem:

Objective function: Maximize total contribution to profit = $4X_1 + $3X_2$

▼ SOLVED PROBLEM B.2

We want to solve the following LP problem for Kevin Caskey Wholesale Inc. using the corner-point method:

Objective: Maximize profit = $9X_1 + $7X_2$
Constraints: $2X_1 + 1X_2 \leq 40$
$X_1 + 3X_2 \leq 30$
$X_1, X_2 \geq 0$

▼ SOLUTION

Figure B.10 illustrates these constraints:

Corner-point a: $(X_1 = 0, X_2 = 0)$ Profit = 0
Corner-point b: $(X_1 = 0, X_2 = 10)$ Profit = 9(0) + 7(10) = $70
Corner-point c: $(X_1 = 20, X_2 = 0)$ Profit = 9(20) + 7(0) = $180

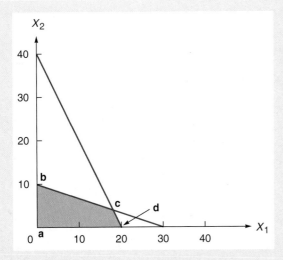

FIGURE B.10   Kevin Caskey Wholesale Inc.'s Feasible Region

Corner-point **c** is obtained by solving equations $2X_1 + 1X_2 = 40$ and $X_1 + 3X_2 = 30$ simultaneously. Multiply the second equation by -2 and add it to the first.

$$2X_1 + 1X_2 = 40$$
$$\underline{-2X_1 + 6X_2 = -60}$$
$$-5X_2 = -20$$
$$\text{Thus } X_2 = 4$$

Hence, the optimal solution is:

$$(x_1 = 18, x_2 = 4)$$
$$\text{Profit} = 9(18) + 7(4) = \$190$$

▼ SOLVED PROBLEM B.3

Holiday Meal Turkey Ranch in the United States is considering buying two different types of turkey feed. Each feed contains, in varying proportions, some or all of the three nutritional ingredients essential for fattening turkeys. Brand Y feed costs the ranch $0.02 per pound. Brand Z costs $0.03 per pound. The rancher would like to determine the lowest-cost diet that meets the minimum monthly intake requirement for each nutritional ingredient.

The following table contains relevant information about the composition of brand Y and brand Z feeds, as well as the minimum monthly requirement for each nutritional ingredient per turkey.

Ingredient	Composition of Each Pound of Feed		
	Brand Y Feed	Brand Z Feed	Minimum Monthly Requirement
A	5 oz	10 oz	90 oz
B	4 oz	3 oz	48 oz
C	0.5 oz	0	1.5 oz
Cost/lb	$0.02	$0.03	

▼ SOLUTION

If we let:

X_1 = number of pounds of brand Y feed purchased

X_2 = number of pounds of brand Z feed purchased

then we may proceed to formulate this linear programming problem as follows:

Objective: Minimize cost (in cents) = $2X_1 + 3X_2$

subject to these constraints:

$$5X_1 + 10X_2 \geq 90 \text{ oz} \quad \textit{(ingredient A constraint)}$$
$$4X_1 + 3X_2 \geq 48 \text{ oz} \quad \textit{(ingredient B constraint)}$$
$$0.5X_1 \geq 1.5 \text{ oz} \quad \textit{(ingredient A constraint)}$$

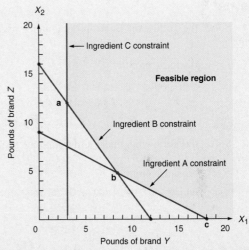

FIGURE B.11   Feasible Region for the Holiday Meal Turkey Ranch Problem

Figure B.11 illustrates these constraints.

The iso-cost line approach may be used to solve LP minimization problems such as that of the Holiday Meal Turkey Ranch. As with iso-profit lines, we need not compute the cost at each corner point, but instead draw a series of parallel cost lines. The last cost point to touch the feasible region provides us with the optimal solution corner.

For example, we start in Figure B.12 by drawing a 54¢ cost line, namely, $54 = 2X_1 + 3X_2$. Obviously, there are many points in the feasible region that would yield a lower total cost. We proceed to move our iso-cost line towards the lower left, in a plane parallel to the 54¢ solution line. The last point we touch while still in contact with the feasible region is the same as corner point **b** of Figure B.11. It has the coordinates ($X_1 = 8.4, X_2 = 4.8$) and an associated cost of 31.2 cents.

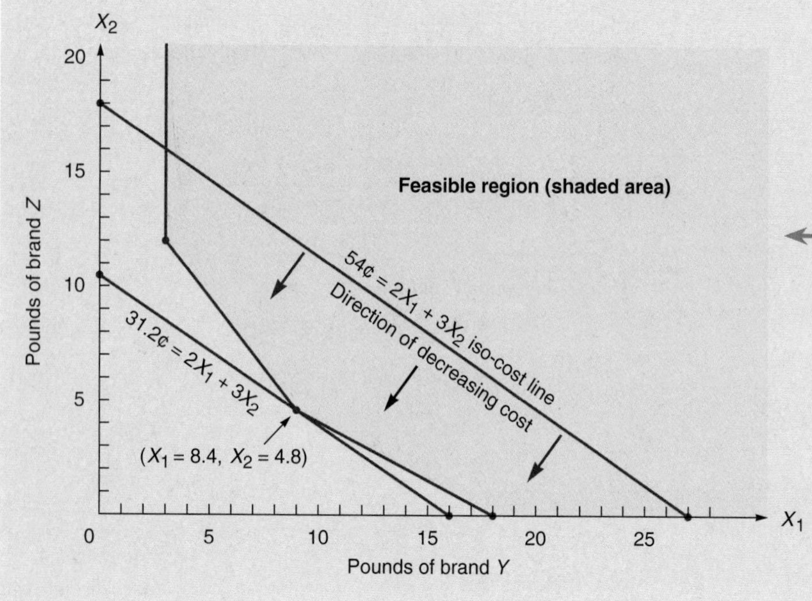

FIGURE B.12
Graphical Solution to the Holiday Meal Turkey Ranch Problem Using the Iso-Cost Line

Problems*

• **B.1** Solve the following linear programming problem graphically:

$$\text{Maximize profit} = 4X + 6Y$$

$$\text{Subject to:} \quad X + 2Y \le 8$$

$$5X + 4Y \le 20$$

$$X, Y \ge 0 \; \textbf{Px}$$

• **B.2** Solve the following linear programming problem graphically:

$$\text{Maximize profit} = X + 10Y$$

$$\text{Subject to:} \quad 4X + 3Y \le 36$$

$$2X + 4Y \le 40$$

$$Y \ge 3$$

$$X, Y \ge 0 \; \textbf{Px}$$

• **B.3** Solve the following linear program graphically:

$$\text{Maximize cost} = X_1 + X_2$$

$$8X_1 + 16X_2 \ge 64$$

$$X_1 \ge 0$$

$$X_2 \ge -2$$

$$X, Y \ge -2 \; \textbf{Px}$$

•• **B.4** Consider the following linear programming problem:

$$\text{Maximize profit} = 30X_1 + 10X_2$$

$$\text{Subject to:} \quad 3X_1 + X_2 \le 300$$

$$X_1 + X_2 \le 200$$

$$X_1 \le 100$$

$$X_2 \ge 50$$

$$X_1 - X_2 \le 0$$

$$X_1, X_2 \ge 0$$

a) Solve the problem graphically.
b) Is there more than one optimal solution? Explain. **Px**

• **B.5** Solve the following LP problem graphically:

$$\text{Maximize cost} = 24X + 15Y_2$$

$$\text{Subject to:} \quad 7X + 11Y \ge 77$$

$$16X + 4Y \ge 80$$

$$X, Y \ge 0 \; \textbf{Px}$$

•• **B.6** Ed Silver Dog Food Company wishes to introduce a new brand of dog biscuits composed of chicken- and liver-flavoured biscuits that meet certain nutritional requirements. The liver-flavoured biscuits contain 1 unit of nutrient A and 2 units of nutrient B; the chicken-flavoured biscuits contain 1 unit of nutrient A and 4 units of nutrient B. According to federal requirements, there must be at least 40 units of nutrient A and 60 units of nutrient B in a package of the new mix. In addition, the company has decided that there can be no more than 15 liver-flavoured biscuits in a package. If it costs 1¢ to make one liver-flavoured biscuit and 2¢ to make one chicken-flavoured biscuit, what is the optimal product mix for a package of the biscuits to minimize the firm's cost?
a) Formulate this as a linear programming problem.
b) Solve this problem graphically, giving the optimal values of all variables.
c) What is the total cost of a package of dog biscuits using the optimal mix? **Px**

• **B.7** The Electrocomp Corporation manufactures two electrical products: air conditioners and large fans. Their assembly processes are similar in that both require a certain amount of wiring and drilling. Each air conditioner takes 3 hours of wiring and 2 hours of drilling. Each fan must go through 2 hours of wiring and 1 hour of drilling. During the next production period, 240 hours of wiring time are available and up to 140 hours of drilling time may be used. Each air conditioner sold yields a profit of $25. Each fan assembled may be sold for a $15 profit.

Note: **Px** means the problem may be solved with POM for Windows and/or Excel OM.

Formulate and solve this LP production-mix situation, and find the best combination of air conditioners and fans that yields the highest profit. **Px**

• **B.8** The Lauren Shur Tub Company manufactures two lines of bathtubs, called model A and model B. Every tub requires blending a certain amount of steel and zinc; the company has available a total of 25 000 kg of steel and 6000 kg of zinc. Each model A bathtub requires a mixture of 125 kg of steel and 20 kg of zinc, and each yields a profit of $90. Each model B tub requires 100 kg of steel and 30 kg of zinc and can be sold for a profit of $70.

Find by graphical linear programming the best production mix of bathtubs. **Px**

•• **B.9** Spitzfire Inc. manufactures specialty industrial machines. It has just opened a new factory where the C1 machine and the T1 machine can both be manufactured. To make either machine, processing in the assembly shop and in the paint shop is required. It takes 1/40 of a day and 1/60 of a day to paint type T1 and type C1 in the paint shop, respectively. It takes 1/50 of a day to assemble either type of machine in the assembly shop.

A T1 machine and a C1 machine yield profits of $300 and $220, respectively, per industrial machine sold.
a) Define the objective function and constraint equations.
b) Graph the feasible region.
c) What is a maximum-profit daily production plan at the new factory?
d) How much profit will such a plan yield, assuming whatever is produced is sold? **Px**

• **B.10** MSA Computer Corporation manufactures two models of minicomputers, the Alpha 4 and the Beta 5. The firm employs five technicians, working 160 hours each per month, on its assembly line. Management insists that full employment (i.e., *all* 160 hours of time) be maintained for each worker during next month's operations. It requires 20 labour-hours to assemble each Alpha 4 computer and 25 labour-hours to assemble each Beta 5 model. MSA wants to see at least 10 Alpha 4s and at least 15 Beta 5s produced during the production period. Alpha 4s generate a $1200 profit per unit, and Beta 5s yield $1800 each. **Px**

Determine the most profitable number of each model of minicomputer to produce during the coming month.

• **B.11** The Sweet Smell Fertilizer Company markets bags of manure labelled "not less than 60 kg dry weight". The packaged manure is a combination of compost and sewage wastes. To provide good-quality fertilizer, each bag should contain at least 30 kg of compost but no more than 40 kg of sewage. Each kilogram of compost costs Sweet Smell 5¢ and each kilogram of sewage costs 4¢. Use a graphical LP method to determine the least-cost blend of compost and sewage in each bag. **Px**

• **B.12** Consider Faud Shatara's following linear programming formulation:

$$\text{Minimize cost} = \$1X_1 + \$2X_2$$
$$\text{Subject to:} \quad X_1 + 3X_2 \geq 90$$
$$8X_1 + 2X_2 \geq 160$$
$$3X_1 + 2X_2 \geq 120$$
$$X_2 \leq 70$$

a) Graphically illustrate the feasible region to indicate to Faud which corner point produces the optimal solution.
b) What is the cost of this solution? **Px**

• **B.13** The LP relationships that follow were formulated by Jeffrey Rummel at the Fort McMurray Chemical Company. Which ones are invalid for use in a linear programming problem, and why?

$$\text{Maximize} = 6X_1 + \tfrac{1}{2}X_1X_2 + 5X_3$$
$$\text{Subject to:} \quad 4X_1X_2 + 2X_3 \leq 70$$
$$7.9X_1 - 4X_2 \geq 15.6$$
$$3X_1 + 3X_2 + 3X_3 \geq 21$$
$$19X_2 - \tfrac{1}{3}X_3 = 17$$
$$-X_1 - X_2 + 4X_3 = 5$$
$$4X_1 + 2X_2 + 3\sqrt{X_3} \leq 80$$

•• **B.14** Kalyan Singhal Corp. makes three products, and it has three machines available as resources as given in the following LP problem:

$$\text{Maximize contribution} = 4X_1 + 4X_2 + 7X_3$$
$$\text{Subject to} \quad 1X_1 + 7X_2 + 4X_3 \leq 100 \text{ (hours on machine 1)}$$
$$2X_1 + 1X_2 + 7X_3 \leq 110 \text{ (hours on machine 2)}$$
$$8X_1 + 4X_2 + 1X_3 \leq 100 \text{ (hours on machine 3)}$$

a) Determine the optimal solution using LP software.
b) Is there unused time available on any of the machines with the optimal solution?
c) What would it be worth to the firm to make an additional hour of time available on the third machine?
d) How much would the firm's profit increase if an extra 10 hours of time were made available on the second machine at no extra cost? **Px**

•• **B.15** Consider the following LP problem developed at Jeff Spencer's Calgary optical scanning firm:

$$\text{Maximize profit} = \$1X_1 + \$1X_2$$
$$\text{Subject to:} \quad 2X_1 + 1X_2 \leq 100$$
$$1X_1 + 2X_2 \leq 100$$

a) What is the optimal solution to this problem? Solve it graphically.
b) If a technical breakthrough occurred that raised the profit per unit of X_1 to $3, would this affect the optimal solution?
c) Instead of an increase in the profit coefficient X_1, to $3, suppose that profit was overestimated and should only have been $1.25. Does this change the optimal solution? **Px**

••• **B.16** The Cold Lake, Alberta, superintendent of education is responsible for assigning students to the three high schools in his jurisdiction. He recognizes the need to bus a certain number of students, because several sectors, A–E, of the region are beyond walking distance to a school. The superintendent partitions the district into five geographic sectors as he attempts to establish a plan that will minimize the total number of student kilometres travelled by bus. He also recognizes that if a student happens to live in a certain sector and is assigned to the high school in that sector, there is no need to bus him because he can walk to school. The three schools are located in sectors B, C, and E.

The accompanying table reflects the number of high-school-age students living in each sector and the distance in kilometres from each sector to each school:

	Distance to School			
Sector	**School in Sector B**	**School in Sector C**	**School in Sector E**	**Number of Students**
A	5	8	6	700
B	0	4	12	500
C	4	0	7	100
D	7	2	5	800
E	12	7	0	400
				2500

Each high school has a capacity of 900 students.

a) Set up the objective function and constraints of this problem using linear programming so that the total number of student kilometres travelled by bus is minimized.
b) Solve the problem. **Px**

•• **B.17** The National Credit Union has $250 000 available to invest in a 12-month commitment. The money can be placed in Treasury bills yielding an 8% return or in municipal bonds at an average rate of return of 9%. Credit union regulations require diversification to the extent that at least 50% of the investment be placed in Treasury notes. Because of defaults in some municipalities, it is decided that no more than 40% of the investment be placed in bonds. How much should the National Credit Union invest in each security so as to maximize its return on investment?

•• **B.18** Edmonton's famous Limoges Restaurant is open 24 hours a day. Servers report for duty at 3:00 a.m., 7:00 a.m., 11:00 a.m., 3:00 p.m., 7:00 p.m., or 11:00 p.m., and each works an eight-hour shift. The following table shows the minimum number of workers needed during the six periods into which the day is divided:

Period	Time	Number of Servers Required
1	3:00 a.m.–7:00 a.m.	3
2	7:00 a.m.–11:00 a.m.	12
3	11:00 a.m.–3:00 p.m.	16
4	3:00 p.m.–7:00 p.m.	9
5	7:00 p.m.–11:00 p.m.	11
6	11:00 p.m.–3:00 a.m.	4

Owner Michelle Limoges's scheduling problem is to determine how many servers should report for work at the start of each time period in order to minimize the total staff required for one day's operation. (*Hint:* Let X_i equal the number of servers beginning work in time period i, where $i = 1, 2, 3, 4, 5, 6$.) **Px**

• **B.19** A local craftsman named Chuck Synovec builds two kinds of birdhouses, one for wrens and a second for bluebirds. Each wren birdhouse takes 4 hours of labour and 4 units of lumber. Each bluebird house requires 2 hours of labour and 12 units of lumber. The craftsman has available 60 hours of labour and 120 units of lumber. Wren houses yield a profit of $6 each and bluebird houses yield a profit of $15 each.
a) Write out the objective and constraints.
b) Solve graphically. **Px**

•• **B.20** Each coffee table produced by Robert West Designers nets the firm a profit of $9. Each bookcase yields a $12 profit. West's firm is small and its resources limited. During any given production period (of 1 week), 10 litres of varnish and 12 lengths of high-quality redwood are available. Each coffee table requires approximately 1 litre of varnish and 1 length of redwood. Each bookcase takes 1 litre of varnish and 2 lengths of wood.

Formulate West's production-mix decision as a linear programming problem, and solve. How many tables and bookcases should be produced each week? What will the maximum profit be? **Px**

•• **B.21** Par Inc. produces a standard golf bag and a deluxe golf bag on a weekly basis. Each golf bag requires time for cutting and dyeing and time for sewing and finishing, as shown in the following table:

	Hours Required per Bag	
Product	**Cutting and Dyeing**	**Sewing and Finishing**
Standard Bag	1/2	1
Deluxe Bag	1	2/3

The profits per bag and weekly hours available for cutting and dyeing and for sewing and finishing are as follows:

Product	**Profit per Unit ($)**
Standard bag	10
Deluxe bag	8

Activity	**Weekly Hours Available**
Cutting and dyeing	300
Sewing and finishing	360

Par Inc. will sell whatever quantities it produces of these two products.
a) Find the mix of standard and deluxe golf bags to produce per week that maximizes weekly profit from these activities.
b) What is the value of the profit? **Px**

• **B.22** Solve the following linear programming problem graphically:

$$\text{Minimize cost} = 4X_1 + 5X_2$$
$$\text{Subject to:} \quad X_1 + 2X_2 \geq 80$$
$$3X_1 + X_2 \geq 75$$
$$X_1, X_2 \geq 0 \quad \textbf{Px}$$

•• **B.23** Thompson Distributors packages and distributes industrial supplies. A standard shipment can be packaged in a class A container, a class K container, or a class T container. A single class A container yields a profit of $9; a class K container, a profit of $7; and a class T container, a profit of $15. Each shipment prepared requires a certain amount of packing material and a certain amount of time.

Resources Needed per Standard Shipment

Class of Container	**Packing Material (kilograms)**	**Packing Time (hours)**
A	2	2
K	1	6
T	3	4

Total amount of resource available each week	130 kilograms	240 hours

Jason Thompson, head of the firm, must decide the optimal number of each class of container to pack each week. He is bound by the previously mentioned resource restrictions but also decides that he must keep his 6 full-time packers employed all 240 hours (6 workers × 40 hours) each week.

Formulate and solve this problem using LP software. **Px**

•• **B.24** How many corner points are there in the feasible region of the following problem?

$$\text{Minimize cost} = X - Y$$

$$\text{Subject to:} \quad X \le 4$$

$$-X \le 2$$

$$X + 2Y \le 6$$

$$-X + 2Y \le 8$$

$$Y \ge 0$$

(*Note:* X values can be negative in this problem.)

•• **B.25** The Toronto advertising agency promoting the new Breem dishwashing detergent wants to get the best exposure possible for the product within the $100 000 advertising budget ceiling placed on it. To do so, the agency needs to decide how much of the budget to spend on each of its two most effective media: (1) television spots during the afternoon hours and (2) large ads in the city's Sunday newspaper. Each television spot costs $3000; each Sunday newspaper ad costs $1250. The expected exposure, based on industry ratings, is 35 000 viewers for each TV commercial and 20 000 readers for each newspaper advertisement. The agency director, Deborah Kellogg, knows from experience that it is important to use both media in order to reach the broadest spectrum of potential Breem customers. She decides that at least 5 but no more than 25 television spots should be ordered, and that at least 10 newspaper ads should be contracted. How many times should each of the two media be used to obtain maximum exposure while staying within the budget? Use the graphical method to solve. **Px**

••• **B.26** Libby Temple Manufacturing has three factories (1, 2, and 3) and three warehouses (A, B, and C). The following table shows the shipping costs between factories and warehouses, the factory manufacturing capabilities (in thousands), and the warehouse capacities (in thousands). Management would like to keep the warehouses filled to capacity in order to generate demand.

a) Write the objective function and the constraint equations. Let $X_1A = 1000s$ of units shipped from factory 1 to warehouse A, and so on.

b) Solve by computer. **Px**

To From	Warehouse A	Warehouse B	Warehouse C	Production Capability
Factory 1	$ 6	$ 5	$ 3	6
Factory 2	$ 8	$10	$ 8	8
Factory 3	$11	$14	$18	10
Capacity	7	12	5	

•••• **B.27** A fertilizer manufacturer has to fulfill supply contracts to its two main customers (650 tons to customer A and 800 tons to customer B). It can meet this demand by shipping existing inventory from any of its three warehouses. Warehouse 1 (W1) has 400 tons of inventory on hand, warehouse 2 (W2) has 500 tons, and warehouse 3 (W3) has 600 tons. The company would like to arrange the shipping for the lowest cost possible, where the per-ton transit costs are as follows:

	W1	W2	W3
Customer A	$7.50	$6.25	$6.50
Customer B	6.75	7.00	8.00

a) Explain what each of the six decision variables (V) is: (*Hint:* Look at the Solver report below.)

V A1: _____

V A2: _____

V A3: _____

V B1: _____

V B2: _____

V B3: _____

b) Write out the objective function in terms of the variables (V A1, V A2, etc.) and the objective coefficients.

c) Aside from nonnegativity of the variables, what are the five constraints? Write a short description for each constraint, and write out the formula (and circle the type of equality/inequality).

Description	Variables and Coefficients	What Type?	RHS
C1: _____	Formula: _____	(= > | = | = <)	_____
C2: _____	Formula: _____	(= > | = | = <)	_____
C3: _____	Formula: _____	(= > | = | = <)	_____
C4: _____	Formula: _____	(= > | = | = <)	_____
C5: _____	Formula: _____	(= > | = | = <)	_____

After you formulate and enter the linear program for Problem B.27 in Excel, the Solver gives you the following sensitivity report:

Variable Cells

Cell	Name	Final Value	Reduced Cost	Objective Coefficient	Allowable Increase	Allowable Decrease
$B$6	V A1	0	1.5	7.5	1.00E+30	1.5
$C$6	V A2	100	0	6.25	0.25	0.75
$D$6	V A3	550	0	6.5	0.75	0.25
$E$6	V B1	400	0	6.75	0.5	1.00E+30
$F$6	V B2	400	0	7	0.75	0.5
$G$6	V B3	0	0.75	8	1.00E+30	0.75

Constraints

Cell	Name	Final Value	Shadow Price	Constraint R.H. Side	Allowable Increase	Allowable Decrease
$H$7	C1	650	6.5	650	50	550
$H$8	C2	800	7.25	800	50	400
$H$9	C3	400	−0.5	400	400	50
$H$10	C4	500	−0.25	500	550	50
$H$11	C5	550	0	600	1E+30	50

d) How many of the constraints are binding?

e) How much slack/surplus is there with the nonbinding constraint(s)?

f) What is the range of optimality on variable V A3?

g) If we could ship 10 tons less to customer A, how much money *might* we be able to save? If we could choose to short *either* customer A or customer B by 10 tons, whom would we prefer to short? Why? **Px**

•••• **B.28** Grand River Hospital in Kitchener, Ontario, is a large, 600-bed facility complete with laboratories, operating rooms, and X-ray equipment. In seeking to optimize government funding, Grand River's administration has decided to make a 90-bed addition on a portion of adjacent land currently used for staff parking. The administrators feel that the labs, operating rooms, and X-ray department are not being fully utilized at present and do not need to be expanded to handle additional patients. The addition of 90 beds, however, involves deciding how many beds should be allocated to the medical staff (for medical patients) and how many to the surgical staff (for surgical patients).

The hospital's accounting and medical records departments have provided the following pertinent information. The average hospital stay for a medical patient is eight days, and the average medical patient generates $2280 in funding. The average surgical patient is in the hospital five days and generates $1515 in funding. The laboratory is capable of handling 15 000 tests per year more than it *was* handling. The average medical patient requires 3.1 lab tests, the average surgical patient 2.6 lab tests. Furthermore, the average medical patient uses one X-ray, the average surgical patient two X-rays. If the hospital were expanded by 90 beds, the X-ray department could handle up to 7000 X-rays without significant additional cost. Finally, the administration estimates that up to 2800 additional operations could be performed in existing operating-room facilities. Medical patients, of course, require no surgery, whereas each surgical patient generally has one surgery performed.

Formulate this problem so as to determine how many medical beds and how many surgical beds should be added to maximize revenues. Assume that the hospital is open 365 days per year. **Px**

•••• **B.29** Charles Watts Electronics manufactures the following six peripheral devices used in computers especially designed for jet fighter planes: internal modems, external modems, graphics circuit boards, jump drives, hard disk drives, and memory expansion boards. Each of these technical products requires time, in minutes, on three types of electronic testing equipment as shown in the following table:

	Internal Modem	External Modem	Circuit Board	Jump Drive	Hard Drive	Memory Board
Test device 1	7	3	12	6	18	17
Test device 2	2	5	3	2	15	17
Test device 3	5	1	3	2	9	2

The first two test devices are available 120 hours per week. The third (device 3) requires more preventive maintenance and may be used only 100 hours each week. The market for all six computer components is vast, and Watts Electronics believes that it can sell as many units of each product as it can manufacture. The table summarizes the revenues and material costs for each product.

Device	Revenue per Unit Sold ($)	Material Cost per Unit ($)
Internal modem	200	35
External modem	120	25
Graphics circuit board	180	40
Jump drive	130	45
Hard disk drive	430	170
Memory expansion board	260	60

In addition, variable labour costs are $15 per hour for test device 1, $12 per hour for test device 2, and $18 per hour for test device 3. Watts Electronics wants to maximize its profits.

a) Formulate this problem as an LP model.

b) Solve the problem by computer. What is the best product mix?

c) What is the value of an additional minute of time per week on test device 1? test device 2? test device 3? Should Watts Electronics add more test device time? If so, on which equipment? **Px**

•••• **B.30** You have just been hired as a planner for the municipal school system, and your first assignment is to redesign the subsidized lunch program. In particular, you are to formulate the least expensive lunch menu that will still meet all Health Canada-mandated nutritional guidelines.

The guidelines are as follows: A meal must be between 500 and 800 calories. It must contain at least 200 calories of protein, at least 200 calories of carbohydrates, and no more than 400 calories of fat. It also needs to have at least 200 calories of a food classified as a fruit or vegetable.

Following this problem is the list of the foods you can consider as possible menu items, with contract-determined prices and nutritional information. Note that all percentages sum to 100% per food—as all calories are protein, carbohydrate, or fat calories. For example, a serving of applesauce has 100 calories, all of which are carbohydrate, and it counts as a fruit/vegetable food. You are allowed to use fractional servings, such as 2.25 servings of turkey breast and a 0.33 portion of salad. Cost and nutritional attributes scale likewise: for example, a 0.33 portion of salad costs $0.30 and has 33 calories.

Formulate and solve as a linear problem. Print out your formulation in Excel showing the objective function coefficients and constraint matrix in standard form.

- Display, on a separate page, the full *Answer Report* as generated by Excel Solver.
- Highlight *and label as* Z the objective value for the optimal solution on the Answer Report.
- Highlight the nonzero decision variables for the optimal solution on the Answer Report.
- Display, on a separate page, the full *Sensitivity Report* as generated by Excel Solver. **Px**

Food	Cost/Serving	Calories/Serving	% Protein	% Carbs	% Fat	Fruit/Veg
Apple sauce	$0.30	100	0%	100%	0%	Y
Canned corn	$0.40	150	20%	80%	0%	Y
Fried chicken	$0.90	250	55%	5%	40%	N
French fries	$0.20	400	5%	35%	60%	N
Macaroni and cheese	$0.50	430	20%	30%	50%	N
Turkey breast	$1.50	300	67%	0%	33%	N
Garden salad	$0.90	100	15%	40%	45%	Y

•••• **B.31** Bowman Builders manufactures steel storage sheds for commercial use. Joe Bowman, president of Bowman Builders, is contemplating producing sheds for home use. The activities necessary to build an experimental model and related data are given in Table B.2.

a) What is the project normal time completion date? (See Chapter 3 for a review of project management.)
b) Formulate an LP problem to crash this project to 10 weeks.

Table B.2 Data for Problem B.31

Activity	Normal Time	Crash Time	Normal Cost ($)	Crash Cost ($)	Immediate Predecessors
A	3	2	1000	1600	—
B	2	1	2000	2700	—
C	1	1	300	300	—
D	7	3	1300	1600	A
E	6	3	850	1000	B
F	2	1	4000	5000	C
G	4	2	1500	2000	D, E

•• **B.32** Rollins Publishing needs to decide what textbooks from the following table to publish.

Textbook	Demand	Fixed Cost	Variable Cost	Selling Price
Book 1	9000	$12 000	$19	$40
Book 2	8000	$21 000	$28	$60
Book 3	5000	$15 000	$30	$52
Book 4	6000	$10 000	$20	$34
Book 5	7000	$18 000	$20	$45

For each book, the maximum demand, fixed cost of publishing, variable cost, and selling price are provided. Rollins has the capacity to publish a total of 20 000 books.

•• **B.33** Porter Investments needs to develop an investment portfolio for Mrs. Singh from the following list of possible investments:

Textbook	Demand	Fixed Cost
A	$10 000	$ 700
B	$12 000	$1000
C	$3500	$ 390
D	$5000	$ 500
E	$8500	$ 750
F	$8000	$ 640
G	$4000	$ 300

Mrs. Singh has a total of $60 000 to invest. The following conditions must be met: (1) If investment F is chosen, then investment G must also be part of the portfolio, (2) at least four investments should be chosen, and (3) of investments A and B, exactly one must be included. Formulate and solve this problem using LP software to determine which stocks should be included in Mrs. Singh's portfolio. **Px**

CASE STUDY

Golding Landscaping and Plants Inc.

Kenneth and Patricia Golding spent a career as a husband-and-wife real estate investment partnership in Calgary. When they finally retired to a 25-acre farm on northern Vancouver Island, they became ardent amateur gardeners. Kenneth planted shrubs and fruit trees, and Patricia spent her hours potting all sizes of plants. When the volume of shrubs and plants reached the point that the Goldings began to think of their hobby seriously, they built a greenhouse adjacent to their home and installed heating and watering systems.

By 2015, the Goldings realized their retirement from real estate had really only led to a second career—in the plant and shrub business—and they filed for a business licence. Within a matter of months, they asked their lawyer to file incorporation documents and formed the firm Golding Landscaping and Plants Inc.

Early in the new business's existence, Kenneth Golding recognized the need for a high-quality commercial fertilizer that he could blend himself, both for sale and for his own nursery. His goal was to keep his costs to a minimum while producing a top-notch product that was especially suited to the Vancouver Island climate.

Working with chemists at the University of Guelph, Golding blended "Golding-Grow". It consists of four chemical compounds, C-30, C-92, D-21, and E-11. The cost per kilogram for each compound is indicated in the following table:

Chemical Compound	Cost per Kilogram
C-30	$0.24
C-92	0.18
D-21	0.22
E-11	0.08

The specifications for Golding-Grow are established as follows:

a) Chemical E-11 must constitute at least 15% of the blend.
b) C-92 and C-30 must together constitute at least 45% of the blend.
c) D-21 and C-92 can together constitute no more than 30% of the blend.
d) Golding-Grow is packaged and sold in 25-kg bags.

Discussion Questions

1. Formulate an LP problem to determine what blend of the four chemicals will allow Golding to minimize the cost of a 25-kg bag of the fertilizer.
2. Solve to find the best solution.

▶ **Additional Case Study:** Visit **MyLab Operations Management** for these additional case studies:

Chase Manhattan Bank: This scheduling case involves finding the optimal number of full-time versus part-time employees at a bank.
Coastal States Chemical: The company must prepare for a shortage of natural gas.

MODULE B | RAPID REVIEW

MyLab Operations Management

Main Heading	Review Material	
WHY USE LINEAR PROGRAMMING? (p. 681)	• **Linear programming (LP)**—A mathematical technique designed to help operations managers plan and make decisions relative to the trade-offs necessary to allocate resources.	
REQUIREMENTS OF A LINEAR PROGRAMMING PROBLEM (p. 682)	• Objective function—A mathematical expression in linear programming that maximizes or minimizes some quantity (often profit or cost, but any goal may be used). • **Constraints**—Restrictions that limit the degree to which a manager can pursue an objective. All LP problems have four properties in common: 1. LP problems seek to maximize or minimize some quantity. We refer to this property as the objective function of an LP problem. 2. The presence of restrictions, or constraints, limits the degree to which we can pursue our objective. We want, therefore, to maximize or minimize a quantity (the objective function) subject to limited resources (the constraints). 3. There must be alternative courses of action to choose from. 4. The objective and constraints in linear programming problems must be expressed in terms of linear equations or inequalities.	
FORMULATING LINEAR PROGRAMMING PROBLEMS (pp. 682–683)	One of the most common linear programming applications is the product-mix problem. Two or more products are usually produced using limited resources. For example, a company might like to determine how many units of each product it should produce to maximize overall profit, given its limited resources. An important aspect of linear programming is that certain interactions will exist between variables. The more units of one product that a firm produces, the fewer it can make of other products.	Virtual Office Hours for Solved Problem: B.1 **ACTIVE MODEL B.1**

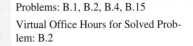

Main Heading	Review Material	
GRAPHICAL SOLUTION TO A LINEAR PROGRAMMING PROBLEM (pp. 683–688)	• **Graphical solution approach**—A means of plotting a solution to a two-variable problem on a graph. • **Decision variables**—Choices available to a decision maker. Constraints of the form $X \geq 0$ are called *nonnegativity constraints*. • **Feasible region**—The set of all feasible combinations of decision variables. Any point inside the feasible region represents a *feasible solution*, while any point outside the feasible region represents an *infeasible solution*. • **Iso-profit line method**—An approach to identifying the optimum point in a graphic linear programming problem. The line that touches a particular point of the feasible region will pinpoint the optimal solution. • **Corner-point method**—A method for solving graphical linear programming problems. The mathematical theory behind linear programming states that an optimal solution to any problem will lie at a *corner point*, or an *extreme point*, of the feasible region. Hence, it is necessary to find only the values of the variables at each corner; the optimal solution will lie at one (or more) of them. This is the corner-point method. 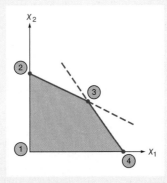	Problems: B.1, B.2, B.4, B.15 Virtual Office Hours for Solved Problem: B.2
SENSITIVITY ANALYSIS (pp. 688–690)	• **Parameter**—A numerical value that is given in a model. • **Sensitivity analysis**—An analysis that projects how much a solution may change if there are changes in the variables or input data. Sensitivity analysis is also called *postoptimality analysis*. There are two approaches to determining just how sensitive an optimal solution is to changes: (1) a trial-and-error approach and (2) the analytic postoptimality method. To use the analytic postoptimality method, after an LP problem has been solved, we determine a range of changes in problem parameters that will not affect the optimal solution or change the variables in the solution. LP software has this capability. While using the information in a sensitivity report to answer what-if questions, we assume that we are considering a change to only a *single* input data value at a time. That is, the sensitivity information does not generally apply to simultaneous changes in several input data values. • **Shadow price (or dual value)**—The value of one additional unit of a scarce resource in LP. The shadow price is valid as long as the right-hand side of the constraint stays in a range within which all current corner points continue to exist. The information to compute the upper and lower limits of this range is given by the entries labelled Allowable Increase and Allowable Decrease in the sensitivity report.	
SOLVING MINIMIZATION PROBLEMS (pp. 690–691)	• **Iso-cost**—An approach to solving a linear programming minimization problem graphically. The iso-cost line approach to solving minimization problems is analogous to the iso-profit approach for maximization problems, but successive iso-cost lines are drawn *inward* instead of outward.	Virtual Office Hours for Solved Problem: B.3 Problems: B.3, B.5, B.6, B.11, B.12, B.22, B.24

Main Heading	Review Material	MyLab Operations Management
LINEAR PROGRAMMING APPLICATIONS (pp. 692–695)	The *diet problem*, known in agricultural applications as the *feed-mix problem*, involves specifying a food or feed ingredient combination that will satisfy stated nutritional requirements at a minimum cost level. *Labour scheduling problems* address staffing needs over a specific time period. They are especially useful when managers have some flexibility in assigning workers to jobs that require overlapping or interchangeable talents.	Problems: B.6, B.7–B.10, B.13, B.14, B.16–B.21, B.23, B.25–B.30
THE SIMPLEX METHOD OF LP (pp. 695–696)	• **Simplex method**—An algorithm for solving linear programming problems of all sizes. The simplex method is actually a set of instructions with which we examine corner points in a methodical fashion until we arrive at the best solution— highest profit or lowest cost. Computer programs (such as Excel OM and POM for Windows) and Excel's Solver add-in are available to solve linear programming problems via the simplex method.	
INTEGER AND BINARY VARIABLES (pp. 696–698)	• **Binary variables**—Decision variables that can only take on the value of 0 or 1. Using computer software, decision variables for linear programs can be forced to be integer or even binary. Binary variables extend the flexibility of linear programs to include such options as mutually exclusive alternatives, either-or constraints, contingent decisions, fixed-charge problems, and threshold levels.	Problems: B.41–B.42

Self-Test

■ **Before taking the self-test,** refer to the learning objectives listed at the beginning of the module.

LO1 Which of the following is *not* a valid LP constraint formulation?
   a) $3X + 4Y \leq 12$
   b) $2X \times 2Y \leq 12$
   c) $3Y + 2Z = 18$
   d) $100 \geq X + Y$
   e) $2.5X + 1.5Z = 30.6$

LO2 Using a graphical solution procedure to solve a maximization problem requires that we:
   a) move the iso-profit line up until it no longer intersects with any constraint equation.
   b) move the iso-profit line down until it no longer intersects with any constraint equation.
   c) apply the method of simultaneous equations to solve for the intersections of constraints.
   d) find the value of the objective function at the origin.

LO3 Consider the following linear programming problem:

$$\text{Maximize} \quad 4X + 10Y$$
$$\text{Subject to:} \quad 3X + 4Y \leq 480$$
$$3X + 2Y \leq 360$$
$$X, Y \geq 0$$

The feasible corner points are (48, 84), (0, 120), (0, 0), and (90, 0). What is the maximum possible value for the objective function?
   a) 1032
   b) 1200
   c) 360
   d) 1600
   e) 840

LO4 A zero shadow price for a resource ordinarily means that:
   a) the resource is scarce.
   b) the resource constraint was redundant.
   c) the resource has not been used up.
   d) something is wrong with the problem formulation.
   e) none of the above.

LO5 For these two constraints, which point is in the feasible region of this minimization problem?

$$14x + 6y \geq 42 \text{ and } x + y \geq 3$$

   a) $x = -1, y = 1$
   b) $x = 0, y = 4$
   c) $x = 2, y = 1$
   d) $x = 5, y = 1$
   e) $x = 2, y = 0$

LO6 When applying LP to diet problems, the objective function is usually designed to:
   a) maximize profits from blends of nutrients.
   b) maximize ingredient blends.
   c) minimize production losses.
   d) maximize the number of products to be produced.
   e) minimize the costs of nutrient blends.

Answers: LO1. b; LO2. a; LO3. b; LO4. c; LO5. d; LO6. e.

MyLab Operations Management

Most of these questions can be found in MyLab Operations Management. Visit MyLab Operations Management to access cases, videos, downloadable software, and much more. MyLab Operations Management Management also features a personalized Study Plan that helps you identify which chapter concepts you've mastered and guides you towards study tools for additional practice.

Transportation Models

Business Analytics Module

C

Learning Objectives

LO1 Develop an initial solution to a transportation model with the northwest-corner and intuitive lowest-cost methods **713**

LO2 Solve a problem with the stepping-stone method **715**

LO3 Balance a transportation problem **719**

LO4 Solve a problem with degeneracy **719**

Transportation Modelling

Because location of a new factory, warehouse, or distribution centre is a strategic issue with substantial cost implications, most companies consider and evaluate several locations. With a wide variety of objective and subjective factors to be considered, rational decisions are aided by a number of techniques. One of those techniques is transportation modelling.

The transportation models described in this module prove useful when considering alternative facility locations *within the framework of an existing distribution system.* Each new potential plant, warehouse, or distribution centre will require a different allocation of shipments, depending on its own production and shipping costs and the costs of each existing facility. The choice of a new location depends on which will yield the minimum cost *for the entire system.*

Transportation modelling finds the least-cost means of shipping supplies from several origins to several destinations. *Origin points* (or *sources*) can be factories, warehouses, car rental agencies like Avis, or any other points from which goods are shipped. *Destinations* are any points that receive goods. To use the transportation model, we need to know the following:

1. The origin points and the capacity or supply per period at each.
2. The destination points and the demand per period at each.
3. The cost of shipping one unit from each origin to each destination.

Transportation modelling
An iterative procedure for solving problems that involves minimizing the cost of shipping products from a series of sources to a series of destinations.

The transportation model is actually a class of the linear programming models discussed in Business Analytics Module B. As it is for linear programming, software is available to solve transportation problems. To fully use such programs, though, you need to understand the assumptions that underlie the model. To illustrate one transportation problem, in this module we look at a company called Yorkton Plumbing, which makes, among other products, a full line of bathtubs. In our example, the firm must decide which of its factories should supply which of its warehouses. Relevant data for Yorkton Plumbing are presented in Table C.1 and Figure C.1. Table C.1 shows, for example, that it costs Yorkton Plumbing $5 to ship one

Table C.1
Transportation Costs per Bathtub for Yorkton Plumbing

From \ To	Regina	Dartmouth	Kingston
Windsor	$5	$4	$3
Toronto	$8	$4	$3
Thunder Bay	$9	$7	$5

FIGURE C.1

Transportation Problem

bathtub from its Windsor factory to its Regina warehouse, $4 to Dartmouth, and $3 to Kingston. Likewise, we see in Figure C.1 that the 300 units required by Yorkton Plumbing's Regina warehouse may be shipped in various combinations from its Windsor, Toronto, and Thunder Bay factories.

The first step in the modelling process is to set up a *transportation matrix*. Its purpose is to summarize all relevant data and to keep track of algorithm computations. Using the information displayed in Figure C.1 and Table C.1, we can construct a transportation matrix as shown in Figure C.2.

FIGURE C.2

Transportation Matrix for Yorkton Plumbing

From \ To	Regina	Dartmouth	Kingston	Factory capacity
Windsor	$5	$4	$3	100
Toronto	$8	$4	$3	300
Thunder Bay	$9	$7	$5	300
Warehouse requirement	300	200	200	700

Windsor capacity constraint

Cell representing a possible source-to-destination shipping assignment (Toronto to Kingston)

Cost of shipping 1 unit from Thunder Bay factory to Dartmouth warehouse

Kingston warehouse demand

Total demand and total supply

Developing an Initial Solution

STUDENT TIP

Here are two ways of finding an initial solution.

Northwest-corner rule

A procedure in the transportation model where one starts at the upper-left-hand cell of a table (the northwest corner) and systematically allocates units to shipping routes.

Once the data are arranged in tabular form, we must establish an initial feasible solution to the problem. A number of different methods have been developed for this step. We now discuss two of them: the northwest-corner rule and the intuitive lowest-cost method.

THE NORTHWEST-CORNER RULE

The **northwest-corner rule** requires that we start in the upper-left-hand cell (or northwest corner) of the table and allocate units to shipping routes as follows:

1. Exhaust the supply (factory capacity) of each row (e.g., Windsor: 100) before moving down to the next row.
2. Exhaust the (warehouse) requirements of each column (e.g., Regina: 300) before moving to the next column on the right.
3. Check to ensure that all supplies and demands are met.

Example C1 applies the northwest-corner rule to our Yorkton Plumbing problem.

LO1 Develop an initial solution to a transportation model with the northwest-corner and intuitive lowest-cost methods

---

Yorkton Plumbing wants to use the northwest-corner rule to find an initial solution to its problem.

APPROACH ▶ Follow the three steps listed above. See Figure C.3.

SOLUTION ▶ To make the initial solution, these five assignments are made:
1. Assign 100 tubs from Windsor to Regina (exhausting Windsor's supply).
2. Assign 200 tubs from Toronto to Regina (exhausting Regina's demand).
3. Assign 100 tubs from Toronto to Dartmouth (exhausting Toronto's supply).
4. Assign 100 tubs from Thunder Bay to Dartmouth (exhausting Dartmouth's demand).
5. Assign 200 tubs from Thunder Bay to Kingston (exhausting Kingston's demand and Thunder Bay's supply).

EXAMPLE C1

The Northwest-Corner Rule

From \ To	(A) Regina	(B) Dartmouth	(C) Kingston	Factory capacity
(D) Windsor	$5	$4	$3	100
	100			
(E) Toronto	$8	$4	$3	300
	200	100		
(F) Thunder Bay	$9	$7	$5	300
		(100)	200	
Warehouse requirement	300	200	200	700

Means that the firm is shipping 100 bathtubs from Thunder Bay to Dartmouth

FIGURE C.3

Northwest-Corner Solution to Yorkton Plumbing Problem

The total cost of this shipping assignment is $4200 (see Table C.2).

Route				
From	**To**	**Tubs Shipped**	**Cost per Unit**	**Total Cost**
D	A	100	$5	$ 500
E	A	200	8	1 600
E	B	100	4	400
F	B	100	7	700
F	C	200	5	1 000
				Total: $4 200

Table C.2

Computed Shipping Cost

INSIGHT ▶ The solution given is feasible because it satisfies all demand and supply constraints. The northwest-corner rule is easy to use, but it totally ignores costs and therefore should be considered only as a starting position.

LEARNING EXERCISE ▶ Does the shipping assignment change if the cost from Windsor to Regina increases from $5 per unit to $10 per unit? Does the total cost change? [Answer: This initial assignment is the same, but cost = $4700.]

RELATED PROBLEMS ▶ C.1a, C.3a, C.9, C.11, C.12

THE INTUITIVE LOWEST-COST METHOD

Intuitive method

A cost-based approach to finding an initial solution to a transportation problem.

The **intuitive method** makes initial allocations based on lowest cost. This straightforward approach uses the following steps:

1. Identify the cell with the lowest cost. Break any ties for the lowest cost arbitrarily.
2. Allocate as many units as possible to that cell without exceeding the supply or demand. Then cross out that row or column (or both) that is exhausted by this assignment.
3. Find the cell with the lowest cost from the remaining (not crossed out) cells.
4. Repeat steps 2 and 3 until all units have been allocated.

EXAMPLE C2

The Intuitive Lowest-Cost Approach

Yorkton Plumbing now wants to apply the intuitive lowest-cost approach.

APPROACH ▶ Apply the four steps listed above to the data in Figure C.2.

SOLUTION ▶ When the firm uses the intuitive approach on the data (rather than the northwest-corner rule) for its starting position, it obtains the solution seen in Figure C.4.

$$\text{The total cost of this approach} = \$3(100) + \$3(100) + \$4(200) + \$9(300) = \$4100$$
$$\qquad\qquad\qquad\qquad (D\text{ to }C) \quad (E\text{ to }C) \quad (E\text{ to }B) \quad (F\text{ to }A)$$

INSIGHT ▶ This method's name is appropriate as most people find it intuitively correct to include costs when making an initial assignment.

LEARNING EXERCISE ▶ If the cost per unit from Windsor to Kingston is not $3, but rather $6, does this initial solution change? [Answer: Yes, now D − B = 100, D − C = 0, E − B = 100, E − C = 200, F − A = 300. Others unchanged at zero. Total cost stays the same.]

RELATED PROBLEMS ▶ C.1b, C.2, C.3b

To From	(A) Regina	(B) Dartmouth	(C) Kingston	Factory capacity	First, cross out top row (D) after entering 100 units in $3 cell because row D is satisfied.
(D) Windsor	$5	$4	$3 100	100	Second, cross out column C after entering 100 units in this $3 cell because column C is satisfied.
(E) Toronto	$8	$4 200	$3 100	300	Third, cross out row E and column B after entering 200 units in this $4 cell because a total of 300 units satisfies row E and column B.
(F) Thunder Bay	$9 300	$7	$5 300		Finally, enter 300 units in the only remaining cell to complete the allocations.
Warehouse requirement	300	200	200	700	

FIGURE C.4 **Intuitive Lowest-Cost Solution to Yorkton Plumbing Problem**

While the likelihood of a minimum-cost solution *does* improve with the intuitive method, we would have been fortunate if the intuitive solution yielded the minimum cost. In this case, as in the northwest-corner solution, it did not. Because the northwest-corner and the intuitive lowest-cost approaches are meant only to provide us with a starting point, we often will have to employ an additional procedure to reach an *optimal* solution.

The Stepping-Stone Method

The **stepping-stone method** will help us move from an initial feasible solution to an optimal solution. It is used to evaluate the cost effectiveness of shipping goods via transportation routes not currently in the solution. When applying it, we test each unused cell, or square, in the transportation table by asking, "What would happen to total shipping costs if one unit of the product (e.g., one bathtub) was tentatively shipped on an unused route?" We conduct the test as follows:

1. Select any unused square to evaluate.
2. Beginning at this square, trace a closed path back to the original square via squares that are currently being used (only horizontal and vertical moves are permissible). You may, however, step over either an empty or an occupied square.
3. Beginning with a plus (+) sign at the unused square, place alternating minus signs and plus signs on each corner square of the closed path just traced.
4. Calculate an improvement index by first adding the unit-cost figures found in each square containing a plus sign and then by subtracting the unit costs in each square containing a minus sign.
5. Repeat steps 1 through 4 until you have calculated an improvement index for all unused squares. If all indices computed are *greater than or equal to zero*, you have reached an optimal solution. If not, the current solution can be improved further to decrease total shipping costs.

Example C3 illustrates how to use the stepping-stone method to move towards an optimal solution. We begin with the northwest-corner initial solution developed in Example C1.

Stepping-stone method
An iterative technique for moving from an initial feasible solution to an optimal solution in the transportation method.

LO2 Solve a problem with the stepping-stone method

Yorkton Plumbing wants to evaluate unused shipping routes.

APPROACH ▶ Start with Example C1's Figure C.3 and follow the five steps listed above. As you can see, the four currently unassigned routes are Windsor to Dartmouth, Windsor to Kingston, Toronto to Kingston, and Thunder Bay to Regina.

SOLUTION ▶ Steps 1 and 2. Beginning with the Windsor–Dartmouth route, first trace a closed path *using only currently occupied squares* (see Figure C.5). Place alternating plus and minus signs in the corners of this path. In the upper left square, for example, we place a minus sign because we have *subtracted* 1 unit from the original 100. Note that we can use only squares currently used for shipping to turn the corners of the route we are tracing. Hence, the path Windsor–Dartmouth to Windsor–Regina to Thunder Bay–Regina to Thunder Bay–Dartmouth to Windsor–Dartmouth would not be acceptable because the Thunder Bay–Regina square is empty. It turns out that *only one closed route exists for each empty square*. Once this one closed path is identified, we can begin assigning plus and minus signs to these squares in the path.

Step 3. How do we decide which squares get plus signs and which squares get minus signs? The answer is simple. Because we are testing the cost-effectiveness of the Windsor–Dartmouth shipping route, we try shipping 1 bathtub from Windsor to Dartmouth. This is 1 *more* unit than we *were* sending between the two cities, so place a plus sign in the box. However, if we ship 1 more unit than before from Windsor to Dartmouth, we end up sending 101 bathtubs out of the Windsor factory. Because the Windsor factory's capacity is only 100 units, we must ship 1 bathtub fewer from Windsor to Regina. This change prevents us from violating the capacity constraint.

To indicate that we have reduced the Windsor–Regina shipment, place a minus sign in its box. As you continue along the closed path, notice that we are no longer meeting our Regina warehouse

EXAMPLE C3

Checking Unused Routes with the Stepping-Stone Method

FIGURE C.5

Stepping-Stone Evaluation of Alternative Routes for Yorkton Plumbing

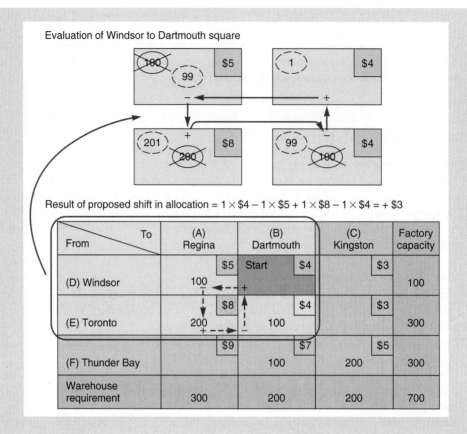

requirement for 300 units. In fact, if we reduce the Windsor–Regina shipment to 99 units, we must increase the Toronto–Regina load by 1 unit, to 201 bathtubs. Therefore, place a plus sign in that box to indicate the increase. You may also observe that those squares in which we turn a corner (and only those squares) will have plus or minus signs.

Finally, note that if we assign 201 bathtubs to the Toronto–Regina route, then we must reduce the Toronto–Dartmouth route by 1 unit, to 99 bathtubs, to maintain the Toronto factory's capacity constraint of 300 units. To account for this reduction, we thus insert a minus sign in the Toronto–Dartmouth box. By so doing, we have balanced supply limitations among all four routes on the closed path.

Step 4. Compute an improvement index for the Windsor–Dartmouth route by adding unit costs in squares with plus signs and subtracting costs in squares with minus signs.

$$\text{Windsor} - \text{Dartmouth index} = \$4 - \$5 + \$8 - \$4 = +\$3$$

This means that for every bathtub shipped via the Windsor–Dartmouth route, total transportation costs will increase by $3 over their current level.

Let us now examine the unused Windsor–Kingston route, which is slightly more difficult to trace with a closed path (see Figure C.6). Again, notice that we turn each corner along the path only at squares on the existing route. Our path, for example, can go through the Toronto–Kingston box but cannot turn a corner; thus, we cannot place a plus or minus sign there. We may use occupied squares only as stepping-stones:

$$\text{Windsor} - \text{Kingston index} = \$3 - \$5 + \$8 - \$4 + \$7 - \$5 = +\$4$$

Again, opening this route fails to lower our total shipping costs.

Two other routes can be evaluated in a similar fashion:

$$\text{Toronto} - \text{Kingston index} = \$3 - \$4 + \$7 - \$5 = +\$1$$
$$(\text{Closed path} = \text{EC} - \text{EB} + \text{FB} - \text{FC})$$
$$\text{Thunder Bay} - \text{Regina index} = \$9 - \$7 + \$4 - \$8 = -\$2$$
$$(\text{Closed path} = \text{FA} - \text{FB} + \text{EB} - \text{EA})$$

INSIGHT ▶ Because this last index is negative, we can realize cost savings by using the (currently unused) Thunder Bay–Regina route.

FIGURE C.6
Testing Windsor to Kingston

From \ To	(A) Regina	(B) Dartmouth	(C) Kingston	Factory capacity
(D) Windsor	$5 100	$4	Start $3	100
(E) Toronto	$8 200+	$4 100	$3	300
(F) Thunder Bay	$9	$7 100	$5 200	300
Warehouse requirement	300	200	200	700

LEARNING EXERCISE ▶ What would happen to total cost if Yorkton used the shipping route from Windsor to Kingston? [Answer: Total cost of the current solution would increase by $400.]

RELATED PROBLEMS ▶ C.1c, C.3c, C.7, C.8, C.10, C.13, C.15, C.16, C.17

EXCEL OM Data File **ModCExC3.xlsx** can be found at **MyLab Operations Management.**

In Example C3, we see that a better solution is indeed possible because we can calculate a negative improvement index on one of our unused routes. *Each negative index represents the amount by which total transportation costs could be decreased if one unit was shipped by the source–destination combination.* The next step, then, is to choose that route (unused square) with the *largest* negative improvement index. We can then ship the maximum allowable number of units on that route and reduce the total cost accordingly.

What is the maximum quantity that can be shipped on our new money-saving route? That quantity is found by referring to the closed path of plus signs and minus signs drawn for the route and then selecting the *smallest number found in the squares containing minus signs*. To obtain a new solution, we add this number to all squares on the closed path with plus signs and subtract it from all squares on the path to which we have assigned minus signs.

One iteration of the stepping-stone method is now complete. Again, of course, we must test to see if the solution is optimal or whether we can make any further improvements. We do this by evaluating each unused square, as previously described. Example C4 continues our effort to help Yorkton Plumbing arrive at a final solution.

Yorkton Plumbing wants to continue solving the problem.

APPROACH ▶ Use the improvement indices calculated in Example C3. We found in Example C3 that the largest (and only) negative index is on the Thunder Bay–Regina route (which is the route depicted in Figure C.7).

EXAMPLE **C4**

Improvement Indices

FIGURE C.7
Transportation Table:
Route FA

From \ To	(A) Regina	(B) Dartmouth	(C) Kingston	Factory capacity
(D) Windsor	$5 100	$4	$3	100
(E) Toronto	$8 200	$4 100	$3	300
(F) Thunder Bay	$9	$7 100	$5 200	300
Warehouse demand	300	200	200	700

STUDENT TIP

FA has a negative index: FA (+9) to FB (−7) to EB (+4) to EA (−8) = −$2

SOLUTION ▶ The maximum quantity that may be shipped on the newly opened route, Thunder Bay–Regina (FA), is the smallest number found in squares containing minus signs—in this case, 100 units. Why 100 units? Because the total cost decreases by $2 per unit shipped, we know we would like to ship the maximum possible number of units. Previous stepping-stone calculations indicate that each unit shipped over the FA route results in an increase of 1 unit shipped from Toronto (E) to Dartmouth (B) and a decrease of 1 unit in amounts shipped both from F to B (now 100 units) and from E to A (now 200 units). Hence, the maximum we can ship over the FA route is 100 units. This solution results in zero units being shipped from F to B. Now we take the following four steps:

1. Add 100 units (to the zero currently being shipped) on route FA.
2. Subtract 100 from route FB, leaving zero in that square (though still balancing the row total for F).
3. Add 100 to route EB, yielding 200.
4. Finally, subtract 100 from route EA, leaving 100 units shipped.

Note that the new numbers still produce the correct row and column totals as required. The new solution is shown in Figure C.8.

Total shipping cost has been reduced by (100 units) × ($2 saved per unit) = $200 and is now $4000. This cost figure, of course, can also be derived by multiplying the cost of shipping each unit by the number of units transported on its respective route, namely: 100($5) + 100($8) + 200($4) + 100($9) + 200($5) = $4000.

FIGURE C.8

Solution at Next Iteration (Still Not Optimal)

From \ To	(A) Regina	(B) Dartmouth	(C) Kingston	Factory capacity
(D) Windsor	$5 100	$4	$3	100
(E) Toronto	$8 100	$4 200	$3	300
(F) Thunder Bay	$9 100	$7	$5 200	300
Warehouse demand	300	200	200	700

INSIGHT ▶ Looking carefully at Figure C.8, however, you can see that it, too, is not yet optimal. Route EC (Toronto–Kingston) has a negative cost improvement index of –$1. Closed path = EC – EA + FA – FC.

LEARNING EXERCISE ▶ Find the final solution for this route on your own. [Answer: Programs C.1 and C.2, at the end of this module, provide an Excel OM solution.]

RELATED PROBLEMS ▶ C.4, C.6, C.7, C.8, C.10, C.13, C.15, C.16, C.17

Dummy sources

Artificial shipping source points created when total demand is greater than total supply to effect a supply equal to the excess of demand over supply.

STUDENT TIP

Let's look at what happens when two issues arise: an unbalanced problem and degeneracy.

Dummy destinations

Artificial destination points created when the total supply is greater than the total demand; they serve to equalize the total demand and supply.

Special Issues in Modelling

DEMAND NOT EQUAL TO SUPPLY

A common situation in real-world problems is the case in which total demand is not equal to total supply. We can easily handle these so-called unbalanced problems with the solution procedures that we have just discussed by introducing **dummy sources** or **dummy destinations**. If total supply is greater than total demand, we make demand exactly equal the surplus by creating a dummy destination. Conversely, if total demand is greater than total supply, we introduce a dummy source (factory) with a supply equal to the excess of demand. Because these units will not in fact be shipped, we assign cost coefficients of zero to each square on the dummy location. In each case, then, the cost is zero. Example C5 demonstrates the use of a dummy destination.

Yorkton Plumbing decides to increase the production in its Windsor factory from 100 tubs to 250 bathtubs. This increases supply over demand and creates an unbalanced problem.

APPROACH ▶ To reformulate this unbalanced problem, we refer back to the data presented in Example C1 and present the new matrix in Figure C.9. First, we use the northwest-corner rule to find the initial feasible solution. Then, once the problem is balanced, we can proceed to the solution in the normal way.

From \ To	(A) Regina	(B) Dartmouth	(C) Kingston	Dummy	Factory capacity
(D) Windsor	$5 250	$4	$3	0	250
(E) Toronto	$8 50	$4 200	$3 50	0	300
(F) Thunder Bay	$9	$7	$5 150	0 150	300
Warehouse requirement	300	200	200	150	850

New Windsor capacity

EXAMPLE C5

Adjusting for Unequal Supply and Demand With a Dummy Column

FIGURE C.9
Northwest-Corner Rule with Dummy

LO3 Balance a transportation problem

SOLUTION ▶

Total cost = 250($5) + 50($8) + 200($4) + 50($3) + 150($5) + 150(0) = $3350

INSIGHT ▶ Excel OM and POM for Windows software automatically perform the balance for you. But if you are solving by hand, be careful to decide first whether a dummy row (source) or a dummy column (destination) is needed.

LEARNING EXERCISE ▶ Yorkton instead increases Windsor's capacity to 350 tubs. Does the initial northwest-corner solution change? [Answer: Yes, now D − A = 300, D − B = 50, E − B = 150, E − C = 150, F − C = 50, F − Dummy = 250. Cost = $3000.]

RELATED PROBLEMS ▶ C.5, C.9, C.14

EXCEL OM Data File **ModCExC5.xlsx** can be found at **MyLab Operations Management**.

DEGENERACY

To apply the stepping-stone method to a transportation problem, we must observe a rule about the number of shipping routes being used: *The number of occupied squares in any solution (initial or later) must be equal to the number of rows in the table plus the number of columns minus 1.* Solutions that do not satisfy this rule are called *degenerate*.

Degeneracy occurs when too few squares or shipping routes are being used. As a result, it becomes impossible to trace a closed path for one or more unused squares. The Yorkton Plumbing problem we just examined was not degenerate, as it had 5 assigned routes (3 rows or factories +3 columns or warehouses − 1).

To handle degenerate problems, we must artificially create an occupied cell: That is, we place a zero or a *very* small amount (representing a fake shipment) in one of the unused squares and *then treat that square as if it were occupied*. Remember that the chosen square must be in such a position as to allow all stepping-stone paths to be closed. We illustrate this procedure in Example C6.

LO4 Solve a problem with degeneracy

Degeneracy
An occurrence in transportation models in which too few squares or shipping routes are being used, so that tracing a closed path for each unused square becomes impossible.

EXAMPLE C6

Dealing With Degeneracy

FIGURE C.10

Martin's Northwest-Corner Rule

Martin Shipping Company has three warehouses from which it supplies its three major retail customers in Cornwall. Martin's shipping costs, warehouse supplies, and customer demands are presented in the transportation table in Figure C.10. The company wants to make an initial shipping assignment.

From \ To	Customer 1	Customer 2	Customer 3	Warehouse supply
Warehouse 1	$8 100	$2	$6	100
Warehouse 2	$10 0	$9 100	$9 20	120
Warehouse 3	$7	$10	$7 80	80
Customer demand	100	100	100	300

APPROACH ▶ To make the initial shipping assignments in that table, we apply the northwest-corner rule.

SOLUTION ▶ The initial solution is degenerate because it violates the rule that the number of used squares must equal the number of rows plus the number of columns minus 1. To correct the problem, we may place a zero in the unused square that permits evaluation of all empty cells. Some experimenting may be needed because not every cell will allow tracing a closed path for the remaining cells. Also, we want to avoid placing the 0 in a cell that has a negative sign in a closed path. No reallocation will be possible if we do this.

For this example, we try the empty square that represents the shipping route from Warehouse 2 to Customer 1. Now we can close all stepping-stone paths and compute improvement indices.

INSIGHT ▶ We must always check the unused squares in a transportation solution to make sure the *Number of rows + Number of columns − 1* = Number of occupied squares.

LEARNING EXERCISES ▶ Explain why the "zero" cannot be placed in the Warehouse 3–Customer 1 square. [Answer: The route, Warehouse 1–Customer 2, cannot be closed now.] Why did this problem become degenerate? [Answer: Our first assignment, 100 units to the Warehouse 1–Customer 1 cell, fully met both the first row and first column's needs in one cell.]

RELATED PROBLEMS ▶ C.11, C.12

EXCEL OM Data File **ModCExC6.xlsx** can be found at **MyLab Operations Management.**

MODULE | SUMMARY

The transportation model, a form of linear programming, is used to help find the least-cost solutions to system-wide shipping problems. The northwest-corner method (which begins in the upper-left corner of the transportation table) or the intuitive lowest-cost method may be used for finding an initial feasible solution. The stepping-stone algorithm is then used for finding optimal solutions. Unbalanced problems are those in which the total demand and total supply are not equal. Degeneracy refers to the case in which the number of rows plus the number of columns minus 1 is not equal to the number of occupied squares. The transportation model approach is one of the four location models described earlier in Chapter 8. Additional solution techniques are presented in Tutorial 4 at MyLab Operations Management.

Discussion Questions

1. What are the three information needs of the transportation model?
2. What are the steps in the intuitive lowest-cost method?
3. Identify the three "steps" in the northwest-corner rule.
4. How do you know when an optimal solution has been reached?
5. Which starting technique generally gives a better initial solution, and why?
6. The more sources and destinations there are for a transportation problem, the smaller the percentage of all cells that will be used in the optimal solution. Explain.

7. All of the transportation examples appear to apply to long distances. Is it possible for the transportation model to apply on a much smaller scale, for example, within the departments of a store or the offices of a building? Discuss.

8. Develop a *northeast*-corner rule and explain how it would work. Set up an initial solution for the Yorkton Plumbing problem analyzed in Example C1.

9. What is meant by "an unbalanced transportation problem," and how would you balance it?

10. How many occupied cells must all solutions use?

11. Explain the significance of a negative improvement index in a transportation-minimizing problem.

12. How can the transportation method address production costs in addition to transportation costs?

13. Explain what is meant by the term *degeneracy* within the context of transportation modelling.

Using Software to Solve Transportation Problems

Excel, Excel OM, and POM for Windows may all be used to solve transportation problems. Excel uses Solver, which requires that you enter your own constraints. Excel OM also uses Solver but is prestructured so that you need enter only the actual data. POM for Windows similarly requires that only demand data, supply data, and shipping costs be entered.

✖ USING EXCEL OM

Excel OM's Transportation module uses Excel's built-in Solver routine to find optimal solutions to transportation problems. Program C.1 illustrates the input data (from Yorkton Plumbing) and total-cost formulas. To reach an optimal solution, we must go to Excel's **Tools** bar, request **Solver**, then select **Solve**. In Excel 2007, **Solver** is in the **Analysis** section of the **Data** tab. The output appears in Program C.2.

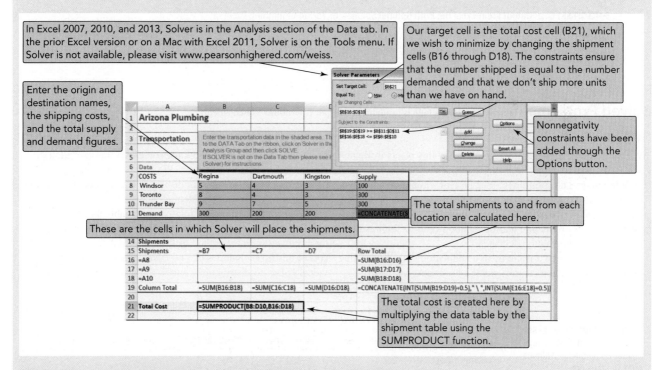

PROGRAM C.1 Excel OM Input Screen and Formulas, Using Yorkton Plumbing Data

🅿 USING POM FOR WINDOWS

The POM for Windows Transportation module can solve both maximization and minimization problems by a variety of methods. Input data are the demand data, supply data, and unit shipping costs. See Appendix IV for further details.

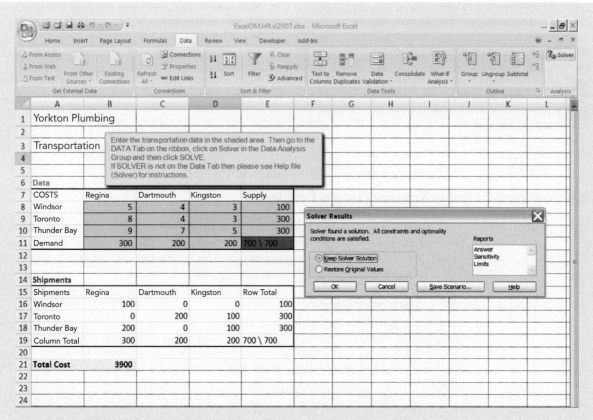

PROGRAM C.2 Output From Excel OM With Optimal Solution to Yorkton Plumbing Problem

Source: Microsoft product screen shot(s) reprinted with permission from Microsoft Corporation.

Solved Problems Virtual Office Hours help is available at MyLab Operations Management.

▼ SOLVED PROBLEM C.1

Williams Auto Top Carriers currently maintains plants in Regina and Edmonton to supply auto top carriers to distribution centres in Vancouver and Winnipeg. Because of expanding demand, Williams has decided to open a third plant and has narrowed the choice to one of two cities—Calgary and Kelowna. Table C.3 provides pertinent production and distribution costs as well as plant capacities and distribution demands.

Which of the new locations, in combination with the existing plants and distribution centres, yields a lower cost for the firm?

▼ SOLUTION

To answer this question, we must solve two transportation problems, one for each combination. We will recommend the location that yields a lower total cost of distribution and production in combination with the existing system.

We begin by setting up a transportation table that represents the opening of a third plant in Calgary (see Figure C.11). Then we use the northwest-corner method to find an initial solution. The total cost of this first solution is $23 600. Note that the cost of each individual "plant-to-distribution-centre" route is found by adding the

Table C.3

Production Costs, Distribution Costs, Plant Capabilities, and Market Demands for Williams Auto Top Carriers

From Plants	To Distribution Centres		Normal Production	Unit Production Cost
	Vancouver	Winnipeg		
Existing plants				
Regina	$8	$5	600	$6
Edmonton	$4	$7	900	$5
Proposed locations				
Calgary	$5	$6	500	$4 (anticipated)
Kelowna	$4	$6[a]	500	$3 (anticipated)
Forecast demand	800	1200	2000	

[a]Indicates distribution cost (shipping, handling, storage) will be $6 per carrier between Kelowna and Winnipeg.

FIGURE C.11

Initial Williams Transportation Table for Calgary

From \ To	Vancouver	Winnipeg	Production capacity
Regina	$14 600	$11	600
Edmonton	$9 200	$12 700	900
Calgary	$9	$10 500	500
Demand	800	1200	2000

distribution costs (in the body of Table C.3) to the respective unit production costs (in the right-hand column of Table C.3). Thus, the total production-plus-shipping cost of one auto top carrier from Regina to Vancouver is $14 (= $8 for shipping plus $6 for production).

$$\text{Total cost} = (600 \text{ units} \times \$14) + (200 \text{ units} \times \$9)$$
$$+ (700 \text{ units} \times \$12) + (500 \text{ units} \times \$10)$$
$$= \$8400 + \$1800 + \$8400 + \$5000$$
$$= \$23\ 600$$

Is this initial solution (in Figure C.11) optimal? We can use the stepping-stone method to test it and compute improvement indices for unused routes:

Improvement index for Regina–Winnipeg route

$$= +\$11(\text{Regina}-\text{Winnipeg}) - \$14(\text{Regina}-\text{Vancouver})$$
$$+ \$9(\text{Edmonton}-\text{Vancouver}) - \$12(\text{Edmonton}-\text{Winnipeg})$$
$$= -\$6$$

Improvement index for Calgary–Vancouver route

$$= +\$9 \ (\text{Calgary}-\text{Vancouver})$$
$$- \$10 \ (\text{Calgary}-\text{Winnipeg})$$
$$+ \$12(\text{Edmonton}-\text{Winnipeg})$$
$$- \$9(\text{Edmonton}-\text{Vancouver})$$
$$= \$2$$

Because the firm can save $6 for every unit shipped from Regina to Winnipeg, it will want to improve the initial solution and send as many units as possible (600, in this case) on this currently unused route (see Figure C.12). You may also want to confirm that the total cost is now $20 000, a savings of $3600 over the initial solution.

Next, we must test the two unused routes to see if their improvement indices are also negative numbers:

Index for Calgary–Vancouver

$$= \$14 - \$11 + \$12 - \$9 = \$6$$

Index for Calgary–Vancouver

$$= \$9 - \$10 + \$12 - \$9 = \$2$$

Because both indices are greater than zero, we have already reached our optimal solution for the Calgary location. If Williams elects to open the Calgary plant, the firm's total production and distribution cost will be $20 000.

This analysis, however, provides only half the answer to Williams's problem. The same procedure must still be followed to determine the minimum cost if the new plant is built in Kelowna. Determining this cost is left as a homework problem. You can help provide complete information and recommend a solution by solving Problem C.8.

FIGURE C.12

Improved Transportation Table for Williams

From \ To	Vancouver	Winnipeg	Production capacity
Regina	$14	$11 600	600
Edmonton	$9 800	$12 100	900
Calgary	$9	$10 500	500
Demand	800	1200	2000

▼ **SOLVED PROBLEM C.2**

In Solved Problem C.1, we examined the Williams Auto Top Carriers problem by using a transportation table. An alternative approach is to structure the same decision analysis using linear programming (LP), which we explained in detail in Business Analytics Module B.

▼ **SOLUTION**

Using the data in Figure C.11, we write the objective function and constraints as follows:

$$\text{Minimize total cost} = \$14X_{R,V} + \$11X_{R,W} + \$9X_{E,V} + \$12X_{E,W} + \$9X_{C,V} + \$10X_{C,W}$$

$$
\begin{aligned}
\text{Subject to:} \quad & X_{R,V} + X_{R,W} && \leq 600 && \text{(production capacity at Regina)} \\
& X_{E,V} + X_{E,W} && \leq 900 && \text{(production capacity at Edmonton)} \\
& X_{C,V} + X_{C,W} && \leq 500 && \text{(production capacity at Calgary)} \\
& X_{R,V} + X_{E,V} + X_{C,V} && \geq 800 && \text{(Vancouver demand constraint)} \\
& X_{R,W} + X_{E,W} + X_{C,W} && \geq 1200 && \text{(Winnipeg demand constraint)}
\end{aligned}
$$

Problems*

•   **C.1** Find an initial solution to the following transportation problem.

From	To Los Angeles	Calgary	Panama City	Supply
Mexico City	$ 6	$18	$ 8	100
Detroit	$17	$13	$19	60
Ottawa	$20	$10	$24	40
Demand	50	80	70	

a) Use the northwest-corner method. What is its total cost?
b) Use the intuitive lowest-cost approach. What is its total cost?
c) Using the stepping-stone method, find the optimal solution. Compute the total cost. **Px**

•   **C.2** Consider the transportation table below. Unit costs for each shipping route are in dollars. What is the total cost of the basic feasible solution that the intuitive least-cost method would find for this problem? **Px**

Destination

Source	A	B	C	D	E	Supply
1	12	8	5	10	4	18
2	6	11	3	7	9	14
Demand	6	8	12	4	2	

•   **C.3** a) Use the northwest-corner method to find an initial feasible solution to the following problem. What must you do before beginning the solution steps?
a) Use the intuitive lowest-cost approach to find an initial feasible solution. Is this approach better than the northwest-corner method?
c) Find the optimal solution using the stepping-stone method.

Note: **Px** means the problem may be solved with POM for Windows and/or Excel OM.

From	To A	B	C	Supply
X	$10	$18	$12	100
Y	$17	$13	$ 9	50
Z	$20	$18	$14	75
Demand	50	80	70	

Px

•   **C.4** Consider the transportation table below. The solution displayed was obtained by performing some iterations of the transportation method on this problem. What is the total cost of the shipping plan that would be obtained by performing *one more iteration* of the stepping-stone method on this problem?

Destination

Source	Sudbury	Toronto	Montreal	Supply
Windsor	$2 10	$8	$1	10
Owen Sound	$4 10	$5 10	$6	20
Sault Ste. Marie	$6	$3 10	$2 20	30
Demand	20	20	20	

••   **C.5** Tharp Air Conditioning manufactures room air conditioners at plants in Montreal, Quebec City, and Ottawa. These are sent to regional distributors in Kingston, Fredericton, and North Bay. The shipping costs vary, and the company would like to find the least-cost way to meet the demands at each of the distribution centres. Kingston needs to receive 800 air conditioners per month, Fredericton needs 600, and North Bay needs 200. Montreal has 850 air conditioners available each month, Quebec City has 650, and Ottawa has 300. The shipping cost per unit from Montreal to Kingston is $8, to Fredericton $12, and to North Bay $10. The cost per unit from Quebec City to Kingston is $10, to Fredericton $14, and to North Bay $9. The cost per unit from Ottawa to Kingston is $11, to Fredericton $8, and to North Bay $12. How many units should owner Devorah Tharp ship from each plant to each regional distribution centre? What is the total transportation cost? (Note that a "dummy" destination is needed to balance the problem.) **Px**

•• **C.6** The following table is the result of one or more iterations:
a) Complete the next iteration using the stepping-stone method.
b) Calculate the "total cost" incurred if your results were to be accepted as the final solution. **Px**

From \ To	1	2	3	Capacity
A	40 [30]	[30]	10 [5]	50
B	[10]	30 [10]	[10]	30
C	[20]	30 [10]	45 [25]	75
Demand	40	60	55	155

•• **C.7** The three blood banks in Kitchener-Waterloo are coordinated through a central office that facilitates blood delivery to four hospitals in the region. The cost to ship a standard container of blood from each bank to each hospital is shown in the table below. Also given are the biweekly number of containers available at each bank and the biweekly number of containers of blood needed at each hospital. How many shipments should be made biweekly from each blood bank to each hospital so that total shipment costs are minimized?

From	Hosp. 1	Hosp. 2	Hosp. 3	Hosp. 4	Supply
Bank 1	$ 8	$ 9	$11	$16	50
Bank 2	$12	$ 7	$ 5	$ 8	80
Bank 3	$14	$10	$ 6	$ 7	120
Demand	90	70	40	50	250

Px

•• **C.8** In Solved Problem C.1, Williams Auto Top Carriers proposed opening a new plant in either Calgary or Kelowna. Management found that the total system cost (of production plus distribution) would be $20 000 for the Calgary site. What would be the total cost if Williams opened a plant in Kelowna? At which of the two proposed locations (Calgary or Kelowna) should Williams open the new facility? **Px**

•• **C.9** For the following William Gehrlein Corp. data, find the starting solution and initial cost using the northwest-corner method. What must you do to balance this problem? **Px**

From	To W	X	Y	Z	Supply
A	$132	$116	$250	$110	220
B	$220	$230	$180	$178	300
C	$152	$173	$196	$164	435
Demand	160	120	200	230	

•• **C.10** The Tara Tripp Clothing Group owns factories in three towns (W, Y, and Z), which distribute to three Walsh retail dress shops in three other cities (A, B, and C). The following table summarizes factory availabilities, projected store demands, and unit shipping costs:

Tara Tripp Clothing Group

From \ To	Dress Shop A	Dress Shop B	Dress Shop C	Factory availability
Factory W	$4	$3	$3	35
Factory Y	$6	$7	$6	50
Factory Z	$8	$2	$5	50
Store demand	30	65	40	135

a) Complete the analysis, determining the optimal solution for shipping at the Tara Tripp Clothing Group.
b) How do you know if it is optimal or not? **Px**

•• **C.11** Consider the following transportation problem at Frank Timoney Enterprises in Clarenville, Newfoundland.

From	To Destination A	Destination B	Destination C	Supply
Source 1	$8	$9	$4	72
Source 2	$5	$6	$8	38
Source 3	$7	$9	$6	46
Source 4	$5	$3	$7	19
Demand	110	34	31	175

a) Find an initial solution using the northwest-corner rule. What special condition exists?
b) Explain how you will proceed to solve the problem.
c) What is the optimal solution? **Px**

•• **C.12** Lawson Mill Works (LMW) ships pre-cut lumber to three building-supply houses from mills in Charlottetown, Summerside, and Wellington. Determine the best shipment schedule for LMW from the data provided by James Lawson, the traffic manager at LMW. Use the northwest-corner starting procedure and the stepping-stone method. Refer to the following table. (*Note:* You may face a degenerate solution in one of your iterations.) **Px**

Lawson Mill Works

From \ To	Supply House 1	Supply House 2	Supply House 3	Mill capacity (in tons)
Charlottetown	$3	$3	$2	25
Summerside	$4	$2	$3	40
Wellington	$3	$2	$3	30
Supply house demand (in tons)	30	30	35	95

··· C.13 Captain Cabell Corp. manufacturers fishing equipment. Currently, the company has a plant in Victoria and a plant in Calgary. David Cabell, the firm's owner, is deciding where to build a new plant—Winnipeg or Terrace. Use the following table to find the total shipping costs for each potential site. Which should Cabell select?

	Warehouse			
Plant	**Sudbury**	**Barrie**	**Windsor**	**Capacity**
Victoria	$100	$75	$50	150
Calgary	$ 80	$60	$90	225
Winnipeg	$ 40	$50	$90	350
Terrace	$110	$70	$30	350
Demand	200	100	400	

·· C.14 Susan Helms Manufacturing Co. has hired you to evaluate its shipping costs. The following table shows present demand, capacity, and freight costs between each factory and each warehouse. Find the shipping pattern with the lowest cost. **Px**

Susan Helms Manufacturing Data

From \ To	Warehouse 1	Warehouse 2	Warehouse 3	Warehouse 4	Plant capacity
Factory 1	4	7	10	12	2000
Factory 2	7	5	8	11	2500
Factory 3	9	8	6	9	2200
Warehouse demand	1000	2000	2000	1200	6700 / 6200

·· C.15 Drew Rosen Corp. is considering adding a fourth plant to its three existing facilities in Gatineau, Napanee, and Kanata. Both Oka and Cornwall are being considered. Evaluating only the transportation costs per unit as shown in the table, decide which site is best.

	From Existing Plants			
To	**Gatineau**	**Napanee**	**Kanata**	**Demand**
Renfrew	$20	$17	$21	250
Arnprior	$25	$27	$20	200
Kingston	$22	$25	$22	350
Capacity	300	200	150	

	From Proposed Plants	
To	**Cornwall**	**Oka**
Renfrew	$29	$27
Arnprior	$30	$28
Kingston	$30	$31
Capacity	150	150

·· C.16 Using the data from Problem C.15 and the unit production costs in the following table, show which locations yield the lowest cost.

Location	Production Costs ($)
Gatineau	$50
Napanee	60
Kanata	70
Cornwall	40
Oka	50

···· C.17 Dalton Pharmaceuticals enjoys a dominant position in most of Canada with over 800 discount retail outlets. These stores are served by twice-weekly deliveries from Dalton's 16 warehouses, which are in turn supplied daily by seven factories that manufacture about 70% of all of the chain's products.

It is clear to Marilyn Helms, VP operations, that an additional warehouse is desperately needed to handle growth and backlogs. Three cities, Montreal, Toronto, and Winnipeg, are under final consideration. The table below illustrates the current and proposed factory/warehouse capacities/demands and shipping costs per average box of supplies.

a) Based on shipping costs only, which city should be selected for the new warehouse?
b) One study shows that Ottawa's capacity can increase to 500 boxes per day. Would this affect your decision in part (a)?
c) Because of a new intraprovincial shipping agreement, rates for shipping from each factory in Ontario to each warehouse in Ontario drop by $1 per carton. How does this factor affect your answer to parts (a) and (b)?

Table for Problem C.17

	Warehouse								Capacity (cartons per day)
Factory	**Yorkton, SK**	**Calgary, AB**	**Miramichi, NB**	**Quebec City, QC**	**Gatineau, QC**	**Charlotte town, PE**	**Wellington, PE**	**Bonavista, NL**	
Saskatoon, SK	$3	$5	$4	$3	$4	$6	$8	$8	350
Ottawa, ON	4	6	5	5	6	7	6	7	300
Regina, SK	1	4	3	2	2	6	7	8	400
Hamilton, ON	3	5	2	6	6	5	5	6	200
Moncton, NB	4	1	4	3	3	8	9	10	600
Fredericton, NB	3	3	1	2	2	6	5	6	400
Summerside, PEI	4	8	8	7	7	2	2	2	500
Requirements (cartons/day)	150	250	50	150	100	200	150	300	

Factory	Warehouse					Alternatives			Capacity (cartons per day)
	Kingston, ON	Windsor, ON	Thunder Bay, ON	Bedeque, PE	Tignish, PE	Montreal, QC	Toronto, ON	Winnipeg, MB	
Saskatoon, SK	$9	$10	$8	$8	$11	$4	$6	$3	350
Ottawa, ON	2	3	2	6	7	5	2	5	300
Regina, SK	7	9	6	8	9	3	5	2	400
Hamilton, ON	2	2	3	5	5	6	3	5	200
Moncton, NB	7	13	9	8	8	2	6	3	600
Fredericton, NB	6	8	7	7	8	3	6	2	400
Summerside, PE	6	8	5	1	2	8	7	8	500
Requirements (cartons/day)	250	300	300	100	150	300	300	300	

CASE STUDY

Custom Vans Inc.

Custom Vans Inc. specializes in converting standard vans into campers. Depending on the amount of work and customizing to be done, the customizing can cost less than $1000 to more than $5000. In less than four years, Tony Rizzo was able to expand his small operation in Gary, Indiana, to other major outlets in Chicago, Milwaukee, Minneapolis, and Detroit.

Innovation was the major factor in Tony's success in converting a small van shop into one of the largest and most profitable custom van operations in the Midwest. Tony seemed to have a special ability to design and develop unique features and devices that were always in high demand by van owners. An example was Shower-Rific, which was developed by Tony only six months after Custom Vans Inc. was started. These small showers were completely self-contained, and they could be placed in almost any type of van and in a number of different locations within a van. Shower-Rific was made of fibreglass, and contained towel racks, built-in soap and shampoo holders, and a unique plastic door. Each Shower-Rific took 2 gallons of fibreglass and 3 hours of labour to manufacture.

Most of the Shower-Rifics were manufactured in Gary in the same warehouse where Custom Vans Inc. was founded. The manufacturing plant in Gary could produce 300 Shower-Rifics in a month, but this capacity never seemed to be enough. Custom Van shops in all locations were complaining about not getting enough Shower-Rifics, and because Minneapolis was farther away from Gary than the other locations, Tony was always inclined to ship Shower-Rifics to the other locations before Minneapolis. This infuriated the manager of Custom Vans at Minneapolis, and after many heated discussions, Tony decided to start another manufacturing plant for Shower-Rifics at Fort Wayne, Indiana. The manufacturing plant at Fort Wayne could produce 150 Shower-Rifics per month.

The manufacturing plant at Fort Wayne was still not able to meet current demand for Shower-Rifics, and Tony knew that the demand for his unique camper shower would grow rapidly in the next year. After consulting with his lawyer and banker, Tony concluded that he should open two new manufacturing plants as soon as possible. Each plant would have the same capacity as the Fort Wayne manufacturing plant. An initial investigation into possible manufacturing locations was made, and Tony decided that the

two new plants should be located in Detroit, Michigan; Rockford, Illinois; or Madison, Wisconsin. Tony knew that selecting the best location for the two new manufacturing plants would be difficult. Transportation costs and demands for the various locations would be important considerations.

The Chicago shop was managed by Bill Burch. This shop was one of the first established by Tony, and it continued to outperform the other locations. The manufacturing plant at Gary was supplying 200 Shower-Rifics each month, although Bill knew that the demand for the showers in Chicago was 300 units. The transportation cost per unit from Gary was $10, and although the transportation cost from Fort Wayne was double that amount, Bill was always pleading with Tony to get an additional 50 units from the Fort Wayne manufacturer. The two additional manufacturing plants would certainly be able to supply Bill with the additional 100 showers he needed. The transportation costs would, of course, vary, depending on which two locations Tony picked. The transportation cost per shower would be $30 from Detroit, $5 from Rockford, and $10 from Madison.

Wilma Jackson, manager of the Custom Van shop in Milwaukee, was the most upset about not getting an adequate supply of showers. She had a demand for 100 units, and at the present time, she was getting only half of this demand from the Fort Wayne manufacturing plant. She could not understand why Tony didn't ship her all 100 units from Gary. The transportation cost per unit from Gary was only $20, while the transportation cost from Fort Wayne was $30. Wilma was hoping that Tony would select Madison for one of the manufacturing locations. She would be able to get all the showers needed, and the transportation cost per unit would only be $5. If not in Madison, a new plant in Rockford would be able to supply her total needs, but the transportation cost per unit would be twice as much as it would be from Madison. Because the transportation cost per unit from Detroit would be $40, Wilma speculated that even if Detroit became one of the new plants, she would not be getting any units from Detroit.

Custom Vans Inc. of Minneapolis was managed by Tom Poanski. He was getting 100 showers from the Gary plant. Demand was 150 units. Tom faced the highest transportation costs of all locations. The transportation cost from Gary was $40 per unit. It would cost $10 more if showers were sent from the Fort Wayne location. Tom was hoping that Detroit would not be one of the new plants, as the transportation cost would be $60 per unit. Rockford and Madison would have a cost of $30 and $25, respectively, to ship one shower to Minneapolis.

The Detroit shop's position was similar to Milwaukee's—only getting half of the demand each month. The 100 units that Detroit did receive came directly from the Fort Wayne plant. The transportation cost was only $15 per unit from Fort Wayne, while it was $25 from Gary. Dick Lopez, manager of Custom Vans Inc. of Detroit, placed the probability of having one of the new plants in Detroit fairly high. The factory would be located across town, and the transportation cost would be only $5 per unit. He could get 150 showers from the new plant in Detroit and the other 50 showers from Fort Wayne. Even if Detroit was not selected, the other two locations were not intolerable. Rockford had a transportation cost per unit of $35, and Madison had a transportation cost of $40.

Tony pondered the dilemma of locating the two new plants for several weeks before deciding to call a meeting of all the managers of the van shops. The decision was complicated, but the objective was clear—to minimize total costs. The meeting was held in Gary, and everyone was present except Wilma.

Tony: Thank you for coming. As you know, I have decided to open two new plants at Rockford, Madison, or Detroit. The two locations, of course, will change our shipping practices, and I sincerely hope that they will supply you with the Shower-Rifics that you have been wanting. I know you could have sold more units, and I want you to know that I am sorry for this situation.

Dick: Tony, I have given this situation a lot of consideration, and I feel strongly that at least one of the new plants should be located in Detroit. As you know, I am now only getting half of the showers that I need. My brother, Leon, is very interested in running the plant, and I know he would do a good job.

Tom: Dick, I am sure that Leon could do a good job, and I know how difficult it has been since the recent layoffs by the auto industry. Nevertheless, we should be considering total costs and not personalities. I believe that the new plants should be located in Madison and Rockford. I am farther away from the other plants than any other shop, and these locations would significantly reduce transportation costs.

Dick: That may be true, but there are other factors. Detroit has one of the largest suppliers of fibreglass, and I have checked prices. A new plant in Detroit would be able to purchase fibreglass for $2 per gallon less than any of the other existing or proposed plants.

Tom: At Madison, we have an excellent labour force. This is due primarily to the large number of students attending the University of Wisconsin. These students are hard workers, and they will work for $1 less per hour than the other locations that we are considering.

Bill: Calm down, you two. It is obvious that we will not be able to satisfy everyone in locating the new plants. Therefore, I would like to suggest that we vote on the two best locations.

Tony: I don't think that voting would be a good idea. Wilma was not able to attend, and we should be looking at all of these factors together in some type of logical fashion.

Discussion Questions

Where would you locate the two new plants? Why?

Source: Quantitative Analysis for Management, Barry Render, 10e, Ralph M. Stair, and Michael E. Hanna. © 2009. Reprinted and electronically reproduced by permission of Pearson Education, Inc., Upper Saddle River, New Jersey.

▶**Additional Case Study:** Visit **MyLab Operations Management** for this case study:

Consolidated Bottling (B): This case involves determining where to add bottling capacity.

MODULE C | RAPID REVIEW

MyLab Operations Management

Main Heading	Review Material
TRANSPORTATION MODELLING (pp. 711–712)	The transportation models described in this module prove useful when considering alternative facility locations *within the framework of an existing distribution system.* The choice of a new location depends on which will yield the minimum cost for the entire system • **Transportation modelling**—An iterative procedure for solving problems that involves minimizing the cost of shipping products from a series of sources to a series of destinations. *Origin points* (or *sources*) can be factories, warehouses, car rental agencies, or any other points from which goods are shipped. *Destinations* are any points that receive goods. To use the transportation model, we need to know the following: 1. The origin points and the capacity or supply per period at each. 2. The destination points and the demand per period at each. 3. The cost of shipping one unit from each origin to each destination.

Main Heading	**Review Material**

The transportation model is a type of linear programming model.

- A *transportation matrix* summarizes all relevant data and keeps track of algorithm computations. Shipping costs from each origin to each destination are contained in the appropriate cross-referenced box.

To⟍ From	Destination 1	Destination 2	Destination 3	Capacity
Source A				
Source B				
Source C				
Demand				

DEVELOPING AN INITIAL SOLUTION (pp. 713–715)	Two methods for establishing an initial feasible solution to the problem are the northwest-corner rule and the intuitive lowest-cost method.	Problems: C.1–C.3, C.9, C.11

- **Northwest-corner rule**—A procedure in the transportation model where one starts at the upper-left-hand cell of a table (the northwest corner) and systematically allocates units to shipping routes.

The northwest-corner rule requires that we:

1. Exhaust the supply (origin capacity) of each row before moving down to the next row.

2. Exhaust the demand requirements of each column before moving to the next column to the right.

3. Check to ensure that all supplies and demands are met.

The northwest-corner rule is easy to use and generates a feasible solution, but it totally ignores costs and, therefore, should be considered only as a starting position.

- **Intuitive method**—A cost-based approach to finding an initial solution to a transportation problem.

The intuitive method uses the following steps:

1. Identify the cell with the lowest cost. Break any ties for the lowest cost arbitrarily.

2. Allocate as many units as possible to that cell, without exceeding the supply or demand. Then cross out that row or column (or both) that is exhausted by this assignment.

3. Find the cell with the lowest cost from the remaining (not crossed out) cells.

4. Repeat steps 2 and 3 until all units have been allocated.

THE STEPPING-STONE METHOD (pp. 715–718)	- **Stepping-stone method**—An iterative technique for moving from an initial feasible solution to an optimal solution in the transportation method.	Problems: C.1d, C.3c, C.4, C.6-C.8, C.10, C.13, C.15, C.16, C.17

The stepping-stone method is used to evaluate the cost effectiveness of shipping goods via transportation routes not currently in the solution. When applying it, we test each unused cell, or square, in the transportation table by asking, "What would happen to total shipping costs if one unit of the product were tentatively shipped on an unused route?" We conduct the test as follows:

1. Select any unused square to evaluate.

2. Beginning at this square, trace a closed path back to the original square via squares that are currently being used (only horizontal and vertical moves are permissible). You may, however, step over either an empty or an occupied square.

3. Beginning with a plus (+) sign at the unused square, place alternative minus signs and plus signs on each corner square of the closed path just traced.

4. Calculate an improvement index by first adding the unit-cost figures found in each square containing a plus sign and then subtracting the unit costs in each square containing a minus sign.

5. Repeat steps 1 through 4 until you have calculated an improvement index for all unused squares. If all indices computed are *greater than or equal to zero*, you have reached an optimal solution. If not, the current solution can be improved further to decrease total shipping costs.

Main Heading	Review Material	
	Each negative index represents the amount by which total transportation costs could be decreased if one unit was shipped by the source–destination combination. The next step, then, is to choose that route (unused square) with the *largest* negative improvement index. We can then ship the maximum allowable number of units on that route and reduce the total cost accordingly. That maximum quantity is found by referring to the closed path of plus signs and minus signs drawn for the route and then selecting the *smallest number found in the squares containing minus sign*s. To obtain a new solution, we add this number to all squares on the closed path with plus signs and subtract it from all squares on the path to which we have assigned minus signs. From this new solution, a new test of unused squares needs to be conducted to see if the new solution is optimal or whether we can make further improvements.	
SPECIAL ISSUES IN MODELLING (pp. 718–720)	• **Dummy sources**—Artificial shipping source points created when total demand is greater than total supply to effect a supply equal to the excess of demand over supply. • **Dummy destinations**—Artificial destination points created when the total supply is greater than the total demand; they serve to equalize the total demand and supply. Because units from dummy sources or to dummy destinations will not in fact be shipped, we assign a cost coefficient of zero to each square on the dummy location. If you are solving a transportation problem by hand, be careful to decide first whether a dummy source (row) or a dummy destination (column) is needed. When applying the stepping-stone method, *the number of occupied squares in any solution (initial or later) must be equal to the number of rows in the table plus the number of columns minus 1.* Solutions that do not satisfy this rule are called *degenerate*. • **Degeneracy**—An occurrence in transportation models in which too few squares or shipping routes are being used, so that tracing a closed path for each unused square becomes impossible. To handle degenerate problems, we must artificially create an occupied cell: That is, we place a zero (representing a fake shipment) into one of the unused squares and *then treat that square as if it were occupied.* Remember that the chosen square must be in such a position as to allow all stepping-stone paths to be closed.	Problem: C.5, C.9, C.11, C.12, C.14

Self-Test

■ **Before taking the self-test,** refer to the learning objectives listed at the beginning of the module.

LO 1 With the transportation technique, the initial solution can be generated in any fashion one chooses. The only restriction(s) is (are) that:
  a) the solution be optimal.
  b) one uses the northwest-corner method.
  c) the edge constraints for supply and demand be satisfied.
  d) the solution not be degenerate.
  e) all of the above.

LO 2 The purpose of the stepping-stone method is to:
  a) develop the initial solution to a transportation problem.
  b) identify the relevant costs in a transportation problem.
  c) determine whether a given solution is feasible.
  d) assist one in moving from an initial feasible solution to the optimal solution.
  e) overcome the problem of degeneracy.

LO 3 The purpose of a *dummy source* or a *dummy destination* in a transportation problem is to:
  a) provide a means of representing a dummy problem.
  b) obtain a balance between total supply and total demand.
  c) prevent the solution from becoming degenerate.
  d) make certain that the total cost does not exceed some specified figure.
  e) change a problem from maximization to minimization.

LO 4 If a solution to a transportation problem is degenerate, then:
  a) it will be impossible to evaluate all empty cells without removing the degeneracy.
  b) a dummy row or column must be added.
  c) there will be more than one optimal solution.
  d) the problem has no feasible solution.
  e) increase the cost of each cell by 1.

Answers: LO1. c; LO2. d; LO3. b; LO4. a.

MyLab Operations Management

Most of these questions can be found in MyLab Operations Management. Visit MyLab Operations Management to access cases, videos, downloadable software, and much more. MyLab Operations Management Management also features a personalized Study Plan that helps you identify which chapter concepts you've mastered and guides you towards study tools for additional practice.

Waiting-Line Models

Learning Objectives

Queuing Theory

The body of knowledge about waiting lines, often called **queuing theory**, is an important part of operations and a valuable tool for the operations manager. **Waiting lines (or queues)** are a common occurrence—they may, for example, take the form of cars waiting for repair at a Midas Muffler Shop, copying jobs waiting to be completed at a Kinko's print shop, or vacationers waiting to enter the Space Mountain ride at Disney. Table D.1 lists just a few OM uses of waiting-line models.

Waiting-line models are useful in both manufacturing and service areas. Analysis of queues in terms of waiting-line length, average waiting time, and other factors helps us to understand service systems (such as bank teller stations), maintenance activities (that might repair broken machinery), and shop-floor control activities. Indeed, patients waiting in a doctor's office and broken drill presses waiting in a repair facility have a lot in common from an OM perspective. Both use human and equipment resources to restore valuable production assets (people and machines) to good condition.

Queuing theory
A body of knowledge about waiting lines.

Waiting lines (or queues)
Items or people in lines awaiting service.

Paris's EuroDisney, Tokyo's Disney Japan, and Disney World and Disneyland in the United States all have one feature in common—long lines and seemingly endless waits. However, Disney is one of the world's leading companies in the scientific analysis of queuing theory. It analyzes queuing behaviours and can predict which rides will draw what sizes of crowds. To keep visitors happy, Disney makes lines appear to be constantly moving forward, entertains people while they wait, and posts signs telling visitors how many minutes until they reach each ride.

Jeff Greenberg/PhotoEdit

Table D.1

Common Queuing Situations

Situation	Arrivals in Queue	Service Process
Supermarket	Grocery shoppers	Checkout clerks at cash register
Highway toll booth	Automobiles	Collection of tolls at booth
Doctor's office	Patients	Treatment by doctors and nurses
Computer system	Programs to be run	Computer processes jobs
Telephone company	Callers	Switching equipment forwards calls
Bank	Customers	Transactions handled by teller
Machine maintenance	Broken machines	Repair people fix machines
Harbour	Ships and barges	Dock workers load and unload

Every queuing system has three parts.

LO1 Describe the characteristics of arrivals, waiting lines, and service systems.

Characteristics of a Waiting-Line System

In this section, we take a look at the three parts of a waiting-line, or queuing, system (as shown in Figure D.1):

1. *Arrivals or inputs to the system:* These have characteristics such as population size, behaviour, and a statistical distribution.
2. *Queue discipline, or the waiting line itself:* Characteristics of the queue include whether it is limited or unlimited in length and the discipline of people or items in it.
3. *The service facility:* Its characteristics include its design and the statistical distribution of service times.

We now examine each of these three parts.

ARRIVAL CHARACTERISTICS

The input source that generates arrivals or customers for a service system has three major characteristics:

1. *Size* of the arrival population
2. *Behaviour* of arrivals
3. *Pattern* of arrivals (statistical distribution)

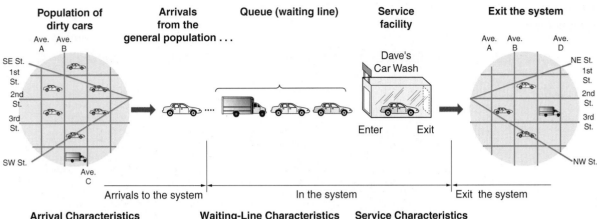

Arrival Characteristics
- Size of arrival population
- Behaviour of arrivals
- Statistical distribution of arrivals

Waiting-Line Characteristics
- Limited vs. unlimited
- Queue discipline

Service Characteristics
- Service design
- Statistical distribution of service

FIGURE D.1 Three Parts of a Waiting-Line, or Queuing System, at Dave's Car Wash

SIZE OF THE ARRIVAL (SOURCE) POPULATION Population sizes are considered either unlimited (essentially infinite) or limited (finite). When the number of customers or arrivals on hand at any given moment is just a small portion of all potential arrivals, the arrival population is considered an **unlimited, or infinite, population**. Examples of unlimited populations include cars arriving at a big city car wash, shoppers arriving at a supermarket, and students arriving to register for classes at a large university. Most queuing models assume such an infinite arrival population. An example of a **limited, or finite, population** is found in a copying shop that has, say, eight copying machines. Each of the copiers is a potential "customer" that may break down and require service.

Unlimited, or infinite, population
A queue in which a virtually unlimited number of people or items could request the services, or in which the number of customers or arrivals on hand at any given moment is a very small portion of potential arrivals.

PATTERN OF ARRIVALS AT THE SYSTEM Customers arrive at a service facility either according to some known schedule (e.g., one patient every 15 minutes or one student every half hour) or else they arrive *randomly*. Arrivals are considered random when they are independent of one another and their occurrence cannot be predicted exactly. Frequently in queuing problems, the number of arrivals per unit of time can be estimated by a probability distribution known as the **Poisson distribution**.[1] For any given arrival time (such as two customers per hour or four trucks per minute), a discrete Poisson distribution can be established by using the formula:

Limited, or finite, population
A queue in which there are only a limited number of potential users of the service.

Poisson distribution
A discrete probability distribution that often describes the arrival rate in queuing theory.

$$P(x) = \frac{e^{-\lambda}\lambda^x}{x!} \quad \text{for } x = 0, 1, 2, 3, 4, \ldots \qquad \text{(D-1)}$$

where $P(x)$ = probability of x arrivals
$\qquad x$ = number of arrivals per unit of time
$\qquad \lambda$ = average arrival rate
$\qquad e$ = 2.7183 (which is the base of the natural logarithms)

With the help of the table in Appendix II that gives the value of $e^{-\lambda}$ for use in the Poisson distribution, these values are easy to compute. Figure D.2 illustrates the Poisson distribution for $\lambda = 2$ and $\lambda = 4$. This means that if the average arrival rate is $\lambda = 2$ customers per hour, the probability of 0 customers arriving in any random hour is about 13%, probability of 1 customer is about 27%, 2 customers about 27%, 3 customers about 18%, 4 customers about 9%, and so on. The chances that 9 or more will arrive are virtually nil. Arrivals are, of course, not always Poisson distributed (they may follow some other distribution). Patterns should therefore be examined to make certain that they are well approximated by Poisson before that distribution is applied.

---

[1] When the arrival rates follow a Poisson process with mean arrival rate λ, the time between arrivals follows a negative exponential distribution with mean time between arrivals of 1/λ. The negative exponential distribution, then, is also representative of a Poisson process but describes the time between arrivals and specifies that these time intervals are completely random.

FIGURE D.2

Two Examples of the Poisson Distribution for Arrival Times

Probability $= P(x) = \dfrac{e^{-\lambda}\,\lambda^x}{x!}$

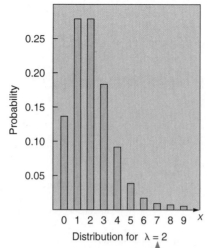

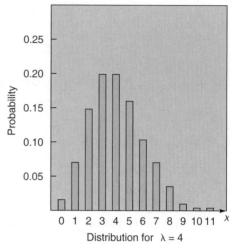

Distribution for $\lambda = 2$

Distribution for $\lambda = 4$

BEHAVIOUR OF ARRIVALS Most queuing models assume that an arriving customer is a patient customer. Patient customers are people or machines that wait in the queue until they are served and do not switch between lines. Unfortunately, life is complicated by the fact that people have been known to balk or to renege. Customers who *balk* refuse to join the waiting line because it is too long to suit their needs or interests. *Reneging* customers are those who enter the queue but then become impatient and leave without completing their transaction. Actually, both of these situations just serve to highlight the need for queuing theory and waiting-line analysis.

WAITING-LINE CHARACTERISTICS

The waiting line itself is the second component of a queuing system. The length of a line can be either limited or unlimited. A queue is *limited* when it cannot, either by law or because of physical restrictions, increase to an infinite length. A small barbershop, for example, will have only a limited number of waiting chairs. Queuing models are treated in this module under an assumption of *unlimited* queue length. A queue is *unlimited* when its size is unrestricted, as in the case of the toll booth serving arriving automobiles.

A second waiting-line characteristic deals with *queue discipline*. This refers to the rule by which customers in the line are to receive service. Most systems use a queue discipline known as the **first-in, first-out (FIFO) rule**. In a hospital emergency room or an express checkout line at a supermarket, however, various assigned priorities may preempt FIFO. Patients who are critically injured will move ahead in treatment priority over patients with broken fingers or noses. Shoppers with fewer than 10 items may be allowed to enter the express checkout queue (but are *then* treated as first-come, first-served). Computer-programming runs also operate under priority scheduling. In most large companies, when computer-produced paycheques are due on a specific date, the payroll program gets highest priority.[2] Please see the video case, "The Winter Park Hotel" at the end of the chapter.

First-in, first-out (FIFO) rule
A queue discipline in which the first customers in line receive the first service.

SERVICE CHARACTERISTICS

The third part of any queuing system is the service characteristics. Two basic properties are important: (1) design of the service system and (2) the distribution of service times.

BASIC QUEUING SYSTEM DESIGNS Service systems are usually classified in terms of their number of channels (e.g., number of servers) and number of phases (e.g., number of service stops that must be made). See Figure D.3. A **single-channel queuing system**, with one server, is typified by the drive-in bank with only one open teller. If, on the other hand, the bank has several tellers

Single-channel queuing system
A service system with one line and one server.

[2] The term *FIFS* (first-in, first-served) is often used in place of FIFO. Another discipline, LIFS (last-in, first-served), also called last-in, first-out (LIFO), is common when material is stacked or piled so that the items on top are used first.

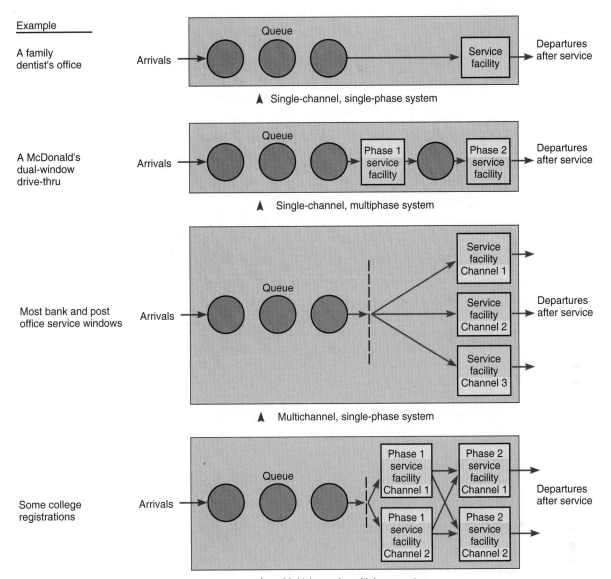

FIGURE D.3 Basic Queuing System Designs

on duty, with each customer waiting in one common line for the first available teller, then we would have a **multiple-channel queuing system**. Most banks today are multichannel service systems, as are most large barbershops, airline ticket counters, and post offices.

In a **single-phase system**, the customer receives service from only one station and then exits the system. A fast-food restaurant in which the person who takes your order also brings your food and takes your money is a single-phase system. So is a driver's licence agency in which the person taking your application also grades your test and collects your licence fee. However, say the restaurant requires you to place your order at one station, pay at a second, and pick up your food at a third. In this case, it is a **multiphase system**. Likewise, if the driver's licence agency is large or busy, you will probably have to wait in one line to complete your application (the first service stop), queue again to have your test graded, and finally go to a third counter to pay your fee. To help you relate the concepts of channels and phases, Figure D.3 presents these four possible channel configurations.

SERVICE TIME DISTRIBUTION Service patterns are like arrival patterns in that they may be either constant or random. If service time is constant, it takes the same amount of time to look after each customer. This is the case in a machine-performed service operation such as an automatic car wash. More often, service times are randomly distributed. In many cases, we can assume that random service times are described by the **negative exponential probability distribution**.

Multiple-channel queuing system

A service system with one waiting line but with several servers.

Single-phase system

A system in which the customer receives service from only one station and then exits the system.

Multiphase system

A system in which the customer receives services from several stations before exiting the system.

Negative exponential probability distribution

A continuous probability distribution often used to describe the service time in a queuing system.

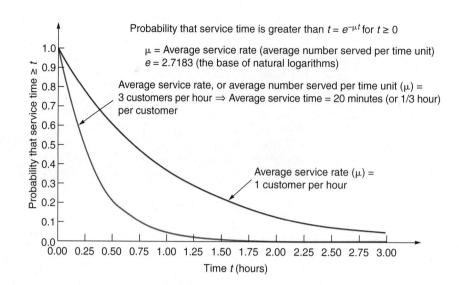

Figure D.4 shows that if *service times* follow a negative exponential distribution, the probability of any very long service time is low. For example, when an average service time is 20 minutes (or three customers per hour), seldom if ever will a customer require more than 1.5 hours in the service facility. If the mean service time is 1 hour, the probability of spending more than 3 hours in service is quite low.

MEASURING A QUEUE'S PERFORMANCE

Queuing models help managers make decisions that balance service costs with waiting-line costs. Queuing analysis can obtain many measures of a waiting-line system's performance, including the following:

1. Average time that each customer or object spends in the queue.
2. Average queue length.
3. Average time that each customer spends in the system (waiting time plus service time).
4. Average number of customers in the system.
5. Probability that the service facility will be idle.
6. Utilization factor for the system.
7. Probability of a specific number of customers in the system.

Queuing Costs

As described in the *OM in Action* box "Belairdirect Puts Its Money Where Its Mouth Is," operations managers must recognize the trade-off that takes place between two costs: the cost of providing good service and the cost of customer or machine waiting time. Managers want queues that are short enough so that customers do not become unhappy and either leave without buying or buy but never return. However, managers may be willing to allow some waiting if it is balanced by a significant savings in service costs.

One means of evaluating a service facility is to look at total expected cost. Total cost is the sum of expected service costs plus expected waiting costs.

As you can see in Figure D.5, service costs increase as a firm attempts to raise its level of service. Managers in *some* service centres can vary capacity by having standby personnel and machines that they can assign to specific service stations to prevent or shorten excessively long lines. In grocery stores, for example, managers and stock clerks can open extra checkout counters. In banks and airport check-in points, part-time workers may be called in to help. As the level of service improves (i.e., speeds up), however, the cost of time spent waiting in lines decreases (refer to Figure D.5). Waiting cost may reflect lost productivity of workers while tools or machines await repairs or may simply be an estimate of the cost of customers lost because of poor service and long queues. In some service systems (e.g., an emergency ambulance service), the cost of long waiting lines may be intolerably high.

OM in Action Belairdirect Puts Its Money Where Its Mouth Is

Customers often express dissatisfaction when contacting call centres, suggesting that they experience long waiting times, being left on hold, and being forced to deal with rude or untrained employees. In the home and auto insurance arena, clients will occasionally express concern that the insurance company is quick to accept their insurance premium but slow to react when a claim is being made. Belair Insurance Company, through Belairdirect call centres, is striving to reduce these types of complaints and in so doing position the firm as a leader in providing excellent customer service.

To achieve this, Belair has put forward a service guarantee. For claims service, it provides toll-free telephone access 24 hours per day, 7 days per week. It also guarantees that within 30 minutes of a client's first telephone call on a claim, a Belairdirect claims representative will respond and confirm the coverage, and provide emergency support and advice. If Belairdirect is unable to respond within 30 minutes, it will write the client a cheque for the amount of the annual premium up to a maximum of $1000. So it is more than lip service the company is paying. It is a meaningful guarantee that pays real money!

Source: www.belairdirect.com; www.belairdirect.com/english/ontario/claims/claims_service_guarantee.htm.

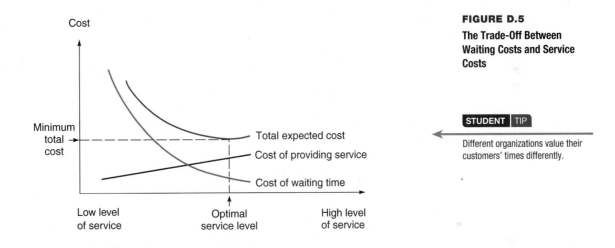

FIGURE D.5

The Trade-Off Between Waiting Costs and Service Costs

> **STUDENT | TIP**
>
> Different organizations value their customers' times differently.

The Variety of Queuing Models

> **STUDENT | TIP**
>
> This is the main section of Module D. We illustrate four important queuing models.

A wide variety of queuing models may be applied in operations management. We will introduce you to four of the most widely used models. These are outlined in Table D.2, and examples of each follow in the next few sections. More complex models are described in queuing theory

Table D.2
Queuing Models Described in This Module

Model	Name (technical name)	Example	Number of Channels	Number of Phases	Arrival Rate Pattern	Service Time Pattern	Population Size	Queue Discipline
A	Single-channel system (M/M/1)	Information counter at department store	Single	Single	Poisson	Exponential	Unlimited	FIFO
B	Multichannel (M/M/S)	Airline ticket counter	Multi-channel	Single	Poisson	Exponential	Unlimited	FIFO
C	Constant service (M/D/1)	Automated car wash	Single	Single	Poisson	Constant	Unlimited	FIFO
D	Limited population (finite population)	Shop with only a dozen machines that might break	Single	Single	Poisson	Exponential	Limited	FIFO

textbooks[3] or can be developed through the use of simulation (the topic of Module F). Note that all four queuing models listed in Table D.2 have three characteristics in common. They all assume:

1. Poisson distribution arrivals
2. FIFO discipline
3. A single-service phase

In addition, they all describe service systems that operate under steady, ongoing conditions. This means that arrival and service rates remain stable during the analysis.

MODEL A (M/M/1): SINGLE-CHANNEL QUEUING MODEL WITH POISSON ARRIVALS AND EXPONENTIAL SERVICE TIMES

LO2 Apply the single-channel queuing model equations

The most common case of queuing problems involves the *single-channel*, or single-server, waiting line. In this situation, arrivals form a single line to be serviced by a single station (see Figure D.3). We assume that the following conditions exist in this type of system:

1. Arrivals are served on a first-in, first-out (FIFO) basis, and every arrival waits to be served, regardless of the length of the line or queue.
2. Arrivals are independent of preceding arrivals, but the average number of arrivals (*arrival rate*) does not change over time.
3. Arrivals are described by a Poisson probability distribution and come from an infinite (or very, very large) population.
4. Service times vary from one customer to the next and are independent of one another, but their average rate is known.
5. Service times occur according to the negative exponential probability distribution.
6. The service rate is faster than the arrival rate.

The giant Moscow McDonald's boasts 900 seats, 800 workers, and $80 million in annual sales (versus approximately $2 million in a Canadian outlet). North Americans would balk at the average waiting time of 45 minutes, but Russians are used to such long lines. McDonald's represents good service in Moscow.

Roy/Science Source

---

[3] See, for example, John F. Shortle et al., *Fundamentals of Queuing Theory*, 4th ed. (New York, NY: Wiley, 2008).

Table D.3
Queuing Formulas for Model A: Single-Channel System, Also Called M/M/1

λ = mean number of arrivals per time period

μ = mean number of people or items served per time period

L_s = average number of units (customers) in the system (waiting and being served)

$$= \frac{\lambda}{\mu - \lambda}$$

W_s = average time a unit spends in the system (waiting time plus service time)

$$= \frac{1}{\mu - \lambda}$$

L_q = average number of units waiting in the queue

$$= \frac{\lambda^2}{\mu(\mu - \lambda)}$$

W_q = average time a unit spends waiting in the queue

$$= \frac{\lambda}{\mu(\mu - \lambda)} = \frac{L_q}{\lambda}$$

ρ = utilization factor for the system

$$= \frac{\lambda}{\mu}$$

P_0 = probability of 0 units in the system (i.e., the service unit is idle)

$$= 1 - \frac{\lambda}{\mu}$$

$P_{n>k}$ = probability of more than k units in the system, where n is the number of units in the system

$$= 1\left(\frac{\lambda}{\mu}\right)^{k+1}$$

When these conditions are met, the series of equations shown in Table D.3 can be developed. Examples D1 and D2 illustrate how Model A (which in technical journals is known as the M/M/1 model) may be used.[4]

EXAMPLE **D1**

A Single-Channel Queue

Tom Jones, the mechanic at Golden Muffler Shop, is able to install new mufflers at an average rate of three per hour (or about one every 20 minutes), according to a negative exponential distribution. Customers seeking this service arrive at the shop on the average of two per hour, following a Poisson distribution. They are served on a first-in, first-out basis and come from a very large (almost infinite) population of possible buyers.

We would like to obtain the operating characteristics of Golden Muffler's queuing system.

APPROACH ▶ This is a single-channel (M/M/1) system and we apply the formulas in Table D.3.

SOLUTION ▶

$$\lambda = 2 \text{ cars arriving per hour}$$
$$\mu = 3 \text{ cars serviced per hour}$$

$$L_s = \frac{\lambda}{\mu - \lambda} = \frac{2}{3 - 2} = \frac{2}{1}$$

$$= 2 \text{ cars in the system, on average}$$

$$W_s = \frac{1}{\mu - \lambda} = \frac{1}{3 - 2} = 1$$

$$= 1 \text{ hour (average time in the system)}$$

$$L_q = \frac{\lambda^2}{\mu(\mu - \lambda)} = \frac{2^2}{3(3 - 2)} = \frac{4}{3(1)} = \frac{4}{3}$$

$$= 1.33 \text{ car waiting in line, on average}$$

---

[4] In queuing notation, the first letter refers to the arrivals (where M stands for Poisson distribution); the second letter refers to service (where M is again a Poisson distribution, which is the same as an exponential rate for service—and a D is a constant service rate); the third symbol refers to the number of servers. So an M/D/1 system (our Model C) has Poisson arrivals, constant service, and one server.

$$W_q = \frac{\lambda}{\mu(\mu - \lambda)} = \frac{2}{3(3 - 2)} = \frac{2}{3} \text{ hour}$$

$$= \text{40-minute average waiting time per car}$$

$$\rho = \frac{\lambda}{\mu} = \frac{2}{3}$$

$$= 66.6\% \text{ of time mechanic is busy}$$

$$P_0 = 1 - \frac{\lambda}{\mu} = 1 - \frac{2}{3}$$

$$= 0.33 \text{ probability there are 0 cars in the system}$$

Probability of More than _k_ Cars in the System

k	$\mathbf{P}_{n>k} = (2/3)^{k+1}$
0	0.667 ← Note that this is equal to $1 - P_0 = 1 - 0.33 = 0.667$
1	0.444
2	0.296
3	0.198 ← Implies that there is a 19.8% chance that more than three cars are in the system.
4	0.132
5	0.088
6	0.058
7	0.039

INSIGHT ▶ Recognize that arrival and service times are converted to the same rate. For example, a service time of 20 minutes is stated as an average *rate* of three mufflers *per hour*. It's also important to differentiate between time in the *queue* and time in the *system*.

LEARNING EXERCISE ▶ If $\mu = 4$ cars/hour instead of the current 3 arrivals, what are the new values of L_s, W_s, L_q, W_q, and P_0? [Answer: 1 car, 30 min., 0.5 cars, 15 min., 50%, 0.50.]

RELATED PROBLEMS ▶ D.1, D.2, D.3, D.4, D.6, D.7, D.8, D.9a–e, D.10, D.11a–c, D.12a–d.

EXCEL OM Data File **ModDExD1.xlsx** can be found at **MyLab Operations Management**.

ACTIVE MODEL D.1 This example is further illustrated in Active Model D.1 at **MyLab Operations Management**.

Once we have computed the operating characteristics of a queuing system, it is often important to do an economic analysis of their impact. Although the waiting-line model described above is valuable in predicting potential waiting times, queue lengths, idle times, and so on, it does not identify optimal decisions or consider cost factors. As we saw earlier, the solution to a queuing problem may require management to make a trade-off between the increased cost of providing better service and the decreased waiting costs derived from providing that service.

Example D2 examines the costs involved in Example D1.

EXAMPLE **D2**

Economic Analysis of Example D1

LO3 Conduct a cost analysis for a waiting line

Golden Muffler Shop's owner is interested in cost factors as well as the queuing parameters computed in Example D1. He estimates that the cost of customer waiting time, in terms of customer dissatisfaction and lost goodwill, is $15 per hour spent *waiting* in line. Jones, the mechanic, is paid $11 per hour.

APPROACH ▶ First compute the average daily customer waiting time, then the daily salary for Jones, and finally the total expected cost.

SOLUTION ▶ Because the average car has a $\frac{2}{3}$-hour wait (W_q) and because there are approximately 16 cars serviced per day (two arrivals per hour multiplied by eight working hours per day), the total number of hours that customers spend waiting each day for mufflers to be installed is:

$$\frac{2}{3}(16) = \frac{32}{3} = 10\frac{2}{3} \text{ hour}$$

Hence, in this case:

$$\text{Customer waiting-time cost} = \$15 \left(10\frac{2}{3} \right) = \$160 \text{ per day}$$

The only other major cost that Golden's owner can identify in the queuing situation is the salary of Jones, the mechanic, who earns $11 per hour, or $88 per day. Thus:

$$\begin{aligned} \text{Total expected costs} &= \$160 + \$88 \\ &= \$248 \text{ per day} \end{aligned}$$

This approach will be useful in Solved Problem D.2.

INSIGHT ▶ L_q and W_q are the two most important queuing parameters when it comes to cost analysis. Calculating customer wait times, we note, is based on average time waiting in the queue (W_q) times the number of arrivals per hour (λ) times the number of hours per day. This is because this example is set on a daily basis. This is the same as using L_q, since $L_q = W_q\lambda$.

LEARNING EXERCISE ▶ If the customer waiting time is actually $20 per hour and Jones gets a salary increase to $15 per hour, what are the total daily expected costs? [Answer: $333.33.]

RELATED PROBLEMS ▶ D.12e–f, D.13, D.22, D.23, D.24

MODEL B (M/M/S): MULTIPLE-CHANNEL QUEUING MODEL

Now let's turn to a multiple-channel queuing system in which two or more servers or channels are available to handle arriving customers. We still assume that customers awaiting service form one single line and then proceed to the first available server. Multichannel, single-phase waiting lines are found in many banks today: A common line is formed, and the customer at the head of the line proceeds to the first free teller. (Refer to Figure D.3 for a typical multichannel configuration.)

The multiple-channel system presented in Example D3 again assumes that arrivals follow a Poisson probability distribution and that service times are exponentially distributed. Service is first-come, first-served, and all servers are assumed to perform at the same rate. Other assumptions listed earlier for the single-channel model also apply.

The queuing equations for Model B (technical name M/M/S) are shown in Table D.4. These equations are obviously more complex than those used in the single-channel model; yet they are used in exactly the same fashion and provide the same type of information as the simpler model. (*Note:* The POM for Windows and Excel OM software described later in this chapter can prove very useful in solving multiple-channel as well as other queuing problems.)

LO4 Apply the multiple-channel queuing model formulas

Photo Courtesy of Costco Wholesale, 2012

To shorten queues, each Costco register is staffed with two servers. This approach, along with new checkout technology, has enabled Costco to serve more customers: The numbers have gone from 37 to 45 customers per register each hour.

Table D.4
Queuing Formulas for Model B: Multichannel System, Also Called M/M/S

Number of channels open = M
Average arrival rate = λ
Average service rate at each channel = μ
Probability that there are zero people or units in the system =

$$P_0 = \frac{1}{\left[\sum_{n=0}^{M-1} \frac{1}{n!}\left(\frac{\lambda}{\mu}\right)^n\right] + \frac{1}{M!}\left(\frac{\lambda}{\mu}\right)^M \frac{M\mu}{M\mu - \lambda}} \quad \text{for } M\mu > \lambda$$

Average number of people or units in the system =

$$L_s = \frac{\lambda\mu(\lambda/\mu)^M}{(M-1)!(M\mu - \lambda)^2} P_0 + \frac{\lambda}{\mu}$$

Average time a unit spends in the waiting line and being serviced (namely, in the system) =

$$W_s = \frac{\mu(\lambda/\mu)^M}{(M-1)!(M\mu - \lambda)^2} P_0 + \frac{1}{\mu} = \frac{L_s}{\lambda}$$

Average number of people or units in line waiting for service = $L_q = L_s - \dfrac{\lambda}{\mu}$

Average time a person or unit spends in the queue waiting for service = $W_q = W_s - \dfrac{1}{\mu} = \dfrac{L_q}{\lambda}$

EXAMPLE D3

A Multiple-Channel Queue

The Golden Muffler Shop has decided to open a second garage bay and hire a second mechanic to handle installations. Customers, who arrive at the rate of about $\lambda = 2$ per hour, will wait in a single line until one of the two mechanics is free. Each mechanic installs mufflers at the rate of about $\mu = 3$ per hour.

The company wants to find out how this system compares with the old single-channel waiting-line system.

APPROACH ▶ Compute several operating characteristics for the $M = 2$ channel system, using the equations in Table D.4, and compare the results with those found in Example D1.

SOLUTION ▶

$$P_0 = \frac{1}{\left[\sum_{n=0}^{1} \frac{1}{n!}\left(\frac{2}{3}\right)^n\right] + \frac{1}{2!}\left(\frac{2}{3}\right)^2 \frac{2(3)}{2(3) - 2}}$$

$$= \frac{1}{1 + \frac{2}{3} + \frac{1}{2}\left(\frac{4}{9}\right)\left(\frac{6}{6-2}\right)} = \frac{1}{1 + \frac{2}{3} + \frac{1}{3}} = \frac{1}{2}$$

$$= 0.5 \text{ probability of 0 cars in the system}$$

Then:

$$L_s = \frac{(2)(3)(2/3)^2}{1![2(3) - 2]^2}\left(\frac{1}{2}\right) + \frac{2}{3} = \frac{8/3}{16}\left(\frac{1}{2}\right) + \frac{2}{3} = \frac{3}{4}$$

$$= 0.75 \text{ average number of cars in the system}$$

$$W_s = \frac{L_s}{\lambda} = \frac{3/4}{2} = \frac{3}{8} \text{ hour}$$

$$= 22.5 \text{ minutes average time a car spends in the system}$$

$$L_q = L_s - \frac{\lambda}{\mu} = \frac{3}{4} - \frac{2}{3} = \frac{9}{12} - \frac{8}{12} = \frac{1}{12}$$

$$= 0.083 \text{ average number of cars in the queue (waiting)}$$

$$W_q = \frac{L_q}{\lambda} = \frac{0.083}{2} = 0.0415 \text{ hour}$$

$$= 2.5 \text{ minutes average time a car spends in the queue (waiting)}$$

INSIGHT ▶ It is very interesting to see the big differences in service performance when an additional server is added.

LEARNING EXERCISE ▶ If $\mu = 4$ per hour, instead of $\mu = 3$, what are the new values for P_0, L_s, W_s, L_q, and W_q? [Answers: 0.6, 0.53 cars, 16 min, 0.033 cars, 1 min.]

RELATED PROBLEMS ▶ D.7h, D.9f, D.11d, D.15, D.20

EXCEL OM Data File **ModDExD3.xlsx** can be found at **MyLab Operations Management.**

ACTIVE MODEL D.2 This example is further illustrated in Active Model D.2 at MyLab Operations Management.

We can summarize the characteristics of the two-channel model in Example D3 and compare them to those of the single-channel model in Example D1 as follows:

	Single Channel	Two Channels
P_0	0.33	0.5
L_s	2 cars	0.75 car
W_s	60 minutes	22.5 minutes
L_q	1.33 cars	0.083 car
W_q	40 minutes	2.5 minutes

The increased service has a dramatic effect on almost all characteristics. For instance, note that the time spent waiting in line drops from 40 minutes to only 2.5 minutes.

USE OF WAITING-LINE TABLES Imagine the work a manager would face in dealing with $M = 3, 4,$ or 5 channel waiting line models if a computer were not readily available. The arithmetic becomes increasingly troublesome. Fortunately, much of the burden of manually examining multiple-channel queues can be avoided by using Table D.5. This table, the result of hundreds of computations, represents the relationship between three things: (1) a ratio we call ρ ([rho], which is simple to find—it's just λ/μ), (2) number of service channels open, and (3) the average number of customers in the queue, L_q (which is what we'd like to find). For any combination of the ratio ρ and $M = 1, 2, 3, 4,$ or 5 open service channels, you can quickly look in the body of the table to read off the appropriate value for L_q.

Example D4 illustrates the use of Table D.5.

EXAMPLE D4

Use of Waiting Line Tables

The Royal Bank is trying to decide how many drive-in teller windows to open on a busy Saturday. Director of operations Ted Eschenbach estimates that customers arrive at a rate of about $\lambda = 18$ per hour, and that each teller can service about $\mu = 20$ customers per hour.

APPROACH ▶ Ted decides to use Table D.5 to compute L_q and W_q.

SOLUTION ▶ The ratio is $\rho = \lambda/\mu = \frac{18}{20} = 0.90$. Turning to the table, under $\rho = 0.90$, Ted sees that if only $M = 1$ service window is open, the average number of customers in line will be 8.1. If two windows are open, L_q drops to 0.2285 customers, to 0.03 for $M = 3$ tellers, and to 0.0041 for $M = 4$ tellers. Adding more open windows at this point will result in an average queue length of 0.

It is also a simple matter to compute the average waiting time in the queue, W_q, since $W_q = L_q/\lambda$. When one channel is open, $W_q = 8.1$ customers/(18 customers per hour) $= 0.45$ hours $= 27$ minutes of waiting time; when two tellers are open, $W_q = 0.2285$ customers/(18 customers per hour) $= 0.0127$ hours $\cong \frac{3}{4}$ minute; and so on.

INSIGHT ▶ If a computer is not readily available, Table D.5 makes it easy to find L_q and to then compute W_q. Table D.5 is especially handy to compare L_q for different numbers of servers (M).

LEARNING EXERCISE ▶ The number of customers arriving on a Thursday afternoon at the Royal Bank is 15/hour. The service rate is still 20 customers/hour. How many people are in the queue if there are 1, 2, or 3 servers? [Answer: 2.25, 0.1227, 0.0147.]

RELATED PROBLEM ▶ D.5

Table D.5

Values of L_q for $M = 1$–5 Service Channels and Selected Values of $\rho = \lambda/\mu$

	Poisson Arrivals, Exponential Service Times				
	Number of Service Channels, M				
ρ	1	2	3	4	5
0.10	0.0111				
0.15	0.0264	0.0008			
0.20	0.0500	0.0020			
0.25	0.0833	0.0039			
0.30	0.1285	0.0069			
0.35	0.1884	0.0110			
0.40	0.2666	0.0166			
0.45	0.3681	0.0239	0.0019		
0.50	0.5000	0.0333	0.0030		
0.55	0.6722	0.0449	0.0043		
0.60	0.9000	0.0593	0.0061		
0.65	1.2071	0.0767	0.0084		
0.70	1.6333	0.0976	0.0112		
0.75	2.2500	0.1227	0.0147		
0.80	3.2000	0.1523	0.0189		
0.85	4.8166	0.1873	0.0239	0.0031	
0.90	8.1000	0.2285	0.0300	0.0041	
0.95	18.0500	0.2767	0.0371	0.0053	
1.0		0.3333	0.0454	0.0067	
1.2		0.6748	0.0904	0.0158	
1.4		1.3449	0.1778	0.0324	0.0059
1.6		2.8444	0.3128	0.0604	0.0121
1.8		7.6734	0.5320	0.1051	0.0227
2.0			0.8888	0.1739	0.0398
2.2			1.4907	0.2770	0.0659
2.4			2.1261	0.4305	0.1047
2.6			4.9322	0.6581	0.1609
2.8			12.2724	1.0000	0.2411
3.0				1.5282	0.3541
3.2				2.3856	0.5128
3.4				3.9060	0.7365
3.6				7.0893	1.0550
3.8				16.9366	1.5184
4.0					2.2164
4.2					3.3269
4.4					5.2675
4.6					9.2885
4.8					21.6384

You might also wish to check the calculations in Example D3 against tabled values just to practise the use of Table D.5. You may need to interpolate if your exact value is not found in the first column. Other common operating characteristics besides L_q are published in tabular form in queuing theory textbooks.

Long check-in lines (left photo) are a common airport sight. This is an M/M/S model—passengers wait in a single queue for one of several agents. But now most airlines have jettisoned the traditional wall of ticket counters. Instead, millions of passengers per year use self-service check-in machines and staffed "bag drop" stations. Looking nothing like a typical airport, the new system dramatically improves an airline's check-in capacity, cutting staff needs in half, all while speeding travellers through in less than 15 minutes, even during peak hours.

MODEL C (M/D/1): CONSTANT-SERVICE-TIME MODEL

LO5 Apply the constant-service-time model equations

Some service systems have constant, instead of exponentially distributed, service times. When customers or equipment are processed according to a fixed cycle, as in the case of an automatic car wash or an amusement park ride, constant service times are appropriate. Because constant rates are certain, the values for L_q, W_q, L_s, and W_s are always less than they would be in Model A, which has variable service rates. As a matter of fact, both the average queue length and the average waiting time in the queue are halved with Model C. Constant-service-model formulas are given in Table D.6. Model C also has the technical name M/D/1 in the literature of queuing theory.

Table D.6
Queuing Formulas for Model C: Constant Service, Also Called M/D/1

Average length of queue: $L_q = \dfrac{\lambda^2}{2\mu(\mu - \lambda)}$

Average waiting time in queue: $W_q = \dfrac{\lambda}{2\mu(\mu - \lambda)}$

Average number of customers in system: $L_s = L_q + \dfrac{\lambda}{\mu}$

Average time in system: $W_s = W_q + \dfrac{1}{\mu}$

Example D5 gives a constant-service-time analysis.

EXAMPLE D5

A Constant-Service Model

Inman Recycling Inc. collects and compacts aluminum cans and glass bottles in Edmonton, Alberta. Its truck drivers currently wait an average of 15 minutes before emptying their loads for recycling. The cost of driver and truck time while they are in queues is valued at $60 per hour. A new automated compactor can be purchased to process truckloads at a *constant* rate of 12 trucks per hour (i.e. 5 minutes per truck). Trucks arrive according to a Poisson distribution at an average rate of 8 per hour. If the new compactor is put in use, the cost will be amortized at a rate of $3 per truck unloaded.

APPROACH ▶ CEO Tony Inman hires a summer college intern to conduct an analysis to evaluate the costs versus benefits of the purchase. The intern uses the equation for W_q in Table D.6.

SOLUTION ▶

$$\text{Current waiting cost/trip} = (1/4 \text{ hr waiting now})(\$60/\text{hr cost}) = \$15/\text{trip}$$

New system: $\lambda = 8$ trucks/hr arriving $\mu = 12$ trucks/hr served

$$\text{Average waiting time in queue} = W_q = \frac{\lambda}{2\mu(\mu - \lambda)} = \frac{8}{2(12)(12 - 8)} = \frac{1}{12} \text{ hr}$$

$$\text{Waiting cost/trip with new compactor} = (1/12 \text{ hr wait})(\$60/\text{hr cost}) = \$5/\text{trip}$$

$$\text{Savings with new equipment} = \$15(\text{current system}) - \$5(\text{new system}) = \$10/\text{trip}$$

$$\text{Cost of new equipment amortized:} = \$3/\text{trip}$$

$$\text{New savings} = \$7/\text{trip}$$

INSIGHT ▶ Constant service times, usually attained through automation, help control the variability inherent in service systems. This can lower average queue length and average waiting time. Note the 2 in the denominator of the equations for L_q and W_q in Table D.6.

LEARNING EXERCISE ▶ With the new constant-service-time system, what are the average waiting time in the queue, average number of trucks in the system, and average waiting time in the system? [Answer: 0.0833 hours, 1.33, 0.1667 hours.]

RELATED PROBLEMS ▶ D.14, D.16, D.21

EXCEL OM Data File **ModDExD5.xlsx** can be found at **MyLab Operations Management**.

ACTIVE MODEL D.3 This example is further illustrated in Active Model D.3 at MyLab Operations Management.

LITTLE'S LAW

A practical and useful relationship in queuing for any system in a *steady state* is called Little's Law. A steady state exists when a queuing system is in its normal operating condition (e.g., after customers waiting at the door when a business opens in the morning are taken care of). Little's Law can be written as either:

$$L = \lambda W \quad \text{(which is the same as } W = L/\lambda) \tag{D-2}$$

or

$$L_q = \lambda W_q \quad \text{(which is the same as } W_q = L_q/\lambda) \tag{D-3}$$

The advantage of these formulas is that once two of the parameters are known, the other one can easily be found. This is important because in certain waiting-line situations, one of these might be easier to determine than the other.

Little's Law is also important because it makes no assumptions about the probability distributions for arrivals and service times, the number of servers, or service priority rules. The law applies to all the queuing systems discussed in this module, except the limited-population model, which we discuss next.

MODEL D: LIMITED-POPULATION MODEL

LO6 Perform a limited-population model analysis

When there is a limited population of potential customers for a service facility, we must consider a different queuing model. This model would be used, for example, if we were considering equipment repairs in a factory that has five machines, if we were in charge of maintenance for a fleet of 10 commuter airplanes, or if we ran a hospital ward that has 20 beds. The limited-population model allows any number of repair people (servers) to be considered.

This model differs from the three earlier queuing models because there is now a *dependent* relationship between the length of the queue and the arrival rate. Let's illustrate the extreme situation: If your factory had five machines and all were broken and awaiting repair, the arrival rate would drop to zero. In general, then, as the *waiting line* becomes longer in the limited-population model, the *arrival rate* of customers or machines drops.

Table D.7 displays the queuing formulas for the limited-population model. Note that they employ a different notation from Models A, B, and C. To simplify what can become time-consuming calculations, finite queuing tables have been developed that determine D and F. D represents the

Table D.7
Queuing Formulas and Notation for Model D: Limited-Population Formulas

Source: Based on L. G. Peck and R. N. Hazelwood, *Finite Queuing Tables* (New York: Wiley, 1958).

Service factor: $X = \dfrac{T}{T + U}$

Average number running: $J = NF(1 - X)$

Average number waiting: $L = N(1 - F)$

Average number being serviced: $H = FNX$

Average waiting time: $W = \dfrac{L(T + U)}{N - L} = \dfrac{T(1 - F)}{XF}$

Number in population: $N = J + L + H$

Notation

D = probability that a unit will have to wait in queue

N = number of potential customers

F = efficiency factor

T = average service time

H = average number of units being served

U = average time between unit service requirements

J = average number of units not in queue or in service

W = average time a unit waits in line

L = average number of units waiting for service

X = service factor

M = number of service channels

probability that a machine needing repair will have to wait in line. F is a waiting-time efficiency factor. D and F are needed to compute most of the other finite model formulas.

A small part of the published finite queuing tables is illustrated in this section. Table D.8 provides data for a population of $N = 5$.[5]

To use Table D.8, we follow four steps:

1. Compute X (the service factor), where $X = T/(T + U)$.
2. Find the value of X in the table and then find the line for M (where M is the number of service channels).
3. Note the corresponding values for D and F.
4. Compute L, W, J, H, or whichever are needed to measure the service system's performance.

Example D6 illustrates these steps.

This isn't Disney World, where waits are made tolerable—or even fun—via amusements and entertainment. This long line of frustrated customers is a frequent sight at many government service outlets. How could the principles in this module be used to improve this queuing system?

Stephen J. Carrera/AP Images

---

[5] Limited, or finite, queuing tables are available to handle arrival populations of up to 250. Although there is no definite number that we can use as a dividing point between limited and unlimited populations, the general rule is this: If the number in the queue is a significant proportion of the arrival population, use a limited-population queuing model. For a complete set of *N*-values, see L. G. Peck and R. N. Hazelwood, *Finite Queuing Tables* (New York, NY: Wiley, 1958).

Table D.8
Finite Queuing Tables for a Population of $N = 5$*

X	M	D	F	X	M	D	F	X	M	D	F	X	M	D	F	X	M	D	F
0.012	1	0.048	0.999		1	0.404	0.945		1	0.689	0.801	0.330	4	0.012	0.999		3	0.359	0.927
0.019	1	0.076	0.998	0.110	2	0.065	0.996	0.210	3	0.032	0.998		3	0.112	0.986	0.520	2	0.779	0.728
0.025	1	0.100	0.997		1	0.421	0.939		2	0.211	0.973		2	0.442	0.904		1	0.988	0.384
0.030	1	0.120	0.996	0.115	2	0.071	0.995		1	0.713	0.783		1	0.902	0.583	0.540	4	0.085	0.989
0.034	1	0.135	0.995		1	0.439	0.933	0.220	3	0.036	0.997	0.340	4	0.013	0.999		3	0.392	0.917
0.036	1	0.143	0.994	0.120	2	0.076	0.995		2	0.229	0.969		3	0.121	0.985		2	0.806	0.708
0.040	1	0.159	0.993		1	0.456	0.927		1	0.735	0.765		2	0.462	0.896		1	0.991	0.370
0.042	1	0.167	0.992	0.125	2	0.082	0.994	0.230	3	0.041	0.997		1	0.911	0.569	0.560	4	0.098	0.986
0.044	1	0.175	0.991		1	0.473	0.920		2	0.247	0.965	0.360	4	0.017	0.998		3	0.426	0.906
0.046	1	0.183	0.990	0.130	2	0.089	0.933		1	0.756	0.747		3	0.141	0.981		2	0.831	0.689
0.050	1	0.198	0.989		1	0.489	0.914	0.240	3	0.046	0.996		2	0.501	0.880		1	0.993	0.357
0.052	1	0.206	0.988	0.135	2	0.095	0.993		2	0.265	0.960		1	0.927	0.542	0.580	4	0.113	0.984
0.054	1	0.214	0.987		1	0.505	0.907		1	0.775	0.730	0.380	4	0.021	0.998		3	0.461	0.895
0.056	2	0.018	0.999	0.140	2	0.102	0.992	0.250	3	0.052	0.995		3	0.163	0.976		2	0.854	0.670
	1	0.222	0.985		1	0.521	0.900		2	0.284	0.955		2	0.540	0.863		1	0.994	0.345
0.058	2	0.019	0.999	0.145	3	0.011	0.999		1	0.794	0.712		1	0.941	0.516	0.600	4	0.130	0.981
	1	0.229	0.984		2	0.109	0.991	0.260	3	0.058	0.994	0.400	4	0.026	0.977		3	0.497	0.883
0.060	2	0.020	0.999		1	0.537	0.892		2	0.303	0.950		3	0.186	0.972		2	0.875	0.652
	1	0.237	0.983	0.150	3	0.012	0.999		1	0.811	0.695		2	0.579	0.845		1	0.996	0.333
0.062	2	0.022	0.999		2	0.115	0.990	0.270	3	0.064	0.994		1	0.952	0.493	0.650	4	0.179	0.972
	1	0.245	0.982		1	0.553	0.885		2	0.323	0.944	0.420	4	0.031	0.997		3	0.588	0.850
0.064	2	0.023	0.999	0.155	3	0.013	0.999		1	0.827	0.677		3	0.211	0.966		2	0.918	0.608
	1	0.253	0.981		2	0.123	0.989	0.280	3	0.071	0.993		2	0.616	0.826		1	0.998	0.308
0.066	2	0.024	0.999		1	0.568	0.877		2	0.342	0.938		1	0.961	0.471	0.700	4	0.240	0.960
	1	0.260	0.979	0.160	3	0.015	0.999		1	0.842	0.661	0.440	4	0.037	0.996		3	0.678	0.815
0.068	2	0.026	0.999		2	0.130	0.988	0.290	4	0.007	0.999		3	0.238	0.960		2	0.950	0.568
	1	0.268	0.978		1	0.582	0.869		3	0.079	0.992		2	0.652	0.807		1	0.999	0.286
0.070	2	0.027	0.999	0.165	3	0.016	0.999		2	0.362	0.932		1	0.969	0.451	0.750	4	0.316	0.944
	1	0.275	0.977		2	0.137	0.987		1	0.856	0.644	0.460	4	0.045	0.995		3	0.763	0.777
0.075	2	0.031	0.999		1	0.597	0.861	0.300	4	0.008	0.999		3	0.266	0.953		2	0.972	0.532
	1	0.294	0.973	0.170	3	0.017	0.999		3	0.086	0.990		2	0.686	0.787	0.800	4	0.410	0.924
0.080	2	0.035	0.998		2	0.145	0.985		2	0.382	0.926		1	0.975	0.432		3	0.841	0.739
	1	0.313	0.969		1	0.611	0.853		1	0.869	0.628	0.480	4	0.053	0.994		2	0.987	0.500
0.085	2	0.040	0.998	0.180	3	0.021	0.999	0.310	4	0.009	0.999		3	0.296	0.945	0.850	4	0.522	0.900
	1	0.332	0.965		2	0.161	0.983		3	0.094	0.989		2	0.719	0.767		3	0.907	0.702
0.090	2	0.044	0.998		1	0.638	0.836		2	0.402	0.919		1	0.980	0.415		2	0.995	0.470
	1	0.350	0.960	0.190	3	0.024	0.998		1	0.881	0.613	0.500	4	0.063	0.992	0.900	4	0.656	0.871
0.095	2	0.049	0.997		2	0.117	0.980	0.320	4	0.010	0.999		3	0.327	0.936		3	0.957	0.666
	1	0.368	0.955		1	0.665	0.819		3	0.103	0.988		2	0.750	0.748		2	0.998	0.444
0.100	2	0.054	0.997	0.200	3	0.028	0.998		2	0.422	0.912		1	0.985	0.399	0.950	4	0.815	0.838
	1	0.386	0.950	0.200	2	0.194	0.976		1	0.892	0.597	0.520	4	0.073	0.991		3	0.989	0.631
0.105	2	0.059	0.997						0										

*See notation in Table D.7.

Past records indicate that each of the five massive laser computer printers at the Ministry of Health in Ottawa needs repair after about 20 hours of use. Breakdowns have been determined to be Poisson distributed. The one technician on duty can service a printer in an average of two hours, following an exponential distribution. Printer downtime costs $120 per hour. Technicians are paid $25 per hour. Should the Ministry of Health hire a second technician?

APPROACH ▶ Assuming the second technician can also repair a printer in an average of two hours, we can use Table D.8 (because there are $N = 5$ machines in this limited population) to compare the costs of one versus two technicians.

SOLUTION ▶
1. First, we note that $T = 2$ hours and $U = 20$ hours.
2. Then, $X = \dfrac{T}{T + U} = \dfrac{2}{2 + 20} = \dfrac{2}{22} = 0.091$ (close to 0.090 [to use for determining D and F]).
3. For $M = 1$ server, $D = 0.350$ and $F = 0.960$.
4. For $M = 2$ servers, $D = 0.044$ and $F = 0.998$.
5. The average number of printers working is $J = NF(1 - X)$.
   For $M = 1$, this is $J = (5)(0.960)(1 - 0.091) = 4.36$.
   For $M = 2$, it is $J = (5)(0.998)(1 - 0.091) = 4.54$.
6. The cost analysis follows:

Number of Technicians	Average Number Printers Down $(N - J)$	Average Cost/Hr for Downtime $(N - J)(\$120/hr)$	Cost/Hr. for Technicians	Total Cost/hr
1	0.64	$76.80	$25.00	$101.80
2	0.46	$55.20	$50.00	$105.20

INSIGHT ▶ This analysis suggests that having only one technician on duty will save a few dollars per hour ($105.20 − $101.80 = $3.402). This may seem like a small amount, but it adds up to over $7000 per year.

LEARNING EXERCISE ▶ The Ministry of Health has just replaced its printers with a new model that seems to break down after about 18 hours of use. Recompute the costs. [Answer: For $M = 1, F = 0.95, J = 4.275$, total cost/hr = $112.00, and $D = 0.386$. For $M = 2, F = 0.997$, $J = 4.487$, total cost/hr = $111.56 and $D = 0.054$.]

RELATED PROBLEMS ▶ D.17, D.18, D.19

Other Queuing Approaches

Many practical waiting-line problems that occur in service systems have characteristics like those of the four mathematical models already described. Often, however, *variations* of these specific cases are present in an analysis. Service times in an automobile repair shop, for example, tend to follow the normal probability distribution instead of the exponential. A college registration system in which seniors have first choice of courses and hours over other students is an example of a first-come, first-served model with a preemptive priority queue discipline. A physical examination for military recruits is an example of a multiphase system, one that differs from the single-phase models discussed earlier in this module. A recruit first lines up to have blood drawn at one station, then waits for an eye exam at the next station, talks to a psychiatrist at the third, and is examined by a doctor for medical problems at the fourth. At each phase, the recruit must enter another queue and wait his or her turn. Many models, some very complex, have been developed to deal with situations such as these.

When the assumptions of the four models we just introduced do not hold true, there are other approaches still available to us.

MODULE SUMMARY

Queues are an important part of the world of operations management. In this module, we describe several common queuing systems and present mathematical models for analyzing them.

The most widely used queuing models include Model A, the basic single-channel, single-phase system with Poisson arrivals and exponential service times; Model B, the multichannel equivalent of Model A; Model C, a constant-service-rate model; and Model D, a limited-population system. All four models allow for Poisson arrivals; first-in, first-out service; and a single-service phase. Typical operating characteristics we examine include average time spent waiting in the queue and system, average number of customers in the queue and system, idle time, and utilization rate.

A variety of queuing models exists for which all the assumptions of the traditional models need not be met. In these cases, we use more complex mathematical models or turn to a technique called *simulation*. The application of simulation to problems of queuing systems is addressed in Module F.

Discussion Questions

1. Name the three parts of a typical queuing system.
2. When designing a waiting-line system, what "qualitative" concerns need to be considered?
3. Name the three factors that govern the structure of "arrivals" in a queuing system.
4. State the seven common measures of queuing system performance.
5. State the assumptions of the "basic" single-channel queuing model (Model A, or M/M/1).
6. Is it good or bad to operate a supermarket bakery system on a strict first-come, first-served basis? Why?
7. Describe what is meant by the waiting-line terms *balk* and *renege*. Provide an example of each.
8. Which is larger, W_s or W_q? Explain.
9. Briefly describe three situations in which the first-in, first-out (FIFO) discipline rule is not applicable in queuing analysis.
10. Describe the behaviour of a waiting line where $\lambda > \mu$. Use both analysis and intuition.
11. Discuss the likely outcome of a waiting-line system where $\mu > \lambda$ but only by a tiny amount (e.g., $\mu = 4.1, \lambda = 4$).
12. Provide examples of four situations in which there is a limited, or finite, waiting line.
13. What are the components of the following queuing systems? Draw and explain the configuration of each.
    a) Barbershop
    b) Car wash
    c) Laundromat
    d) Small grocery store
14. Do doctors' offices generally have random arrival rates for patients? Are service times random? Under what circumstances might service times be constant?
15. What happens if two single-channel systems have the same mean arrival and service rates, but the service time is constant in one and exponential in the other?
16. What dollar value do you place on yourself per hour that you spend waiting in lines? What value do your classmates place on themselves? Why do the values differ?
17. Why is Little's Law a useful queuing concept?

Using Software to Solve Queuing Problems

Both Excel OM and POM for Windows may be used to analyze all but the last two homework problems in this module.

X USING EXCEL OM

Excel OM's Waiting-Line program handles all four of the models developed in this module. Program D.1 illustrates our first model, the M/M/1 system, using the data from Example D1.

P USING POM FOR WINDOWS

There are several POM for Windows queuing models from which to select in that program's Waiting-Line module. The program can include an economic analysis of cost data, and, as an option, you may display probabilities of various numbers of people/items in the system. See Appendix IV for further details.

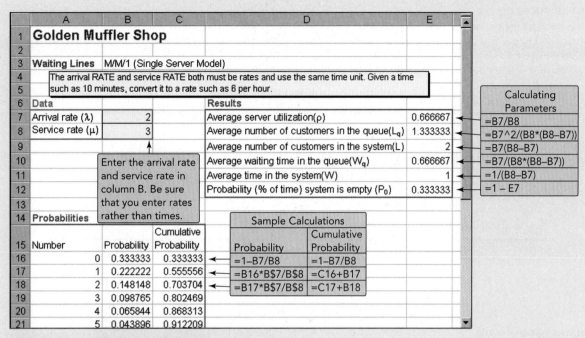

PROGRAM D.1 Using Excel OM for Queuing

Example D1's (Golden Muffler Shop) data are illustrated in the M/M/1 model.

Source: Microsoft product screen shot(s) reprinted with permission from Microsoft Corporation.

Solved Problems Virtual Office Hours help is available at MyLab Operations Management.

▼ SOLVED PROBLEM D.1

Sid Das Brick Distributors currently employs one worker whose job is to load bricks on outgoing company trucks. An average of 24 trucks per day, or three per hour, arrive at the loading platform, according to a Poisson distribution. The worker loads them at a rate of four trucks per hour, following approximately the exponential distribution in his service times.

Das believes that adding an additional brick loader will substantially improve the firm's productivity. He estimates that a two-person crew loading each truck will double the loading rate (μ) from four trucks per hour to eight trucks per hour. Analyze the effect on the queue of such a change and compare the results to those achieved with one worker. What is the probability that there will be more than three trucks either being loaded or waiting?

▼ SOLUTION

	Number of Brick Loaders	
	1	**2**
Truck arrival rate (λ)	3/hr	3/hr
Loading rate (μ)	4/hr	8/hr
Average number in system (L_s)	3 trucks	0.6 truck
Average time in system (W_s)	1 hr	0.2 hr
Average number in queue (L_q)	2.25 trucks	0.225 truck
Average time in queue (W_q)	0.75 hr	0.075 hr
Utilization rate (ρ)	0.75	0.375
Probability system empty (P_0)	0.25	0.625

Probability of More Than k Trucks in System

	Probability $> k$	
k	**One Loader**	**Two Loaders**
0	0.75	0.375
1	0.56	0.141
2	0.42	0.053
3	0.32	0.020

These results indicate that when only one loader is employed, the average truck must wait three-quarters of an hour before it is loaded. Furthermore, there is an average of 2.25 trucks waiting in line to be loaded. This situation may be unacceptable to management. Note also the decline in queue size after the addition of a second loader.

▼ SOLVED PROBLEM D.2

Truck drivers working for Sid Das (see Solved Problem D.1) earn an average of $10 per hour. Brick loaders receive about $6 per hour. Truck drivers waiting *in the queue or at the loading platform* are drawing a salary but are productively idle and unable to generate revenue during that time. What would be the *hourly* cost savings to the firm if it employed two loaders instead of one?

Referring to the data in Solved Problem D.1, we note that the average number of trucks *in the system* is three when there is only one loader and 0.6 when there are two loaders.

▼ SOLUTION

	Number of Loaders	
	1	**2**
Truck driver idle time costs [(Average number of trucks) × (Hourly rate)] =	$30 = (3)($10)	$6 = (0.6)($10)
Loading costs	6	12 = (2)($6)
Total expected cost per hour	$36	$18

The firm will save $18 per hour by adding another loader.

▼ SOLVED PROBLEM D.3

Sid Das is considering building a second platform or gate to speed the process of loading trucks. This system, he thinks, will be even more efficient than simply hiring another loader to help out on the first platform (as in Solved Problem D.1).

Assume that each worker at each platform will be able to load four trucks per hour and that trucks will continue to arrive at the rate of three per hour. Then apply the appropriate equations to find the waiting line's new operating conditions. Is this new approach indeed speedier than the other two that Das has considered?

▼ SOLUTION

$$P_0 = \cfrac{1}{\left[\displaystyle\sum_{n=0}^{1} \frac{1}{n!}\left(\frac{3}{4}\right)^n\right] + \frac{1}{2!}\left(\frac{3}{4}\right)^2 \frac{2(4)}{2(4) - 3}}$$

$$= \cfrac{1}{1 + \frac{3}{4} + \frac{1}{2}\left(\frac{3}{4}\right)^2\left(\frac{8}{8 - 3}\right)} = 0.4545$$

$$L_s = \frac{3(4)(3/4)^2}{(1)!(8 - 3)^2}(0.4545) + \frac{3}{4} = 0.873$$

$$W_s = \frac{0.873}{3} = 0.291 \text{ hr}$$

$$L_q = 0.873 - 3/4 = 0.123$$

$$W_q = \frac{0.123}{3} = 0.041 \text{ hr}$$

Looking back at Solved Problem D.1, we see that although length of the *queue* and average time in the queue are lowest when a second platform is open, the average number of trucks in the *system* and average time spent waiting in the system are smallest when two workers are employed at a *single* platform. Thus, we would probably recommend not building a second platform.

▼ SOLVED PROBLEM D.4

Mount Sinai Hospital's orthopedic care unit has 5 beds, which are virtually always occupied by patients who have just undergone orthopedic surgery. One registered nurse is on duty in the unit in each of the three 8-hour shifts. About every 2 hours (following a Poisson distribution), one of the patients requires a nurse's attention. The nurse will then spend an average of 30 minutes (negative exponentially distributed) assisting the patient and updating medical records regarding the problem and care provided.

Because immediate service is critical to the 5 patients, two important questions are: What is the average number of patients either waiting for or being attended by the nurse? What is the average time that a patient spends waiting for the nurse to arrive?

▼ SOLUTION

$$\lambda = .5 \text{ arrivals/hour}$$

$$\mu = 2 \text{ served/hour}$$

$$N = 5 \text{ patients}$$

$$P_0 = \dfrac{1}{\displaystyle\sum_{n=0}^{5} \dfrac{5!}{(5-n)!}\left(\dfrac{.5}{2}\right)^n} = 0.20$$

$$L_q = 5 - \left(\frac{.5 + 2}{.5}\right)(1 - 0.20) = 1 \text{ patient}$$

$$L_s = 1 + (1 - 0.20) = 1.8 \text{ patients}$$

$$W_q = \frac{1}{(5 - 1.8)(.5)} = .62 \text{ hours} = 37.28 \text{ min.}$$

$$W_s = .62 + \frac{1}{2} = 1.12 \text{ hours} = 67.28 \text{ min}$$

So the average number of patients in the system = 1.8

Average wait time in the queue = .62 hours = 37.28 minutes

Problems*

• **D.1** Customers arrive at Paul Harrold's Styling Shop at a rate of three per hour, distributed in a Poisson fashion. Paul can perform haircuts at a rate of five per hour, distributed exponentially.
a) Find the average number of customers waiting for haircuts.
b) Find the average number of customers in the shop.
c) Find the average time a customer waits until it is his or her turn.
d) Find the average time a customer spends in the shop.
e) Find the percentage of time that Paul is busy. **PX**

• **D.2** There is only one copying machine in the student lounge of the business school. Students arrive at the rate of $\lambda = 40$ per hour (according to a Poisson distribution). Copying takes an average of 40 seconds, or $\mu = 90$ per hour (according to an exponential distribution). Compute the following:
a) The percentage of time that the machine is used.
b) The average length of the queue.
c) The average number of students in the system.
d) The average time spent waiting in the queue.
e) The average time in the system. **PX**

• **D.3** Glen Schmidt owns and manages a chili-dog and soft drink stand near the Simon Fraser campus. While Glen can service 30 customers per hour on the average (μ), he gets only 20 customers per hour (λ). Because Glen could wait on 50% more customers than actually visit his stand, it doesn't make sense to him that he should have any waiting lines.

Glen hires you to examine the situation and to determine some characteristics of his queue. After looking into the problem, you find it follows the six conditions for a single-channel waiting line (as seen in Model A). What are your findings? **PX**

• **D.4** Sam Certo, a Nanaimo vet, is running a rabies vaccination clinic for dogs at the local grade school. Sam can "shoot" a dog every three minutes. It is estimated that the dogs will arrive independently and randomly throughout the day at a rate of one dog every six minutes according to a Poisson distribution. Also assume that Sam's shooting times are exponentially distributed. Compute the following:
a) The probability that Sam is idle.
b) The proportion of the time that Sam is busy.
c) The average number of dogs being vaccinated and waiting to be vaccinated.
d) The average number of dogs waiting to be vaccinated.
e) The average time a dog waits before getting vaccinated.
f) The average amount of time a dog spends waiting in line and being vaccinated. **PX**

•• **D.5** The pharmacist at Saskatoon City Hospital, Saad Alwan, receives 12 requests for prescriptions each hour, Poisson distributed. It takes him a mean time of four minutes to fill each, following a negative exponential distribution. Using the waiting-line table (Table D.5) and $W_q = L_q/\lambda$, answer these questions.
a) What is the average number of prescriptions in the queue?
b) How long will the average prescription spend in the queue?
c) Alwan decides to hire a second pharmacist, Ajay Aggerwal, whom he went to school with and who operates at the same speed in filling prescriptions. How will the answers to parts (a) and (b) change? **PX**

• **D.6** Calls arrive at James Hamann's hotel switchboard at a rate of two per minute. The average time to handle each is 20 seconds. There is only one switchboard operator at the current time. The Poisson and exponential distributions appear to be relevant in this situation.
a) What is the probability that the operator is busy?
b) What is the average time that a customer must wait before reaching the operator?
c) What is the average number of calls waiting to be answered? **PX**

•• **D.7** Automobiles arrive at the drive-through window at the downtown Fort McMurray post office at the rate of four every 10 minutes. The average service time is two minutes. The Poisson distribution is appropriate for the arrival rate and service times are exponentially distributed.
a) What is the average time a car is in the system?
b) What is the average number of cars in the system?
c) What is the average number of cars waiting to receive service?
d) What is the average time a car is in the queue?
e) What is the probability that there are no cars at the window?
f) What percentage of the time is the postal clerk busy?
g) What is the probability that there are exactly two cars in the system?
h) By how much would your answer to part (a) be reduced if a second drive-through window, with its own server, were added? **PX**

• **D.8** Manitoba's Stephen Allen Electronics Corporation retains a service crew to repair machine breakdowns that occur on an average of $\lambda = 3$ per 8-hour workday (approximately Poisson in nature). The crew can service an average of $\mu = 8$ machines per workday, with a repair time distribution that resembles the exponential distribution.
a) What is the utilization rate of this service system?
b) What is the average downtime for a broken machine?
c) How many machines are waiting to be serviced at any given time?
d) What is the probability that more than one machine is in the system? The probability that more than two are broken and waiting to be repaired or being serviced? More than three? More than four? **PX**

---

*Note: **PX** means the problem may be solved with POM for Windows and/or Excel OM.

•• **D.9** Scotiabank is the only bank in the small town of St. Thomas. On a typical Friday, an average of 10 customers per hour arrive at the bank to transact business. There is one teller at the bank, and the average time required to transact business is four minutes. It is assumed that service times may be described by the exponential distribution. A single line would be used, and the customer at the front of the line would go to the first available bank teller. If a single teller is used, find:

a) The average time in the line.
b) The average number in the line.
c) The average time in the system.
d) The average number in the system.
e) The probability that the bank is empty.
f) Scotiabank is considering adding a second teller (who would work at the same rate as the first) to reduce the waiting time for customers. She assumes that this will cut the waiting time in half. If a second teller is added, find the new answers to parts (a) to (e). **PX**

•• **D.10** Susan Slotnick manages a Burlington, Ontario, movie theatre complex called Cinema I, II, III, and IV. Each of the four auditoriums plays a different film; the schedule staggers starting times to avoid the large crowds that would occur if all four movies started at the same time. The theatre has a single ticket booth and a cashier who can maintain an average service rate of 280 patrons per hour. Service times are assumed to follow an exponential distribution. Arrivals on a normally active day are Poisson distributed and average 210 per hour.

To determine the efficiency of the current ticket operation, Susan wishes to examine several queue-operating characteristics.

a) Find the average number of moviegoers waiting in line to purchase a ticket.
b) What percentage of the time is the cashier busy?
c) What is the average time that a customer spends in the system?
d) What is the average time spent waiting in line to get to the ticket window?
e) What is the probability that there are more than two people in the system? More than three people? More than four? **PX**

•• **D.11** Bill Youngdahl has been collecting data at the TU student grill. He has found that, between 5:00 p.m. and 7:00 p.m., students arrive at the grill at a rate of 25 per hour (Poisson distributed) and service time takes an average of two minutes (exponential distribution). There is only one server, who can work on only one order at a time.

a) What is the average number of students in line?
b) What is the average time a student is in the grill area?
c) Suppose that a second server can be added to team up with the first (and, in effect, act as one faster server). This would reduce the average service time to 90 seconds. How would this affect the average time a student is in the grill area?
d) Suppose a second server is added and the two servers act independently, with *each* taking an average of two minutes. What would be the average time a student is in the system? **PX**

••• **D.12** The wheat harvesting season in the Canadian Prairies is short, and farmers deliver their truckloads of wheat to a giant central storage bin within a two-week span. Because of this, wheat-filled trucks waiting to unload and return to the fields have been known to back up for a block at the receiving bin. The central bin is owned cooperatively, and it is to every farmer's benefit to make the unloading/storage process as efficient as possible. The cost of grain deterioration caused by unloading delays and the cost of truck rental and idle driver time are significant concerns to the cooperative members. Although farmers have difficulty quantifying crop damage, it is easy to assign a waiting and unloading cost for truck and driver of $18 per hour. During the two-week harvest season, the storage bin is open and operated 16 hours per day, 7 days per week, and can unload 35 trucks per hour according to an exponential distribution. Full trucks arrive all day long (during the hours the bin is open) at a rate of about 30 per hour, following a Poisson pattern.

To help the cooperative get a handle on the problem of lost time while trucks are waiting in line or unloading at the bin, find the following:

a) The average number of trucks in the unloading system.
b) The average time per truck in the system.
c) The utilization rate for the bin area.
d) The probability that there are more than three trucks in the system at any given time.
e) The total daily cost to the farmers of having their trucks tied up in the unloading process.
f) As mentioned, the cooperative uses the storage bin heavily only two weeks per year. Farmers estimate that enlarging the bin would cut unloading costs by 50% next year. It will cost $9000 to do so during the off-season. Would it be worth the expense to enlarge the storage area? **PX**

••• **D.13** Radovilsky's Department Store in Richmond Hill maintains a successful catalogue sales department in which a clerk takes orders by telephone. If the clerk is occupied on one line, incoming phone calls to the catalogue department are answered automatically by a recording machine and asked to wait. As soon as the clerk is free, the party who has waited the longest is transferred and serviced first. Calls come in at a rate of about 12 per hour. The clerk can take an order in an average of four minutes. Calls tend to follow a Poisson distribution, and service times tend to be exponential.

The cost of the clerk is $10 per hour, but because of lost goodwill and sales, Radovilsky's loses about $25 per hour of customer time spent waiting for the clerk to take an order.

a) What is the average time that catalogue customers must wait before their calls are transferred to the order clerk?
b) What is the average number of customers waiting to place an order?
c) Radovilsky's is considering adding a second clerk to take calls. The store's cost would be the same $10 per hour. Should it hire another clerk? Explain your decision. **PX**

• **D.14** Karen Brown's Coffee Shop decides to install an automatic coffee vending machine outside one of its stores to reduce the number of people standing in line inside. Karen charges $3.50 per cup. However, it takes too long for people to make change. The service time is a constant 3 minutes, and the arrival rate is 15 per hour (Poisson distributed).

a) What is the average wait in line?
b) What is the average number of people in line?
c) Karen raises the price to $5 per cup and takes 60 seconds off the service time. However, because the coffee is now so expensive, the arrival rate drops to 10 per hour. Now what are the average wait time and the average number of people in the queue (waiting)? **PX**

••• **D.15** The typical subway station in Toronto has six turnstiles, each of which can be controlled by the station supervisor to be used for either entrance or exit control—but never for both. The supervisor must decide at different times of the day how many turnstiles to use for entering passengers and how many to use for exiting passengers.

At the Old Mill Station, passengers enter the station at a rate of about 84 per minute between the hours of 7:00 a.m. and 9:00 a.m. Passengers exiting trains at the stop reach the exit turnstile area at a rate of about 48 per minute during the same morning rush hours. Each turnstile can allow an average of 30 passengers per minute to enter or exit. Arrival and service times have been thought to follow Poisson and exponential distributions, respectively. Assume riders form a common queue at both entry and exit turnstile areas and proceed to the first empty turnstile.

The Old Mill station supervisor, Ernie Forman, does not want the average passenger at his station to have to wait in a turnstile line for more than six seconds, nor does he want more than eight people in any queue at any average time.

a) How many turnstiles should be opened in each direction every morning?

b) Discuss the assumptions underlying the solution of this problem using queuing theory. **PX**

•• **D.16** Yvette Freeman's Car Wash takes a constant time of 4.5 minutes in its automated car wash cycle. Autos arrive following a Poisson distribution at the rate of 10 per hour. Yvette wants to know:

a) The average waiting time in line.

b) The average length of the line. **PX**

••• **D.17** Debra Bishop's cabinet-making shop in Niagara Falls has five tools that automate the drilling of holes for the installation of hinges. These machines need setting up for each order of cabinets. The orders appear to follow the Poisson distribution, averaging three per eight-hour day. There is a single technician for setting these machines. Her service times are exponential, averaging two hours each.

a) What is the service factor for this system?

b) What is the average number of these machines in service?

c) What impact on machines in service would there be if a second technician were available? **PX**

••• **D.18** Two technicians, working separately, monitor a group of five computers that run an automated manufacturing facility. It takes an average of 15 minutes (exponentially distributed) to adjust a computer that develops a problem. Computers run for an average of 85 minutes (Poisson distributed) without requiring adjustments. Determine the following:

a) The average number of computers waiting for adjustment.

b) The average number being adjusted.

c) The average number of computers not in working order. **PX**

••• **D.19** One mechanic services five drilling machines for a steel plate manufacturer. Machines break down on an average of once every six working days, and breakdowns tend to follow a Poisson distribution. The mechanic can handle an average of one repair job per day. Repairs follow an exponential distribution.

a) On the average, how many machines are waiting for service?

b) On the average, how many drills are in running order?

c) How much would waiting time be reduced if a second mechanic were hired? **PX**

••• **D.20** Richard Insinga, the administrator at the Moncton Hospital emergency room, faces the problem of providing treatment for patients who arrive at different rates during the day. There are four doctors available to treat patients when needed. If not needed, they can be assigned other responsibilities (such as doing lab tests, reports, X-ray diagnoses) or else rescheduled to work at other hours.

It is important to provide quick and responsive treatment, and Richard feels that, on the average, patients should not have to sit in the waiting area for more than five minutes before being seen by a doctor. Patients are treated on a first-come, first-served basis and see the first available doctor after waiting in the queue. The arrival pattern for a typical day is as follows:

Time	Arrival Rate
9 a.m.–3 p.m.	6 patients/hour
3 p.m.–8 p.m.	4 patients/hour
8 p.m.–midnight	12 patients/hour

Arrivals follow a Poisson distribution, and treatment times, 12 minutes on the average, follow the exponential pattern.

a) How many doctors should be on duty during each period to maintain the level of patient care expected?

b) What condition would exist if only one doctor were on duty between 9 a.m. and 3 p.m.? **PX**

••• **D.21** A proposal has been presented to the government of Newfoundland and Labrador to build a new section of highway that would provide improved access for residents of a remote coastal area near Bonavista. The highway would be 16 kilometres in length. The initial proposal called for seven toll booths, each staffed by an employee. But a subsequent proposal recommended replacing the employees with machines. Many factors must be considered because the intended employees are unionized. However, one of the government's concerns is the effect that replacing the employees with machines will have on the times the drivers spend in the system. Customers will arrive to any one toll booth at a rate of 10 per minute. In the exact-change lanes with employees, the service time is essentially constant at five seconds for each driver. With machines, the average service time would still be five seconds, but it would be exponential rather than constant, because it takes time for the coins to rattle around in the machine. Contrast the two systems for a single lane. **PX**

••• **D.22** The registration area has just opened at a large convention of building contractors in Banff. There are 200 people arriving per hour (Poisson distributed), and the cost of their waiting time in the queue is valued at $100 per person per hour. The local convention bureau provides servers to register guests at a fee of $15 per person per hour. It takes about one minute to register an attendee (exponentially distributed). A single waiting line, with multiple servers, is set up.

a) What is the minimum number of servers for this system?

b) What is the optimal number of servers for this system?

c) What is the cost for the system, per hour, at the optimum number of servers?

d) What is the server utilization rate with the minimum number of servers? **PX**

•• **D.23** Refer to Problem D.22. A new registration manager, Lisa Houts, is hired who initiates a program to entertain the people in line with a juggler whom she pays $15/hour. This reduces the waiting costs to $50 per hour.

a) What is the optimal number of servers?

b) What is the cost for the system, per hour, at the optimal service level?

•••• **D.24** The Kitchener Furniture store gets an average of 50 customers per shift. Marilyn Helms, the manager, wants to calculate whether she should hire one, two, three, or four salespeople. She has determined that average waiting times will be seven minutes with one salesperson, four minutes with two salespeople, three minutes with three salespeople, and two minutes with four salespeople. She has estimated the cost per minute that customers wait at $1. The cost per salesperson per shift (including fringe benefits) is $70.

How many salespeople should be hired?

•• **D.25** During the afternoon peak hours the First Bank of Halifax has an average of 40 customers arriving every hour. There is also an average of eight customers at First Bank at any time. The probability of the arrival distribution is unknown. How long does the average customer spend in the bank?

•• **D.26** An average of nine cars can be seen in the system (both the drive-through line and the drive-through window) at Burger Universe. Approximately every 20 seconds, a car attempts to enter the drive-through line; however, 40% of cars simply leave the restaurant because they're discouraged by the length of the line. On average, how long does a car spend going through the drive-through at Burger Universe?

•• **D.27** Lobster World stores approximately 1000 pounds of fish on average. In a typical day, the busy restaurant cooks and sells 360 (raw) pounds of fish. How long do the fish stay in storage on average?

•• **D.28** Gamma Bank processes a typical loan application in 2.4 weeks. Customers fill out 30 loan applications per week. On average how many loan applications are being processed somewhere in the system at Gamma Bank?

•• **D.29** Fisher's Furniture Store sells $800 000 worth of furniture to customers on credit each month. The Accounts Receivable balance in the accounting books averages $2 million. On average, how long are customers taking to pay their bills?

CASE | STUDIES

Labrador Foundry Inc.

For more than 75 years, Labrador Foundry Inc. (LFI) has manufactured wood stoves for home use. In recent years, with increasing energy prices, president George Mathison has seen sales triple. This dramatic increase has made it difficult for George to maintain quality in all his wood stoves and related products.

Unlike other companies manufacturing wood stoves, LFI is in the business of making *only* stoves and stove-related products. Its major products are the Warmglo I, the Warmglo II, the Warmglo III, and the Warmglo IV. The Warmglo I is the smallest wood stove, with a heat output of 30 000 BTU, and the Warmglo IV is the largest, with a heat output of 60 000 BTU.

The Warmglo III outsells all other models by a wide margin. Its heat output and available accessories are ideal for the typical home. The Warmglo III also has a number of other outstanding features that make it one of the most attractive and heat-efficient stoves on the market. These features, along with the accessories, have resulted in expanding sales and have prompted George to build a new factory to manufacture the Warmglo III model. An overview diagram of the factory is shown in Figure D.6.

The new foundry uses the latest equipment, including a new Disamatic that helps in manufacturing stove parts. Regardless of new equipment or procedures, casting operations have remained basically unchanged for hundreds of years. To begin with, a wooden pattern is made for every cast iron piece in the stove. The wooden pattern is an exact duplicate of the cast iron piece that is to be manufactured. All LFI patterns are made by Precision Patterns Inc. and are stored in the pattern shop and maintenance room. Next, a specially formulated sand is moulded around the wooden pattern. There can be two or more sand moulds for each pattern. The sand is mixed and the moulds are made in the moulding room. When the wooden pattern is removed, the resulting sand moulds form a negative image of the desired casting. Next, moulds are transported to the casting room, where molten iron is poured into them and allowed to cool. When the iron has solidified, moulds are moved into the cleaning, grinding, and preparation room, where they are dumped into large vibrators that shake most of the sand from the casting. The rough castings are then subjected to both sandblasting to remove the rest of the sand and grinding to finish some of their surfaces. Castings are then painted with a special heat-resistant paint, assembled into workable stoves, and inspected for manufacturing defects that may have gone undetected. Finally, finished stoves are moved to storage

and shipping, where they are packaged and transported to the appropriate locations.

At present, the pattern shop and the maintenance department are located in the same room. One large counter is used by both maintenance personnel, who store tools and parts (that are mainly used by the casting department); and sand moulders, who need various patterns for the moulding operation. Pete Nawler and Bob Dillman, who work behind the counter, can service a total of 10 people per hour (about five per hour each). On the average, four people from casting and three from moulding arrive at the counter each hour. People from moulding and casting departments arrive randomly, and to be served, they form a single line.

Pete and Bob have always had a policy of first come, first served. Because of the location of the pattern shop and maintenance department, it takes an average of three minutes for an individual from the casting department to walk to the pattern and maintenance room, and it takes about one minute for an individual to walk from the moulding department to the pattern and maintenance room.

After observing the operation of the pattern shop and maintenance room for several weeks, George decided to make some changes to the factory layout. An overview of these changes appears in Figure D.7.

Separating the maintenance shop from the pattern shop would have a number of advantages. It would take people from the casting

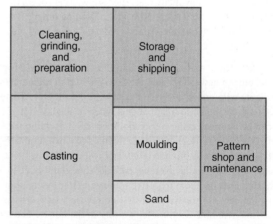

FIGURE D.6 Overview of Factory

department only one minute instead of three to get to the new main-tenance room. The time from moulding to the pattern shop would be unchanged. Using motion and time studies, George was also able to determine that improving the layout of the maintenance room would allow Bob to serve six people from the casting department per hour; improving the layout of the pattern department would allow Pete to serve seven people from the moulding shop per hour.

Discussion Questions

1. How much time would the new layout save?
2. If casting personnel were paid $9.50 per hour and moulding per-sonnel were paid $11.75 per hour, how much could be saved per hour with the new factory layout?
3. Should George have made the change in layout?

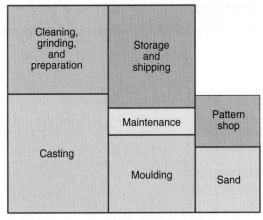

FIGURE D.7 Overview of Factory After Changes

The Winter Park Hotel

Donna Shader, manager of the Winter Park Hotel, is considering how to restructure the front desk to reach an optimum level of staff efficiency and guest service. At present, the hotel has five clerks on duty, each with a separate waiting line, during peak check-in time of 3:00 p.m. to 5:00 p.m. Observation of arrivals during this period shows that an average of 90 guests arrive each hour (although there is no upward limit on the number that could arrive at any given time). It takes an average of three minutes for the front-desk clerk to register each guest.

Shader is considering three plans for improving guest ser-vice by reducing the length of time that guests spend waiting in line. The first proposal would designate one employee as a quick-service clerk for guests registering under corporate accounts, a market segment that fills about 30% of all occupied rooms. Because corporate guests are preregistered, their registration takes just 2 minutes. With these guests separated from the rest of the clien-tele, the average time for registering a typical guest would climb to 3.4 minutes. Under this plan, noncorporate guests would choose any of the remaining four lines.

The second plan is to implement a single-line system. All guests could form a single waiting line to be served by whichever of five clerks became available. This option would require sufficient lobby space for what could be a substantial queue.

The use of an automated teller machine (ATM) for check-ins is the basis of the third proposal. This ATM would provide about the same service rate as would a clerk. Because initial use of this technology might be minimal, Shader estimates that 20% of cus-tomers, primarily frequent guests, would be willing to use the machines.

(This might be a conservative estimate if guests perceive direct benefits from using the ATM, as bank customers do. Citibank reports that some 95% of its Manhattan customers use its ATMs.) Shader would set up a single queue for customers who prefer human check-in clerks. This line would be served by the five clerks, although Shader is hopeful that the ATM will allow a reduction to four.

Discussion Questions*

1. Determine the average amount of time that a guest spends check-ing in. How would this change under each of the stated options?
2. Which option do you recommend?

---

*You may wish to view the video that accompanies this case before answering these questions.

▶**Additional Case Study:** Visit **MyLab Operations Management** for this additional case study:
Pantry Shopper: The case requires the redesign of a checkout system for a supermarket.

MODULE D | RAPID REVIEW

Main Heading	Review Material
QUEUING THEORY (pp. 731–732)	• **Queuing theory**—A body of knowledge about waiting lines. • **Waiting lines (or queues)**—Items or people in lines awaiting service.

CHARACTERISTICS OF A WAITING-LINE SYSTEM (pp. 732–736)

The three parts of a waiting-line, or queuing, system are:

Arrivals or inputs to the system; queue discipline, or the waiting line itself; and the service facility:

• **Unlimited, or infinite, population**—A queue in which a virtually unlimited number of people or items could request the services, or in which the number of customers or arrivals on hand at any given moment is a very small portion of potential arrivals.

• **Limited, or finite, population**—A queue in which there are only a limited number of potential users of the service.

• **Poisson distribution**—A discrete probability distribution that often describes the arrival rate in queuing theory:

$$P(x) = \frac{e^{-\lambda}\lambda^x}{x!} \text{ for } x = 0, 1, 2, 3, 4,\dots \qquad \textbf{(D-1)}$$

A queue is *limited* when it cannot, either by law or because of physical restrictions, increase to an infinite length. A queue is *unlimited* when its size is unrestricted.

Queue discipline refers to the rule by which customers in the line are to receive service:

• **First-in, first-out (FIFO) rule**—A queue discipline in which the first customers in line receive the first service.

• **Single-channel queuing system**—A service system with one line and one server.

• **Multiple-channel queuing system**—A service system with one waiting line but with several servers (channels).

• **Single-phase system**—A system in which the customer receives service from only one station and then exits the system.

• **Multiphase system**—A system in which the customer receives services from several stations before exiting the system.

• **Negative exponential probability distribution**—A continuous probability distribution often used to describe the service time in a queuing system.

QUEUING COSTS (pp. 736–737)

Operations managers must recognize the trade-off that takes place between two costs: the cost of providing good service and the cost of customer or machine waiting time.

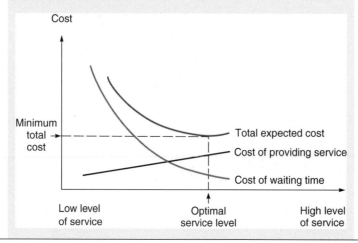

Main Heading	**Review Material**	

**THE VARIETY OF
QUEUING MODELS**
(pp. 737–738)

Model A: Single-Channel System (M/M/1):

Queuing Formulas:

λ = mean number of arrivals per time period

μ = mean number of people or items served per time period

L_s = average number of units in the system = $\lambda/(\mu - \lambda)$

W_s = average time a unit spends in the system = $1/(\mu - \lambda)$

L_q = average number of units waiting in the queue = $\lambda^2/[\mu(\mu - \lambda)]$

W_q = average time a unit spends waiting in the queue = $\lambda/[\mu(\mu - \lambda)]$

$\quad = L_q/\lambda$

ρ = utilization factor for the system = λ/μ

P_0 = probability of 0 units in the system (i.e., the service unit is idle)

$\quad = 1 - (\lambda/\mu)$

$P_{n>k}$ = probability of > k units in the system = $(\lambda/\mu)^{k+1}$

Model B: Multichannel System (M/M/S):

$$P_0 = \frac{1}{\left[\sum_{n=0}^{M-1}\frac{1}{n!}\left(\frac{\lambda}{\mu}\right)^n\right] + \frac{1}{M!}\left(\frac{\lambda}{\mu}\right)^M \frac{M\mu}{M\mu - \lambda}} \quad \text{for } M\mu > \lambda$$

$$L_s = \frac{\lambda\mu(\lambda/\mu)^M}{(M-1)!(M\mu - \lambda)^2} P_0 + \frac{\lambda}{\mu}$$

$$W_s = L_s/\lambda \quad L_q = L_s - (\lambda/\mu) \quad W_q = L_q/\lambda$$

Model C: Constant Service (M/D/1):

$$L_q = \lambda^2/[2\mu(\mu - \lambda)] \qquad W_q = \lambda/[2\mu(\mu - \lambda)]$$
$$L_s = L_q + (\lambda/\mu) \qquad W_q = \lambda/[2\mu(\mu - \lambda)]$$

Little's Law

A useful relationship in queuing for any system in a steady state is called
Little's Law:

$$L = \lambda W \quad \text{(which is the same as } W = L/\lambda) \quad \textbf{(D-2)}$$
$$L_q = \lambda W_q \quad \text{(which is the same as } W_q = L_q/\lambda) \quad \textbf{(D-3)}$$

Model D: Limited Population

With a limited population, there is a *dependent* relationship between the
length of the queue and the arrival rate. As the *waiting* line becomes longer,
the *arrival rate* drops.

Problems: D.1–D.24

Virtual Office Hours for
Solved Problems: D.1–D.4

**ACTIVE MODEL
D.1, D.2, D.3**

**OTHER QUEUING
APPROACHES**
(p. 749)

Often, *variations* of the four basic queuing models are present in an analysis.
Many models, some very complex, have been developed to deal with such
variations.

Self-Test

■ **Before taking the self-test,** refer to the learning objectives listed at the beginning of the module.

LO1 Which of the following is *not* a key operating characteristic for a
queuing system?
  a) Utilization rate
  b) Percent idle time
  c) Average time spent waiting in the system and in the queue
  d) Average number of customers in the system and in the queue
  e) Average number of customers who renege

LO2 Customers enter the waiting line at a cafeteria's only cash register on
a first-come, first-served basis. The arrival rate follows a Poisson distribution, whereas service times follow an exponential distribution. If
the average number of arrivals is 6 per minute and the average service
rate of a single server is 10 per minute, what is the average number
of customers in the system?
  a) 0.6   **b)** 0.9   **c)** 1.5
  d) 0.25   **e)** 1.0

LO3 In performing a cost analysis of a queuing system, the waiting-time cost is sometimes based on the time in the queue and sometimes based on the time in the system. The waiting cost should be based on time in the system for which of the following situations?

a) Waiting in line to ride an amusement park ride

b) Waiting to discuss a medical problem with a doctor

c) Waiting for a picture and an autograph from a rock star

d) Waiting for a computer to be fixed so it can be placed back in service

LO4 Which of the following is *not* an assumption in a multichannel queuing model?

a) Arrivals come from an infinite, or very large, population.

b) Arrivals are Poisson distributed.

c) Arrivals are treated on a first-in, first-out basis and do not balk or renege.

d) Service times follow the exponential distribution.

e) Servers each perform at their own individual speeds.

LO5 If everything else remains the same, including the mean arrival rate and service rate, except that the service time becomes constant instead of exponential:

a) the average queue length will be halved.

b) the average waiting time will be doubled.

c) the average queue length will increase.

d) we cannot tell from the information provided.

LO6 A company has one computer technician who is responsible for repairs on the company's 20 computers. As a computer breaks, the technician is called to make the repair. If the repair person is busy, the machine must wait to be repaired. This is an example of:

a) a multichannel system.

b) a finite population system.

c) a constant service rate system.

d) a multiphase system.

e) all of the above.

Answers: LO1. e; LO2. c; LO3. d; LO4. e; LO5. a; LO6. b.

MyLab Operations Management

Most of these questions can be found in MyLab Operations Management. Visit MyLab Operations Management to access cases, videos, downloadable software, and much more. MyLab Operations Management Management also features a personalized Study Plan that helps you identify which chapter concepts you've mastered and guides you towards study tools for additional practice.

Learning Curves

Learning Objectives

LO1 Define *learning curve* **761**

LO2 Use the arithmetic concept to estimate times **763**

LO3 Compute learning-curve effects with the logarithmic and learning-curve coefficient approaches **763**

LO4 Describe the strategic implications of learning curves **766**

What Is a Learning Curve?

Most organizations learn and improve over time. As firms and employees perform a task over and over, they learn how to perform more efficiently. This means that task times and costs decrease.

Learning curves are based on the premise that people and organizations become better at their tasks as the tasks are repeated. A learning-curve graph (illustrated in Figure E.1) displays labour-hours per unit versus the number of units produced. From it we see that the time needed to produce a unit decreases, usually following a negative exponential curve, as the person or company produces more units. In other words, *it takes less time to complete each additional unit a firm produces*. However, we also see in Figure E.1 that the time *savings* in completing each subsequent unit *decreases*. These are the major attributes of the learning curve.

Learning curves were first applied to industry in a report by T. P. Wright of Curtis-Wright Corporation in 1936.[1] Wright described how direct labour costs of making a particular airplane decreased with learning, a theory since confirmed by other aircraft manufacturers. Regardless of the time needed to produce the first plane, learning curves are found to apply to various categories of air frames (e.g., jet fighters versus passenger planes versus bombers). Learning curves have since been applied not only to labour but also to a wide variety of other costs, including material and purchased components. The power of the learning curve is so significant that it plays a major role in many strategic decisions related to employment levels, costs, capacity, and pricing.

The learning curve is based on a *doubling* of production: That is, when production doubles, the decrease in time per unit affects the rate of the learning curve. So, if the learning curve is an 80% rate, the second unit takes 80% of the time of the first unit, the fourth unit takes 80% of the time of the second unit, the eighth unit takes 80% of the time of the fourth unit, and so forth. This principle is shown as:

$$T \times L^n = \text{Time required for the } n\text{th unit} \qquad \text{(E-1)}$$

where
T = unit cost or unit time of the first unit
L = learning-curve rate
n = number of times T is doubled

LO1 Define *learning curve*

Learning curves
The premise that people and organizations get better at their tasks as the tasks are repeated; sometimes called experience curves.

---

[1] T. P. Wright, "Factors Affecting the Cost of Airplanes," *Journal of the Aeronautical Sciences* (February 1936).

(a)

Exponential graph of learning

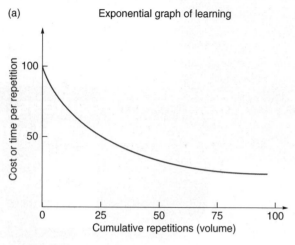

(b)

Log-log graph of learning

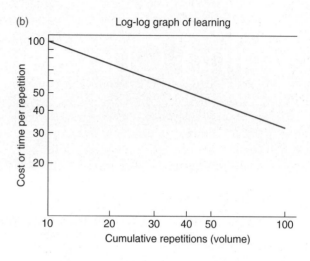

FIGURE E.1

The Learning-Curve Effect States that Time per Repetition Decreases as the Number of Repetitions Increases

Both curves show that the labour-hours to build an airplane decline by 20% each time the production volume doubles. The left graph (a) shows the exponential decline. The log-log graph (b) yields a straight line that is easier to extrapolate.

If the first unit of a particular product took 10 labour-hours, and if a 70% learning curve is present, the hours the fourth unit will take require doubling twice—from 1 to 2 to 4. Therefore, the formula is:

$$\text{Hours required for unit } 4 = 10 \times (0.7)^2 = 4.9 \text{ hours}$$

Learning Curves in Services and Manufacturing

Different organizations—indeed, different products—have different learning curves. The rate of learning varies depending on the quality of management and the potential of the process and product. *Any change in process, product, or personnel disrupts the learning curve.* Therefore, caution should be exercised in assuming that a learning curve is continuing and permanent.

As you can see in Table E.1, industry learning curves vary widely. The lower the number (say, 70% compared to 90%), the steeper the slope and the faster the drop in costs. By tradition, learning curves are defined in terms of the *complements* of their improvement rates. For example, a 70% learning curve implies a 30% decrease in time each time the number of repetitions is doubled. A 90% curve means there is a corresponding 10% rate of improvement.

Table E.1
Examples of Learning-Curve Effects

Example	Improving Parameter	Cumulative Parameter	Learning-Curve Slope (%)
1. Model-T Ford production	Price	Units produced	86
2. Aircraft assembly	Direct labour-hours per unit	Units produced	80
3. Equipment maintenance at GE	Average time to replace a group of parts	Number of replacements	76
4. Steel production	Production worker labour-hours per unit produced	Units produced	79
5. Integrated circuits	Average price per unit	Units produced	72*
6. Hand-held calculator	Average factory selling price	Units produced	74
7. Disk memory drives	Average price per bit	Number of bits	76
8. Heart transplants	1-year death rates	Transplants completed	79
9. Caesarean section baby deliveries	Average operation time	Number of surgeries	93

*Constant dollars

Sources: W. Y. Fok, L. Y. S. Chan, and T. K. H. Chung. "The Effect of Learning Curves on the Outcome of a Caesarean Section." *BSOG* (November 2006): 1259–1263; James A. Cunningham, "Using the Learning Curve as a Management Tool," *IEEE Spectrum* (June 1980): 45, © 1980 IEEE; and Davis B. Smith and Jan L. Larsson, "The Impact of Learning on Cost: The Case of Heart Transplantation." *Hospital and Health Services Administration* (Spring 1989): 85–97.

Stable, standardized products and processes tend to have costs that decline more steeply than others. Between 1920 and 1955, for instance, the steel industry was able to reduce labour-hours per unit to 79% each time cumulative production doubled.

Learning curves have application in services as well as industry. For example, one-year death rates of heart transplant patients follow a 79% learning curve. The results of that three-year study of 62 patients receiving transplants found that every three operations resulted in a halving of the one-year death rate. As more hospitals face pressure from both insurance companies and the government to enter fixed-price negotiations for their services, their ability to learn from experience becomes increasingly critical. In addition to having applications in both services and industry, learning curves are useful for a variety of purposes. These include:

1. *Internal:* Labour forecasting, scheduling, establishing costs and budgets.
2. *External:* Supply chain negotiations (see the SMT case study at the end of this module).
3. *Strategic:* Evaluation of company and industry performance, including costs and pricing.

The consequences of learning curves can be far-reaching. For example, there are major problems in scheduling if the learning improvement is not considered: Labour and plants may sit idle a portion of the time. Firms may also refuse more work because they ignore their own efficiency improvements.

Applying the Learning Curve

STUDENT TIP

Here are the three ways of solving learning-curve problems.

A mathematical relationship enables us to express the time required to produce a certain unit. This relationship is a function of how many units have been produced before the unit in question and how long it took to produce them. To gain a mastery of this relationship, we will work through learning-curve scenarios using three different approaches: arithmetic analysis, logarithmic analysis, and learning-curve coefficients.

ARITHMETIC APPROACH

The arithmetic approach is the simplest approach to learning-curve problems. As we noted at the beginning of this module, each time production doubles, labour per unit declines by a constant factor, known as the learning rate. So, if we know that the learning rate is 80% and that the first unit produced took 100 hours, the hours required to produce the 2nd, 4th, 8th, and 16th units are as follows:

LO2 Use the arithmetic concept to estimate times

Nth Unit Produced	Hours for Nth Unit
1	100
2	$80.0 = (0.8 \times 100)$
4	$64.0 = (0.8 \times 80)$
8	$51.2 = (0.8 \times 64)$
16	$41.0 = (0.8 \times 51.2)$

As long as we wish to find the hours required to produce N units and N is one of the doubled values, then this approach works. Arithmetic analysis does not tell us how many hours will be needed to produce other units. For this flexibility, we must turn to the logarithmic approach.

LO3 Compute learning-curve effects with the logarithmic and learning-curve coefficient approaches

LOGARITHMIC APPROACH

The logarithmic approach allows us to determine labour for *any* unit, T_N, by the formula:

$$T_N = T_1(N^b) \tag{E-2}$$

where
T_N = time for the Nth unit
T_1 = hours to produce the first unit
b = (log of the learning rate)/(log 2) = slope of the learning curve

Some of the values for b are presented in Table E.2. Example E1 shows how this formula works.

Table E.2
Learning-Curve Values of b

Learning Rate (%)	b
70	−0.515
75	−0.415
80	−0.322
85	−0.234
90	−0.152

Using Table E.3 requires that we know how long it takes to complete the first unit. Yet what happens if our most recent or most reliable information available pertains to some other unit? The answer is that we must use these data to find a revised estimate for the first unit and then apply the table coefficient to that number. Example E4 illustrates this concept.

EXAMPLE E4

Revising Learning-Curve Estimates

Great Lakes Services Inc. believes that unusual circumstances in producing the first boat (see Example E2) imply that the time estimate of 125 000 hours is not as valid a base as the time required to produce the third boat. Boat 3 was completed in 100 000 hours. It wants to solve for the revised estimate for boat 1.

APPROACH ▶ We return to Table E.3, with a unit value of $N = 3$ and a learning-curve coefficient of $C = 0.773$ in the 85% column.

SOLUTION ▶ To find the revised estimate, divide the actual time for boat 3, 100 000 hours, by $C = 0.773$:

$$\text{Revised Estimate} = \frac{100\ 000}{0.773} = 129\ 366 \text{ hours}$$

So, 129 366 hours is the new (revised) estimate for boat 1.

INSIGHT ▶ Any change in product, process, or personnel will change the learning curve. The new estimate for boat 1 suggests that related cost and volume estimates need to be revised.

LEARNING EXERCISE ▶ Boat 4 was just completed in 90 000 hours. Great Lakes thinks the 85% learning rate is valid but isn't sure about the 125 000 hours for the first boat. Find a revised estimate for boat 1 ($C = 0.723$). [Answer: 124 481, suggesting that boat 1's time was fairly accurate after all.]

RELATED PROBLEMS ▶ E.8, E.12, E.13, E.17, E.18, E.20b, E.21, E.23

EXCEL OM Data File **ModEExE4.xlsx** can be found at **MyLab Operations Management.**

Strategic Implications of Learning Curves

LO4 Describe the strategic implications of learning curves

So far, we have shown how operations managers can forecast labour-hour requirements for a product. We have also shown how purchasing agents can determine a supplier's cost, knowledge that can help in price negotiations. Another important application of learning curves concerns strategic planning.

An example of a company cost line and industry price line are so labelled in Figure E.2. These learning curves are straight because both scales are log scales. When the *rate* of change is constant, a *log–log graph* yields a straight line. If an organization believes its cost line to be the "company cost" line, and the industry price is indicated by the dashed horizontal line, then the company must have costs at the points below the dashed line (e.g., point *a* or *b*) or else operate at a loss (point *c*).

FIGURE E.2

Industry Learning Curve for Price Compared with Company Learning Curve for Cost

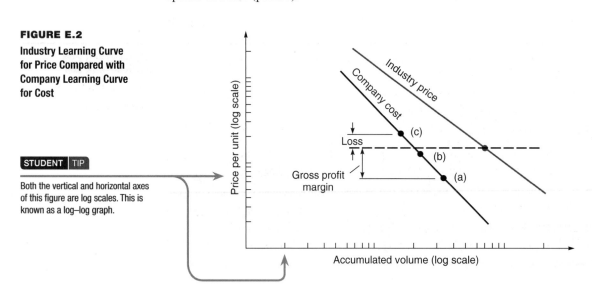

STUDENT TIP

Both the vertical and horizontal axes of this figure are log scales. This is known as a log–log graph.

Lower costs are not automatic; they must be managed down. When a firm's strategy is to pursue a curve steeper than the industry average (the company cost line in Figure E.2), it does this by:

1. Following an aggressive pricing policy.
2. Focusing on continuing cost reduction and productivity improvement.
3. Building on shared experience.
4. Keeping capacity growing ahead of demand.

Costs may drop as a firm pursues the learning curve, but volume must increase for the learning curve to exist. Moreover, managers must understand competitors before embarking on a learning-curve strategy. Weak competitors are undercapitalized, stuck with high costs, or do not understand the logic of learning curves. However, strong and dangerous competitors control their costs, have solid financial positions for the large investments needed, and have a track record of using an aggressive learning-curve strategy. Taking on such a competitor in a price war may help only the consumer.

Limitations of Learning Curves

Before using learning curves, some cautions are in order:

- Because learning curves differ from company to company, as well as industry to industry, estimates for each organization should be developed rather than applying someone else's.
- Learning curves are often based on the time necessary to complete the early units; therefore, those times must be accurate. As current information becomes available, re-evaluation is appropriate.
- Any changes in personnel, design, or procedure can be expected to alter the learning curve, causing the curve to spike up for a short time, even if it is going to drop in the long run.
- While workers and processes may improve, the same learning curves do not always apply to indirect labour and material.
- The culture of the workplace, as well as resource availability and changes in the process, may alter the learning curve. For instance, as a project nears its end, worker interest and effort may drop, curtailing progress down the curve.

MODULE | SUMMARY

The learning curve is a powerful tool for the operations manager. This tool can assist operations managers in determining future cost standards for items produced as well as purchased. In addition, the learning curve can provide understanding about company and industry performance. We saw three approaches to learning curves: arithmetic analysis, logarithmic analysis, and learning-curve coefficients found in tables. Software can also help analyze learning curves.

Discussion Questions

1. What are some of the limitations of learning curves?
2. Identify three applications of the learning curve.
3. What are the approaches to solving learning-curve problems?
4. Refer to Example E2. What are the implications for Great Lakes Services Inc. if the engineering department wants to change the engine in the third and subsequent tugboats that the firm purchases?
5. Why isn't the learning-curve concept as applicable in a high-volume assembly line as it is in most other human activities?
6. What are the elements that can disrupt the learning curve?
7. Explain the concept of the *doubling* effect in learning curves.
8. What techniques can a firm use to move to a steeper learning curve?

Using Software for Learning Curves

Excel, Excel OM, and POM for Windows may all be used in analyzing learning curves. You can use the ideas in the following section on Excel OM to build your own Excel spreadsheet if you wish.

✗ USING EXCEL OM

Program E.1 shows how Excel OM develops a spreadsheet for learning-curve calculations. The input data come from Example E2 and Example E3. In cell B7, we enter the unit number for the base unit (which does not have to be 1), and in B8 we enter the time for this unit.

These are used for computations. Do not touch these cells. In cell B11, the time for the first unit is computed, allowing us to use initial units other than unit 1. In cell B12, the power to be raised to is computed, making the formulas in the rest of column B much simpler.

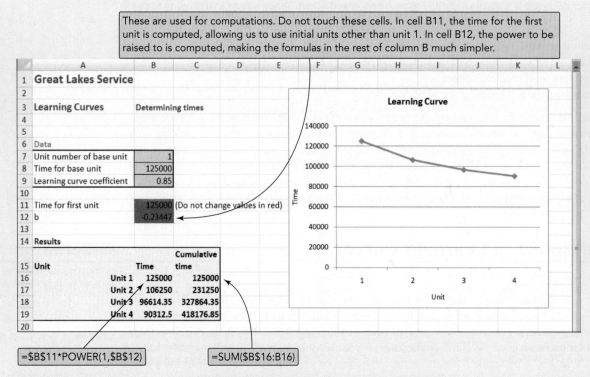

`=$B$11*POWER(1,$B$12)`

`=SUM($B$16:B16)`

PROGRAM E.1 Excel OM's Learning-Curve Module, Using Data From Example E2 and Example E3

Source: Microsoft product screen shot(s) reprinted with permission from Microsoft Corporation.

P USING POM FOR WINDOWS

The POM for Windows Learning-Curve module computes the length of time that future units will take, given the time required for the base unit and the learning rate (expressed as a number between 0 and 1). As an option, if the times required for the first and Nth units are already known, the learning *rate* can be computed. See Appendix IV for further details.

Solved Problems   Virtual Office Hours help is available at MyLab Operations Management.

▼ SOLVED PROBLEM E.1

Digicomp produces a new telephone system with built-in TV screens. Its learning rate is 80%.

a) If the first one took 56 hours, how long will it take Digicomp to make the 11th system?

b) How long will the first 11 systems take in total?

c) As a purchasing agent, you expect to buy units 12 through 15 of the new phone system. What would be your expected cost for the units if Digicomp charges $30 for each labour-hour?

▼ SOLUTION

a) $T_N = T_1 C$ ⟵ From Table E.3, coefficient for 80% unit time

$T_{11} = (56 \text{ hours})(0.462) = 25.9 \text{ hours}$

b) Total time for the first 11 units $= (56 \text{ hours})(6.777) = 379.5 \text{ hours}$

from Table E.3, coefficient for 80% total time ⟶

c) To find the time for units 12 through 15, we take the total cumulative time for units 1 to 15 and subtract the total time for units 1 to 11, which was computed in part (b). Total time for the first 15 units $= (56 \text{ hours})(8.511) = 476.6 \text{ hours}$. So, the time for units 12 through 15 is $476.6 - 379.5 = 97.1$ hours. (This figure could also be confirmed by computing the times for units 12, 13, 14, and 15 separately using the unit-time coefficient column and then adding them.) Expected cost for units 12 through 15 $= (97.1 \text{ hours})(\$30 \text{ per hour}) = \$2913$.

Equations are rounded to 3 decimal places and answers are rounded to one decimal place.

▼ **SOLVED PROBLEM E.2**

If the first time you performed a job took 60 minutes, how long will the eighth job take if you are on an 80% learning curve?

▼ **SOLUTION**

Three doublings from 1 to 2 to 4 to 8 implies 8^3. Therefore, we have:

$$60 \times (0.8)^3 = 60 \times 0.512 = 30.72 \text{ minutes}$$

or, using Table E.3, we have $C = 0.512$. Therefore:

$$60 \times 0.512 = 30.72 \text{ minutes}$$

Problems*

• **E.1** Amanda Heinl, a CRA auditor, took 45 minutes to process her first tax return. The CRA uses an 85% learning curve. How long will the:
a) second return take?
b) fourth return take?
c) eighth return take? **PX**

• **E.2** Seton Hall Trucking Co. just hired Sally Kissel to verify daily invoices and accounts payable. She took 9 hours and 23 minutes to complete her task on the first day. Prior employees in this job have tended to follow a 90% learning curve. How long will the task take at the end of:
a) the second day?
b) the fourth day?
c) the eighth day?
d) the 16th day? **PX**

• **E.3** If Professor Tracy Quinn takes 15 minutes to grade the first exam and follows an 80% learning curve, how long will it take her:
a) to grade the 25th exam?
b) to grade the first 10 exams? **PX**

• **E.4** If it took 563 minutes to complete a hospital's first cornea transplant, and the hospital uses a 90% learning rate, what is the cumulative time to complete:
a) the first three transplants?
b) the first six transplants?
c) the first eight transplants?
d) the first 16 transplants? **PX**

•• **E.5** A new concept hospital, one that is mobile and will serve remote areas, has received initial certification from the Ministry of Health to become a centre for liver transplants. The hospital must complete its first 18 transplants under great scrutiny, however, and with no additional transfer payments from the Ministry. The very first transplant, just completed, required 30 hours. On the basis of research at the hospital, management estimates that it will have an 80% learning curve. Estimate the time it will take to complete:
a) the fifth liver transplant.
b) all of the first five transplants.
c) the 18th transplant.
d) all 18 transplants. **PX**

•• **E.6** Refer to Problem E.5. Management at the new concept hospital has just been informed that only the first 10 transplants must be performed at the hospital's expense and come out of its own operating budget. The cost per hour of surgery is estimated to

be $5000. Again, the learning rate is 80% and the first surgery took 30 hours.
a) How long will the 10th surgery take?
b) How much will the 10th surgery cost?
c) How much will all 10 cost the hospital? **PX**

• **E.7** Manceville Air has just produced the first unit of a large industrial compressor that incorporated new technology in the control circuits and a new internal venting system. The first unit took 112 hours of labour to manufacture. The company knows from past experience that this labour content will decrease significantly as more units are produced. In reviewing past production data, it appears that the company has experienced a 90% learning curve when producing similar designs. The company is interested in estimating the total time to complete the next seven units. Your job as the production cost estimator is to prepare the estimate. **PX**

• **E.8** John Howard, a student at the University of Lethbridge, bought six bookcases for his dorm room. Each required unpacking of parts and assembly, which included some nailing and bolting. John completed the first bookcase in five hours and the second in four hours.
a) What is his learning rate?
b) Assuming the same rate continues, how long will the third bookcase take?
c) The fourth, fifth, and sixth cases?
d) All six cases? **PX**

•• **E.9** Professor Mary Beth Marrs took six hours to prepare the first lecture in a new course. Traditionally, she has experienced a 90% learning factor. How much time should it take her to prepare the 15th lecture? **PX**

• **E.10** The first vending machine that Michael Vest Inc. assembled took 80 labour-hours. Estimate how long the fourth machine will require for each of the following learning rates:
a) 95%   b) 87%   c) 72% **PX**

• **E.11** Kara-Smith Systems is installing networks for Advantage Insurance. The first installation took 46 labour-hours to complete. Estimate how long the fourth and the eighth installations will take for each of the following learning rates:
a) 92%   b) 84%   c) 77% **PX**

••• **E.12** Dartmouth Assessment Centre screens and trains employees for a computer assembly firm in Halifax. The progress of all trainees is tracked and those not showing the proper progress are moved to less demanding programs. By the 10th repetition, trainees must be able to complete the assembly task in one hour or less. Torri Olson-Alves has just spent five hours on the fourth unit and four hours completing her eighth unit, while another trainee, Julie Burgmeier, took four hours on the third and three hours on the sixth unit. Should you encourage either or both of the trainees to continue? Why? **PX**

••• **E.13** The better students at Dartmouth Assessment Centre (see Problem E.12) have an 80% learning curve and can do a task

*Note: **PX** means the problem may be solved with POM for Windows and/or Excel OM.

in 20 minutes after just six times. You would like to identify the weak students sooner and decide to evaluate them after the third unit. How long should the third unit take? **Px**

• • E.14 Wanda Fennell, the purchasing agent for Northeast Airlines, is interested in determining what she can expect to pay for the fourth airplane if the third plane took 20 000 hours to produce. What would Fennell expect to pay for the fifth plane? The sixth plane? Use an 85% learning curve and a $40-per-hour labour charge. **Px**

• • E.15 Using the data from Problem E.14, how long will it take to complete the 12th plane? the 15th plane? How long will it take to complete planes 12 through 15 inclusive? At $40 per hour, what can Fennell, as purchasing agent, expect to pay for all four planes? **Px**

• • E.16 Dynamic RAM Corp. produces semiconductors and has a learning curve of 0.7. The price per bit is 100 millicents when the volume is 7×10^{12} bits.
a) What is the expected price at 1.4×10^{12} bits?
b) What is the expected price at 89.6×10^{12} bits? **Px**

• • E.17 Central Power owns 25 small power generating plants. It has contracted with Genco Services to overhaul the power turbines of each of the plants. The number of hours that Genco billed Central to complete the third turbine was 460. Central pays Genco $60 per hour for its services. As the maintenance manager for Central, you are trying to estimate the cost of overhauling the fourth turbine. How much would you expect to pay for the overhaul of the fifth and sixth? All the turbines are similar and an 80% learning curve is appropriate. **Px**

• • E.18 It takes 28 718 hours to produce the eighth locomotive at a large French manufacturing firm. If the learning factor is 80%, how long does it take to produce the 10th locomotive? **Px**

• • E.19 Eric Krassow's firm is about to bid on a new radar system. Although the product uses new technology, Krassow believes that a learning rate of 75% is appropriate. The first unit is expected to take 700 hours, and the contract is for 40 units.
a) What is the total amount of hours to build the 40 units?
b) What is the average time to build each of the 40 units?
c) Assume that a worker works 2080 hours per year. How many workers should be assigned to this contract to complete it in a year? **Px**

• • • E.20 As the estimator for Arup Mukherjee Enterprises, your job is to prepare an estimate for a potential customer service contract. The contract is for the service of diesel locomotive cylinder heads. The shop has done some of these in the past on a sporadic basis. The time required to service the first cylinder head in each job has been exactly four hours, and similar work has been accomplished at an 85% learning curve. The customer wants you to quote the total time in batches of 12 and 20.
a) Prepare the quote.
b) After preparing the quote, you find a labour ticket for this customer for five locomotive cylinder heads. From the notations on the labour ticket, you conclude that the fifth unit took 2.5 hours. What do you conclude about the learning curve and your quote? **Px**

• • E.21 Sara Bredbenner and Blake DeYoung are teammates at a discount store; their new job is assembling swing sets for customers. Assembly of a swing set has a learning rate of 90%. They forgot to time their effort on the first swing set but spent four hours on the second set. They have six more sets to do. Determine approximately how much time will be (was) required for:
a) the first unit.
b) the eighth unit.
c) all eight units. **Px**

• • E.22 Kelly-Lambing Inc., a builder of government-contracted small ships, has a steady workforce of 10 very skilled craftspeople. These workers can supply 2500 labour-hours each per year. Kelly-Lambing is about to undertake a new contract, building a new style of boat. The first boat is expected to take 6000 hours to complete. The firm thinks that 90% is the expected learning rate.
a) What is the firm's "capacity" to make these boats—that is, how many units can the firm make in one year?
b) If the operations manager can increase the learning rate to 85% instead of 90%, how many units can the firm make?

• • • E.23 The service times for a new data entry clerk have been measured and sequentially recorded as shown below:

Report	Time (minutes)
1	66
2	56
3	53
4	48
5	47
6	45
7	44
8	41

a) What is the learning-curve rate, based on this information?
b) Using an 85% learning-curve rate and the above times, estimate the length of time the clerk will take to complete the 48th report. **Px**

• • E.24 If the first unit of a production run takes one hour and the firm is on an 80% learning curve, how long will unit 100 take? (*Hint:* Apply the coefficient in Table E.3 twice.) **Px**

• • • • E.25 Using the accompanying log–log graph, answer the following questions:
a) What are the implications for management if it has forecast its cost on the optimum line?
b) What could be causing the fluctuations above the optimum line?
c) If management forecast the 10th unit on the optimum line, what was that forecast in hours?
d) If management built the 10th unit as indicated by the actual line, how many hours did it take?

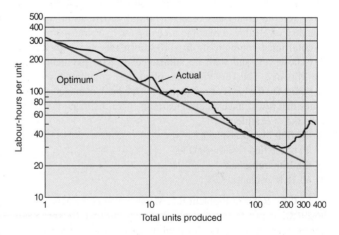

• • • E.26 Boeing spent $270 million to make the eleventh 787 in its production line. The first 787 cost $448 million. What was the learning-curve rate at this point?

SMT's Negotiation with IBM

SMT and one other, much larger company were asked by IBM to bid on 80 more units of a particular computer product. The request for quote asked that the overall bid be broken down to show the hourly rate, the parts and materials component in the price, and any charges for subcontracted services. SMT quoted $1.62 million and supplied the cost breakdown as requested. The second company submitted only one total figure, $5 million, with no cost breakdown. The decision was made to negotiate with SMT.

The IBM negotiating team included two purchasing managers and two cost engineers. One cost engineer had developed manufacturing cost estimates for every component, working from engineering drawings and cost-data books that he had built up from previous experience and that contained time factors, both setup and run times, for a large variety of operations. He estimated materials costs by working both from data supplied by the IBM corporate purchasing staff and from purchasing journals. He visited SMT facilities to see the tooling available so that he would know what processes were being used. He assumed that there would be perfect conditions and trained operators, and he developed cost estimates for the 158th unit (previous orders were for 25, 15, and 38 units). He added 5% for scrap-and-flow loss; 2% for the use of temporary tools, jigs, and fixtures; 5% for quality control; and 9% for purchasing burden. Then, using an 85% learning curve, he backed up his costs to get an estimate for the first unit. He next checked the data on hours and materials for the 25, 15, and 38 units already made and found that his estimate for the first unit was within 4% of actual cost. His check, however, had indicated a 90% learning-curve effect on hours per unit.

In the negotiations, SMT was represented by one of the two owners of the business, two engineers, and one cost estimator. The sessions opened with a discussion of learning curves. The IBM cost estimator demonstrated that SMT had in fact been operating on a 90% learning curve. But, he argued, it should be possible to move to an 85% curve, given the longer runs, reduced setup time, and increased continuity of workers on the job that would be possible with an order for 80 units. The owner agreed with this analysis and was willing to reduce his price by 4%.

However, as each operation in the manufacturing process was discussed, it became clear that some IBM cost estimates were too low because certain crating and shipping expenses had been overlooked. These oversights were minor, however, and in the following discussions, the two parties arrived at a common understanding of specifications and reached agreements on the costs of each manufacturing operation.

At this point, SMT representatives expressed great concern about the possibility of inflation in material costs. The IBM negotiators volunteered to include a form of price escalation in the contract, as previously agreed among themselves. IBM representatives suggested that if overall material costs changed by more than 10%, the price could be adjusted accordingly. However, if one party took the initiative to have the price revised, the other could require an analysis of *all* parts and materials invoices in arriving at the new price.

Another concern of the SMT representatives was that a large amount of overtime and subcontracting would be required to meet IBM's specified delivery schedule. IBM negotiators thought that a relaxation in the delivery schedule might be possible if a price concession could be obtained. In response, the SMT team offered a 5% discount, and this was accepted. As a result of these negotiations, the SMT price was reduced almost 20% below its original bid price.

In a subsequent meeting called to negotiate the prices of certain pipes to be used in the system, it became apparent to an IBM cost estimator that SMT representatives had seriously underestimated their costs. He pointed out this apparent error because he could not understand why SMT had quoted such a low figure. He wanted to be sure that SMT was using the correct manufacturing process. In any case, if SMT estimators had made a mistake, it should be noted. It was IBM's policy to seek a fair price both for itself and for its suppliers. IBM procurement managers believed that if a vendor was losing money on a job, there would be a tendency to cut corners. In addition, the IBM negotiator felt that by pointing out the error, he generated some goodwill that would help in future sessions.

Discussion Questions

1. What are the advantages and disadvantages to IBM and SMT from this approach?
2. How does SMT's proposed learning rate compare with that of other industries?
3. What are the limitations of the learning curve in this case?

Source: Based on E. Raymond Corey, *Procurement Management: Strategy, Organization, and Decision Making* (New York, NY Van Nostrand Reinhold).

MODULE E | RAPID REVIEW

MyLab Operations
Management

Main Heading	Review Material	

WHAT IS A LEARNING CURVE? (pp. 761–762)	• **Learning curves**—The premise that people and organizations get better at their tasks as the tasks are repeated; sometimes called experience curves.
	
	Learning usually follows a negative exponential curve.
	
	It takes less time to complete each additional unit a firm produces; however, the time *savings* in completing each subsequent unit *decreases.*
	
	Learning curves were first applied to industry in a report by T. P. Wright of Curtis-Wright Corp. in 1936. Wright described how direct labour costs of making a particular airplane decreased with learning.
	
	Learning curves have been applied not only to labour but also to a wide variety of other costs, including material and purchased components.
	
	The power of the learning curve is so significant that it plays a major role in many strategic decisions related to employment levels, costs, capacity, and pricing.
	
	The learning curve is based on a *doubling* of production: That is, when production doubles, the decrease in time per unit affects the rate of the learning curve.
	
	$$T \times L^n = \text{Time required for the } n\text{th unit} \qquad \textbf{(E-1)}$$
	where T = unit cost or time of the first unit
	          L = learning-curve rate
	          n = number of times T is doubled	

LEARNING CURVES IN SERVICES AND MANUFACTURING (pp. 762–763)	Different organizations—indeed, different products—have different learning curves. The rate of learning varies, depending on the quality of management and the potential of the process and product. *Any change in process, product, or personnel disrupts the learning curve.* Therefore, caution should be exercised in assuming that a learning curve is continuing and permanent. The steeper the slope of the learning curve, the faster the drop in costs. By tradition, learning curves are defined in terms of the *complements* of their improvement rates (i.e., a 75% learning rate is better than an 85% learning rate). Stable, standardized products and processes tend to have costs that decline more steeply than others. Learning curves are useful for a variety of purposes, including: 1. *Internal:* Labour forecasting, scheduling, establishing costs and budgets. 2. *External:* Supply chain negotiations. 3. *Strategic:* Evaluation of company and industry performance, including costs and pricing.	
APPLYING THE LEARNING CURVE (pp. 763–766)	If learning-curve improvement is ignored, potential problems could arise, such as scheduling mismatches, leading to idle labour and productive facilities, refusal to accept new orders because capacity is assumed to be full, or missing an opportunity to negotiate with suppliers for lower purchase prices as a result of large orders. Three ways to approach the mathematics of learning curves are (1) arithmetic analysis, (2) logarithmic analysis, and (3) learning-curve coefficients. The arithmetic approach uses the production doubling equation, Equation (E-1).	Problems: E.1–E.23 Virtual Office Hours for Solved Problems: E.1, E.2 **ACTIVE MODEL E.1**

Main Heading	**Review Material**

	The logarithmic approach allows us to determine labour for *any* unit, T_N, by the formula:
	
	$$T_N = T_1(N^b) \qquad \text{(E-2)}$$
	
	where T_N = time for the Nth unit
	          T_1 = hours to produce the first unit
	          b = (log of the learning rate)/(log 2) = slope of the learning curve
	
	The learning-curve coefficient approach makes use of Table E.3 and uses the formula:
	
	$$T_N = T_1 C \qquad \text{(E-3)}$$
	
	where T_N = number of labour-hours required to produce the Nth unit
	          T_1 = number of labour-hours required to produce the first unit
	          C = learning-curve coefficient found in "Unit Time Coefficient" columns of Table E.3
	
	The learning-curve coefficient, C, depends on both the learning rate and the unit number of interest.
	
	Equation (E-3) can also use the "Total Time Coefficient" columns of Table E.3 to provide the total cumulative number of hours needed to complete the specified number of units.
	
	If the most recent or most reliable information available pertains to some unit other than the first, these data should be used to find a revised estimate for the first unit, and then the applicable formulas should be applied to that revised number.

STRATEGIC IMPLICATIONS OF LEARNING CURVES (pp. 766–767)	When a firm's strategy is to pursue a learning cost curve steeper than the industry average, it can do this by: 1. Following an aggressive pricing policy. 2. Focusing on continuing cost reduction and productivity improvement. 3. Building on shared experience. 4. Keeping capacity growing ahead of demand. Managers must understand competitors before embarking on a learning-curve strategy. For example, taking on a strong competitor in a price war may help only the consumer.
LIMITATIONS OF LEARNING CURVES (p. 767)	Before using learning curves, some cautions are in order: • Because learning curves differ from company to company, as well as industry to industry, estimates for each organization should be developed rather than applying someone else's. • Learning curves are often based on the time necessary to complete the early units; therefore, those times must be accurate. As current information becomes available, re-evaluation is appropriate. • Any changes in personnel, design, or procedure can be expected to alter the learning curve, causing the curve to spike up for a short time, even if it is going to drop in the long run. • While workers and process may improve, the same learning curves do not always apply to indirect labour and material. • The culture of the workplace, as well as resource availability and changes in the process, may alter the learning curve. For instance, as a project nears its end, worker interest and effort may drop, curtailing progress down the curve.

Self-Test

■ **Before taking the self-test,** refer to the learning objectives listed at the beginning of the module.

LO1 A learning curve describes:
a) the rate at which an organization acquires new data.
b) the amount of production time per unit as the total number of units produced increases.
c) the increase in production time per unit as the total number of units produced increases.
d) the increase in number of units produced per unit time as the total number of units produced increases.

LO2 A surgical procedure with a 90% learning curve required 20 hours for the initial patient. The fourth patient should require approximately how many hours?
a) 18
b) 16.2
c) 28
d) 30
e) 54.2

LO3 The first transmission took 50 hours to rebuild at Bob's Auto Repair, and the learning rate is 80%. How long will it take to rebuild the third unit? (Include at least three decimals in the exponent if you use the logarithmic approach.)
a) Under 30 hours
b) About 32 hours
c) About 35 hours
d) About 60 hours
e) About 45 hours

LO4 Which one of the following courses of action would *not* be taken by a firm wanting to pursue a learning curve steeper than the industry average?
a) Following an aggressive pricing policy
b) Focusing on continuing cost reduction
c) Keeping capacity equal to demand to control costs
d) Focusing on productivity improvement
e) Building on shared experience

Answers: LO1. b; LO2. b; LO3. c; LO4. c.

MyLab Operations Management

Most of these questions can be found in MyLab Operations Management. Visit MyLab Operations Management to access cases, videos, downloadable software, and much more. MyLab Operations Management Management also features a personalized Study Plan that helps you identify which chapter concepts you've mastered and guides you towards study tools for additional practice.

Simulation

Learning Objectives

LO1 List the advantages and disadvantages of modelling with simulation **777**

LO2 Perform the five steps in a Monte Carlo simulation **777**

LO3 Simulate a queuing problem **780**

LO4 Simulate an inventory problem **783**

LO5 Use Excel spreadsheets to create a simulation **787**

What Is Simulation?

Simulation models abound in our world. Cities use them to control traffic. Bombardier uses them to test the aerodynamics of proposed jets. The Canadian Forces simulates war games on computers. Business students use management gaming to simulate realistic business competition. And thousands of organizations such as hospitals develop simulation models to help make operations decisions.

Most of the large companies in the world use simulation models. Table F.1 lists just a few areas in which simulation is now being applied.

Simulation is the attempt to duplicate the features, appearance, and characteristics of a real system. In this module, we will show how to simulate part of an operations management system by building a mathematical model that comes as close as possible to representing the reality of the system. The model will then be used to estimate the effects of various actions. The idea behind simulation is threefold:

Simulation

The attempt to duplicate the features, appearance, and characteristics of a real system, usually via a computerized model.

1. To imitate a real-world situation mathematically.
2. Then to study its properties and operating characteristics.
3. Finally to draw conclusions and make action decisions based on the results of the simulation.

In this way, a real-life system need not be touched until the advantages and disadvantages of a major policy decision are first measured on the model.

To use simulation, an OM manager should:

1. Define the problem.
2. Introduce the important variables associated with the problem.
3. Construct a numerical model.
4. Set up possible courses of action for testing by specifying values of variables.
5. Run the experiment.
6. Consider the results (possibly modifying the model or changing data inputs).
7. Decide what course of action to take.

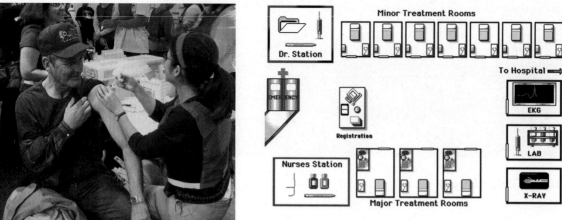

When hospitals and medical centres face severe overcrowding at their outpatient clinics, they turn to computer simulation to try to reduce bottlenecks and improve patient flow. A simulation language called Micro Saint analyzes current data relating to patient service times between clinic rooms. By simulating different numbers of doctors and staff, simulating the use of another clinic for overflow, and simulating a redesign of the existing clinic, hospital management is able to make decisions based on an understanding of both costs and benefits. This results in better patient service at lower cost.

Table F.1

Some Applications of Simulation

Ambulance location and dispatching	Bus scheduling
Assembly-line balancing	Design of library operations
Parking lot and harbour design	Taxi, truck, and railroad dispatching
Distribution system design	Production facility scheduling
Scheduling aircraft	Plant layout
Labour-hiring decisions	Capital investments
Personnel scheduling	Production scheduling
Traffic-light timing	Sales forecasting
Voting pattern prediction	Inventory planning and control

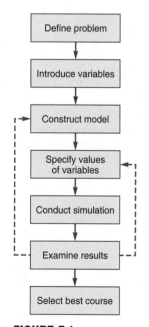

FIGURE F.1

The Process of Simulation

These steps are illustrated in Figure F.1.

The problems tackled by simulation may range from very simple to extremely complex, from bank-teller lines to an analysis of the Canadian economy. Although small simulations can be conducted by hand, effective use of the technique requires a computer. Large-scale models, simulating perhaps years of business decisions, are virtually all handled by computer.

In this module, we examine the basic principles of simulation and then tackle some problems in the areas of waiting-line analysis and inventory control. Why do we use simulation in these areas when mathematical models described in other chapters can solve similar problems? The answer is that simulation provides an alternative approach for problems that are very complex mathematically. It can handle, for example, inventory problems in which demand or lead time is not constant.

Advantages and Disadvantages of Simulation

Simulation is a tool that has become widely accepted by managers for several reasons. The main *advantages* of simulation are as follows:

1. Simulation is relatively straightforward and flexible.
2. It can be used to analyze large and complex real-world situations that cannot be solved by conventional operations management models.

3. Real-world complications can be included that most OM models cannot permit. For example, simulation can use *any* probability distribution the user defines; it does not require standard distributions.

4. *Time compression* is possible. The effects of OM policies over many months or years can be obtained by computer simulation in a short time.

5. Simulation allows "what-if" types of questions. Managers like to know in advance what options will be most attractive. With a computerized model, a manager can try out several policy decisions within a matter of minutes.

6. Simulations do not interfere with real-world systems. It may be too disruptive, for example, to experiment physically with new policies or ideas in a hospital or manufacturing plant.

7. Simulation can study the interactive effects of individual components or variables in order to determine which ones are important.

LO1 List the advantages and disadvantages of modelling with simulation

The main *disadvantages* of simulation are as follows:

1. Good simulation models can be very expensive; they may take many months to develop.

2. It is a trial-and-error approach that may produce different solutions in repeated runs. It does not generate optimal solutions to problems (as does linear programming).

3. Managers must generate all of the conditions and constraints for solutions that they want to examine. The simulation model does not produce answers without adequate, realistic input.

4. Each simulation model is unique. Its solutions and inferences are not usually transferable to other problems.

Monte Carlo Simulation

STUDENT **TIP**

This approach is named after the random behaviour of a roulette wheel.

When a system contains elements that exhibit *chance* in their behaviour, the **Monte Carlo method** of simulation may be applied. The basis of Monte Carlo simulation is experimentation on chance (or *probabilistic*) elements by means of random sampling.

The technique breaks down into five simple steps:

1. Setting up a probability distribution for important variables.
2. Building a cumulative probability distribution for each variable.
3. Establishing an interval of random numbers for each variable.
4. Generating random numbers.
5. Actually simulating a series of trials.

Let's examine these steps in turn.

Monte Carlo method

A simulation technique that uses random elements when chance exists in their behaviour.

LO2 Perform the five steps in a Monte Carlo simulation

STEP 1. ESTABLISHING PROBABILITY DISTRIBUTIONS

The basic idea in the Monte Carlo simulation is to generate values for the variables making up the model under study. In real-world systems, a lot of variables are probabilistic in nature. To name just a few: inventory demand; lead time for orders to arrive; times between machine breakdowns; times between customer arrivals at a service facility; service times; times required to complete project activities; and number of employees absent from work each day.

One common way to establish a *probability distribution* for a given variable is to examine historical outcomes. We can find the probability, or relative frequency, for each possible outcome of a variable by dividing the frequency of observation by the total number of observations.

Here's an example. The daily demand for radial tires at Barry's Auto Tire over the past 200 days is shown in columns 1 and 2 of Table F.2. Assuming that past arrival rates will hold in the future, we can convert this demand to a probability distribution by dividing each demand frequency by the total demand, 200. The results are shown in column 3.

Table F.2

Demand for Barry's Auto Tire

	(1)	(2)	(3)	(4)
	Demand for Tires	Frequency	Probability of Occurrence	Cumulative Probability
	0	10	10/200 = 0.05	0.05
	1	20	20/200 = 0.10	0.15
	2	40	40/200 = 0.20	0.35
	3	60	60/200 = 0.30	0.65
	4	40	40/200 = 0.20	0.85
	5	30	30/200 = 0.15	1.00
		200 days	200/200 = 1.00	

STUDENT TIP

To establish a probability distribution for tires, we assume that historical demand is a good indicator of future demand.

STEP 2. BUILDING A CUMULATIVE PROBABILITY DISTRIBUTION FOR EACH VARIABLE

Cumulative probability distribution

The accumulation of individual probabilities of a distribution.

The conversion from a regular probability distribution, such as in column 3 of Table F.2, to a **cumulative probability distribution** is an easy job. In column 4, we see that the cumulative probability for each level of demand is the sum of the number in the probability column (column 3) added to the previous cumulative probability.

STEP 3. SETTING RANDOM-NUMBER INTERVALS

Random-number intervals

Sets of numbers to represent each possible value or outcome in a computer simulation.

Random number

A digit that has been selected by a totally random process.

Once we have established a cumulative probability distribution for each variable in the simulation, we must assign a set of numbers to represent each possible value or outcome. These are referred to as **random-number intervals**. Basically, a **random number** is a series of digits (say, two digits from 01, 02, . . ., 98, 99, 00) that have been selected by a totally random process—a process in which each random number has an equal chance of being selected.

If, for example, there is a 5% chance that demand for Barry's radial tires will be zero units per day, then we will want 5% of the random numbers available to correspond to a demand of zero units. If a total of 100 two-digit numbers are used in the simulation, we could assign a demand of zero units to the first five random numbers: 01, 02, 03, 04, and 05.[1] Then a simulated demand for zero units would be created every time one of the numbers 01 to 05 was drawn. If there is also a 10% chance that demand for the same product will be one unit per day, we could let the next 10 random numbers (06, 07, 08, 09, 10, 11, 12, 13, 14, and 15) represent that demand—and so on for other demand levels.

Similarly, we can see in Table F.3 that the length of each interval on the right corresponds to the probability of one of each of the possible daily demands. Thus, in assigning random numbers to the daily demand for three radial tires, the range of the random-number interval (36 through 65) corresponds *exactly* to the probability (or proportion) of that outcome. A daily demand for three radial tires occurs 30% of the time. All of the 30 random numbers greater than 35 up to and including 65 are assigned to that event.

Table F.3

The Assignment of Random-Number Intervals for Barry's Auto Tire

Daily Demand	Probability	Cumulative Probability	Interval of Random Numbers
0	0.05	0.05	01 through 05
1	0.10	0.15	06 through 15
2	0.20	0.35	16 through 35
3	0.30	0.65	36 through 65
4	0.20	0.85	66 through 85
5	0.15	1.00	86 through 00

STUDENT TIP

You may start random-number intervals at either 01 or 00, but the text starts at 01 so that the top of each range is the cumulative probability.

[1] Alternatively, we could have assigned the random numbers 00, 01, 02, 03, and 04 to represent a demand of zero units. The two digits 00 can be thought of as either 0 or 100. As long as five numbers out of 100 are assigned to the zero demand, it does not make any difference which five they are.

Table F.4
Table of Two-Digit Random Numbers

52	06	50	88	53	30	10	47	99	37	66	91	35	32	00	84	57	07
37	63	28	02	74	35	24	03	29	60	74	85	90	73	59	55	17	60
82	57	68	28	05	94	03	11	27	79	90	87	92	41	09	25	36	77
69	02	36	49	71	99	32	10	75	21	95	90	94	38	97	71	72	49
98	94	90	36	06	78	23	67	89	85	29	21	25	73	69	34	85	76
96	52	62	87	49	56	59	23	78	71	72	90	57	01	98	57	31	95
33	69	27	21	11	60	95	89	68	48	17	89	34	09	93	50	44	51
50	33	50	95	13	44	34	62	64	39	55	29	30	64	49	44	30	16
88	32	18	50	62	57	34	56	62	31	15	40	90	34	51	95	26	14
90	30	36	24	69	82	51	74	30	35	36	85	01	55	92	64	09	85
50	48	61	18	85	23	08	54	17	12	80	69	24	84	92	16	49	59
27	88	21	62	69	64	48	31	12	73	02	68	00	16	16	46	13	85
45	14	46	32	13	49	66	62	74	41	86	98	92	98	84	54	33	40
81	02	01	78	82	74	97	37	45	31	94	99	42	49	27	64	89	42
66	83	14	74	27	76	03	33	11	97	59	81	72	00	64	61	13	52
74	05	81	82	93	09	96	33	52	78	13	06	28	30	94	23	37	39
30	34	87	01	74	11	46	82	59	94	25	34	32	23	17	01	58	73
59	55	72	33	62	13	74	68	22	44	42	09	32	46	71	79	45	89
67	09	80	98	99	25	77	50	03	32	36	63	65	75	94	19	95	88
60	77	46	63	71	69	44	22	03	85	14	48	69	13	30	50	33	24
60	08	19	29	36	72	30	27	50	64	85	72	75	29	87	05	75	01
80	45	86	99	02	34	87	08	86	84	49	76	24	08	01	86	29	11
53	84	49	63	26	65	72	84	85	63	26	02	75	26	92	62	40	67
69	84	12	94	51	36	17	02	15	29	16	52	56	43	26	22	08	62
37	77	13	10	02	18	31	19	32	85	31	94	81	43	31	58	33	51

Source: Reprinted from A *Million Random Digits with 100,000 Normal Deviates,* ©1955, RAND Corporation. Used by permission.

STEP 4. GENERATING RANDOM NUMBERS

Random numbers may be generated for simulation problems in two ways. If the problem is large and the process under study involves many simulation trials, computer programs are available to generate the needed random numbers. If the simulation is being done by hand, the numbers may be selected from a table of random digits.

STEP 5. SIMULATING THE EXPERIMENT

We may simulate outcomes of an experiment by simply selecting random numbers from Table F.4. Beginning anywhere in the table, we note the interval in Table F.3 into which each number falls. For example, if the random number chosen is 81 and the interval 66 through 85 represents a daily demand for four tires, then we select a demand of four tires. Example F1 carries the simulation further.

Naturally, it would be risky to draw any hard and fast conclusions about the operation of a firm from only a short simulation like Example F1. Seldom would anyone actually want to go to the effort of simulating such a simple model containing only one variable. Simulating by hand does, however, demonstrate the important principles involved and may be useful in small-scale studies.

Simulating Demand

Barry's Auto Tire wants to simulate 10 days of demand for radial tires.

APPROACH ▶ Earlier, we went through Steps 1 and 2 in the Monte Carlo method (in Table F.2) and Step 3 (in Table F.3). Now, we need to generate random numbers (Step 4) and simulate demand (Step 5).

SOLUTION ▶ We select the random numbers needed from Table F.4, starting in the upper-left-hand corner and continuing down the first column, and record the corresponding daily demand:

Day Number	Random Number	Simulated Daily Demand
1	52	3
2	37	3
3	82	4
4	69	4
5	98	5
6	96	5
7	33	2
8	50	3
9	88	5
10	90	5

39 Total 10-day demand

39/10 = 3.9 = tires average daily demand

INSIGHT ▶ It is interesting to note that the average demand of 3.9 tires in this 10-day simulation differs substantially from the *expected* daily demand, which we may calculate from the data in Table F.3:

$$\text{Expected demand} = \sum_{i=1}^{5} (\text{probability of } i \text{ units}) \times (\text{demand of } i \text{ units})$$

$$= (0.05)(0) + (0.10)(1) + (0.20)(2) + (0.30)(3) + (0.20)(4) + (0.15)(5)$$

$$= 0 + 0.1 + 0.4 + 0.9 + 0.8 + 0.75$$

$$= 2.95 \text{ tires}$$

However, if this simulation were repeated hundreds or thousands of times, the average *simulated* demand would be nearly the same as the *expected* demand.

LEARNING EXERCISE ▶ Resimulate the 10 days, this time with random numbers from column 2 of Table F.4. What is the average daily demand? [Answer: 2.5.]

RELATED PROBLEMS ▶ F.1, F.2, F.3, F.4, F.5, F.7, F.9, F.10, F.14, F.20

Simulation of a Queuing Problem

An important use of simulation is in the analysis of waiting-line problems. As we saw in Module D, the assumptions required for solving queuing problems are quite restrictive. For most realistic queuing systems, simulation may be the only approach available, as we see in the Starbucks *OM in Action* box.

Example F2 illustrates the use of simulation for a large unloading dock and its associated queue. Arrivals of barges at the dock are not Poisson-distributed, and unloading rates (service times) are not exponential or constant. As such, the mathematical waiting-line models of Module D cannot be used.

OM in Action — Simulation Software Takes the Kinks Out of Starbucks's Lines

The animation on the computer screen is not encouraging. Starbucks is running a digital simulation of customers ordering new warm sandwiches and pastries at a "virtual" store.

At first, things seem to go well, as animated workers rush around, preparing orders. But then they can't keep up. Soon the customers are stacking up in line, and the goal of serving each person in less than three minutes is blown. The line quickly reaches the point at which customers decide the snack or drink isn't worth the wait—called the "balking point" in queuing theory.

Fortunately for Starbucks, the customers departing without their frappuccinos and decaf slim lattes are digital. The simulation software is helping operations managers find out what caused the backup before the scene repeats itself in the real world.

Simulation software is also used to find the point where capital expenditures will pay off. In large chains such as Starbucks, adding even a minor piece of equipment can

add up. A $200 blender in each of Starbucks's more than 10 000 stores globally would cost the firm over $2 million.

Sources: *The Wall Street Journal* (August 4, 2009): A1, A10; and *Business Wire* (February 13, 2006): 1 and (June 15, 2005): 1.

Following long trips up and down the St. Lawrence River from various cities and towns, fully loaded barges arrive at night in Montreal. Barges are unloaded on a first-in, first-out basis. Any barges not unloaded on the day of arrival must wait until the following day. However, tying up barges in dock is an expensive proposition, and the superintendent cannot ignore the angry phone calls from barge owners reminding him that "Time is money!" He decides that before going to the Port of Montreal controller to request additional unloading crews, he should conduct a simulation study of arrivals, unloadings, and delays. A 100-day simulation would be ideal, but for purposes of illustration, the superintendent can begin with a shorter 15-day analysis.

APPROACH ▶ Follow the five steps in Monte Carlo simulation: (1) Establish probability distributions for the important variables (i.e., barge arrivals and barge unloadings); (2 and 3) create cumulative distributions and random-number intervals for each variable; (4) draw random numbers from Table F.4; and (5) simulate the experiment.

SOLUTION ▶ The number of barges docking on any given night ranges from 0 to 5. The probability of 0, 1, 2, 3, 4, and 5 arrivals is displayed in Table F.5. In the same table, we establish cumulative probabilities and corresponding random-number intervals for each possible value.

EXAMPLE F2

A Barge-Unloading Simulation With Two Variables

Table F.5

Overnight Barge Arrival Rates and Random-Number Intervals

Number of Arrivals	Probability	Cumulative Probability	Random-Number Interval
0	0.13	0.13	01 through 13
1	0.17	0.30	14 through 30
2	0.15	0.45	31 through 45
3	0.25	0.70	46 through 70
4	0.20	0.90	71 through 90
5	0.10	1.00	91 through 00
	1.00		

The dock superintendent believes that the number of barges unloaded also tends to vary from day to day. In Table F.6, the superintendent provides information from which we can create a probability distribution for the variable *daily unloading rate*. As we just did for the arrival variable, we can set up an interval of random numbers for the unloading rates.

Table F.6

Unloading Rates and Random-Number Intervals

Daily Unloading Rates	Probability	Cumulative Probability	Random-Number Interval
1	0.05	0.05	01 through 05
2	0.15	0.20	06 through 20
3	0.50	0.70	21 through 70
4	0.20	0.90	71 through 90
5	0.10	1.00	91 through 00
	1.00		

Random numbers are drawn from the top row of Table F.4 to generate daily arrival rates. To create daily unloading rates, they are drawn from the second row of Table F.4. Table F.7 shows the day-to-day port simulation.

INSIGHT ▶ The superintendent will likely be interested in at least three useful and important pieces of information:

$$\left(\begin{array}{c}\text{Average number of barges} \\ \text{delayed to the next day}\end{array}\right) = \frac{20 \text{ delays}}{15 \text{ days}}$$

$$= 1.33 \text{ barges delayed per day}$$

$$\text{Average number of nightly arrivals} = \frac{41 \text{ arrivals}}{15 \text{ days}}$$

$$= 2.73 \text{ arrivals per night}$$

$$\text{Average number of barges unloaded each day} = \frac{39 \text{ unloadings}}{15 \text{ days}}$$

$$= 2.60 \text{ unloadings per day}$$

The simulation in Table F.7 by itself provides interesting data, but these three averages are management information to help make decisions.

Table F.7

Queuing Simulation of Port of Montreal Barge Unloadings

(1) Day	(2) Number Delayed from Previous Day	(3) Random Number	(4) Number of Nightly Arrivals	(5) Total to Be Unloaded	(6) Random Number	(7) Number Unloaded
1	—a	52	3	3	37	3
2	0	06	0	0	63	0b
3	0	50	3	3	28	3
4	0	88	4	4	02	1
5	3	53	3	6	74	4
6	2	30	1	3	35	3
7	0	10	0	0	24	0c
8	0	47	3	3	03	1
9	2	99	5	7	29	3
10	4	37	2	6	60	3
11	3	66	3	6	74	4
12	2	91	5	7	85	4
13	3	35	2	5	90	4
14	1	32	2	3	73	3d
15	0	00	5	5	59	3
	20		41			39
	Total delays		Total arrivals			Total unloadings

aWe can begin with no delays from the previous day. In a long simulation, even if we started with five overnight delays, that initial condition would be averaged out.

bThree barges could have been unloaded on day 2. Yet, because there were no arrivals and no backlog existed, zero unloadings took place.

cThe same situation as noted in footnote b takes place.

dThis time, four barges could have been unloaded, but because only three were in the queue, the number unloaded is recorded as three.

When the data from Example F2 are analyzed in terms of delay costs, idle labour costs, and the cost of hiring extra unloading crew, the dock superintendent and port controller can make a better staffing decision. They may even choose to resimulate the process assuming different unloading rates that correspond to increased crew sizes. Although simulation cannot guarantee an optimal solution to problems such as this, it can be helpful in recreating a process and identifying good decision alternatives.

Simulation and Inventory Analysis

In Chapter 12, we introduced inventory models. The commonly used EOQ models are based on the assumption that both product demand and reorder lead time are known, constant values. In most real-world inventory situations, though, demand and lead time are variables, so accurate analysis becomes extremely difficult to handle by any means other than simulation. This is discussed in the *OM in Action* box "Toronto General Hospital Uses Computer Simulation for Scheduling".

LO4 Simulate an inventory problem

In this section, we present an inventory problem with two decision variables and two probabilistic components. The owner of the hardware store in Example F3 would like to establish *order quantity* and *reorder point* decisions for a particular product that has probabilistic (uncertain) daily demand and reorder lead time. He wants to make a series of simulation runs, trying out various order quantities and reorder points, to minimize his total inventory cost for the item. Inventory costs in this case will include ordering, holding, and stockout costs.

OM in Action **Toronto General Hospital Uses Computer Simulation for Scheduling**

There are quite a few operating rooms in the Toronto General Hospital (TGH), and they are busy. They have a full slate of surgeries, including emergency cases, transplants, and elective surgeries. In order to optimize the use of the facilities, TGH implemented a computerized decision support tool that aids hospital administrators in more efficient scheduling of operating rooms in the institution. They used computer simulation to assess the impact of the many different factors on operating room utilization and ultimately improve the utilization ratio.

Most hospitals with a fixed budget, similar to TGH, find that operating rooms represent a bottleneck. Operating rooms consume scarce and expensive resources and a significant portion of the hospital's annual budget. Thus, most

Canadian hospitals could benefit from tools and methods for effective scheduling of operating rooms in order to reduce expenditures while maintaining top quality of care.

The overall numbers and types of operating rooms in a hospital can be found in their master surgical schedules. This master schedule contains their operating time and the service or surgeon assigned to rooms in a specific period of time. Developing an optimized master surgical schedule is a complex task since there are many factors impacting the operating room scheduling. Toronto General Hospital determined this to be a worthwhile investment in time and resources.

Source: www.uhn.ca.

Simkin's Hardware Store in Canmore, Alberta, sells the Ace model electric drill. Daily demand for this particular product is relatively low but subject to some variability. Lead times tend to be variable as well. Mark Simkin wants to develop a simulation to test an inventory policy of ordering 10 drills, with a reorder point of five. In other words, every time the on-hand inventory level at the end of the day is five or fewer, Simkin will call his supplier that evening and place an order for 10 more drills. Simkin notes that if the lead time is one day, the order will not arrive the next morning but rather at the beginning of the following workday. Stockouts become lost sales, not back orders.

APPROACH ▶ Simkin wants to follow the five steps in the Monte Carlo simulation process.

SOLUTION ▶ Over the past 300 days, Simkin has observed the sales shown in column 2 of Table F.8. He converts this historical frequency into a probability distribution for the variable daily demand (column 3). A cumulative probability distribution is formed in column 4 of Table F.8. Finally, Simkin establishes an interval of random numbers to represent each possible daily demand (column 5).

Table F.8

Probabilities and Random-Number Intervals for Daily Ace Drill Demand

(1) Demand for Ace Drill	(2) Frequency	(3) Probability	(4) Cumulative Probability	(5) Interval of Random Numbers
0	15	0.05	0.05	01 through 05
1	30	0.10	0.15	06 through 15
2	60	0.20	0.35	16 through 35
3	120	0.40	0.75	36 through 75
4	45	0.15	0.90	76 through 90
5	30	0.10	1.00	91 through 00
	300 days	1.00		

When Simkin places an order to replenish his inventory of drills, there is a delivery lag of from one to three days. This means that lead time may also be considered a probabilistic variable. The number of days that it took to receive the past 50 orders is presented in Table F.9. In a fashion similar to the creation of the demand variable, Simkin establishes a probability distribution for the lead-time variable (column 3 of Table F.9), computes the cumulative distribution (column 4), and assigns random-number intervals for each possible time (column 5).

Table F.9

Probabilities and Random-Number Intervals for Reorder Lead Time

(1) Lead Time (days)	(2) Frequency	(3) Probability	(4) Cumulative Probability	(5) Random-Number Interval
1	10	0.20	0.20	01 through 20
2	25	0.50	0.70	21 through 70
3	15	0.30	1.00	71 through 00
	50 orders	1.00		

Table F.10

Simkin Hardware's First Inventory Simulation. Order Quantity = 10 Units; Reorder Point = 5 units

(1) Day	(2) Units Received	(3) Beginning Inventory	(4) Random Number	(5) Demand	(6) Ending Inventory	(7) Lost Sales	(8) Order?	(9) Random Number	(10) Lead Time
1		10	06	1	9	0	No		
2	0	9	63	3	6	0	No		
3	0	6	57	3	3[a]	0	Yes	02[b]	1
4	0	3	94[c]	5	0	2	No[d]		
5	10[e]	10	52	3	7	0	No		
6	0	7	69	3	4	0	Yes	33	2
7	0	4	32	2	2	0	No		
8	0	2	30	2	0	0	No		
9	10[f]	10	48	3	7	0	No		
10	0	7	88	4	3	0	Yes	14	1
					Totals: 41	2			

[a]This is the first time inventory dropped to the reorder point of five drills. Because no prior order was outstanding, an order is placed.

[b]The random number 02 is generated to represent the first lead time. It was drawn from column 2 of Table F.4 as the next number in the list being used. A separate column could have been used from which to draw lead-time random numbers if we had wanted to do so, but in this example, we did not do so.

[c]Again, notice that the random digits 02 were used for lead time (see footnote b). So the next number in the column is 94.

[d]No order is placed on day 4 because there is an order outstanding from the previous day that has not yet arrived.

[e]The lead time for the first order placed is one day, but as noted in the text, an order does not arrive the next morning but rather the beginning of the following day. Thus, the first order arrives at the start of day 5.

[f]This is the arrival of the order placed at the close of business on day 6. Fortunately for Simkin, no lost sales occurred during the two-day lead time before the order arrived.

The entire process is simulated in Table F.10 for a 10-day period. We assume that beginning inventory (column 3) is 10 units on day 1. We took the random numbers (column 4) from column 2 of Table F.4.

Table F.10 was filled in by proceeding one day (or line) at a time, working from left to right. It is a four-step process:

1. Begin each simulated day by checking to see whether any ordered inventory has just arrived. If it has, increase current inventory by the quantity ordered (10 units, in this case).
2. Generate a daily demand from the demand probability distribution for the selected random number.
3. Compute: Ending inventory = Beginning inventory − Demand. If on-hand inventory is insufficient to meet the day's demand, satisfy as much demand as possible and note the number of lost sales.
4. Determine whether the day's ending inventory has reached the reorder point (five units). If it has, and if there are no outstanding orders, place an order. Lead time for a new order is simulated for the selected random number corresponding to the distribution in Table F.9.

INSIGHT ▶ Simkin's inventory simulation yields some interesting results. The average daily ending inventory is:

$$\text{Average ending inventory} = \frac{41 \text{ total units}}{10 \text{ days}} = 4.1 \text{ units/day}$$

We also note the average lost sales and number of orders placed per day:

$$\text{Average lost sales} = \frac{2 \text{ sales lost}}{10 \text{ days}} = 0.2 \text{ units/day}$$

$$\text{Average number of orders placed} = \frac{3 \text{ orders}}{10 \text{ days}} = 0.3 \text{ orders/day}$$

LEARNING EXERCISE ▶ How would these three averages change if the random numbers for day 10 were 04 and 93 instead of 88 and 14? [Answer: 4.5, 0.2 (no change), and 0.2.]

RELATED PROBLEMS ▶ F.11, F.16a

Example F4 shows how these data can be useful in studying the inventory costs of the policy being simulated.

EXAMPLE F4

Adding Costs to Example F3

Simkin wants to put a cost on the ordering policy simulated in Example F3.

APPROACH ▶ Simkin estimates that the cost of placing each order for Ace drills is $10, the holding cost per drill held at the end of each day is $0.50, and the cost of each lost sale is $8. This information enables us to compute the total daily inventory cost.

SOLUTION ▶ Here are the three cost components:

Daily order cost = (Cost of placing 1 order) × (Number of orders placed per day)

= $10 per order × 0.3 order per day = $3

Daily holding cost = (Cost of holding 1 unit for 1 day) × (Average ending inventory)

= $0.50 per unit per day × 4.1 units per day = $2.05

Daily stockout cost = (Cost per lost sale) × (Average number of lost sales per day)

= $8 per lost sale × 0.2 lost sales per day = $1.60

Total daily inventory cost = Daily order cost + Daily holding cost + Daily stockout cost = $6.65

INSIGHT ▶ This cost will help Simkin decide if the $Q = 10$, $ROP = 5$ order policy is a good one.

LEARNING EXERCISE ▶ If the cost of placing an order is really $20 (instead of $10), what is the correct total daily inventory cost? [Answer: $9.65.]

RELATED PROBLEMS ▶ F.12, F.13, F.16b, F.17, F.18

Now that we have worked through Example F3 and Example F4, we want to emphasize something very important: This simulation should be extended many more days before we draw any conclusions as to the cost of the order policy being tested. If a hand simulation is being conducted, 100 days would provide a better representation. If a computer is doing the calculations, 1000 days would be helpful in reaching accurate cost estimates. (Moreover, remember that even with a 1000-day simulation, the generated distribution should be compared with the desired distribution to ensure valid results.)

Let us say that Simkin *does* complete a 1000-day simulation of the policy from Example F3 (order quantity = 10 drills, reorder point = 5 drills). Does this complete his analysis? The answer is no—this is just the beginning! Simkin must now compare *this* potential strategy with other possibilities. For example, what about order quantity = 10, reorder point = 4? Or order quantity = 12, reorder point = 6? Or order quantity = 14, reorder point = 5? Perhaps every combination of values—of order quantity from 6 to 20 drills and reorder points from 3 to 10—should be simulated. After simulating all reasonable combinations of order quantities and reorder points, Simkin would likely select the pair yielding the lowest total inventory cost. Problem F.12 later in this module gives you a chance to help Simkin begin this series of comparisons.

MODULE SUMMARY

Simulation involves building mathematical models that attempt to act like real operating systems. In this way, a real-world situation can be studied without imposing on the actual system. Although simulation models can be developed manually, simulation by computer is generally more desirable. The Monte Carlo approach uses random numbers to represent variables, such as inventory demand or people waiting in line, which are then simulated in a series of trials. Simulation is widely used as an operations tool because its advantages usually outweigh its disadvantages.

Discussion Questions

1. State the seven steps, beginning with "Define the problem," that an operations manager should perform when using simulation to analyze a problem.
2. List the advantages of simulation.
3. List the disadvantages of simulation.
4. Explain the difference between *simulated* average demand and *expected* average demand.
5. What is the role of random numbers in a Monte Carlo simulation?
6. Why might the results of a simulation differ each time you make a run?
7. What is Monte Carlo simulation? What principles underlie its use, and what steps are followed in applying it?
8. List six ways that simulation can be used in business.
9. Why is simulation such a widely used technique?
10. What are the advantages of special-purpose simulation languages?
11. In the simulation of an order policy for drills at Simkin's hardware (Example F3), would the results (of Table F.10) change significantly if a longer period were simulated? Why is the 10-day simulation valid or invalid?
12. Why is a computer necessary in conducting a real-world simulation?
13. Why might a manager be forced to use simulation instead of an analytical model in dealing with a problem of:
   (a) inventory order policy?
   (b) ships docking in a port to unload?
   (c) bank-teller service windows?
   (d) the Canadian economy?

Using Software in Simulation

Computers are critical in simulating complex tasks. They can generate random numbers, simulate thousands of time periods in a matter of seconds or minutes, and provide management with reports that improve decision making. A computer approach is almost a necessity in order to draw valid conclusions from a simulation.

Computer programming languages can help the simulation process. *General-purpose languages*, such as BASIC or C++, constitute one approach. *Special-purpose simulation languages*, such as GPSS and SIMSCRIPT, have a few advantages: (1) they require less programming time for large simulations, (2) they are usually more efficient and easier to check for errors, and (3) random-number generators are already built in as subroutines.

Commercial, easy-to-use prewritten simulation programs are also available. Some are generalized to handle a wide variety of situations ranging from queuing to inventory. These include programs such

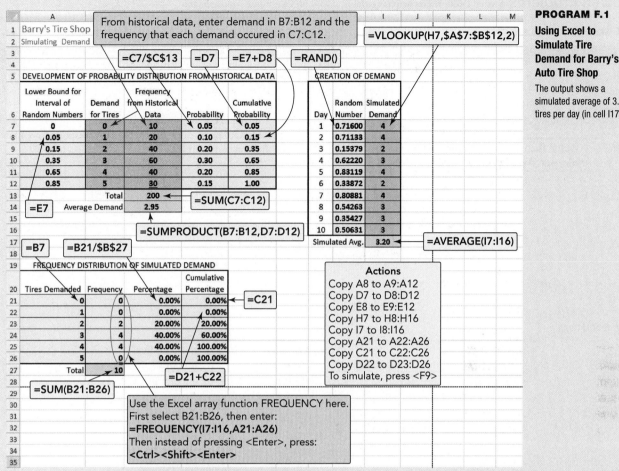

PROGRAM F.1

Using Excel to Simulate Tire Demand for Barry's Auto Tire Shop

The output shows a simulated average of 3.2 tires per day (in cell I17).

as Extend, Modsim, Witness, MAP/1, Enterprise Dynamics, Simfactory, ProModel, Micro Saint, and ARENA.

Spreadsheet software such as Excel can also be used to develop simulations quickly and easily. Such packages have built-in random-number generators and develop outputs through "data-fill" table commands.

✗USING EXCEL SPREADSHEETS

The ability to generate random numbers and then "look up" these numbers in a table to associate them with a specific event makes spreadsheets excellent tools for conducting simulations. Program F.1 illustrates an Excel simulation for Example F1.

Notice that the cumulative probabilities are calculated in column E of Program F.1. This procedure reduces the chance of error and is useful in larger simulations involving more levels of demand.

The VLOOKUP function in column I looks up the random number (generated in column H) in the leftmost column of the defined lookup table. The VLOOKUP function moves downward through this column until it finds a cell that is bigger than the random number. It then goes to the previous row and gets the value from column B of the table.

In column H, for example, the first random number shown is .716. Excel looked down the left-hand column of the lookup table ($A$7:$B$12) of Program F.1 until it found .85. From the previous row it retrieved the value in column B which is 4. Pressing the F9 function key recalculates the random numbers and the simulation.

LO5 Use Excel spreadsheets to create a simulation

✗USING POM FOR WINDOWS AND EXCEL OM

POM for Windows and Excel OM are capable of handling any simulation that contains only one random variable, such as Example F1. For further details, please refer to Appendix IV.

Solved Problems Virtual Office Hours help is available at MyLab Operations Management.

▼ SOLVED PROBLEM F.1

Higgins Plumbing and Heating maintains a stock of 113-litre water heaters that it sells to homeowners and installs for them. Owner Jim Higgins likes the idea of having a large supply on hand to meet any customer demand. However, he also recognizes that it is expensive to do so. He examines water heater sales over the past 50 weeks and notes the following:

Water Heater Sales per Week	Number of Weeks this Number Was Sold
4	6
5	5
6	9
7	12
8	8
9	7
10	3
	50 weeks total data

a) If Higgins maintains a constant supply of eight water heaters in any given week, how many times will he stockout during a 20-week simulation? We use random numbers from the seventh column of Table F.4, beginning with the random digit 10.

b) What is the average number of sales per week over the 20-week period?

c) Using an analytic nonsimulation technique, determine the expected number of sales per week. How does this compare with the answer in part (b)?

▼ SOLUTION

Heater Sales	Probability	Cumulative Probability	Random-Number Intervals
4	0.12	0.12	01 through 12
5	0.10	0.22	13 through 22
6	0.18	0.40	23 through 40
7	0.24	0.64	41 through 64
8	0.16	0.80	65 through 80
9	0.14	0.94	81 through 94
10	0.06	1.00	95 through 00
	1.00		

a)

Week	Random Number	Simulated Sales	Week	Random Number	Simulated Sales
1	10	4	11	08	4
2	24	6	12	48	7
3	03	4	13	66	8
4	32	6	14	97	10
5	23	6	15	03	4
6	59	7	16	96	10
7	95	10	17	46	7
8	34	6	18	74	8
9	34	6	19	77	8
10	51	7	20	44	7

a) With a supply of eight heaters, Higgins will stock out three times during the 20-week period (in weeks 7, 14, and 16).

b) Average sales by simulation = Total sales/20 weeks = 135/20 = 6.75 per week

c) Using expected values, we obtain:

E (sales) = 0.12(4 heaters) + 0.10(5)
   + 0.18(6) + 0.24(7) + 0.16(8)
   + 0.14(9) + 0.06(10)
   = 6.88 heaters

With a longer simulation, these two approaches will lead to even closer values.

▼ SOLVED PROBLEM F.2

Random numbers may be used to simulate continuous distributions. As a simple example, assume that fixed cost equals $300, profit contribution equals $10 per item sold, and you expect an equally likely chance of 0 to 99 units to be sold. That is, profit equals –$300 + $10X, where X is the number sold. The mean amount you expect to sell is 49.5 units.

a) Calculate the expected value.
b) Simulate the sale of five items, using the following double-digit randomly selected numbers of items sold: 37; 77; 13; 10; 85.
b) Calculate the expected value of part (b) and compare with the results of part (a).

▼ SOLUTION

a) Expected value = –300 + 10(49.5) = $195
b) – 300 + $10(37) = $70
    – 300 + $10(77) = $470
    – 300 + $10(13) = –$170
    – 300 + $10(10) = –$200
    – 300 + $10(85) = $550
c) The mean of these simulated sales is $144. If the sample size were larger, we would expect the two values to be closer.

Problems*

The problems that follow involve simulations that can be done by hand. However, to obtain accurate and meaningful results, long periods must be simulated. This task is usually handled by a computer. If you are able to program some of the problems in Excel or a computer language with which you are familiar, we suggest you try to do so. If not, the hand simulations will still help you understand the simulation process.

•   **F.1**   The daily demand for tuna sandwiches at a cafeteria vending machine is either 8, 9, 10, or 11, with probabilities 0.4, 0.3, 0.2, or 0.1, respectively. Assume the following random numbers have been generated: 09, 55, 73, 67, 53, 59, 04, 23, 88, and 84. Using these numbers, generate daily sandwich sales for 10 days. **Px**

•   **F.2**   The number of machine breakdowns per day at Kristen Hodge's factory is either 0, 1, or 2, with probabilities 0.5, 0.3, or 0.2, respectively. The following random numbers have been generated: 13, 14, 02, 18, 31, 19, 32, 85, 31, and 94. Use these numbers to generate the number of breakdowns for 10 consecutive days. What proportion of these days had at least one breakdown? **Px**

•   **F.3**   The table below shows the partial results of a Monte Carlo simulation. Assume that the simulation began at 8:00 a.m., and there is only one server.

Customer Number	Arrival Time	Service Time
1	8:01	6
2	8:06	7
3	8:09	8
4	8:15	6
5	8:20	6

a) When does service begin for customer 3?
b) When will customer 5 leave?
c) What is the average waiting time in line?
d) What is the average time in the system?

•   **F.4**   Barbara Flynn sells papers at a newspaper stand for $0.35. The papers cost her $0.25, giving her a $0.10 profit on each one she sells. From past experience Barbara knows that:
a) 20% of the time she sells 100 papers.
b) 20% of the time she sells 150 papers.

c) 30% of the time she sells 200 papers.
d) 30% of the time she sells 250 papers.

Assuming that Barbara believes the cost of a lost sale to be $0.05 and any unsold papers cost her $0.25, simulate her profit outlook over five days if she orders 200 papers for each of the five days. Use the following random numbers: 52, 06, 50, 88, and 53. **Px**

••   **F.5**   Children's Hospital is studying the number of emergency surgery kits that it uses on weekends. Over the last 40 weekends the number of kits used is as follows:

Number of Kits	Frequency
4	4
5	6
6	10
7	12
8	8

The following random numbers have been generated: 11, 52, 59, 22, 03, 03, 50, 86, 85, 15, 32, 47. Simulate 12 nights of emergency kit usage. What is the average number of kits used during these 12 nights? **Px**

•   **F.6**   Susan Sherer's grocery store has noted the following figures with regard to the number of people who arrive at the store's three checkout stands and the time it takes to check them out:

Arrivals/Minute	Frequency
0	0.3
1	0.5
2	0.2

Service Time (minute)	Frequency
1	0.1
2	0.3
3	0.4
4	0.2

Simulate the utilization of the three checkout stands over five minutes, using the following random numbers: 07, 60, 77, 49, 76, 95, 51, 16, and 14. Record the results at the end of the five-minute period. Start at time = 0. **Px**

---

*Note: **Px** means the problem may be solved with POM for Windows and/or Excel OM or Excel.

• **F.7** A warehouse manager at Mary Beth Marrs Corporation needs to simulate the demand placed on a product that does not fit standard models. The concept being measured is "demand during lead time," where both lead time and daily demand are variable. The historical record for this product, along with the cumulative distribution, appears in the table. Random numbers have been generated to simulate the next five order cycles; they are 91, 45, 37, 65, and 51. What are the five demand values? What is their average?

Demand During Lead Time	Probability	Cumulative Probability
100	0.01	0.01
120	0.15	0.16
140	0.30	0.46
160	0.15	0.61
180	0.04	0.65
200	0.10	0.75
220	0.25	1.00

•• **F.8** The time between arrivals at the drive-through window of Barry Harmon's fast-food restaurant follows the distribution given in the table. The service-time distribution is also given. Use the random numbers provided to simulate the activity of the first four arrivals. Assume that the window opens at 11:00 a.m. and that the first arrival occurs afterward, based on the first interarrival time generated.

Time Between Arrivals	Probability	Service Time	Probability
1	0.2	1	0.3
2	0.3	2	0.5
3	0.3	3	0.2
4	0.2		

a) Random numbers for arrivals: 14, 74, 27, 03
b) Random numbers for service times: 88, 32, 36, 24
c) At what time does the fourth customer leave the system? **Px**

• **F.9** Phantom Controls monitors and repairs control circuit boxes on elevators installed in multistorey buildings in downtown Calgary. The company has the contract for 108 buildings. When a box malfunctions, Phantom installs a new one and rebuilds the failed unit in its repair facility in Yorkton, Saskatchewan. The data for failed boxes over the last two years are shown in the following table:

Number of Failed Boxes per Month	Probability
0	0.10
1	0.14
2	0.26
3	0.20
4	0.18
5	0.12

Simulate two years (24 months) of operation for Phantom, and determine the average number of failed boxes per month from the simulation. Was it common to have fewer than seven failures over three months of operation? (Start your simulation at the top of the 10th column of Table F.4, $RN = 37$, and go down in the table.) **Px**

• **F.10** The number of cars arriving at Terry Haugen's Car Wash during the last 200 hours of operation is observed to be the following:

Number of Cars Arriving	Frequency
3 or fewer	0
4	20
5	30
6	50
7	60
8	40
9 or more	0
	200

a) Set up a probability and cumulative probability distribution for the variable of car arrivals.
b) Establish random-number intervals for the variable.
c) Simulate 15 hours of car arrivals and compute the average number of arrivals per hour. Select the random numbers needed from column 1, Table F.4, beginning with the digits 52. **Px**

•• **F.11** Leonard Presby's newsstand uses naive forecasting to order tomorrow's papers. The number of newspapers ordered corresponds to the previous day's demands. Today's demand for papers was 22. Presby buys the newspapers for $0.20 and sells them for $0.50. Whenever there is unsatisfied demand, Presby estimates the lost goodwill cost at $0.10. Complete the accompanying table, and answer the questions that follow.

Demand	Probability
21	0.25
22	0.15
23	0.10
24	0.20
25	0.30

Day	Papers Ordered	Random Number	Demand	Revenue	Cost	Goodwill Cost	Net Profit
1	22	37					
2		19					
3		52					
4		8					
5		22					
6		61					

a) What is the demand on day 3?
b) What is the total net profit at the end of the six days?
c) What is the lost goodwill on day 6?
d) What is the net profit on day 2?
e) How many papers has Presby ordered for day 5? **Px**

•• **F.12** Simkin's Hardware simulated an inventory-ordering policy for Ace electric drills that involved an order quantity of 10 drills, with a reorder point of five. This first attempt to develop a cost-effective ordering strategy was illustrated in Table F.10 of Example F3. The brief simulation resulted in a total daily inventory cost of $6.65 in Example F4.

Simkin would now like to compare this strategy to one in which he orders 12 drills, with a reorder point of six. Conduct a 10-day simulation (using random numbers from the right-hand column of Table F.4, starting with 07, and using a beginning inventory of 12). Discuss the cost implications. **Px**

•• **F.13** Every home hockey game for the last eight years at McMaster University has been sold out. The revenues from ticket sales are significant, but the sale of food, beverages, and souvenirs has contributed greatly to the overall profitability of the hockey program. One particular souvenir is the hockey program for each game. The number of programs sold at each game is described by the probability distribution given in the table:

Numbers of Programs Sold	Probability
2300	0.15
2400	0.22
2500	0.24
2600	0.21
2700	0.18

Each program costs $0.80 to produce and sells for $2.00. Any programs that are not sold are donated to a recycling centre and do not produce any revenue.

a) Simulate the sales of programs at 10 hockey games. Use the last column in the random-number table (Table F.4) and begin at the top of the column.

b) If the university decided to print 2500 programs for each game, what would the average profits be for the 10 games that were simulated?

c) If the university decided to print 2600 programs for each game, what would the average profits be for the 10 games that were simulated? **Px**

• **F.14** Refer to the data in Solved Problem F.1, which deals with Higgins Plumbing and Heating. Higgins has now collected 100 weeks of data and finds the following distribution for sales:

Water Heater Sales per Week	Number of Weeks This Number Was Sold	Water Heater Sales per Week	Number of Weeks This Number Was Sold
3	2	8	12
4	9	9	12
5	10	10	10
6	15	11	5
7	25		100

a) Assuming that Higgins maintains a constant supply of eight heaters, simulate the number of stockouts incurred over a 20-week period (using the seventh column of Table F.4).

b) Conduct this 20-week simulation two more times and compare your answers with those in part (a). Did they change significantly? Why or why not?

c) What is the new expected number of sales per week? **Px**

••• **F.15** Taboo Tattoo and Tanning has two tanning beds. One bed serves the company's regular members exclusively. The second bed serves strictly walk-in customers (those without appointments) on a first-come, first-served basis. Gary Clendenen, the store manager, has noticed on several occasions during the busy five hours of the day (2:00 p.m. until 7:00 p.m.) that potential walk-in customers

will most often walk away from the store if they see one person already waiting for the second bed. He wonders if capturing this lost demand would justify adding a third bed. Leasing and maintaining a tanning bed costs Taboo $600 per month. The price paid per customer varies according to the time in the bed, but Gary has calculated the average net income for every 10 minutes of tanning time to be $2. A study of the pattern of arrivals during the busy hours and the time spent tanning has revealed the following:

Time Between Arrivals (minutes)	Probability	Time in Tanning Bed (minutes)	Probability
5	0.30	10	0.20
10	0.25	15	0.30
15	0.20	20	0.40
20	0.15	25	0.10
25	0.10		

a) Simulate four hours of operation (arrivals over four hours). Use the 14th column of Table F.4 for arrival times and the 8th column for tanning times. Assume there is one person who has just entered the bed at 2:00 p.m. for a 20-minute tan. Indicate which customers balk at waiting for the bed to become available. How many customers were lost over the four hours?

b) If the store is open an average of 24 days a month, will capturing all lost sales justify adding a new tanning bed?

••• **F.16** Erin Davis owns and operates one of the largest Mercedes-Benz auto dealerships in British Columbia. In the past 36 months, her monthly sales have ranged from a low of six new cars to a high of 12 new cars, as reflected in the following table:

Sales of New Cars/Month	Frequency (months)
6	3
7	4
8	6
9	12
10	9
11	1
12	1
	36

Davis believes that sales will continue during the next 24 months at about the same historical rates, and that delivery times will also continue to follow the following pace (stated in probability form):

Delivery Time (months)	Probability
1	0.44
2	0.33
3	0.16
4	0.07
	1.00

Davis's current policy is to order 14 cars at a time (two full truckloads, with seven vehicles on each truck), and to place a new order whenever the stock on hand reaches 12 cars.

a) What are the results of this policy when simulated over the next two years?

b) Davis establishes the following relevant costs: (1) carrying cost per Mercedes per month is $600; (2) cost of a lost sale averages $4350; and (3) cost of placing an order is $570. What is the total inventory cost of this policy?

•• **F.17** Dumoor Appliance Centre sells and services several brands of major appliances. Past sales for a particular model of refrigerator have resulted in the following probability distribution for demand:

Demand per week	0	1	2	3	4
Probability	0.20	0.40	0.20	0.15	0.05

The lead time in weeks is described by the following distribution:

Lead time (weeks)	1	2	3
Probability	0.15	0.35	0.50

Based on cost considerations as well as storage space, the company has decided to order 10 of these each time an order is placed. The holding cost is $1 per week for each unit that is left in inventory at the end of the week. The stockout cost has been set at $40 per stockout. The company has decided to place an order whenever there are only two refrigerators left at the end of the week. Simulate 10 weeks of operation for Dumoor Appliance, assuming that there are currently five units in inventory. Determine what the weekly stockout cost and weekly holding cost would be for the problem. Use the random numbers in the first column of Table F.4 for demand and the second column for lead time.

•• **F.18** Repeat the simulation in Problem F.17, assuming that the reorder point is four units rather than two. Compare the costs for these two situations. Again use the same random numbers as in Problem F.17.

••• **F.19** Johnny's Dynamo Dogs has a drive-through line. Customers arriving at this line during the busy hours (11:00 a.m. to 1:00 p.m.) order items either à la carte or on a value-meal basis. Currently 25% of meals are sold as value meals at an average contribution margin of $2.25. The à la carte meals earn $3.00 per meal but take longer to prepare and this slows the line. The following are the interarrival times that were recorded over the last three weeks of operation.

Interarrival Times for 500 Observations	
Time Between Arrivals (minutes)	**Number of Occurrences**
1	100
2	150
3	125
4	100
5	25

In addition, the following service times for à la carte and value meals were recorded:

Customer Service Times for 500 Orders of Each Type			
Service Time (minutes)	À la Carte	Service Time (minutes)	Value Meals
1	50	1	100
2	125	2	175
3	175	3	125
4	150	4	100

John Cottrell ("Johnny") has observed that because of street traffic the store loses all the potential customers who arrive when four cars are in the drive-through line (i.e., the line never exceeds four customers).

a) Simulate a one-hour time period for the current mix of à la carte and value-meal orders. To start, assume two cars are in the line, each with a two-minute service time. Determine the number of meals served, the income from those meals, and the number of missed sales because customers go elsewhere.

b) Johnny is contemplating a reduction of $0.25 in the prices of value meals. He believes that this will increase the percentage of meals that are value meals from 25% to 40%. This will result in faster service times and fewer lost sales. Using simulation, determine if this change will be financially beneficial. Assume that the benefits will be available for two hours a day over a 20-day month.

••• **F.20** The Toronto General Hospital has an emergency room that is divided into six departments: (1) an initial exam station to treat minor problems or to make a diagnosis; (2) an X-ray department; (3) an operating room; (4) a cast-fitting room; (5) an observation room (for recovery and general observation before final diagnosis or release); and (6) an outprocessing department (where clerks check out patients).

The probabilities that a patient will go from one department to another are presented in the following table:

From	To	Probability
Initial exam at emergency room entrance	X-ray department	0.45
	Operating room	0.15
	Observation room	0.10
	Outprocessing clerk	0.30
X-ray department	Operating room	0.10
	Cast-fitting room	0.25
	Observation room	0.35
	Outprocessing clerk	0.30
Operating room	Cast-fitting room	0.25
	Observation room	0.70
	Outprocessing clerk	0.05
Cast-fitting room	Observation room	0.55
	X-ray department	0.05
	Outprocessing clerk	0.40
Observation room	Operating room	0.15
	X-ray department	0.15
	Outprocessing clerk	0.70

a) Simulate the trail followed by 10 emergency room patients. Proceed, one patient at a time, from each one's entry at the initial exam station until he or she leaves through outprocessing. You should be aware that a patient can enter the same department more than once.

b) Using your simulation data, determine the chances that a patient enters the X-ray department twice.

•••• **F.21** The management of Scotiabank are concerned over a loss of customers at its Georgetown branch. One proposed solution calls for adding one or more drive-through teller stations so that customers can get quick service without parking. Director of operations David Pentico thinks the bank should risk only the cost of installing one drive-through. He is informed by his staff that the cost (amortized over a 20-year period) of building a drive-through is $12 000 per year. It also costs $16 000 per year in wages and benefits to staff each new teller window.

The director of management analysis, Marilyn Hart, believes that the following two factors encourage the immediate construction of two drive-through stations. According to a recent article in *Banking Research* magazine, customers who wait in long lines for drive-through teller service will cost banks an average of $1 per minute in lost goodwill. Also, although adding a second drive-through will cost an additional $16 000 in staffing, amortized construction costs can be cut to a total of $20 000 per year if two drive-throughs are installed simultaneously, instead of one at a time. To complete her analysis, Hart collected one month's worth of arrival and service rates at a competing bank. These data follow:

Interarrival Times for 1000 Observations

Time Between Arrivals (minutes)	Number of Occurrences
1	200
2	250
3	300
4	150
5	100

Customer Service Time for 1000 Customers

Service Time (minutes)	Number of Occurrences
1	100
2	150
3	350
4	150
5	150
6	100

a) Simulate a one-hour time period, from 1:00 p.m. to 2:00 p.m., for a single-teller drive-through.

b) Simulate a one-hour time period, from 1:00 p.m. to 2:00 p.m., for a two-teller system.

c) Conduct a cost analysis of the two options. Assume that the bank is open seven hours per day and 200 days per year.

•••• F.22 The Alfredo Fragrance Company produces only one product, a perfume called Hint of Elegance. Hint of Elegance consists of two secret ingredients blended into an exclusive fragrance that is marketed in Zurich. An economic expression referred to as the Cobb-Douglas function describes the production of Hint of Elegance, as follows:

$$X = \sqrt{(\text{Ingredient 1})(\text{Ingredient 2})}$$

where X is the amount of perfume produced.

The company operates at a level where ingredient 1 is set daily at 25 units and ingredient 2 at 36 units. Although the price Alfredo pays for ingredient 1 is fixed at $50 per unit, the cost of ingredient 2 and the selling price for the final perfume are both probabilistic. The sales price for Hint of Elegance follows this distribution:

Sales Price ($)	Probability
300	0.2
350	0.5
400	0.3

The cost for ingredient 2 is as follows:

Ingredient 2 Cost ($)	Probability
35	0.1
40	0.6
45	0.3

a) What is the profit equation for Alfredo Fragrance Company?
b) What is the expected profit to the firm?
c) Simulate the firm's profit for a period of nine days, using these random numbers from Table F.4's top row: 52, 06, 50, 88, 53, 30, 10, 47, 99 for sales price, and 37, 66, 91, 35, 32, 00, 84, 57, 07 for ingredient 2 cost.
d) What is the expected daily profit as simulated in part (c)?

CASE | STUDY

Canadian Shield Airlines Call Centre

Canadian Shield Airlines opened its doors in December 2001 as a commuter service with its headquarters and hub located in Yellowknife. The airline was started and managed by two former pilots, Steve Hobbs and Joseph Magill. It acquired a fleet of 12 used prop-jet planes and the airport gates vacated by a bankrupt regional airline.

With business growing quickly, Hobbs turned his attention to Canadian Shield's "800" reservations system. Between midnight and 6:00 a.m., only one telephone reservations agent had been on duty. The times between incoming calls during this period are distributed as shown in Table 1. Carefully observing and timing the

Table 1
Incoming Call Distribution

Time Between Calls (minutes)	Probability
1	0.11
2	0.21
3	0.22
4	0.20
5	0.16
6	0.10

Main Heading	Review Material	
	One common way to establish a *probability distribution* for a given variable is to examine historical outcomes. We can find the probability, or relative frequency, for each possible outcome of a variable by dividing the frequency of observation by the total number of observations. • **Cumulative probability distribution**—The accumulation of individual probabilities of a distribution. • **Random-number intervals**—Sets of numbers to represent each possible value or outcome in a computer simulation. • **Random number**—A digit that has been selected by a totally random process. Random numbers may be generated for simulation problems in two ways: (1) If the problem is large and the process under study involves many simulation trials, computer programs are available to generate the needed random numbers; or (2) if the simulation is being done by hand, the numbers may be selected from a table of random digits.	
SIMULATION OF A QUEUING PROBLEM (pp. 780–783)	An important use of simulation is in the analysis of waiting-line problems. The assumptions required for solving queuing problems are quite restrictive. For most realistic queuing situations, simulation may be the only approach available.	Problems: F.6, F.8, F.15, F.19, F.21
SIMULATION AND INVENTORY ANALYSIS (pp. 783–786)	The commonly used EOQ models are based on the assumption that both product demand and reorder lead time are known, constant values. In most real-world inventory situations, though, demand and lead time are variables, so accurate analysis becomes extremely difficult to handle by any means other than simulation.	Problems: F.12, F.13, F.16b, F.17, F.18

Self-Test

■ **Before taking the self-test**, refer to the learning objectives listed at the beginning of the module.

LO1 Which of the following is *not* an advantage of simulation?
 a) Simulation is relatively straightforward and flexible.
 b) Good simulation models are usually inexpensive to develop.
 c) *Time compression* is possible.
 d) Simulation can study the interactive effects of individual variables.
 e) Simulations do not interfere with real-world systems.

LO2 The five steps required to implement the Monte Carlo simulation technique are __, __, __, __, and __.

LO3 Using simulation for a queuing problem:
 a) would be rare in a realistic situation.
 b) is an unreasonable alternative if the arrival rate is not Poisson distributed but can be plotted on a curve.
 c) would be appropriate if the service time were not exponential or constant.
 d) all of the above.

LO4 Two particularly good candidates to be probabilistic components in the simulation of an inventory problem are:
 a) order quantity and reorder point.
 b) setup cost and holding cost.
 c) daily demand and reorder lead time.
 d) order quantity and reorder lead time.
 e) reorder point and reorder lead time.

LO5 One important reason that spreadsheets are excellent tools for conducting simulations is that they can:
 a) generate random numbers.
 b) easily provide animation of the simulation.
 c) provide more security than manual simulations.
 d) prohibit *time compression* from corrupting the results.
 e) be easily programmed.

Answers: LO1. b; LO2. Set up a probability distribution for each of the important variables, build a cumulative probability distribution for each of the important variables, establish an interval of random numbers for each variable, generate sets of random numbers, actually simulate a set of trials; LO3. c; LO4. c; LO5. a.

APPENDIX | SOLUTIONS TO EVEN-NUMBERED PROBLEMS

Chapter 1

1.2 (a) 2 valves/hr.; (b) 2.25 valves/hr.; (c) 12.5%

1.4 Varies by site, source, and time.

1.6 Productivity of labour: 9.3%
Productivity of resin: 11.1%
Productivity of capital: −10.0%
Productivity of energy: 6.1%

1.8 (a) 0.0096 rugs/labour-dollar; (b) 0.00787 rugs/dollar

1.10 Productivity of capital dropped; labour and energy productivity increased.

1.12 (a) Before: 25 boxes/hr.; After: 27.08 boxes/hr.
(b) Increase: 8.3%
(c) 29.167 boxes/hr.

1.14 (a) 0.293 loaves/dollar
(b) 0.359 loaves/dollar
(c) Labour change: 0%; Investment change: 22.5%

1.16 (a) 220 hours per labourer; (b) 66 000 labour-hours

Chapter 2

2.2 Venezuela, China, United States, Switzerland, Denmark

2.4 Differentiation is evident when comparing most restaurants or restaurant chains.

2.6 (a) Focus more on standardization, make fewer product changes, find optimum capacity, and stabilize manufacturing process are a few possibilities
(b) New human resource skills, added capital investment for new equipment/processes
(c) Same as (b)

2.8 (a) Canada, 1.7; (b) No change

2.10 (a) Worldwide, 81.5 weighted *average*, 815 weighted *total*
(b) No change
(c) Overnight Shipping now preferred, weighted total 5 880

2.12 Company C, 1.0 ... w ... 25.0

Chapter 3

3.2 Here are some detailed activities for the first two activities for Mefford's WBS:

1.11 Set initial goals for fundraising
1.12 Set strategy including identifying sources and solicitation
1.13 Raise the funds
1.21 Identify voters' concerns
1.22 Analyze competitor's voting record
1.23 Establish positions on issues
1.31 Hire campaign manager and political advisor
1.32 Get volunteers
1.33 Hire a staff
1.34 Hire media consultants
1.41 Identify filing deadlines
1.42 File for candidacy
1.51 Train staff for audit planning

3.4

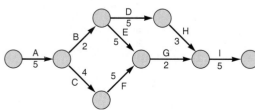

A–C–F–G–I is critical path; 21 days.
This is an AOA network.

3.6 (a)

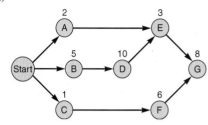

(b) B–D–E–G
(c) 26 days
(d) A=13, B=0, C=11, D=0, E=0, F=11, and G=0

3.8

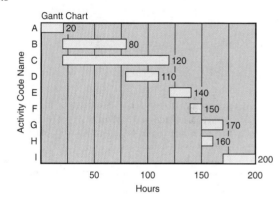

3.10

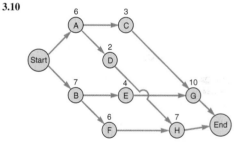

3.12 (a)

(b) A–B–E–G–I is critical path.
(c) 34

3.14 (a)

A, 5.83, 0.69		G, 2.17, 0.25
B, 3.67, 0.11		H, 6.00, 1.00
C, 2.00, 0.11		I, 11.00, 0.11
D, 7.00, 0.11		J, 16.33, 1.00
E, 4.00, 0.44		K, 7.33, 1.78
F, 10.00, 1.78		

(b) Critical path is C–D–E–F–H–K. Time = 36.33 days.
(c) Slacks are 7.17, 5.33, 0, 0, 0, 0, 2.83, 0, 2.83, 18, and 0, respectively, for A through K.
(d) P = 0.946

3.16 Crash C to three weeks at $200 total for one week. Now both paths are critical. Not worth it to crash further.

3.18 Critical path currently is C–E for 12 days. $1100 to crash by four days. Watch for parallel critical paths as you crash.

3.20 (a) 16 (A–D–G)
(b) $12 300
(c) D; 1 wk. for $75
(d) 7 wk.; $1600

3.22 (a) A–C–E–H–I–K–M–N; 50 days
(b) 82.1%
(c) 58 days

3.24 (a) 0.0228; (b) 0.3085; (c) 0.84134; (d) 0.97725; (e) 24 mo.

3.26 (a)

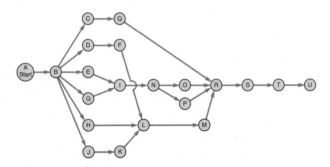

(b) Critical path is A–B–J–K–L–M–R–S–T–U for 18 days.
(c) i. No, transmissions and drivetrains are not on the critical path.
ii. No, halving engine-building time will reduce the critical path by only one day.
iii. No, it is not on the critical path.
(d) Reallocating workers not involved with critical-path activities to activities along the critical path will reduce the critical path length.

Chapter 4

4.2 (a) None obvious.
(b) 7.0, 7.7, 9.0, 10.0, 11.0, 11.0, 11.3, 11.0, 9.0
(c) 6.4, 7.8, 11.0, 9.6, 10.9, 12.2, 10.5, 10.6, 8.4
(d) The 3-yr. moving average.

4.4 (a) 41.6; (b) 42.3; (c) Banking industry's seasonality.

4.6 (a)

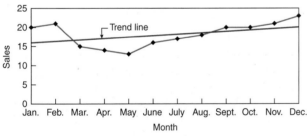

(b) Naive = 23; 3-mo. moving = 21.33; 6-mo. weighted = 20.6; exponential smoothing = 20.62; trend = 20.67
(c) Trend projection.

4.8 (a) 91.3; (b) 89; (c) MAD = 2.7; (d) MSE = 13.35; (e) MAPE = 2.99%

4.10 (a) 4.7, 5.0, 6.3, 7.7, 8.3, 8.0, 9.3, 11.7, 13.7
(b) 4.5, 5.0, 7.3, 7.8, 8.0, 8.3, 10.0, 12.3, 14.0
(c) Forecasts are about the same.

4.12 72

4.14 Method 1: MAD = 0.125; MSE = 0.021
Method 2: MAD = 0.1275; MSE = 0.018

4.16 $y = 421 + 33.6x$ When $x = 6$, $y = 622.8$.

4.18 49

4.20 $\alpha = 0.1$, $\beta = 0.2$, August forecast = $71 303; MSE = 12.7 for $\beta = 0.8$ vs. MSE = 18.87 for $\beta = 0.2$ in Problem 4.19.

4.22 Confirm that you match the numbers in Table 4.1.

4.24 (a) Observations do not form a straight line but do cluster about one.
(b) $y = 0.676 + 1.03x$
(c) 10 drums
(d) $r^2 = 0.68$; $r = 0.82$

4.26 270, 390, 189, 351 for fall, winter, spring, and summer, respectively.

4.28 Index is 0.709, winter; 1.037, spring; 1.553, summer; 0.700, fall.

4.30 (a) 337; (b) 380; (c) 423

4.32 (a) $y = 50 + 18x$
(b) $410

4.34 (a) 28; (b) 43; (c) 58

4.36 (a) $452.50
(b) Request is higher than predicted, so seek additional documentation.
(c) Include other variables (such as a destination cost index) to try to increase r and r^2.

4.38 (a) $y = -0.158 + 0.1308x$
(b) 2.719 million
(c) $r = 0.966$; $r^2 = 0.934$

4.40 131.2 → 72.7 patients; 90.6 → 50.6 patients

4.42 (a) They need more data and must be able to address seasonal *and* trend factors.
(b) Try to create your own naive model because seasonality is strong.
(c) Compute and graph your forecast.

4.44 Trend adjustment does not appear to give any significant improvement.

4.46 (a) $y = 1.03 + 0.0034x$, $r^2 = 0.479$
(b) For $x = 350$; $y = 2.22$
(c) For $x = 800$; $y = 3.75$
(Some rounding may occur, depending on software.)

4.48 (a) Sales $(y) = -9.349 + 0.1121$ (contracts)
(b) $r = 0.8963$; $S_{xy} = 1.3408$

Chapter 5

5.2 House of quality for a lunch:

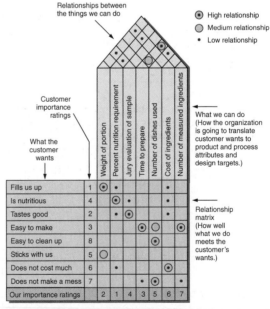

5.4 Individual answer. Build a house of quality similar to the one shown in Problem 5.2, entering the *wants* on the left and entering the *hows* at the top.

5.6 An assembly chart for the eyeglasses is shown below:

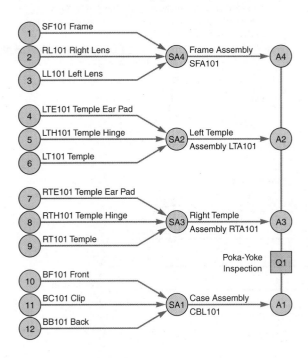

5.8 Assembly chart for a table lamp:

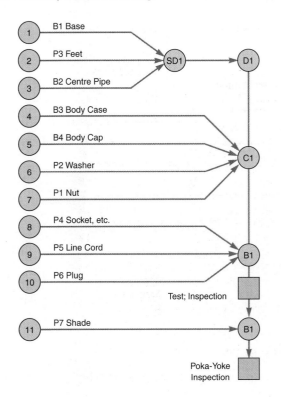

5.10 Possible strategies:
  Kindle 2 (growth phase):
    Increase capacity and improve balance of production system.
    Attempt to make production facilities more efficient.
  Netbook (introductory phase):
    Increase R&D to better define required product characteristics.
    Modify and improve production process.
    Develop supplier and distribution systems.
  Hand calculator (decline phase):
    Concentrate on production and distribution cost reduction
    Attempt to develop improved product
    Attempt to develop supplementary product
    Unless product is of special importance to overall competitive strategy, consider terminating production

5.12 EMV of Proceeding = $49 500 000
EMV of Do Value Analysis = $55 025 000
Therefore, do value analysis.

5.14

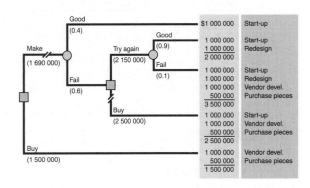

(a) The best decision would be to buy the semiconductors. This decision has an expected payoff of $1 500 000.
(b) Expected monetary value, minimum cost.
(c) The worst that can happen is that Ritz ends up buying the semiconductors and spending $3 500 000.
   The best that can happen is that they make the semiconductors and spend only $1 000 000.

5.16 EMV (Design A) = $875 000; EMV (Design B) = $700 000
5.18 Use K1 with EMV = $27 500

Chapter 6

6.2 Individual answer, in the style of Figure 6.6(b).
6.4 Individual answer, in the style of Figure 6.6(f).
6.6 Partial flowchart for planning a party:

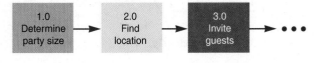

6.8 See figure below.

6.10 Individual answer, in the style of Figure 6.7 in the chapter.

6.12 Pareto chart, in the style of Example 1 with parking/drives most frequent, pool second, etc.

6.14 Materials: 4, 12, 14; Methods: 3, 7, 15, 16; Manpower: 1, 5, 6, 11; Machines: 2, 8, 9, 10, 13.

6.16 (a) A scatter diagram in the style of Figure 6.6(b) that shows a strong positive relationship between shipments and defects.

(b) A scatter diagram in the style of Figure 6.6(b) that shows a mild relationship between shipments and turnover.

(c) A Pareto chart in the style of Figure 6.6(d) that shows frequency of each type of defect.

(d) A fishbone chart in the style of Figure 6.6(c) with the 4 Ms showing possible causes of increasing defects in shipments.

Figure for Problem 6.8.

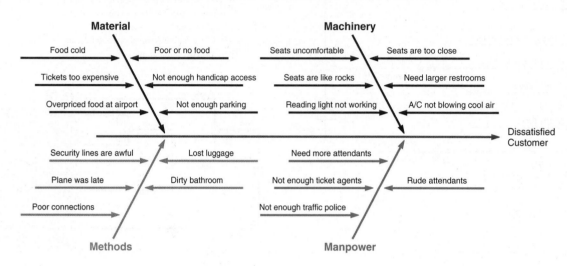

Cause-and-Effect Diagram for Dissatisfied Airline Customer

Figure for Problem 6.14

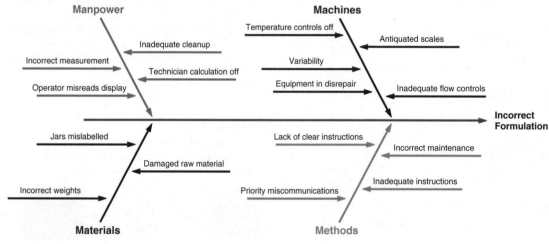

Chapter 6 Supplement

S6.2 (a) $\text{UCL}_{\bar{x}} = 52.31$
$\text{LCL}_{\bar{x}} = 47.69$

(b) $\text{UCL}_{\bar{x}} = 51.54$
$\text{LCL}_{\bar{x}} = 48.46$

S6.4 (a) $\text{UCL}_{\bar{x}} = 440$ calories
$\text{LCL}_{\bar{x}} = 400$ calories

(b) $\text{UCL}_{\bar{x}} = 435$ calories
$\text{LCL}_{\bar{x}} = 405$ calories

S6.6 $\text{UCL}_{\bar{x}} = 3.728$
$\text{LCL}_{\bar{x}} = 2.236$
$\text{UCL}_R = 2.336$
$\text{LCL}_R = 0.0$
The process is in control.

S6.8 (a) $\text{UCL}_{\bar{x}} = 16.08$
$\text{LCL}_{\bar{x}} = 15.92$

(b) $\text{UCL}_{\bar{x}} = 16.12$
$\text{LCL}_{\bar{x}} = 15.88$

S6.10 (a) 1.36, 0.61

(b) Using $\sigma_{\bar{x}}$, $\text{UCL}_{\bar{x}} = 11.83$, and $\text{LCL}_{\bar{x}} = 8.17$.

(c) Using A_2, $\text{UCL}_{\bar{x}} = 11.90$, and $\text{LCL}_{\bar{x}} = 8.10$;
$\text{UCL}_R = 6.98$; $\text{LCL}_R = 0$

(d) Yes

S6.12 $\text{UCL}_R = 6.058$; $\text{LCL}_R = 0.442$
Averages are increasing.

S6.14

UCL_p	LCL_p
0.062	0
0.099	0
0.132	0
0.161	0
0.190	0.01

S6.16 $UCL_p = 0.0313$; $LCL_p = 0$

S6.18 (a) $UCL_p = 0.077$; $LCL_p = 0.003$
   (b) Because the percent defective can never be less than zero.
   (c) The industry standards are not as strict as those at Royal Bank. Royal Bank sets its upper control limit at $0.077 = 7.7\%$ defective, while the industry allows as high as 10% before claiming that the sample is out of control.

S6.20 (a) $UCL_p = 0.0581$; $LCL_p = 0$
   (b) in control
   (c) $UCL_p = 0.1154$; $LCL_p = 0$

S6.22 (a) c-chart
   (b) $UCL_c = 13.35$; $LCL_c = 0$
   (c) in control
   (d) not in control

S6.24 (a) $UCL_c = 26.063$; $LCL_c = 3.137$
   (b) No point out of control.

S6.26 $C_p = 1.0$. The process is barely capable.

S6.28 $C_{pk} = 1.125$. Process *is* centred and will produce within tolerance.

S6.30 $C_{pk} = 0.1667$

S6.32 $AOQ = 2.2\%$

S6.34 (a) $UCL_{\bar{x}} = 61.131, LCL_{\bar{x}} = 38.421, UCL_R = 41.62, LCL_R = 0$
   (b) Yes, the process is in control for both $\bar{x}$- and R-charts.
   (c) They support West's claim. But variance from the mean needs to be reduced and controlled.

Chapter 7

7.2

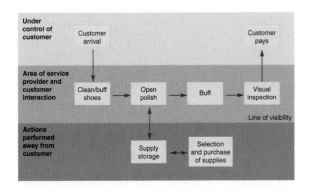

7.4.

7.6 GPE is best below 100 000.
   FMS is best between 100 000 and 300 000.
   DM is best over 300 000.

7.8 Optimal process will change at 100 000 and 300 000.

7.10 (a)

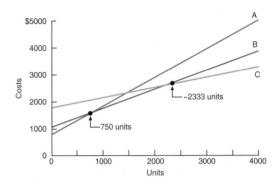

   (b) Plan C
   (c) Plan B

7.12 Rent HP software since projected volume of 80 is above the cross-over point of 75.

7.14 (a) Intermittent; (b) $200 000

Chapter 7 Supplement

S7.2 69.2%

S7.4 88.9%

S7.6 Design = 88 920
   Fabrication = 160 680
   Finishing = 65 520

S7.8 5.17 (or 6) bays

S7.10 15 min/unit

S7.12 (a) Process cycle time = 40 min
   (b) System process time = 12 min/unit
   (c) Weekly capacity = 240 units

S7.14 (a) Workstation C at 20 min/unit; (b) 3 units/hr.

S7.16 (a) 2000 units; (b) $1500

S7.18 (a) $150 000; (b) $160 000

S7.20 (a) $BEP_A = 1667$ pizzas;
   $BEP_B = 2353$ pizzas
   (b, c) Oven A slightly more profitable
   (d) 13 333 pizzas

S7.22 (a) $BEP_s = \$18\,750$
   (b) $BEP_x = 375\,000$ copies

S7.24 Option B, purchase new equipment and raise price. Profit = $2500

S7.26 (a) $BEP_\$ = \$7584.83$ per month; (b) Daily meals = 9

S7.28 Option B; $74 000

S7.30 $4590

S7.32 $NPV = \$1764$

S7.34 (a) Purchase two large ovens; (b) Equal quality, equal production capacity; (c) Payments are made at end of each time period. Future interest rates are known.

Chapter 8

8.2 China, $1.44

8.4 India is $0.05 less than elsewhere.

8.6 (a) Red Deer = 53; Camrose = 60; select Camrose.
   (b) Camrose now = 66.

8.8 (a) Hyde Park, with 54.5 points.
   (b) Present location = 51 points.

8.10 (a) Location C, with a total *weighted* score of 1530.
   (b) Location B = 1360
   (c) B can never be in first place.

8.12 (a) Britain, at 36;
   (b) Britain is now 31; Netherlands is 30.

8.14 (a) Italy is highest.
   (b) Spain is always lowest.
8.16 (a) Site 1 up to 125, site 2 from 125 to 233, site 3 above 233
   (b) Site 2
8.18 (a) Above 10 000 cars, site C is lowest cost.
   (b) Site A optimal from 0 to 10 000 cars.
   (c) Site B is never optimal.
8.20 (a) (5.15, 7.31)
   (b) (5.13, 7.67)
8.22 (a) (6.23, 6.08)
   (b) Safety, space, traffic, etc.
8.24 (a) Site C is best, with a score of 374.
   (b) For all positive values of w_7 such that $w_7 \le 14$.

Chapter 9

9.2 (a) $23 400; (b) $20 600; (c) $22 000; (d) Plan B is the lowest
9.4 Benders to area 1; Materials to 2; Welders to 3; Drills to 4; Grinder to 5; and Lathes to 6; Trips × Distance = 13 000 ft.
9.6 Layout #1, distance = 600 with areas fixed
   Layout #2, distance = 602 with areas fixed
9.8 Layout #4, distance = 609
   Layout #5, distance = 478
9.10 (a) 1.68 minutes
   (b) 4.76 ≈ 5
   (c) cleaning
9.12 (a) Cycle time = 9.6 min
   (b) 6 stations
   (c)

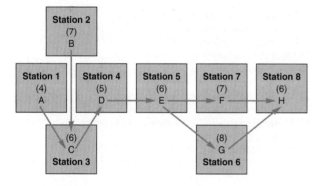

   (d) Idle time/cycle = 15 min
   (e) 15 hours/day idle
   (f) 8 workstations with 76.6% efficiency is possible

9.14 (a)

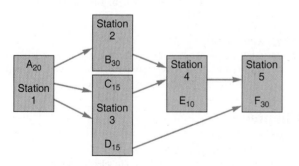

   (b) Cycle time = 30 sec./unit
   (c) 4 stations = *theoretical* minimum
   (d) Station 1–Task A; 2–B; 3–C, D; 4–E; 5–F
   (e) Total idle = 30 sec.
   (f) E = 80% with 5 stations; E = 66.6% with 6 stations

9.16 (a, b) Cycle time = 6.67 min./unit. Multiple solutions with 5 stations. Here is a sample: A, F, G to station 1; B, C to station 2; D, E to station 3; H to station 4; and I, J to station 5. (c) Actual efficiency with 5 stations = 83% (d) Idle time = 5 min./cycle.
9.18 (a) Minimum no. of workstations = 2.6 (or 3).
   (b) Efficiency = 86.7%.
   (c) Cycle time = 6.67 min./unit with 400 min./day; minimum no. of workstations = 1.95 (or 2).
9.20 Minimum (theoretical) = 4 stations. Efficiency = 93.3% with 5 stations and 6 min. cycle time. Several assignments with 5 are possible.
9.22 (a) Theoretical min. no. workstations = 5
   (b) There are several possibilities. For example, Station 1–Task A; 2–C; 3–B and F; 4–D and G; 5–E, H, and I; 6–J. Or 1–A; 2–C; 3–B and F; 4–D and G; 5–E, H and I; 6–J.
   (c) $n = 6$
   (d) Efficiency = 0.7611

Chapter 10

10.2

Time	Operator	Time	Machine	Time
	Prepare Mill			
1	Load Mill	1	Idle	1
2		2		2
3	Idle	3	Mill Operating (Cutting Material)	3
4		4		4
5	Unload Mill	5	Idle	5
6		6		6

10.4 The first 10 steps are shown below. The remaining 10 steps are similar.

OPERATIONS CHART		SUMMARY						
PROCESS: CHANGE ERASER		SYMBOL		PRESENT		DIFF.		
ANALYST:				LH	RH	LH	RH	LH	RH
DATE:		○ OPERATIONS	1	8				
SHEET: 1 of 2		⇨ TRANSPORTS	3	8				
METHOD: PRESENT PROPOSED		☐ INSPECTIONS	1					
REMARKS:		D DELAYS	15	4				
		▽ STORAGE						
		TOTALS	20	20				

LEFT HAND	DIST.	SYMBOL	SYMBOL	DIST.	RIGHT HAND
1 Reach for pencil		⇨	D		Idle
2 Grasp pencil		○	D		Idle
3 Move to work area		⇨	⇨		Move to pencil top
4 Hold pencil		D	○		Grasp pencil top
5 Hold pencil		D	○		Remove pencil top
6 Hold pencil		D	⇨		Set top aside
7 Hold pencil		D	⇨		Reach for old eraser
8 Hold pencil		D	○		Grasp old eraser
9 Hold pencil		D	○		Remove old eraser
10 Hold pencil		D	⇨		Set aside old eraser

10.6 Individual solution.

10.8

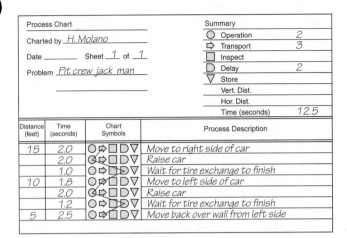

10.10 The first portion of the activity chart is shown below.

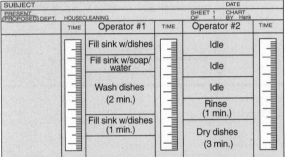

10.12 The first portion of the process chart is shown below.

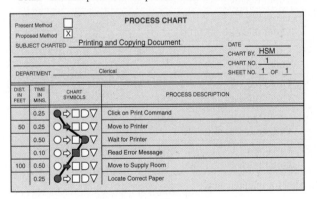

10.14 $NT = 7.65$ sec.; slower than normal

10.16 (a) 6.525 sec.; (b) 6.2 sec.; (c) 6.739 sec.

10.18 (a) 12.6 min.; (b) 15 min.

10.20 (a) 12.0 sec.; (b) 14.12 sec.

10.22 10.12 min.

10.24 (a) 3.24 min.; (b) 4.208 min.

10.26 $n = 14.06$, or 15 observations

10.28 (a) 45.36, 13.75, 3.6, 15.09; (b) 91.53 min.; (c) 96 samples

10.30 (a) 47.6 min.; (b) 75 samples

10.32 $n = 348$

10.34 73.8%

10.36 6.55 sec.

10.38 (a) 240 min.
   (b) 9000 min.
   (c) Clean 8 rooms; refresh 16 rooms; 38 housekeepers needed
   (d) 50 employees

Chapter 11

11.2 Donna, Inc., 8.2; Kay Corp., 9.8

11.4 Individual responses. Issues might include: academics, location, financial support, size, facilities, etc.

11.6 (a) $3.13; (b) $7.69

11.8 (a) Option (a) is most economical.
   (b) The customer requirements may demand a faster schedule.

11.10 (a) Go with faster subcontractor.
   (b) Internal production or testing may require a faster schedule.

11.12 (a) Weeks of supply = 3.85
   (b) % of assets in inventory = 11.63%
   (c) Turnover = 13.5
   (d) No, but note they are in different industries

11.14 (a) Last year = 10.4; (b) This year = 9.67

11.16 25% decrease in material costs is required.

Chapter 11 Supplement

S11.2 Two supplies best, $42 970

S11.4 (a) $P(2) = 0.017463$
   (b) $P(2) = 0.018866$
   (c) Option 1 (2 local suppliers) has lower risk.

S11.6 (a) 2.5; (b) 1.2; (c) 1.25; (d) 1.8; (e) Retailer

S11.8 (a) 1.20
   (b) Bullwhip = 0 if order sizes all the same.

S11.10 Donna, Inc., 8.2; Kay Corp., 9.8

S11.12 Individual responses. Issues might include academics, location, financial support, size, facilities, etc.

S11.14 Use faster shipping, option (a), since daily holding cost is more than daily cost of faster shipping.

S11.16 $20.34

S11.18 Paper Products 1,2; Dishes, Glasses, and Silverware 5–8; Cleaning Agents 3 9,10; Cooking Oils and Seasonings 3,4; Pots and Pans 11–16

Chapter 12

12.2 (a) A items are G2 and F3; B items are A2, C7, and D1; all others are C. (b) save ordering costs on his less important C items by ordering only when A or B items are being ordered from the same supplier. (c) A2 could move to A category based on annual dollar volume.

12.4 108 items

12.6 (a) 600 units; (b) 424.26 units; (c) 848.53 units

12.8 (a) 80 units; (b) 73 units

12.10 (a) 2100 units; (b) 4200 units; (c) 1050 units

12.12 (a) 189.74 units; (b) 94.87; (c) 31.62; (d) 7.91; (e) $1897.30;
   (f) $601 897.30

12.14 (a) Order quantity variations have limited impact on total cost.
   (b) EOQ = 50

12.16 (a) 671 units; (b) 18.63; (c) 559 = max. inventory; (d) 16.7%;
   (e) $1117.90

12.18 (a) 1217 units
   (b) 1095 = max. inventory
   (c) 8.22 production runs
   (d) $657.30

12.20 (a) EOQ = 200, total cost = $1 446 380
   (b) EOQ = 200, total cost = $1 445 880

12.22 (a) 16 970.56 units; (b) $530.33; (c) $530.33; (d) $56 250;
   (e) $57 310.66

12.24 (a) EOQ = 410
   (b) Vendor Allen has slightly lower cost.
   (c) Optimal order quantity = 1000 @ total cost of $128 920

12.26 (a) EOQ (1) = 336; EOQ (2) = 335
    (b) Order 1200 from Vendor 2.
    (c) At 1200 lb., total cost = $161 275.
    (d) Storage space and perishability
12.28 (a) $Z = 1.88$
    (b) Safety stock = $Z\sigma = 1.88(5) = 9.4$ drives
    (c) ROP = 59.4 drives
12.30 100 kilograms of safety stock
12.32 (a) 2291 towels; (b) 291 towels
12.34 (a) ROP = 1718 cigars
    (b) 1868 cigars
    (c) A higher service level means a lower probability of stocking out.
12.36 103 pounds
12.38 (a) $3; (b) $0.90; (c) 63 675 programs; (d) 23.1%
12.40 (a) Q = 400 lb.
    (b) $600
    (c) $600
    (d) ROP = 369.99
    (e) 69.99
    (f) $209.97
    (g) Safety stock = 61.61

Chapter 13

13.2 (a) $109 120 = total cost
    (b) $106 640 = total cost
    (c) No, plan 2 is better at $105 152.
13.4 Cost = $214 000 for plan B
13.6 (a) Plan D, $122 000; (b) Plan E, $129 000
13.8 Extra total cost = $2960.
13.10 (a) Plan C, $92 000; (b) plan D, $81 800, assuming initial inventory = 0
13.12 (a) Cost is $314 000.
    (b) Cost is $329 000 (but an alternative approach yields $259 500).
13.14 $1 186 810
13.16 $100 750
13.18 $90 850
13.20 (a, b) Cost using O.T. and Forrester = $195 625.
    (c) A case could be made for either position.
13.22 (a) Current model = $9200 in sales; (b) proposed model yields $9350, which is only slightly better.

Chapter 14

14.2 The time-phased plan for the gift bags is:

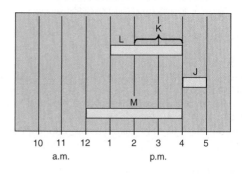

Someone should start on item M by noon.

14.4 Gross material requirements plan:

Item		Week								Lead Time (wk.)
		1	2	3	4	5	6	7	8	
S	Gross req.							100		
	Order release					100				2
T	Gross req.						100			
	Order release				100					1
U	Gross req.						200			
	Order release			200						2
V	Gross req.					100				
	Order release		100							2
W	Gross req.					200				
	Order release	200								3
X	Gross req.					100				
	Order release			100						1
Y	Gross req.			400						
	Order release	400								2
Z	Gross req.			600						
	Order release		600							1

14.6 Gross material requirements plan, modified to include the 20 units of U required for maintenance purposes:

Item		Week								Lead Time (wk.)
		1	2	3	4	5	6	7	8	
S	Gross req.							100		
	Order release					100				2
T	Gross req.						100			
	Order release				100					1
U	Gross req.					200	20*			
	Order release			200	20					2
V	Gross req.					100				
	Order release		100							2
W	Gross req.					200				
	Order release	200								3
X	Gross req.					100				
	Order release			100						1
Y	Gross req.			400	40					
	Order release	400	40							2
Z	Gross req.			600	60					
	Order release		600	60						1

*Needed for maintenance.

14.8 (a)

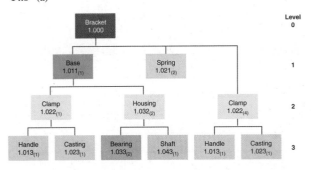

(b) For 50 brackets, the gross requirements are for 50 bases, 100 springs, 250 clamps, 250 handles, 250 castings, 100 housings, 200 bearings, and 100 shafts.

(c) For 50 brackets, net requirements are 25 bases, 100 springs, 125 clamps, 125 handles, 125 castings, 50 housings, 100 bearings, and 50 shafts.

14.10 (a) Gross material requirements plan for the first three items:

		Week												
Item		1	2	3	4	5	6	7	8	9	10	11	12
X1	Gross req.							50		20			100
	Order release						50		20		100		
B1	Gross req.							50		20			100
	Order release					50		20		100			
B2	Gross req.							100		40			200
	Order release					100		40		200			

(b) The net materials requirement plan for the first two items:

Level: 0	Parent:	Quantity:
Item: X1	Lead Time:	Lot Size: L4L

Week No.	1	2	3	4	5	6	7	8	9	10	11	12
Gross Requirement							50		20			100
Scheduled Receipt												
On-Hand Inventory							50		0			0
Net Requirement							0		20			100
Planned Order Receipt									20			100
Planned Order Release								20		100		

Level: 1	Parent: X1	Quantity: 1X
Item: B1	Lead Time: 2	Lot Size: L4L

Week No.	1	2	3	4	5	6	7	8	9	10	11	12
Gross Requirement								20		100		
Scheduled Receipt												
On-Hand Inventory								20		0		
Net Requirement								0		100		
Planned Order Receipt										100		
Planned Order Release								100				

14.12 (a) Net material requirements schedule (only items A and H are shown):

		Week											
	1	2	3	4	5	6	7	8	9	10	11	12
A Gross Required								100		50			150
On Hand								0		0			0
Net Required								100		50			150
Order Receipt								100		50			150
Order Release							100		50		150		
H Gross Required								100		50			
On Hand								0		0			
Net Required								100		50			
Order Receipt								100		50			
Order Release							100		50				

(b) Net material requirements schedule (only items B and C are shown; schedule for items A and H remains the same as in part a).

		Week											
	1	2	3	4	5	6	7	8	9	10	11	12	13
B Gross Requirements							200		100		300		
Scheduled Receipts													
Projected On Hand	100							100		0		0	
Net Requirements							100		100		300		
Planned Order Receipts							100		100		300		
Planned Order Releases						100		100		300			
C Gross Requirements							200	200	100	100	300		
Scheduled Receipts													
Projected On Hand	50							50		0		0	
Net Requirements							150	200	100	100	300		
Planned Order Receipts							150	200	100	100	300		
Planned Order Releases						150	200	100	100	300			

14.14 (a)

Level	Description		Qty
0	A		1
1	B		1
2	C		1
2	D		1
3		E	1
1	F		1
2	G		1
2	H		1
3		E	1
3		C	1

Note: with low-level coding "C" would be a level-3 code

(b) Solution for Items A, B, F:

Lot Size	Lead Time	On Hand	Safety Stock	Allo-cated	Low-Level Code	Item ID		1	2	3	4	5	6	7	8
Lot for Lot	1	0	—	—	0	A	Gross Requirement								10
							Scheduled Receipt								
							Projected On Hand								0
							Net Requirement								10
							Planned Receipt								10
							Planned Release							10	
Lot for Lot	1	2	—	—	1	B	Gross Requirement								10
							Scheduled Receipt								
							Projected On Hand	2	2	2	2	2	2	2	0
							Net Requirement								8
							Planned Receipt								8
							Planned Release							8	
Lot for Lot	1	5	—	—	1	F	Gross Requirement								10
							Scheduled Receipt								
							Projected On Hand	5	5	5	5	5	5	5	0
							Net Requirement								5
							Planned Receipt								5
							Planned Release							5	

14.16 (a) Only item G changes.

(b) Component F and 4 units of A will be delayed 1 week.

(c) Options include: delaying 4 units of A for 1 week; asking supplier of G to expedite production; reducing production time for item F or A.

14.18 EOQ = 57; Total cost $ = $1630

14.20 $650

14.22 $455

14.24 Selection for first five weeks:

Table for 14.24

Week	Units	Capacity Required (time)	Capacity Available (time)	Over/ (Under)	Production Scheduler's Action
1	60	3900	2250	1650	Lot split. Move 300 minutes (4.3 units) to week 2 and 1350 minutes to week 3.
2	30	1950	2250	(300)	
3	10	650	2250	(1600)	
4	40	2600	2250	350	Lot split. Move 250 minutes to week 3. Operations split. Move 100 minutes to another machine, overtime, or subcontract.
5	70	4550	2250	2300	Lot split. Move 1600 minutes to week 6. Overlap operations to get product out door. Operations split. Move 700 minutes to another machine, overtime, or subcontract.

14.26 Here are the order releases for the table and the top:

Lot Size	Lead Time (# of periods)	On Hand	Safety Stock	Allo-cated	Low-Level Code	Item ID		1	2	3	4	5	6	7	8
Lot for Lot	1	—	—	—	0	Table	Gross Requirements					640	640	128	128
							Scheduled Receipts								
							Projected on Hand								
							Net Requirements					640	640	128	128
							Planned Order Receipts					640	640	128	128
							Planned Order Releases				640	640	128	128	
Lot for Lot	1	—	—	—	1	Top	Gross Requirements					640	640	128	128
							Scheduled Receipts								
							Projected on Hand								
							Net Requirements					640	640	128	128
							Planned Order Receipts					640	640	128	128
							Planned Order Releases				640	640	128	128	

Chapter 15

15.2

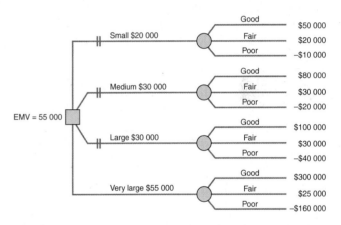

Now

15.4 **(a)** 1–D, 2–A, 3–C, 4–B
(b) 40
15.6 Chris–Finance, Steve–Marketing, Juana–H.R., Rebecca–Operations, $210
15.8 Ajay–Jackie, Jack–Barbara, Gray–Stella, Raul–Dona, 230.
15.10 **(a)** A, B, C, D, E; **(b)** B, A, D, E, C; **(c)** E, D, A, B, C; **(d)** C, B, A, D, E
SPT is best.
15.12 **(a)** A, B, C, D; **(b)** B, C, A, D; **(c)** D, A, C, B; **(d)** C, B, D, A; **(e)** D, C, A, B
SPT is best on all measures.
15.14 **(a)** A, B, C, D, E; **(b)** C, A, B, E, D; **(c)** C, D, E, A, B; **(d)** B, A, E, D, C
EDD, then FCFS are best on lateness; SPT on other two measures.
15.16 1, 3, 4, 2, 5
15.18 E, D, C, A, B, F
15.20 7 employees needed; 6 have two consecutive days off. The 7th works only 3 days/week.

Chapter 16

16.2 3.75, or 4 kanbans
16.4 Size of kanban = 66; number of kanbans = 5.9 or 6
16.6 **(a)** EOQ = 10 lamps; **(b)** 200 orders/yr.; **(c)** $200
16.8 7.26 min.
16.10 **(a)** Setup cost = $5.74; **(b)** Setup time = 8.61 min.

Chapter 17

17.2 From Figure 17.2, about 13% overall reliability.
17.4 Expected daily breakdowns = 2.0
Expected cost = $100 daily
17.6 **(a)** 5.0%; **(b)** 0.00001026 failures/unit-hr.; **(c)** 0.08985; **(d)** 98.83
17.8 R_s = 0.9941
17.10 R_p = 0.99925
17.12 **(a)** R_p = 0.984; **(b)** Increase by 11.1%.
17.14 R = 0.7918
17.16 **(a)** 0.972; **(b)** 0.9801
17.18 System B is slightly higher, at 0.9397.

Business Analytics Module A

A.2 **(a)**

Size of First Station	Good Market ($)	Fair Market ($)	Poor Market ($)	EV Under Equally Likely
Small	50 000	20 000	−10 000	20 000
Medium	80 000	30 000	−20 000	30 000
Large	100 000	30 000	−40 000	30 000
Very large	300 000	25 000	−160 000	55 000

(b) Maximax: Build a very large station.
(c) Maximin: Build a small station.
(d) Equally likely: Build a very large station.
(e)

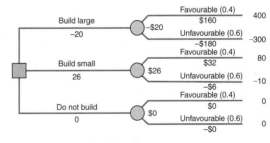

A.4 **(a)** Alternatives: N, M, L, D. States of nature: Fixed, Slight Increase, Major Increase
(b) Use maximin criterion. No floor space (N).
A.6 Buying equipment at $733 333
A.8 **(a)** E(cost full-time) = $520
(b) E(cost part-timers) = $475
A.10 Alternative B; 74
A.12 8 cases; EMV = $352.50
A.14 **(a)**

(b) Small plant with EMV = $26 000
(c) EVPI = $134 000
A.16 **(a)** Max EMV = $11 700
(b) EVPI = $13 200 − $11 700 = $1500

A.18

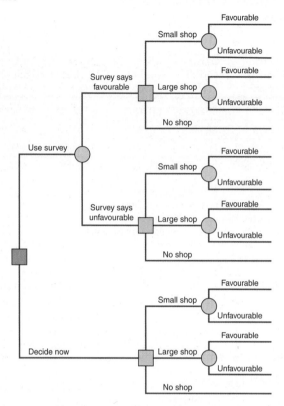

A.20 Do not gather additional information. Build a large video section; $4500.

A.22 (a)

Decision	At X	At Y	At X	At Y
X	45–27	9–27	18	–18
Y	6–15	30–15	–9	15
X&Y	(45 + 6)–(27 + 15)	(30 + 9)–(27 + 15)	9	–3
Nothing	0	0	0	0
Probability	0.45	0.55	0.45	0.55

(b) EMV(Y) = 4.2, which is best

Business Analytics Module B

B.2 Profit = $100 at X = 0, Y = 10

B.4 (a) Corner points (0, 50), (50, 50), (0, 200), (75, 75), (50, 150)
(b) Yes; $P = \$3000$ at (75, 75) and (50, 150)

B.6 (a) Min $X_1 + 2X_2$
Subject to: $X_1 + X_2 \geq 40$
$2X_1 + 4X_2 \geq 60$
$x_1 \leq 15$
(b) Cost = $0.65 at (15, 25)
(c) 65¢

B.8 $x_1 = 200, x_2 = 0$, profit = $18 000

B.10 10 Alpha 4s, 24 Beta 5s, profit = $55 200

B.12 (a) $x_1 = 25.71, x_2 = 21.43$
(a) Cost = $68.57

B.14 (a) $x_1 = 7.95, x_2 = 5.95, x_3 = 12.6, P = \$143.76$
(b) No unused time
(c) 26¢
(d) $7.86

B.16 (a) Let X_{ij} = number of students bussed from sector i to school j.
Objective: minimize total travel kilometres =
$5X_{AB} + 8X_{AC} + 6X_{AE}$
$+ 0X_{BB} + 4X_{BC} + 12X_{BE}$
$+ 4x_{CB} + 0X_{CC} + 7X_{CE}$
$+ 7X_{DB} + 2X_{DC} + 5x_{DE}$
$+ 12X_{EB} + 7X_{EC} + 0X_{EE}$
Subject to:
$X_{AB} + X_{AC} + X_{AE} = 700$ (number of students in sector A)
$X_{BB} + X_{BC} + X_{BE} = 500$ (number students in sector B)
$X_{CB} + X_{CC} + X_{CE} = 100$ (number of students in sector C)
$X_{DB} + X_{DC} + X_{DE} = 800$ (number of students in sector D)
$X_{EB} + X_{EC} + X_{EE} = 400$ (number of students in sector E)
$X_{AB} + X_{BB} + X_{CB} + X_{DB} + X_{EB} \leq 900$ (school B capacity)
$X_{AC} + X_{BC} + X_{CC} + X_{DC} + X_{EC} \leq 900$ (school C capacity)
$X_{AE} + X_{BE} + X_{CE} + X_{DE} + X_{EE} \leq 900$ (school E capacity)
(b) Solution: $X_{AB} = 400$
$X_{AE} = 300$
$X_{BB} = 500$
$X_{CC} = 100$
$X_{DC} = 800$
$X_{EE} = 400$
Distance = 5400 "student kilometres"

B.18 Hire 30 workers; three solutions are feasible; two of these are:
16 begin at 7:00 a.m.
9 begin at 3:00 p.m.
2 begin at 7:00 p.m.
3 begin at 11:00 p.m.
An alternative optimum is:
3 begin at 3:00 a.m.
9 begin at 7:00 a.m.
7 begin at 11:00 a.m.
2 begin at 3:00 p.m.
9 begin at 7:00 p.m.
0 begin at 11:00 p.m.

B.20 Max $P = 9x_1 + 12x_2$
Subject to:
$x_1 + x_2 \leq 10$
$x_1 + 2x_2 \leq 12$
$x_1 = 8, x_2 = 2$; profit = $96

B.22 $x_1 = 14, x_2 = 33$, cost = 221

B.24 5 corner points

B.26 (a) Minimize = $6X_{1A} + 5X_{1B} + 3X_{1C} + 8X_{2A} + 10X_{2B} + 8X_{2C} + 11X_{3A} + 14X_{3B} + 18X_{3C}$
Subject to:
$X_{1A} + X_{2A} + X_{3A} = 7$
$X_{1B} + X_{2B} + X_{3B} = 12$
$X_{1C} + X_{2C} + X_{3C} = 5$
$X_{1A} + X_{1B} + X_{1C} \leq 6$
$X_{2A} + X_{2B} + X_{2C} \leq 8$
$X_{3A} + X_{3B} + X_{3C} \leq 10$
(b) Minimum cost = $219 000

B.28 One approach results in 2790 medical patients and 2104 surgical patients, with a revenue of $9 551 659 per year (which can change slightly with rounding). This yields 61 integer medical beds and 29 integer surgical beds.

B.30 Apple sauce = 0, Canned corn = 1.33, Fried chicken = 0.46, French fries = 0, Macaroni & Cheese = 1.13, Turkey = 0, Garden salad = 0,
Cost = $1.51.

Business Analytics Module C

C.2 $208

C.4 $170

C.6 (a) A–1, 10; B–1, 30; C–2, 60; A–3, 40; C–3, 15
(b) $1775

C.8 Kelowna, $19 500

C.10 Total cost = $505

C.12 Initial cost = $260
Final solution = $230

C.14 F1–W1, 1000; F1–W4, 500; F2–W2, 2000; F2–W3, 500; F3–W3, 1500; F3–W4, 700; cost = $39 300

C.16 $60 900 with Cornwall; $62 250 with Oka

Business Analytics Module D

D.2 (a) 44%; (b) 0.356 people; (c) 0.8 people; (d) 0.53 min.; (e) 1.2 min.

D.4 (a) 0.5; (b) 0.5; (c) 1; (d) 0.5; (e) 0.05 hr.; (f) 0.1 hr.

D.6 (a) 0.667; (b) 0.667 min.; (c) 1.33

D.8 (a) 0.375
(b) 1.6 hr. (or 0.2 days)
(c) 0.225
(d) 0.141, 0.053, 0.020, 0.007

D.10 (a) 2.25
(b) 0.75
(c) 51.4 sec.
(d) 38.6 sec.
(e) 0.422, 0.316, 0.237

D.12 (a) 6 trucks
(b) 12 min.
(c) 0.857
(d) 0.54
(e) $1728/day
(f) Yes, save $3096 in the first year.

D.14 (a) 0.075 hr. (4.5 min.)
(b) 1.125 people
(c) 0.0083 hr. (0.5 min.), 0.083 people

D.16 (a) 0.113 hr. (6.8 min.)
(b) 1.13 cars

D.18 (a) 0.05; (b) 0.743; (c) 0.793

D.20 (a) 3, 2, 4 MDs, respectively
(b) Because $\lambda > \mu$, an indefinite queue buildup can occur.

D.22 (a) 4 servers; (b) 6 servers; (c) $109; (d) 83.33%

D.24 2 salespeople ($340)

D.26 5 min.

D.28 72 loans

Business Analytics Module E

E.2 (a) 507 min.; (b) 456 min.; (c) 410 min.; (d) 369 min.

E.4 (a) 1546 min.; (b) 2872 min.; (c) 3701 min.; (d) 6779 min.

E.6 (a) 14.31 hr.; (b) $71 550; (c) $947 250

E.8 (a) 80%; (b) 3.51; (c) 3.2, 2.98, 2.81; (d) 21.5

E.10 (a) 72.2 hr.; (b) 60.55 hr.; (c) 41.47 hr.

E.12 Torri will take 3.73 hr. and Julie 2.43 hr. Neither trainee will reach 1 hr. by the 10th unit.

E.14 $748 240 for fourth, $709 960 for fifth, $679 960 for sixth

E.16 (a) 70 millicents/bit; (b) 8.2 millicents/bit

E.18 26 755 hr.

E.20 (a) 32.98 hr., 49.61 hr.; (b) Initial quote is high.

E.22 (a) Four boats can be completed; (b) Five boats can be completed.

E.24 0.227 hr.

E.26 Just over 85%

Business Analytics Module F

F.2 0, 0, 0, 0, 0, 0, 0, 2, 0, 2; Proportion = 20%

F.4 Profits = 20, −15, 20, 17.50, 20; average equals $12.50.

F.6 At the end of 5 min., two checkouts are still busy and one is available.

F.8

Arrivals	Arrival Time	Service Time	Departure Time
1	11:01	3	11:04
2	11:04	2	11:06
3	11:06	2	11:08
4	11:07	1	11:09

F.10 (a, b)

No. Cars	Prob.	Cum. Prob.	R.N. Interval
3 or fewer	0	0	—
4	0.10	0.10	01 through 10
5	0.15	0.25	11 through 25
6	0.25	0.50	26 through 50
7	0.30	0.80	51 through 80
8	0.20	1.00	81 through 00
9 or more	0	—	—

(c) Average no. arrivals/hr. = 105/15 = 7 cars

F.12 Each simulation will differ. Using random numbers from right-hand column of Table F.4, reading top to bottom, in the order used, results in a $9.20 cost. This is greater than the $6.65 in Example F3.

F.14 (a) 5 times
(b) 6.95 times; yes
(c) 7.16 heaters

F.16 (a) Expected average demand is about 8.75, average lead time is 1.86, average end inventory = 6.5, average lost sales = 4.04. Values and costs will vary with different sets of random numbers.
(b) $520 110, or $21 671 per month

F.18 Total stockout cost = $80; total holding cost = $40; so total cost = $120 with ROP = 4 vs. total cost = $223 with ROP = 2 in Problem F.17. Weekly costs are found by dividing by 10.

F.20 (a) Here are the random-number intervals for the first two departments. Random number intervals correspond to probability of occurrence.

From	To	R.N. Interval
Initial exam	X-ray	01 through 45
	OR	46 through 60
	Observ.	61 through 70
	Out	71 through 00

From	To	R.N. Interval
X-ray	OR	01 through 10
	Cast	11 through 35
	Observ.	36 through 70
	Out	71 through 00

(b) Each simulation could produce different results. Some will indeed show a person entering X-ray twice.

F.22 (a) Profit = 30 (sales price) − $1250 − 36 (ingredient 2 cost)
(b) Expected profit = $7924/day
(c) $69 930
(d) Expected profit from simulation = $7770/day

Table for F.22 (c)

Day	Random Number	Sales Price	Gross* Sales	Random Number	Ingred. 2 Cost/Unit	Daily** Ingred. 2 Cost Total	Ingred. 1 Cost	Profit
1	52	$350	10 500	37	$40	$1 440	$1 250	$7 810
2	06	300	9 000	66	40	1 440	1 250	6 310
3	50	350	10 500	91	45	1 620	1 250	7 630
4	88	400	12 000	35	40	1 440	1 250	9 310
5	53	350	10 500	32	40	1 440	1 250	7 810
6	30	350	10 500	00	45	1 620	1 250	7 630
7	10	300	9 000	84	45	1 620	1 250	6 130
8	47	350	10 500	57	40	1 440	1 250	7 810
9	99	400	12 000	07	35	1 260	1 250	9 490
								$69 930

*Sales price $\times$ 30
**Ingredient 2 cost/unit $\times$ 36
Total profit = $69 930
Random number intervals for sales price: Random number intervals for cost 2:
        01–20 = $300   01–10 = $35
        21–70 = $350   11–70 = $40
        71–00 = $400   71–00 = $45

Online Tutorial 1

T1.2 5.45; 4.06
T1.4 (a) 0.2743; (b) 0.5
T1.6 0.1587; 0.2347; 0.1587
T1.8 (a) 0.0548; (b) 0.6554; (c) 0.6554; (d) 0.2119

Online Tutorial 2

T2.2 (selected values)

Fraction Defective	Mean of Poisson	$P(x \le 1)$
0.01	0.05	0.999
0.05	0.25	0.974
0.10	0.50	0.910
0.30	1.50	0.558
0.60	3.00	0.199
1.00	5.00	0.040

T2.4 The plan meets neither the producer's nor the consumer's requirement.

Online Tutorial 3

T3.2 (a) $x_1 + 4x_2 + s_1 = 24$
         $x_1 + 2x_2 + s_2 = 16$
(b) See the steps in the tutorial.
(c) Second tableau:

c_j	Mix	x_1	x_2	s_1	s_2	Qty.
9	x_2	0.25	1	0.25	0	6
0	s_2	0.50	0	−0.50	1	4
	z_j	2.25	9	2.25	0	54
	$c_j - z_j$	0.75	0	−2.25	0	

(d) $x_1 = 8, x_2 = 4$, Profit = $60
T3.4 Basis for 1st tableau:
        $A_1 = 80$
        $A_2 = 75$

Basis for 2nd tableau:
        $A_1 = 55$
        $X_1 = 25$
Basis for 3rd tableau:
        $X_1 = 14$
        $X_2 = 33$
        Cost = $221 at optimal solution
T3.6 (a) x_1; (b) A_1

Online Tutorial 4

T4.2 Cost = $980; 1–A = 20; 1–B = 50; 2–C = 20; 2–Dummy = 30; 3–A = 20; 3–C = 40
T4.4 Total = 3100 mi.; Morgantown–Coaltown = 35; Youngstown–Coal Valley = 30; Youngstown–Coaltown = 5; Youngstown–Coal Junction = 25; Pittsburgh–Coaltown = 5; Pittsburgh–Coalsburg = 20
T4.6 (a) Using VAM, cost = 635; A–Y = 35; A–Z = 20; B–W = 10; B–X = 20; B–Y = 15; C–W = 30.
(b) Using MODI, cost is also 635 (i.e., initial solution was optimal). An alternative optimal solution is A–X = 20; A–Y = 15; A–Z = 20; B–W = 10; B–Y = 35; C–W = 30.

Online Tutorial 5

T5.2 (a) $I_{13} = 12$
(b) $I_{35} = 7$
(c) $I_{51} = 4$
T5.4 (a) Tour: 1–2–4–5–7–6–8–3–1; 37.9 mi.
(b) Tour: 4–5–7–1–2–3–6–8–4; 39.1 mi.
T5.6 (a) Vehicle 1: Tour 1–2–4–3–5–1 = $134
(b) Vehicle 2: Tour 1–6–10–9–8–7–1 = $188
T5.8 The cost matrix is shown below:

	1	2	3	4	5	6	7	8
1	—	107.26	118.11	113.20	116.50	123.50	111.88	111.88
2		—	113.53	111.88	118.10	125.30	116.50	118.10
3			—	110.56	118.70	120.50	119.90	124.90
4				—	109.90	119.10	111.88	117.90
5					—	111.88	106.60	118.50
6						—	111.88	123.50
7							—	113.20
8								—

Bibliography

Chapter 1

Broedner, P., S. Kinkel, and G. Lay. "Productivity Effects of Outsourcing." *International Journal of Operations and Production Management* 29, no. 2 (2009): 127.

Hounshell, D. A. *From the American System to Mass Production 1800–1932: The Development of Manufacturing.* Baltimore, MD Johns Hopkins University Press, 1985.

Lewis, William W. *The Power of Productivity.* Chicago: University of Chicago Press, 2004.

Maroto, A., and L. Rubalcaba. "Services Productivity Revisited." *The Service Industries Journal* 28, no. 3 (April 2008): 337.

Sahay, B. S. "Multi-factor Productivity Measurement Model for Service Organization." *International Journal of Productivity and Performance Management* 54, no. 1–2 (2005): 7–23.

San, G., T. Huang, and L. Huang. "Does Labor Quality Matter on Productivity Growth?" *Total Quality Management and Business Excellence* 19, no. 10 (October 2008): 1043.

Sprague, Linda G. "Evolution of the Field of Operations Management," *Journal of Operations Management* 25, no. 2 (March 2007): 219–238.

Tangen, S. "Demystifying Productivity and Performance." *International Journal of Productivity and Performance Measurement* 54, no. 1–2 (2005): 34–47.

Taylor, F. W. *The Principles of Scientific Management.* New York, NY: Harper & Brothers, 1911.

van Biema, Michael, and Bruce Greenwald. "Managing Our Way to Higher Service-Sector Productivity." *Harvard Business Review* 75, no. 4 (July–August 1997): 87–95.

Wren, Daniel A. *The Evolution of Management Thought,* New York, NY: Wiley, 1994.

Chapter 2

Beckman, S. L., and D. B. Rosenfield. *Operations Strategy: Competing in the 21st Century.* New York, NY: McGraw-Hill, 2008.

Crotts, J. C., D. R. Dickson, and R. C. Ford. "Aligning Organizational Processes with Mission." *Academy of Management Executive* 19, no. 3 (August 2005): 54–68.

Flynn, B. B., R. G. Schroeder, and E. J. Flynn. "World Class Manufacturing." *Journal of Operations Management* 17, no. 3 (March 1999): 249–269.

Friedman, Thomas. *The World Is Flat: A Brief History of the Twenty-first Century.* New York, NY: Farrar, Straus, and Giroux, 2005.

Greenwald, Bruce, and Judd Kahn. "All Strategy Is Local." *Harvard Business Review* 83, no. 9 (September 2005): 94–104.

Kaplan, Robert S., and David P. Norton. *Strategy Maps.* Boston, MA: Harvard Business School Publishing, 2003.

Kathuria, R., M. P. Joshi, and S. Dellande. "International Growth Strategies of Service and Manufacturing Firms: The Case of Banking and Chemical Industries." *International Journal of Operations and Production Management* 28, no. 10 (2008): 968–990.

Porter, Michael, and Nicolaj Siggelkow. "Contextuality within Activity Systems and Sustainability of Competitive Advantage." *Academy of Management Perspectives* 22, no. 2 (May 2008): 34–36.

Rudberg, Martin, and B. M. West. "Global Operations Strategy." *Omega* 36, no. 1 (February 2008): 91.

Skinner, Wickham. "Manufacturing Strategy: The Story of Its Evolution." *Journal of Operations Management* 25, no. 2 (March 2007): 328–334.

Slack, Nigel, and Mike Lewis. *Operation Strategy,* 2nd ed. Upper Saddle River, NJ: Prentice Hall, 2008.

Wolf, Martin. *Why Globalization Works.* London, UK: Yale University Press, 2004.

Zakaria, Fareed. *The Post American World.* New York, NY: W.W. Norton, 2008.

Chapter 3

Balakrishnan, R., B. Render, and R. M. Stair. *Managerial Decision Modeling with Spreadsheets,* 2nd ed. Upper Saddle River, NJ: Prentice Hall, 2007.

Cleland, D. L., and L. R. Ireland. *Project Management,* 5th ed. New York, NY: McGraw-Hill/Irwin, 2007.

Gray, C. L., and E. W. Larson. *Project Management with MS Project.* New York, NY: McGraw-Hill/Irwin, 2008.

Helgadottir, Hilder. "The Ethical Dimension of Project Management." *International Journal of Project Management* 26, no. 7 (October 2008): 743.

Karlos, A., et al. "Foundations of Project Management." *International Journal of Project Management* 27, no. 1 (January 2009): 1.

Kerzner, H. *Project Management Case Studies,* 3rd ed. New York, NY: Wiley, 2009.

Kumar, P. P. "Effective Use of Gantt Chart for Managing Large-Scale Projects." *Cost Engineering* 47, no. 7 (July 2005): 14–21.

Ling, F. Y. Y., et al. "Key Project Management Practices Affecting Singaporean Firms' Project Performance in China." *International Journal of Project Management* 27, no. 1 (January 2009): 59.

Matta, N. F., and R. N. Ashkenas. "Why Good Projects Fail Anyways." *Harvard Business Review* (September 2003): 109–114.

Maylor, Harvey. *Project Management,* 4th ed. Upper Saddle River, NJ: Prentice Hall, 2008.

Meredith, J. R., and S. Mantel. *Project Management,* 7th ed. New York, NY: Wiley, 2008.

Oates, David. "Understanding and Solving the Causes of Project Failure." *Knowledge Management Review* 9, no. 5 (May–June 2006): 5.

Render, B., R. M. Stair, and M. Hanna. *Quantitative Analysis for Management,* 10th ed. Upper Saddle River, NJ: Prentice Hall, 2009.

Verzuh, Eric. *The Fast Forward MBA in Project Management.* New York, NY: Wiley, 2008.

Wysocki, R. K. *Effective Project Management,* 5th ed. New York, NY: Wiley, 2009.

Chapter 4

Balakrishnan, R., B. Render, and R. M. Stair. *Managerial Decision Modeling with Spreadsheets,* 2nd ed. Upper Saddle River, NJ: Prentice Hall, 2007.

Berenson, Mark, Tim Krehbiel, and David Levine. *Basic Business Statistics,* 11th ed. Upper Saddle River, NJ: Prentice Hall, 2009.

Campbell, Omar. "Forecasting in Direct Selling Business: Tupperware's Experience." *The Journal of Business Forecasting* 27, no. 2 (Summer 2008): 18–19.

Diebold, F. X. *Elements of Forecasting,* 5th ed. Cincinnati, OH: South-Western College Publishing, 2010.

Fildes, Robert, and Paul Goodwin. "Against Your Better Judgment? How Organizations Can Improve Their Use of Management Judgment in Forecasting." *Decision Sciences* 37, no. 6 (November–December 2007): 570–576.

Georgoff, D. M., and R. G. Murdick. "Manager's Guide to Forecasting." *Harvard Business Review* 64 (January–February 1986): 110–120.

Gilliland, M., and M. Leonard. "Forecasting Software—The Past and the Future." *The Journal of Business Forecasting* 25, no. 1 (Spring 2006): 33–36.

Hanke, J. E., and D. W. Wichern. *Business Forecasting,* 9th ed. Upper Saddle River, NJ: Prentice Hall, 2009.

Heizer, Jay. "Forecasting with Stagger Charts." *IIE Solutions* 34 (June 2002): 46–49.

Jain, Chaman L. "Benchmarking Forecasting Software and Systems." *The Journal of Business Forecasting* 26, no. 4 (Winter 2007/2008): 30–34.

Onkal, D., M. S. Gonul, and M. Lawrence. "Judgmental Adjustments of Previously Adjusted Forecasts." *Decision Sciences* 39, no. 2 (May 2008): 213–238.

Render, B., R. M. Stair, and M. Hanna. *Quantitative Analysis for Management,* 10th ed. Upper Saddle River, NJ: Prentice Hall, 2009.

Shah, Piyush. "Techniques to Support Better Forecasting." *APICS Magazine* (November/December 2008): 49–50.

Tabatabai, Bijan. "Improving Forecasting." *Financial Management* (October 2008): 48–49.

Urs, Rajiv. "How to Use a Demand Planning System for Best Forecasting and Planning Results." *The Journal of Business Forecasting* 27, no. 2 (Summer 2008): 22–25.

Wilson, J. H., B. Keating, and J. Galt. *Business Forecasting,* 6th ed. New York, NY: McGraw-Hill, 2009.

Yurklewicz, Jack. "Forecasting at Steady State." *Analytics* (Summer 2008): 42–45.

Chapter 5

Ambec, Stefan, and Paul Lanoie. "Does It Pay to Be Green? A Systematic Overview." *Academy of Management Perspectives* 22, no. 4 (November 2008): 13–20.

Brockman, Beverly K., and Robert M. Morgan. "The Role of Existing Knowledge in New Product Innovativeness and Performance." *Decision Sciences* 34, no. 2 (Spring 2003): 385–419.

Camevalli, J. A., and P. A. C. Miguel. "Review, Analysis, and Classification of the Literature on QFD." *International Journal of Production Economics* 114, no. 2 (August 2008): 737.

Ernst, David, and James Bamford. "Your Alliances Are Too Stable." *Harvard Business Review* 83, no. 5 (June 2005): 133–141.

Gerwin, Donald. "Coordinating New Product Development in Strategic Alliances." *The Academy of Management Review* 29, no. 2 (April 2004): 241–257.

Krishnan, V., and Karl T. Ulrich. "Product Development Decisions: A Review of the Literature." *Management Science* 47, no. 1 (January 2001): 1–21.

Loch, C. H., and C. Terwiesch. "Rush and Be Wrong or Wait and Be Late?" *Production and Operations Management* 14, no. 3 (Fall 2005): 331–343.

Miguel, P. A. C., and J. A. Camevalli. "Benchmarking Practices of Quality Function Deployment." *Benchmarking* 15, no. 6 (2008): 657.

Phyper, J. D., and P. MacLean. *Good to Green: Managing Business Risks and Opportunities in the Age of Environmental Awareness.* New York, NY: Wiley, 2009.

Pisano, Gary P., and Roberto Verganti. "Which Kind of Collaboration Is Right for You?" *Harvard Business Review* 86, no. 12 (December 2008): 78–86.

Saaksvuori, A., and A. Immonen. *Product Lifecycle Management.* Berlin: Springer-Verlag, 2004.

Seider, Warren D., et al. *Product and Process Design Principles.* 3rd. ed. New York, NY: Wiley, 2008.

Ulrich, K., and S. Eppinger. *Product Design and Development,* 4th ed. New York, NY: McGraw-Hill, 2008.

Chapter 5 Supplement

Ambec, Stefan, and Paul Lanoie. "Does It Pay to Be Green? A Systematic Overview." *Academy of Management Perspectives* 22, no. 4 (November 2008): 13–20.

Banerjee, S. B. "Embedding Sustainability Across the Organization: A Critical Perspective." *Academy of Management, Learning & Education* 10, no. 4 (December 2011): 719–731.

Epstein, Marc J. *Making Sustainability Work.* San Francisco, CA Berrett-Koehler Publisher, 2008.

Haugh, Helen M., and A. Talwar. "How Do Corporations Embed Sustainability Across the Organization?" *Academy of Management, Learning & Education* 9, no. 3 (September 2010): 384–396.

Laszlo, Chris. *Sustainable Value.* Stanford, CA: Stanford University Press, 2008.

Laszlo, Chris, and N. Zhexembayeva. *Embedded Sustainability.* Stanford, CA: Stanford University Press, 2011.

Nidumolu, Ram, C. K. Prahalad, and M. R. Rangaswami. "Why Sustainability Is Now the Key Driver of Innovation." *Harvard Business Review* 87, no. 9 (September 2009): 56–64.

Stoner, J. A. F., and C. Wankel (Ed). *Global Sustainability Initiatives.* Charlotte, NC: Information Age Publishing, 2008.

Chapter 6

Besterfield, Dale H. *Quality Control,* 8th ed. Upper Saddle River, NJ: Prentice Hall, 2009.

Brown, Mark G. *Baldrige Award Winning Quality,* 19th ed. University Park, IL: Productivity Press, 2010.

Crosby, P. B. *Quality Is Still Free.* New York, NY: McGraw-Hill, 1996.

Evans, J. R., and W. M. Lindsay. *Managing for Quality and Performance Excellence,* 7th ed. Mason, OH: Thompson-Southwestern, 2008.

Feigenbaum, A. V. "Raising the Bar." *Quality Progress* 41, no. 7 (July 2008): 22–28.

Gitlow, Howard S. A *Guide to Lean Six Sigma Management Skills.* University Park, IL: Productivity Press, 2009.

Gonzalez-Benito, J., and O. Gonzalez-Benito. "Operations Management Practices Linked to the Adoption of ISO 14001." *International Journal of Production Economics* 113, no. 1 (May 2008): 60.

Gryna, F. M., R. C. H. Chua, and J. A. DeFeo. *Juran's Quality Planning and Analysis for Enterprise Quality,* 5th ed. New York, NY: McGraw-Hill, 2007.

Harrington, D. R., M. Khanna, and G. Deltas. "Striving to Be Green: The Adoption of Total Quality Environmental Management." *Applied Economics* 40, no. 23 (December 2008): 2995.

Mitra, Amit. *Fundamentals of Quality Control and Improvement.* New York, NY: Wiley, 2009.

Pande, P. S., R. P. Neuman, R. R. Cavanagh. *What Is Design for Six Sigma?* New York, NY: McGraw-Hill, 2005.

Schroeder, Roger G., et al. "Six Sigma: Definition and Underlying Theory." *Journal of Operations Management* 26, no. 4 (2008): 536–554.

Soltani, E., P. Lai, and P. Phillips. "A New Look at Factors Influencing Total Quality Management Failure." *New Technology, Work, and Employment* 23, no. 1–2 (March 2008): 125.

Stewart, D. M. "Piecing Together Service Quality: A Framework for Robust Service." *Production and Operations Management* (Summer 2003): 246–265.

Summers, Donna. *Quality Management,* 2nd ed. Upper Saddle River, NJ: Prentice Hall, 2009.

Chapter 6 Supplement

Bakir, S. T. "A Quality Control Chart for Work Performance Appraisal." *Quality Engineering* 17, no. 3 (2005): 429.

Besterfield, Dale H. *Quality Control,* 8th ed. Upper Saddle River, NJ: Prentice Hall, 2009.

Elg, M., J. Olsson, and J. J. Dahlgaard. "Implementing Statistical Process Control." *The International Journal of Quality and Reliability Management* 25, no. 6 (2008): 545.

Goetsch, David L., and Stanley B. Davis. *Quality Management,* 5th ed. Upper Saddle River, NJ: Prentice Hall, 2006.

Gryna, F. M., R. C. H. Chua, and J. A. DeFeo. *Juran's Quality Planning and Analysis,* 5th ed. New York, NY: McGraw-Hill, 2007.

Lin, H., and G. Sheen. "Practical Implementation of the Capability Index C_{pk} Based on Control Chart Data." *Quality Engineering* 17, no. 3 (2005): 371.

Matthes, N., et al. "Statistical Process Control for Hospitals." *Quality Management in Health Care* 16, no. 3 (July–September 2007): 205.

Mitra, Amit. *Fundamentals of Quality Control and Improvement,* 3rd ed. New York, NY: Wiley, 2008.

Montgomery, D. C. *Introduction to Statistical Quality Control,* 6th ed. New York, NY: Wiley, 2008.

Roth, H. P. "How SPC Can Help Cut Costs." *Journal of Corporate Accounting and Finance* 16, no. 3 (March–April 2005): 21–30.

Summers, Donna. *Quality Management,* 2nd ed. Upper Saddle River, NJ: Prentice Hall, 2009.

Chapter 7

Davenport, T. H. "The Coming Commoditization of Processes." *Harvard Business Review* 83, no. 6 (June 2005): 101–108.

Debo, L. G., L. B. Toktay, and L. N. Van Wassenhove. "Market Segmentation and Product Technology Selection for Remanufacturable Products." *Management Science* 51, no. 8 (August 2005): 1193–1205.

Duray, R. "Mass Customization Origins: Mass or Custom Manufacturing." *International Journal of Operations and Production Management* 22, no. 3 (2002): 314–328.

Duray, R., P. T. Ward, G. W. Milligan, and W. L. Berry. "Approaches to Mass Customization: Configurations and Empirical Validation." *Journal of Operations Management* 18, no. 6 (November 2000): 605–625.

Gilmore, James H., and B. Joseph Pine II (eds.). *Markets of One: Creating Customer-Unique Value through Mass Customization.* Boston: Harvard Business Review Press, 2000.

Hall, Joseph M., and M. Eric Johnson. "When Should a Process Be Art, Not Science?" *Harvard Business Review* 87, no. 3 (March 2009): 58–65.

Hegde, V. G., et al. "Customization: Impact on Product and Process Performance." *Production and Operations Management* 14, no. 4 (Winter 2005): 388–399.

Inderfurth, Karl, and I. M. Langella. "An Approach for Solving Disassembly-to-Order Problems under Stochastic Yields." *In Logistik Management.* Heidelberg: Physica, 2004: 309–331.

Moeeni, F. "From Light Frequency Identification to Radio Frequency Identification in the Supply Chain," *Decision Line* 37, no. 3 (May 2006): 8–13.

Rugtusanatham, M. Johnny, and Fabrizio Salvador. "From Mass Production to Mass Customization." *Production and Operations Management* 17, no. 3 (May–June 2008): 385–396.

Su, J. C. P., Y. Chang, and M. Ferguson. "Evaluation of Postponement Structures to Accommodate Mass Customization." *Journal of Operations Management* 23, no. 3–4 (April 2005): 305–318.

Swamidass, Paul M. *Innovations in Competitive Manufacturing.* Dordrecht, NL: Kluwer, 2000.

Welborn, Cliff. "Mass Customization." *OR/MS Today* (December 2007): 38–42.

Zipkin, Paul. "The Limits of Mass Customization." *MIT Sloan Management Review* 40, no. 1 (Spring 2001): 81–88.

Chapter 7 Supplement

Anupindi, Ravi, S. Deshmukh, and S. Chopra. *Managing Business Process Flows*, 2nd ed. Upper Saddle River, NJ: Prentice Hall, 2007.

Atamturk, A., and D. S. Hochbaum. "Capacity Acquisition, Subcontracting, and Lot-Sizing." *Management Science* 47, no. 8 (August 2001): 1081–1100.

Bowers, John, et al. "Modeling Outpatient Capacity for a Diagnosis and Treatment Center." *Health Care Management Science* 8, no. 3 (August 2005): 205.

Brandl, Dennis. "Capacity and Constraints." *Control Engineering* (February 2008): 24.

Chambers, Chester, Eli M. Snir, and Asad Ata. "The Use of Flexible Manufacturing Capacity in Pharmaceutical Product Introductions." *Decision Sciences* 40, no. 2 (May 2009): 243–268.

Cheng, H. K., K. Dogan, and R. A. Einicki. "Pricing and Capacity Decisions for Non-Profit Internet Service Providers." *Information Technology and Management* 7, no. 2 (April 2006): 91.

Goldratt, Eliyaha. *The Choice*. Great Barrington, MA: North River Press, 2009.

Goodale, John C., Rohit Verma, and Madeleine E. Pullman. "A Market Utility-Based Model for Capacity Scheduling in Mass Services." *Production and Operations Management* 12, no. 2 (Summer 2003): 165–185.

Gupta, M. C., and L. H. Boyd. "Theory of Constraints: A Theory for Operations Management." *International Journal of Operations Management* 28, no. 10 (2008): 991.

Jack, Eric P., and Amitabh S. Raturi. "Measuring and Comparing Volume Flexibility in the Capital Goods Industry." *Production and Operations Management* 12, no. 4 (Winter 2003): 480–501.

Jonsson, Patrik, and Stig-Arne Mattsson. "Use and Applicability of Capacity Planning Methods." *Production and Inventory Management Journal* (3rd/4th Quarter 2002): 89–95.

Kekre, Sunder, et al. "Reconfiguring a Remanufacturing Line at Visteon, Mexico." *Interfaces* 33, no. 6 (November–December 2003): 30–43.

Tibben-Lembke, Ronald S. "Theory of Constraints at UniCo." *International Journal of Production Research* 47, no. 7 (January 2009): 1815.

Watson, Kevin J., John H. Blackstone, and Stanley C. Gardiner. "The Evolution of a Management Philosophy: The Theory of Constraints." *Journal of Operations Management* 25, no. 2 (March 2007): 387–402.

Chapter 8

Ballou, Ronald H. *Business Logistics Management*, 5th ed. Upper Saddle River, NJ: Prentice Hall, 2004.

Bartness, A. D. "The Plant Location Puzzle." *Harvard Business Review* 72, no. 2 (March–April 1994).

Denton, B. "Decision Analysis, Location Models, and Scheduling Problems." *Interfaces* 30, no. 3 (May–June 2005): 262–263.

Drezner, Z. *Facility Location: Applications and Theory*. Berlin: Springer-Verlag, 2002.

Florida, R. *The Flight of the Creative Class: The New Global Competition for Talent*. New York, NY: HarperCollins, 2005.

Klamroth, K. *Single Facility Location Problems*. Berlin: Springer-Verlag, 2002.

Kennedy, M. *Introducing Geographic Information Systems with ArcGIS*. New York, NY: Wiley, 2006.

Mentzer, John T. "Seven Keys to Facility Location." *Supply Chain Management Review* 12, no. 5 (May 2008): 25.

Partovi, F. Y. "An Analytic Model for Locating Facilities Strategically." *Omega* 34, no. 1 (January 2006): 41.

Porter, Michael E., and Scott Stern. "Innovation: Location Matters." *MIT Sloan Management Review* (Summer 2001): 28–36.

Render, B., R. M. Stair, and M. Hanna. *Quantitative Analysis for Management*, 10th ed. Upper Saddle River, NJ: Prentice Hall, 2009.

Snyder, L. V. "Facility Location Under Uncertainty." *IIE Transactions* 38, no. 7 (July 2006): 547.

Tallman, Stephen, et al. "Knowledge, Clusters, and Competitive Advantage." *The Academy of Management Review* 29, no. 2 (April 2004): 258–271.

White, G. "Location, Location, Location." *Nation's Restaurant News* 42, no. 27 (July 14, 2008): S10–S11.

Chapter 9

Birchfield, J. C., and J. Birchfield. *Design and Layout of Foodservice Facilities*, 3rd ed. New York, NY: Wiley, 2007.

Francis, R. L., L. F. McGinnis, and J. A. White. *Facility Layout and Location*, 3rd ed. Upper Saddle River, NJ: Prentice Hall, 1998.

Gultekin, H., O. Y. Karasan, and M. S. Akturk. "Pure Cycles in Flexible Robotic Cells." *Computers & Operations Research* 36, no. 2 (February 2009): 329.

Heragu, S. S. *Facilities Design*, 3rd ed. New York, NY: CRC Press, 2008.

Heyer, N., and U. Wemmerlöv. *Reorganizing the Factory: Competing through Cellular Manufacturing*. Portland, OR: Productivity Press, 2002.

Johnson, Alan. "Getting the Right Factory Layout." *Manufacturer's Monthly* (July 2008): 16.

Kator, C. "Crossdocking on the Rise." *Modern Materials Handling* 63, no. 6 (June 2008): 15.

Kee, Micah R. "The Well-Ordered Warehouse." *APICS: The Performance Advantage* (March 2003): 20–24.

Keeps, David A. "Out-of-the-Box Offices." *Fortune* 159, no. 1 (January 19, 2009): 45.

Larson, S. "Extreme Makover—OR Edition." *Nursing Management* (November 2005): 26.

Panchalavarapu, P. R., and V. Chankong. "Design of Cellular Manufacturing System with Assembly Considerations." *Computers & Industrial Engineering* 48, no. 3 (May 2005): 448.

Roodbergen, K. J., and I. F. A. Vis. "A Model for Warehouse Layout." *IIE Transactions* 38, no. 10 (October 2006): 799–811.

Stanowy, A. "Evolutionary Strategy for Manufacturing Cell Design." *Omega* 34, no. 1 (January 2006): 1.

Tompkins, James A. *Facility Planning*, 4th ed. New York, NY: Wiley, 2009.

Upton, David. "What Really Makes Factories Flexible?" *Harvard Business Review* 73, no. 4 (July–August 1995): 74–84.

Zeng, A. Z., M. Mahan, and N. Fleut. "Designing an Efficient Warehouse Layout to Facilitate the Order-Filling Process." *Production and Inventory Management Journal* 43, no. 3–4 (3rd/4th Quarter 2002): 83–88.

Zhao, T., and C. L. Tseng. "Flexible Facility Interior Layout." *The Journal of the Operational Research Society* 58, no. 6 (June 2007): 729–740.

Chapter 10

Aft, Larry, and Neil Schmeidler. "Work Measurement Practices." *Industrial Engineer* 35, no. 11 (November 2003): 44.

Barber, Felix, and Rainer Strack. "The Surprising Economics of a People Business." *Harvard Business Review* 83, no. 6 (June 2005): 81–90.

Barnes, R. M. *Motion and Time Study, Design and Measurement of Work*, 7th ed. New York, NY: Wiley, 1980.

Bridger, R. S. *Introduction to Ergonomics*, 3rd ed. New York, NY: CRC Press, 2008.

De Jong, A., K. De Ruyter, and J. Lemmink. "Service Climate in Self-Managing Teams." *The Journal of Management Studies* 42, no. 8 (December 2005): 1593.

Elnekave, M., and I. Gilad. "Rapid Video-Based Analysis System for Advanced Work Measurement." *International Journal of Production Research* 44, no. 2 (January 2006): 271.

Freivalds, Andris, and B. W. Niebel. *Methods, Standards, and Work Design*, 12th ed. New York, NY: Irwin/McGraw-Hill, 2009.

Huselid, Mark A., Richard W. Beatty, and Brian E. Becker. "'A Players' or 'A Positions'? The Strategic Logic of Workforce Management." *Harvard Business Review* (December 2005): 110–117.

Konz, S., and Steven Johnson. *Work Design: Industrial Ergonomics*, 6th ed. Scottsdale, AZ: Holcomb Hathaway, 2004.

Muthusamy, S. K., J. V. Wheeler, and B. L. Simmons. "Self-Managing Work Teams." *Organization Development Journal* 23, no. 3 (Fall 2005): 53–66.

Pfeffer, Jeffrey. "Producing Sustainable Competitive Advantage Through the Effective Management of People." *Academy of Management Executive* 19, no. 4 (2005): 95.

Sadikoglu, E. "Integration of Work Measurement and Total Quality Management." *Total Quality Management and Business Excellence* 16, no. 5 (July 2005): 597.

Salvendy, G., ed. *Handbook of Human Factors and Ergonomics*, 3rd ed. New York, NY: Wiley, 2006.

Tolo, B. "21st-Century Stopwatch." *Industrial Engineer* 37, no. 7 (July 2005): 34–37.

Walsh, Ellen. "Get Results with Workload Management." *Nursing Management* (October 2003): 16.

Chapter 11

Blackburn, Joseph, and Gary Scudder. "Supply Chain Strategies for Perishable Products." *Production and Operations Management* 18, no. 2 (March–April 2009): 129–137.

Boyer, Kenneth K., and G. Tomas M. Hult. "Extending the Supply Chain: Integrating Operations and Marketing in the Online Grocery Industry." *Journal of Operations Management* 23, no. 6 (September 2005): 642–661.

Chopra, Sunil, and Peter Meindl. *Supply Chain Management*, 4th ed. Upper Saddle River, NJ: Prentice Hall, 2010.

Crook, T. Russell, and James G. Combs. "Sources and Consequences of Bargaining Power in Supply Chains." *Journal of Operations Management* 25, no. 2 (March 2007): 546–555.

Hu, J., and C. L. Munson. "Speed versus Reliability Trade-offs in Supplier Selection." *International Journal Procurement Management* 1, no. 1/2 (2007): 238–259.

Kersten, Wolfgang, and Thorsten Blecker (eds.). *Managing Risk in Supply Chains*. Berlin: Erich Schmidt Verlag GmbH & Co., 2006.

Kreipl, Stephan, and Michael Pinedo."Planning and Scheduling in Supply Chains." *Production and Operations Management* 13, no. 1 (Spring 2004): 77–92.

Linton, J. D., R. Klassen, and V. Jayaraman. "Sustainable Supply Chains: An Introduction." *Journal of Operations Management* 25, no. 6 (November 2007): 1075–1082.

Monczka, R. M., R. B. Handfield, L. C. Gianipero, and J. L. Patterson. *Purchasing and Supply Chain Management*, 4th ed. Mason, OH: Cengage, 2009.

Narayanan, Sriram, Ann S. Marucheck, and Robert B. Handfield. "Electronic Data Interchange: Research Review and Future Directions." *Decisions Sciences* 40, no. 1 (February 2009): 121–163.

Pisano, Gary P., and Roberto Verganti. "Which Kind of Collaboration Is Right for You?" *Harvard Business Review* 86, no. 12 (December 2008): 78–86.

Sinha, K. K., and E. J. Kohnke. "Health Care Supply Chain Design." *Decision Sciences* 40, no. 2 (May 2009): 197–212.

Stanley, L. L., and V. R. Singhal. "Service Quality Along the Supply Chain." *Journal of Operations Management* 19, no. 3 (May 2001): 287–306.

Wisner, Joel, K. Tan, and G. Keong Leong. *Principles of Supply Chain Management*, 3rd ed., Mason, OH: Cengage, 2009.

Chapter 11 Supplement

Berger, Paul D., Arthur Gerstenfeld, and Amy Z. Zeng. "How Many Suppliers Are Best? A Decision-Analysis Approach." *Omega* 32, no. 1 (February 2004): 9–15.

Chopra, Sunil, and Peter Meindl. *Supply Chain Management,* 4th ed. Upper Saddle River, NJ: Prentice Hall (2010).

Disney, Stephen M., and Marc R. Lambrecht. "On Replenishment Rules, Forecasting, and the Bullwhip Effect in Supply Chains." *Foundations and Trends in Technology, Information and Operations Management* 2, no. 1 (2007), 1–80.

Wang, Phanich P., S. Kara, and B. Kayis. "Analysis of the Bullwhip Effect in Multi-product, Multi-stage Supply Chain Systems—A Simulation Approach." *International Journal of Production Research* 48, no. 15 (August 2010): 4501–4517.

Chapter 12

Abernathy, Frederick H., et al. "Control Your Inventory in a World of Lean Retailing." *Harvard Business Review* 78, no. 6 (November–December 2000): 169–176.

Arnold, J. R., S. N. Chapman, and L. M. Clive. *Introduction to Materials Management*, 6th ed. Upper Saddle River, NJ: Prentice Hall, 2008.

Bradley, James R., and Richard W. Conway. "Managing Cyclic Inventories." *Production and Operations Management* 12, no. 4 (Winter 2003): 464–479.

Burt, D. N., S. Petcavage, and R. Pinkerton. *Supply Management*, 8th ed. Burr Ridge, IL: Irwin/McGraw, 2010.

Chapman, Stephen. *Fundamentals of Production Planning and Control*. Upper Saddle River, NJ: Prentice Hall, 2006.

Chopra, Sunil, Gilles Reinhardt, and Maqbool Dada. "The Effect of Lead Time Uncertainty on Safety Stocks." *Decision Sciences* 35, no. 1 (Winter 2004): 1–24.

Keren, Baruch. "The Single Period Inventory Model." *Omega* 37, no. 4 (August 2009): 801.

Liu, X., and Z. Lian. "Cost-effective Inventory Control in a Value-added Manufacturing System." *European Journal of Operational Research* 196, no. 2 (July 2009): 534.

McDonald, Stan C. *Materials Management*. New York, NY: Wiley, 2009.

Noblitt, James M. "The Economic Order Quantity Model: Panacea or Plague?" *APICS—The Performance Advantage* (February 2001): 53–57.

Render, B., R. M. Stair, and M. Hanna. *Quantitative Analysis for Management*, 11th ed. Upper Saddle River, NJ: Prentice Hall, 2011.

Rubin, Paul A., and W. C. Benton. "A Generalized Framework for Quantity Discount Pricing Schedules." *Decision Sciences* 34, no. 1 (Winter 2003): 173–188.

Vollmann, T. E., W. L. Berry, D. C. Whybark, and F. R. Jacobs. *Manufacturing Planning and Control for Supply Chain Management*, 5th ed. Burr Ridge, IL: Irwin/McGraw, 2005.

Witt, Clyde E. "Mobile Warehouse Supplies U.S. Marines in Iraq." *Material Handling Management* 60, no. 8 (August 2005): 24–25.

Chapter 13

Chen, Fangruo. "Salesforce Initiative, Market Information, and Production/Inventory Planning." *Management Science* 51, no. 1 (January 2005): 60–75.

Hopp, Wallace J., and Mark L. Spearman. *Factory Physics*, 3rd ed. New York, NY: Irwin/McGraw-Hill, 2008.

Kimes, S. E., and G. M. Thompson. "Restaurant Revenue Management at Chevy's." *Decision Sciences* 35, no. 3 (Summer 2004): 371–393.

Metters, R., K. King-Metters, M. Pullman, and S. Walton. *Successful Service Operations Management*, 2nd ed. Mason, OH: Thompson-South-Western, 2006.

Metters, Richard, et al. "The 'Killer Application' of Revenue Management: Harrah's Cherokee Casino and Hotel." *Interfaces* 38, no. 3 (May–June 2008): 161–178.

Mukhopadhyay, S., S. Samaddar, and G. Colville. "Improving Revenue Management Decision Making for Airlines." *Decision Science* 38, no. 2 (May 2007): 309–327.

Plambeck, Erica L., and Terry A. Taylor. "Sell the Plant? The Impact of Contract Manufacturing on Innovation, Capacity, and Profitability." *Management Science* 51, no. 1 (January 2005): 133–150.

Silver, E. A., D. F. Pyke, and R. Peterson. *Inventory Management and Production Planning and Scheduling*. New York, NY: Wiley, 1998.

Vollmann, T. E., W. L. Berry, D. C. Whybark, and F. R. Jacobs. *Manufacturing Planning and Control for Supply Chain Management*, 5th ed. Burr Ridge, IL: Irwin, 2005.

Chapter 14

Barba-Gutierrez, Y., B. Adenso-Diaz, and S. M. Gupta. "Lot Sizing in Reverse MRP for Scheduling Disassembly." *International Journal of Production Economics* 111, no. 2 (February 2008): 741.

Bell, Steve. "Time Fence Secrets." *APICS* 16, no. 4 (April 2006): 44–48.

Bolander, Steven, and Sam G. Taylor. "Scheduling Techniques: A Comparison of Logic." *Production and Inventory Management Journal* 41, no. 1 (1st Quarter 2000): 1–5.

Crandall, Richard E. "The Epic Life of ERP." *APICS* 16, no. 2 (February 2006): 17–19.

Gattiker, Thomas "Anatomy of an ERP Implementation Gone Awry." *Production and Inventory Management* 43, nos. 3–4 (3rd/4th Quarter 2002): 96–105.

Kanet, J., and V. Sridharan. "The Value of Using Scheduling Information in Planning Material Requirements." *Decision Sciences* 29, no. 2 (Spring 1998): 479–498.

Koh, S. C. L., and S. M. Saad. "Managing Uncertainty in ERP-controlled Manufacturing Environments." *International Journal of Production Economics* 101, no. 1 (May 2006): 109.

Krupp, James A. G. "Integrating Kanban and MRP to Reduce Lead Time." *Production and Inventory Management Journal* 43, no. 3–4 (3rd/4th quarter 2002): 78–82.

Lawrence, Barry F., Daniel F. Jennings, and Brian E. Reynolds. *ERP in Distribution*. Florence, KY: Thomson South-Western, 2005.

Moncrief, Stephen. "Push and Pull." *APICS—The Performance Advantage* (June 2003): 46–51.

Norris, G. *E-Business & ERP*. New York, NY: Wiley, 2005.

O'Sullivan, Jill, and Gene Caiola. *Enterprise Resource Planning*, 2nd ed. New York, NY: McGraw-Hill, 2008.

Segerstedt, A. "Master Production Scheduling and a Comparison of MRP and Cover-Time Planning." *International Journal of Production Research* 44, no. 18–19 (September 2006): 3585.

Summer, M. *Enterprise Resource Planning*. Upper Saddle River, NJ: Prentice Hall, 2005.

Wagner, H. M., and T. M. Whitin. "Dynamic Version of the Economic Lot Size Model." *Management Science* 5, no. 1 (1958): 89–96.

Wu, Jen-Hur, et al. "Using Multiple Variables Decision-Making Analysis for ERP Selection." *International Journal of Manufacturing Technology and Management* 18, no. 2 (2009): 228.

Chapter 15

Baker, Kenneth A., and Dan Trietsch. *Principles of Sequencing and Scheduling*. New York, NY: Wiley, 2009.

Bard, Jonathan F. "Staff Scheduling in High Volume Service Facilities with Downgrading." *IIE Transactions* 36 (2004): 985–997.

Bolander, Steven, and Sam G. Taylor. "Scheduling Techniques: A Comparison of Logic." *Production and Inventory Management Journal* (1st quarter 2000): 1–5.

Cayirli, Tugba, and Emre Veral. "Outpatient Scheduling in Health Care: A Review of Literature." *Production and Operations Management* 12, no. 4 (Winter 2003): 519–549.

Chapman, Stephen. *Fundamentals of Production Planning and Control*. Upper Saddle River, NJ: Prentice Hall, 2006.

Deng, Honghui, Q. Wang, G. K. Leong, and S. X. Sun. "Usage of Opportunity Cost to Maximize Performance in Revenue Management." *Decision Sciences* 38, no. 4 (November 2008): 737–758.

Dietrich, Brenda, G. A. Paleologo, and L. Wynter. "Revenue Management in Business Services." *Production and Operations Management* 17, no. 4 (July–August 2008): 475–480.

Farmer, Adam, Jeffrey S. Smith, and Luke T. Miller. "Scheduling Umpire Crews for Professional Tennis Tournaments." *Interfaces* 37, no. 2 (March–April 2007): 187–196.

Geraghty, Kevin. "Revenue Management and Digital Marketing." *OR/MS Today* 35, no. 6 (December 2008): 22–28.

Kellogg, Deborah L., and Steven Walczak. "Nurse Scheduling." *Interfaces* 37, no. 4 (July–August 2007): 355–369.

Lopez, P., and F. Roubellat. *Production Scheduling*. New York, NY: Wiley, 2008.

Mondschein, S. V., and G. Y. Weintraub. "Appointment Policies in Service Operations." *Production and Operations Management* 12, no. 2 (Summer 2003): 266–286.

Morton, Thomas E., and David W. Pentico. *Heuristic Scheduling Systems*. New York, NY: Wiley, 1993.

Pinedo, M. *Scheduling: Theory, Algorithms, and Systems*, 2nd ed. Upper Saddle River, NJ: Prentice Hall, 2002.

Plenert, Gerhard, and Bill Kirchmier. *Finite Capacity Scheduling*. New York, NY: Wiley, 2000.

Render, B., R. M. Stair, and M. Hanna. *Quantitative Analysis for Management*, 10th ed. Upper Saddle River, NJ: Prentice Hall, 2009.

Chapter 16

Burke, Robert, and Gregg Messel. "From Simulation to Implementation: Cardinal Health's Lean Journey." *Target: Innovation at Work* 19, no. 2 (2nd Quarter 2003): 27–32.

Flinchbauh, Jamie. *The Hitchhiker's Guide to Lean*. Dearborn, MI: Society of Manufacturing Engineers, 2006.

Graban, Mark. *Lean Hospitals*. New York, NY: CRC Press, 2009.

Hall, Robert W. "'Lean' and the Toyota Production System." *Target* 20, no. 3 (3rd Issue 2004): 22–27.

Keyte, Beau, and Drew Locher. *The Complete Lean Enterprise*. University Park, IL: Productivity Press, 2004.

Morgan, James M., and Jeffrey K. Liker. *The Toyota Product Development System*. New York, NY: Productivity Press, 2007.

Nelson-Peterson, Dana L., and Carol J. Leppa, "Creating an Environment of Caring Using Lean Principles of the Virginia Mason Production System," *Journal of Nursing Administration* 37 (2007): 289.

Parks, Charles M. "The Bare Necessities of Lean." *Industrial Engineer* 35, no. 8 (August 2003): 39.

Schonberger, Richard J. "Lean Extended." *Industrial Engineer* (December 2005): 26–31.

van Veen-Dirks, Paula. "Management Control and the Production Environment." *International Journal of Production Economics* 93 (January 8, 2005): 263.

Womack, James P., and Daniel T. Jones. "Lean Consumption." *Harvard Business Review* 83 (March 2005): 58–68.

Womack, James P., and Daniel T. Jones. *Lean Solutions: How Companies and Customers Can Create Value and Wealth Together*. New York, NY: The Free Press, 2005.

Chapter 17

Bauer, Eric, X. Zhang, and D. A. Kimber. *Practical System Reliability*. New York, NY: Wiley, 2009.

Blank, Ronald. *The Basics of Reliability*. University Park, IL: Productivity Press, 2004.

Cua, K. O., K. E. McKone, and R. G. Schroeder. "Relationships between Implementation of TQM, JIT, and TPM and Manufacturing Performance." *Journal of Operations Management* 19, no. 6 (November 2001): 675–694.

Finigen, Tim, and Jim Humphries. "Maintenance Gets Lean." *IE Industrial Systems* 38, no. 10 (October 2006): 26–31.

Sova, Roger, and Lea A. P. Tonkin. "Total Productive Maintenance at Crown International." *Target: Innovation at Work* 19, no. 1 (1st Quarter 2003): 41–44.

Stephens, M. P. *Productivity and Reliability-Based Maintenance Management*. Upper Saddle River, NJ: Prentice Hall, 2004.

Weil, Marty. "Beyond Preventive Maintenance." *APICS* 16, no. 4 (April 2006): 40–43.

Module A

Balakrishnan, R., B. Render, and R. M. Stair Jr. *Managerial Decision Modeling with Spreadsheets*, 2nd ed. Upper Saddle River, NJ: Prentice Hall, 2007.

Buchannan, Leigh, and Andrew O'Connell. "A Brief History of Decision Making." *Harvard Business Review* 84, no. 1 (January, 2006): 32–41.

Hammond, J. S., R. L. Kenney, and H. Raiffa. "The Hidden Traps in Decision Making." *Harvard Business Review* 84, no. 1 (January 2006): 118–126.

Keefer, Donald L. "Balancing Drug Safety and Efficacy for a Go/No-Go Decision." *Interfaces* 34, no. 2 (March–April 2004): 113–116.

Miller, C. C., and R. D. Ireland. "Intuition in Strategic Decision Making." *Academy of Management Executive* 19, no. 1 (February 2005): 19.

Parmigiani, G., and L. Inoue. *Decision Theory: Principles and Approaches*. New York, NY: Wiley, 2010.

Raiffa, H., and R. Schlaifer. *Applied Statistical Decision Theory*. New York, NY: Wiley, 2000.

Render, B., R. M. Stair Jr., and M. Hanna. *Quantitative Analysis for Management*, 10th ed. Upper Saddle River, NJ: Prentice Hall, 2009.

Module B

Bard, J. F. "Staff Scheduling in High Volume Services with Downgrading." *IIE Transactions* 36 (October 2004): 985.

Brown, G., R. F. Dell, and A. M. Newman. "Optimizing Military Capital Planning." *Interfaces* 34, no. 6 (November–December 2004): 415–425.

daSilva, C. G., et al. "An Interactive Decision Support System for an Aggregate Planning Production Model." *Omega* 34 (April 2006): 167.

Denton, Brian T. "AusWest Timbers Uses an Optimization Model to Improve Its Manufacturing Process." *Interfaces* 38, no. 4 (July–August 2008): 341–344.

Duran, G., et al. "Scheduling the Chilean Soccer League by Integer Programming." *Interfaces* 37, no. 6 (November–December 2007): 539–555.

Harrod, Steven. "A Spreadsheet-Based, Matrix Formulation Linear Programming Lesson." *Decision Sciences Journal of Innovative Education* 7, no. 1 (January 2009): 249.

Martin, C. H. "Ohio University's College of Business Uses Integer Programming to Schedule Classes." *Interfaces* 34 (November–December 2004): 460–465.

Neureuther, B. D., G. G. Polak, and N. R. Sanders. "A Hierarchical Production Plan for a Make-to-Order Steel Fabrication Plant." *Production Planning & Control* 15 (April 2004): 324.

Pasupathy, K., and A. Medina-Borja. "Integrating Excel, Access, and Visual Basic to Deploy Performance Measurement and Evaluation at the American Red Cross." *Interfaces* 38, no. 4 (July–August 2008): 324–340.

Render, B., R. M. Stair, and Michael Hanna. *Quantitative Analysis for Management*, 10th ed. Upper Saddle River, NJ: Prentice Hall, 2009.

Render, B., R. M. Stair, and R. Balakrishnan. *Managerial Decision Modeling with Spreadsheets*, 2nd ed. Upper Saddle River, NJ: Prentice Hall, 2007.

Sodhi, M. S., and S. Norri. "A Fast and Optimal Modeling Approach Applied to Crew Rostering at London Underground." *Annals of OR* 127 (March 2004): 259.

Taylor, Bernard. *Introduction to Management Science*, 10th ed. Upper Saddle River, NJ: Prentice Hall, 2011.

Module C

Balakrishnan, R., B. Render, and R. M. Stair. *Managerial Decision Modeling with Spreadsheets*, 2nd. ed. Upper Saddle River, NJ: Prentice Hall, 2007.

Drezner, Z. *Facility Location: A Survey of Applications and Methods*. Secaucus, NJ: Springer-Verlag, 1995.

Koksalan, M., and H. Sural. "Efes Beverage Group Makes Location and Distribution Decisions for Its Malt Plants." *Interfaces* 29 (March–April 1999): 89–103.

Ping, J., and K. F. Chu. "A Dual-Matrix Approach to the Transportation Problem." *Asia-Pacific Journal of Operations Research* 19 (May 2002): 35–46.

Render, B., R. M. Stair, and M. Hanna. *Quantitative Analysis for Management*, 10th ed. Upper Saddle River, NJ: Prentice Hall, 2009.

Schmenner, R. W. "Look Beyond the Obvious in Plant Location." *Harvard Business Review* 57, no. 1 (January–February 1979): 126–132.

Taylor, B. *Introduction to Management Science*, 10th ed. Upper Saddle River, NJ: Prentice Hall, 2011.

Module D

Canonaco, P., et al. "A Queuing Network Model for the Management of Berth Crane Operations." *Computers & Operations Research* 35, no. 8 (August 2008): 2432.

Cochran, J. K., and K. Roche. "A Queuing-Based Decision Support Methodology to Estimate Hospital Inpatient Bed Demand." *Journal of the Operational Research Society* 59, no. 11 (November 2008): 1471–1483.

Gross, Donald, John F. Shortle, James M. Thompson, and Carl M. Harris. *Fundamentals of Queuing Theory*, 4th ed. New York, NY: Wiley, 2008.

Parlar, M., and M. Sharafali. "Dynamic Allocation of Airline Check-In Counters: A Queueing Optimization Problem." *Management Science* 54, no. 8 (August 2008): 1410–1425.

Prabhu, N. U. *Foundations of Queuing Theory*. Dordecht, Netherlands: Kluwer Academic Publishers, 1997.

Ramaswami, V., et al. "Ensuring Access to Emergency Services in the Presence of Long Internet Dial-Up Calls." *Interfaces* 35, no. 5 (September–October 2005): 411–425.

Render, B., R. M. Stair, and R. Balakrishnan. *Managerial Decision Modeling with Spreadsheets*, 2nd ed. Upper Saddle River, NJ: Prentice Hall, 2007.

Render, B., R. M. Stair, and M. Hanna. *Quantitative Analysis for Management*, 10th ed. Upper Saddle River, NJ: Prentice Hall, 2009.

Stanford, D. A., E. Renouf, and V. C. McAlister. "Waiting for Liver Transplantation in Canada." *Health Care Management Science* 11, no. 2 (June 2008): 196–208.

Module E

Boh, W. F., S. A. Slaughter, and J. A. Espinosa. "Learning from Experience in Software Development." *Management Science* 53, no. 8 (August 2007): 1315–1332.

Couto, J. P., and J. C. Teixeira. "Using a Linear Model for Learning Curve Effect on Highrise Floor Construction." *Construction Management & Economics* 23 (May 2005): 355.

McDonald, A., and L. Schrattenholzer. "Learning Curves and Technology Assessment." *International Journal of Technology Management* 23 (2002): 718.

Morrison, J. Bradley. "Putting the Learning Curve into Context." *Journal of Business Research* 61, no. 1 (November 2008): 1182.

Ngwenyama, O., A. Guergachi, and T. McLaren. "Using the Learning Curve to Maximize IT Productivity." *International Journal of Production Economics* 105, no. 2 (February 2007): 524.

Smunt, T. L., and C. A. Watts. "Improving Operations Planning with Learning Curves." *Journal of Operations Management* 21 (January 2003): 93.

Weston, M. *Learning Curves*. New York, NY: Crown Publishing, 2000.

Module F

Al-Zubaidi, H., and D. Tyler. "A Simulation Model of Quick Response Replenishment of Seasonal Clothing." *International Journal of Retail and Distribution Management* 32 (2004): 320.

Balakrishnan, R., B. Render, and R. M. Stair. *Managerial Decision Modeling with Spreadsheets*, 2nd ed. Upper Saddle River, NJ: Prentice Hall, 2007.

Banks, J., J. S. Carson, B. L. Nelson, and D. M. Nicol. *Discrete-Event System Simulation*, 5th ed. Upper Saddle River, NJ: Prentice Hall, 2010.

Banks, Jerry, and Randall R. Gibson "The ABC's of Simulation Practice." *Analytics* (Spring 2009): 16–23.

Gavirneni, S., D. J. Morrice, and P. Mullarkey. "Simulation Helps Maxager Shorten Its Sales." *Interfaces* 2 (March–April, 2004): 87–96.

Huang, H. C., et al. "Sim Man—A Simulation Model for Workforce Capacity Planning." *Computers & Operations Research* 196, no. 3 (August 1, 2009): 1147.

Kelton, W. D., R. P. Sadowski, and N. B. Swets, *Simulation with Arena*, 5th ed. New York, NY: McGraw-Hill, 2010.

Law, A. *Simulation Modeling and Analysis*, 4th ed. New York, NY: McGraw-Hill, 2007.

Render, B., R. M. Stair, and M. Hanna. *Quantitative Analysis for Management*, 10th ed. Upper Saddle River, NJ: Prentice Hall, 2009.

Rossetti, Manuel D. *Simulation Modeling and ARENA*. New York, NY: Wiley, 2009.

Saltzman, Robert M., and Vijay Mehrotra. "A Call Center Uses Simulation to Drive Strategic Change." *Interfaces* 31, no. 3 (May–June 2001): 87–101.

Sud, V. P., et al. "Reducing Flight Delays Through Better Traffic Management." *Interfaces* 39, no. 1 (January/February 2009): 35–51.

Taylor, S. J .E., et al. "Simulation Modelling Is 50." *The Journal of the Operational Research Society* 60, no. S1 (May 2009): S69–S13.

Thompson, G. M., and R. Verma. "Computer Simulation in Hospitality Teaching, Practice and Research." *Cornell Hotel and Restaurant Administration Quarterly* 44 (April 2003): 85.

Name Index

Subject Index

Note: Bold page numbers denotes definitions and figures and tables are denoted with f and t.